Biological Concepts of Health

Custom Edition for University of Guelph
BIOL 1080

Taken from

Health: The Basics, Fifth Canadian Edition
by Rebecca J. Donatelle and Angela M. Thompson

Biology of Humans: Concepts, Applications, and Issues, Third Edition
by Judith Goodenough and Betty McGuire

An Introduction to Health Psychology, Second Edition
by Val Morrison and Paul Bennett

Principles of Human Physiology, Fourth Edition
by Cindy L. Stanfield

Learning Solutions

New York Boston San Francisco
London Toronto Sydney Tokyo Singapore Madrid
Mexico City Munich Paris Cape Town Hong Kong Montreal

Cover image courtesy of Andre Nantel

Taken from:

Health: The Basics, Fifth Canadian Edition
by Rebecca J. Donatelle and Angela M. Thompson

Published by Benjamin Cummings
Toronto, Ontario

Biology of Humans: Concepts, Applications, and Issues, Third Edition
by Judith Goodenough and Betty McGuire

Published by Benjamin Cummings
San Francisco, California 94111

An Introduction to Health Psychology, Second Edition
by Val Morrison and Paul Bennett

Published by Prentice Hall
Edinburgh Gate, Harlow

Principles of Human Physiology, Fourth Edition
by Cindy L. Stanfield

Published by Benjamin Cummings
San Francisco, California 94111

This special edition published in cooperation with Pearson Learning Solutions.

Pearson Learning Solutions, 501 Boylston Street, Suite 900, Boston, MA 02116
A Pearson Education Company
www.pearsoned.com

Printed in Canada

3 4 5 6 7 8 9 10 XXXX 15 14 13 12 11

000200010270569054

MHB

ISBN 10: 0-558-79699-0
ISBN 13: 978-0-558-79699-0

CONTENTS

PART I THE HUMAN ORGANISM 1

PART II WHAT IS HEALTH AND ILLNESS? 77

Part III SYSTEM CONTROL AND COMMUNICATION AS THE FOUNDATION OF INDIVIDUAL HEALTH 107

PART IV HOMEOSTASIS, ALLOSTASIS AND STRESS 257

PART V LIFESTYLE FACTORS AND HEALTH 277

PART VI AGING, DEATH AND DYING 439

*** Posted on course website at http://www.pearsoncustom.com/can/uguelph_biohealth**

Please see credit lines thoughout text for details on original source information.

PART I: THE HUMAN ORGANISM

CHAPTER 1a

HUMANS IN THE WORLD OF BIOLOGY

Taken from *Biology of Humans: Concepts, Applications, and Issues*, Third Edition, by Judith Goodenough and Betty McGuire

The rain forest is a fitting place to begin considering human biology. The forest's incredible diversity of life—the bewildering variety of plants, the brilliant colors of the flowers, the haunting songs of exotic birds—reminds us that humans are just a small part of life on Earth.

As we look around, we can see that life has many levels of organization: individual, population, community, ecosystem, and biosphere. Throughout most of this book, we focus on the human individual—how the individual human body functions and the biological principles that govern those functions. However, we also examine many of the larger health, social, and environmental issues that we must be aware of, because they can affect all of us. Our actions as individuals can affect the health of the rain forest. At the same time, the rain forest is a source of biological substances that may be used to improve the health of humans.

BASIC CHARACTERISTICS OF ALL LIVING THINGS

As you continue exploring the rain forest, how do you determine if something unfamiliar to you is alive? In most cases, the question is easy to answer. Although the leaves around you have different shapes and sizes, a brief examination assures you that they are leaves, and the tree whose trunk you are exploring is clearly a tree—thus telling you that the tree specimen you are examining is indeed alive. But what about the gray material adhering to the trunk? Is it also alive?

Defining life might seem to be easy, but it is not. In fact, no single definition satisfies all life scientists. For example, if we say you can tell something is alive if it reproduces, someone is likely to note that a page with a wet ink spot can fall on top of another page and reproduce itself almost exactly. If we say you can tell something is alive if it grows, what should we conclude about crystals? They grow, but they are not alive. And so it goes.

No single definition applies to all forms of life, so we find that instead of defining life, we can only characterize it. That is, we can only list the traits associated with life. Most biologists agree that, in general, the following statements characterize life.

1. **Living things contain nucleic acids, proteins, carbohydrates, and lipids.** The same set of slightly more than 100 elements is present in various combinations in everything on Earth—living or nonliving. However, living things can combine certain of these elements to create molecules that are found in all living organisms. These include nucleic acids, proteins, carbohydrates, and lipids. The nucleic acid DNA (deoxyribonucleic acid) is especially important because DNA molecules can make copies of themselves, an ability that enables organisms to reproduce (Figure 1a.1).
2. **Living things are composed of cells. Cells** are the smallest units of life. Some organisms (called unicellular organisms) have only a single cell; others (multicellular organisms), such as humans, are composed of trillions of cells. All cells come from preexisting cells. Because cells can divide to form new cells, reproduction, growth, and repair are possible
3. **Living things grow and reproduce.** Living things grow and ultimately generate new individuals that carry some of the genetic material of the parents. Some organisms, such as bacteria, reproduce simply by making new and virtually exact copies of themselves. Other organisms, including humans, reproduce by combining genetic material with another individual. Many organisms have stages of life. Humans progress from embryo to fetus, child, adolescent, and then adult.
4. **Living things use energy and raw materials.** The term **metabolism** refers to all chemical reactions that occur within the cells of living things. Through metabolic activities, organisms extract energy from various nutrients and transform it to do many kinds of work. Metabolism maintains life and allows organisms to grow.
5. **Living things respond to their environment.** A boxer weaves and ducks to avoid the blow of an opponent. A chameleon takes aim at and captures its prey. For a living thing to respond, it must first detect a stimulus and then have a way to react. Your sensory organs detect stimuli. Your nervous system processes sensory input, and your skeletal and muscular systems enable you to respond.
6. **Living things maintain homeostasis. Homeostasis** is the relatively constant and self-correcting internal environment of a living organism. We generally find that life can exist only within certain limits and that living things tend to behave in ways that will keep their body systems functioning within those limits. For example, if you become too cold, you shiver (a metabolic response). Shivering produces heat that warms your body. Alternatively, if you become too hot, your sweat glands will be activated to cool you down. In addition to these and other physiological responses, the sensation of being hot or cold may motivate you to behave in ways that cool you down or warm you up.
7. **Populations of living things evolve and have adaptive traits.** Members of a population of reproducing organisms possessing beneficial genetic traits will survive and reproduce better than members of the population that lack these traits. As a

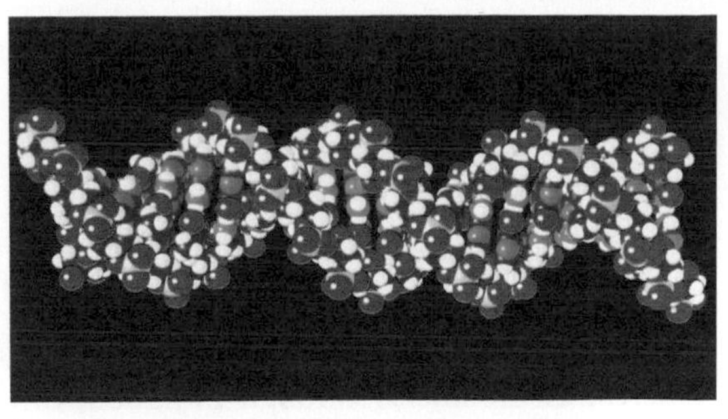

1. Living things contain nucleic acids, proteins, carbohydrates, and lipids.
This is a computer-generated model of the nucleic acid DNA, which carries genetic information.

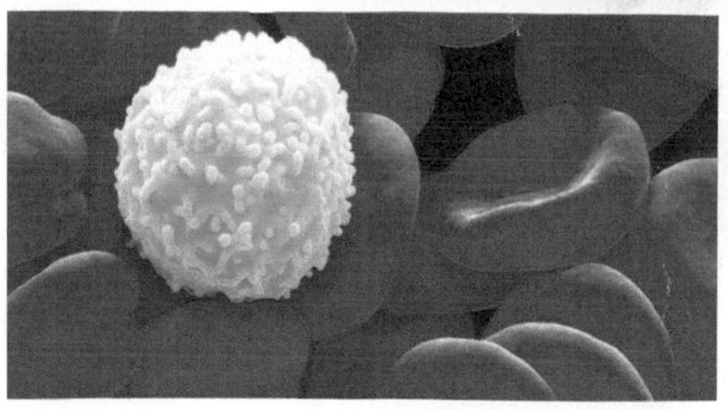

2. Living things are composed of cells.
These are red blood cells (disks) and a white blood cell (sphere).

3. Living things grow and reproduce.
All organisms reproduce their own kind.

4. Living things use energy and raw materials.
This mother orangutan is sharing bananas with her offspring. This food will provide energy and raw materials for the maintenance, repair, and growth of their bodies.

5. Living things respond to their environment.
This chameleon sees and catches its prey.

6. Living things maintain homeostasis.
This person's body temperature will remain about 37°C (98.6° F) in spite of extreme environmental temperature.

7. Populations of living things evolve and have adaptive traits.
The orchid is adapted to live perched on branches of trees. It uses other plants for support so that it can receive enough sunlight to produce its own food by photosynthesis.

FIGURE 1.a.1 **Characteristics of life**

result of this process, called *natural selection*, each of the amazing organisms you see around you has **adaptive traits**—that is, traits that help it survive and reproduce in its natural environment. For example, most plants in the rain forest have shallow root systems, because the topsoil in the Amazon is thin and nutrients are near the surface. As a result, tall trees have acquired, through evolution, supports like cathedral buttresses to hold them up, while vines climb over both roots and trees to reach the light. Many plants do not grow in the ground at all but live high above it in the canopy for greater exposure to sunlight, which provides energy to produce sugar. These plants, called epiphytes, are rooted on the surfaces of other plants. Rain forest animals also have adaptations—the ability to fly or climb, for example—that enable them to reach the plants for food.

stop and THINK

Scientists have discovered vents of water similar to geysers spouting on the surface of a small moon of Saturn called Enceladus. Locations near these vents may be the most likely place in the solar system to find extraterrestrial life. If samples of water from Enceladus were brought back to scientists on Earth, what characteristics of life could they look for to determine whether the samples contain anything that is or was once alive?

CLASSIFICATION BY EVOLUTIONARY RELATIONSHIP

At least 10 million species of organisms live on Earth. Organisms are unified because all species descended from the first cells. However, as organisms adapted to different environments through evolution, diversity among species arose.

Scientists organize, or classify, living organisms in a way that shows evolutionary relationships among them. This means, for the most part, that organisms with the greatest similarity are grouped together.

Several classification systems have been proposed over the years. One system recently favored by many biologists recognizes three domains. Two of the domains, Bacteria and Archaea, consist of the various kinds of prokaryotes—all very small, single-celled organisms that lack a nucleus or other internal compartments. All other organisms, including humans, belong to the third domain, Eukarya. Organisms in domain Eukarya have eukaryotic cells, which contain a nucleus and complex internal compartments called organelles. Domain Eukarya is subdivided into four kingdoms—protists, fungi, plants, and animals—as shown in Figure 1a.2. Within each kingdom, organisms are further categorized into groups whose members share characteristics that distinguish them from members of other groups in the kingdom. These groups in turn are subdivided into smaller groups to show successively closer relationships.

As humans, we belong to a subdivision of the animal kingdom called vertebrates (animals with a nerve

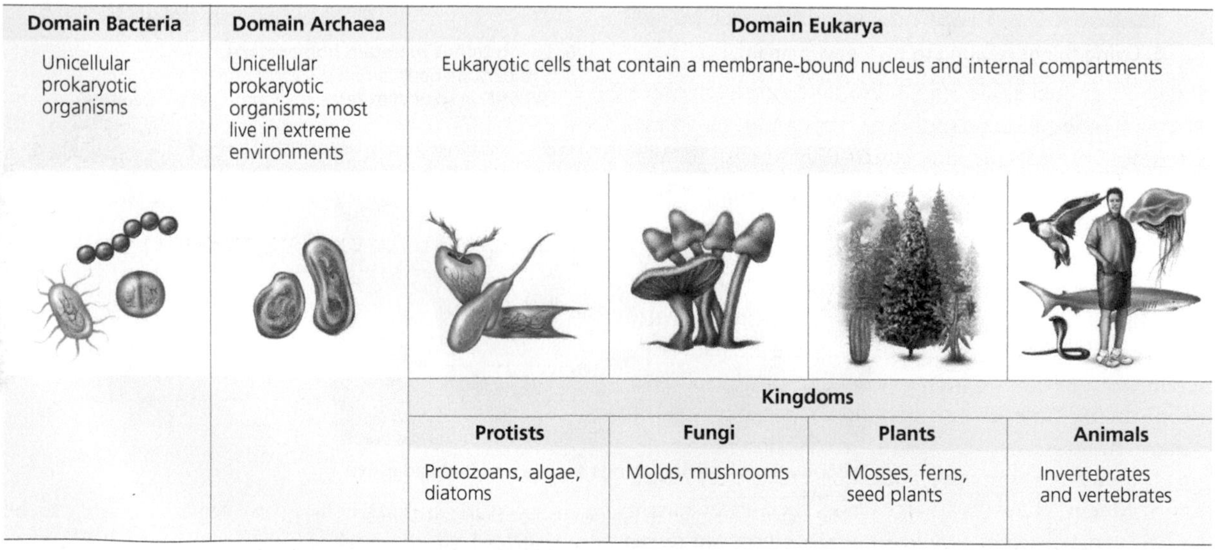

Domain Bacteria	Domain Archaea	Domain Eukarya			
Unicellular prokaryotic organisms	Unicellular prokaryotic organisms; most live in extreme environments	Eukaryotic cells that contain a membrane-bound nucleus and internal compartments			
		Kingdoms			
		Protists	Fungi	Plants	Animals
		Protozoans, algae, diatoms	Molds, mushrooms	Mosses, ferns, seed plants	Invertebrates and vertebrates

FIGURE 1a.2 One classification scheme showing three domains and four kingdoms of life

FIGURE 1a.3 **Social interactions are an important thread in the fabric of human life.**

cord protected by a backbone), and more specifically to the group called mammals. Two characteristics that make us mammals are that we have hair and that we feed our young milk produced by mammary glands. However, we are further defined as belonging to the primates, along with lemurs, monkeys, and apes, because we share a suite of features that includes forward-looking eyes and a particularly well-developed brain. Humans, monkeys, and apes also have opposable thumbs (a thumb that can touch the tips of the other four fingers). Smaller details, such as tooth structure and skeletal characteristics, serve to divide the primates into smaller subgroupings.

What most sets humans apart from all other living species? Human characteristics include a large brain size relative to body size and a two-legged gait. But nothing distinguishes humans more than culture. *Culture* may be regarded as a set of social influences that produce an integrated pattern of knowledge, belief, and behavior (Figure 1a.3). Other animals have social interactions, from various forms of cooperation and mating behavior to territoriality, competition, and social hierarchies. But social influences are much less pronounced in other animals than in corresponding human interactions. Consider, for example, our rituals—weddings, graduation, burial of the dead—and the way our lives are enriched with art, music, and dance.

Of course, there is not one human culture but many. If you were a scientist following native guides through the Amazon rain forest, you would quickly learn that their culture is different from ours. In fact, there are many different cultures within the rain forest. Separate groups of people in the same environment do not adapt to it in the same way. If you were to describe your culture to someone from a rain forest tribe, your description might elicit astonishment and even howls of laughter. However, you and your native guide would soon recognize that some things, especially love of children and the need to belong to a group, seem the same across cultures.

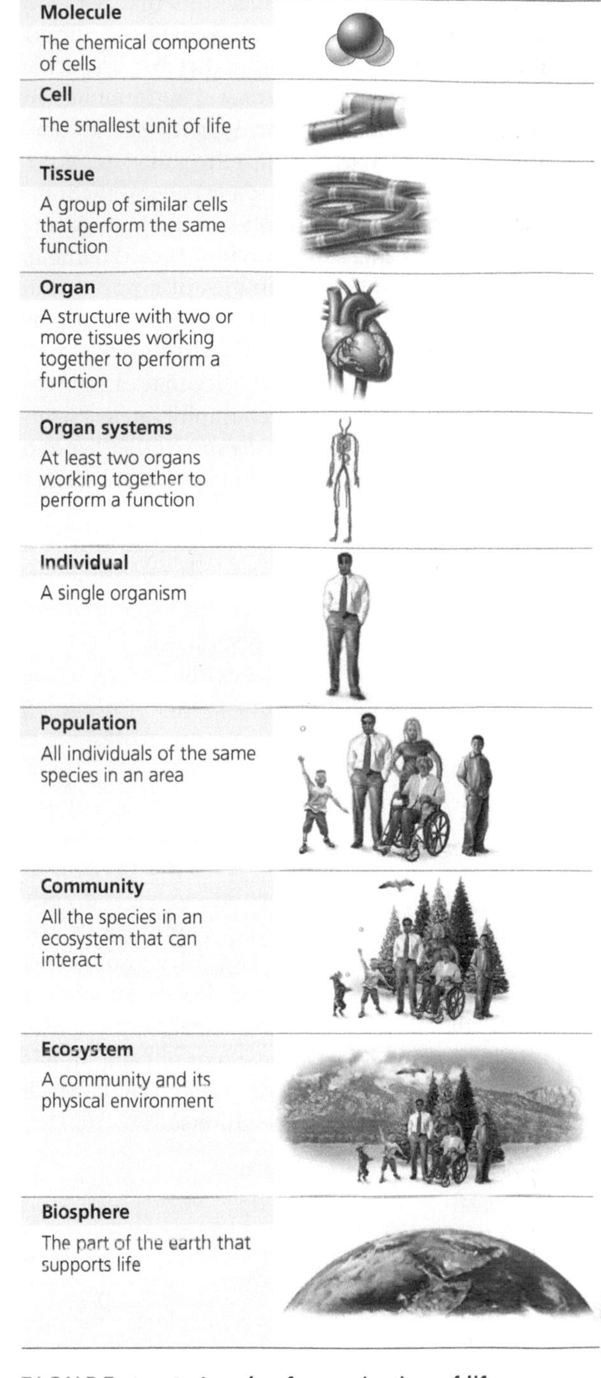

FIGURE 1a.4 **Levels of organization of life**

LEVELS OF BIOLOGICAL ORGANIZATION

As we study human biology, we learn that life can be organized on many levels (Figure 1a.4). Cells, the smallest unit of life, are themselves composed of molecules. A multicellular organism may consist of different tissues, groups of similar cells that perform specific functions. Organs also may consist of different types of tissue that work together for a specific function. Two or more organs working together to perform specific functions form an organ system. Humans are described as having 11 organ systems.

Life can also be organized at levels beyond the individual organism. A **population** is individuals of the same species (individuals that can interbreed) living in a distinct geographic area. Examples of a population include yellow-bellied marmots living in an alpine meadow or four-eyed butterfly fish living in a coral reef. A **community** is all living species that can potentially interact in a particular geographic area. Examples of a community include *all the species* that live and interact in an alpine meadow or all the species living in a coral reef.

An **ecosystem** includes all the living organisms in a community along with their physical environment. The size of the locality that defines the ecosystem varies with the interest of the person studying it. In other words, an ecosystem can be defined as the whole Earth, a particular forest, or even a single rotting log within a forest. Whatever its size, an ecosystem is viewed as being relatively self-contained.

The **biosphere** is that part of Earth where life is found. It encompasses all of Earth's living organisms and their habitats. In essence, the biosphere is the narrow zone in which the interplay of light, minerals, water, and gases produces environments where life can exist on Earth. The biosphere extends only about 11 km (7 mi) above sea level and the same distance below, to the deepest trenches of the sea. If Earth were the size of a basketball, the biosphere would have the depth of about one coat of paint. In this thin layer covering one small planet, we find all of the life we currently know of in the entire universe.

SCIENTIFIC METHOD

It is not surprising that scientists are exploring the rain forest in search of any secrets it may reveal, including any plants that may have healing qualities. Humans are an irrepressibly curious species, constantly asking questions about the things they observe. **Science** is a systematic approach to answering those questions, a way of acquiring knowledge through carefully documented investigation and experimentation.

There is no such thing as *the* scientific method in the sense of a single, formalized set of steps to follow for doing an experiment. Instead, the **scientific method** is a way of learning about the natural world by applying certain rules of logic to the way information is gathered and conclusions are drawn. It often begins with an observation that raises a question. Next, a possible explanation is formulated to answer the question, but that explanation must be testable. Generally, the tentative explanation will lead to a prediction. If the prediction holds true when it is tested, the test results support the explanation. If the original explanation is not supported, an alternative explanation is generated and tested. For example, if you were a scientist looking for potentially useful compounds in the rain forest, you might proceed as follows:

1. **Make careful observations and ask a question about the observations.** If, while walking through the rain forest, you came across a patch of small trees—that you later identify as lemon ant trees—growing in a cluster, with no other trees or plants growing among them, you might record and describe that observation (Figure 1a.5). Considering the density of different plants that you see on most of the forest floor, the relative isolation of this group of plants strikes you as odd. You are aware that some of the chemicals that plants produce to protect themselves from damage by insects or other plants have been found to have medicinal value and wonder if this plant or the lemon ants living on it might also be producing a chemical with medicinal value. You make up your mind to discover why other plants don't grow alongside lemon ant trees. You begin your study of the situation by collecting information about the plant and its surroundings. This includes, among other things, measuring the area of the patch and counting the approximate number of each type of plant in it.

FIGURE 1a.5 A patch of lemon ant trees, shown in the foreground, usually consists of only lemon ant trees. Other regions of the rain forest, as shown in the background, generally have a wide variety of organisms.

2. **Develop a testable hypothesis (possible explanation) as a possible answer to your question.** Now you start to formulate ideas about why other plants do not grow within patches of lemon ant trees. This statement is your **hypothesis**—an explanation for your observation. A good hypothesis can be tested. If a hypothesis cannot be tested, it is not useful in a scientific investigation because it cannot be supported or refuted. For example, the local people call a patch of lemon ant trees a devil's garden because they believe that the trees are planted by an evil forest spirit. You cannot test the hypothesis that an evil spirit is to blame, so it cannot advance your scientific understanding of why other plants don't grow with lemon ant trees. So, you develop your own possible explanation: the lemon ant trees are producing a chemical that inhibits the growth of other plants within their midst. This hypothesis can be tested, and even if it is found to be incorrect, it can still be useful in developing alternative hypotheses. Note that a hypothesis cannot be *proven* true; it can only be proven untrue.

3. **Make a prediction based on your hypothesis and test it with a controlled experiment.** Now you must plan an experiment to test your hypotheses. Ideally, your experiment will be designed in such a way that there can be only one explanation for the results. In such an experiment, called a **controlled experiment**, the research subjects (in this case, Spanish cedar saplings) are randomly divided into two groups. One group is designated as the **control group** and the other one is designated as the **experimental group.** Both groups are treated in the same way except for the *one* factor, called the **variable**, whose effect the experiment is designed to reveal. You would predict that, if the lemon ant trees were secreting a chemical into the soil of the patch that inhibited growth of invading plants, then a sapling of a tree other than the lemon ant tree would grow well outside of the patch, but not inside the patch.

   To test the hypothesis that lemon ant trees inhibit the growth of other plants you identify another tree, the Spanish cedar, that is common in the rain forest but is not usually found within a patch of lemon ant trees. You plant cedar saplings outside the patch of lemon ant trees (control group) and inside the patch (experimental group because this group is exposed to the hypothesized chemical from lemon ant trees). You find that the cedar saplings within the patch of lemon ant trees lose many of their leaves within 5 days.

   Do these results support your hypothesis? They seem to . . . but, without intending to, you actually had two variables: the lemon ant trees and the lemon ants that call these trees home. Lemon ants are common within a patch of lemon ant trees, but they are rare outside a patch. Could the lemon ants be inhibiting the growth of other invading plants? In a scientific study, additional variables that have not been controlled for and may have affected the outcome are called *confounding variables.* When there are confounding variables, we cannot say for sure which variable or variables caused the effect. So you experiment again. This time, you control for the lemon ants.

   You predict that if the ants were responsible, then preventing ants from reaching a different type of tree would allow the different tree to survive in the midst of lemon ant trees. Knowing that lemon ants almost never leave the patch of lemon ant trees, you randomly divide cedar saplings into four groups: (1) planted within the lemon ant tree patch with ants having access to them, (2) planted within the lemon ant tree patch with a sticky barrier preventing the ants from having access to them, (3) planted outside the lemon ant tree patch with ants having access to them (though few lemon ants travel outside their own patch of trees), (4) planted outside the lemon ant tree patch with a sticky barrier preventing the ants from having access to them (Figure 1a.6). You measure the number of dead cedar leaves on the forest floor after 5 days.

> **stop and THINK**
>
> Predict the results of this experiment. Which group(s) of cedar saplings would suffer the most leaf damage if chemicals from the lemon ant trees inhibit the growth of other plants? Which group(s) of cedar saplings would suffer the most leaf damage if lemon ants are inhibiting the growth of other plants?

4. **Draw a conclusion based on the results of the experiment.** Next, you arrive at a **conclusion**, which is an interpretation of the data. The results of a scientific experiment are often summarized in a graph, such as the one shown in Figure 1a.7, which presents the results of the experiment we just described. When you read a graph, first look at the axes. The horizontal line, or x-axis, shows the independent variables—the variables altered by the researcher. In this case, the independent variables are the four treatment groups. The vertical line is the y-axis; it presents the dependent variable, that is, the variable that was changed by the independent variables. In your experiment, the dependent variable was the number of dead cedar

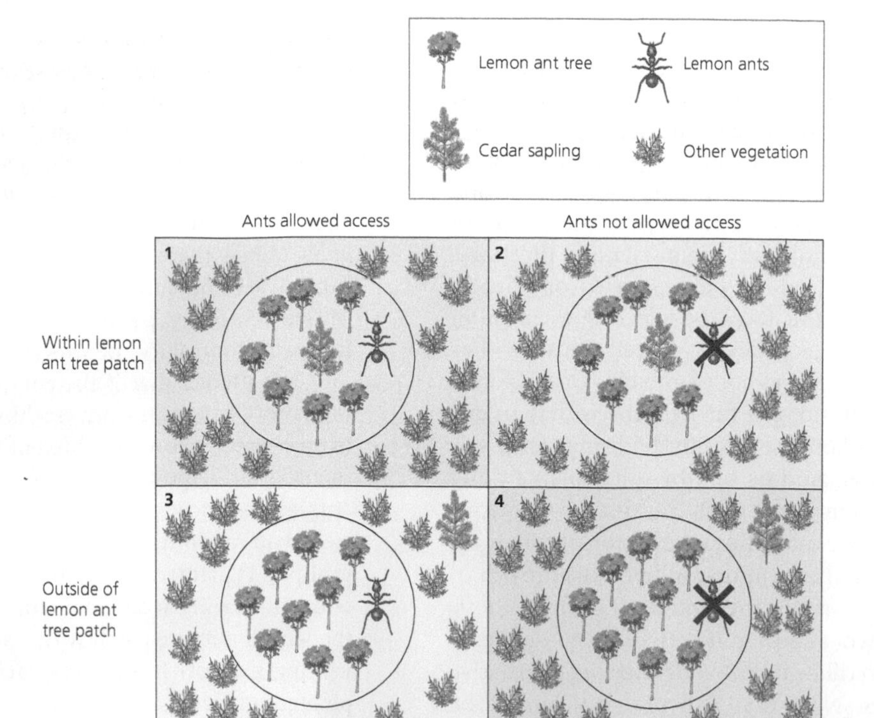

FIGURE 1a.6 **The experimental design used to test the hypothesis that lemon ants kill plants that invade the patch of lemon ant trees.**

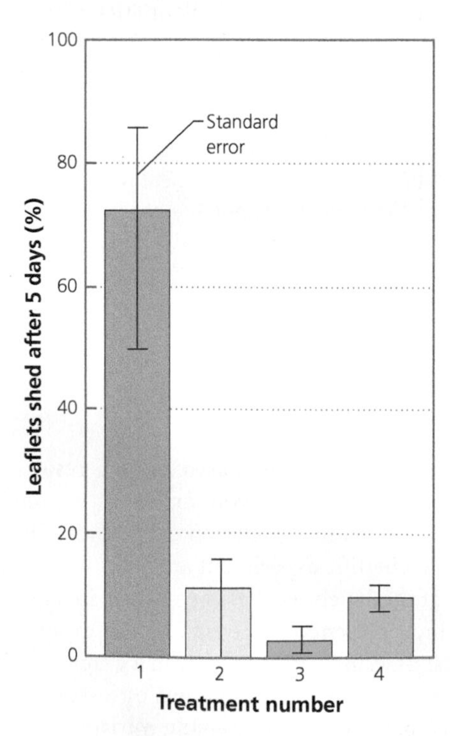

FIGURE 1a.7 **Leaf damage to cedar saplings planted within and outside of a patch of lemon ant trees. Lemon ants were excluded from two treatment areas—one inside and one outside the patch of lemon ant trees. These results indicate that lemon ants kill plants that invade a patch of lemon ant trees.**

leaves on the forest floor. Read the labels on the axes to see what the graph pertains to, and notice the scale to appreciate the extent of variation. This is a bar graph, and the height of the bar indicates the number of dead cedar leaves in each treatment. A bar graph is appropriate here because each treatment is a discrete category. (Variables that vary continuously, such as the change in factor x over time, would be better represented by a line graph.) Thus, the results of this experiment are that the number of dead leaves (a measure of damage to the cedar sapling) is greater in treatment 1 (sapling planted inside the patch of lemon ant trees with the ant permitted access to it) than in any other treatment group. We might have predicted that there would also be a greater number of dead leaves in treatment group 3 (sapling planted outside the patch of lemon ant trees with the ant permitted access to it), but few lemon ants leave the patch. A reasonable conclusion based on these results is that the lemon ants are inhibiting the growth of other plants, at least cedar trees, within the patch. Indeed, thanks to actual scientific research into this matter, we now know that lemon ants inject formic acid into the leaves of plants other than lemon ant trees. Once injected, the leaf dies within hours. Scientists suggest that lemon ants kill plants that invade a lemon ant tree patch to preserve and expand their habitat.

But what about your original hypothesis? Does the lemon ant tree itself also produce a chemical that inhibits the growth of other saplings? To answer this question, we compare the leaf damage to cedar saplings within the patch but with ants excluded (treatment 2) to leaf damage to cedar saplings outside the patch (treatments 3 and 4). The leaf damage to cedars within the patch is slightly greater. Scientists base conclusions on the **statistical significance** of the data, which is a measure of the possibility that the results were due to chance. A probability of less than 5% (written as $p < 0.05$) that the results are due to chance is generally acceptable. The lower the number, the more confidence we have in the accuracy of the results. The *standard error* reflects the degree of certainty of the results. In a graph, the standard error is shown as a vertical bar extending above and below the data point. If standard error bars overlap, the results are not statistically significant. Notice in Figure 1a.7 that the standard error bars for treatment groups 2, 3, and 4 overlap. Thus, the differences in leaf damage in those treatment groups could be due to chance alone. Using leaf damage as a measure, we cannot conclude that a chemical from the lemon ant tree inhibits new plant growth. Thus, even successful experiments often lead to revised hypotheses and further experimentation (Figure 1a.8).

Another requirement of scientific inquiry is that experiments must be repeated and yield similar results. Other scientists following the same procedure should obtain a similar outcome. Note, however, that it can be very difficult to identify all the factors that might affect the outcome of an experiment. In our rain forest experiment, for example, over time the rainfall, amount of light, and soil characteristics might all influence the results. Each time an experiment is repeated, additional factors may be identified as important.

The testing and refinement of a hypothesis represents one level of the scientific process. As time passes, related hypotheses that have been confirmed repeatedly can be fit together to form a **theory**—a well-supported and wide-ranging explanation of some aspect of the physical universe. Because of its breadth, a theory cannot be tested by a single experiment but instead emerges from many observations, hypotheses, and experiments. Nevertheless, a theory, like a hypothesis, leads to additional predictions and continued experimentation. Among the few explanations that have been tested thoroughly enough to be considered theories are the cell theory of life (which says all cells come from preexisting cells) and the theory of evolution by natural selection.

Inductive and Deductive Reasoning

As you examined the lemon ant tree, asked questions about it, and devised experiments to answer those questions, you made use of two types of logical reasoning: inductive and deductive.

Q *How would you modify this diagram to indicate that testing alternative hypotheses is also part of the scientific process?*

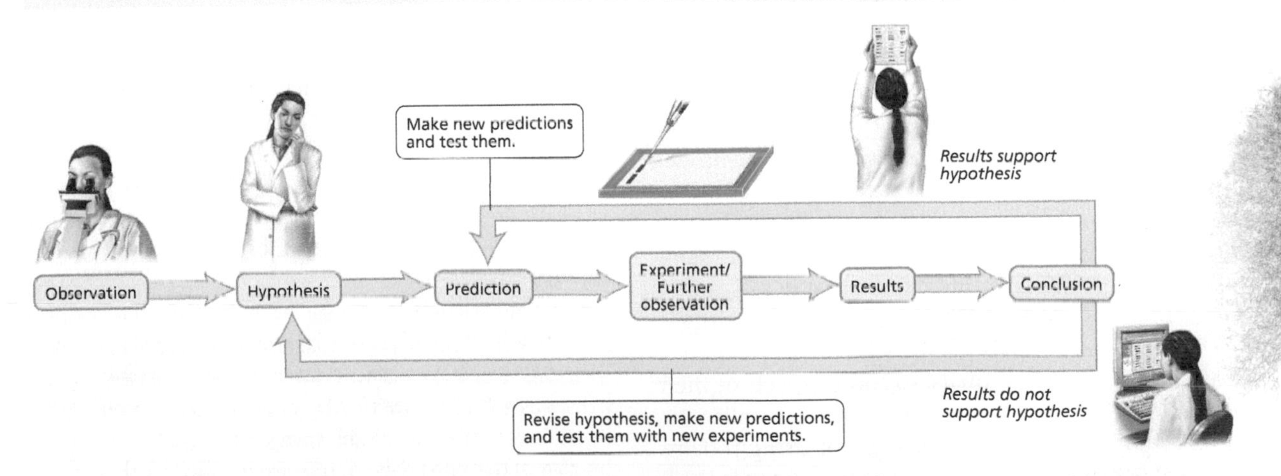

FIGURE 1a.8 **The scientific process consists of observation, creating testable hypotheses, experimentation, drawing conclusions, revising hypotheses, and designing new experiments.**

A *Add another arrow from "Observation" indicating Hypothesis 2. All the steps that are currently shown leading from "Hypothesis" would be repeated for Hypothesis 2.*

In **inductive reasoning,** facts are accumulated through observation until the sheer weight of the evidence allows some logical general statement to be made. An example is the way you collected as much information as you could about the lemon ant tree, other plants in the area, the soil, the light, and anything else that might have a bearing on your question. You then used those specific facts to draw the initial general conclusion that the lemon ant tree could be interfering with the growth of other plants in the area. You used inductive reasoning to develop a testable hypothesis.

Deductive reasoning, begins with a general statement that leads logically to one or more deductions, or conclusions. The process can usually be described as an "if-then" series of associations. *If* lemon ants are producing something that interferes with the growth of other plants, *then* there should be few plants other than lemon ant trees in areas where lemon ants live; *then* other plants should grow in areas without lemon ants; and so on. You used deductive reasoning to make predictions that would support your hypothesis and to decide whether the results of your experiment supported or refuted the hypothesis.

Clinical Trials

Recall that the reason for your interest in chemicals from plants in the rain forest was the hope that some of them might yield drugs to treat human ailments. You interviewed several native healers, collected many species of plants they use for healing, and made extensive notes on how the plants are used and what maladies the plants are used to treat. Now, you will preserve the plants for the trip home, where their extracts will undergo extensive testing and possible development into pharmaceuticals.

Each plant you collected is used by native people to treat a particular illness, so the first step for researchers is to identify all the chemicals in the extract and determine which one is the active ingredient; that is, which chemical is effective in treatment of the illness. That chemical is then purified to be tested as a drug.

Before testing a new drug or treatment on humans, scientists must take steps to ensure that it will not do more harm than good (Table 1a.1). Usually a drug is tested first on animals such as laboratory rodents. Rats and mice are mammals, so some aspects of their physiology are similar to, and can generalize to, human physiology. The advantages of using rodents for testing drugs include that they are relatively inexpensive to use, have short life spans, and reproduce quickly. Research on animals also helps determine how the drug is handled by the body, which helps determine dosage. Most medical advances, including vaccinations, chemotherapy, new surgical techniques, and organ transplants, began with animal studies. Strict rules safeguard the care and use of animals in research and testing.

TABLE 1a.1 Tests Performed on a New Drug before It Is Approved by the Food and Drug Administration (FDA)

Tests on laboratory animals	
Is the drug safe for use on animals?	
Clinical trials	
Phase I	Is the drug safe for humans?
Phase II	Does the drug work for its intended purpose?
Phase III	How does the new drug compare with other available treatments?

If no ill effects are discovered in animals receiving the drug, then studies on humans, called *clinical trials,* may begin. In all phases of clinical testing, the studies are done on people who volunteer. In phase I of a clinical trial, the drug is screened for safety on fewer than 100 healthy people. At this stage, researchers hope to learn whether they can safely give the drug to humans, determine the effective dosage range, and identify side effects.

If the drug is found to be safe, it is tested further. In phase II of a clinical trial, a few hundred people with the target disease are given the drug to see if it works for its intended purpose. If it does, the new drug will be compared with alternative treatments in phase III

what would you do?

The job of the FDA is to ensure the safety and effectiveness of new drugs and treatments. It must balance the patients' desires for access to new treatments against the government's desire to protect patients from treatments that may be unsafe or ineffective. The drug approval process is painstakingly slow, usually taking more than 8 years. Do you think that the FDA should bypass certain steps of the approval process to make new drugs available to critically ill patients who may not be able to wait? If you do, what criteria should be used to decide the degree of illness that would warrant treatment with a drug that was not yet approved? Who should be held responsible if early access to a drug of unknown safety causes a patient to suffer serious side effects or premature death? If you were ill and there was a drug for your illness in clinical trials, would you participate in those trials? What factors would influence your decision?

trials. Thousands of participants are involved in phase III of a clinical trial. The Food and Drug Administration (FDA) approves only those drugs or treatments that have passed all three phases of human-subjects testing.

Recall that a well-designed experiment has both an experimental group and a control group. Clinical studies are no different. In a drug trial, the experimental group receives the drug under consideration. The control group receives a **placebo,** an innocuous, nondrug substance made to look like the drug being tested. Study participants are randomly assigned to either the control group or the experimental group and do not know whether they are receiving the treatment or a placebo. When neither the researchers nor the study participants know which people are receiving treatment and which are receiving the placebo, the study is described as being *double-blind.* It is important that participants do not know whether they are receiving the placebo or the drug, because their expectations about the drug could affect the way they respond. Similarly, researchers should not know which people are in the experimental or control groups, because their expectations or desire for a particular result could affect their interpretation of the data.

Finally, it is extremely important, and legally required, that study participants give their **informed consent** before participating. An informed consent document lists all the possible harmful effects of the drug or treatment and must be signed before a person can take part in the study. To give informed consent, study participants must be mentally capable of understanding the treatment and risks, so they cannot be mentally impaired due to mental retardation, mental or other illness, or substance abuse.

Epidemiological Studies

Human health can also be studied without clinical trials. In an *epidemiological study*, researchers look at patterns that occur within large populations. For example, an epidemiological study to investigate the effects of air pollution on asthma (a condition in which airway constriction causes breathing problems) would look for a correlation of some kind between the variable of interest (air pollution) and its suspected effects (worsening of asthma). If the researchers' hypothesis is that air pollution aggravates asthma, they might predict and then look for evidence that the number of people admitted to hospitals for asthma-related problems increases with increased levels of air pollution.

Recent epidemiological studies have asked the question, "Does using a cell phone increase your risk of developing brain cancer?" Cell phones emit radiofrequency waves and are usually used by holding them to one's ear. A Danish study published in 2006[1] compared cancer rates of 426,000 cell phone users, some of whom had used cell phones for more than 20 years, with cancer rates of the general public, as recorded in the Danish national cancer registry. Researchers determined the amount of cell phone use by examining billing records, and people who had cancer before using a cell phone were excluded from the study. The cancer rates (in the brain, central nervous system, salivary gland, and the eye) among cell phone users was statistically the same as the cancer rates in the general population. Thus, this study does not demonstrate a link between cell phone use and cancer. Indeed, nearly all studies to date have failed to show such a link. Although these results are reassuring, additional research must be done. Cell phone use is a relatively new practice, and many cancers take years to develop. You can find current information on cell phones and cancer on the website of the American Cancer Society.

CRITICAL THINKING TO EVALUATE SCIENTIFIC CLAIMS

Few of us perform controlled experiments in our everyday lives, but all of us must evaluate the likely validity of scientific claims. We encounter them in many forms—as advertisements, news stories, and anecdotes told by friends. We often must make decisions based on these claims, but how can we decide whether they are valid? Critical-thinking skills can help us analyze the information and make prudent decisions.

The key to becoming a critical thinker is to ask questions. The following list is not exhaustive, but it may help guide your thinking process.

1. **Is the information consistent with information from other sources?** The best way to answer this question is to gather as much information as possible, from a variety of sources. Do not passively accept a report as true. Do some research.
2. **How reliable is the source of the information?** Investigate the source of the information to determine whether that person or group has the necessary scientific expertise. Is there any reason to think the claim may be biased? Who stands to

[1] Joachim Schütz and others, "Cellular Telephone Use and Cancer Risk: Update of a Nationwide Danish Cohort," *Journal of the National Cancer Institute* 98, no. 23 (December 6, 2006): 1707–13.

gain if you accept it as true? For example, the Food and Drug Administration (FDA) is probably a more reliable source of information on the effectiveness of a drug than is the drug company marketing the drug. If a claim is controversial, listen to both sides of the debate and be aware of who is arguing on each side.

3. **Was the information obtained through proper scientific procedures?** Information gathered through controlled experiments is more reliable than anecdotal evidence, which cannot be verified. For example, your friend might tell you that his muscles have gotten larger since he started using some special exercise equipment. But you cannot be sure unless measurements were taken before and after he began to use it. Even if your friend can prove his muscles are bigger with such measurements, there is no guarantee that exercising with this equipment will build *your* muscles.
4. **Were experimental results interpreted correctly?** Consider, for example, a headline advertising capsules containing fish oils: "Fish Oils Increase Longevity." It may be tempting to conclude from this headline that you will live longer if you take fish oil supplements, but in fact the headline is referring to an experiment in which *dietary* fish oil increased longevity in *rats*. Rats fed a diet high in fish oils lived longer than did rats on a diet low in fish oil. The claim that taking fish oil supplements will increase longevity is not a valid conclusion based on the experiment. First, the study was done on rats, not on humans. Not all aspects of rat physiology generalize to humans. For example, rats are more resistant to heart disease than are humans. Second, the amount of dietary fish oil, not the amount of fish oil from capsules that supplement dietary fish oil, was the variable in the study the headline refers to. Supplements of fish oil may not have the same effect as dietary fish oils. It could be that taking fish oil supplements would boost the amount of fish oil in your body to unhealthy levels.
5. **Are there other possible explanations for the results?** Suppose you learn that the fish oil headline is based on a study showing that people who eat fish at least three times a week live longer than those who eat fish less frequently. In this case, the data indicate that there is a correlation between fish in the diet and length of life. However, a correlation between two factors does not prove that one *caused* the other. Instead, the two factors may *both* be caused by a third factor. In this case, the difference in longevity may be due to other differences in the lifestyles of the two groups. For instance, people who eat fish may exercise more frequently or have less stressful jobs or live in areas with less pollution.

Throughout your life you will be asked to make many decisions about scientific issues. Some will affect your community and even beyond. For example, should we eliminate genetically modified food? Should stem cell research be permitted? Should we vaccinate the general public against smallpox? Should companies polluting the atmosphere be taxed at a higher rate? We will raise these and similar questions throughout this textbook. You will find others every day in the local and national news media.

Although you may never be one of the lawmakers deciding these issues, you are a voter who can help choose the lawmakers and voice your opinions to the lawmakers, who will decide. Scientists can provide facts that may be useful as we all struggle to answer the complex questions facing society, but they cannot provide simple answers. As scientific knowledge grows and our choices become increasingly complex, each of us must stay informed and review the issues critically.

CHAPTER 1b

CHEMISTRY COMES TO LIFE

Taken from *Biology of Humans: Concepts, Applications, and Issues*, Third Edition, by Judith Goodenough and Betty McGuire

THE NATURE OF ATOMS

The world around you contains an amazing variety of physical substances: the grass or concrete you walk on, the water you drink, the air you breathe, and even this book that you are reading. All of these substances that make up our world are called matter. Fundamentally, **matter** is anything that takes up space and has mass. All forms of matter are made up of atoms.

Atoms are units of matter that cannot be broken down into simpler substances by ordinary chemical means. Each atom is composed of even smaller, subatomic particles, such as protons, neutrons, and electrons. These subatomic particles are characterized by their location within the atom, their electrical charge, and their mass.

Each atom has a nucleus at its center and a surrounding spherical "cloud" of electrons. As you can see in Figure 1b.1, the nucleus contains protons and neutrons. Electrons, on the other hand, move around the nucleus and occur at certain energy levels called shells. Note that shells are three-dimensional spaces, although they are often depicted in textbook figures as two-dimensional circles for convenience. The shell closest to the nucleus can hold up to 2 electrons. The next shell out can hold up to 8 electrons. Atoms with more than 10 electrons have additional shells. Electrons have different amounts of energy; those with the most energy are found furthest from the nucleus. The chemical properties of an atom are determined by the number of electrons in its outermost shell. As we will see, those atoms whose outermost shells are not full tend to interact with other atoms.

Neutrons, as their name implies, are neutral: they have no electrical charge. In contrast, protons have a positive charge and electrons have a negative charge. The negatively charged electrons stay near the nucleus because they are attracted to the positively charged protons in it. Most atoms have the same number of positively charged protons and negatively charged electrons. As a result, they are "neutral," having no net charge. Table 1b.1 summarizes the basic characteristics of protons, neutrons, and electrons.

TABLE 1b.1 Review of Subatomic Particles

Particle	Location	Charge	Mass
Proton	Nucleus	1 positive unit	1 atomic mass unit
Neutron	Nucleus	None	1 atomic mass unit
Electron	Outside the nucleus	1 negative unit	Negligible

Elements

An **element** is a "pure" form of matter containing only one kind of atom. You are probably familiar with many elements, such as gold, silver, iron, and oxygen. Earth and everything on it or in its atmosphere is made up of a little more than 100 elements. Only about 20 elements are found in the human body, which consists mostly of carbon, oxygen, hydrogen, and nitrogen. Each element consists of atoms containing a certain number of protons in the nucleus. For example, all carbon atoms have 6 protons. The number of protons in the atom's nucleus is called the *atomic number*.

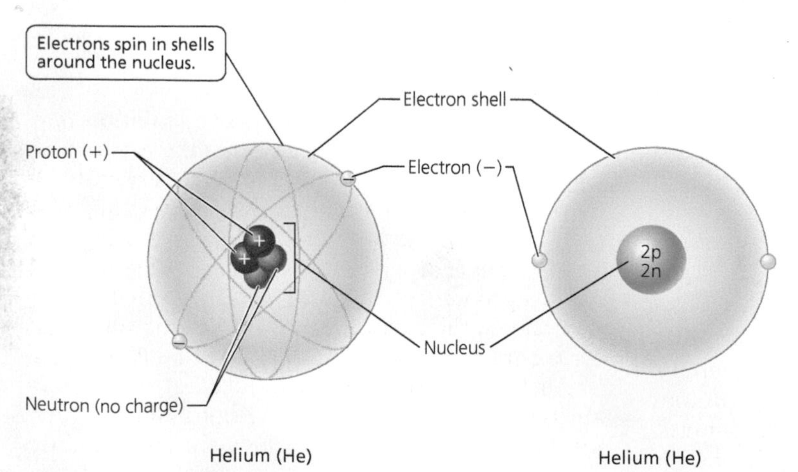

(a) A three-dimensional representation of an atom of helium, showing protons and neutrons in the nucleus and electrons occupying a region around the nucleus.

(b) A two-dimensional representation of an atom of helium.

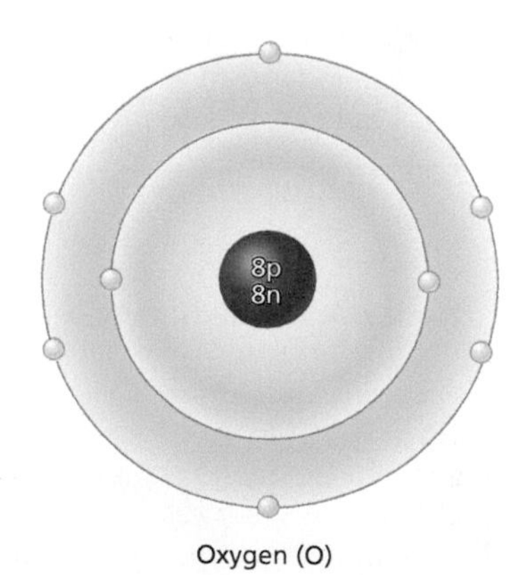

(c) A two-dimensional representation of an atom of oxygen.

FIGURE 1b.1 **Atoms can be represented in different ways.**

1 (Atomic number) H (Atomic symbol) 1.00 (Atomic mass)																	2 He 4.00
3 Li 6.94	4 Be 9.01											5 B 10.81	6 C 12.01	7 N 14.01	8 O 16.00	9 F 19.00	10 Ne 20.18
11 Na 22.99	12 Mg 24.31											13 Al 26.98	14 Si 28.09	15 P 30.97	16 S 32.06	17 Cl 35.45	18 Ar 39.95
19 K 39.10	20 Ca 40.08	21 Sc 44.96	22 Ti 47.88	23 V 50.94	24 Cr 52.00	25 Mn 54.94	26 Fe 55.85	27 Co 58.93	28 Ni 58.69	29 Cu 63.55	30 Zn 63.38	31 Ga 69.72	32 Ge 72.59	33 As 74.92	34 Se 78.96	35 Br 79.90	36 Kr 83.80
37 Rb 85.47	38 Sr 87.62	39 Y 88.91	40 Zr 91.22	41 Nb 92.91	42 Mo 95.94	43 Tc (98)	44 Ru 101.1	45 Rh 102.9	46 Pd 106.4	47 Ag 107.9	48 Cd 112.4	49 In 114.8	50 Sn 118.7	51 Sb 121.8	52 Te 127.6	53 I 126.9	54 Xe 131.3
55 Cs 132.9	56 Ba 137.3	57 La 138.9	72 Hf 178.5	73 Ta 180.9	74 W 183.9	75 Re 186.2	76 Os 190.2	77 Ir 192.2	78 Pt 195.1	79 Au 197.0	80 Hg 200.6	81 Tl 204.4	82 Pb 207.2	83 Bi 209.0	84 Po (209)	85 At (210)	86 Rn (222)
87 Fr (223)	88 Ra 226	89 Ac (227)	104 Rf (261)	105 Db (262)	106 Sg (263)	107 Bh (262)	108 Hs (265)	109 Mt (266)	110 — (269)	111 — (272)	112 — (277)						

58 Ce 140.1	59 Pr 140.9	60 Nd 144.2	61 Pm (145)	62 Sm 150.4	63 Eu 152.0	64 Gd 157.3	65 Tb 158.9	66 Dy 162.5	67 Ho 164.9	68 Er 167.3	69 Tm 168.9	70 Yb 173.0	71 Lu 175.0
90 Th 232.0	91 Pa (231)	92 U 238.0	93 Np (237)	94 Pu (244)	95 Am (243)	96 Cm (247)	97 Bk (247)	98 Cf (251)	99 Es (252)	100 Fm (257)	101 Md (258)	102 No (259)	103 Lr (260)

FIGURE 1b.2 **The periodic table**

The periodic table lists the elements and describes many of their characteristics. Figure 1b.2 depicts the periodic table. Note that each element has a name and a one- or two-letter symbol. The symbol for the element carbon, for example, is C, and that for chlorine is Cl. (The abbreviations are not always as intuitive; for example, the abbreviation for gold is Au, based on the Latin name for the metal.) Besides an atomic number, each atom also has an atomic weight. Each proton and neutron has an approximate mass of 1 atomic mass unit, or amu. The mass of an electron is so small that it is usually considered zero. Because electrons have negligible mass, and protons and neutrons each have an atomic mass of 1, the *atomic weight* for any atom equals the number of protons plus the number of neutrons. Oxygen has an atomic weight of 16, indicating that it has 8 protons (we know this from its atomic number) and 8 neutrons in its nucleus.

Isotopes and Radioisotopes

All the atoms of a particular element contain the same number of protons; they can, however, have different numbers of neutrons. Such differences result in atoms of the same element having slightly different atomic weights. Atoms that have the same number of protons but differ in the number of neutrons are called **isotopes.** More than 300 isotopes occur naturally on Earth. The element carbon, for example, has 3 isotopes. All carbon atoms have 6 protons in the nucleus. Most carbon atoms also have 6 neutrons, but some have 7 or 8. The isotopes of carbon thus have atomic weights of 12, 13, and 14, respectively, depending on the number of neutrons in the nucleus. These isotopes are written ^{12}C (the most common form in nature), ^{13}C, and ^{14}C.

Radiation is energy moving through space. Examples include radio waves, light, heat, and the excess energy or particles given off by unstable isotopes as they break down. Some elements have both stable and unstable isotopes. Unstable, radiation-emitting isotopes are called **radioisotopes.** About 60 occur naturally, and many more have been made in laboratories.

Radiation can be dangerous or useful, depending on the context. When dangerous, it can damage the body directly or indirectly. Direct damage to a person absorbing harmful radiation may include a low white blood cell count, development of some cancers, and damage to organs and glands. Short-term, high-level exposure to radiation can cause skin burns (Figure 1b.3). In other cases, radiation may not produce any noticeable injury to the person who was exposed; but it may alter the hereditary material in the cells of his or her reproductive system, possibly causing defects in the individual's offspring. For an example of the harmful effects of radiation and how to protect yourself from radiation that occurs naturally in the environment, see the Environmental Issue essay, *Radon Gas: A Killer That Can Be Stopped.*

In stark contrast to the harmful effects of radiation are its medical uses. Medical professionals use radiation for diagnosis and therapy. Perhaps the most familiar diagnostic use of radiation is the x-ray. A less common diagnostic procedure is the use of small doses of radiation to generate visual images of internal body parts. Radioactive iodine, for example, is often used to identify disorders of the thyroid gland. This gland, located in the

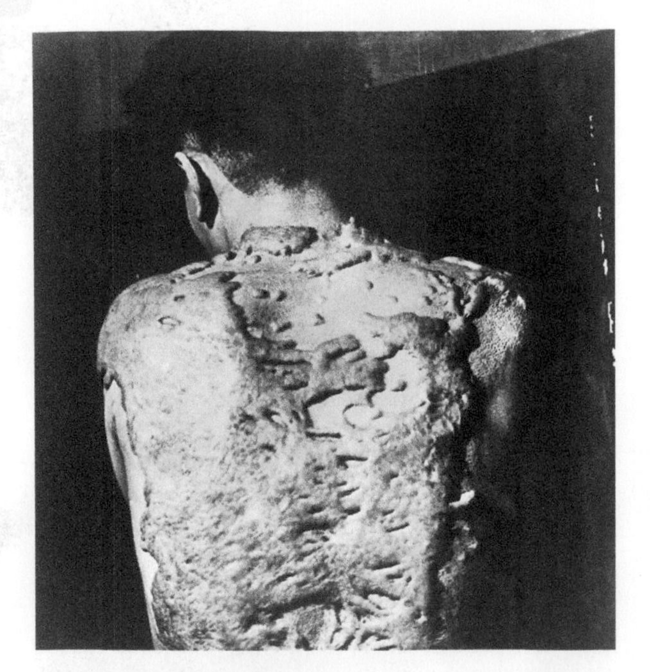

FIGURE 1b.3 **An example of direct damage caused by radiation. This individual survived the atomic explosion at Nagasaki, Japan, on August 9, 1945. Damage to the reproductive cells of people exposed to radiation has proved more difficult to recognize. Children of atomic bomb survivors are still being monitored.**

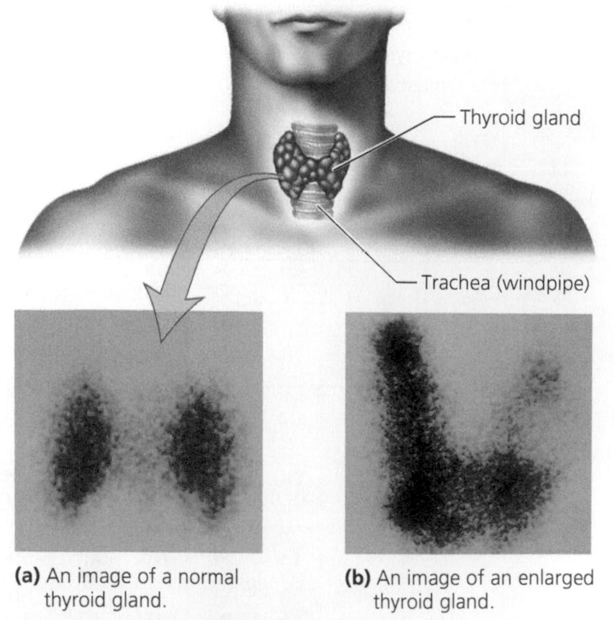

FIGURE 1b.4 **Radioactive iodine can be used to generate images of the thyroid gland. Such images may be used to diagnose metabolic disorders.**

neck, normally accumulates the element iodine, which it uses to regulate growth and metabolism. Small doses of iodine-131 (^{131}I), a radioactive isotope, can be given to a patient suspected of having metabolic problems. The radioactive iodine is taken up by the patient's thyroid gland and detected by medical instruments, as shown in Figure 1b.4. The small amount of radioactive iodine used in imaging does not damage the thyroid gland or surrounding structures. However, larger doses can be used to kill thyroid cells when the gland is enlarged and overactive.

Radiation can also be used to kill cancer cells. Cancer cells divide more rapidly and have higher rates of metabolic activity than do most normal cells. For these reasons, cancer cells are more susceptible to the destructive effects of radiation. Still, when medical professionals aim an outside beam of radiation at a tumor to kill the cancer cells inside it, they must also take steps to shield the surrounding healthy tissue. Sometimes a radiation source is placed within the body to treat a cancer. For example, one treatment for prostate cancer (the prostate gland is an accessory reproductive gland in males) involves the placement of radioactive seeds (pellets) directly in the prostate gland (Figure 1b.5). Once in place, the seeds emit radiation that damages or kills nearby cancer cells. In most cases, the seeds are left in place, even though they stop emitting radiation within 1 year.

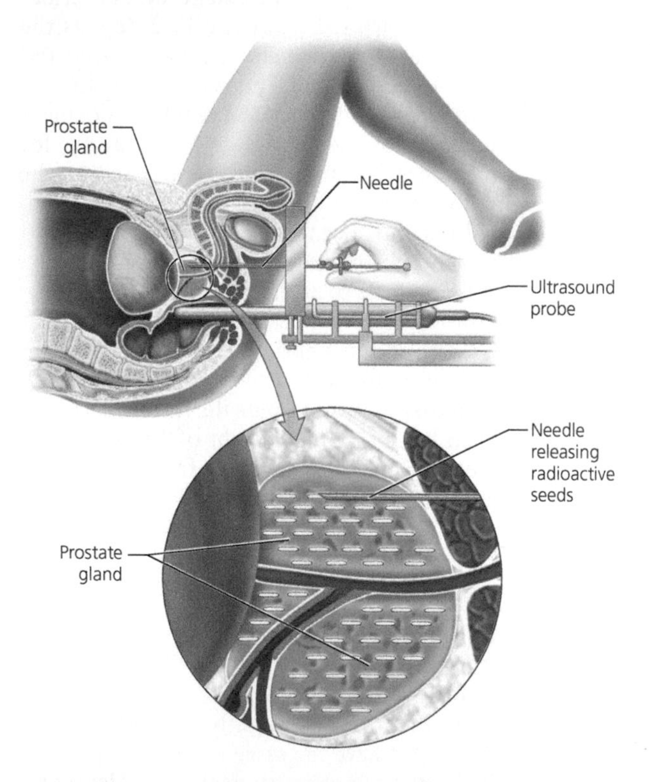

FIGURE 1b.5 **Prostate cancer can be treated by the implantation of radioactive seeds in the prostate gland. A physician injects the seeds through needles, with guidance from an ultrasound probe placed in the rectum.**

what would you do?

Irradiation is the process in which an item is exposed to radiation. Many foods today are intentionally irradiated for various reasons, such as (1) removing harmful microorganisms (pathogens), insect pests, and parasites; (2) delaying spoilage and increasing shelf life; and (3) sterilizing the material in which the food is packaged. The food does not become radioactive as a result. Supporters of the practice note that test animals fed on irradiated food show no adverse effects. Opponents, however, point to the environmental risks of building and operating food irradiation plants. Opponents also note that carefully controlled experiments are still needed to verify that irradiated food is safe for people of all ages and nutritional states. Several foods, including wheat flour, poultry, and white potatoes, have been approved for irradiation in the United States. These irradiated foods have a distinctive logo (Figure 1b.6) on their packaging. Would you eat irradiated food? What would you base your decision on?

FIGURE 1b.6 **Logo for irradiated foods. This logo and words such as "Treated with radiation" must appear on food that has been irradiated.**

COMPOUNDS AND CHEMICAL BONDS

Two or more elements may combine to form a new chemical substance called a **compound.** A compound's characteristics are usually different from those of its elements. Consider what happens when the element sodium (Na) combines with the element chlorine (Cl). Sodium is a silvery metal that explodes when it comes into contact with water. Chlorine is a deadly yellow gas. In combination, however, they form a crystalline solid called sodium chloride (NaCl)—plain table salt (Figure 1b.7).

The atoms (or, as we will soon see, ions) in a compound are held together by chemical bonds. There are two types of chemical bond: covalent and ionic. Recall that atoms have outer shells, which are the regions surrounding the nucleus where the electrons are most likely to be found. Figure 1b.8 depicts the first two shells as concentric circles around the nucleus. As discussed earlier, a full innermost shell contains 2 electrons. A full second shell contains 8 electrons. Atoms with a total of more than 10 electrons have additional shells. When atoms form bonds, they lose, gain, or share the electrons in their outermost shell.

(a) The element sodium is a solid metal.

(b) Elemental sodium reacts explosively with water.

(c) The element chlorine is a yellow gas.

(d) When the elements sodium and chlorine join, they form table salt, a compound quite different from its elements.

FIGURE 1b.7 **The characteristics of compounds are usually different from those of their elements.**

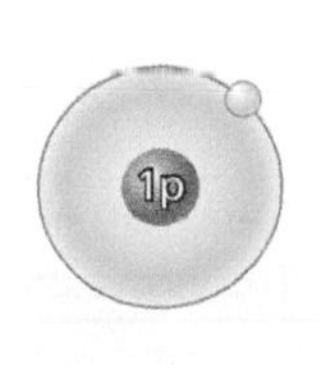

1p
Hydrogen atom
(atomic number = 1)

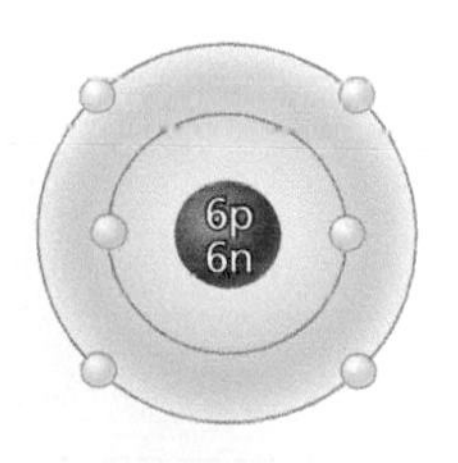

6p
6n
Carbon atom
(atomic number = 6)

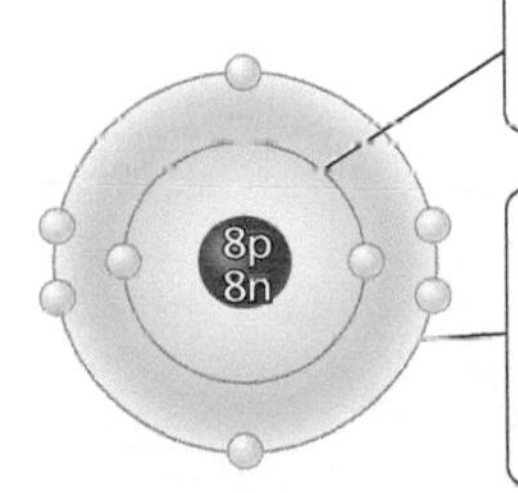

8p
8n
Oxygen atom
(atomic number = 8)
The shell closest to the nucleus can hold up to 2 electrons.
The next shell out can hold up to 8 electrons (the shell shown here has 6). Atoms with more than 10 electrons have additional shells.

FIGURE 1b.8 **Atoms of hydrogen, carbon, and oxygen. Each of the concentric circles around the nucleus represents a shell occupied by electrons.**

Covalent Bonds

A **covalent bond** forms when two or more atoms *share* electrons in their outer shells. Consider the compound methane (CH_4). Methane is formed by the sharing of electrons between one atom of carbon and four atoms of hydrogen. Notice in Figure 1b.9 that the outer shell of an isolated carbon atom contains only 4 electrons, even though it can hold as many as 8. Also note that hydrogen atoms only have 1 electron, although the first shell can hold up to 2 electrons. A carbon atom can fill its outer shell by joining with four atoms of hydrogen. At the same time, by forming a covalent bond with the carbon atom, each hydrogen atom fills its first shell. We see, then, that the covalent bonds between the carbon atom and hydrogen atoms of methane result in filled outer shells for all five atoms involved.

A **molecule** is a chemical structure held together by covalent bonds. Recall that compounds are formed by two or more elements, so molecules that contain only one kind of atom are not considered compounds. For example, oxygen gas, formed by the joining of two oxygen atoms, is *not* a compound, but it *is* a molecule. Molecules are described by a formula that contains the symbols for all of the elements included in that molecule. If more than one atom of a given element is present

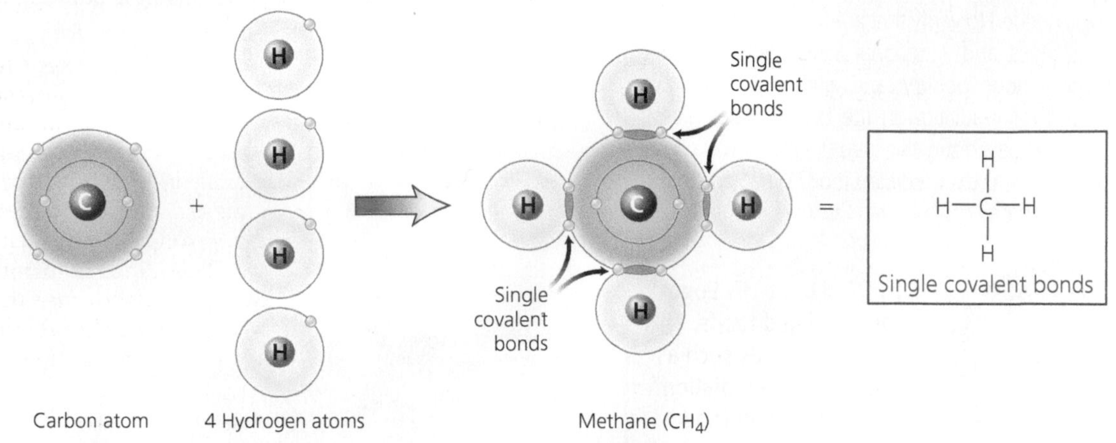

(a) The molecule methane (CH_4) is formed by the sharing of electrons between one carbon atom and four hydrogen atoms. Because in each case one pair of electrons is shared, the bonds formed are single covalent bonds.

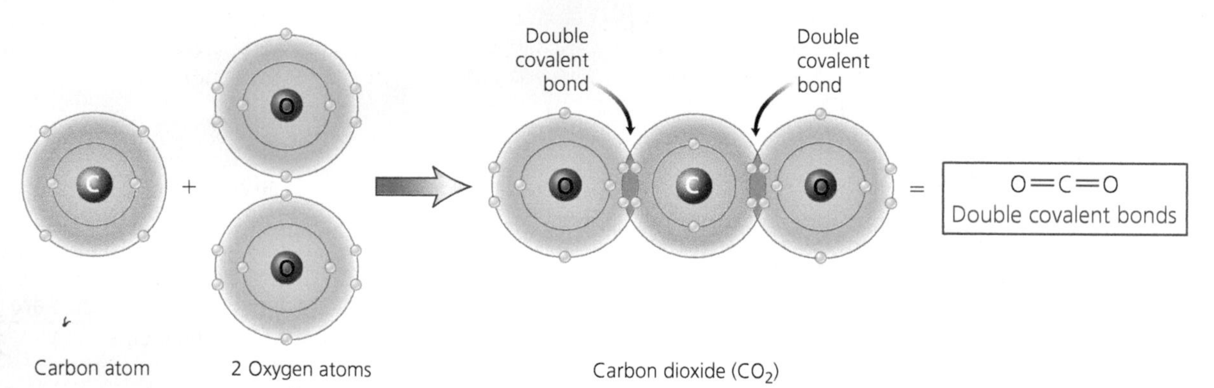

(b) The oxygen atoms in a molecule of carbon dioxide (CO_2) form double covalent bonds with the carbon atom. In double bonds, two pairs of electrons are shared.

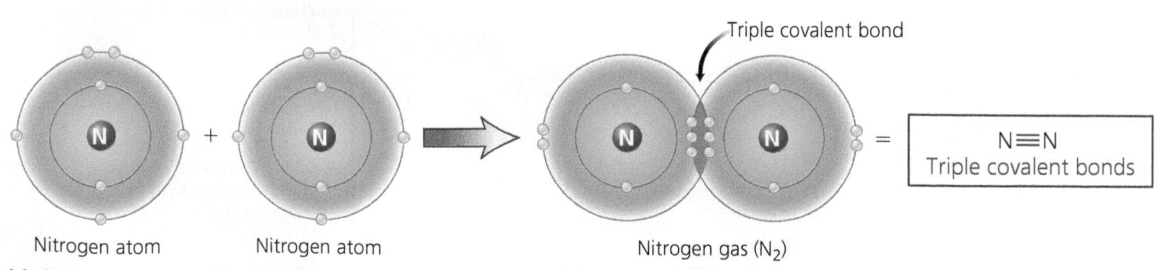

(c) The nitrogen atoms in nitrogen gas (N_2) form a triple covalent bond in which three pairs of electrons are shared.

FIGURE 1b.9 Covalent bonds form when electrons are shared between atoms. Shown here are examples of single, double, and triple covalent bonds. For each example, the structural formula is shown on the far right.

in the molecule, a subscript is used to show the precise number of that kind of atom. For example, the molecular formula of sucrose (table sugar) is $C_{12}H_{22}O_{11}$, showing that one molecule of sucrose contains 12 atoms of carbon, 22 atoms of hydrogen, and 11 atoms of oxygen. Numbers placed in front of the molecular formula indicate more than one molecule. For example, three molecules of sucrose are described by the formula $3C_{12}H_{22}O_{11}$.

As shown in the methane molecule in Figure 1b.9a, the bond between each of the four hydrogen atoms and the carbon atom consists of a single pair of electrons. A bond in which a single pair of electrons is shared is called a single bond; in this example, the methane molecule contains four single covalent bonds. Sometimes, however, two atoms share two or three pairs of electrons. These bonds are called double and triple covalent bonds, respectively. For example, carbon dioxide, CO_2, produced by chemical reactions inside our cells, has double covalent bonds between the carbon atom and each of two oxygen atoms (Figure 1b.9b). And the nitrogen atoms in nitrogen gas, N_2, are joined by triple covalent bonds (Figure 1b.9c).

Covalent bonds in molecules are sometimes depicted by a structural formula. Notice in the box at the right of Figure 1b.9a that one straight line is drawn between the carbon atom and each hydrogen atom in the structural formula for the methane molecule. The single line indicates a single covalent bond resulting from a pair of shared electrons. In the box to the right of Figure 1b.9b, the double lines between the carbon and oxygen atoms in the carbon dioxide molecule indicate a double covalent bond, or two pairs of shared electrons. In Figure 1b.9c, three lines drawn between the two nitrogen atoms in gaseous nitrogen depict a triple covalent bond, or three pairs of shared electrons.

Ionic Bonds

We have all heard the phrase "opposites attract" in reference to human relationships—and it is no different for ions. An **ion** is an atom or group of atoms that carries either a positive (+) or a negative (–) electrical charge. Electrical charges result from the *transfer* (as opposed to sharing) of electrons between atoms. Recall that a neutral atom has the same number of positively charged protons and negatively charged electrons. An atom that loses an electron has one more proton than electrons and therefore has a positive charge. An atom that gains an electron has one more electron than protons and has a negative charge. Oppositely charged ions are attracted to one another. An **ionic bond** results from the mutual attraction of oppositely charged ions.

Ions form because of the tendency of atoms to attain a complete outermost shell. Consider, again, the atoms of sodium and chlorine that join to form sodium chloride. As shown in Figure 1b.10, an atom of sodium has 1 electron in its outer shell. An atom of chlorine has 7 electrons in its outer shell. Sodium chloride is formed when the sodium atom transfers the single electron in its outer shell to the chlorine atom. The sodium atom now has a full outer shell. This comes about because the sodium atom loses its third shell, making the second shell its outermost shell. The sodium atom, having lost an electron, has one more proton than electrons and therefore now has a positive charge (Na^+). The chlorine atom, having gained an electron to fill its outer shell, has one more electron than protons and now has a negative charge (Cl^-). These oppositely charged ions are attracted to one another, and an ionic bond forms. Because they do not contain shared electrons, ionic bonds are weaker than covalent bonds.

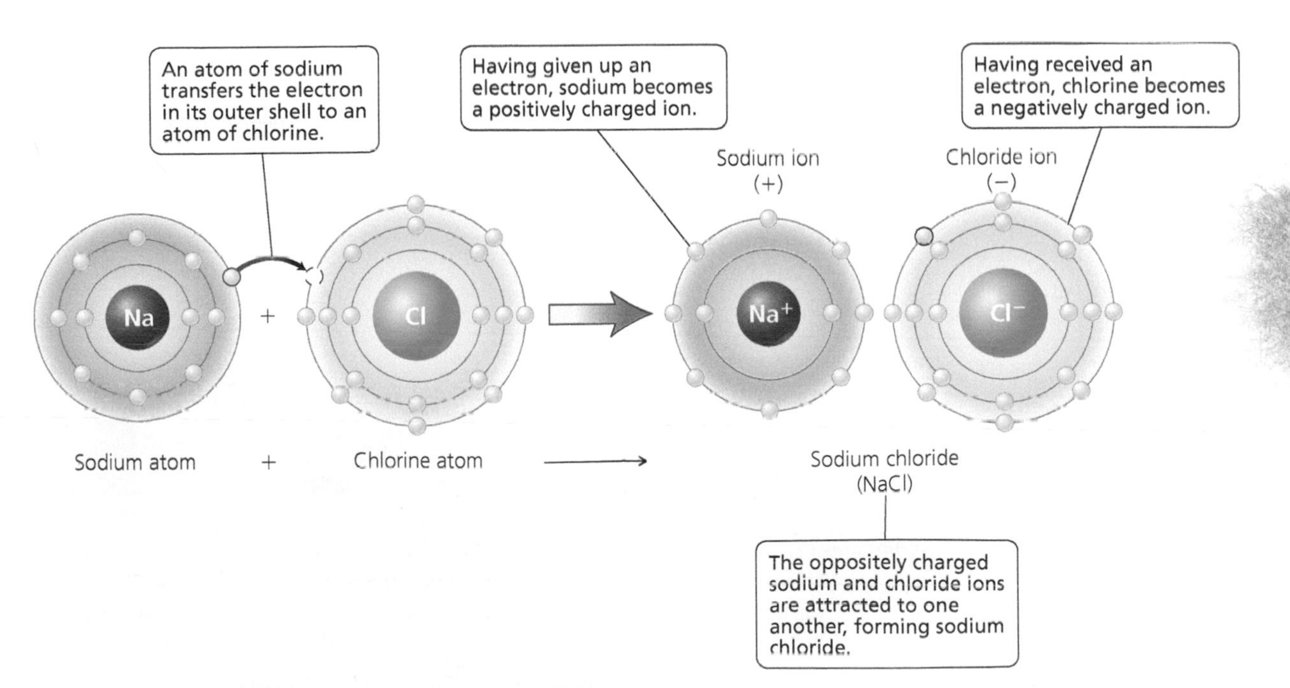
An atom of sodium transfers the electron in its outer shell to an atom of chlorine.
Having given up an electron, sodium becomes a positively charged ion.
Having received an electron, chlorine becomes a negatively charged ion.
Sodium ion (+)
Chloride ion (–)
Na
+
Cl
Na+
Cl−
Sodium atom
+
Chlorine atom
Sodium chloride (NaCl)
The oppositely charged sodium and chloride ions are attracted to one another, forming sodium chloride.

FIGURE 1b.10 **An ionic bond involves the transfer of electrons between atoms. Such a transfer creates oppositely charged ions that are attracted to one another.**

THE ROLE OF WATER IN LIFE

Water is such a familiar part of our everyday lives that we often overlook its unusual qualities. Unique properties of water include its virtuosity as a dissolving agent, its high heat capacity, and its high heat of vaporization. As it turns out, water's unusual qualities can be traced to its polarity (tendency of its molecules to have positive and negative regions) and the hydrogen bonds between its molecules.

Polarity and Hydrogen Bonds

In covalently bonded molecules, electrons may be shared equally or unequally between atoms. When the sharing of electrons is unequal, different ends of the same molecule can have slight opposite charges. Unequal covalent bonds are called *polar*, and molecules with unevenly distributed charges are called polar molecules. In water (H_2O), for example, the electrons shared by oxygen and hydrogen spend more time near the oxygen atom than near the hydrogen atom. As a result, the oxygen atom has a slight negative charge; each hydrogen atom has a slight positive charge; and water molecules are polar (Figure 1b.11a). The hydrogen atoms of one water molecule are attracted to the oxygen atoms of other water molecules. The attraction between a slightly positively charged hydrogen atom and a slightly negatively charged atom nearby is called a **hydrogen bond.** In the case of water, the hydrogen bonding occurs between hydrogen and oxygen. However, sometimes hydrogen bonds form between hydrogen and atoms of other elements.

Hydrogen bonds are weaker than either ionic or covalent bonds. For this reason, they are generally illustrated by dotted lines rather than solid lines, as shown in Figure 1b.11b. Even though individual hydrogen bonds are very weak, collectively they can be significant. Hydrogen bonds maintain the shape of proteins and our hereditary material, DNA, and they account for some of the unique physical properties of water.

Covalent bonds, ionic bonds, and hydrogen bonds are summarized in Table 1b.2.

TABLE 1b.2 Review of Chemical Bonds

Type	Basis for Attraction	Strength	Example
Covalent	Sharing of electrons between atoms; the sharing between atoms may be equal or unequal	Strongest	CH_4 (methane)
Ionic	Transfer of electrons between atoms creates oppositely charged ions that are attracted to one another	Strong	NaCl (table salt)
Hydrogen	Attraction between a hydrogen atom with a slight positive charge and another atom (often oxygen) with a slight negative charge	Weak	Between a hydrogen atom on one water molecule and an oxygen atom on another water molecule

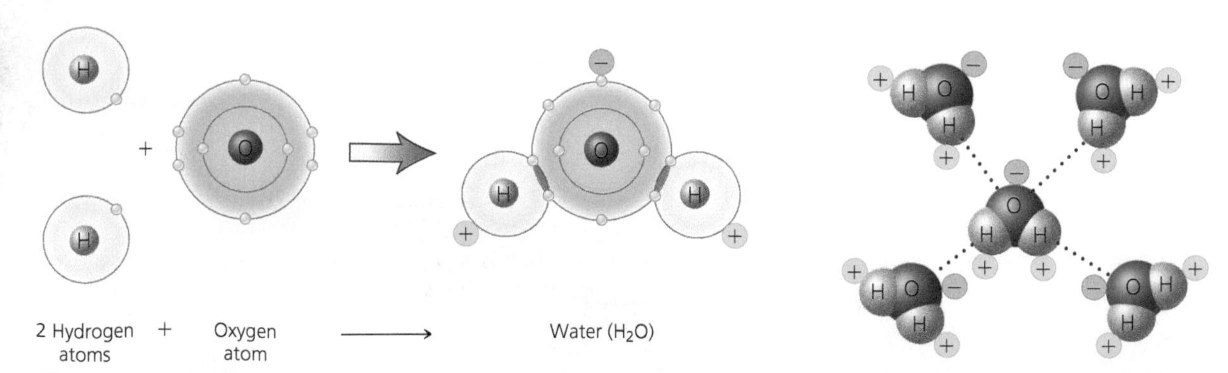

(a) Water is formed when an oxygen atom covalently bonds (shares electrons) with two hydrogen atoms. Due to unequal sharing of electrons, oxygen carries a slight negative charge and the hydrogen atoms carry a slight positive charge.

(b) The hydrogen atoms from one water molecule are attracted to the oxygen atoms of other water molecules. This relatively weak attraction (shown by dotted lines) is called a hydrogen bond.

FIGURE 1b.11 **The hydrogen bonds of water**

Properties of Water

Life depends on the properties of water. Let's consider some of the ways that the polarity and hydrogen bonding of water give water the properties that make it so vital to life.

Due to the polarity of its molecules, water interacts with many substances. This interactivity makes it an excellent solvent, easily dissolving both polar and charged substances. Ionic compounds, such as NaCl, dissolve into independent ions in water. The sodium ions and chloride ions separate from one another in water because the sodium ions are attracted to the negative regions of water molecules and the chloride ions are attracted to the positive regions. Because of its excellence as a solvent, water serves as the body's main transport medium. As the liquid component of blood, it carries dissolved nutrients, gases, and wastes through the circulatory system. Metabolic wastes are excreted from the body in urine, another watery medium.

Water also helps prevent dramatic changes in body temperature. About 67% of the human body is water (thus, if a person weighs 68 kg (150 lb), water makes up about 45 kg (100 lb) of the body weight). Because humans, as well as many other organisms, are made up largely of water, they are well suited to resist changes in body temperature and to keep a relatively stable internal environment. This ability comes from water's *high heat capacity*, which simply means that a great deal of heat is required to raise its temperature. Hydrogen bonds hold multiple water molecules together, so a large amount of heat is required to break these bonds (a higher temperature corresponds to an increase in the movement of the molecules). Water in blood also helps redistribute heat within our bodies. Our fingers don't usually freeze on a frigid day because heat is carried to them by blood from muscles where the heat is generated.

Another property of water that helps prevent the body from overheating is its *high heat of vaporization*, which means that a great deal of heat is required to make water evaporate (that is, change from a liquid to a gas). Water's high heat of vaporization is also due to its hydrogen bonds, which must be broken before water molecules can leave the liquid and enter the air. (These bonds, by the way, remain broken as long as water is in the gaseous phase known as water vapor.) Water molecules that evaporate from a surface carry away a lot of heat, cooling the surface. We rely on the evaporation of water in sweat to cool the body surface and prevent overheating (Figure 1b.12). By the same token, water vapor in the air can inhibit the evaporation of sweat—which is why we tend to feel hotter on a humid day.

It is clear that water is essential for human life and for the lives of many other organisms we share the planet with. Despite our reliance on water, we continue to pollute both seawater and freshwater. Equally alarming is the global shortage of freshwater, caused largely by the burgeoning human population.

FIGURE 1b.12 The evaporation of water in sweat cools the surface of this runner's body. Water has a high heat of vaporization, so when water molecules in sweat evaporate, they carry away a lot of heat.

stop and THINK

Sharp increases in body temperature can cause heat stroke, a condition that may damage the brain. Explain why heat stroke is more likely to occur on a hot, humid day than on an equally hot, dry day.

Acids and Bases

Sometimes a water molecule dissociates, or breaks up, forming a positively charged hydrogen ion (H^+) and a negatively charged hydroxide ion (OH^-):

$$\underset{\text{H—O—H}}{\text{H—O—H}} \rightleftharpoons \underset{\text{Hydrogen ion}}{H^+} + \underset{\text{Hydroxide ion}}{OH^-}$$

(Note that in equations describing chemical reactions, an arrow should be read as "yields.")

In any sample of water, the fraction of water molecules that are dissociated is extremely small, so water molecules are much more common in the human body than are H^+ and OH^-. In fact, the amount of H^+ in the body must be precisely regulated. Even slight changes in the concentration of H^+ can be disastrous, disrupting chemical reactions within cells. Substances called acids and bases influence the concentration of H^+ in solutions.

Acids and bases are defined by what happens when they are added to water. An **acid** is anything that releases hydrogen ions (H^+) when placed in water. A **base** is anything that releases hydroxide ions OH^- when placed in water. Hydrochloric acid (HCl), for example, dissociates in water to produce hydrogen ions (H^+) and chloride ions (Cl^-). Because HCl increases the concentration of H^+ in solution, it is classified as an acid. Sodium hydroxide (NaOH), on the other hand, dissociates in water to produce sodium ions (Na^+) and hydroxide ions (OH^-). Because NaOH increases the concentration of in solution, it is classified as a base. The OH^- produced when NaOH dissociates reacts with H^+ to form water molecules and thus reduces the concentration of H^+ in solution. Therefore, acids increase the concentration of H^+ in solution, and bases decrease the concentration of H^+ in solution.

The pH Scale

We often want to know more than simply whether a substance is an acid or a base. For example, how strong an acid is battery acid? How strong a base is household ammonia? Questions like these can be answered by knowing the pH of these solutions and understanding the pH scale (Figure 1b.13). The **pH** of a solution is a measure of hydrogen ion concentration. The **pH scale** ranges from 0 to 14, with a pH of 7 being neutral (the substance does not increase H^+ or OH^-), a pH of less than 7 being acidic, and a pH of greater than 7, basic.

Usually, the amount of H^+ in a solution is very small. For example, the concentration of H^+ in a solution with a pH of 6 is 1×10^{-6} (or 0.000001) moles per liter (a mole, here, is not a small furry animal with a star-shaped nose, but a unit of measurement that indicates a specific number of atoms, molecules, or ions). Similarly, the concentration of H^+ in a solution with a pH of 5 is 1×10^{-5} (or 0.00001) moles per liter. Technically, pH is the negative logarithm of the concentration of H^+ in a solution. According to the pH scale, the lower the pH, the greater the acidity—or concentration of H^+—in a solution. Each reduction of pH by one unit represents a tenfold increase in the amount of H^+. So a solution with a pH of 5 is 10 times more acidic than a solution with a pH of 6. And a solution with a pH of 4 is 100 times more acidic than one with a pH of 6. Some characteristics of acids and bases, including their values on the pH scale, are summarized in Table 1b.3.

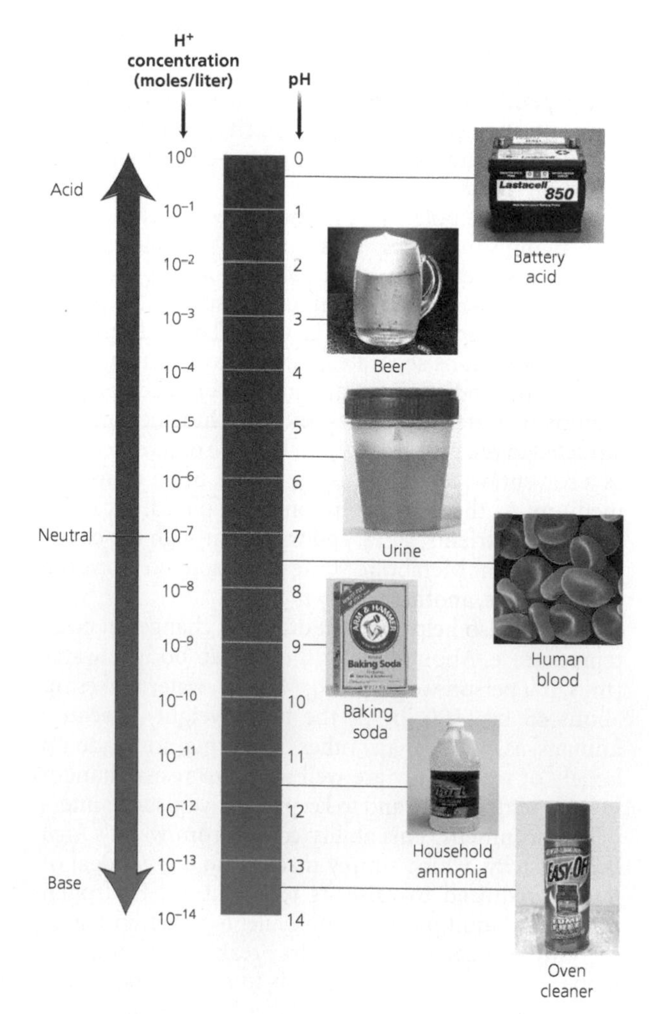

FIGURE 1b.13 The pH scale and the pH of some body fluids and other familiar substances

TABLE 1b.3 Review of the Characteristics of Acids and Bases

Characteristic	Acid	Base
Behavior in water	Releases H^+	Releases OH^-
pH	Less than 7	Greater than 7
Example	HCl (hydrochloric acid)	NaOH (sodium hydroxide)

Buffers

Most biological systems must keep their fluids within a narrow range of pH values. Substances called **buffers** keep pH values from changing dramatically. Buffers remove excess H^+ from solution when concentrations of H^+ increase. Buffers add H^+ when concentrations of H^+ decrease. For example, an important buffering system that keeps the pH of blood at about 7.4 is the carbonic acid–bicarbonate system. When carbon dioxide is added to water it forms carbonic acid (H_2CO_3), which dissociates into hydrogen ions and bicarbonate ions (HCO_3^-):

$$\underset{\text{Carbon dioxide}}{CO_2} + \underset{\text{Water}}{H_2O} \rightleftharpoons \underset{\text{Carbonic acid}}{H_2CO_3} \rightleftharpoons \underset{\text{Hydrogen ion}}{H^+} + \underset{\text{Bicarbonate ion}}{HCO_3^-}$$

Carbonic acid and bicarbonate have a buffering action because when levels of H^+ decrease in the blood, carbonic acid dissociates, adding H^+ to solution. When levels of H^+ increase in the blood, the H^+ combines with bicarbonate and is removed from solution. Such action is essential because even slight changes in the pH of blood—say, a drop from 7.4 to 7.0 or an increase to 7.8—can cause death in a few minutes.

In the human body, almost all biochemical reactions occur around pH 7 and are maintained at that level by powerful buffering systems. An important exception occurs in the stomach, where hydrochloric acid (HCl) produces pH values from about 1 to 3. In the stomach, HCl kills bacteria swallowed with food or drink and promotes the initial breakdown of proteins. These activities require an acid stomach, and the stomach has several ways of protecting itself from the acid. However, sometimes stomach acid backs up into the esophagus, and "heartburn" is the uncomfortable result. Taking an antacid can ease the discomfort of heartburn. Antacids consist of weak bases that temporarily relieve the pain of stomach acid in the esophagus by neutralizing some of the hydrochloric acid.

The critical link between pH and life is illustrated by the impact of acid rain on our environment and health. Acid rain is usually defined as rain with a pH lower than 5.6, the pH of natural precipitation. It is caused largely by the burning of fossil fuels in cars, factories, and power plants. The sulfur dioxide and nitrogen oxides produced by these activities react with water in the atmosphere to form sulfuric acid (H_2SO_4) and nitric acid (HNO_3). These acids fall to Earth as rain, snow, or fog, with pH values sometimes as low as 1.5.

The effects of acid rain on the environment have been devastating (Figure 1b.14). On land, acid rain has been linked to the decline of forests. Trees, for example, become stressed and more susceptible to disease when their nutrient uptake is disrupted by increased acidity in the soil. In aquatic environments, acid rain has been linked to the decrease and sometimes total elimination of populations of fish and amphibians. Embryos of spotted salamanders, for example, develop abnormally under somewhat acidic conditions and die when pH values are less than about 5. Acid rain is harmful to human health, as well. The pollutants that cause acid rain form fine particles of sulfate and nitrate that are easily inhaled. Once inside us, they cause irritation and respiratory illnesses such as asthma and bronchitis.

Because most acid rain is caused by human activity, it is within our power to reduce, if not eliminate, the problem. Power plants and automobile manufacturers have taken steps to reduce emissions of sulfur dioxide and nitrogen oxides, leading to significant progress in reducing acid rain.

MAJOR MOLECULES OF LIFE

Most of the molecules we have discussed so far have been small and simple. Many of the molecules of life, however, are enormous by comparison and have complex architecture. Some proteins, for example, are made up of thousands of atoms linked together in a chain that

(a) Acid rain has destroyed parts of our forests.

(b) In some areas, acid rain has reduced or eliminated populations of aquatic organisms. Acidic conditions have been shown, for example, to disrupt the development of spotted salamanders or to kill the embryos outright.

FIGURE 1b.14 **Effects of acid rain**

repeatedly coils and folds upon itself. Exceptionally large molecules, including many important biological molecules, are known as **macromolecules.**

Macromolecules that consist of many small, repeating molecular subunits linked in a chain are called **polymers.** The small molecular subunits that form the building blocks of the polymer are called **monomers.** We might think of a polymer as a pearl necklace, with each monomer representing a pearl. As we shall see, a protein is a polymer, or chain, of amino acid monomers linked together. And glycogen, the storage form of carbohydrates in animals, is a polymer of glucose monomers.

Polymers form through **dehydration synthesis** (sometimes called the condensation reaction). In this process, the reaction that bonds one monomer covalently to another releases a water molecule: one of the monomers donates OH, and the other donates H. The reverse process, called **hydrolysis,** which the body uses to break many polymers apart, requires the addition of water across the covalent bonds. The H from the water molecule attaches to one monomer and the OH attaches to the adjoining monomer, thus breaking the covalent bond between the two. Hydrolysis plays a critical role in digestion. Most foods consist of polymers too large to pass from our digestive tract into the bloodstream and on to our cells. Thus, the polymers are hydrolyzed into their component monomers. The monomers can then be absorbed into the bloodstream for transport throughout the body. Dehydration synthesis and hydrolysis are summarized in Figure 1b.15.

Carbohydrates

The **carbohydrates** known commonly as sugars and starches provide fuel (energy) for the human body. Carbohydrates are compounds made entirely of carbon, hydrogen, and oxygen, with each molecule having twice as many hydrogen atoms as oxygen atoms. Sugars and starches can be classified by size into monosaccharides, oligosaccharides, and polysaccharides. Some common carbohydrates are described in Table 1b.4.

Monosaccharides

Monosaccharides, also called simple sugars, are the smallest molecular units of carbohydrates. They contain from three to seven carbon atoms and, in fact, can be classified by the number of carbon atoms they contain. A sugar that contains five carbons is *pent*ose; one with six carbons is *hex*ose; and so on. Glucose, fructose, and galactose are examples of six-carbon sugars (Table 1b.4). Monosaccharides can be depicted in several ways (Figure 1b.16).

Oligosaccharides

Oligosaccharides (*oligo* means "few") are chains of a few monosaccharides joined together by dehydration synthesis. **Disaccharides,** one type of oligosaccharide, are double sugars that form when two monosaccharides covalently bond to each other. The disaccharide sucrose (table sugar) consists of the monosaccharides glucose and fructose (Figure 1b.17). Two glucose molecules form the disaccharide maltose, an important ingredient of beer. Another disaccharide is lactose, the principal carbohydrate of milk and milk products. Lactose is formed by the joining of glucose and galactose.

Polysaccharides

Polysaccharides (*poly* means "many") are complex carbohydrates that form when monosaccharides (most commonly glucose) join together in long chains. Most

(a) Polymers are formed by dehydration synthesis, in which a water molecule is removed and two monomers are joined.

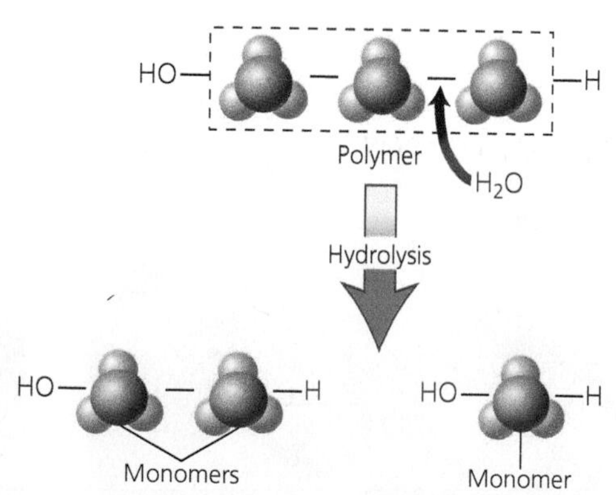

(b) Polymers are broken down by hydrolysis, in which the addition of a water molecule disrupts the bonds between two monomers.

FIGURE 1b.15 **Formation and breaking apart of polymers**

TABLE 1b.4 Review of Some Common Carbohydrates

Carbohydrate	Molecular Formula	Source	Monomers
Monosaccharides			
Glucose	$C_6H_{12}O_6$	Blood, fruit, honey	
Fructose	$C_6H_{12}O_6$	Fruit, honey	
Galactose	$C_6H_{12}O_6$	From hydrolysis of lactose (milk sugar)	
Disaccharides			
Sucrose	$C_{12}H_{22}O_{11}$	Sugar cane, maple syrup	Glucose, fructose
Maltose	$C_{12}H_{22}O_{11}$	From hydrolysis of starch; ingredient in beer	Glucose
Lactose	$C_{12}H_{22}O_{11}$	Component of milk	Glucose, galactose
Polysaccharides			
Starch	*	Potatoes, corn, some grains	Glucose
Glycogen	*	Stored in muscle and liver cells	Glucose
Cellulose	*	Cell walls of plants	Glucose

*These complex carbohydrates consist of chains containing hundreds of glucose molecules joined to each other in long strings.

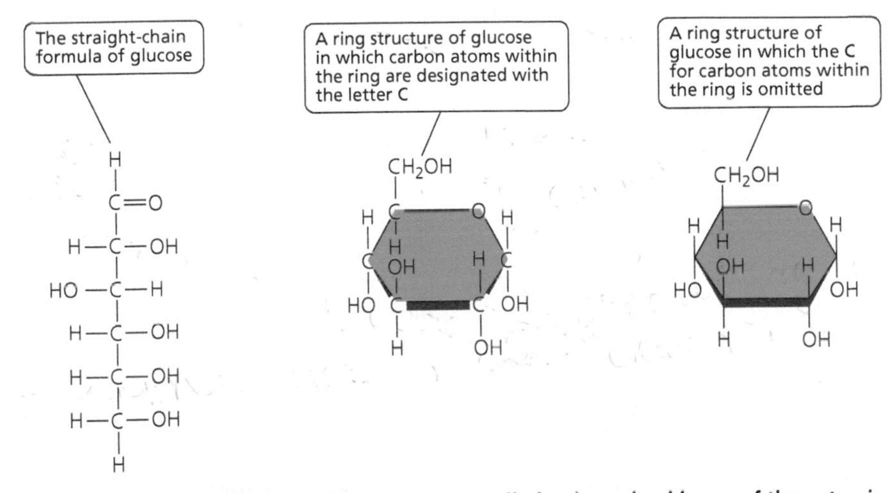

FIGURE 1b.16 **Monosaccharides are simple sugars, generally having a backbone of three to six carbon atoms. Many of these carbon atoms are also bonded to hydrogen (H) and a hydroxyl group (OH). In the fluid within our cells, the carbon backbone usually forms a ringlike structure. Here, three representations of the monosaccharide glucose ($C_6H_{12}O_6$) are shown.**

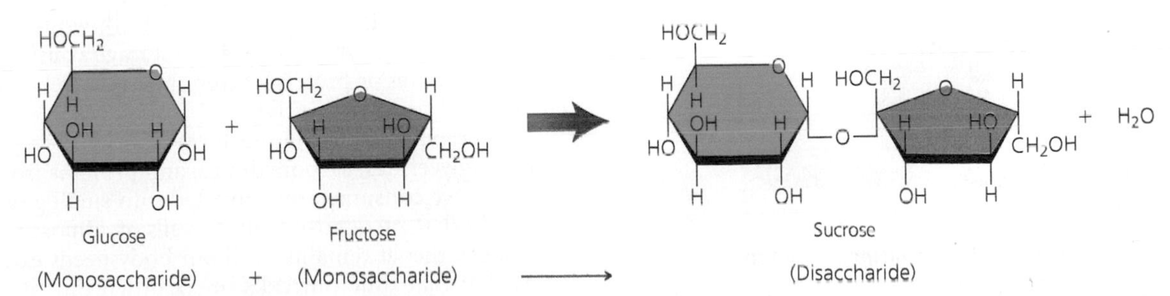

FIGURE 1b.17 **Disaccharides are built from two monosaccharides. Here, a molecule of glucose and one of fructose combine to form sucrose.**

polysaccharides store energy or provide structure. In plants, the storage polysaccharide is **starch;** in animals it is **glycogen,** a short-term energy source that can be broken down to release energy-laden glucose molecules. Humans store glycogen mainly in the cells of the liver and muscles (Figure 1b.18a).

Cellulose is a structural polysaccharide found in the cell walls of plants (Figure 1b.18b). Humans lack the enzymes necessary to digest cellulose and, as a result, it passes unchanged through our digestive tract. (Enzymes are discussed later in this chapter.) Nevertheless, cellulose is an important form of dietary fiber

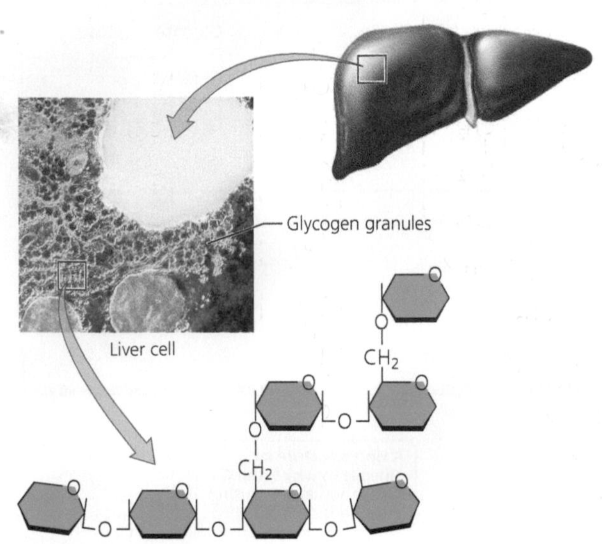

(a) Glycogen is the storage polysaccharide in animals. Granules of glycogen are stored in cells of the liver.

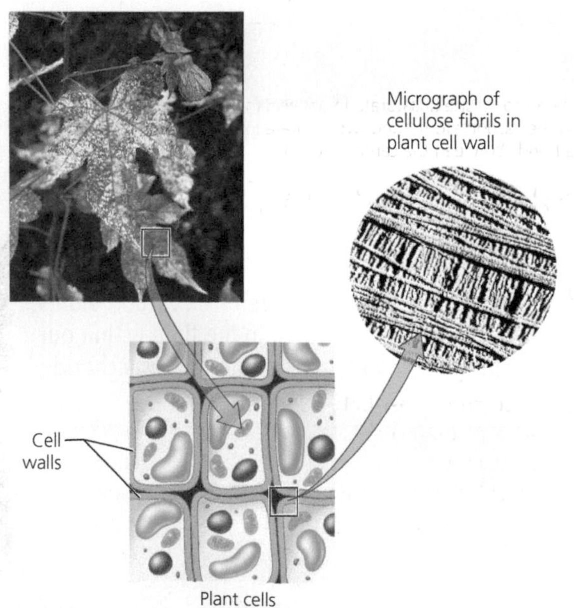

(b) Cellulose is a structural polysaccharide found in the cell walls of plants.

FIGURE 1b.18 **Polysaccharides may function in storage (as in glycogen) or provide structure (as in cellulose).**

(roughage) that helps fecal matter move through the large intestines. Including fiber in our diet may reduce the incidence of colon cancer.

Lipids

Lipids, such as fats, are compounds that do not dissolve in water. Lipids are nonpolar (having no electrical charges), while water is polar. Because of this difference, water shows no attraction for lipids and vice versa, so water and lipids do not mix. Three types of lipids that are important to human health are triglycerides, phospholipids, and steroids.

Triglycerides

Fats and oils are **triglycerides,** compounds made of one molecule of glycerol and three fatty acids. **Fatty acids** are chains of carbon atoms also bonded to hydrogens and having the acidic group COOH at one end. The fatty acids bond to glycerol through dehydration synthesis (Figure 1b.19a). Triglycerides are classified as saturated or unsaturated, depending on the presence or absence of double bonds between the carbon atoms in their fatty acids (Figure 1b.19b). Saturated fatty acids have only single covalent bonds linking the carbon atoms. They are described as "saturated with hydrogen" because their carbon atoms are bonded to as many hydrogen atoms as possible. Saturated fats are made from saturated fatty acids. Butter, a saturated fat, is solid at room temperature because its fatty acids can pack closely together. Fatty acids with one or more double bond between carbon atoms are described as unsaturated—that is, not saturated with hydrogen—because they could bond to more hydrogen atoms if the double bonds between their carbon atoms were broken. The double bonds cause "kinks" in the fatty acids and prevent molecules of unsaturated fat from packing tightly into a solid. Thus, unsaturated fats, such as olive oil, are liquid at room temperature. Sometimes hydrogens are added to unsaturated fats to stabilize them, with the goal of lengthening their shelf life, or to solidify them. For example, hydrogens are added to vegetable oil to make margarine. These partially hydrogenated fats are called trans fats and are found in many packaged snacks, such as cookies and potato chips.

Fats and oils provide about twice the energy per gram that carbohydrates or proteins do. This high energy density makes fat an ideal way for the body to store energy for the long term. Our bulk would be much greater if most of our energy storage consisted of carbohydrates or proteins, given their relatively low energy yield compared with fat.

In preparation for long-term energy storage, excess triglycerides, carbohydrates, and proteins from the foods we consume are converted into small globules of fat that are deposited in the cells of adipose tissue. There, the fat remains until our body needs extra energy; at that time our cells break down the fat to release the energy needed to keep vital processes going. Besides long-term energy storage, fat serves a protec-

Q *Would the triglyceride shown in part (b) be a solid or a liquid at room temperature? Why?*

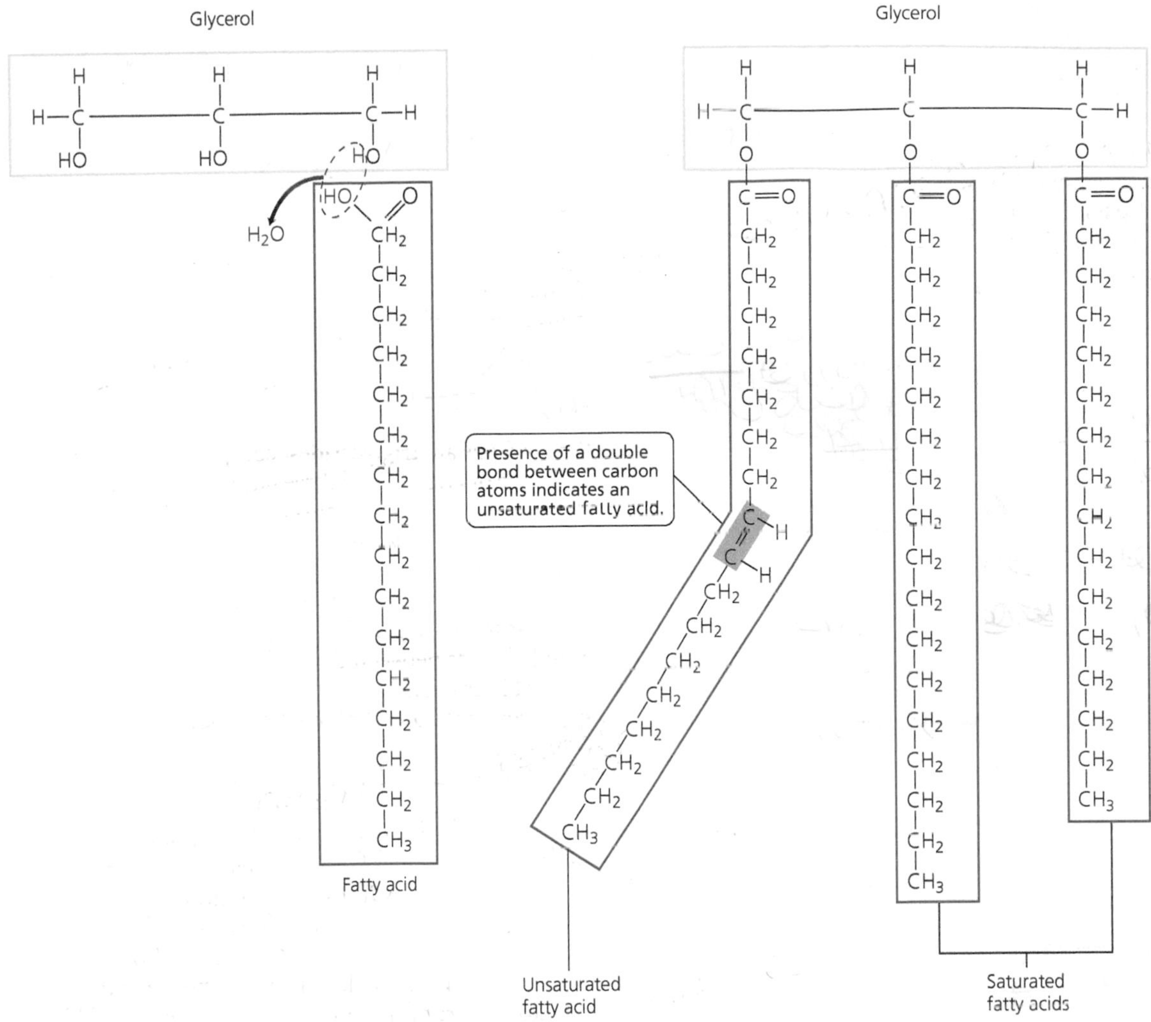

(a) A fatty acid bonds to glycerol through dehydration synthesis.

(b) This triglyceride contains one unsaturated fatty acid (note the presence of a double bond between the carbon atoms) and two saturated fatty acids (note the absence of any double bonds between the carbon atoms).

FIGURE 1b.19 **Triglycerides are composed of a molecule of glycerol joined to three fatty acids.**

A *The triglyceride would be a liquid at room temperature because the kink in the unsaturated fatty acid in part (b) would prevent close packing of adjacent molecules.*

tive function in the body. Thin layers of fat surround major organs such as the kidneys, cushioning the organs against physical shock from falls or blows. Fat also serves as insulation and as a means of absorbing lipid-soluble vitamins from the intestines and transporting them to the cells that use them. Despite the importance of fats and oils to human health, in excess they can be dangerous, particularly to our circulatory system.

Phospholipids

A **phospholipid** is made of a molecule of glycerol bonded to two fatty acids and a negatively charged phosphate group. Another small molecule of some kind—usually polar, called the variable group—is linked to the phosphate group. This general structure provides phospholipids with two regions having very different characteristics. As you will notice in Figure 1b.20a, the region made up of fatty acids is nonpolar; it is described as a **hydrophobic,** or "water-fearing," tail. The other, polar region consists of the **hydrophilic,** or "water-loving," head. The tails, being hydrophobic, do not mix with water. The heads, being hydrophilic, interact readily with water. The hydrophilic heads and hydrophobic tails of phospholipids are responsible for the structure of plasma (cell) membranes. In the membrane surrounding a cell, phospholipids are arranged in a double layer, called a bilayer (Figure 1b.20b), with the hydrophilic heads of each layer facing away from each

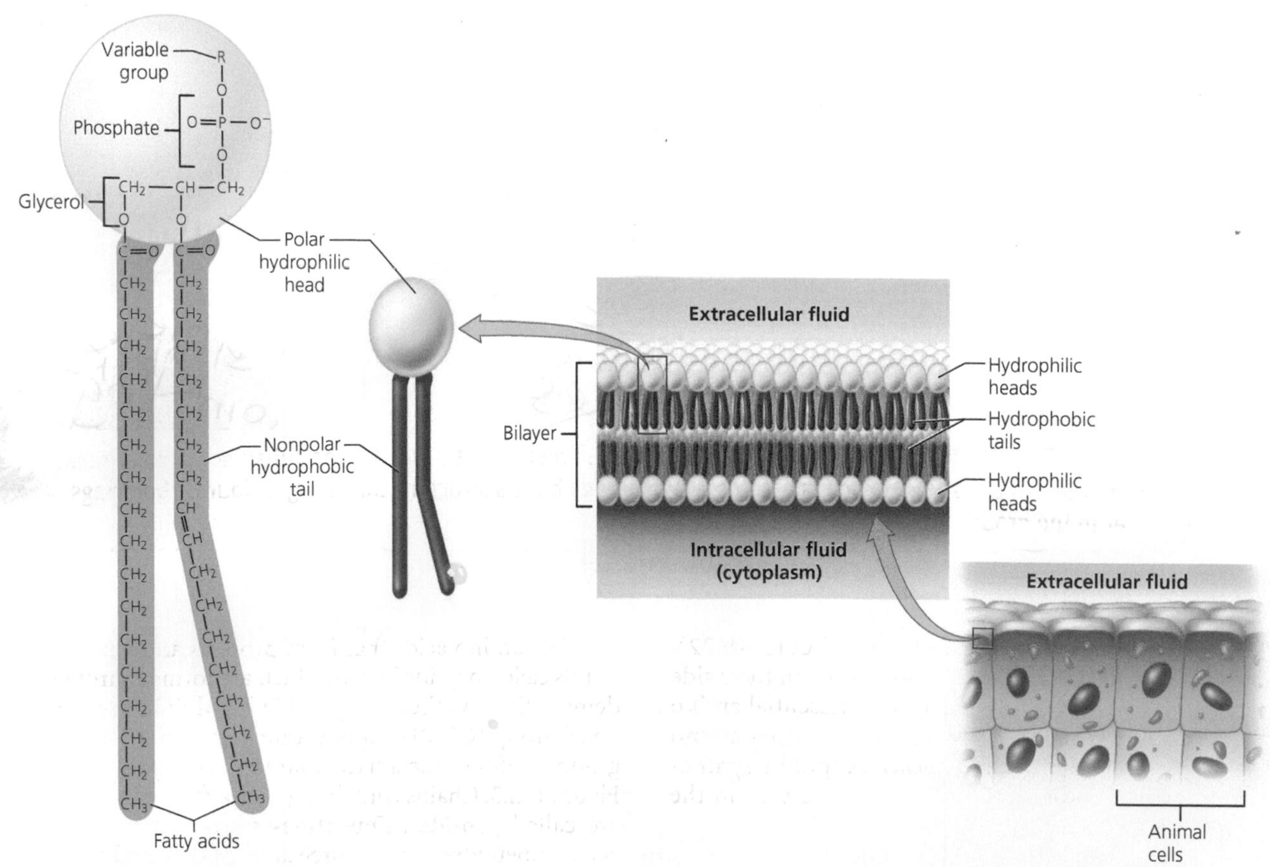

(a) A phospholipid consists of a variable group designated by the letter R, a phosphate, a glycerol, and two fatty acids. Because the variable group is often polar and the fatty acids nonpolar, phospholipids have a polar hydrophilic (water-loving) head and a nonpolar hydrophobic (water-fearing) tail.

(b) Within the phospholipid bilayer of the plasma membrane, the hydrophobic tails point inward and help hold the membrane together. The outward-pointing hydrophilic heads mix with the watery environments inside and outside the cell.

FIGURE 1b.20 **Structure of a phospholipid. Phospholipids are the main components of the plasma membrane encasing a cell and separating its internal and external watery environments.**

other. That way, each surface of the membrane consists of hydrophilic heads in contact with the watery solutions inside and outside the cell. The hydrophobic tails of the two layers point toward each other and help hold the membrane together.

Steroids

A **steroid** is a type of lipid made up of four carbon rings attached to molecules that vary from one steroid to the next. Cholesterol, one of the most familiar steroids, is a component of the plasma membrane and is also the foundation from which steroid hormones, such as estrogen and testosterone, are made. Cholesterol in our blood comes from two sources, our liver and our diet. A high level of cholesterol in the blood is considered a risk factor for heart disease. Cholesterol, estrogen, and testosterone are shown in Figure 1b.21.

Proteins

A **protein** is a polymer made of one or more chains of amino acids. In many proteins, the chains are twisted, turned, and folded to produce complicated structures. Thousands upon thousands of different proteins are found in the human body, contributing to structural support, transport, movement, and regulation of chemical reactions. Despite their great diversity in structure and function, all proteins are made from a set of only about 20 kinds of amino acids.

Amino acids

Amino acids are the building blocks of proteins. They consist of a central carbon atom bound to a hydrogen atom (H), an amino group (NH_2), an acidic carboxyl group (COOH), and a side chain,

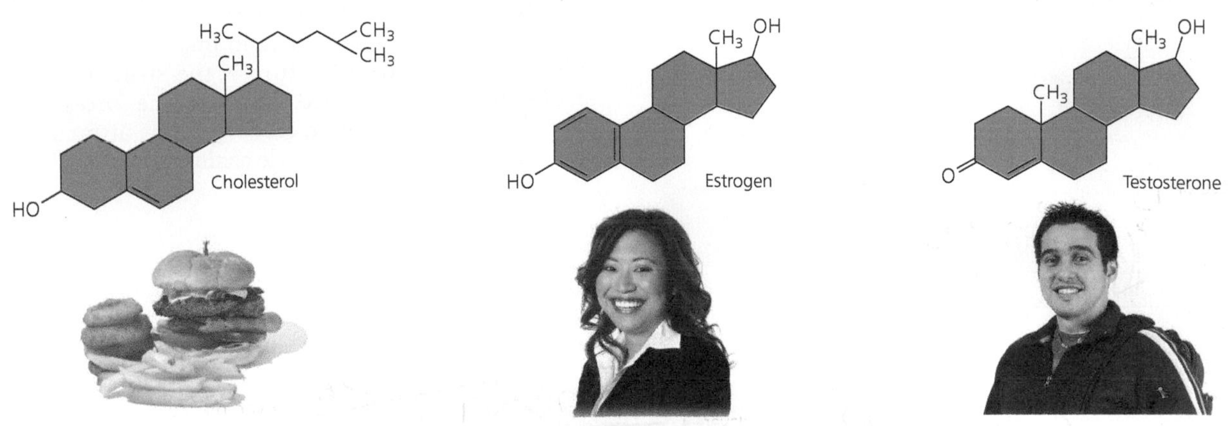

FIGURE 1b.21 **The steroid cholesterol is a component of cell membranes, and it is the substance used to make steroid hormones such as estrogen and testosterone. All steroids have a structure consisting of four carbon rings. Steroids differ in the groups attached to these rings.**

often designated by the letter R (Figure 1b.22). Amino acids differ from each other only in their side chains. Some amino acids, called nonessential amino acids, can be synthesized by our bodies. Other amino acids, called *essential amino acids*, cannot be synthesized by our bodies and must be obtained from the foods we eat.

Central carbon
Hydrogen atom
Amino group
Side chain
Carboxyl group

FIGURE 1b.22 **Structure of an amino acid. Amino acids differ from one another in the type of R group (side chain) they contain.**

The amino acids that form proteins are linked by bonds called peptide bonds, which are formed through dehydration synthesis. A peptide bond links the carboxyl group (COOH) of one amino acid to the amino group (NH_2) of the adjacent amino acid, as shown in Figure 1b.23. Chains containing only a few amino acids are called **peptides.** *Di*peptides contain two amino acids, *tri*peptides contain three amino acids, and so on. Chains containing 10 or more amino acids are called **polypeptides.** The term *protein* is used for polypeptides with at least 50 amino acids.

Protein structure

Proteins have four levels of structure: primary, secondary, tertiary, and quaternary (see Figure 1b.24). The **primary structure** of a protein is the particular sequence of amino acids. This sequence, determined by the genes, dictates a protein's structure and function. Even slight changes in primary structure can alter a protein's shape and ability to function. The inherited blood disorder sickle-cell anemia provides an example. This disease primarily affects populations in central Africa, but it also occurs in approximately 1 in 500 African Americans. It results from the substitution of

Amino acid glycine
Amino acid alanine
Dehydration synthesis
Peptide bond
Dipeptide glycylalanine
+ H_2O

FIGURE 1b.23 **Formation of a peptide bond between two amino acids through dehydration synthesis. The carboxyl group (COOH) of one amino acid bonds to the amino group (NH_2) of the adjacent amino acid, releasing water.**

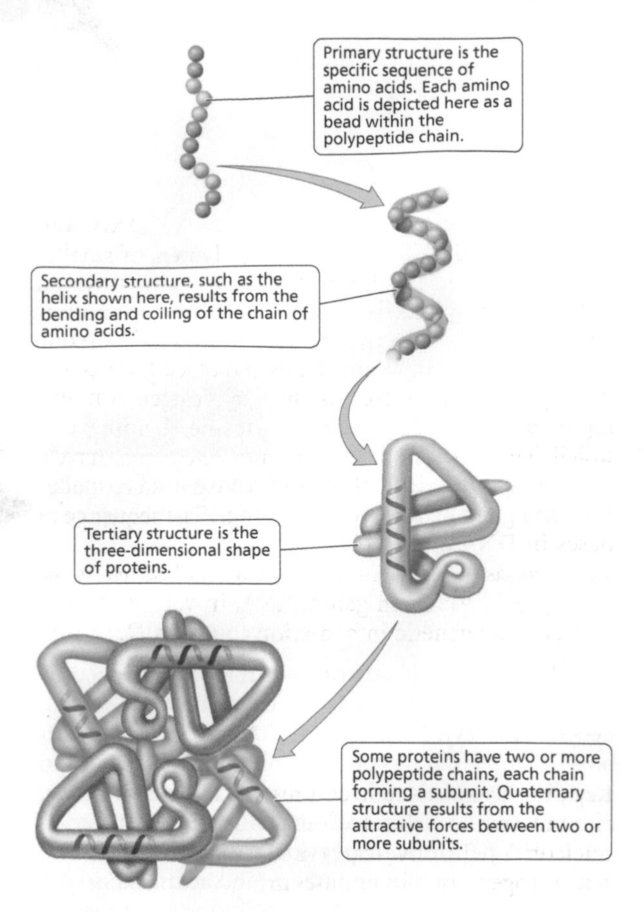

Primary structure is the specific sequence of amino acids. Each amino acid is depicted here as a bead within the polypeptide chain.
Secondary structure, such as the helix shown here, results from the bending and coiling of the chain of amino acids.
Tertiary structure is the three-dimensional shape of proteins.
Some proteins have two or more polypeptide chains, each chain forming a subunit. Quaternary structure results from the attractive forces between two or more subunits.

FIGURE 1b.24 **Levels of protein structure**

one amino acid for another during synthesis of the protein hemoglobin, which carries oxygen in our red blood cells. This single substitution in a molecule that contains hundreds of amino acids creates a misshapen protein that then alters the shape of red blood cells. Death can result when the oddly shaped cells clog the tiny vessels of the brain and heart.

The **secondary structure** of proteins consists of patterns known as pleated sheets and helices, which are formed by certain kinds of bends and coils in the chain, as a result of hydrogen bonding. Alterations in the secondary structure of a protein normally found on the surface of nerve cells can transform the protein into an infectious agent known as a prion. Prions have been implicated in several diseases, including Creutzfeldt-Jakob disease in humans and "mad cow disease" in cattle.

The **tertiary structure** is the overall three-dimensional shape of the protein. Hydrogen, ionic, and covalent bonds between different side chains may all contribute to tertiary structure. Changes in the environment of a protein, such as increased heat or changes in pH, can cause the molecule to unravel and lose its three-dimensional shape. This process is called **denaturation.** Even a minor change in the shape of a protein can result in loss of function.

Finally, some proteins consist of two or more polypeptide chains. Each chain, in this case, is called a subunit. **Quaternary structure** is the structure that results from the assembled subunits. The forces that hold the subunits in place are largely the attractions between oppositely charged side chains.

Enzymes

Life is possible because of enzymes. Without them, most chemical reactions within our cells would occur far too slowly to sustain life. **Enzymes** are substances—almost always proteins, but occasionally RNA molecules—that speed up chemical reactions without being consumed in the process. Typically, reactions with enzymes proceed 10,000 to 1,000,000 times faster than the same reactions without enzymes.

The basic process by which an enzyme speeds up a chemical reaction can be summarized by the following equation:

$$\underset{\text{Enzyme}}{E} + \underset{\text{Substrate}}{S} \longrightarrow \underset{\text{Enzyme–substrate complex}}{ES} \longrightarrow \underset{\text{Enzyme}}{E} + \underset{\text{Product}}{P}$$

The particular substance that an enzyme works on is called its substrate. For example, the enzyme sucrase speeds up the reaction in which sucrose is broken down into glucose and fructose. In this reaction, sucrose is the substrate, and glucose and fructose are products. Similarly, the enzyme maltase speeds up the breakdown of maltose (the substrate) into molecules of glucose (the product). From these examples you can see that an enzyme's name may resemble the name of its substrate. These particular examples are decomposition reactions, in which a substance is broken down into its component parts. Enzymes also increase the speed of many synthesis reactions.

During reactions promoted by enzymes, the substrate binds to a specific location, called the **active site,** on the enzyme, to form an **enzyme–substrate complex.** This binding orients the substrate molecules so they can react. The substrate is converted to one or more products that then leave the active site, allowing the enzyme to bind to another substrate molecule. The entire process occurs very rapidly. One estimate suggests that a typical enzyme can convert about 1000 molecules of substrate into product every second. Figure 1b.25 summarizes the steps of enzymatic reactions.

Enzymes are very specific in their activity; each is capable of binding to and acting on only one or at most a few particular substrates. Maltase, for example, acts only on maltose and not on sucrose, a structurally similar compound. This specificity is due to the unique shape of each enzyme's active site. The enzyme's active site and the substrate fit together like pieces of a jigsaw puzzle.

Sometimes enzymes need *cofactors,* nonprotein substances that help them convert substrate to product. Some cofactors permanently reside at the enzyme's

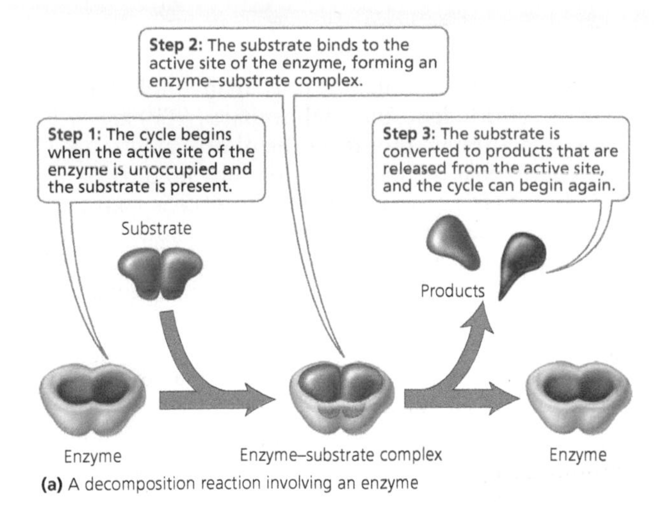
Step 2: The substrate binds to the active site of the enzyme, forming an enzyme–substrate complex.
Step 1: The cycle begins when the active site of the enzyme is unoccupied and the substrate is present.
Step 3: The substrate is converted to products that are released from the active site, and the cycle can begin again.
Substrate
Products
Enzyme
Enzyme–substrate complex
Enzyme

(a) A decomposition reaction involving an enzyme

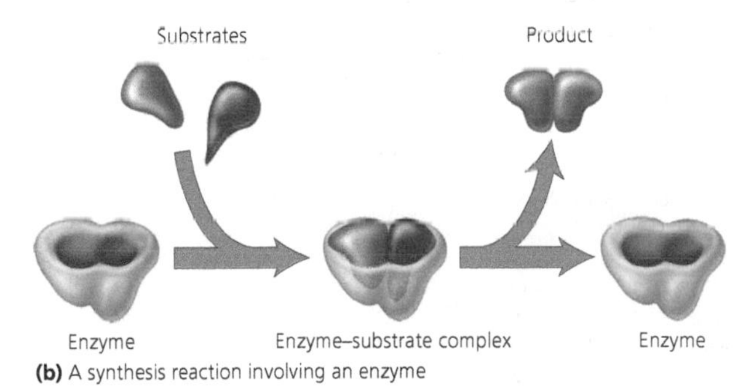
Substrates
Product
Enzyme
Enzyme–substrate complex
Enzyme

(b) A synthesis reaction involving an enzyme

FIGURE 1b.25 **The working cycle of an enzyme**

active site. Other cofactors bind to the active site at the same time as the substrate. Some cofactors are the organic (carbon-containing) substances we know as vitamins. Organic cofactors are called *coenzymes*. Other cofactors are inorganic (non-carbon-containing) substances such as zinc or iron.

Enzyme deficiencies sometimes occur and affect our health. Lactase deficiency is a relatively common example. Lactase is the enzyme needed to digest the lactose in milk products, breaking it down to its two component monosaccharides, glucose and galactose. Infants and young children usually produce adequate amounts of lactase, but many adults do not. For them, consumption of milk and milk products can lead to diarrhea, cramps, and bloating, caused by undigested lactose passing into the large intestine where it feeds resident bacteria. The bacteria, in turn, produce gas and lactic acid that irritate the bowels. The milk industry has responded to this problem (often called "lactose intolerance") by marketing lactose-reduced milk, and tablets and caplets that contain the enzyme lactase are also available.

Nucleic Acids and Nucleotides

In our discussion of protein structure we mentioned that genes determine the protein's primary structure, which is the sequence of amino acids. Genes, our units of inheritance, are segments of long polymers called **deoxyribonucleic acid (DNA).** DNA is one of the two types of nucleic acids.

Nucleotides

The two nucleic acids in our cells are DNA and **ribonucleic acid (RNA).** Both are polymers of smaller units called **nucleotides,** joined into chains through dehydration synthesis. Every nucleotide monomer consists of a five-carbon (pentose) sugar bonded to one of five nitrogen-containing bases and at least one phosphate group (Figure 1b.26). The five nitrogen-containing bases are adenine, guanine, cytosine, thymine, and uracil. The bases cytosine, thymine, and uracil have a single ring made of carbon and nitrogen atoms; adenine and guanine have two such rings. The sequence of bases in DNA and RNA determines the sequence of amino acids in a protein. DNA, as we said earlier, is the nucleic acid found in genes. RNA, in various forms, converts the genetic information found in DNA into proteins.

DNA and RNA

Key differences in the structures of RNA and DNA are summarized in Table 1b.5. RNA is a single strand of nucleotides. The five-carbon sugar in RNA is ribose. The nitrogen-containing bases in RNA are cytosine (C),

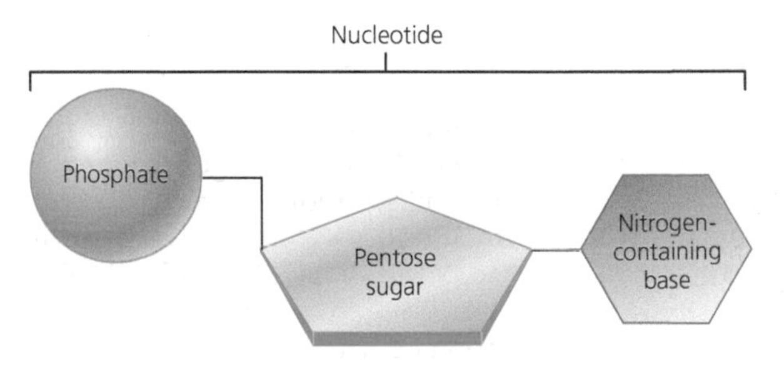
Nucleotide
Phosphate
Pentose sugar
Nitrogen-containing base

FIGURE 1b.26 **Structure of a nucleotide. Nucleotides consist of a five-carbon (pentose) sugar bonded to a phosphate molecule and one of five nitrogen-containing bases. Nucleotides are the building blocks of nucleic acids.**

TABLE 1b.5 Review of the Structural Differences between RNA and DNA

Characteristic	RNA	DNA
Sugar	Ribose	Deoxyribose
Bases	Adenine, guanine, cytosine, uracil	Adenine, guanine, cytosine, thymine
Number of strands	One	Two; twisted to form double helix

adenine (A), guanine (G), and uracil (U; Figure 1b.27). In contrast, DNA is a double-stranded chain. Its two parallel strands, held together by hydrogen bonds between the nitrogen-containing bases, twist around one another to form a double helix. The five-carbon sugar in DNA is deoxyribose. The nitrogen-containing bases in DNA are adenine (A), thymine (T), cytosine (C), and guanine (G; Figure 1b.28).

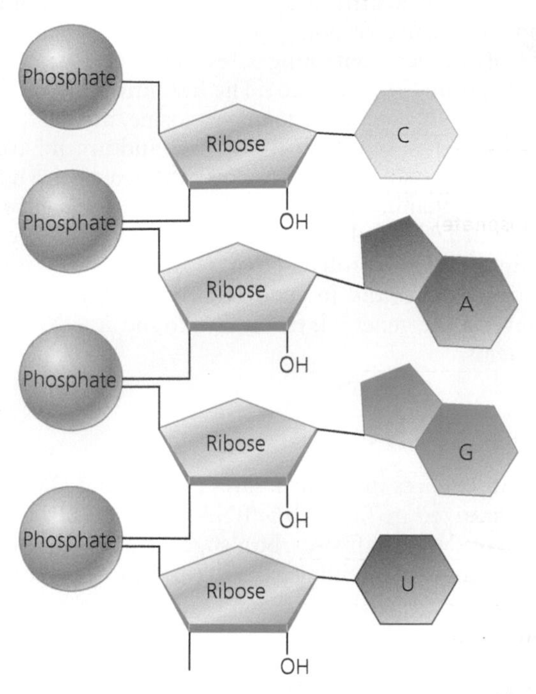

FIGURE 1b.27 RNA is a single-stranded nucleic acid. It is formed by the linking together of nucleotides composed of the sugar ribose, a phosphate group, and the nitrogen-containing bases cytosine (C), adenine (A), guanine (G), and uracil (U).

exploring further

In Chapter 1b we learned about the important roles that water plays in the human body. Recall that water serves as the body's main transport medium and helps to prevent dramatic changes in body temperature. Foodborne illnesses are caused by the ingestion of contaminated food or water, and they wreak havoc on the body's water balance. These illnesses are usually associated with severe diarrhea and vomiting, which rob the body of its water.

ATP

At this moment within your cells, many molecules of the nucleotide **adenosine triphosphate** (ATP) are each losing a phosphate group. As the phosphate group is lost, energy that the molecule stored by holding on to the phosphate group is released. Your cells trap that energy and use it to perform work. It is because of this activity that you are able to sit up and read this book. ATP consists of the sugar ribose, the base adenine, and three phosphate groups, attached to the molecule by phosphate bonds. It is formed from adenosine diphosphate (ADP) by covalent bonding of a phosphate group to the ADP in an energy-requiring reaction. The

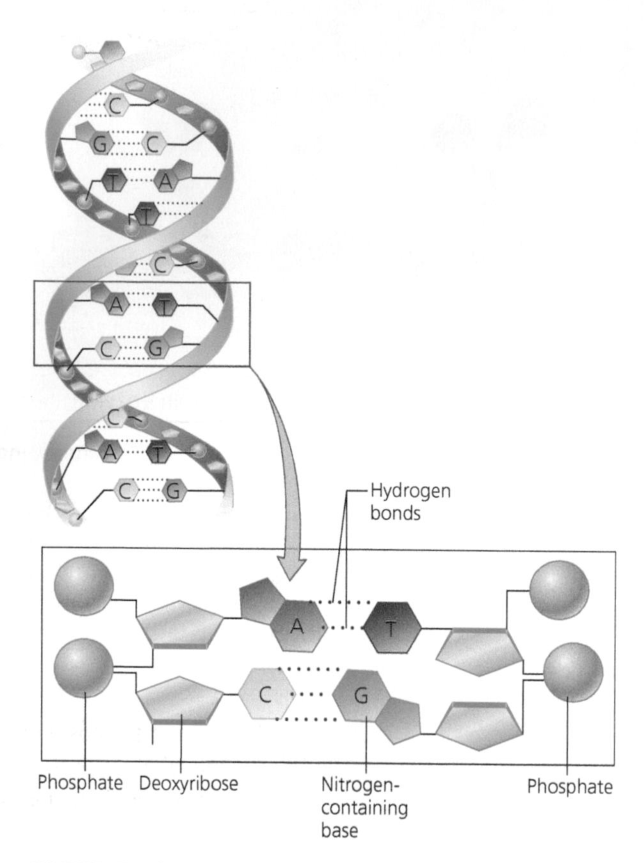

FIGURE 1b.28 DNA is a nucleic acid in which two chains of nucleotides twist around one another to form a double helix. The two chains are held together by hydrogen bonds between the nitrogen-containing bases. Each nucleotide of DNA contains the pentose sugar deoxyribose, a phosphate group, and one of the following four nitrogen-containing bases: adenine (A), thymine (T), cytosine (C), and guanine (G).

energy absorbed during the reaction is stored in the new phosphate bond. This high-energy phosphate bond is easily broken when the cell requires energy (Figure 1b.29).

ATP is often described as the energy currency of cells. All energy from the breakdown of molecules such as glucose must be channeled through ATP before it can be used by the body.

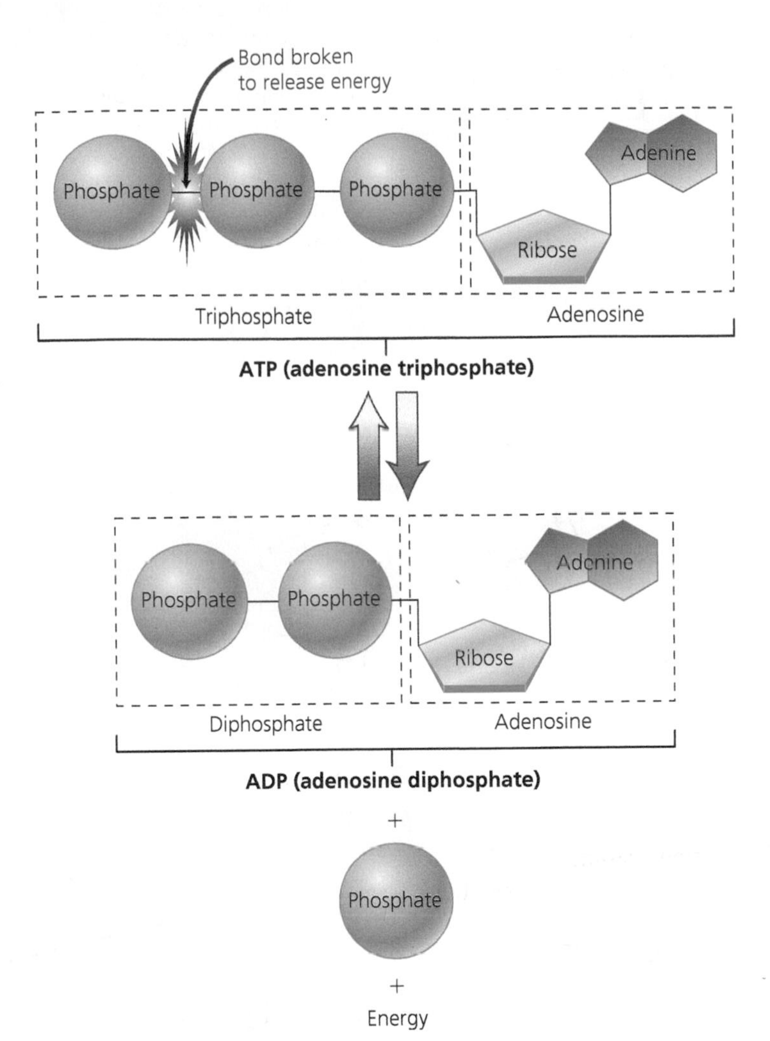

FIGURE 1b.29 **Structure and function of adenosine triphosphate (ATP). This nucleotide consists of the sugar ribose, the base adenine, and three phosphate groups. The phosphate bonds of ATP are unstable. When cells need energy, the last phosphate bond is broken, yielding adenosine diphosphate (ADP), a phosphate molecule, and energy.**

CHAPTER 1c

THE CELL

Taken from *Biology of Humans: Concepts, Applications, and Issues*, Third Edition, by Judith Goodenough and Betty McGuire

EUKARYOTIC CELLS COMPARED WITH PROKARYOTIC CELLS

The **cell theory** is a fundamental organizing principle of biology, guiding the way biologists think about and study living things. A theory, you may recall from Chapter 1a, is a well-researched and well-supported explanation for some aspect of the physical universe. The cell theory states that (1) a cell is the smallest unit of life; (2) cells make up all living things, from unicellular to multicellular organisms; and (3) new cells can arise only from preexisting cells.

There are two basic types of cells—eukaryotic cells and prokaryotic cells. **Prokaryotic cells,** as shown in Figure 1c.1, are structurally simpler and typically smaller than eukaryotic cells. They are limited to bacteria and another group of microscopic organisms called archaea. You are probably already aware of bacteria, some of which inhabit your body. Many bacterial inhabitants are harmless, but others can cause illness. Archaea may be less familiar to you. They include species that inhabit extreme environments such as the high-saline Great Salt Lake or the hot sulfur springs of Yellowstone National Park. Most prokaryotic cells are surrounded by a rigid cell wall.

The cells of plants, animals, and all other organisms except bacteria and archaea are eukaryotic. All the cells that make up your body, therefore, are eukaryotic. The difference between eukaryotic and prokaryotic cells relates to the presence or absence of membrane-bound organelles. An **organelle** or "little organ" is a component within a cell that carries out specific functions. Some organelles have membranes, others do not. Nonmembranous organelles such as ribosomes and cytoskeletal elements are found in both prokaryotic and eukaryotic cells. Unique to **eukaryotic cells,** however, are membrane-bound organelles such as mitochondria and endoplasmic reticulum (Figure 1c.2). Another of the membrane-bound organelles found in all typical eukaryotic cells is a well-defined nucleus containing DNA. Note that in prokaryotes, a membrane does not surround the DNA (refer, again, to Figure 1c.1). Among eukaryotes, plant cells have cell walls, but animal cells do not. Table 1c.1 reviews the major differences between eukaryotic and prokaryotic cells.

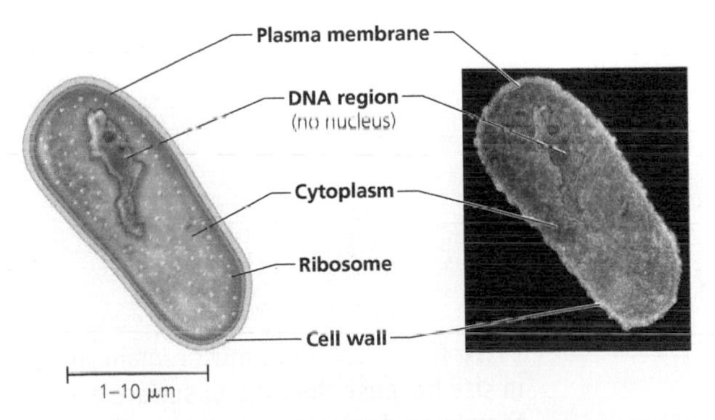

FIGURE 1c.1 **Prokaryotic cells, such as a bacterium, lack internal membrane-bound organelles.**

TABLE 1c.1 Review of Features of Prokaryotic and Eukaryotic Cells

Feature	Prokaryotic Cells	Eukaryotic Cells
Organisms	Bacteria, archaea	Plants, animals, fungi, protists
Size	1–10 µm across	10–100 µm across
Membrane-bound organelles	Absent	Present
DNA form	Circular	Coiled, linear strands
DNA location	Cytoplasm	Nucleus
Internal membranes	Rare	Many
Cytoskeleton	Present	Present

CELL SIZE AND MICROSCOPY

Most eukaryotic and prokaryotic cells are so small they are typically measured in micrometers (µm), which are equal to 1/1000 meters (m). (An obvious exception is the chicken egg.) The small size of cells is dictated by a physical relationship known as the **surface-to-volume ratio.** This relationship says that as a cell gets larger, its surface area increases much more slowly than its volume (Figure 1c.3). Nutrients enter a cell, and wastes leave a cell at its surface. Therefore, a large cell would have difficulty moving all the nutrients it needs and all the wastes it produces across its inadequate surface and would die. A small cell, on the other hand, has sufficient surface for the uptake and removal of substances and would survive.

Due to the small size of most cells, you need a microscope to see them. Throughout this book you will see micrographs, which are photographs obtained using a microscope (Figure 1c.4). Microscopic specimens can be imaged using beams of either light or electrons. Light microscopes, which are used in many classrooms, have the advantage that they are relatively inexpensive and simple to operate. Electron microscopes, though more complex and expensive, have the capacity to reveal finer details because the wavelength of an electron beam is smaller than the wavelengths of visible light. Whether using light or electrons, the beam can be either transmitted through a thinly sliced specimen or bounced off of the specimen's surface.

Q *The nucleus is a membrane-bound organelle. Look closely at the other organelles in the cell and read their functions. Based on the structure and functions of the organelles shown, list those that you think are membrane-bound organelles and those that are nonmembranous organelles.*

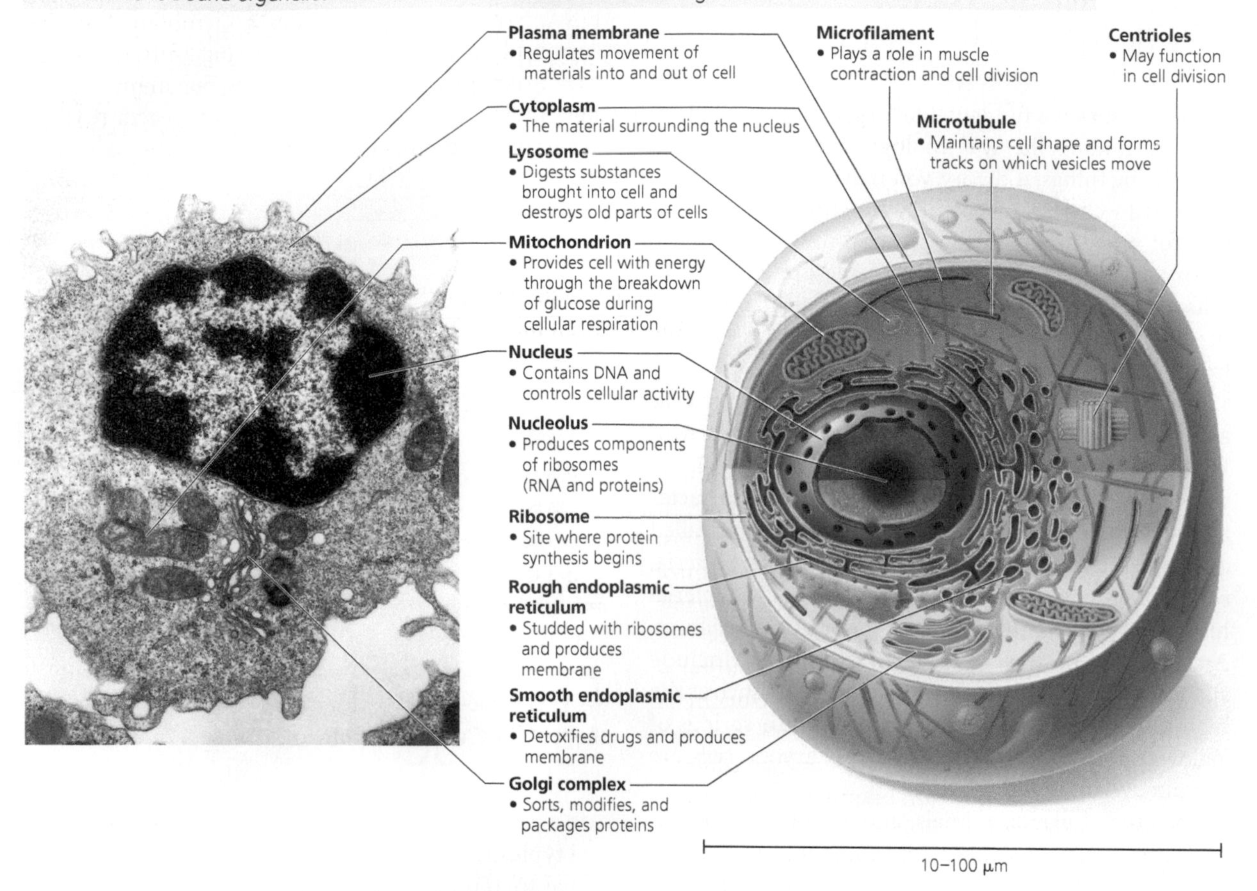
Plasma membrane
• Regulates movement of materials into and out of cell
Cytoplasm
• The material surrounding the nucleus
Lysosome
• Digests substances brought into cell and destroys old parts of cells
Mitochondrion
• Provides cell with energy through the breakdown of glucose during cellular respiration
Nucleus
• Contains DNA and controls cellular activity
Nucleolus
• Produces components of ribosomes (RNA and proteins)
Ribosome
• Site where protein synthesis begins
Rough endoplasmic reticulum
• Studded with ribosomes and produces membrane
Smooth endoplasmic reticulum
• Detoxifies drugs and produces membrane
Golgi complex
• Sorts, modifies, and packages proteins
Microfilament
• Plays a role in muscle contraction and cell division
Centrioles
• May function in cell division
Microtubule
• Maintains cell shape and forms tracks on which vesicles move
10–100 μm

FIGURE 1c.2 Eukaryotic cells, such as the generalized animal cell shown here, have internal membrane-bound organelles.

A *The membrane-bound organelles include the nucleus, rough endoplasmic reticulum, smooth endoplasmic reticulum, Golgi complex, mitochondrion, and lysosome. The nonmembranous organelles include ribosomes, microfilaments, centrioles, and microtubules.*

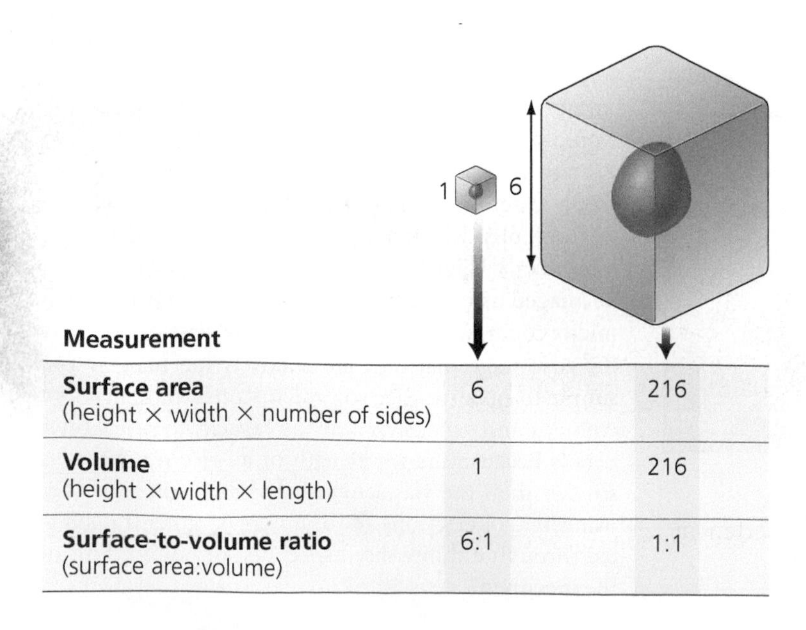
1
6

Measurement		
Surface area (height × width × number of sides)	6	216
Volume (height × width × length)	1	216
Surface-to-volume ratio (surface area:volume)	6:1	1:1

FIGURE 1c.3 Cells must remain small in size because the ratio of surface area to volume decreases rapidly as cell size increases.

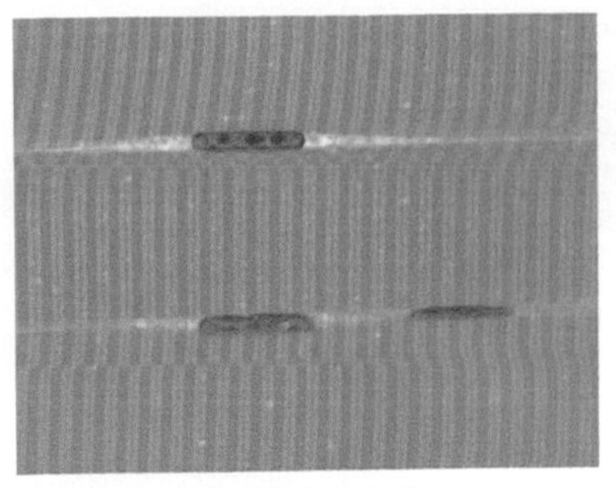

(a) Striated muscle cells viewed with a light microscope.

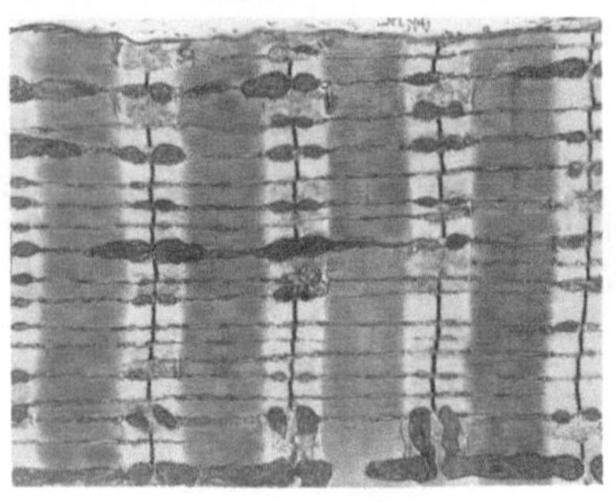

(b) Striated muscle cells viewed with a transmission electron microscope.

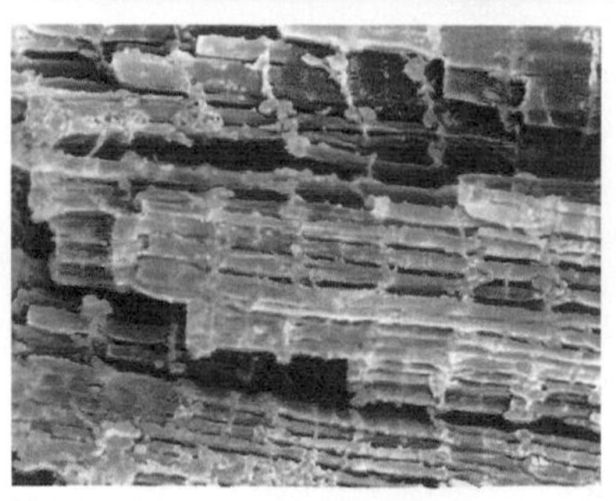

(c) Striated muscle cells viewed with a scanning electron microscope.

FIGURE 1c.4 **Micrographs are photographs taken through a microscope. Here, striated muscle cells have been photographed using three different types of microscope. Electron microscopes use beams of electrons to produce images with finer details than those viewed with light microscopes.**

Figure 1c.4a is a transmitted light micrograph through three striated muscle cells that have been stained with biological dyes to increase the contrast between different cellular components. The three nuclei visible in this picture are colored dark purple because the dye used has an affinity for acidic components in the cell such as DNA. Figure 1c.4b is a transmitted electron micrograph that shows the structure of striated muscle cells in more detail than is possible using light to image the tissue. In this case, the contrast between different cellular components is produced by staining the tissue with heavy metals such as lead and uranium. Different components of the cells absorb different amounts of these heavy metals. Components that readily absorb the metals differentially block the electron beam from passing through the sample. Figure 1c.4c is a scanning electron micrograph produced by bouncing an electron beam off the surface of several striated muscle cells. The beam is scanned across the surface of the sample, and electrons that bounce off the surface are collected by a detector. For every point that is scanned, the number of electrons reaching the detector is used to calculate the relative brightness of that spot on the sample. This information is used to construct the image. Images produced with electron beams are not in color. The pictures shown in Figures 1c.4b and 1c.4c have been colored to highlight certain features, an improvement made possible by computer-assisted processing of images. Other micrographs in the text have also been colored.

CELL STRUCTURE AND FUNCTION

The structure of a cell exquisitely reflects its functions (Figure 1c.5). For example, few human cells are more specialized than sperm or eggs, the cells that carry genetic information and other materials needed to make a new individual of the next generation. A sperm

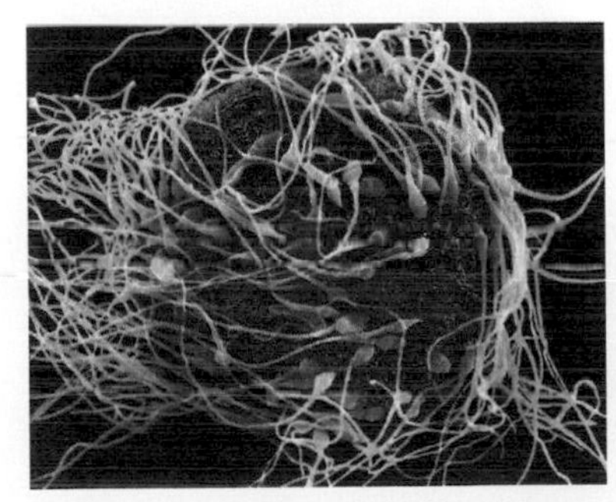

(a) A sperm is specialized to be highly mobile. In contrast, an egg is specialized to be large, immobile, and packed with material needed to initiate development.

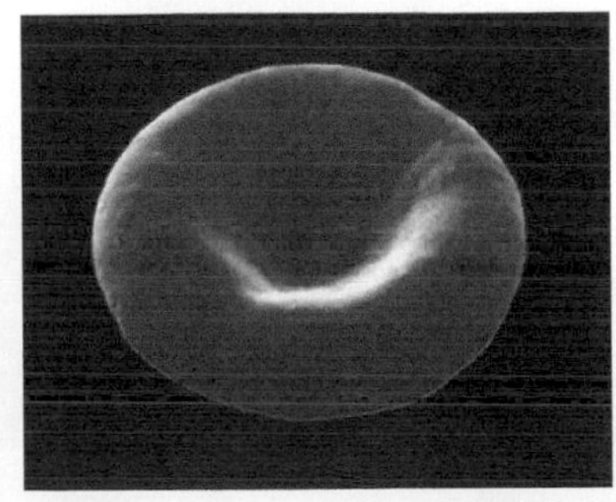

(b) A mature red blood cell, devoid of most organelles, is specialized for carrying oxygen.

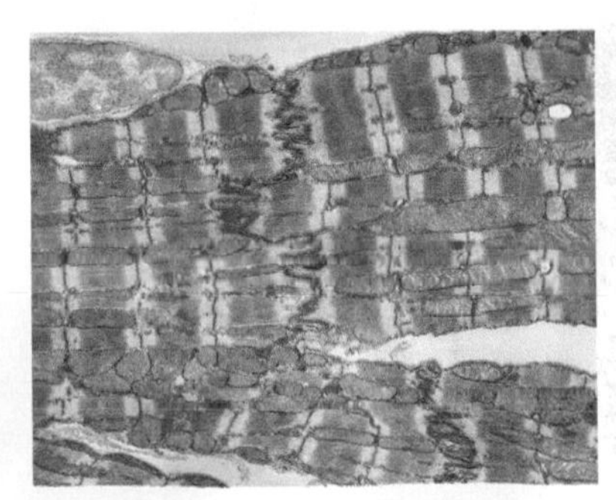

(c) A cardiac muscle cell is specialized for contraction and for propagating the signal for contraction.

FIGURE 1c.5 **A cell's structure reflects its specific function. These cell types from the human body illustrate the close tie between structure and function.**

is specialized for swimming to the egg and fertilizing it. As such, a sperm is streamlined and equipped with a whiplike tail. In the head of the sperm is an enzyme-containing sac that spills open to release enzymes that digest a path through the layers of cells surrounding the egg. In contrast, the egg is immobile and much larger than a typical cell because it is literally packed with nutrients and other materials needed to initiate development. A mature red blood cell is another example of a cell whose structure reflects its function. As the red blood cell matures, it extrudes its nucleus and most organelles, leaving more space for hemoglobin, the protein that transports oxygen. A mature red blood cell is thus an exception to the rule that eukaryotic cells have a well-defined nucleus and other membrane-bound organelles. Consider, also, a cardiac muscle cell. This cell is specialized for contraction, and for propagating the signal for contraction from one muscle cell to the next. Thus it is filled with contractile proteins and joined to adjacent cells by specialized junctions that strengthen cardiac tissue and promote rapid conduction of impulses throughout the heart. In each of these cases, careful study of the cell's structure provides excellent clues to its function, and vice versa.

PLASMA MEMBRANE

We begin our examination of the cell at its outer surface—the **plasma membrane.** This remarkably thin outer covering controls the movement of substances both into and out of the cell. Because the concentrations of substances in a cell's interior are critically balanced, molecules and ions are not permitted to move randomly in and out.

Both prokaryotic and eukaryotic cells have a plasma membrane, but only eukaryotic cells also contain internal membranes that divide the cell into many compartments. Each compartment contains its own assortment of enzymes and is specialized for particular functions. In general, the principles described for the plasma membrane also apply to the membranes inside the cell.

Plasma Membrane Structure

The plasma membrane is made of lipids, proteins, and carbohydrates. Phospholipids are the major components of the plasma membrane. These molecules, with their hydrophilic (water-loving) heads and hydrophobic (water-fearing) tails, form a double layer, called the phospholipid bilayer, at the surface of the cell (Figure 1c.6). The hydrophilic heads facing outside the cell interact with the **extracellular fluid** (also known as interstitial fluid), which is the watery solution outside cells. The hydrophilic heads facing inside the cell interact with the **cytoplasm,** which is the jellylike solution inside the cell. The cytoplasm includes all contents of the cell between the plasma membrane and the nucleus. Within the phospholipid bilayer, the hydrophobic tails point toward each other and hold the plasma membrane together.

Interspersed in the phospholipid bilayer are proteins, as seen in Figure 1c.6. Some proteins are embedded in the membrane, and some of these span the bilayer completely. Other proteins are simply attached to the inner or outer surface of the membrane. In

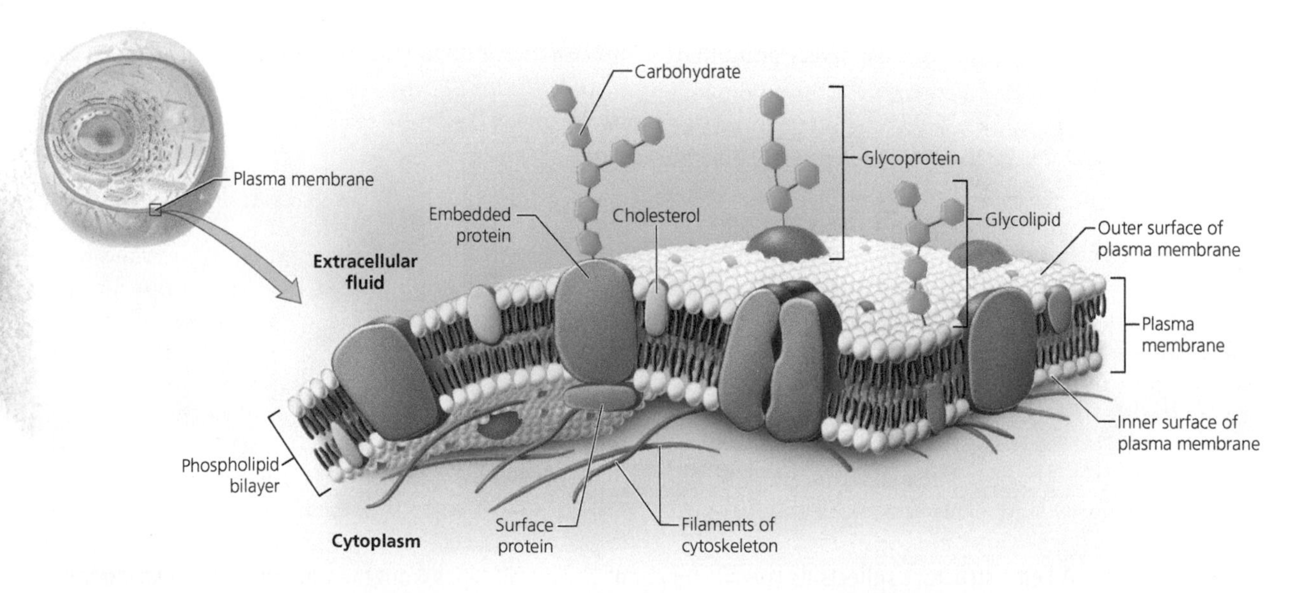

FIGURE 1c.6 **The structure of the plasma membrane of a cell according to the fluid mosaic model**

many cases, such surface proteins are attached to an exposed portion of an embedded protein. Molecules of cholesterol are also scattered throughout the bilayer.

As you can see in Figure 1c.6, carbohydrates attach only to the outer surface of the plasma membrane. Most of these carbohydrates are attached to proteins, forming glycoproteins. We will see that glycoproteins often function in cell recognition. Other carbohydrates are attached to lipids, forming glycolipids.

The structure of the plasma membrane is often described as a **fluid mosaic.** The proteins are interspersed among the lipid molecules like tiles of different colors within a mosaic. Many of the proteins are able to move sideways through the bilayer to some degree, giving the membrane its fluid quality.

Plasma Membrane Functions

The plasma membrane performs several vital functions for the cell. First, by imposing a boundary between the cell's internal and external environment, the plasma membrane maintains the cell's structural integrity. Second, the structure of the plasma membrane regulates the movement of substances into and out of the cell, permitting entry to some substances but not others. For this reason, the membrane is often described as being **selectively permeable.** You will read more about the transport of materials across the plasma membrane in the next section of this chapter.

The plasma membrane also functions in cell–cell recognition. Cells distinguish one type of cell from another by recognizing molecules—often glycoproteins—on their surface. Membrane glycoproteins differ from one species of organism to another and among individuals of the same species. Even different cell types within an individual have different membrane glycoproteins. This variation allows the body to recognize foreign invaders such as bacteria. Your own body, for example, would recognize such invaders because the bacteria lack the surface molecules found on your cells. The bacteria, in turn, "read" the different surface molecules of your cells to settle preferentially on some kinds of cells but not others.

Another important function of the plasma membrane is communication between cells. Such communication relies on *receptors,* specialized proteins in the plasma membrane (or inside the cell) that bind particular substances that affect cell activities. For example, hormones secreted by one group of cells may bind to receptors in the plasma membranes of other cells. The receptors then relay a signal to proteins inside the cell, which transmit the message to other nearby molecules. Through a series of chemical reactions, the hormone's "message" ultimately initiates a response by the recipient cell, perhaps causing it to release a certain chemical.

Finally, the plasma membrane plays an important role in binding pairs or groups of cells together. **Cell adhesion molecules** (CAMs) extend from the plasma membranes of most cells and help attach the cells to one another, especially during the formation of tissues and organs in an embryo. Table 1c.2 reviews the functions of the plasma membrane.

stop and THINK

Of the five functions of the plasma membrane summarized in Table 1c.2, which might explain the difficulty of transplanting tissues and organs successfully from one body to another? Why would rejection of such transplants occur? Under what circumstances might one body accept a tissue graft or organ from another?

TABLE 1c.2 Review of Plasma Membrane Functions

Maintain structural integrity of the cell
Regulate movement of substances into and out of the cell
Provide recognition between cells
Provide communication between cells
Stick cells together to form tissues and organs

Movement Across the Plasma Membrane

Recall that an important function of the plasma membrane is to control which substances move into and out of the cell. Substances cross the plasma membrane in several ways. These methods are described as either active—requiring the cell to expend energy—or passive—requiring no energy expenditure by the cell.

Simple diffusion

Some materials cross the plasma membrane passively through **simple diffusion,** the random movement of a substance from a region of higher concentration to a region of lower concentration. *Concentration* is the number of molecules of a substance in a particular volume, while a **concentration gradient** is a difference in the relative number of molecules or ions of a given substance in two adjacent areas. The end result of simple diffusion is an equal distribution of the substance in the two areas; in other words, diffusion tends to eliminate the concentration gradient. Consider what happens when someone is cooking bacon in the kitchen. At first, the smell of bacon is localized in the kitchen. Soon, however, the smell permeates adjoining rooms, too, as odor molecules move from where they are more concentrated (the kitchen) to where they are less concentrated (other parts of the house). Eventually the odor molecules are equally distributed, but they still move randomly in all directions. Likewise, when a substance diffuses across a membrane from a region of higher concentration to a region of lower concentration, the movement of its molecules does not stop once the concentration has equalized. Instead, the molecules continue to move randomly back and forth across the membrane. The rate of movement in each direction, however, is now the same. Substances such as carbon dioxide and oxygen diffuse through the plasma membrane of our cells (Figure 1c.7).

Facilitated diffusion

Water-soluble substances are repelled by lipids and so cannot move through the phospholipid bilayer by simple diffusion. If they are to cross a cell membrane, their transport must be assisted, or "facilitated," by certain proteins within the membrane. Some of these proteins, called carrier proteins, bind to a particular water-soluble substance. Such binding prompts a change in the protein's shape and has the effect of carrying the substance to the other side of the membrane. Other proteins form channels through which certain water-soluble substances can move. **Facilitated diffusion** is the movement of a substance from a region of higher concentration to a region of lower concentration with the aid of a membrane protein. Molecules of glucose, for example, enter fat cells by facilitated diffusion. In this example, a molecule of glucose in the extracellular fluid binds to a carrier protein in the plasma membrane, which helps to move the glucose molecule from outside to inside the fat cell (Figure 1c.8). Facilitated diffusion does not require energy and is thus a form of passive transport.

Osmosis

Osmosis is a type of diffusion in which water moves across a plasma membrane or any other selectively permeable membrane from a region of higher water concentration to a region of lower water concentration. The movement of water occurs in response to a concentration gradient of a dissolved substance (solute). Consider what happens when a substance such as table sugar (in this case, our solute) is dissolved in water (our solvent) in a membranous bag through which water, but not sugar, can move. Keep in mind that when solute concentration is low, water concentration is high; and when solute concentration is high, water concentration is low. If the membranous bag is placed into a **hypertonic solution,** meaning a solution whose solute concentration is higher than that inside the bag, more water moves out of the bag than in,

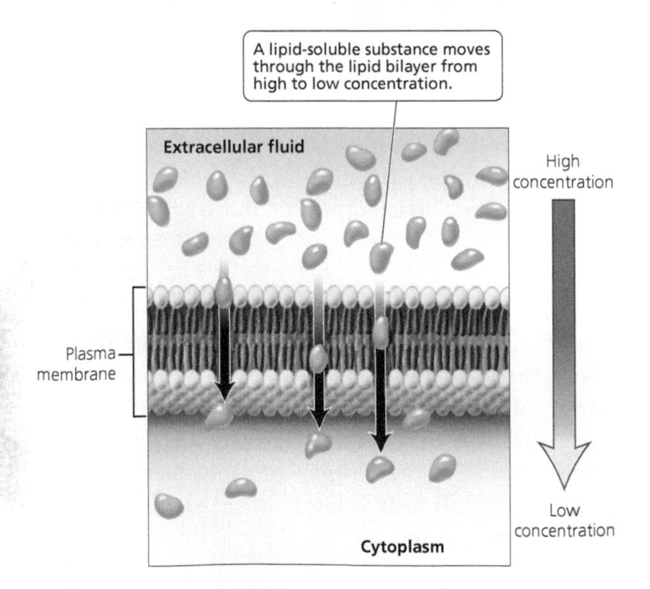

FIGURE 1c.7 Simple diffusion is the random movement of a substance from a region of higher concentration to a region of lower concentration.

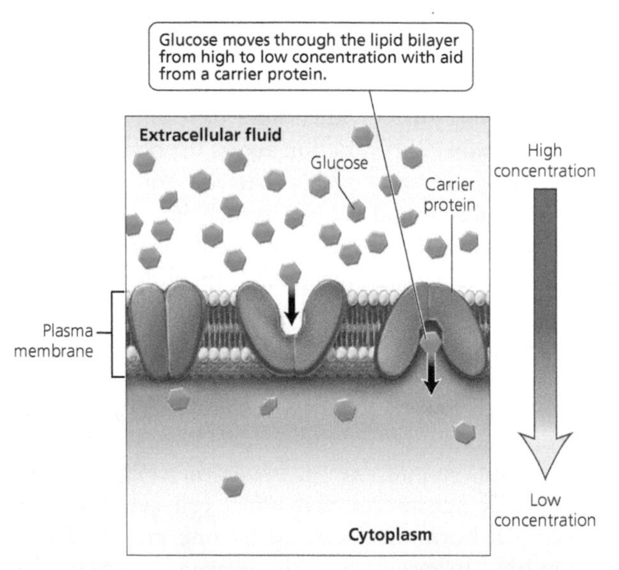

FIGURE 1c.8 Facilitated diffusion is the movement through the plasma membrane of a substance from a region of higher concentration to a region of lower concentration with the aid of a membrane protein that acts as a channel or a carrier protein.

causing the bag to shrivel (Figure 1c.9a). If, on the other hand, the bag is placed into an **isotonic solution,** one with the same solute (sugar) concentration as inside the bag, there is no net movement of water in either direction, and the bag maintains its original shape (Figure 1c.9b). When the bag is placed into a **hypotonic solution,** in which the concentration of solute is lower than that inside the bag, more water moves into the bag than out, causing the bag to swell and possibly burst (Figure 1c.9c). Osmosis does not require energy and is thus a form of passive transport.

Red blood cells behave the same way the bag in our example does, as shown at the bottom of Figure 1c.9. Red blood cells move through a fluid, called plasma. As the figure illustrates, the shape of red blood cells responds to different levels of solute concentration in the plasma.

Active transport

Active transport is a mechanism that moves substances across plasma membranes with the aid of a carrier protein and energy supplied by the cell (through the breakdown of ATP; see Chapter 1b). So far in our discussion of movement across plasma membranes, we have described substances moving from regions of higher concentration to regions of lower concentration. However, in most cases of active transport, substances are moved from regions of lower concentration to higher concentration, as shown in Figure 1c.10. This type of movement is described as going "against the concentration gradient" and occurs when cells need to concentrate certain substances. For example, the cells in our bodies contain higher concentrations of potassium ions (K^+) and lower concentrations of sodium ions (Na^+) than their surroundings. Through active transport, proteins in the plasma membrane help maintain these conditions, pumping potassium ions into the cell and sodium ions out of the cell. In this example, both potassium and sodium are moving from regions of lower concentration to regions of higher concentration.

Endocytosis

Most small molecules cross the plasma membrane by simple diffusion, facilitated diffusion, or active transport. Large molecules, single-celled organisms

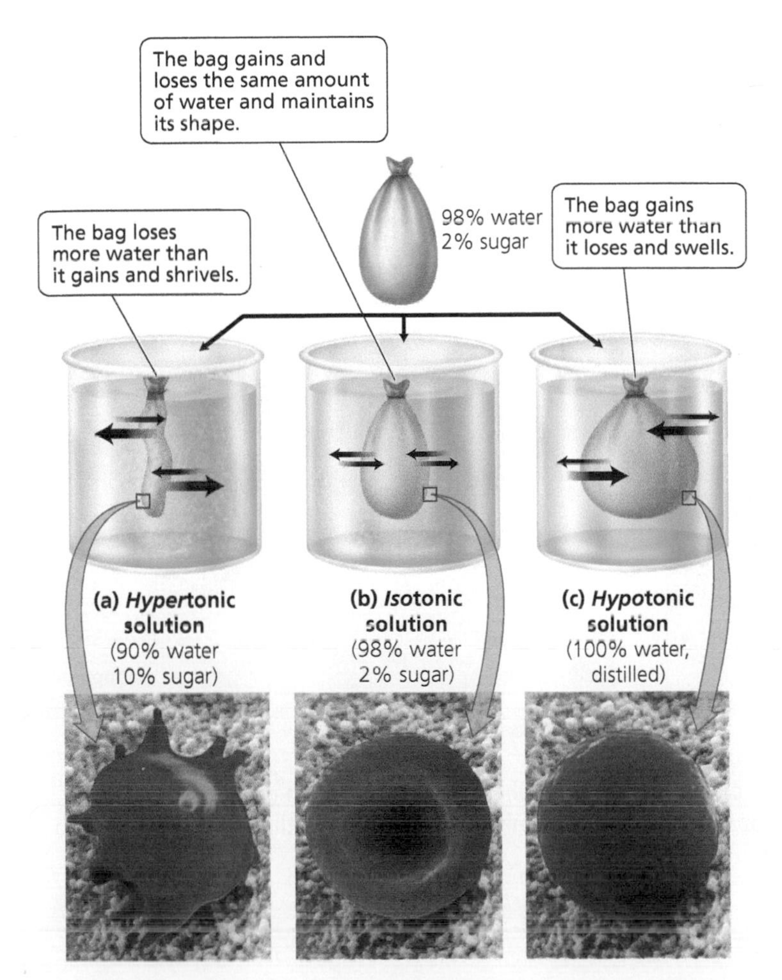

The bag gains and loses the same amount of water and maintains its shape.
98% water
2% sugar
The bag loses more water than it gains and shrivels.
The bag gains more water than it loses and swells.
(a) *Hypertonic* solution
(90% water 10% sugar)
(b) *Isotonic* solution
(98% water 2% sugar)
(c) *Hypotonic* solution
(100% water, distilled)

FIGURE 1c.9 Osmosis is diffusion of water across a selectively permeable membrane. The drawings show what happens when a membranous bag through which water but not sugar can move is placed in solutions that are (a) hypertonic, (b) isotonic, or (c) hypotonic to the solution inside the bag. The width of the black arrows corresponds to the amount of water moving into and out of the bag. The photographs show what happens to red blood cells when placed in the three kinds of solutions. Red blood cells are normally shaped like flattened disks, as in part b.

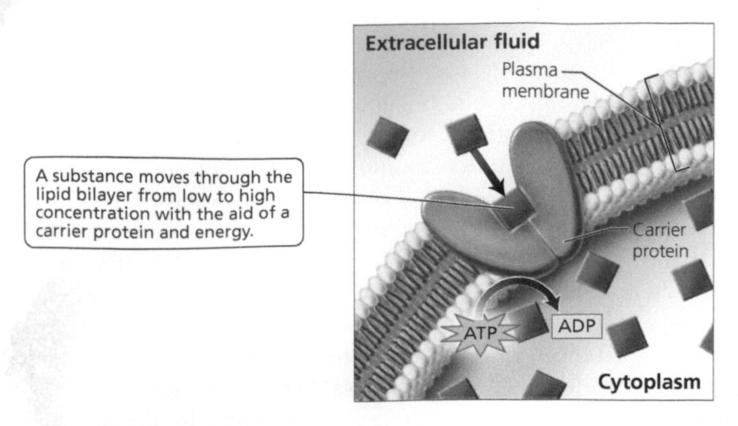

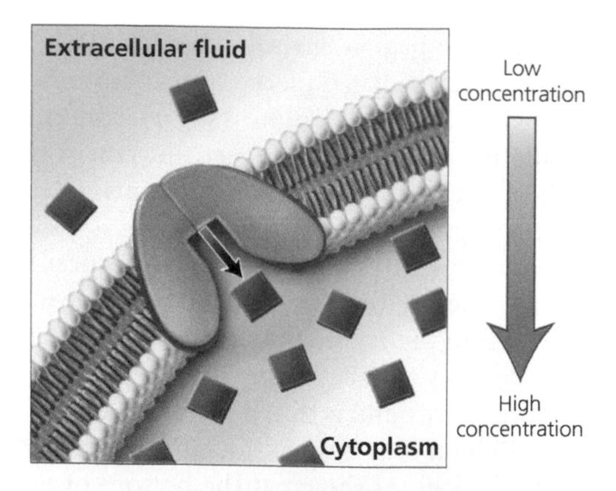

FIGURE 1c.10 **Active transport is the movement of molecules across the plasma membrane, often from an area of lower concentration to one of higher concentration with help from a carrier protein and energy, usually in the form of ATP.**

such as bacteria, and droplets of fluid containing dissolved substances enter cells through endocytosis (Figure 1c.11). In **endocytosis,** a region of the plasma membrane engulfs the substance to be ingested and then pinches off from the rest of the membrane, in this way enclosing the substance in a saclike structure called a **vesicle.** The vesicle then travels through the cytoplasm. Two types of endocytosis are phagocytosis ("cell eating") and pinocytosis ("cell drinking"). In **phagocytosis,** cells engulf large particles or bacteria (Figure 1c.11a). In **pinocytosis,** they engulf droplets of fluid (Figure 1c.11b), thus bringing all of the substances dissolved in the droplet into the cell.

Exocytosis

The process by which large molecules leave cells is **exocytosis.** In a cell that produces hormones, for example, the hormones are enclosed in membrane-bound vesicles that travel through the cell's cytoplasm toward the plasma membrane. When the vesicle reaches the plasma membrane, the vesicle membrane fuses with the plasma membrane and then the vesicle opens up to

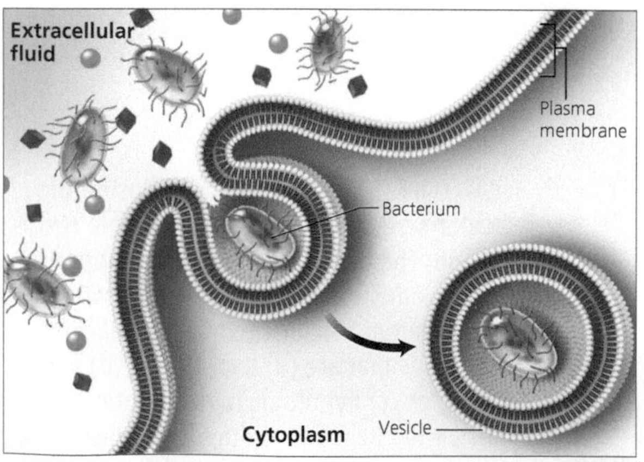

(a) Phagocytosis ("cell eating") occurs when cells engulf bacteria or other large particles.

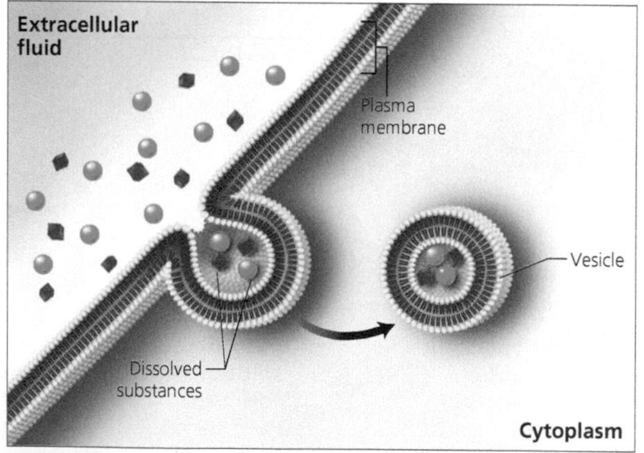

(b) Pinocytosis ("cell drinking") occurs when cells engulf droplets of extracellular fluid and the dissolved substances therein.

FIGURE 1c.11 **Endocytosis—phagocytosis or pinocytosis—occurs when a localized region of the plasma membrane surrounds a bacterium, large molecule, or fluid containing dissolved substances and then pinches inward to form a vesicle that moves into the cell.**

release the hormone outside the cell. Nerve cells also release chemicals by exocytosis. Exocytosis is shown in Figure 1c.12.

Table 1c.3 reviews the ways in which substances move across the plasma membrane.

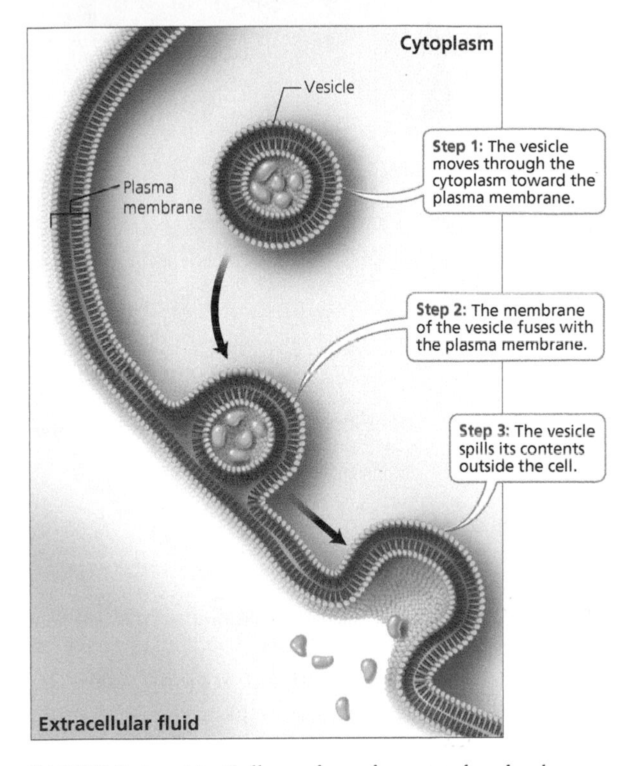

FIGURE 1c.12 **Cells package large molecules in membrane-bound vesicles, which then spill their contents by exocytosis.**

TABLE 1c.3 Review of Mechanisms of Transport Across the Plasma Membrane

Mechanism	Description
Simple diffusion	Random movement from region of higher concentration to region of lower concentration
Facilitated diffusion	Movement from region of higher concentration to region of lower concentration with the aid of a carrier or channel protein
Osmosis	Movement of water from region of higher water concentration (lower solute concentration) to region of lower water concentration (higher solute concentration)
Active transport	Movement often from region of lower concentration to region of higher concentration with the aid of a carrier protein and energy usually from ATP
Endocytosis	Process by which materials are engulfed by plasma membrane and drawn into cell in a vesicle
Exocytosis	Process by which a membrane-bound vesicle from inside the cell fuses with the plasma membrane and spills contents outside of cell

stop and THINK

People with kidney disorders may need dialysis to remove waste products from their blood. The blood is passed through a long, coiled tube submerged in a tank filled with dialyzing fluid. The tubing is porous, allowing small molecules to diffuse out of the blood into the dialyzing fluid. Urea is a waste product that must be removed from the blood. Glucose molecules, on the other hand, should remain in the blood. To achieve these goals, what should the concentrations of urea and glucose be like in the dialyzing fluid?

ORGANELLES

Inside the eukaryotic cell, the primary role of membranes is to create separate compartments where specific chemical processes critical to the life of the cell are carried out. The membrane-bound organelles distributed in the cells' cytoplasm have different functions—just like the different offices within a large company, some of which are responsible for production, some for purchasing, and others for shipping. The compartmentalization allows segregated combinations of molecules to carry out specific tasks (see Figure 1c.2). Some organelles give directions for manufacturing cell products. Others make or modify the products or transport them. Still other organelles process energy or break down substances for use or disposal. Nonmembranous organelles also perform specific functions for the cell.

Nucleus

The cell **nucleus** contains almost all of the cell's genetic information (Figure 1c.13). The DNA within the nucleus controls cellular structure and function because it contains a code for the production of proteins. All our cells contain the same genetic information. The characteristics of a particular cell—what makes it a muscle cell or a liver cell—are determined largely by the specific directions it receives from its nucleus.

A double membrane called the **nuclear envelope** surrounds the nucleus and separates it from the cytoplasm, as shown in Figure 1c.13. Communication between the nucleus and cytoplasm occurs through openings in the envelope called **nuclear pores.** The traffic of selected materials across the nuclear envelope allows the contents of the cytoplasm to influence the nucleus, and vice versa.

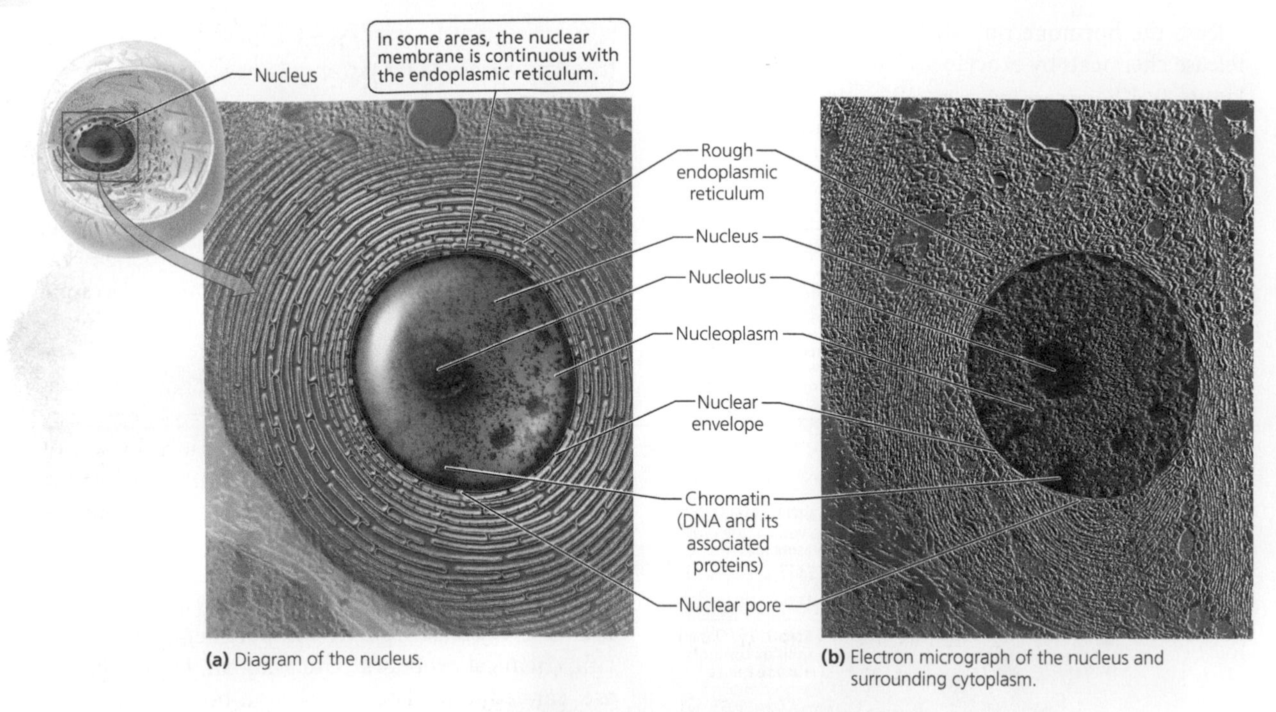

(a) Diagram of the nucleus.

(b) Electron micrograph of the nucleus and surrounding cytoplasm.

FIGURE 1c.13 **The nucleus contains almost all the genetic information of a cell.**

Genetic information within the nucleus is organized into **chromosomes,** threadlike structures made of DNA and associated proteins. The number of chromosomes varies from one species to another. For example, humans have 46 chromosomes (23 pairs), house mice have 40 chromosomes, and domestic dogs have 78. Individual chromosomes are visible with a light microscope during cell division, when they shorten and condense (Figure 1c.14a). At all other times, however, the chromosomes are extended and not readily visible. In this dispersed state, the genetic material is called *chromatin* (Figure 1c.14b). The chromatin and other contents of the nucleus constitute the *nucleoplasm.*

The **nucleolus,** a specialized region within the nucleus (see Figure 1c.13), forms and disassembles during the course of the cell cycle. It is not surrounded by a membrane but is simply a region where DNA has gathered to produce a type of RNA called ribosomal RNA (rRNA). Ribosomal RNA is a component of **ribosomes,** which are sites where protein synthesis begins. Ribosomes may be suspended in the cytoplasm (free ribosomes) or attached to the endoplasmic reticulum (bound ribosomes).

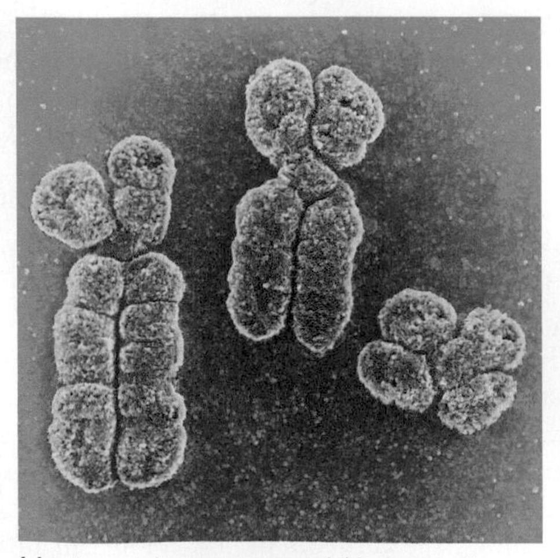

(a) Individual chromosomes are visible during cell division, when they shorten and condense.

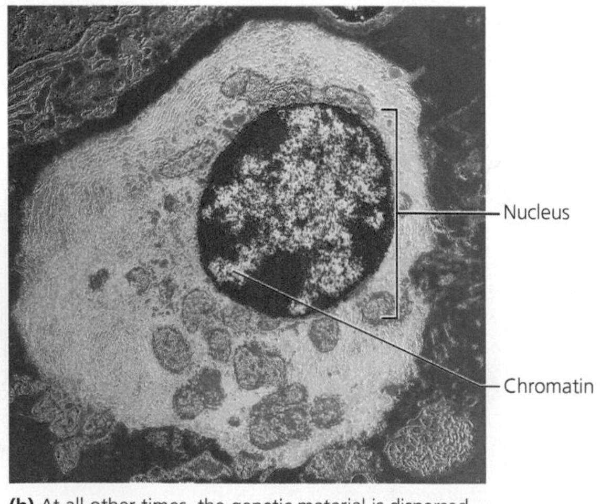

(b) At all other times, the genetic material is dispersed and called chromatin.

FIGURE 1c.14 **Chromosomes are composed of DNA and associated proteins.**

Endoplasmic Reticulum

The **endoplasmic reticulum** (**ER**) is part of an extensive network of channels connected to the nuclear envelope and certain organelles (Figure 1c.15). In some regions, the ER is studded with ribosomes and because of this is called **rough endoplasmic reticulum** (**RER**). The amino acid chains made by the attached ribosomes are threaded through the RER's membrane to its internal spaces. There the chains are processed and modified, enclosed in vesicles formed from the RER membrane, and transferred to the Golgi complex (discussed later) for additional processing and packaging. Proteins made by ribosomes bound to ER will be incorporated into membranes or eventually secreted by the cell. Proteins produced by free ribosomes will remain in the cell.

Smooth endoplasmic reticulum (**SER**) lacks ribosomes. The SER (particularly in liver cells) detoxifies alcohol and other drugs such as phenobarbital. Typically, enzymes of SER modify the drugs to make them more water soluble and easier to eliminate from the body. Another function of SER is the production of phospholipids. These phospholipids, along with proteins from the RER, are used to make the RER membrane. Because the RER membrane is continually used to form vesicles for shipping, it must be replenished constantly.

Golgi Complex

Resembling a stack of dinner plates, the **Golgi complex** consists of a series of interconnected, flattened membranous sacs. This organelle is the cell's protein processing and packaging center (Figure 1c.16). Protein-filled vesicles from the RER arrive at the "receiving side" of the Golgi complex, fuse with its membrane, and empty their contents inside. The Golgi complex then chemically modifies many of the proteins as they move, by way of vesicles, from one membranous disk in the stack to the next. When the processing is finished, the Golgi complex sorts the proteins, much as a postal worker sorts letters, and sends them to their various destinations. Some of the proteins emerging from the "shipping side" are packaged in vesicles and sent to the plasma membrane for export from the cell or to become membrane proteins. Other proteins are packaged in lysosomes. Figure 1c.17 summarizes the movement of protein-filled vesicles from the rough endoplasmic reticulum to the Golgi complex for processing and eventual release.

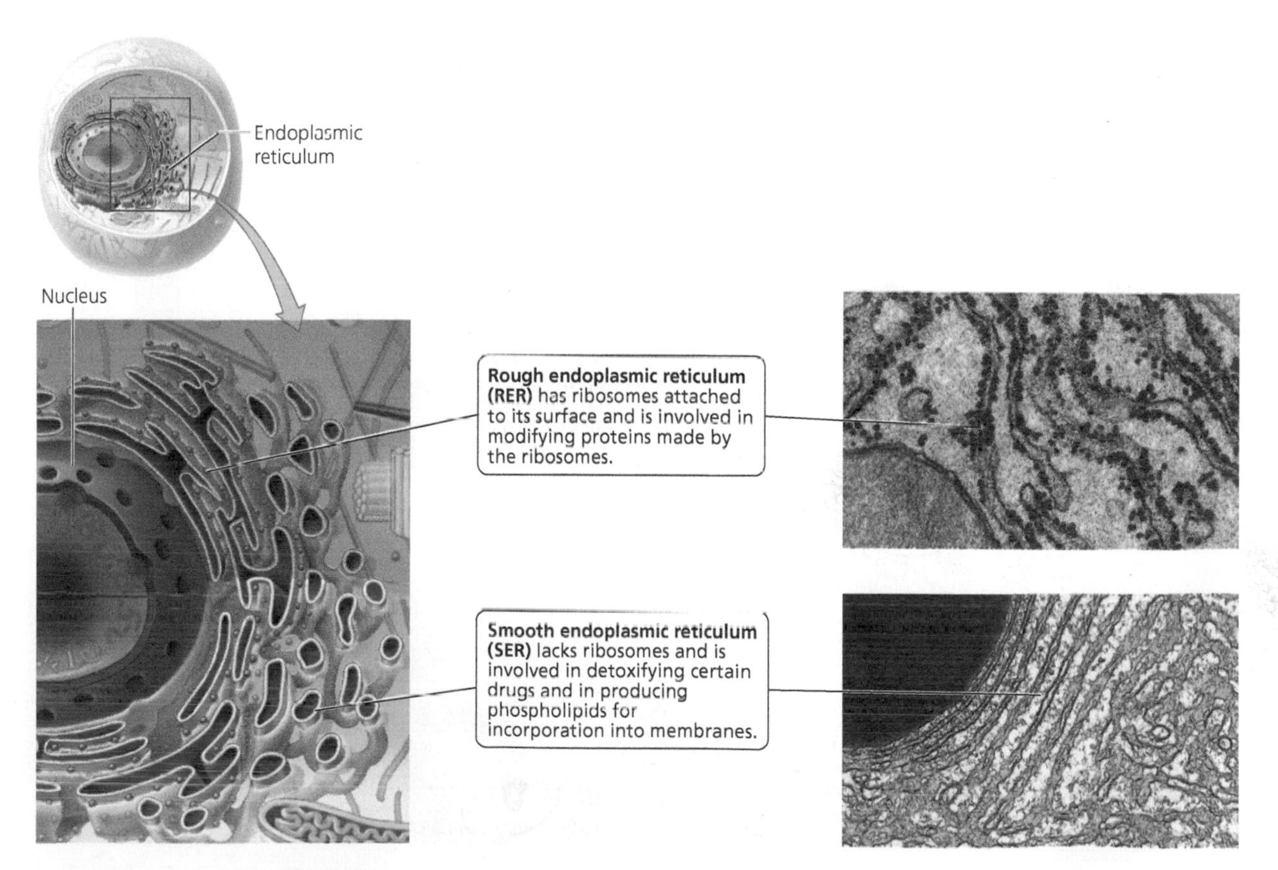

Endoplasmic reticulum
Nucleus
Rough endoplasmic reticulum (RER) has ribosomes attached to its surface and is involved in modifying proteins made by the ribosomes.
Smooth endoplasmic reticulum (SER) lacks ribosomes and is involved in detoxifying certain drugs and in producing phospholipids for incorporation into membranes.

FIGURE 1c.15 The endoplasmic reticulum (ER) is continuous with the nuclear membrane and consists of two regions: rough ER and smooth ER.

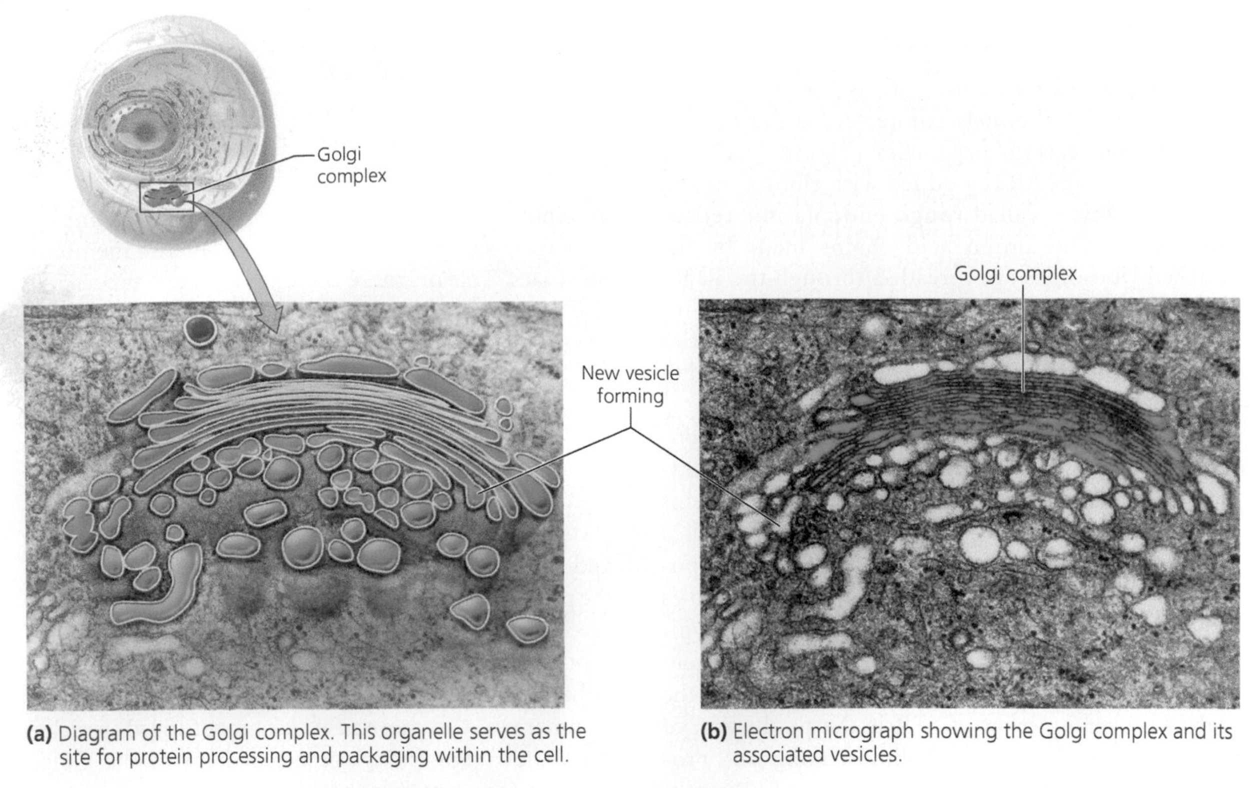

(a) Diagram of the Golgi complex. This organelle serves as the site for protein processing and packaging within the cell.

(b) Electron micrograph showing the Golgi complex and its associated vesicles.

FIGURE 1c.16 **The Golgi complex**

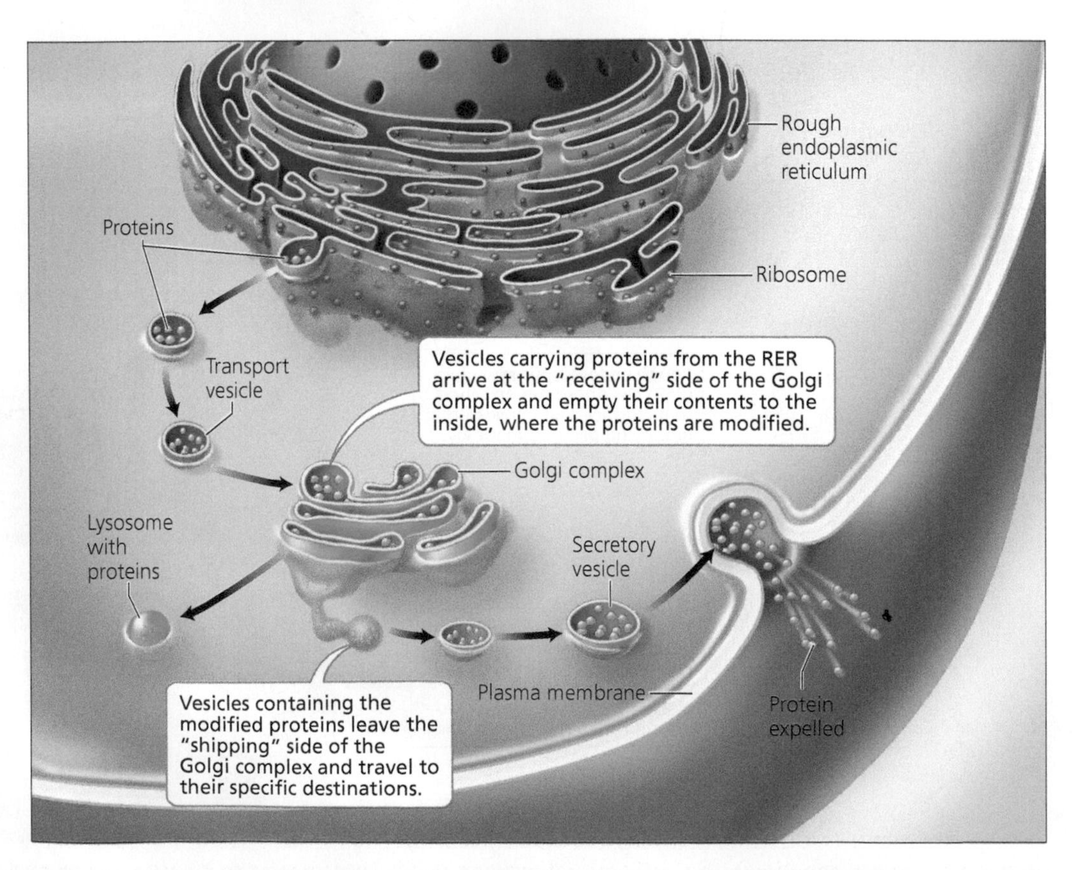

FIGURE 1c.17 **The route by which protein-filled vesicles from the rough endoplasmic reticulum travel to the Golgi complex for processing and eventual release**

Lysosomes

How does the cell break down worn-out parts or digest large objects that it takes in by phagocytosis? If it simply released digestive enzymes into its cytoplasm, for example, it would soon destroy itself. Instead, intracellular digestion occurs mainly within lysosomes. **Lysosomes** are roughly spherical organelles consisting of a single membrane packed with about 40 different digestive enzymes. The enzymes and membranes of lysosomes are made by the RER and then sent to the Golgi complex for additional processing. Eventually, enzyme-filled lysosomes bud and then pinch off from the Golgi complex (see Figure 1c.17) and begin their diverse roles in digestion within the cell. These roles include destroying foreign invaders, such as bacteria, and breaking down worn-out organelles.

Consider, for example, what happens when a cell engulfs a bacterium. You can follow this process in Figure 1c.18 (see pathway on right). During the process of phagocytosis (Step 1), a vesicle encircles the bacterium. A lysosome released from the Golgi complex then fuses with the vesicle (Step 2), and the lysosome's digestive enzymes break the bacterium down into smaller molecules. These molecules diffuse out of the vesicle into the cytoplasm, where they can be used by the cell (Step 3). Indigestible residues may be expelled from the cell by exocytosis (Step 4), or they may be stored indefinitely in vesicles inside the cell (Step 5).

Lysosomes also break down obsolete parts of the cell itself. Worn-out organelles and macromolecules are broken down into smaller components that can be reused (see Figure 1c.18, pathway on left). For example, an organelle called a mitochondrion (discussed later) lasts only about 10 days in a typical liver cell before being destroyed by lysosomes. After worn-out mitochondria are destroyed, their component monomers, such as amino acids, are returned to the cytoplasm for reuse. Such "housecleaning" keeps the cell functioning properly and promotes the recycling of essential materials.

The absence of a single kind of lysosomal enzyme can have devastating consequences. Molecules that would normally be broken down by the missing enzyme start to collect in the lysosomes and cause them to swell. Ultimately, the accumulating molecules interfere with cell function. These lysosomal storage diseases are inherited and progress with age.

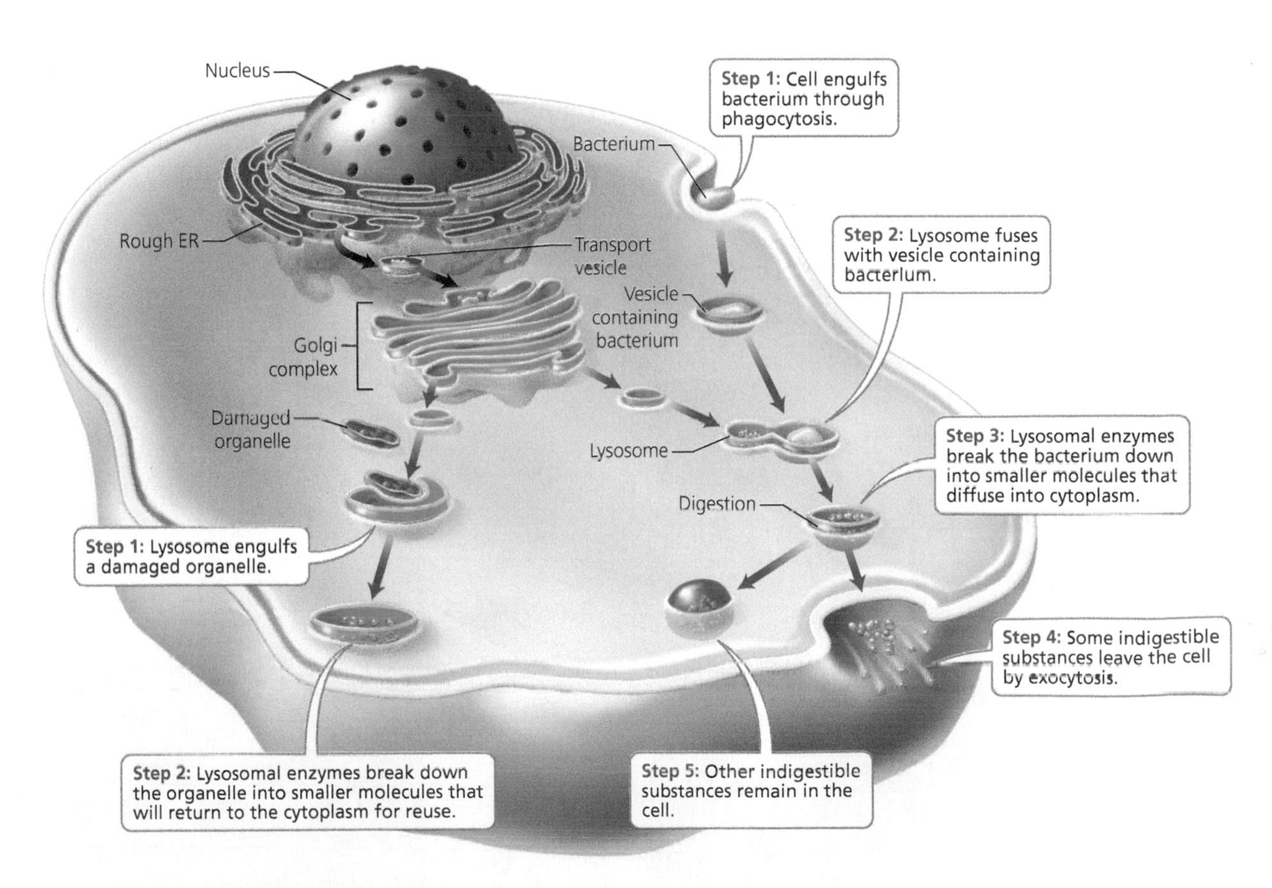

FIGURE 1c.18 Lysosome formation and function in intracellular digestion. Lysosomes, released from the Golgi complex, digest a bacterium engulfed by the cell (see pathway on right). Lysosomes also digest obsolete parts of the cell itself (see pathway on left).

what would you do?

Imagine that you and your spouse want to start a family, but both of you are carriers of Tay-Sachs disease and could pass the gene to your children. The possible outcomes for any child you might conceive are as follows: the child may not have the gene for Tay-Sachs and may be healthy, may have the disease and die in early childhood, or may be a carrier as you are. Your parents urge adoption. Your spouse prefers not to adopt but to use prenatal screening to check if your fetus has the disease. What would you do?

Tay-Sachs disease is a lysosomal storage disease caused by the absence of the lysosomal enzyme hexosaminidase (Hex A), which breaks down lipids in nerve cells. When Hex A is missing, the lysosomes swell with undigested lipids. Infants with Tay-Sachs disease appear normal at birth but begin to deteriorate by about 6 months of age as abnormal amounts of lipid accumulate in the nervous system. By the age of 4 or 5, Tay-Sachs causes paralysis and death. At present there is no cure for this disease. However, there is a blood test to detect individuals who carry the gene for Tay-Sachs. Called carriers, these individuals do not have the disease but could pass the gene to their offspring.

Certain environmental factors cause disease by interfering with lysosomes.

Mitochondria

Most cellular activities require energy. Energy is needed to transport certain substances across the plasma membrane and to fuel many of the chemical reactions that occur in the cytoplasm. Specialized cells such as muscle cells and nerve cells require energy to perform their particular activities. The energy needed by cells is provided by **mitochondria** (singular, mitochondrion), the organelles within which most of cellular respiration occurs. Cellular respiration, discussed later in the chapter, is a four-phase process in which oxygen and an organic fuel such as glucose are consumed and energy in the form of ATP is released. The first phase takes place in the cytoplasm. The remaining three phases occur in the mitochondria.

The number of mitochondria varies considerably from cell to cell and is roughly correlated with a cell's demand for energy. Most cells contain several hundred to thousands of mitochondria. Like the nucleus, but unlike other organelles, mitochondria are bounded by a double membrane (Figure 1c.19). The inner and outer membranes create two separate compartments that serve as sites for some of the reactions in cellular respiration. The infoldings of the inner membrane of a mitochondrion are called *cristae*, and these are the sites of the last phase of cellular respiration. Finally, mitochondria contain ribosomes and a small percentage of a cell's total DNA (the rest being found in the nucleus, as noted earlier). Mitochondria contain ribosomes and DNA because they are likely descendants of once free-living bacteria that invaded or were engulfed by ancient cells. Table 1c.4 reviews the functions of organelles.

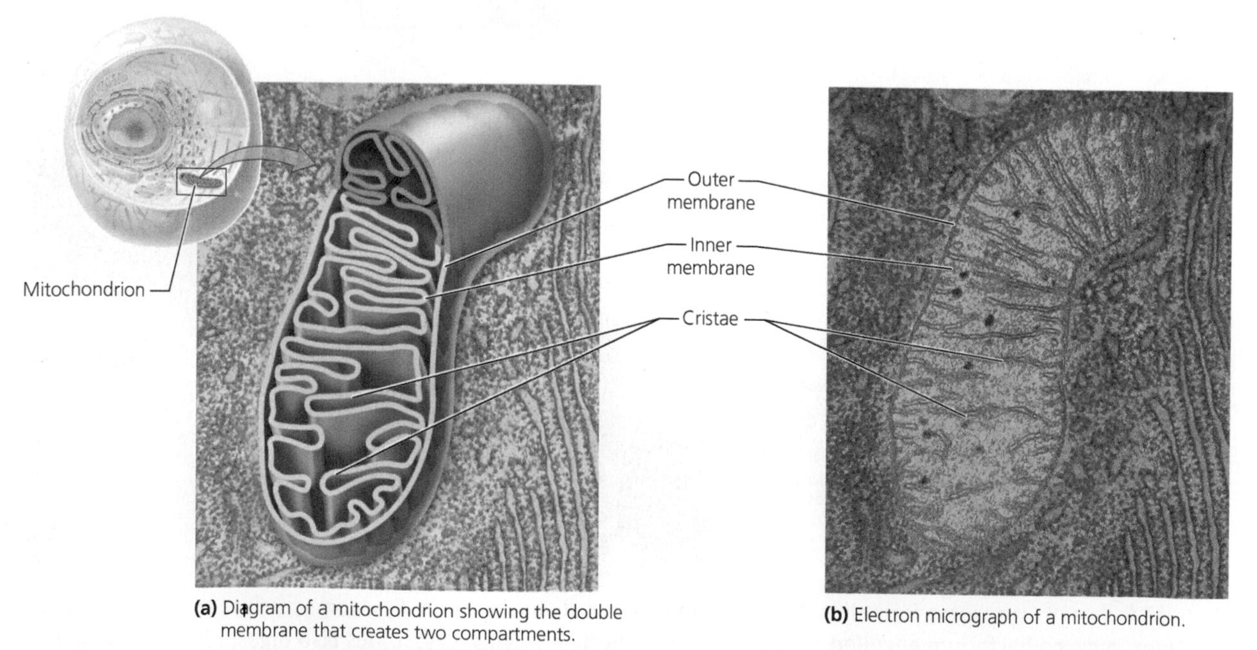

(a) Diagram of a mitochondrion showing the double membrane that creates two compartments.

(b) Electron micrograph of a mitochondrion.

FIGURE 1c.19 **Mitochondria are sites of energy conversion in the cell.**

TABLE 1c.4 Review of Major Organelles and Their Functions

Organelle	Function
Nucleus	Contains almost all the genetic information and influences cellular structure and function
Rough endoplasmic reticulum (RER)	Studded with ribosomes (sites where the synthesis of proteins begins); produces membrane
Smooth endoplasmic reticulum (SER)	Detoxifies drugs; produces membrane
Golgi complex	Sorts, modifies, and packages products of RER
Lysosomes	Digest substances imported from outside the cell; destroy old or defective cell parts
Mitochondria	Provide cell with energy through the breakdown of glucose during cellular respiration

CYTOSKELETON

Traversing the cytoplasm of the cell is a complex network of fibers called the **cytoskeleton**. The fibers are divided into three types: microtubules are the thickest; microfilaments are the thinnest; and intermediate filaments are the diverse group in between. Microtubules and microfilaments are seen to disassemble and reassemble, whereas intermediate filaments tend to be more permanent.

Microtubules are straight, hollow rods made of the protein tubulin. Some microtubules near the plasma membrane maintain cell shape. Microtubules also form tracks along which organelles or vesicles travel (Figure 1c.20). For example, secretory vesicles (membrane-bound vesicles containing material to be released from the cell) that have budded from the Golgi complex make their way to the plasma membrane by moving along a microtubule track. Finally, microtubules play a role in the separation of chromosomes during cell division. A microtubule-organizing center, located near the nucleus, contains a pair of **centrioles**, each composed of nine sets of triplet (three) microtubules arranged in a ring (Figure 1c.21). Centrioles may function in cell division and in the formation of cilia and flagella.

Microtubules serve as the working parts of two types of cell extensions called cilia (singular, cilium) and flagella (singular, flagellum). **Cilia** are numerous, short extensions on a cell, resembling hairs that move with the back-and-forth motion of oars. They are found, for example, on the surfaces of cells lining the respiratory tract (Figure 1c.22a), where they sweep debris trapped in mucus away from the lungs. Smoking destroys these cilia and hampers cleaning of respiratory surfaces. A **flagellum** resembles a whip and moves in an undulating manner. Flagella are much longer than cilia. The only cell with a flagellum in humans is the sperm cell (Figure 1c.22b).

Cilia and flagella differ in length, number per cell, and pattern of movement. Nevertheless, they have a similar arrangement of microtubules, called a 9 + 2 pattern (Figure 1c.22c), at their core. This arrangement

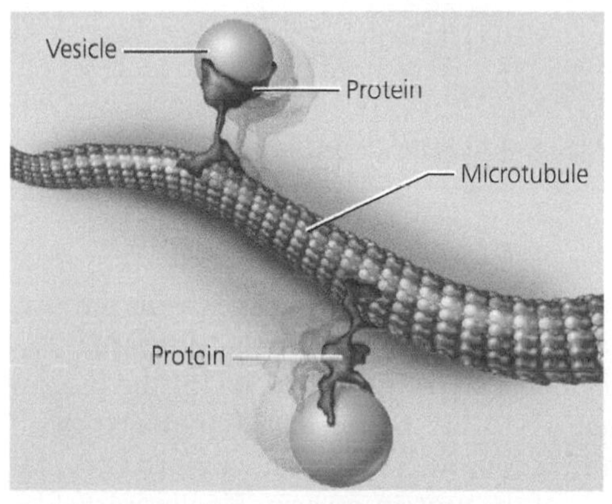

(a) Vesicles carried by proteins travel along a microtubule.

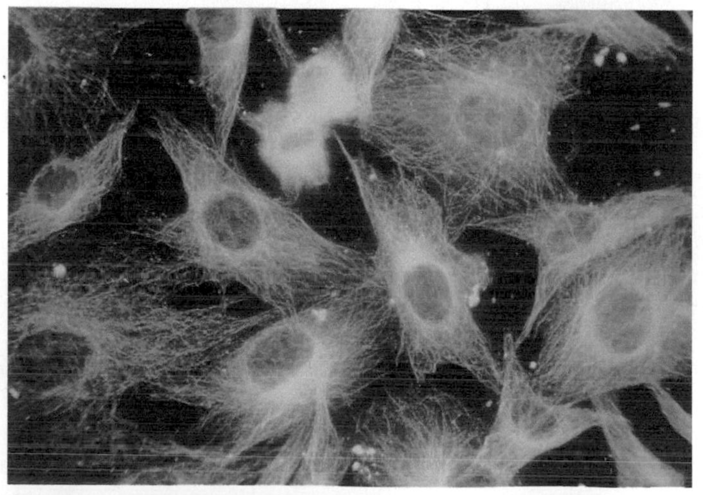

(b) A micrograph showing the microtubule component of the cytoskeleton for several cells. The round area in the center of each cell is the nucleus.

FIGURE 1c.20 **Microtubules serve as tracks along which organelles or vesicles move.**

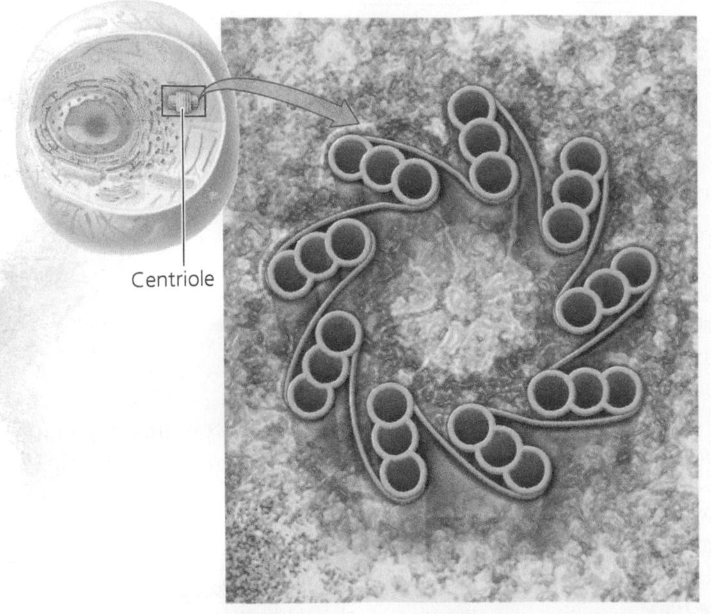

(a) Diagram of a centriole. Each centriole is composed of nine sets of triplet microtubules arranged in a ring.

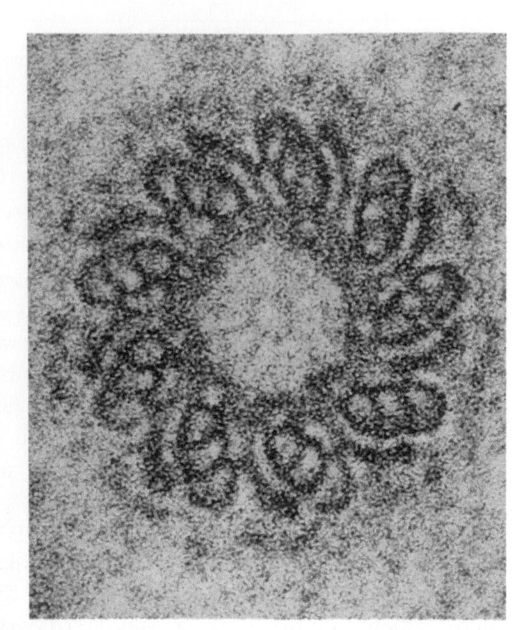

(b) Electron micrograph showing the microtubules of a centriole

FIGURE 1c.21 **Centrioles may play a role in cell division.**

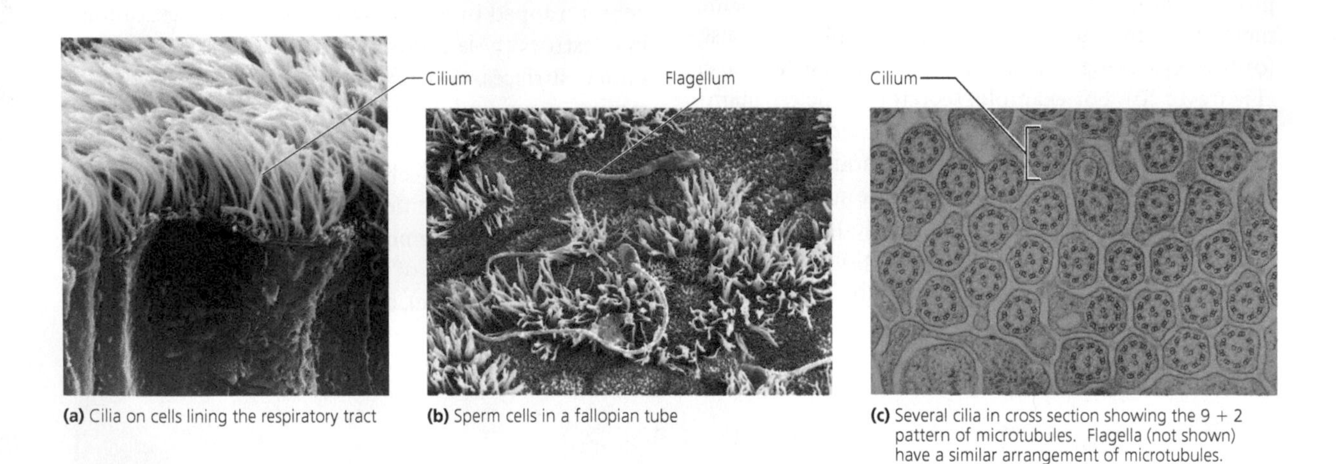

(a) Cilia on cells lining the respiratory tract

(b) Sperm cells in a fallopian tube

(c) Several cilia in cross section showing the 9 + 2 pattern of microtubules. Flagella (not shown) have a similar arrangement of microtubules.

FIGURE 1c.22 **Microtubules are responsible for the movement of cilia and flagella.**

consists of nine pairs of microtubules arranged in a ring with two microtubules at the center. The microtubules of a cilium or flagellum are anchored to the cell by a *basal body*. Like the centrioles described earlier, basal bodies contain nine triplets of microtubules arranged in a ring. Loss of ciliary and flagellar function appears to be caused by the absence of armlike structures that normally link the nine pairs of microtubules in the 9 + 2 pattern. Immotile cilia syndrome is a genetic disorder characterized by severe loss of function in cilia and flagella throughout the body. People with immotile cilia syndrome experience chronic respiratory problems, and men with the syndrome may be sterile because of immotile sperm.

Microfilaments are solid rods made of the protein actin. These fibers are best known for their role in muscle contraction, where they slide past thicker filaments made of the protein myosin. Finally, microfilaments play a role in cell division, forming a band that contracts and pinches the cell in two.

Intermediate filaments are a diverse group of ropelike fibers helping to maintain cell shape and anchoring certain organelles in place. Their protein composition varies from one type of cell to another.

CELLULAR RESPIRATION AND FERMENTATION IN THE GENERATION OF ATP

Living requires work, and work requires energy. Logic tells us, therefore, that living requires energy.

We get our energy from the food we eat. Our digestive system breaks down complex macromolecules such as carbohydrates, proteins, and fats into their simpler components, such as glucose, amino acids, and fatty acids. These simpler molecules are then absorbed into the bloodstream and carried to our cells, where some of the energy stored in the molecules' chemical bonds is used to make ATP, the energy-rich molecule that our cells use to do their work. (Some energy is also given off as heat.) Although carbohydrates, proteins, and fats are all sources of cellular energy, we will focus on carbohydrates. Cells have two ways of breaking glucose molecules apart for energy: cellular respiration and fermentation. Cellular respiration requires oxygen; fermentation does not.

All the chemical reactions that take place in a cell constitute its **metabolism**. These chemical reactions are organized into metabolic pathways. Each pathway consists of a series of steps in which a starting molecule is modified, eventually resulting in a particular product. Specific enzymes speed up each step of the pathway. Cellular respiration and fermentation are examples of *catabolic pathways*, pathways in which complex molecules, such as carbohydrates, are broken down into simpler compounds, releasing energy. *Anabolic pathways*, on the other hand, build complex molecules from simpler ones and consume energy in the process.

Cellular Respiration

Cellular respiration is the oxygen-requiring pathway in which glucose is broken down by cells. It is an elaborate series of chemical reactions whose final products are carbon dioxide, water, and energy. In a laboratory beaker, glucose and oxygen can be combined to produce those products in a single step. However, under those circumstances, the glucose burns, and all the energy is lost as heat. The process used by cells, in which glucose is broken down in a series of steps, enables the cells to obtain much of the energy in a usable form—specifically, as a high-energy chemical bond in ATP. Recall that ATP is formed from ADP (adenosine diphosphate) and inorganic phosphate (P*i*) in a process that requires energy.

Cellular respiration has four phases: (1) glycolysis, (2) the transition reaction, (3) the citric acid cycle, and (4) the electron transport chain. All four phases occur continuously within cells. Glycolysis takes place in the cytoplasm of the cell. The transition reaction, the citric acid cycle, and the electron transport chain take place in mitochondria. You will see that some of these phases consist of a series of reactions in which the **products** from one reaction become the **substrates** (raw materials) for the next reaction. You will also see that the transfer of electrons from one atom or molecule to another is a key feature of the process our cells use to capture energy from fuel. As the electrons are passed along a chain of intermediate compounds, their energy is used to make ATP.

Glycolysis

The first phase of cellular respiration, called **glycolysis** (*glyco*, sugar; *lysis*, splitting), begins with glucose, a six-carbon sugar, being split into 2 three-carbon sugars. These three-carbon sugars are then converted into two molecules of **pyruvate** (Figure 1c.23), another three-carbon compound. Glycolysis occurs in several steps, each requiring a different, specific enzyme. During the first steps, two molecules of ATP are consumed because energy is needed to prepare glucose for splitting. During the remaining steps, four molecules of ATP are produced, for a net gain of two ATP. Glycolysis also produces two molecules of nicotine adenine dinucleotide (NADH), which are generated when electrons are donated to the coenzyme NAD^+. Glycolysis does not require oxygen and releases only a small amount of the chemical energy stored in glucose. Most of the energy remains in the two molecules of pyruvate. These molecules move from the cytoplasm into the inner compartment of the mitochondrion.

Transition reaction

Once inside the inner compartment of the mitochondrion, pyruvate reacts with a substance called coenzyme A (CoA) in a reaction called the transition reaction. The transition reaction results in the removal of one carbon (in the form of carbon dioxide, CO_2) from each pyruvate (Figure 1c.24). The resulting two-carbon molecule, called an acetyl group, then binds to CoA to form acetyl CoA. A molecule of NADH is also produced from each pyruvate.

Citric acid cycle

Still in the inner compartment of the mitochondrion, acetyl CoA reacts with a four-carbon compound in the first of a cyclic series of eight chemical reactions known as the **citric acid cycle**, named after the first

Glycolysis (in cytoplasm)

Cytoplasm

During the first steps, two molecules of ATP are *consumed* in preparing glucose for splitting.

Glucose

C C C C C C

Energy-investment phase

2 ATP

2 ADP

During the remaining steps, four molecules of ATP are *produced.*

4 ADP

4 ATP

Energy-yielding phase

2 NAD^+

2 NADH

The two molecules of pyruvate then diffuse from the cytoplasm into the inner compartment of the mitochondrion, where they pass through a few preparatory steps (the transition reaction) before entering the citric acid cycle.

C C C

2 Pyruvate

C C C

Two molecules of nicotine adenine dinucleotide (NADH), a carrier of high-energy electrons, also are produced.

FIGURE 1c.23 **Glycolysis is a several-step sequence of reactions in the cytoplasm. Glucose, a six-carbon sugar, is split into 2 three-carbon molecules of pyruvate.**

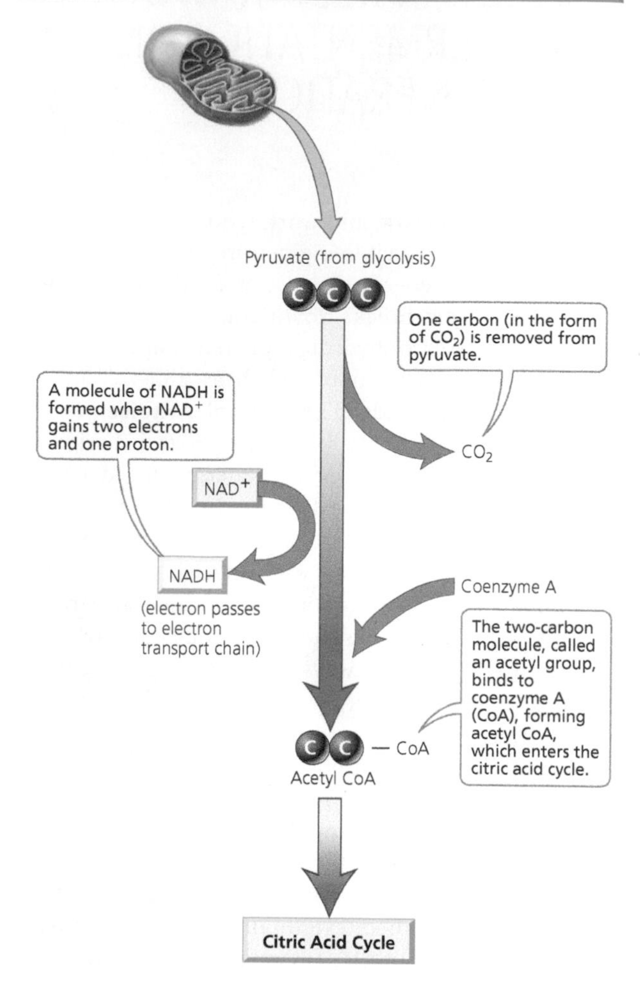

Transition Reaction (in mitochondrion)
Pyruvate (from glycolysis)
C C C
One carbon (in the form of CO_2) is removed from pyruvate.
A molecule of NADH is formed when NAD^+ gains two electrons and one proton.
CO_2
NAD^+
NADH
(electron passes to electron transport chain)
Coenzyme A
The two-carbon molecule, called an acetyl group, binds to coenzyme A (CoA), forming acetyl CoA, which enters the citric acid cycle.
C C — CoA
Acetyl CoA
Citric Acid Cycle

FIGURE 1c.24 **The transition reaction takes place inside the mitochondrion and is the link between glycolysis and the citric acid cycle.**

product (citric acid, or citrate) formed along its route (Figure 1c.25). The cycle is also called the Krebs cycle—after the scientist Hans Krebs, who described many of the reactions. Rather than considering each of the chemical reactions in the citric acid cycle, we will simply say that it completes the loss of electrons from glucose and yields two molecules of ATP (one from each acetyl CoA that enters the cycle) and several molecules of NADH and $FADH_2$ (flavin adenine dinucleotide). NADH and $FADH_2$ are carriers of high-energy electrons. The NADH and $FADH_2$ produced in glycolysis, in the transition reaction, and in the citric acid cycle enter the electron transport chain, the final phase of cellular respiration. The citric acid cycle also produces CO_2 as waste.

Electron transport chain

During the final phase of cellular respiration, the molecules of NADH and $FADH_2$ produced by earlier phases pass their electrons to a series of carrier proteins embedded in the inner membrane of the mitochondrion. These proteins are known as the **electron transport chain** (Figure 1c.26). (Recall that the inner membrane of the mitochondrion is highly folded, providing space for thousands of sets of carrier proteins.) During the transfer of electrons from one protein to the next, energy is released and used to make ATP. Eventually, the electrons are passed to oxygen, the final electron acceptor, which then combines with two hydrogen ions to form water. Oxygen has a critical role in cellular respiration. When oxygen is absent, elec-

Citric Acid Cycle (in mitochondrion)

Acetyl CoA, the two-carbon compound formed during the transition reaction, enters the citric acid cycle.

The citric acid cycle also yields several molecules of $FADH_2$ and NADH, carriers of high-energy electrons that enter the electron transport chain.

Acetyl CoA

— CoA

CoA

Oxaloacetate

Citrate

NADH

NAD^+

CO_2 leaves cycle

Malate

Citric Acid Cycle

NAD^+

$FADH_2$

NADH

ATP

ADP + Pi

FAD

α-Ketoglutarate

Succinate

CO_2 leaves cycle

NAD^+

NADH

The citric acid cycle yields one ATP from each acetyl CoA that enters the cycle, for a net gain of two ATP.

FIGURE 1c.25 **The citric acid cycle is a cyclic series of eight chemical reactions that occurs inside the mitochondrion and yields two molecules of ATP and several molecules of NADH and FADH2 per molecule of glucose.**

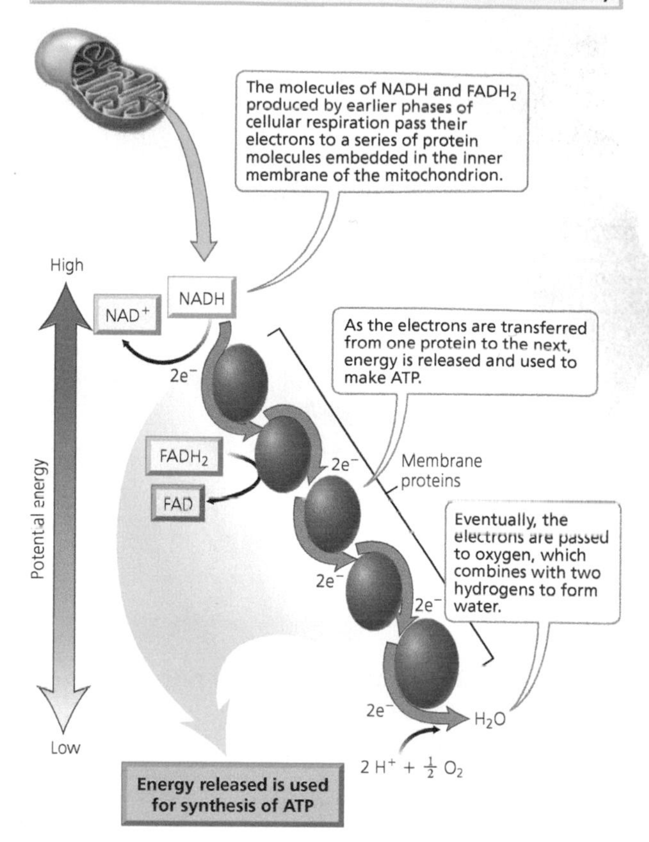
Electron Transport Chain (inner membrane of mitochondrion)
The molecules of NADH and $FADH_2$ produced by earlier phases of cellular respiration pass their electrons to a series of protein molecules embedded in the inner membrane of the mitochondrion.
High
NADH
NAD^+
$2e^-$
As the electrons are transferred from one protein to the next, energy is released and used to make ATP.
$FADH_2$
$2e^-$
Membrane proteins
FAD
Potential energy
Eventually, the electrons are passed to oxygen, which combines with two hydrogens to form water.
$2e^-$
$2e^-$
$2e^-$
H_2O
Low
$2 H^+ + \frac{1}{2} O_2$
Energy released is used for synthesis of ATP

FIGURE 1c.26 **The electron transport chain is the final phase of cellular respiration. This phase yields 32 ATP per molecule of glucose.**

trons accumulate in the carrier proteins, halting the citric acid cycle and cellular respiration. But when oxygen is present, and accepts the electrons, respiration continues. The electron transport chain produces 32 molecules of ATP per molecule of glucose.

Altogether, cellular respiration generally produces 36 molecules of ATP per molecule of glucose: 2 ATP from glycolysis, 2 ATP from the citric acid cycle, and 32 ATP from the electron transport chain. The results of cellular respiration are summarized in Figure 1c.27. Basic descriptions of each phase can be found in Table 1c.5.

Fermentation

As noted earlier, cellular respiration depends on oxygen as the final electron acceptor in the electron transport chain. Without oxygen, the transport chain comes to a halt, blocking the citric acid cycle and stopping cellular

TABLE 1c.5 Review of Cellular Respiration

Phase	Location	Description	Main Products
Glycolysis	Cytoplasm	Several-step process by which glucose is split into 2 pyruvate	2 pyruvate 2 ATP 2 NADH
Transition reaction	Mitochondria	One CO_2 is removed from each pyruvate; the resulting molecules bind to CoA, forming 2 acetyl CoA	2 acetyl CoA 2 NADH
Citric acid cycle	Mitochondria	Cyclic series of eight chemical reactions by which acetyl CoA is broken down	2 ATP 2 $FADH_2$ 6 NADH
Electron transport chain	Mitochondria	Electrons from NADH and $FADH_2$ are passed from one protein to the next, releasing energy for ATP synthesis	32 ATP H_2O

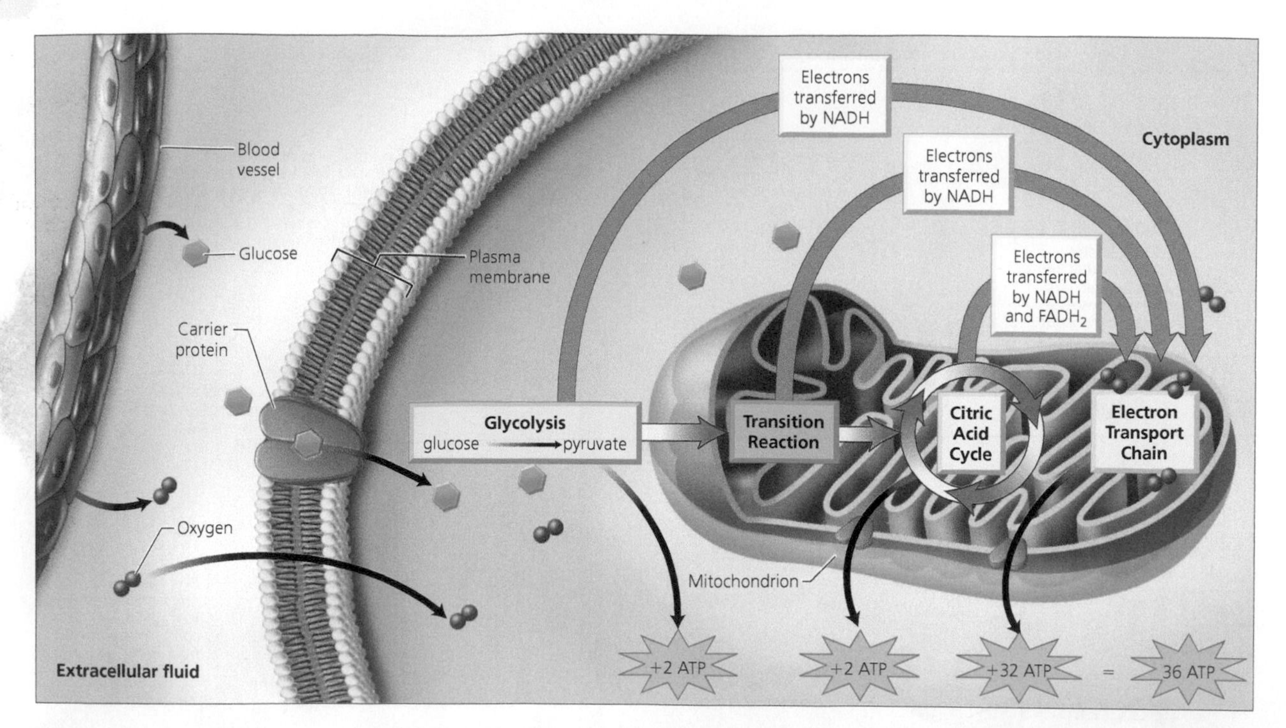

FIGURE 1c.27 **Summary of cellular respiration. Cellular respiration produces 36 ATP per molecule of glucose (2 ATP from glycolysis, 2 ATP from the citric acid cycle, and 32 ATP from the electron transport chain).**

respiration. Is there a way for cells to harvest energy when molecules of oxygen are scarce? The answer is yes, and the pathway is fermentation.

Fermentation is the breakdown of glucose without oxygen. It begins with glycolysis, which as you recall occurs in the cytoplasm and does not require oxygen. From one molecule of glucose, glycolysis produces two molecules each of pyruvate, the electron carrier NADH, and ATP. The remaining fermentation reactions also take place in the cytoplasm, transferring electrons from NADH to pyruvate or a derivative of pyruvate. This transfer of electrons is critical because it regenerates NAD^+, which is essential for the production of ATP through glycolysis. Recall that in cellular respiration, oxygen is the final electron acceptor in the electron transport chain, whereas in fermentation it is pyruvate or a pyruvate derivative. Fermentation therefore nets only 2 molecules of ATP compared with the 36 molecules of ATP produced by cellular respiration (refer, again, to Figure 1c.27). In short, fermentation is a very inefficient way for cells to harvest energy.

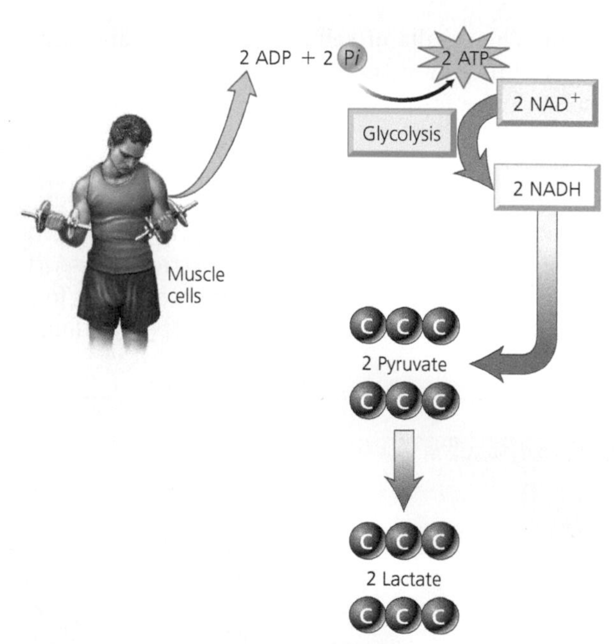

FIGURE 1c.28 **Lactic acid fermentation. Fermentation occurs in the cytoplasm, does not require oxygen, and yields only two molecules of ATP per molecule of glucose. The symbol *Pi* stands for inorganic phosphate (PO_4^{-2}).**

Different types of fermentation found in different organisms differ in the waste products formed from pyruvate. The fermentation that takes place in the human body is **lactic acid fermentation,** in which NADH passes electrons directly to pyruvate to produce lactate or lactic acid as a waste product (Figure 1c.28). During strenuous exercise, the oxygen supply in our muscle cells runs low. Under these conditions, the cells increase lactic acid fermentation to ensure the continued production of ATP. The muscle pain we often experience after intense exercise is caused partly by the accumulation of lactic acid due to fermentation. In time, the soreness disappears as the lactic acid moves into the bloodstream and is carried to the liver, where it is converted back to pyruvate.

CHAPTER 1d

BODY ORGANIZATION AND HOMEOSTASIS

Taken from *Biology of Humans: Concepts, Applications, and Issues*, Third Edition, by Judith Goodenough and Betty McGuire

FROM CELLS TO ORGAN SYSTEMS

Think for a moment about the multitude of functions taking place in your body at this very instant. Your heart is beating. Your lungs are taking in oxygen and eliminating carbon dioxide. Your eyes are forming an image of these words, and your brain is thinking about them. Your body can carry out these functions and more because its cells are specialized to perform specific tasks. But cell specialization is only the beginning. Specialized cells are organized into tissues, organs, and organ systems.

Tissues

A **tissue** is a group of cells of similar type that work together to serve a common function. Human tissues come in four primary types: epithelial tissue, connective tissue, muscle tissue, and nervous tissue. **Epithelial tissue** covers body surfaces, lines body cavities and organs, and forms glands. **Connective tissue** serves as a storage site for fat, plays an important role in immunity, and provides the body and its organs with protection and support. **Muscle tissue** is responsible for body movement and for movement of substances through the body. **Nervous tissue** conducts nerve impulses from one part of the body to another. As you read this chapter, you learn more about each of these types of tissue.

Epithelial tissue

All epithelial tissues share two characteristics: a free surface and a basement membrane. The free surface may be specialized for protection, secretion, or absorption. The **basement membrane** is a noncellular layer that binds the epithelial cells to underlying connective tissue and helps the epithelial tissue resist stretching.

The three basic shapes of epithelial cells are suited to their functions. **Squamous** (skwá-mus) **epithelium** is made up of flattened, or scale-like, cells. These cells form linings—in the blood vessels or lungs, for instance—where their flattened shape allows oxygen and carbon dioxide to diffuse across the lining easily. In blood vessels, the smooth surface of the blood vessel lining reduces friction. **Cuboidal epithelium** is made up of cube-shaped cells. Cuboidal cells are found in many glands and in the lining of kidney tubules, where they provide some protection and are specialized for secretion and absorption. **Columnar epithelium**, consisting of elongated, column-shaped cells, is specialized for absorption and secretion. The small intestine is lined with columnar cells. These, like many examples of columnar cells, have numerous small, fingerlike folds on their exposed surfaces, greatly increasing the surface area for absorption. The goblet cells of this lining produce mucus to ease the passage of food and protect the cells of the lining.

Squamous, cuboidal, and columnar epithelium can be either simple (a single layer of cells) or stratified (multiple layers of cells). Stratified epithelium often serves a protective role, because its multiple layers provide additional thickness that makes it more difficult for molecules to pass through. Table 1d.1 and Figure 1d.1 summarize the types of epithelial tissue.

A **gland** is epithelial tissue that secretes a product. **Exocrine glands** secrete their products into ducts leading to body surfaces, cavities, or organs. Examples of exocrine glands include the glands that produce digestive enzymes, milk glands, and the oil and sweat glands of the skin. **Endocrine glands** lack ducts and secrete their products, hormones, into spaces just outside the cells. Ultimately, hormones diffuse into the bloodstream and are carried throughout the body.

Connective tissue

Connective tissue has many forms and functions. Sometimes described as the body's glue, its most common role is to bind (tendons and ligaments) and support the other tissues (cartilage and bone). However, certain connective tissues specialize in transport (blood) and energy storage (adipose tissue). Connective tissue is the most abundant and widely distributed tissue in the body.

All connective tissues contain cells embedded in an extracellular **matrix**. This matrix consists of protein fibers and a noncellular material called ground substance. The **ground substance** may be solid (as in bone), fluid (as in blood), or gelatinous (as in cartilage). It is secreted by the connective tissue cells themselves or by other cells nearby. Whereas all other types of tissue consist primarily of cells, connective tissue is made up mostly of its matrix. The cells are distributed in the matrix much like pieces of fruit suspended in a gelatin dessert.

The connective-tissue matrix contains three types of protein fibers in proportions that depend on the type of connective tissue. **Collagen fibers** are strong and ropelike and can withstand pulling because of their great tensile strength. **Elastic fibers** contain random coils and can stretch and recoil like a spring. They are common in structures where great elasticity is needed, including the skin, lungs, and blood vessels. **Reticular fibers** are thin strands of collagen[1] that branch extensively, forming interconnecting networks suitable for supporting soft tissues (for example, they support the liver and spleen).

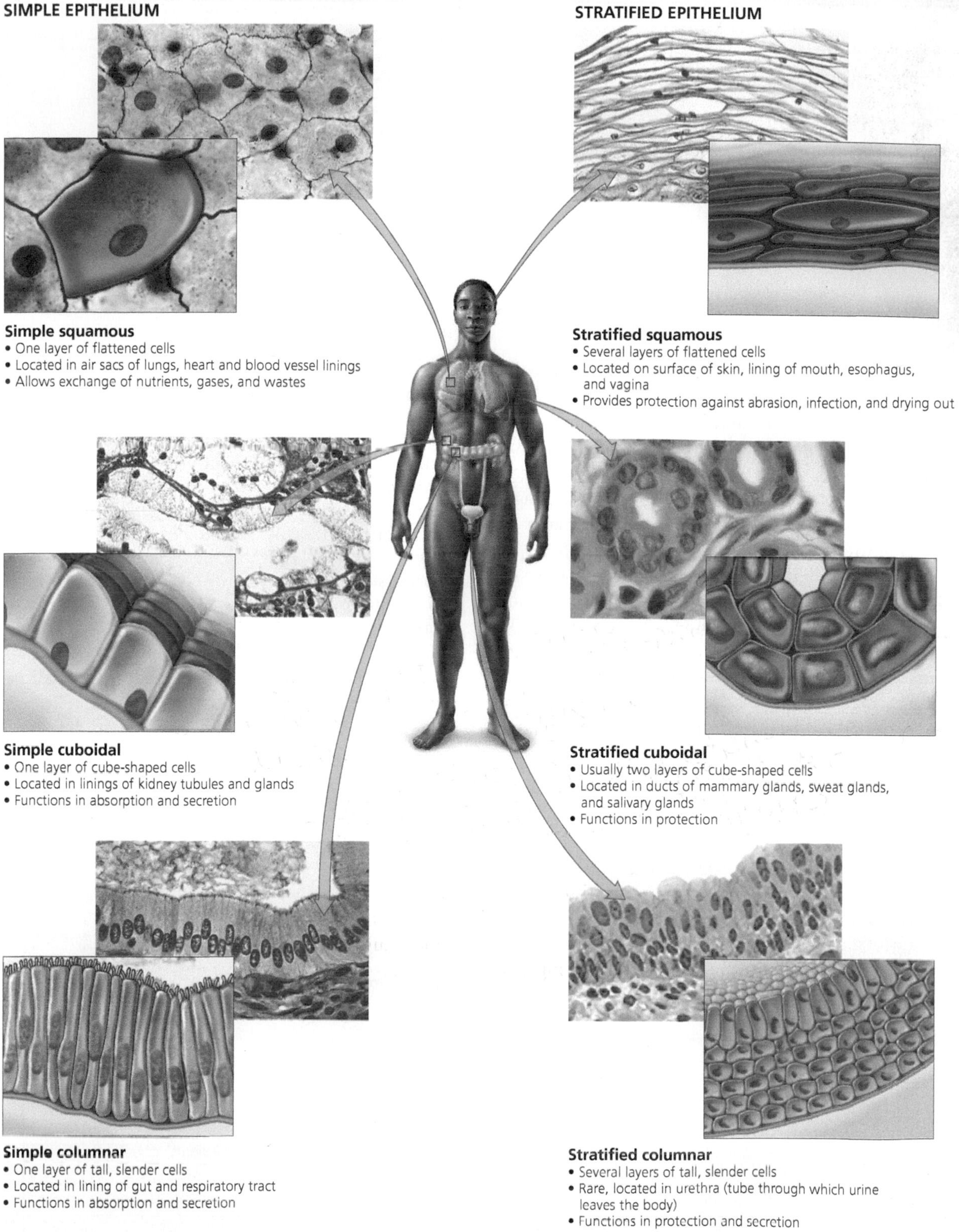

SIMPLE EPITHELIUM

Simple squamous
- One layer of flattened cells
- Located in air sacs of lungs, heart and blood vessel linings
- Allows exchange of nutrients, gases, and wastes

Simple cuboidal
- One layer of cube-shaped cells
- Located in linings of kidney tubules and glands
- Functions in absorption and secretion

Simple columnar
- One layer of tall, slender cells
- Located in lining of gut and respiratory tract
- Functions in absorption and secretion

STRATIFIED EPITHELIUM

Stratified squamous
- Several layers of flattened cells
- Located on surface of skin, lining of mouth, esophagus, and vagina
- Provides protection against abrasion, infection, and drying out

Stratified cuboidal
- Usually two layers of cube-shaped cells
- Located in ducts of mammary glands, sweat glands, and salivary glands
- Functions in protection

Stratified columnar
- Several layers of tall, slender cells
- Rare, located in urethra (tube through which urine leaves the body)
- Functions in protection and secretion

FIGURE 1d.1 Types of epithelial tissue. These are named for the shape of the cell and the number of cell layers.

TABLE 1d.1 Review of Epithelial Tissue

Shape	Number of Layers	Example Locations	Functions
Squamous (flat, scale-like cells)	Simple (single layer)	Lining of heart and blood vessels, air sacs of lungs	Allows passage of materials by diffusion
	Stratified (more than one layer)	Linings of mouth, esophagus, and vagina; outer layer of skin	Protects underlying areas
Cuboidal (cube-shaped cells)	Simple	Kidney tubules, secretory portion of glands and their ducts	Secretes; absorbs
	Stratified	Ducts of sweat glands, mammary glands, and salivary glands	Protects underlying areas
Columnar	Simple	Most of digestive tract (stomach to anus), air tubes of lungs (bronchi), excretory ducts of some glands, uterus	Absorbs; secretes mucus, enzymes, and other substances
	Stratified	Rare; urethra, junction of esophagus and stomach	Protects underlying areas, secretes

All three types of protein fibers—collagen, elastic, and reticular—are produced by cells called **fibroblasts** in the connective tissue. Fibroblasts also repair tears in body tissues. For example, when skin is cut, fibroblasts move to the area of the wound and produce collagen fibers that help close the wound, cover the damage, and provide a surface upon which the outer layer of skin can grow back.

Table 1d.2 and Figure 1d.2 group the many types of connective tissue into two broad categories—connective tissue proper (loose and dense connective tissue) and specialized connective tissue (cartilage, bone, and blood)—and summarize the characteristics of each type. The characteristics of any specific connective tissue are determined more by its matrix than by its cells.

Connective Tissue Proper Loose and dense connective tissues differ in the ratio of cells to extracellular fibers. **Loose connective tissue** contains many cells but has fewer and more loosely woven fibers than are seen in the matrix of dense connective tissue (Figure 1d.2). One type of loose connective tissue, **areolar** (ah-ré-o-lar) **connective tissue,** functions as a universal packing material between other tissues. Its many cells are embedded in a gelatinous matrix that is soft and easily shaped. Areolar con-nective tissue is found, for example, between muscles, where it permits one muscle to move freely over another. It also anchors the skin to underlying tissues and organs.

The second type of loose connective tissue is **adipose tissue,** which contains cells that are specialized for fat storage. Most of the body's long-term energy stores are fat. Fat also serves as insulation and, around certain organs, as a shock absorber.

Dense connective tissue forms strong bands because of its large amounts of tightly woven fibers. It is found in

TABLE 1d.2 Review of Connective Tissue

Type	Example Locations	Functions
Connective tissue proper		
Loose, areolar	Between muscles, surrounding glands, wrapping small blood vessels and nerves	Wraps and cushions organs
Loose, adipose (fat)	Under skin, around kidneys and heart	Stores energy, insulates, cushions organs
Dense	Tendons, ligaments	Attaches bone to bone (ligaments) or bone to muscle (tendons)
Specialized connective tissue		
Cartilage (semisolid)	Nose (tip); rings in respiratory air tubules; external ear	Provides support and protection (by enclosing) and serves as lever for muscles to act on
Bone (solid)	Skeleton	Provides support and protection (by enclosing), and levers for muscles to act on
Blood (fluid)	Within blood vessels	Transports oxygen and carbon dioxide, nutrients, hormones, and wastes; helps fight infections

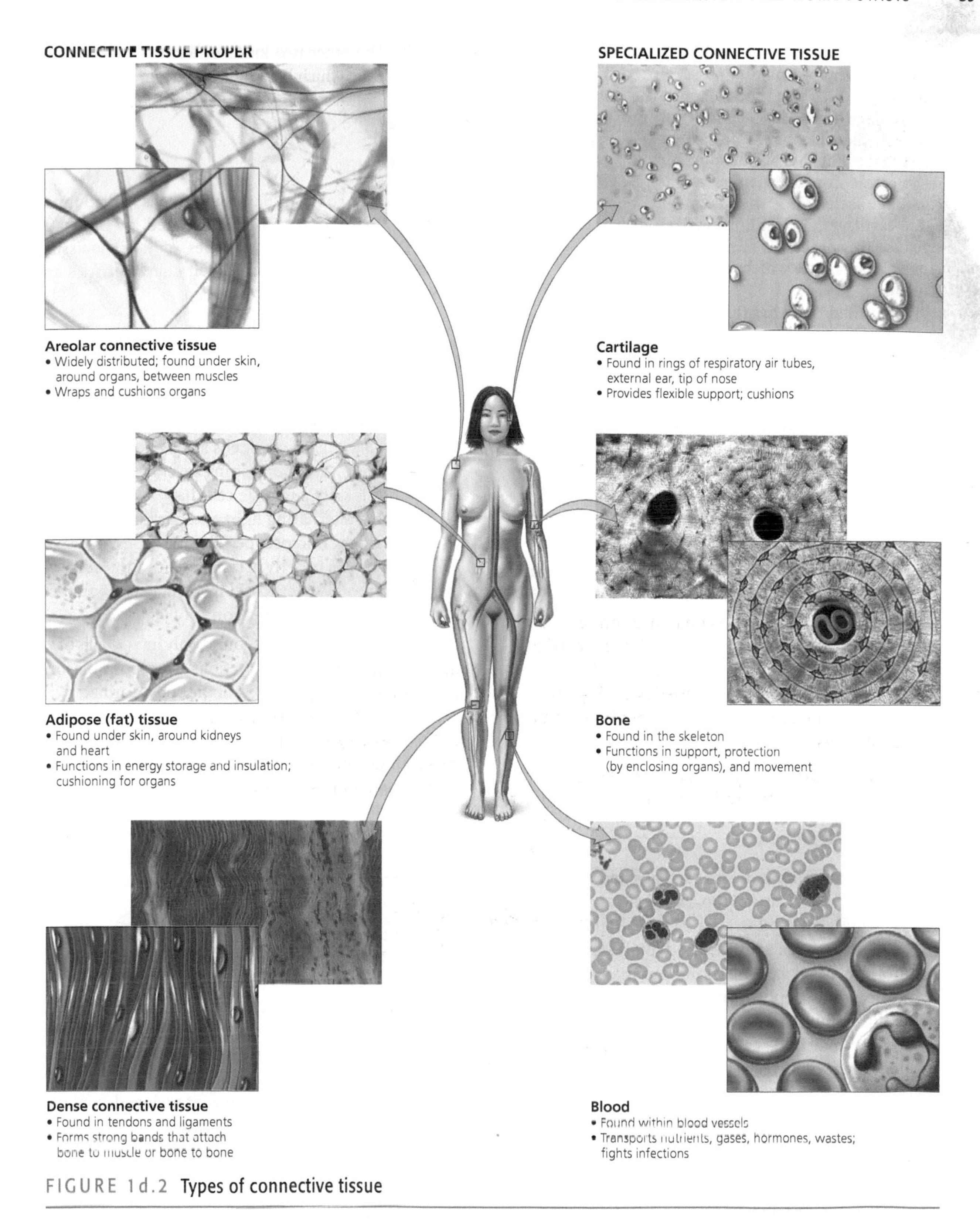

CONNECTIVE TISSUE PROPER
SPECIALIZED CONNECTIVE TISSUE
Areolar connective tissue
• Widely distributed; found under skin, around organs, between muscles
• Wraps and cushions organs
Cartilage
• Found in rings of respiratory air tubes, external ear, tip of nose
• Provides flexible support; cushions
Adipose (fat) tissue
• Found under skin, around kidneys and heart
• Functions in energy storage and insulation; cushioning for organs
Bone
• Found in the skeleton
• Functions in support, protection (by enclosing organs), and movement
Dense connective tissue
• Found in tendons and ligaments
• Forms strong bands that attach bone to muscle or bone to bone
Blood
• Found within blood vessels
• Transports nutrients, gases, hormones, wastes; fights infections

FIGURE 1d.2 Types of connective tissue

ligaments (structures that join bone to bone), tendons (structures that join muscle to bone), and the dermis (layer of skin below the epidermis).

Specialized Connective Tissue Specialized connective tissue, as shown in Figure 1d.2, comes in three types: cartilage, bone, and blood. Cartilage is tough

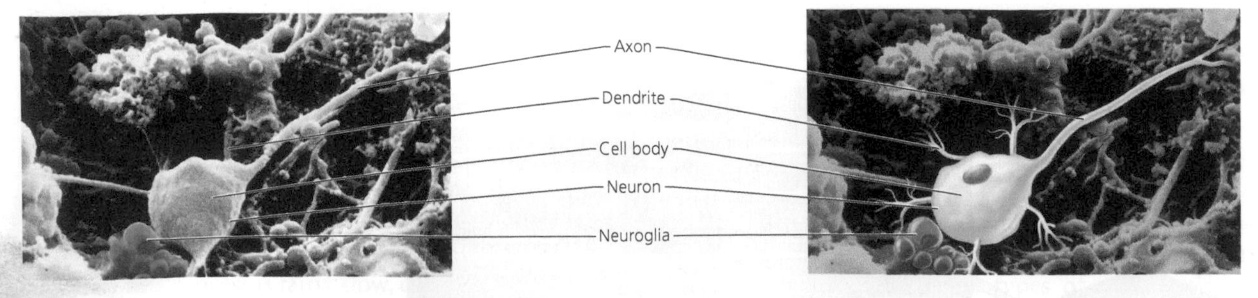

FIGURE 1d.4 Neurons and neuroglia

Cell Junctions

In many tissues, especially epithelial tissue, the cell membranes have structures for forming attachments between adjoining cells. There are three kinds of junctions between cells: tight junctions, adhesion junctions, and gap junctions. Each type of junction suits the function of the tissue. In **tight junctions** (Figure 1d.5a), the membranes of neighboring cells are attached so securely that they form a leakproof seal. Tight junctions are found in the linings of the urinary tract and intestines, where secure seals between cells prevent urine or digestive juices from passing through the epithelium. Less rigid than tight junctions, **adhesion junctions** (also called desmosomes; Figure 1d.5b) resemble rivets holding adjacent tissue layers together. The plasma membranes of adjacent cells do not actually touch but are instead bound together

(a) Tight junction
- Creates an impermeable junction that prevents the exchange of materials between cells
- Found between epithelial cells of the digestive tract, where they prevent digestive enzymes and microorganisms from entering the blood

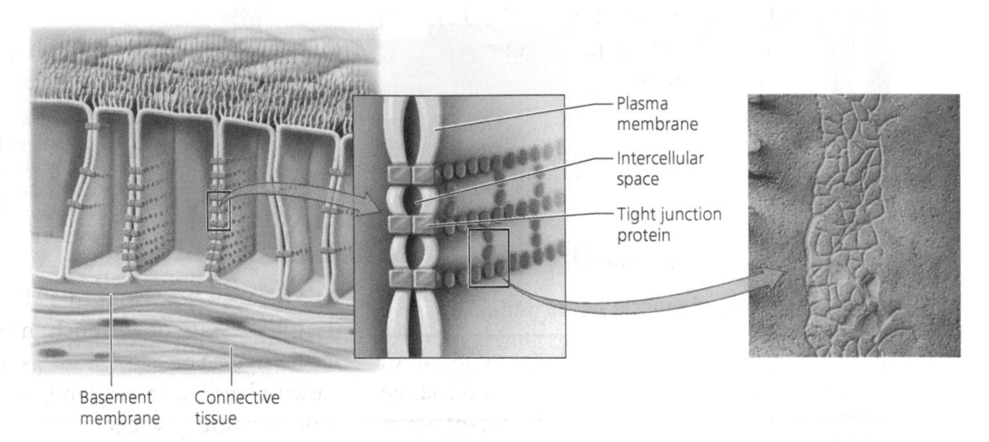

(b) Adhesion junction
- Holds cells together despite stretching
- Found in tissues that are often stretched, such as the skin and the opening of the uterus

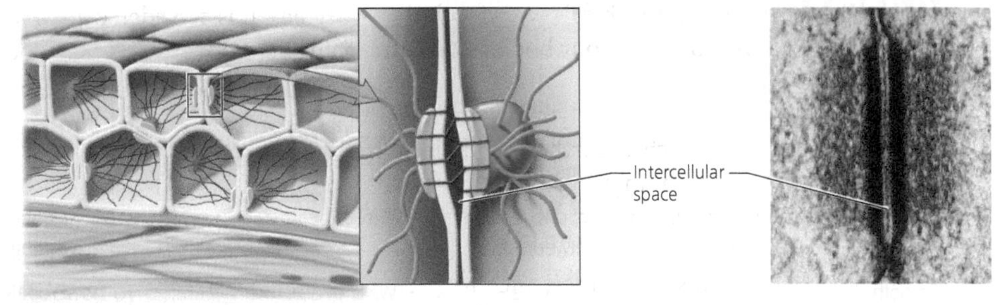

(c) Gap junction
- Allows cells to communicate by allowing small molecules and ions to pass from cell to cell
- Found in epithelia in which the movement of ions coordinates functions, such as the beating of cilia; found in excitable tissue such as heart and smooth muscle

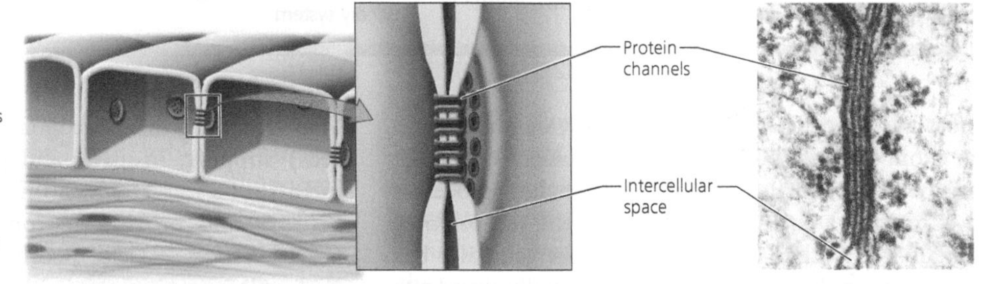

FIGURE 1d.5 Specialized cell junctions

by intercellular filaments attached to a thickening in the membrane. Thus, the cells are connected but can still slide slightly relative to one another. Adhesion junctions are common in tissues that must withstand stretching, such as the skin and heart muscle. **Gap junctions** (Figure 1d.5c) connect the cytoplasm of adjacent cells through small holes, allowing certain small molecules and ions to flow directly from one cell into the next. In heart and smooth muscle cells, gap junctions help synchronize electrical activity and thus contraction.

Organs and Organ Systems

An **organ** is a structure composed of two or more different tissues that work together to perform a specific function. Organs themselves do not usually function as independent units but instead form part of an **organ system**—a group of organs with a common function. For example, organs such as the trachea, bronchi, and lungs constitute the respiratory system. The common function of these organs is to bring oxygen into the body and remove carbon dioxide. The human body includes the 11 major organ systems, as described and illustrated in Figure 1d.6.

Body Cavities Lined with Membranes

Most of our organs are suspended in internal body cavities (Figure 1d.7). These cavities have two important functions. First, they help protect the vital organs from being damaged when we walk or jump. Second, they allow organs to slide past one another and change shape. Sliding and changing shape are important when the lungs fill with air, the stomach fills with food, the urinary bladder fills with urine, or our bodies bend or stretch.

There are two main body cavities—the ventral and dorsal cavities—each of which is further subdivided. The ventral (toward the abdomen) cavity is divided into the *thoracic* (chest) *cavity* and the *abdominal cavity*. The thoracic cavity is subdivided again into the pleural cavities, which house the lungs, and the pericardial cavity, which holds the heart. The abdominal cavity contains the digestive system, the urinary system, and the reproductive system. A muscle sheet called the diaphragm separates the thoracic and abdominal cavities. The dorsal (toward the back) cavity is subdivided into the *cranial cavity*, which encloses the brain, and the *spinal cavity*, which houses the spinal cord.

Body cavities and organ surfaces are covered with membranes—sheets of epithelium supported by connective tissue. Membranes form physical barriers that protect underlying tissues. The body has four types of membrane.

1. **Mucous membranes** line passageways that open to the exterior of the body, such as those of the respiratory, digestive, reproductive, and urinary systems. Some mucous membranes, including the mucous membrane of the small intestine, are specialized for absorption. Others, those of the respiratory system, for instance, secrete mucus that traps bacteria and viruses that could cause illness.
2. **Serous membranes** line the thoracic and abdominal cavities and the organs within them. They secrete a fluid that lubricates the organs within these cavities.
3. **Synovial membranes** line the cavities of freely movable joints, such as the knee. These membranes secrete a fluid that lubricates the joint, easing movement.
4. **Cutaneous membrane**, or skin, covers the outside of the body. Unlike other membranes, it is thick, relatively waterproof, and relatively dry.

We will consider the structure and function of the skin in the next section. Details about the structure and functions of the other organ systems are presented in subsequent chapters.

SKIN: AN ORGAN SYSTEM

We have all been told that "beauty is only skin deep," but our skin does much more than just make us attractive. The skin and its derivatives—hair, nails, sweat glands, and oil glands—are sometimes called the **integumentary system** (an *integument* is an outer covering). It is considered an organ system because the skin and its derivatives function together to provide many services for the body.

Skin Functions

A major function of our skin is protection. It serves as a physical barrier that shields the contents of the body from invasion by foreign bacteria and other harmful particles, from ultraviolet (UV) radiation, and from physical and chemical insult. Besides offering this somewhat passive form of protection, skin contains cells called *macrophages* that have a more active way of fighting infection.

The skin has many other functions, as well. For example, because its outermost layer of cells contains the water-resistant protein keratin, the skin plays a vital role in preventing excessive water loss from underlying tissues. It plays a role in temperature regulation, too. Although we perspire (imperceptively)

Integumentary system
- Protects underlying tissues
- Provides skin sensation
- Helps regulate body temperature
- Synthesizes vitamin D

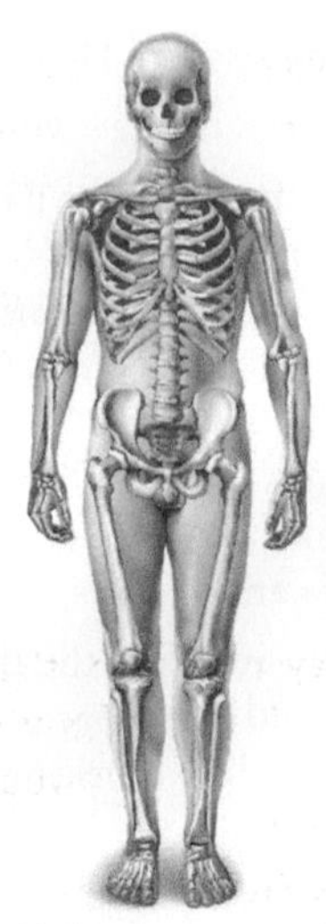

Skeletal system
- Attachment for muscles
- Protects organs
- Stores calcium and phosphorus
- Produces blood cells

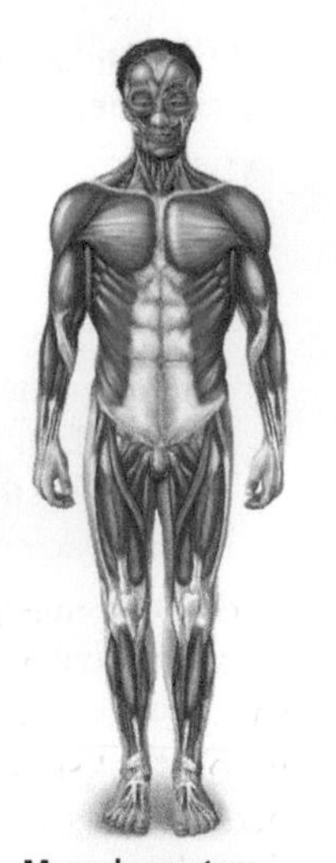

Muscular system
- Moves body and maintains posture
- Internal transport of fluids
- Generation of heat

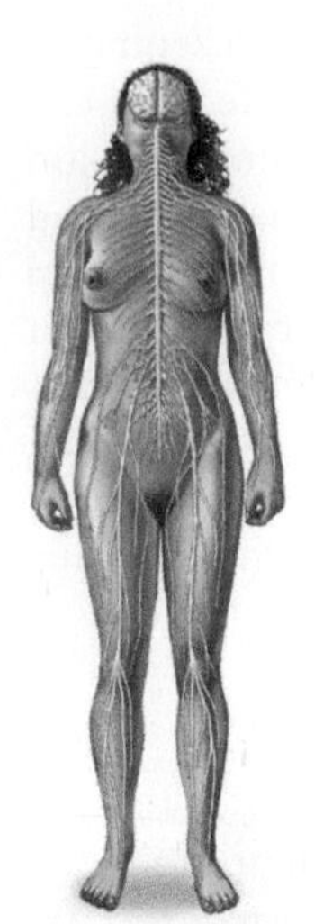

Nervous system
- Regulates and integrates body functions via neurons

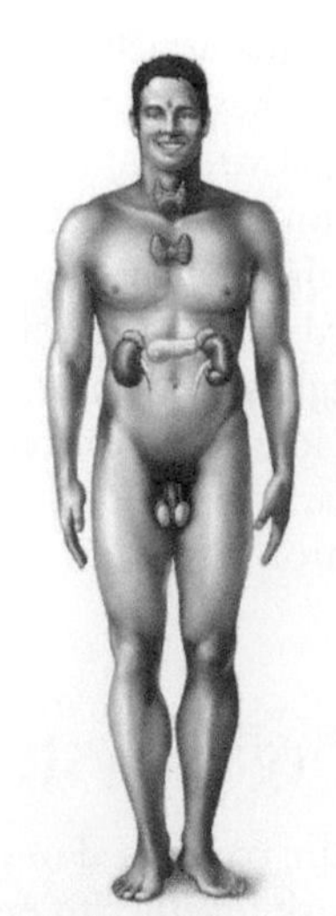

Endocrine system
- Regulates and integrates body functions via hormones

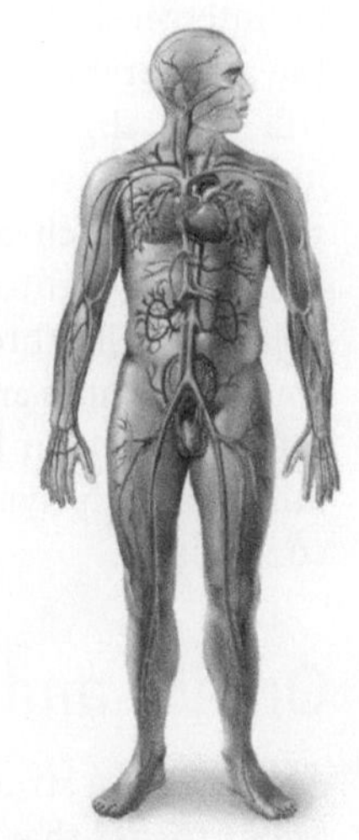

Cardiovascular system
- Transports nutrients, respiratory gases, wastes, and heat
- Transports immune cells and antibodies
- Transports hormones
- Regulates pH

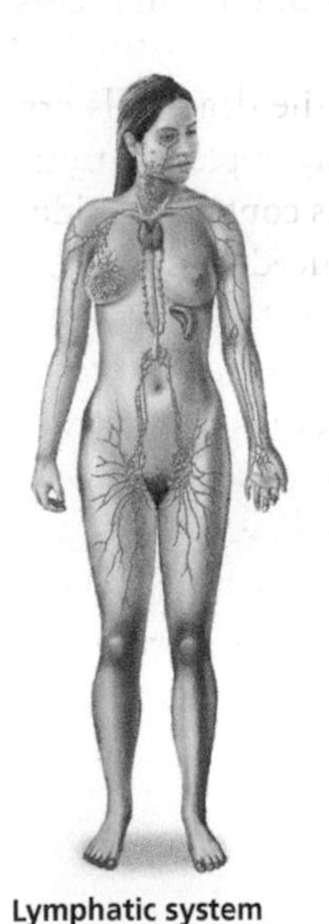

Lymphatic system
- Returns tissue fluids to bloodstream
- Protects against infection and disease

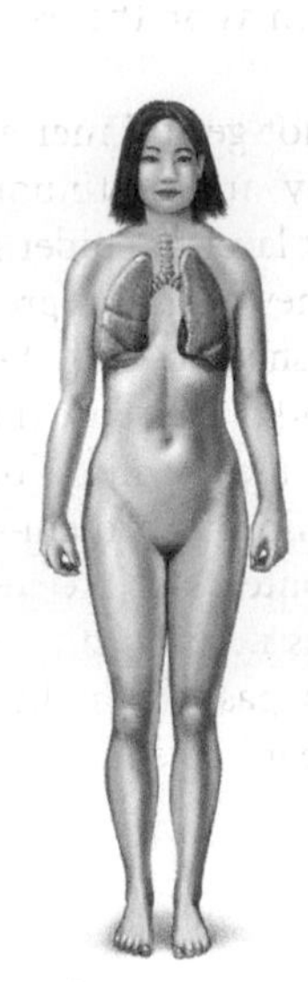

Respiratory system
- Exchanges respiratory gases with the environment

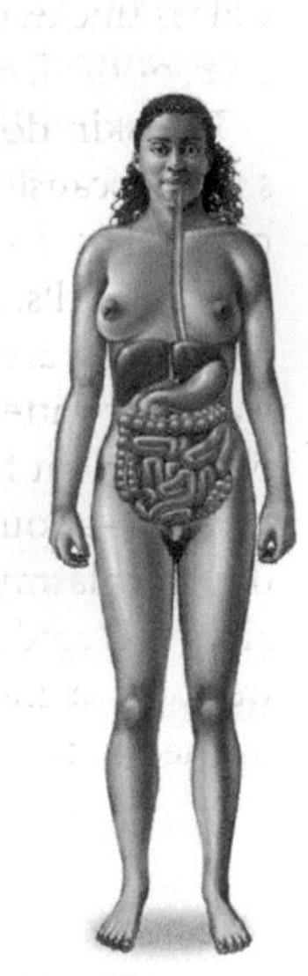

Digestive system
- Physical and chemical breakdown of food
- Absorbs, processes, stores food

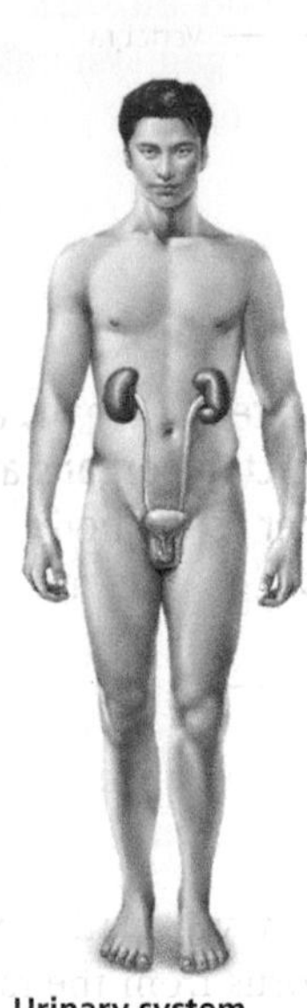

Urinary system
- Maintains constant internal environment through the excretion of nitrogenous waste

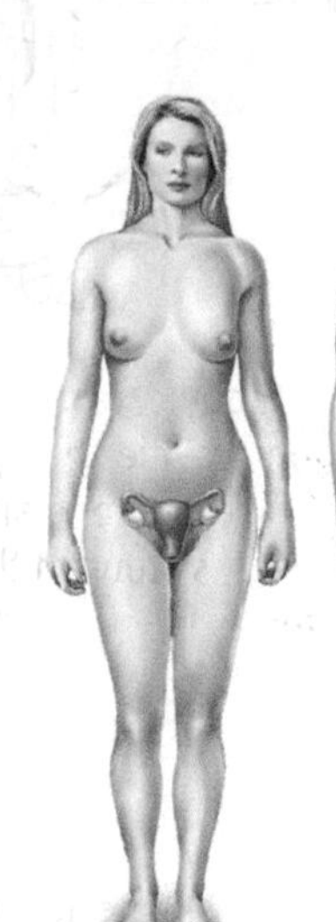

Reproductive system
- Produces and secretes hormones
- Produces and releases egg and sperm cells
- Houses embryo/fetus (females only)

FIGURE 1d.6 **Major organ systems of the human body**

through our skin almost constantly, during times of strenuous exercise or high environmental temperatures our sweat glands become active and increase their output of perspiration dramatically. The evaporation of this perspiration from the skin's surface helps rid the body of excess heat. Later we will see how changes in the flow of blood to the skin help regulate body temperature. The skin even functions in the production of vitamin D. Modified cholesterol molecules in the skin's outer layer are converted to vitamin D by UV radiation. The vitamin D then travels in the bloodstream to the liver and kidneys, where it is chem-

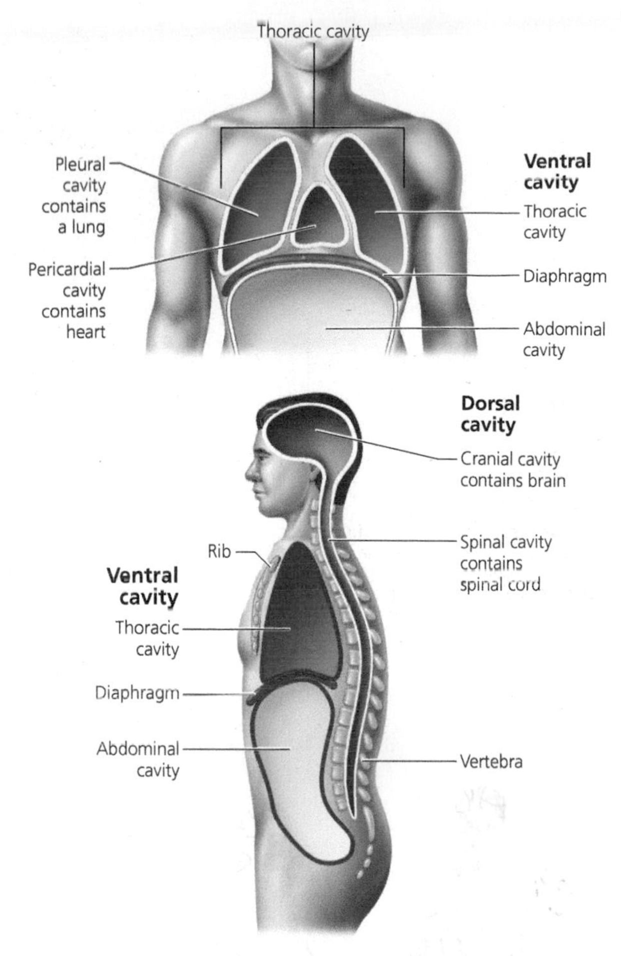

FIGURE 1d.7 **Body cavities. The internal organs are suspended in body cavities that protect the organs and allow organs to slide past one another as the body moves. Ventral means "toward the abdomen," and dorsal means "toward the back."**

ically modified to assume its role in stimulating the absorption of calcium and phosphorus from the food we eat.

In addition, the skin contains structures for detecting temperature, touch, pressure, and pain stimuli. These receptors—components of the nervous system—help keep us informed about conditions in our external environment. Keep these many functions of the integumentary system in mind as you read on about the structure of the skin and its derivatives.

Skin Layers

On most parts of your body, the skin is less than 5 mm (less than a quarter of an inch) thick, yet it is one of your largest organs. It represents about one-twelfth of your body weight and has a surface area of 1.5 to 2 m^2 (1.8 to 2.4 yd^2).

The skin has two principal layers, as shown in Figure 1d.8. The thin, outer layer, the **epidermis**, forms a protective barrier against environmental hazards. The inner layer, the **dermis**, contains blood vessels, nerves, sweat and oil glands, and hair follicles. Beneath the skin is a layer of loose connective tissue called the *hypodermis* or *subcutaneous layer*, which anchors the skin to the tissues of other organ systems that lie beneath.

The epidermis

The outermost layer of skin, the epidermis, is itself composed of several layers of epithelial cells. The outer surface of epidermis, the part you can touch, is made up of dead skin cells. Thus, when we look at another person, most of what we see on the person's surface is dead. These dead cells are constantly being shed, at a rate of about 30,000 to 40,000 each minute. In fact, much of the dust in any room consists of dead skin cells. When you go swimming or soak in the bathtub for a long time, the dead cells on your skin's surface absorb water and swell, causing the skin to wrinkle. This is particularly noticeable where the layer of dead cells is thickest, such as on the palms of the hands and soles of the feet.

The skin does not get thinner as the dead cells are shed, because they are continuously replaced from below. The deepest layer of epidermis contains rapidly dividing cells. As new cells are produced in this layer, older cells are pushed toward the surface. On their way, they flatten and die because they no longer receive nourishment from the dermis. Along this death route, keratin—a tough, fibrous protein—gradually replaces the cytoplasmic contents of the cells. It is keratin that gives the epidermis its protective properties. About 2 weeks to a month pass from the time a new cell is formed to the time it is shed.

what would you do?

To speed up the movement of a drug from a transdermal patch to the patient's blood supply, the patch is prepared with a higher concentration of the drug than would be found in a pill. In transdermal patches that deliver hormones for birth control, the blood levels of hormones may also be higher than would result with birth control pills. During the last few years, several young women using a transdermal patch for birth control have had heart attacks or strokes; some have died. There are warning labels with contraceptive patches informing women of these increased risks. Do you think that women or their families should be able to sue the patch manufacturer for their losses?

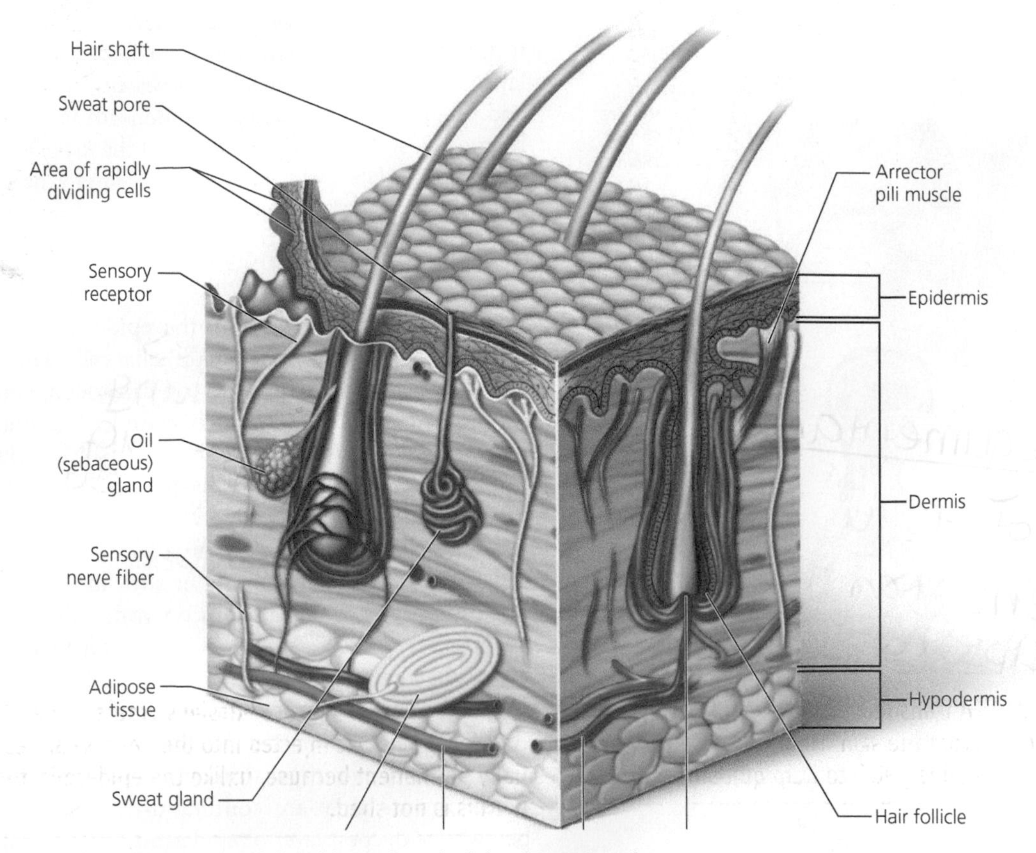

FIGURE 1d.8 **Structures of the skin and underlying hypodermis**

Drugs that must be continuously administered are often given across the skin (transdermally) using a drug-containing patch that adheres to the skin (Figure 1d.9). Although the epidermis is a water-resistant protective barrier, lipid-soluble materials are able to cross the lipid cell membranes of the cells of the epidermis. Thus, if you dissolve a drug in a lipid solvent, it can cross the epidermis, diffuse into the underlying connective tissue, and be absorbed into the blood. Today, transdermal drug administration is commonly used to provide hormones for birth control or the treatment of menopausal symptoms, nicotine to ease the urge to smoke while trying to quit, and anti-emetics to stop nausea from motion sickness.

The dermis

Over most parts of the body, the dermis is a much thicker layer than the epidermis. The dermis lies just beneath the epidermis and consists primarily of connective tissue. In addition, it contains blood vessels, hair follicles, oil glands, the ducts of sweat glands, sensory structures, and nerve endings. Unlike the epidermis, the dermis does not wear away. This durability explains why tattoos—designs created when tiny droplets of ink are injected into the dermal layer—are permanent (Figure 1d.10). Because the dermis is laced with nerves and sensory receptors, getting a tattoo hurts. In the past, the only way to remove a tattoo was by surgical means, such as "shaving" (abrading) of the

stop and THINK

Burns–tissue damage caused by heat, radiation, electric shock, or chemicals–can be classified according to how deep the damage penetrates. First-degree burns are confined to the upper layers of epidermis, where they cause reddening and slight swelling. In second-degree burns, damage extends through the epidermis into the upper regions of the dermis. Blistering, pain, and swelling occur. Third-degree burns extend through the epidermis and dermis into underlying tissues. Severe burns, particularly if they cover large portions of the body, are life threatening. Given your knowledge of skin functions, what would you predict the immediate medical concerns to be when a patient has third-degree burns?

FIGURE 1d.9 A transdermal patch continuously delivers a drug across the skin. Here, a cigarette smoker uses a nicotine patch to help quit smoking.

FIGURE 1d.10 Tattoos—designs created when droplets of ink are injected into the dermis—are essentially permanent because, unlike the epidermis, the dermis is not shed.

skin. Today, laser treatments that destroy the pigments of the tattoo can often be used for tattoo removal.

Blood vessels are present in the dermis but not in the epidermis. Nutrients reach the epidermis by passing out of dermal blood vessels and diffusing through tissue fluid into the layer above. Such tissue fluid is probably quite familiar to you. Where skin is traumatized by, for example, a burn or an ill-fitting shoe rubbing against your heel, this fluid accumulates between the epidermis and dermis, separating the layers and forming blisters.

The lower layer of the dermis consists of dense connective tissue containing collagen and elastic fibers, a combination that allows the skin to stretch and then return to its original shape. Unfortunately, the skin's elasticity has limits. Pregnancy or substantial weight gain may exceed the skin's ability to return completely to its earlier size after stretching; instead, the dermis tears, and stretch marks appear. The resilience of our skin also decreases as we age. The most pronounced effects begin in the late forties, when collagen fibers begin to stiffen and decrease in number and elastic fibers thicken and lose elasticity. These changes, combined with reductions in moisture and the amount of fat in the hypodermis, lead to wrinkles and sagging skin.

Certain wrinkles, such as frown lines, are caused by the contraction of facial muscles. A controversial and popular treatment for these wrinkles is to inject Botox, the toxin from the bacterium that causes botulism. When Botox is injected into facial muscles, they become temporarily paralyzed. The muscle contractions that form the wrinkles cannot occur, and the skin smoothes out. The muscles regain the ability to contract over the next several months, however, and the injection has to be repeated (Figure 1d.11).

The hypodermis

The **hypodermis**, a layer of loose connective tissue just below the epidermis and dermis, is not usually considered part of the skin. It does, however, share some of the skin's functions, including cushioning blows and helping to prevent extreme changes in body temperature, because it contains about half of the body's fat stores. In infants and toddlers, this layer of fat that lies under the skin—often called baby fat—covers the entire body, but as we mature, some of the fat stores are redistributed. In women, subcutaneous fat tends to accumulate in the breasts, hips, and thighs. In both sexes, it has a tendency to accumulate in the abdominal hypodermis, contributing to the all-too-familiar potbelly, and in the sides of the lower back, forming "love handles."

Liposuction, a procedure for vacuuming fat from the hypodermis, is a way to reshape the body. The

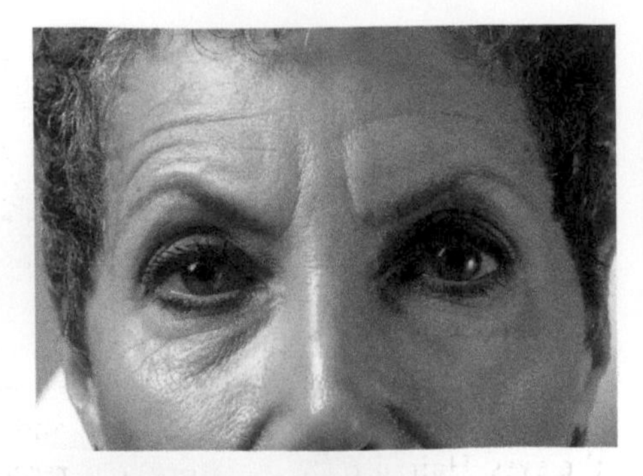
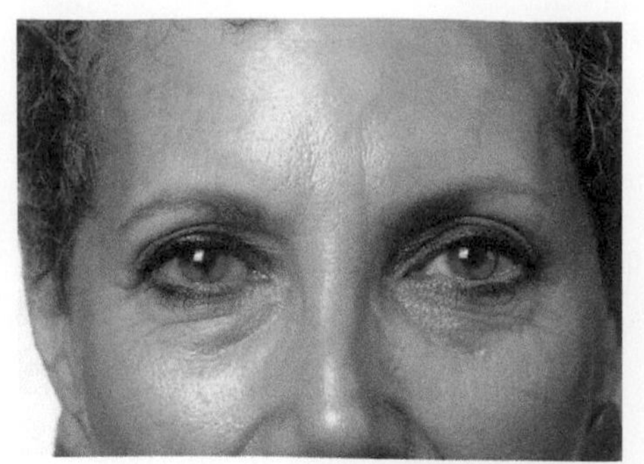

FIGURE 1d.11 Before and after Botox injections

physician makes a small incision in the skin above the area of unwanted fat, inserts a fine tube, and moves the tube back and forth to loosen the fat cells, which are then sucked into a container. Liposuction is not a way of losing a lot of weight, because only a small amount of fat—not more than a few pounds—can be removed. However, it is a way of sculpting the body and removing bulges. Furthermore, because liposuction removes the cells that store the fat, fat does not usually return to those areas. The procedure is generally safe, but it is not risk free. In some patients, it has produced blood clots that traveled to the lungs, causing death. People who are considering liposuction should choose their doctor carefully.

what would you do?

Many social issues are connected to liposuction. One is the procedure's increasing popularity among teenagers. What does this trend say about the value we place on physical beauty? Should there be age restrictions on liposuction? If you decided to have liposuction, what criteria would you use to choose a physician?

Skin Color

Two interacting factors produce skin color: (1) the quantity and distribution of pigment and (2) blood flow. The pigment, called **melanin**, is produced by cells called **melanocytes** at the base of the epidermis. These cells, with their spiderlike extensions, produce two kinds of melanin: a yellow-to-red form and the more common black-to-brown form. The melanin is then taken up by surrounding epidermal cells, thus coloring the entire epidermis.

All people have about the same number of melanocytes. Differences in skin color are due to differences in the form of melanin produced and the size and number of pigment granules. A person's genetic makeup determines the combination of the yellowish red or the brown form of melanin produced.

Albinism is an inherited condition in which an individual's melanocytes are incapable of producing melanin. It occurs in about 1 in 10,000 people and is not specific to a particular race. Individuals with this condition, known as albinos, lack pigment in their eyes, hair, and skin (Figure 1d.12a). The eyes and skin of albinos have a pinkish color because the underlying

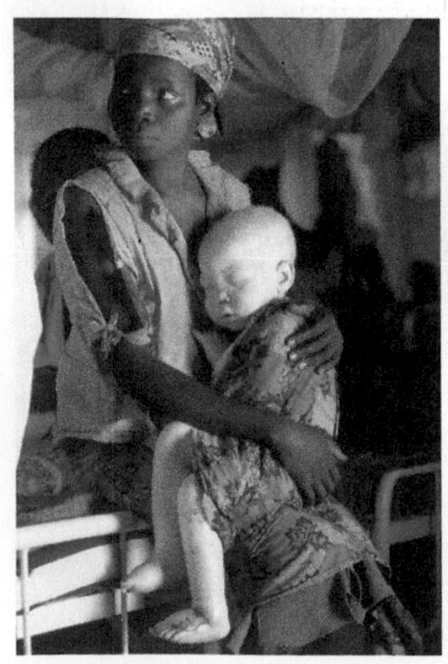

(a)

(b)

FIGURE 1d.12 Conditions caused by abnormalities in melanocytes. (a) Albinism, a genetic condition in which an individual's melanocytes cannot produce melanin, occurs throughout the world. Here, an Angolan mother holds her albino child. (b) Vitiligo is a condition in which melanocytes disappear from areas of the skin, leaving white patches.

blood supply shows through. Vitiligo, in contrast, is a condition in which melanocytes disappear either partially or completely from certain areas of the skin, leaving white patches in their wake (Figure 1d.12b).

Circulation influences skin color in non-albinos, as well. When well-oxygenated blood flows through vessels in the dermis, the skin has a pinkish or reddish tint that is most easily seen in light-skinned people. Intense embarrassment can increase the blood flow, causing the rosy color to heighten, particularly in the face and neck. This response, known as blushing, is impossible to stop. Other intense emotions may cause color to disappear temporarily from the skin. A sudden fright, for example, can cause a rapid drop in blood supply, making a person pale. Skin color may also change in response to changing levels of oxygen in the blood. Compared to well-oxygenated blood, which is ruby red, poorly oxygenated blood is a much deeper red that gives the skin a bluish appearance. Poor oxygenation is why the lips appear blue in extremely cold conditions. When it is cold, your body shunts blood away from the skin to the body's core, which conserves heat and keeps vital organs warm. This shunting reduces the oxygen supply to the blood in the small vessels near the surface of the skin. The oxygen-poor blood seen through the thin skin of the lips makes them look blue. When you do not get enough sleep, the amount of oxygen in your blood may be slightly lower than usual, causing the color to darken. In some people, the darker color of blood is visible through the thin skin under their eyes as dark circles.

Tanning is a change in skin color from exposure to the sun. Melanocytes respond to the UV radiation in sunlight by increasing the production of melanin. This is a protective response, because melanin absorbs some UV radiation, preventing it from reaching the lower epidermis and the dermis. The skin requires some UV radiation for the production of vitamin D, but too much can be harmful. See the Health Issue essay, *Fun in the Sun? Sunlight and Skin Cancer.*

Hair, Nails, and Glands

Many seemingly diverse structures are derived from the epidermis: hair, nails, oil glands, sweat glands, and teeth. We will now consider the first four of these in view of their structure and roles in everyday life.

Hair

Hair usually grows all over the body, except on a few areas such as the lips, palms of the hands, and soles of the feet. Although hair is not essential for our survival, its presence or absence in certain places can have a strong psychological impact. Indeed, the strong emotional response of some individuals to the growth or loss of hair seems surprising when we learn that hair is essentially nothing more than dead cells filled with keratin and packed into a column.

What functions do these dead cells serve? An important one is protection. Hair on the scalp protects the head from UV radiation. Hair in the nostrils and external ear canals keeps particles and bugs from entering. Likewise, eyebrows and eyelashes help keep unwanted particles and glare (and perspiration and rain) out of the eyes. Hair also has a sensory role: receptors associated with hair follicles are sensitive to touch.

A hair consists of a shaft and a root (see Figure 1d.8). The shaft projects above the surface of the skin, and the root extends below the surface into the dermis or hypodermis, where it is embedded in a structure called the hair follicle. Nerve endings surround the follicle and are so sensitive to touch that we are aware of even slight movements of the hair shaft. (Try to move just one hair without feeling it.) Each hair is also supplied with an oil gland that opens onto the follicle and supplies the hair with an oily secretion that makes it soft and pliant. In the dermis, a tiny smooth muscle called the arrector pili is attached to the hair follicle. Contraction of this muscle—which pulls on the follicle, causing the hair to stand up—is associated with fear and with cold. The tiny mound of flesh that forms at the base of the erect hair is sometimes called a goose bump.

A strand of hair, as we said earlier, is made up of dead, keratinized cells. The cuticle, or outermost layer of the strand, consists of a single layer of thin, flat, scale-like cells that are packed with keratin. Exposure to the elements and abrasion can cause the cuticle to wear off at the hair's tip, making the underlying cortex frizz and thus producing dreaded split ends.

Nails

Nails protect the sensitive tips of fingers and toes. Although the nail itself is dead and lacks sensory receptors, it is embedded in tissue so sensitive that we detect even the slightest pressure of an object on the nail. In this way, nails serve as sensory "antennas." They also help us manipulate objects, as when we undo a tight knot in a shoelace.

Like hair, nails are modified skin tissue hardened by the protein keratin. Nails differ from hair, however, in that they grow continuously (a hair stops growing after 2 to 6 years) but much more slowly.

Glands

Three types of glands—oil, sweat, and wax—are found in the skin. Although all three types develop from epidermal cells, they differ in their locations, structures, and functions.

Health Issue

Fun in the Sun? Sunlight and Skin Cancer

It's a sunny day, and the beach is packed with people. Some jump in the surf; some build sand castles, and others lie on blankets or towels. It is hardly a scene we would equate with disfigurement and death. Nonetheless, that is a connection we should make, because skin cancers are increasing at an alarming rate, largely due to our enjoyment of the sun.

The ultraviolet (UV) radiation of sunlight causes the melanocytes of the skin to increase their production of the pigment melanin. The melanin, taken up by surrounding epidermis, absorbs UV radiation before the radiation can travel any deeper into the body and damage the genetic information of the cells.

Unfortunately, this protective buildup of melanin is not instantaneous. Sunburn—damage to skin accompanied by reddening and peeling—is a typical sequel to the first day at the beach. Excessive exposure to sun destroys the cells at the surface of the skin, causing blood vessels in the dermis to dilate, which turns the skin red. The large-scale destruction of epidermis provokes an increased production of new cells. These push the burned cells off the skin surface, and the skin peels—sometimes in small strands, but in severe cases, in large sheets.

In skin cancer, the genetic material in skin cells is altered by UV radiation so that the cells grow and divide uncontrollably, forming a tumor. Some experts fear that the rates of skin cancer will increase dramatically if the ozone layer, which blocks some of the UV radiation before it reaches Earth, continues to become thinner. Three types of skin cancer are caused by overexposure to the sun (Figure **1d.A**):

- Basal cell carcinoma arises in the rapidly dividing cells of the deepest layer of epidermis. It is the most common type of skin cancer.
- Squamous cell carcinoma arises in the newly formed skin cells as they flatten and move toward the skin surface. It is the second most common form of skin cancer.
- Melanoma is the least common and most dangerous type of skin cancer. It arises in melanocytes, the pigment-producing cells of the skin. Unlike basal or squamous cell carcinomas, melanomas, when left untreated, often metastasize (spread rapidly) throughout the body, first infiltrating the lymph nodes and later the vital organs. The survival rate in persons whose melanoma is found before it has metastasized is about 90% but drops to about 14% if the cancerous cells have spread throughout the body.

You can catch melanomas at an early stage if you carefully examine your skin while applying the ABCD mnemonic of the American Cancer Society:

A—stands for asymmetry. Most melanomas are irregular in shape.

B—stands for border. Melanomas often have a diffuse, unclear border.

C—stands for color. Melanomas usually have a mottled appearance and contain colors such as brown, black, red, white, and blue.

D—stands for diameter. Growths with a diameter of more than 5 mm (about 0.2 in.) are threatening.

Most skin cancers are treated either by excision, along with nearby tissue, or by radiation. Sometimes laser surgery, cryosurgery (freezing), or electrodesiccation (drying by electric current) are used to destroy cancerous cells. Many skin cancers occur on the face, and disfigurement caused by removal of large chunks of the nose or ears may necessitate reconstructive surgery.

The best way to avoid getting skin cancer is to avoid prolonged exposure to the sun. If you must be out in the sun, wear a hat, long sleeves, and sunglasses. Use a sunscreen and avoid exposure between 10:00 A.M. and 3:00 P.M., when the UV rays are the strongest. Use sunscreen even when it is overcast, because UV rays can penetrate the clouds. Sunscreens should have a sun protection factor (SPF) of at least 15. Apply your sunscreen about 45 minutes before going out into the sun, allowing time for it to be absorbed by the skin so that it is less likely to wash away with perspiration. Reapply it after swimming.

Always remember that sunscreens are not foolproof. Most block the higher-energy portion of the sun's UV radiation, known as UV-B, while providing only limited protection against the lower-energy portion, called UV-A. Whereas UV-B causes skin to burn, recent research suggests that exposure to UV-A weakens the body's immune system, possibly impairing its ability to

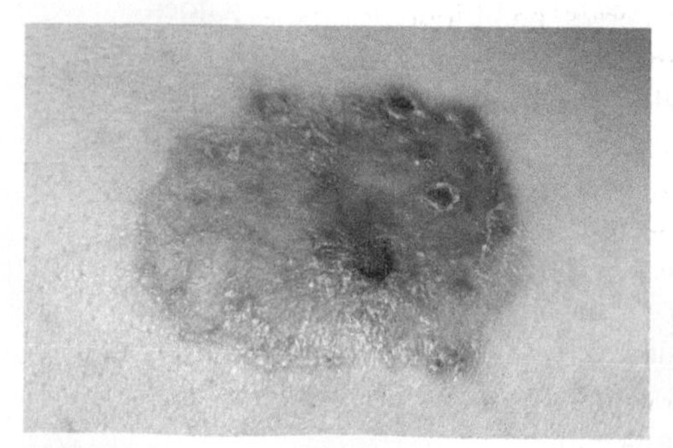

(a) Basal cell carcinoma

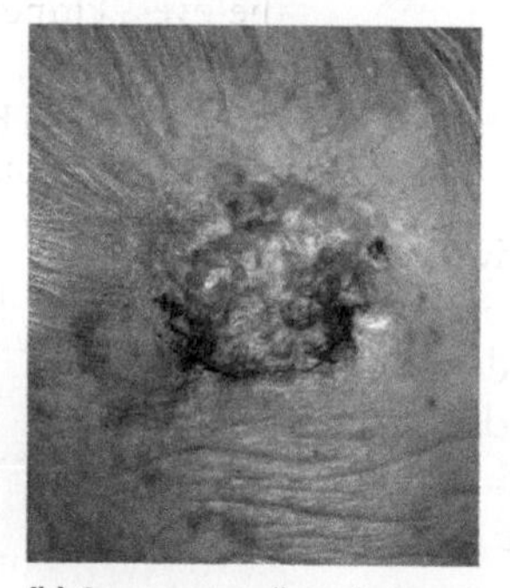

(b) Squamous cell carcinoma

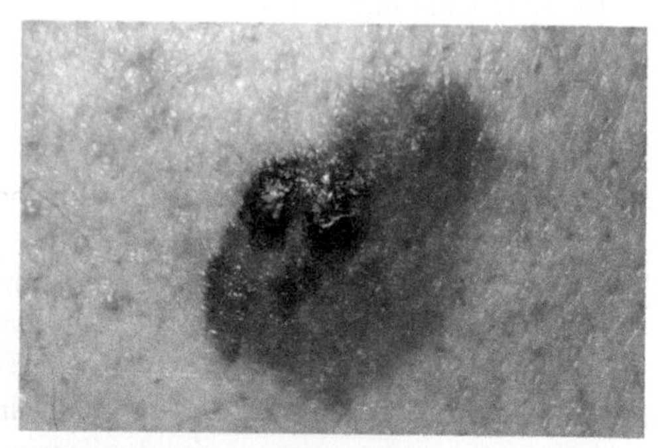

(c) Melanoma

FIGURE 1d.A Three skin cancers

CONTINUED ON PAGE 71

Health Issue CONTINUED

fight melanoma. Ironically, by providing protection from sunburn, sunscreens have had the potentially devastating effect of enabling people to spend more time in the sun, possibly increasing their risk of developing melanoma.

Sunblocks such as zinc oxide, the white ointment used by lifeguards and others who spend long hours in the sun, differ from sunscreens in that they totally deflect ultraviolet rays. For this reason, sunblocks are recommended for particularly sensitive or already burned areas of the face, such as the nose and lips.

Avoid tanning salons. For many years, tanning salons claimed to use "safe" wavelengths of UV radiation because they did not use skin-reddening UV-B. But these "safe" wavelengths are actually UV-A. Given the apparent link between UV-A and increased risk of melanoma, the potential danger of these "safe" wavelengths is now obvious.

Oil (sebaceous) **glands** are found virtually all over the body except on the palms of the hands and soles of the feet. They secrete sebum, an oily substance made of fats, cholesterol, proteins, and salts. The secretory part of these glands is located in the dermis, as shown in Figure 1d.8. Sebum lubricates hair and skin and contains substances that inhibit growth of certain bacteria. Sometimes, however, the duct of an oil gland becomes blocked, causing sebum to accumulate and disrupt the gland's proper function. Then, bacteria can invade the gland and hair follicle, resulting in a condition called acne. See the Health Issue essay, *Acne: The Misery, the Myths, and the Medications.*

As their name implies, **sweat glands** produce sweat, which is largely water plus some salts, lactic acid, vitamin C, and metabolic wastes such as urea. Although some wastes are eliminated through sweating, the principal function of sweat is to help regulate body temperature by evaporating from the skin surface. Wax glands are modified sweat glands found in the external ear canal. As their name implies, they produce wax, which protects the ear by trapping small particles.

HOMEOSTASIS

To remain healthy, the organ systems of the body must constantly adjust their functioning in response to changes in the internal and external environment. We have already learned that the body's organ systems are interdependent, working together to provide the basic needs of all cells—water, nutrients, oxygen, and a normal body temperature. Just as city dwellers breathe the same air and drink the same city water, the cells of the body are surrounded by the same extracellular fluid. Changes in the makeup of that fluid will affect every cell.

One advantage of our body's multicellular, multi-organ-system organization is its ability to provide a controlled environment for the cells. Although conditions outside the body sometimes vary dramatically, our organ systems interact to maintain relatively stable conditions within. This ability to maintain a relatively stable internal environment despite changes in the surroundings is called **homeostasis** (meaning "to stay the same"). But, conditions within the body never stay the same. As internal conditions at any level vary, the body's processes must shift to counteract the variation. Homeostatic mechanisms do not maintain absolute internal constancy, but they do dampen fluctuations around a set point to keep internal conditions within a certain range. Thus, homeostasis is not a static state but a dynamic one.

Illness can result if homeostasis fails. We see this in diabetes, a condition in which either the pancreas does not produce enough of the hormone insulin or the body cells are unable to use insulin. Normally, as a meal is digested and nutrients are absorbed into the bloodstream, the rising level of glucose in the blood stimulates the pancreas to release insulin. The general effect of insulin is to lower the blood level of glucose, returning it to a more desirable value. Without insulin, blood glucose can rise to a point that causes damage to the eyes, kidney, nerves, and blood vessels. A healthy diet, exercise, medication, and sometimes insulin injections can help people with diabetes regulate their blood glucose level.

Homeostasis depends on communication within the body. The nervous and endocrine systems are the two primary means of communication. The nervous system can bring about quick responses to changes in internal and external conditions. The endocrine system produces hormones, which bring about slower and longer-lasting responses to change.

stop and THINK

When you exercise, your breathing rate, blood pressure, and heart rate increase. Is this a violation of homeostasis?

Health Issue

Acne: The Misery, the Myths, and the Medications

Acne and adolescence go hand in hand. In fact, about four out of five teenagers have acne, a skin condition that will probably annoy, if not distress, them well into their twenties and possibly beyond. What is acne, and what causes it? Is it really brought on by the chocolate, potato chips, and sodas so prevalent in the teenage diet? Why do males usually experience more severe acne than females do? Can acne be treated?

Simple acne is a condition that affects hair follicles associated with oil glands. During the teenage years, oil glands increase in size and produce larger amounts of oily sebum. These changes are prompted by increasing levels of "male" hormones called androgens in the blood of both males and females; the androgens are secreted by the testes, ovaries, and adrenal glands. The changes thus induced in the activity and structure of oil glands set the stage for acne. It should come as no surprise, then, that acne occurs most often on areas of the body where oil glands are largest and most numerous: the face, chest, upper back, and shoulders.

Acne is the inflammation that results when sebum and dead cells clog the duct where the oil gland opens onto the hair follicle (Figure **1d.B**). A follicle obstructed by sebum and cells is called a whitehead. Sometimes the sebum in plugged follicles mixes with the skin pigment melanin, forming a blackhead. Thus, melanin, not dirt or bacteria, lends the dark color to these blemishes. The next stage of acne is pimple formation, beginning with the formation of a red, raised bump, often with a white dot of pus at the center. The bump occurs when obstructed follicles rupture and spew their contents into the surrounding epidermis. Such ruptures may occur naturally by the general buildup of sebum and cells or may be induced by squeezing the area. The sebum, dead cells, and bacteria that thrive on them then cause a small infection—a pimple or pustule—that will usually heal within a week or two without leaving a scar.

Eating nuts, chocolate, pizza, potato chips, or any of the other "staples" of the teenage diet does not cause acne. Also, acne is not caused by poor hygiene. Follicles plug from below, so dirt or oil on the skin surface is not responsible. (Most doctors do, however, recommend washing the face two or three times a day with hot water to help open plugged follicles.)

Treatments for acne fall into two main categories: topical (those applied to the skin) and oral (those taken by mouth). Most topical medicines must be used for several weeks before improvements are noticed. One topical preparation is a 5% solution of benzoyl peroxide sometimes sold over the counter. Applied once or twice a day as a cream after the affected area has been washed, benzoyl peroxide kills bacteria living in the follicles. Another topical option, tretinoin (retinoic acid, Retin-A), available only by prescription, is a derivative of vitamin A that helps thin the epidermis, reduce the stickiness of dead cells, and increase the rate at which the cells are sloughed off. These actions help keep follicles clear and speed the removal of existing whiteheads and blackheads.

Severe cases of acne may call for oral, or systemic, medicines—such as tetracycline or minocycline—that work by inhibiting the bacteria in the follicle. Isotretinoin (Accutane), another prescription-only derivative of vitamin A, is probably the most effective treatment for severe acne. This drug works by poisoning the oil glands, causing them to shrink and reduce their output of sebum. Some of the shrinkage is permanent, making Accutane different from other treatments in that it suppresses acne even after the treatment has stopped.

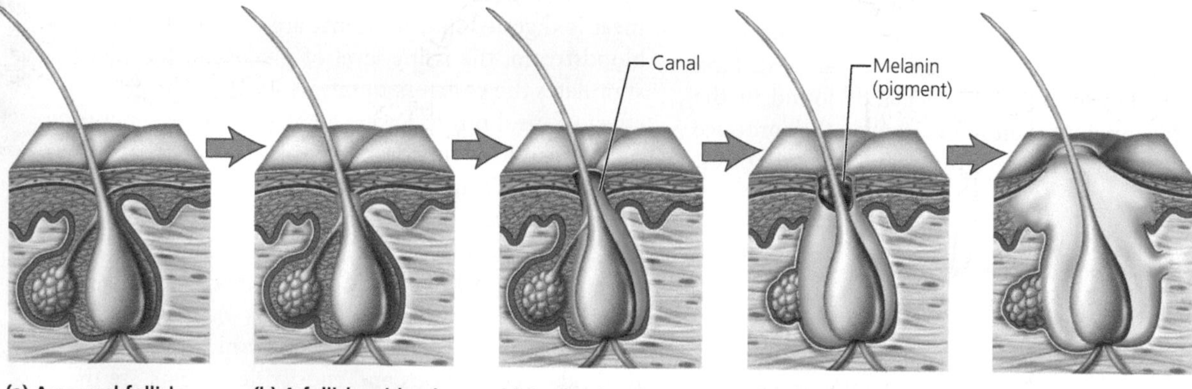

(a) A normal follicle Note the tiny hair and cells of the oil gland.

(b) A follicle with sebum The canal becomes clogged with sebum, dead cells, and bacteria.

(c) A whitehead Sebum, cells, and bacteria accumulate in the follicle.

(d) A blackhead Sebum in the clogged follicle oxidizes and mixes with melanin.

(e) An inflamed pimple The follicle wall ruptures, releasing the contents of a whitehead or blackhead into the surrounding epidermis.

FIGURE 1d.B The stages of acne

Negative Feedback Mechanisms

Homeostasis is maintained primarily through **negative feedback mechanisms**—corrective measures that slow or reverse a variation from the normal value of a factor, such as blood glucose level or body temperature, and return the factor to its normal value. When the normal value is reached, the corrective measures cease; the normal value is the feedback that turns off the response. (In contrast, a positive feedback mechanism causes a change that promotes continued change in the same direction.)

Homeostatic mechanisms have three components (Figure 1d.13):

1. A *receptor* detects change in the internal or external environment. A receptor, in this context, is a sensor that monitors the environment. When the receptor detects a change in some factor or event—some variable—it sends that information to the control center, the second of the three components.
2. A *control center* determines the factor's set point—the level or range that is normal for the factor in question. The control center integrates information coming from all the pertinent receptors and selects an appropriate response. In most of the body's homeostatic systems, the control center is located in the brain.
3. An *effector,* often a muscle or gland, carries out the selected response.

Consider how a negative feedback mechanism controls the temperature in your home during the frigid winter months. A thermostat in the heating

Q *Stable blood calcium levels are important to many physiological processes. Calcitonin is a hormone from the thyroid gland that lowers blood calcium levels. Parathyroid hormone from the parathyroid glands is a hormone that raises blood calcium levels. Describe a negative feedback relationship involving these hormones as effectors that would maintain homeostasis by keeping blood calcium levels stable.*

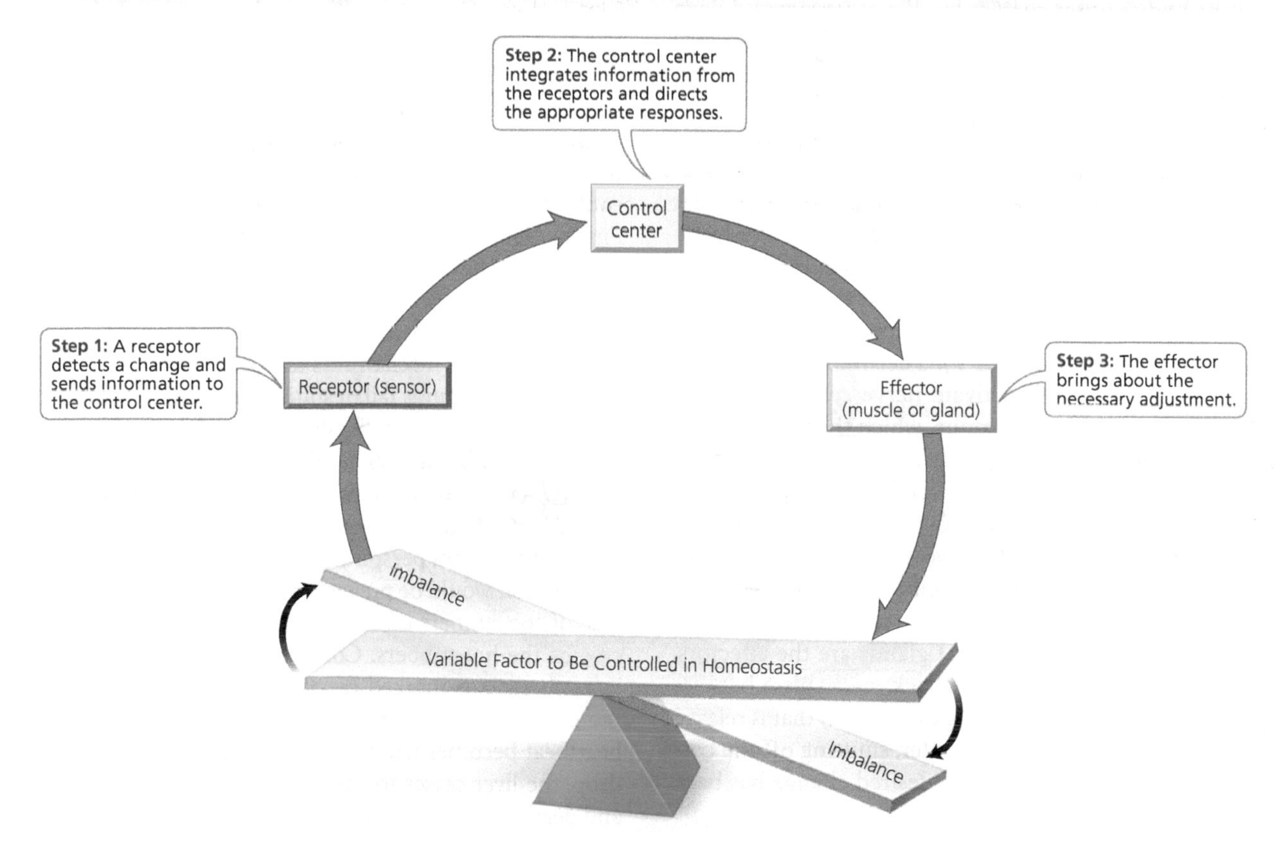

FIGURE 1d.13 **The components of a homeostatic control system maintained by negative feedback mechanisms**

A *An elevation in blood calcium level would be sensed by receptors. In response, a control center in the brain would stimulate the thyroid gland to increase production of calcitonin, which lowers blood calcium level. If the calcium level dropped too low, receptors would signal the control center in the brain. In response, the control center would stimulate the parathyroid glands to increase production of parathyroid hormone, which would raise blood calcium levels.*

PART II: WHAT IS HEALTH AND ILLNESS?

*Posted on course website at http://www.pearsoncustom.com/can/uguelph_biohealth

CHAPTER 2a

WHAT IS HEALTH? CHANGING PERSPECTIVES

Taken from *An Introduction to Health Psychology*, Second Edition, by Val Morrison and Paul Bennett

WHAT IS HEALTH? CHANGING PERSPECTIVES

Stone (1979) pointed out that until we can agree on the meaning of health and how it can be measured we are going to be unable to answer questions about how we can protect, enhance and restore health. The root word of health is 'wholeness', and indeed 'holy' and 'healthy' share the same root word in Anglo-Saxon, which is perhaps why so many cultures associate one with the other: e.g. medicine men have both roles. Having its roots in 'wholeness' also suggests the early existence of a broad view of health that included mental and physical aspects. This view has not held dominance throughout history, as the next section illustrates.

Models of Health and Illness

One needs first to be clear about what health is. Health is a word that most people will use, but without realising that it may hold different meanings for different people, at different times in history, in different cultures, in different social classes, or even within the same family, depending, for example, on age. Some different, but not necessarily oppositional, views of health are described below.

Mind–body Relationships

Archaeological finds of human skulls from the Stone Age have attributed the small neat holes found in some skulls to the process of 'trephination' (or trepanation), whereby a hole is made in order for evil spirits to leave the ailing body. Disease appeared to be attributed to evil spirits. However, by the time of ancient Greece the association between mind and body was viewed somewhat differently. The ancient Greek physician Hippocrates (*circa* 460–377 BC) considered the mind and body as one unit, but did not attribute illness to evil spirits but to the balance between four circulating bodily fluids (called humours): yellow bile, phlegm, blood and black bile. It was thought that when a person was healthy the four humours were in balance, and when they were ill-balanced due to external 'pathogens', illness occurred. The humours were attached to seasonal variations and to conditions of hot, cold, wet and dry, where phlegm was attached to winter (cold–wet), blood to spring (wet–hot), black bile to autumn (cold–dry), and yellow bile to summer (hot–dry). Furthermore, it was thought that the level of specific bodily humours related to particular personalities: excessive yellow bile was linked to a choleric or angry temperament; black bile was attached to sadness; excessive blood was associated with an optimistic or sanguine personality; and excessive phlegm with a calm or phlegmatic temperament. Interestingly, as far back as Hippocrates, it was suggested that eating healthily would help to preserve the balance of the humours, showing an early awareness of a relationship between nutrition and health (Helman 1978). This humoral **theory** of illness therefore attributed disease states to bodily functions but also acknowledged that bodily factors impacted on the mind.

This view continued with Galen (*circa* AD 129–199), another influential Greek physician. Galen considered there to be a physical basis for all ill health (physical or mental) and believed not only that the four bodily humours underpinned the four dominant temperaments (the sanguine, the choleric, the phlegmatic and the melancholic) but also that these temperaments could contribute to the experience of specific illnesses. For example, he proposed that melancholic women were more likely to get breast cancer, offering not a psychological explanation but a physical one because melancholia was itself thought to be underpinned by high levels of black bile. This view was therefore that the mind and body were interrelated, but only in terms of physical and mental disturbances both having an underlying physical cause. The mind was not thought to play a role in illness **aetiology**. This view dominated thinking for many centuries to come but lost predominance in the eighteenth century as organic medicine, and in particular cellular pathology, developed and failed to support the humoral underpinnings. However, Galen's descriptions of personality types were still in use in the latter half of the twentieth century (Marks *et al.* 2000: 76–7).

In the early Middle Ages (fifth–sixth century), however, Galen's theories lost dominance as health became increasingly tied to faith and spirituality. Illness was at this time seen as God's punishment for misdeeds or, similar to very early views, the result of evil spirits entering one's soul. Individuals were considered to have little control over their health, whereas priests, in their perceived ability to restore health by driving out demons, did. As the Church was at the forefront of society, science developed slowly. The mind and body were generally viewed as working together, or at least in parallel, but because medical understanding was limited in its development through the prohibition of scientific investigation such as dissection, mental and mystical explanations of illness predominated.

theory a general belief or beliefs about some aspect of the world we live in or those in it, which may or may not be supported by evidence. For example, women are worse drivers than men.

aetiology (etiology): the cause of disease.

Such causal explanations therefore called for treatment along the lines of self-punishment, abstinence from sin, prayer or hard work.

These religious views persisted for many centuries until the early fourteenth and fifteenth centuries when a period of 'rebirth', a Renaissance, began, with individual thinking becoming increasingly dominant and thus a religious perspective became only one among many. The scientific revolution of the early 1600s led to a huge upsurge in scholarly and scientific study and developments in physical medicine; as a result, the understanding of the human body, and therefore the explanations for illness, became increasingly organic and physiological, with little room for psychological explanations.

During the early seventeenth century, the French philosopher René Descartes (1596–1650), like the ancient Greeks, proposed that the mind and body were separate entities. However, Descartes also proposed that interaction between the two 'domains' was possible, although initially the understanding of how mind–body interactions could happen was limited. For example, how could a mental thought, with no physical properties, cause a bodily reaction (e.g. a neuron to fire) (Solmes and Turnbull 2002)? This is defined as **dualism**, where the mind is considered to be 'non-material' (i.e. not objective or visible, such as thoughts and feelings) and the body is 'material' (i.e. made up of real 'stuff', physical matter such as our brain, heart and cells). The material and the non-material were considered independent. Physicians acted as guardians of the body, which was viewed as a machine amenable to scientific investigation and explanation. In contrast, theologians acted as guardians of the mind, a place not amenable to scientific investigation. The suggested communication between mind and body was thought to be under the control of the pineal gland in the midbrain, but the process of this interaction was unclear. Because Descartes believed that the soul left humans at the time of death, dissection and autopsy study now became acceptable to the Church, and the eighteenth and nineteenth centuries witnessed a huge growth in medical understanding. Anatomical research, autopsy work and cellular pathology concluded that disease was located in human cells, not in ill-balanced humours.

Dualists developed the notion of the body as a machine (a **mechanistic** viewpoint), understandable only in terms of its constituent parts (molecular, biological, biochemical, genetic), with illness understood through the study of cellular and physiological processes. Treatment during these centuries became more technical, diagnostic and focused on the body internal, with individuals perhaps more passively involved than previously, when they had been called upon to pray or exorcise their demons in order to return to health. This approach underpins the **biomedical model** of illness.

dualism the idea that the mind and body are separate entities (cf. Descartes).

mechanistic a reductionist approach that reduces behaviour to the level of the organ or physical function. Associated with the **biomedical model.**

Biomedical Model of Illness

In this model, a symptom of illness is considered to have an underlying pathology that will hopefully, but not inevitably, be cured through medical intervention. Adhering rigidly to the biomedical model would lead to proponents dealing with objective facts and assuming a direct causal relationship between illness, its symptoms or underlying pathology (disease), and adjustment outcomes. The assumption is that removal of the pathology will lead to restored health, i.e. illness results from disease. This relatively mechanistic view of how our bodies and its organs work, fail and can be treated allows little room for subjectivity. The biomedical view has been described as reductionist: i.e. the basic idea that mind, matter (body) and human behaviour can all be reduced to, and explained at, the level of cells, neural activity or biochemical activity. Reductionism tends to ignore evidence that different people respond in different ways to the same underlying disease because of differences, for example, in personality, cognition, social support resources or cultural beliefs.

Biopsychosocial Model of Illness

What is perhaps getting closer to the 'truth', as we understand it today, is the view of dual-aspect monists: those with this viewpoint would agree that there is one type of 'stuff' (monist) but would suggest that it can be perceived in two different ways: objectively and subjectively. For example, many illnesses have organic underlying causes, but they also elicit uniquely individual responses due to the action of the mind, i.e. subjective responses. So, while aspects of reductionism and dualistic thinking have been useful, for example in furthering our understanding of the aetiology and course of many acute and infectious diseases (Larson 1999) such as coronary heart disease and AIDS, we would propose that the role of the 'mind' in the manifestation of, and response to, illness is crucial to the advancement of our understanding of the

biomedical model a view that diseases and symptoms have an underlying physiological explanation.

FIGURE 2a.1 **Having a disability does not equate with a lack of health and fitness as Oscar Pistorius has shown the world.**

complex nature of health and illness. Consider for example the extensive evidence of 'phantom limb pain' in amputees—how can pain exist in an absent limb? Consider the widespread acknowledgement of the placebo effect—how can an inactive (dummy) substance lead to similar levels of reported pain or other symptom reduction in that described by those receiving an active pharmaceutical substance or treatment? Subjectivity in terms of beliefs, expectations and emotions interact with bodily reactions to play an important role in the illness or stress experience. This text aims to illustrate that psychological and social factors can add to biological or biomedical explanations and understanding of health and illness experiences. This is known as the **biopsychosocial** model, and it is employed in health psychology as well as in several allied health professions, such as occupational therapy and, to a growing extent, in the medical profession (Turner 2001; Wade and Halligan 2004).

Challenging Dualism: Psychosocial Models of Health and Illness

Evidence of changed thinking is illustrated in an editorial in the *British Medical Journal* (Bracken and Thomas 2002) suggesting that it is time to 'move beyond the mind–body split'. The authors note that simply because neuroscience now enables us to explore the 'mind' and its workings by the use of increasingly sophisticated scanning devices and measurements, this does not mean we are furthering our understanding of the 'mind'—the thoughts, feelings and the like that make up our lives and give it meaning. They comment that 'conceptualising our mental life as some sort of enclosed world living inside our skull does not do justice to the reality of human experience' (p. 1434). The fact that this editorial succeeded in being published in a medical journal with a traditionally biomedical stance suggests that Descartes's 'legacy' is finally weakening.

The tension between those who viewed the mind and body as separate (dualists) and those who saw them as a unit (monists) has lessened as understanding of the bi-directional relationship between mind and body has grown. Psychology has played a significant role in this altering perspective. A key influence was Sigmund Freud in the 1920s and 1930s, who redefined the mind–body problem as one of 'consciousness'. Freud postulated the existence of an 'unconscious mind', following examination of patients with conversion hysteria. Unconscious conflicts were identified, using hypnosis and free association techniques, as the 'cause' of physical disturbances such as the paralysis and loss of sensation seen in some patients, for whom no underlying physical explanation was present (i.e. hysterical paralysis, e.g. Freud and Breuer 1895).

biopsychosocial a view that diseases and symptoms can be explained by a combination of physical, social, cultural and psychological factors (cf. Engel 1977).

Freud stimulated much work into unconscious conflict, personality and illness, which ultimately led to the development of the field of *psychosomatic medicine* as we now know it. Psychologists have highlighted the need for medicine to become more holistic and to consider the role played in the aetiology, course and outcomes of illness, by psychological and social factors. The biopsychosocial model signals a broadening of a disease or biomedical model of health to one encompassing and emphasising the interaction between biological processes and psychological and social influences (Engel 1977, 1980). In doing so, it offers a complex and multivariate, but potentially more comprehensive, model with which to examine the human experience of illness. It burgeoned in popularity as a result of the many challenges to the biomedical approach as briefly illustrated above, but it was also due to increasing recognition of the role individual behaviour plays in health and illness.

Behaviour and Health

The dramatic increases in life expectancy witnessed in Western countries in the twentieth century, partially due to advances in medical technology and treatments, led to a general belief, in Western cultures at least, in the efficacy of traditional medicine and its power to eradicate disease. This was most notable following the introduction of antibiotics in the 1940s; although Fleming discovered penicillin in 1928, it was some years before it and other antibiotics were generally available. Such drug treatments, alongside increased control of infectious disease through vaccination and improved sanitation, are partial explanations of UK life expectancy at birth increasing from 47 years in 1900 to 74.6 years in 1980 (Whelan 1988). A continued increase is seen in the 2005 figures whereby the life expectancy at birth for females born in UK was 80.7 compared with 85.2 years for women born in Japan. For men the differential is slightly less: 76.1 years for UK-born men compared with 78.3 years for those born in Japan. These cultural variations can be explained to a large extent by differences in lifestyle and diet. In fact, much of the fall in mortality seen in the developed world preceded the major immunisation programmes and therefore it is the wider social and environmental changes, such as developments in education and agriculture, which led to changes in diet, or the development of sewerage and waste disposal systems, which are mainly responsible for improved public health.

One hundred years ago, the ten leading causes of death were infectious diseases such as tuberculosis and pneumonia, with diseases such as diphtheria and tetanus highly common. If people living then had been asked what they thought being healthy meant, they may have replied 'avoiding infections, drinking clean water, living into my 50s/60s'. Death was frequently a result of highly infectious disease becoming epidemic in communities unprotected by immunisation or adequate sanitary conditions. However, in the last century, at least in developed countries, there has been a downturn in deaths resulting from infectious disease, and the 'top killers' make no mention of TB, typhoid or measles but instead list for example cancer, heart, lung and liver disease and accidents. Table 2a.1 shows the leading 'physical' causes of mortality as recorded at various points over the past 106 years. It should be noted that the dementias are also attributed as the cause of death in significant numbers, e.g. over 13,000 deaths in 2006 in England and Wales, however the table presents only those causes considered applicable to all ages groups. These diseases have a behavioural component in that they have been linked to behaviour such as smoking, excessive alcohol consumption, increasingly sedentary lifestyles and poor diet. It has been estimated that approximately two-thirds (Doll and Peto 1981) to three-quarters (Peto and Lopez 1990) of cancer deaths are attributable, in part at least, to our behaviour (note that Peto increased this estimate over the nine years between the two publications cited). The upturn in cancer deaths over the last 100 years is in part because people are living longer with illnesses they previously would have died from; thus they are reaching ages where cancer **incidence** is greater. Although such figures are not wholly attributable to the increase in smoking and other cancer-related behaviour, a person's own behaviour does increase such disease risk significantly. By 2006, diabetes is seen to have regained its 1995 position as 8th; this slight rise from 9th position in 2000 obscures the fact that prevalence almost doubled between 1995 and 2006. Perhaps this finding reflects what has been described as the 'obesity' epidemic. As Table 2a.1 (overleaf) shows, the leading causes of death have however been relatively stable over the past decade.

Worldwide, the leading causes of death include heart disease, cancer, accidents and respiratory disorders, with AIDS predominating in many African and Asian countries and globally being the fourth leading cause of death. The World Health Organization (2002) has cited life expectancy at birth in sub-Saharan Africa as being 47 years but notes that this would be approximately 62 years if there were no AIDS. Projected worldwide mortality estimates place heart disease,

incidence the number of new cases of disease occurring during a defined time interval—not to be confused with prevalence, which refers to the number of established cases of a disease in a population at any one time.

ries from lung, colon and prostate and breast and colorectal cancers in

gets and policy documents assume a clear ıship between people's behaviour, lifestyle and th. However, what they less clearly acknowledge nd what is often not explicitly addressed are the socio-economic and cultural influences on health, illness and health decisions. These important in-fluences on health are addressed in the next chapter. The WHO definition also fails to make explicit mention of the role of the 'psyche' which, as this text will show, plays a major role in the experience of health and illness.

CROSS-CULTURAL PERSPECTIVES ON HEALTH

What is considered to be 'normal' health varies across cultures and as a result of the economic, political and cultural climate of the era in which a person lives. Think of how pregnancy is treated in most Western civilisations (i.e. medicalised) as opposed to many Third World regions (naturalised). The stigma of physical impairment or disability among South Asian communities may have consequences for the family which would not be considered in Caucasian families: for example, having a sibling with a disability may affect the other siblings' marriage chances or even the social standing of the family (Ahmad 2000). The way in which certain behaviour is viewed also differs across time and between cultures. For example, alcohol dependence has shifted from being seen as a legal and moral problem, with abusers seen as deviant to a disease treated in clinics; and smoking has shifted from being considered as glamorous and even desirable to being socially undesirable and indicative of a weak will. Perhaps reflecting this shift, the prevalence of males over age 16 currently smoking in England has dropped significantly over the past thirty years, although the decline is less pronounced for females (The Health Survey for England (2007), Health and Social Care Information Centre (2008).

What is normal and what is defined as sick in a given culture can have all sorts of consequences. If a particular behaviour is labelled as a sickness, the consequences will differ greatly from those received if the behaviour is labelled as deviant; for example, societal responses to illicit drug use have ranged from prohibition through criminalisation to an illness requiring treatment.

There is growing evidence that Westernised views of health differ in various ways from conceptualisations of health in non-Westernised civilisations. Chalmers (1996) astutely notes that Westerners divide the mind, body and soul in terms of allocation of care between psychologists and psychiatrists, medical professions and the clergy. She observes that this is not the case in some African cultures, where these three 'elements of human nature' are integrated in terms of how a person views them, and in how they are cared for. This holistic view considers the social as well as the biological, the spiritual as well as the interpersonal, and health as an integrated state consisting of all these elements. Until recently, with the development of quality of life research, spiritual wellbeing was rarely considered as contributing to a person's perception of health. Furthermore, attributing continued health to a satisfied ancestor would be likely to raise a few eyebrows if stated aloud in a conversation with peers. Spiritual explanations are present in Western reports, if uncommon: for example, supernatural forces such as faith, God's reward, may be perceived as supporting health. Negative supernatural forces such as 'hexes' or the 'evil eye' can also share the blame for illness and disability, as evidenced by cross-cultural studies of illness attributions (e.g. Landrine and Klonoff 1992, 1994) and, as we described above, in earlier historical periods. Among some ethnic groups, Hindus and Sikhs in particular, it has been reported that disability is considered a punishment for past sins within the family (Katbamna *et al.* 2000). These belief systems can have profound effects on living with illness or indeed caring for someone with an illness or disability.

In addition to beliefs of spiritual influences on health, studies of some African regions consider that the community or family work together for the wellbeing of all. This **collectivist** approach to staying healthy and avoiding illness is far different to our **individualistic** approach to health (consider how long the passive smoking evidence was ignored). For example, in a study of preventive behaviour to avoid endemic tropical disease in Malawians, the social actions to prevent infection (e.g. clearing reed beds) were adhered to more consistently than the personal preventive actions (e.g. bathing in piped water or taking one's dose of chloroquine) (Morrison *et al.* 1999). Collectivist cultures emphasise group needs to a greater degree than individualistic ones, which emphasise the uniqueness of its members (Matsumoto *et al.* 1996, cited in Marks *et al.* 2000: 56). Several Eastern cultures (Japanese,

collectivist a cultural philosophy that emphasises the individual as part of a wider unit and places emphasis on actions motivated by collective, rather than individual, needs and wants.

individualistic a cultural philosophy that places responsibility at the feet of the individual; thus behaviour is often driven by individual needs and wants rather than by community needs or wants.

Chinese) also exhibit **holistic** and collectivist approaches to health. For example, following a comparative study of Canadian and Japanese students, Heine and Lehman (1995) highlighted a need to 'distinguish between cultures that promote and validate "independent selfs", i.e. find meaning through uniqueness and autonomy, and cultures that promote and validate "interdependent selfs", i.e. find meaning through links with others and one's community' (Morrison *et al.* 1999: 367). Cultures that promote an interdependent self are more likely to view health in terms of social functioning rather than simply personal functioning, fitness, etc. Several research studies by George Bishop and colleagues (e.g. Quah and Bishop 1996; Bishop and Teng 1992) have noted that Chinese Singaporean adults view health as a harmonious state where the internal and external systems are in balance, and on occasions where they become imbalanced, health is compromised. *Yin*—the positive energy—needs to be kept in balance with the *yang*—the negative energy (also considered to be female!). Eastern cultures hold spiritual beliefs about health and illness, with illness or misfortune commonly being attributed to predestination. Obviously, to maximise effectiveness of health promotion efforts, it is important to acknowledge the existence and effects of such different underlying belief systems.

In the Western world, there is a growing recognition of the value of alternative remedies for health maintenance or treatment of symptoms, and the alternative medicine and complementary therapy industries have grown enormously. A mixture of Western and non-medical/traditional medicine can be found in many regions of sub-Saharan Africa, where, for example in Malawi, a person may visit a faith healer or a herbalist as well as a local Western clinic for antibiotics (Ager *et al.* 1996). Similarly, among some Aboriginal tribes spiritual beliefs in illness causation coexist with the use of Western medicines for symptom control (Devanesen 2000). The biomedical view is therefore seen to be acknowledged and assimilated within the culture's belief system as both the availability of Western medicine and the population's understanding of its methods and efficacy grows. However, our understanding of culturally relevant cognitions regarding illness and health behaviour is still limited, and further cross-cultural research is required.

The use of health care, either traditional or Western, will in part be determined by the nature and strength of an individual's cultural values and beliefs. Illness discourse will reflect the dominant conceptualisations of individual cultures, and it should become clear at various points throughout this text that how people think about health and illness shapes their expectations, health behaviour, and their use of health promotion and health-care resources.

holistic root word 'wholeness'; holistic approaches are concerned with the whole being and its wellbeing, rather than addressing the purely physical or observable.

LIFESPAN, AGEING AND BELIEFS ABOUT HEALTH

Psychological wellbeing, social and emotional health are not only influenced by the ageing process, they are also affected by illness, disability and hospitalisation, all of which can be experienced at any age. Although growing older is associated with decreased functioning and increased disability or dependence, it is not only older people who live with chronic illness. For example, a survey of young people aged 2–24 (using parent proxy reports for those aged under 13) found that approximately a quarter of the young people had a longstanding illness (predominantly respiratory conditions such as asthma) (statistics from the Health Survey for England, www.doh.gov.uk/stats/selfrep.htm).

There are, however, developmental issues which health professionals should be aware of if they are to promote the physical, psychological, social and emotional wellbeing of their patient or client. While the subsequent section considers lifespan issues in relation to health perceptions, it is recommended that interested readers also consult a health psychology text focusing specifically on such issues, e.g. Penny *et al.*'s edited collection (1994).

Developmental Theories

The developmental process is a function of the interaction between three factors:

1. *Learning*: a relatively permanent change in knowledge, skill or ability as a result of experience.
2. *Experience*: what we do, see, hear, feel, think.
3. *Maturation*: thought, behaviour or physical growth, attributed to a genetically determined sequence of development and ageing rather than to experience.

Erik Erikson (Erikson 1959; Erikson *et al.* 1986) described eight major life stages (five related to childhood development, three related to adult development), which varied across different dimensions, including:

- cognitive and intellectual functioning;
- language and communication skills;
- the understanding of illness;
- health care and maintenance behaviour.

It is important that each of these dimensions be taken into consideration when examining health and illness perceptions or behaviour. Deficits or limitations in cognitive functioning (due to age, accident or illness) may, for example, influence the extent to which an individual can understand medical instructions, report their emotions or have their health-care needs assessed. Communication deficits or limited language skills can impair a person's willingness to place themselves in social situations, or impede their ability to express their pain or distress to health professionals or family members. The understanding that an individual has of their symptoms or their illness is crucial to health-care-seeking behaviour and to adherence, and individual health behaviour influences one's perceived and/or actual risk of illness and varies hugely across the lifespan.

Piaget (1930, 1970) was largely responsible for developing a maturational framework for understanding cognitive development, which has also provided a good basis for understanding the developmental course of concepts regarding health, illness and health procedures. Piaget proposed a staged structure to which, he considered, all individuals follow in the sequence described below:

1. *Sensorimotor* (birth–2 years): an infant understands the world through sensations and movement, lacks symbolic thought. Moves from reflexive to voluntary action.
2. *Pre-operational* (2–7 years): symbolic thought develops by around age 2, thereafter simple logical thinking and language develop, generally **egocentric.**
3. *Concrete operational* (7–11 years): abstract thought and logic develop hugely; can perform mental operations (e.g. mental arithmetic) and manipulate objects.
4. *Formal operational* (age 12 to adulthood): abstract thought and imagination develop as does deductive reasoning. Not everyone may attain this level.

egocentric self-centred, such as in the pre-operational stage (age 2–7 years) of children, when they see things only from their own perspective (cf. Piaget).

Piaget's work is influential in terms of providing an overarching structure within which to view cognitive development. For example, his work describes how an infant, from birth to 2 years, slowly acquires symbolic thinking and language and the ability to imitate the actions of others, but that it is only in the latter part of the second stage that children begin to develop logical thought (albeit generally very egocentric thought). Of more relevance is work that has more specifically addressed children's developing beliefs and understanding of health and illness constructs. The subsequent sections describe this work, using Piagetian stages as a broad framework.

Sensorimotor and Pre-operational Stage Children

Little work with infants at the sensorimotor stage is possible in terms of identifying health and illness cognitions, as language is very limited until the end of this stage. At the pre-operational stage, children develop linguistically and cognitively, and symbolic thought means that young children develop awareness of how they can affect the external world through imitation and learning, although they remain very **egocentric.** Health and illness are considered in black and white, i.e. as two opposing states rather than as existing on a continuum. Children here are slow to see or adopt other people's viewpoints or perspectives. This ability is crucial if one is to empathise with others, and thus a pre-operational child is not very sympathetic to a family member being ill, not understanding why this means they can no longer expect the same amount of play, for example.

Illness Concept

It is important that children learn over time some responsibility for maintaining their own health; however, few studies have examined children's conception of health, which would be likely to influence their behaviour. Research has instead focused more often on generating illness concepts. For example, Bibace and Walsh (1980) suggest, on the basis of asking children aged 3–13 questions about health and illness, that an illness concept develops gradually. The questions were about knowledge—'What is a cold?'; experience—'Were you ever sick?'; attributions—'How does someone get a cold'; and recovery—'How does someone get better?' They revealed that there is a progression of understanding and attribution for causes of illness and described six developmentally ordered descriptions of how illness is defined, caused and treated.

Under-7s generally explain illness on a 'magical' level—explanations are based on association.

- *Incomprehension*: child gives irrelevant answers or evades question: e.g. sun causes heart attacks.
- *Phenomenonism*: illness is usually a sign or sound that the child has at some time associated with the illness, but with little grasp of cause and effect: e.g. a cold is when you sniff a lot.
- *Contagion*: illness is usually from a person or object that is close by, but not necessarily touching the child; or it can be attributed to an activity that occurred before the illness: e.g: 'You get measles from people'. If asked how? 'Just by walking near them'.

Concrete Operational Stage Children

Children over 7 are described by Piaget as capable of thinking logically about objects and events, although they are still unable to distinguish between mind and body until around age 11, when adolescence begins.

Illness Concept

Bibace and Walsh describe explanations of illness at around 8 to 11 years as being more concrete and based on a causal sequence:

- *Contamination*: i.e. children at this stage understand that illness can have multiple symptoms, and they recognise that germs, or even their own behaviour, can cause illness: e.g. 'You get a cold if you take your jacket off outside, and it gets into your body'.
- *Internalisation*: i.e. illness is within the body, but the process by which symptoms occur can be partially understood. The cause of a cold may come from outside germs that are inhaled or swallowed. These children can differentiate between body organs and function and can understand specific, simple information about their illness. They can also see the role of treatment and/or personal action as returning them to health.

In this concrete operational stage, medical staff are still seen as having absolute authority, but their actions might be criticised/avoided: e.g. reluctance to give blood, accusations of hurting unnecessarily, etc. Children can, like adults, be encouraged to take some personal control over their illness or treatment at this stage in development, and this can help the child to cope. They also need to be encouraged to express their fears. Parents need to strike a balance between monitoring a sick child's health and behaviour and being overprotective, as this can detrimentally affect a child's social, cognitive and personal development and may encourage feelings of dependency and disability.

Adolescence and Formal Operational Thought

Adolescence is a socially and culturally created concept only a few generations old. Many primitive societies do not acknowledge adolescence, and children move from childhood to adulthood with a ritual performance, not years of transition as viewed by many Western societies as a distinct period in life. Puberty is a period of both physical and psychosocial change that can influence self-perception; indeed, during early adolescence (11–13 years), as individuals prepare for independence and peers take on more credence than parents, much of life's health-damaging behaviour commences, e.g. smoking.

Illness Concept

Bibace and Walsh describe illness concepts at this stage as those at an abstract level—explanations based on interactions between the person and their environment:

- *Physiological*: children from around 11 years reach a stage of physiological understanding, and most can now define illness in terms of specific bodily organs or functions, and with age begin to appreciate multiple physical causes, e.g. genes plus pollution plus behaviour.
- *Psychophysiological*: in later adolescence (from around 14 years) and adulthood, many people grasp the idea that mind and body interact, and they understand or accept the role of stress, worry, etc. in the exacerbation and even the cause of illness. It is worth noting that many adults may not achieve this level of understanding about illness and may continue to use more cognitively simplistic explanations.

It should be noted that Bibace and Walsh's study focuses predominantly on the issue of illness causality. Other work has shown that children and young people are able to think about health and illness in terms of other dimensions, such as controllability and severity (e.g. Goldman *et al.* 1991).

Adolescents perceive themselves as having more control over the onset and cure of illness and are more aware that personal actions can influence outcomes. This means that advice and interventions are understood more and may be acted upon as they can understand complex remedial and therapeutic procedures: e.g. they understand that taking blood can help to monitor the progress of disease.

Childhood is an important period for the development of health and illness concepts, also for the development of attitudes and patterns of health behaviour that will impact on future health status. According to these staged theories, a child's ability to understand their condition and associated treatment is determined by the level of cognitive development attained. This level of understanding will subsequently determine how children communicate their symptom experience to parents and health-care staff, their ability to act on health advice, and the level of personal responsibility for disease management that is feasible. These aspects should not be overlooked when care and educational programmes are developed. While cognitive development is important, such staged theories have not met with universal support (e.g. Dimigen and Ferguson 1993, in relation to concepts of cancer). Illness concepts are now thought to derive more from a range of influences, such as experience and knowledge, rather than from relatively fixed stages of cognitive development.

Adulthood 17/18+

Adulthood tends to be divided between early (17–40), middle age (40–60) and elderly (60/65+). Early adulthood blends out of adolescence as the person forges their identity and assumes the roles and responsibility of adulthood—a time of consolidation. Early adulthood has been described as the prime of life, when all sorts of transitions occur, such as graduation, new careers, pregnancy, marriage, childbirth; many will divorce, some will lose a parent. While Piaget did not describe further developments in cognitive processes during adulthood, new perspectives develop from experience, and what is/has been learned is applied with a view to achieving life goals. The shift from acquisition of learning to application of what has been learned means that health education should be more practical in orientation, emphasising application of information. Adults are less likely than adolescents to adopt new health-risk behaviour and are generally more likely to engage in protective behaviour: e.g. screening, exercise, etc. for health reasons. Transitions in adulthood do not affect all sectors of the adult population in the same way: for example, marriage has been found to benefit health in men—i.e. they have lower illness scores than men living alone, whereas for women, being married carries no such protection (Blaxter 1987; Macintyre 1986), suggesting differential social support perhaps.

In contrast to the generally positive view of early adulthood, middle age has been identified as a period of uncertainty, anxiety and change, where some question their achievements, goals and values, or experience uncertainty of roles when children become adults and leave home themselves.

what do YOU think?

Is middle age a state of mind? Are you 'as young as you feel'? Think of your parents, aunts and uncles or of family friends in their forties. Do they seem to share outlooks on life, expectancies and behaviours that are significantly different to those of you and your friends? How do you view growing older? Think about how it makes you feel and question these feelings.

Ageing and health

In the UK, as elsewhere in the world, the ageing population (accepting the cut-off age for 'older people' to be 65 or over) has burgeoned, but more particularly the percentage of persons living into their late 70s or 80s has increased (Office for National Statistics, *Social Trends 29*, 1999) and is projected to increase further. The United Nations Secretariat (2002) have predicted an increase in those aged over 60 from 10 per cent of the population to 20 per cent by 2050. The implications for health and social care resources are obvious, given the **epidemiology** of illness: i.e. the fact that the incidence of many diseases increases with longevity. Not all elderly people are ill or infirm, but even among the minority who go on without chronic health problems (physical and/or mental), episodes of acute illness are commonplace. The 2000 Health Survey for England (www.doh.gov.uk/public/healtholderpeople2000pres.htm) reports that of those aged 65 and above, 13 per cent of those living at home (10 per cent of those aged 65–79; 25 per cent of those over 80) have a serious disability, compared with 69 per cent of men and 79 per cent of women living in residential homes. This figure suggests that there is a considerable extent of disability in the community. This was confirmed in the 2005 Health Survey for England

epidemiology the study of patterns of disease in various populations and the association with other factors such as lifestyle factors. Key concepts include mortality, morbidity, prevalence, incidence, absolute risk and relative risk. Type of question: Who gets this disease? How common is it?

where arthritis was found to be the most common chronic condition reported by women aged over 65 years (47 per cent women, 32 per cent men) and for men, the most common condition was cardiovascular disease (37 per cent men, 31 per cent women). Two-fifths of the older people sampled reported limitations in performing at least one functional activity, usually walking without stopping or discomfort. Does the process of ageing influence how an older person thinks about themselves and their health?

Empirical research has shown that **self-concept** is relatively stable through ageing (e.g. Baltes and Baltes 1990) and that changes in self-concept are not an inevitable part of the ageing process. In fact, *ageing is not necessarily a negative experience* (although it may become so because of the ageist attitudes that exist in many industrialised countries). Growing older may present an individual with new challenges, but this should not be seen as implying that ageing is itself a problem (Coleman 1999).

With increasing age, sensory and motor losses are most common, with a large proportion of our elderly being physically impaired in some way. In an ageing society disability is common; 85 per cent may experience some chronic condition (Woods 2008). Elderly people often report expecting to have poor health, which can result in poor health-care checks and maintenance as they regard it as pointless; they may think loss of mobility, poor foot health and poor digestion as an inevitable and unavoidable part of growing old, so they may not respond to symptoms as they should (e.g. Leventhal and Prohaska 1986; Sarkisian *et al.* 2001). Exercise tends to decline in old age as it may be avoided in the belief that it will over-exert the joints, heart, etc.; the elderly tend to underestimate their own physical capacities, yet as we shall see, exercise is both possible and beneficial. There is growing interest in 'successful ageing'—what it is and how it can be achieved.

self-concept those conscious thoughts and beliefs about yourself that allow you to feel are distinct from others and that you exist as a separate person.

This section has described what is often meant by 'health'. In focusing on health, we have acknowledged that health is a continuum, not simply a dichotomy of sick versus healthy. Most of us will experience in our lifetime varying degrees of health and wellbeing, with periods of illness at one extreme and optimal wellness at the other. Some may never experience optimal wellness. 'Health refers to a state of being that is largely taken for granted' (Radley 1994: 5) and is often only appreciated when lost through illness.

CHAPTER 2c

THE SEVEN DIMENSIONS OF HEALTH AND WELLNESS

Taken from *Health: The Basics,* Fifth Canadian Edition, by Rebecca J. Donatelle and Angela M. Thompson

The Seven Dimensions of Health & Wellness

Biologist and philosopher Rene Dubos provides a multi-dimensional definition of health, noting that it "involves social, emotional, mental, spiritual, and biological fitness on the part of the individual, which results from adaptations to the environment." The concept of adaptability or the ability to successfully cope with life's ups and downs is a key element of this definition. In recent decades, the term **wellness** has become popular. It includes the previously mentioned elements and implies as well that there are levels to obtain in each category: to achieve a high level of wellness, a person attempts to move progressively higher on a continuum of positive health indicators. Today, *health* and *wellness* are often used interchangeably to refer to the dynamic, ever-changing process of trying to achieve one's individual potential in each of the interrelated dimensions. These dimensions typically include those presented in Figure 2c.1.

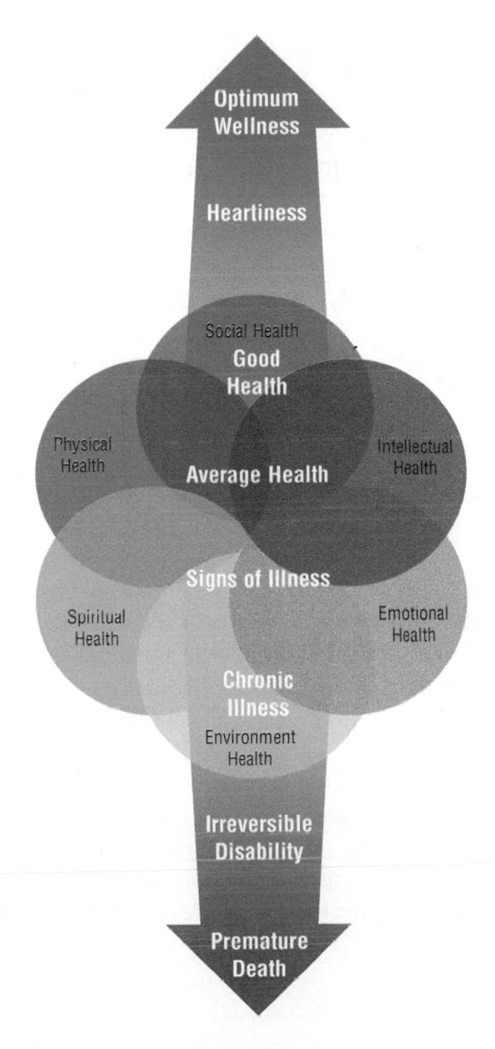

FIGURE 2c.1
The Dimensions of Health and the Wellness Continuum

- **Physical health.** Includes physical characteristics such as body size and shape, sensory acuity, susceptibility to disease and disorders, body functioning, and recuperative ability. Newer definitions of physical health include the ability to perform activities of daily living, such as getting out of bed in the morning, bending to tie up shoes, and shoulder checking while driving.
- **Social health.** Refers to the capacity for satisfying interpersonal relationships, interacting with others, and adapting to various social situations. It also includes communication skills and other daily activities.
- **Mental health.** Refers to the ability to think clearly, reason objectively, analyze critically, and use brain power effectively to meet life's challenges. It includes learning from successes and failures and making responsible decisions.
- **Occupational health.** Refers to the satisfaction a person gets from his or her career or stage of career development. It also involves attaining and maintaining a satisfying balance between work and leisure.
- **Emotional health.** Refers to the "feeling" component of health and to the ability to effectively and appropriately express emotions. Feelings of self-esteem, self-confidence, self-efficacy, trust, love, and others are part of emotional health.
- **Environmental health.** Refers to an appreciation of the external environment and the role individuals play in preserving, protecting, and improving it. Biophilia specifically refers to the instinctive bond between people and their environment. It also includes a student's personal studying environment—the desk, room, lighting, noise level, comfortable emotional atmosphere, and so on.
- **Spiritual health.** Your spirit refers to the deepest or innermost part of you, the part that helps you to understand the world and your role in it. Spirituality is what we draw strength and hope from. It is through understanding our spiritual selves that we

Mortality: Death rate.

Morbidity: Illness rate.

Health: Dynamic, ever-changing process of trying to achieve individual potential in the physical, social, mental, occupational, emotional, environmental, and spiritual dimensions.

Wellness: Similar to health, a dynamic, ever-changing process in which a person attempts to reach his or her potential in each of health's components.

know who we are and what our specific purpose is. Spiritual health may involve a belief in a supreme being or a specified way of living prescribed by a particular religion or it may relate to personal relationships with others and/or being at peace with nature.

Whether the term used is *health* or *wellness*, the focus is on personal attempts to achieve optimal well-being within a realistic framework of individual potential. In Figure 2c.1, a continuum from illness to optimal well-being describes health and wellness. Where you are on this continuum may vary from day to day, week to week, month to month, and year to year. That said, if you persist in your attempts to change attitudes and behaviours to reduce risk and/or improve health, your chances of remaining on the positive end of the continuum greatly improve. Each of us must try to achieve this optimal level of being in a sometimes hostile environment and come to terms with obstacles by focusing on our positive attributes whenever possible, changing what negative aspects we can, and learning to recognize and manage the aspects we can't change.

Individuals who are well take an honest look at their capabilities and limitations and make an effort to change what is within their control. They attempt to achieve balance in each health and wellness dimension while trying to achieve a positive position on the imaginary wellness continuum. Many people believe wellness can best be achieved by adopting a holistic approach in which emphasis is placed on integrating and balancing mind, body, and spirit. Persons on the illness and disability end of the continuum may have failed to achieve this integration and balance, and may be deficient in one or more of the wellness dimensions.

The disability component of the wellness continuum does not imply that a person with a physical and/or mental disability is not well or cannot achieve wellness. Such a person can be healthy in all aspects of wellness—within his or her potential, recognizing physical and/or mental limitations. In contrast, a person who spends hours in front of a mirror lifting weights to perfect the size and shape of each muscle may be less healthy in the other aspects of wellness—even though he or she is physically and mentally able. Appearance and physical performance are only two signs of a person's overall health and thus provide a limited indication of how well or healthy a person may be.

Typically, the closer you get to your potential in the seven wellness components, the healthier you are. Keep in mind that optimal health and wellness is not a static state that one achieves but rather an ongoing, active process that includes positive attitudes and behaviours in each dimension. Complete the appraisal in the Rate Yourself box, and get a better perspective on how you measure up in each of the wellness dimensions discussed in this section.

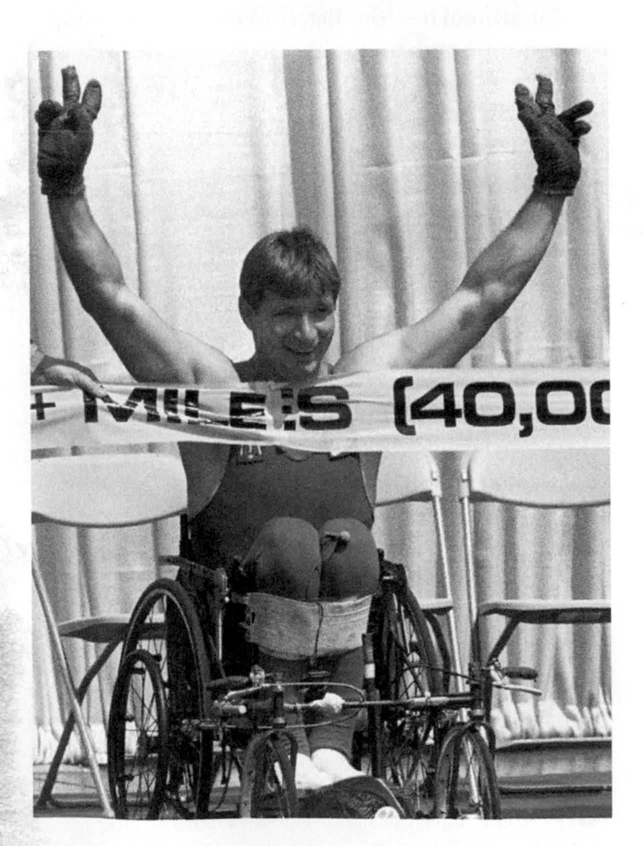

Having the motivation to improve the quality of life within the framework of your unique capabilities and limitations is crucial to achieving optimal health and wellness.

✓• Health Promotion: Helping You Stay Healthy

In discussions of health and wellness, the term **health promotion** is often used. Health promotion requires educational, organizational, environmental, and financial supports to help individuals and groups build positive health attitudes and behaviours and to change negative ones. In other words, health promotion does not just involve telling people to lose weight and to eat better. Efforts are also made to promote learning (*educational supports*), provide programs and services that encourage participation (*organizational supports*), establish rules governing attitudes and behaviours and

Health promotion: Combines educational, organizational, policy, financial, and environmental supports to enhance healthy lifestyle choices and to help people change negative health attitudes and behaviours.

RATE YOURSELF

How Healthy Are You?

Although many of us recognize the importance of healthy attitudes and behaviours, we often do not maintain a healthy regimen. Rate your health status in each of the following dimensions by circling the number of the response that best describes you.

	Very Unhealthy	Somewhat Unhealthy	Somewhat Healthy	Very Healthy
Physical Health	1	2	3	4
Social Health	1	2	3	4
Emotional Health	1	2	3	4
Environmental Health	1	2	3	4
Spiritual Health	1	2	3	4
Mental Health	1	2	3	4
Occupational Health	1	2	3	4

After completing the above section, how healthy do you think you are? Which area(s), if any, do you think you should work on improving? Respond to the following questions regarding each dimension of health by circling the number for the response that best describes you.

PHYSICAL HEALTH

	Rarely, If Ever	Sometimes	Most of the Time	Always
1. I maintain a desirable weight.	1	2	3	4
2. I engage in vigorous exercises such as brisk walking, jogging, swimming, or running for at least 30 minutes per day, 3–4 times per week.	1	2	3	4
3. I do exercises designed to strengthen my muscles and joints.	1	2	3	4
4. I warm up and cool down by stretching before and after vigorous exercise.	1	2	3	4
5. I feel good about the condition of my body.	1	2	3	4
6. I get 7–8 hours of sleep each night.	1	2	3	4
7. My immune system is strong and I am able to avoid most infectious diseases.	1	2	3	4
8. My body heals itself quickly when I get sick or injured.	1	2	3	4
9. I have lots of energy and can get through the day without being overly tired.	1	2	3	4
10. I listen to my body; when there is something wrong, I seek professional advice.	1	2	3	4

SOCIAL HEALTH

	Rarely, If Ever	Sometimes	Most of the Time	Always
1. When I meet people, I feel good about the impression I make on them.	1	2	3	4
2. I am open, honest, and get along well with other people.	1	2	3	4
3. I participate in a wide variety of social activities and enjoy being with people who are different from me.	1	2	3	4

	Rarely, If Ever	Sometimes	Most of the Time	Always
4. I try to be a "better person" and work on behaviours that have caused problems in my interactions with others.	1	2	3	4
5. I get along well with the members of my family.	1	2	3	4
6. I am a good listener.	1	2	3	4
7. I am open and accessible to a loving and responsible relationship.	1	2	3	4
8. I have someone I can talk to about my private feelings.	1	2	3	4
9. I consider the feelings of others and do not act in hurtful or selfish ways.	1	2	3	4
10. I consider how what I say might be perceived by others before I speak.	1	2	3	4

EMOTIONAL HEALTH

	Rarely, If Ever	Sometimes	Most of the Time	Always
1. I find it easy to laugh about things that happen in my life.	1	2	3	4
2. I avoid using alcohol as a means of helping me forget my problems.	1	2	3	4
3. I can express my feelings without feeling silly.	1	2	3	4
4. When I am angry, I try to let others know in non-confrontational and non-hurtful ways.	1	2	3	4
5. I am a chronic worrier and tend to be suspicious of others.	4	3	2	1
6. I recognize when I am stressed and take steps to relax through exercise, quiet time, or other activities.	1	2	3	4
7. I feel good about myself and believe others like me for who I am.	1	2	3	4
8. When I am upset, I talk to others and actively try to work through my problems.	1	2	3	4
9. I am flexible and adapt or adjust to change in a positive way.	1	2	3	4
10. My friends regard me as a stable, emotionally well-adjusted person.	1	2	3	4

ENVIRONMENTAL HEALTH

	Rarely, If Ever	Sometimes	Most of the Time	Always
1. I am concerned about environmental pollution and actively try to preserve and protect natural resources.	1	2	3	4
2. I report people who intentionally hurt the environment.	1	2	3	4
3. I recycle my garbage.	1	2	3	4
4. I reuse plastic and paper bags and tin foil.	1	2	3	4
5. I vote for pro-environmental candidates in elections.	1	2	3	4
6. I write my elected leaders about environmental concerns.	1	2	3	4
7. I consider the amount of packaging covering a product when I buy groceries.	1	2	3	4
8. I try to buy products that are recyclable.	1	2	3	4
9. I use both sides of the paper when taking class notes or doing assignments.	1	2	3	4
10. I try not to leave the tap running too long when I brush my teeth, shave, or bathe.	1	2	3	4

SPIRITUAL HEALTH

	Rarely, If Ever	Sometimes	Most of the Time	Always
1. I believe life is a precious gift that should be nurtured.	1	2	3	4
2. I take time to enjoy nature and the beauty around me.	1	2	3	4
3. I take time alone to think about what's important in life—who I am, what I value, where I fit in, and where I'm going.	1	2	3	4
4. I have faith in a greater power, be it a God-like force, nature, or the connectedness of all living things.	1	2	3	4
5. I engage in acts of caring and goodwill without expecting anything in return.	1	2	3	4
6. I feel sorrow for those who are suffering and try to help them through difficult times.	1	2	3	4
7. I feel confident that I have touched the lives of others in a positive way.	1	2	3	4
8. I work for peace in my interpersonal relationships, in my community, and in the world at large.	1	2	3	4
9. I am content with who I am.	1	2	3	4
10. I go for the gusto and experience life to the fullest.	1	2	3	4

MENTAL HEALTH

	Rarely, If Ever	Sometimes	Most of the Time	Always
1. I tend to let my emotions get the better of me and I act without thinking.	4	3	2	1
2. I learn from my mistakes and try to act differently the next time.	1	2	3	4
3. I follow directions or recommended guidelines and act in ways likely to keep myself and others safe.	1	2	3	4
4. I consider the alternatives before making decisions.	1	2	3	4
5. I am alert and ready to respond to life's challenges in ways that reflect thought and sound judgment.	1	2	3	4
6. I tend to act impulsively without thinking about the consequences.	4	3	2	1
7. I actively try to learn all I can about products and services before making decisions.	1	2	3	4
8. I manage my time well, rather than allowing time to manage me.	1	2	3	4
9. My friends and family trust my judgment.	1	2	3	4
10. I think about my self-talk (the things I tell myself) and then examine the real evidence for my perceptions and feelings.	1	2	3	4

OCCUPATIONAL HEALTH

	Rarely, If Ever	Sometimes	Most of the Time	Always
1. I am happy with my career choice.	1	2	3	4
2. I look forward to work.	1	2	3	4
3. My work responsibilities are consistent with my values.	1	2	3	4
4. The advantages in my career are consistent with my values.	1	2	3	4
5. I am happy with the balance between my work and leisure time.	1	2	3	4
6. I am happy with the amount of control I have in my work.	1	2	3	4
7. My work gives me personal satisfaction and stimulation.	1	2	3	4
8. I am happy with the professional and personal growth provided by my job.	1	2	3	4
9. I feel my work allows me to make a difference in the world.	1	2	3	4
10. My work contributes positively to my overall well-being.	1	2	3	4

PERSONAL CHECKLIST

Now, total your scores in each of the health dimensions and compare them to the ideal score. Which areas do you need to work on? How does your score compare with how you rated yourself in the first part of the questionnaire?

	Ideal Score	Your Score
Physical Health	40	______
Social Health	40	______
Emotional Health	40	______
Environmental Health	40	______
Spiritual Health	40	______
Mental Health	40	______
Occupational Health	40	______

WHAT YOUR SCORES MEAN

Scores of 35–40: Outstanding! Your answers show you are aware of the importance of this component of your health. More important, you are putting your knowledge to work by practising good health habits. As long as you continue to do so, this component will not pose a serious health risk. It's likely that you are a role model for your family, friends, and classmates.

Scores of 30–35: Your health practices in this area are good, but there is room for improvement. Look again at the items where you scored one or two points. What changes could you make to improve your score? Even a small change in behaviour can help you achieve better health.

Scores of 20–30: Your health risks are showing! Do you need more information about the risks you are facing and why it is important for you to change these behaviours? Perhaps you need help in deciding how to make the changes you desire. In either case, help is available from this book, from your professor, and from your student health services.

Scores below 20: You may be taking serious and unnecessary risks with your health. Perhaps you are not aware of the risks and what to do about them. Perhaps you are not sure what lifestyle attitudes and behaviours lead to good health and wellness. In this book, you will find the information you need to attain and maintain optimal health and wellness.

Source: Adapted from the U.S. Health and Human Services, "Health Style: A Self Test" (Washington, DC: Public Health Service, 1981).

supporting decisions to change (*environmental supports*), and provide monetary incentives to motivate them toward healthful decision making (*financial supports*). In short, health promotion enhances the likelihood that, once a person decides to change a behaviour, conditions are optimal for success. In health promotion, healthy people at risk for disease are identified and efforts made to motivate them to improve their health. Further, various health promotion efforts encourage those whose health and wellness are already sound to maintain and improve their relevant health-enhancing activities.

In 2005, the Pan-Canadian Healthy Living Strategy was released (see the Focus on Canada box). Actions proposed through this Strategy should improve the health status and health outcomes of the Canadian population. Further, the proposed actions should reduce the current burden and contribute to the efficiency and sustainability of Canada's universal health-care delivery system. Rather than focusing on individual behaviour change, the Healthy Living Strategy takes a population health approach, recognizing that sustainable changes in individual behaviours are difficult to achieve without addressing living and working conditions. Thus, one of the key elements of the Strategy is to recognize and address linkages between lifestyle choices and the surrounding social, economic, and environmental influences.

The Strategy primarily emphasizes healthy eating and physical activity, and their relationship to healthy weight. Other healthy living priorities will be addressed in upcoming initiatives. As mentioned, a population health approach guides the Healthy Living Strategy. Using this approach, healthy living refers to the attitudes and behaviours that improve or maintain the health of the entire population and its subgroups. When this approach is applied to individuals, healthy living refers to enhancing healthy behaviours, making healthy choices, and living in healthy ways. At all levels, the social, economic, political, cultural, and environmental conditions must be supportive of healthy living.

FOCUS ON CANADA

The Integrated Pan-Canadian Healthy Living Strategy 2005

An extensive pan-Canadian consultation process resulted in the release of the *Integrated Pan-Canadian Healthy Living Strategy 2005.* The federal, provincial, and territorial Ministers of Health noted a need for a pan-Canadian healthy living approach in 2002. Various consultations followed across the country, and the Strategy is the culmination of these discussions. This first Strategy focused on healthy eating, physical activity, and their relationship to healthy weight; plans exist for future Strategies to cover topics such as mental health and injury prevention.

THE HEALTHY LIVING STRATEGY

The Healthy Living Strategy provides a conceptual framework for sustained action that focuses on improving the health of all Canadians as a group. With the population focus for the strategy, it is necessary to address the inequalities in health status among various groups. The Healthy Living Strategy visualizes Canada as a healthy nation, with conditions that support the attainment of optimal health and wellness for all. Thus, the goals of the Healthy Living Strategy are to improve overall health outcomes and to reduce health disparities.

HEALTHY LIVING TARGETS

Given the current overweight and obesity epidemic, along with Canadians' eating and physical activity habits, the proposed pan-Canadian Healthy Living targets "seek to obtain a 20 percent increase in the proportion of Canadians who are physically active, eat healthily, and are at healthy body weights." The year 2015 is considered the first marker for ongoing monitoring and evaluation to assess progress and allow for adjustments as appropriate. The specific targets of the Healthy Living Strategy are as follows:

Healthy Eating: By 2015, increase by 20 percent the proportion of Canadians who make healthy food choices according to the Canadian Community Health Survey (CCHS) and Statistics Canada (SC)/Canadian Institute for Health Information (CIHI) health indicators. This target would measure the food insecurity index and the consumption of vegetables and fruits, among other things.

Physical Activity: By 2015, increase by 20 percent the proportion of Canadians who participate in regular physical activity based on 30 minutes per day of moderate to vigorous activity as measured by the CCHS and the Physical Activity Benchmarks/Monitoring Program.

Healthy Weights: By 2015, increase by 20 percent the proportion of Canadians at a "normal" body weight based on a Body Mass Index (BMI) of 18.5 to 24.9, as measured by the National Population Health Survey (NPHS), CCHS, and SC/CIHI health indicators.

The *Integrated Pan-Canadian Healthy Living Strategy 2005* is available from www.phac-aspc.gc.ca/hl-vs-strat/pdf/hls_e.pdf.

Information about the *Canadian Community Health Survey* can be obtained from www.hc-sc.gc.ca/fn-an/surveill/nutrition/commun/index_e.html.

Information from Statistics Canada is available from www.statcan.gc.ca.

Information from the Canadian Institute for Health Information is available from www.cihi.ca.

Canadian Guidelines for Body Weight Classification in Adults, 2003 is available from www.hc-sc.gc.ca/fn-an/nutrition/weights-poids/guide-ld-adult/cg_quick_ref-ldc_rapide_ref_e.html.

QUESTIONS

1. Identify problems that affect the health of Canadians. How many of these problems are directly (or indirectly) a result of poor dietary practices, physical inactivity, or overweight?
2. Do you think the Healthy Living targets are reasonable? Why or why not? What targets would you choose? Why?
3. Why are integrated efforts among the various sectors a critical component in the pursuit of public health? What contributions to population health could these other sectors provide? How would these other sectors benefit from improvements in health and the conditions that influence health?

Source: Adapted from The Secretariat for the Intersectoral Healthy Living Network in partnership with the F/P/T Healthy Living Task Group and the F/P/T Advisory Committee on Population Health and Health Security (ACPHHS), "The Integrated Pan-Canadian Healthy Living Strategy 2005." Retrieved on May 31, 2006 from www.phac-aspc.gc.ca/hl-vs-strat/pdf/hls_e.pdf.

Whether we use the term *health* or *wellness*, we are talking about a person's overall responses to the challenges of living. Occasional dips into the ice cream bucket, a missed daily walk, an outburst of anger, or other deviations from optimal behaviours should not be viewed as major failures in attaining or maintaining your wellness. In fact, the ability to recognize that each of us is an imperfect being trying

YOUR SPIRITUAL AND EMOTIONAL HEALTH

Breast Cancer Hope: Yukon River Quest

Many of us have heard of dragon boat races. More importantly, we are aware of the reasoning behind them. Participants of dragon boat races are most often survivors of breast cancer or individuals paddling in memory or support of a wife, mother, sister, daughter, aunt, grandmother, cousin, or friend who has had breast cancer. What do you do if you can't find a body of water that's available or suitable for a dragon boat race? What if you don't have a dragon boat? You adjust or adapt to your natural terrain and find a boat that works, just as the Yukon River Quest does for a number of breast cancer survivors in the Yukon.

Inaugurated in 1999 with kayaks and small canoes as the only participating vessels, the Yukon River Quest is the world's longest annual canoe and kayak race that begins in Whitehorse and ends approximately 740 kilometres later in Dawson City. Many of the 11 women who came together to compete in 2001 had never paddled before. They paddled in a Voyageur canoe under the team name Paddlers Abreast and finished their first race in just under 86 hours. In 2005, the team whittled their time down to 60 hours and 25 minutes, placing fourth behind the winning team that came in at just over 55 hours.

The teams that form the Yukon River Quest develop a camaraderie that goes beyond their similarities in experiences with breast cancer. This camaraderie reflects the hope these women have for their future—one without cancer. The women (and their friends) who choose to participate in the Yukon River Quest take part because of their need to share hope, to live beyond their experiences with breast cancer, and to grab hold of life again.

A Yukon filmmaker Werner Walcher created a documentary about the paddlers and their experiences. He tells the story of all breast cancer survivors who participated for five years in the Yukon River Quest. In this documentary, Walcher shows that women with breast cancer lead full and active lives. Further, he attempts to present the male partner's view because he feels that as a male, it is difficult to understand what a woman with breast cancer really goes through. Walcher's wife had a breast cancer scare, and experienced the procedures of being tested and waiting for results. It was this experience that fuelled his interest in a documentary on women's and their partners' experiences with breast cancer. He hopes that national interest will develop as a result of the film and that it will provide hope to those diagnosed with the disease in the future.

Source: Adapted from N. Reveler, "Paddlers Abreast–Yukon River Quest," *Network News: Essential News for Canadians Affected by Breast Cancer* 10 (Winter/Spring 2006). Retrieved on December 18, 2006, from www.cbcn.ca/en/?page=7181§ion=4.

to adapt in an imperfect world signals individual well-being. Further, living life means that you savour some less healthy foods in smaller quantities, infrequently, and that there are times when your usual level of physical activity is not possible or you get a short night's sleep. This means that it is your *overall* approach to healthy eating, physical activity, and other lifestyle habits that is of greater importance than any one element in that approach, and this should be your focus in your efforts to attain and maintain optimal health and wellness.

We must also remember to be tolerant of others who are trying to improve their health. We need to be supportive, understanding, and nonjudgmental in our interactions with those attempting to make positive changes to their lifestyle. Further, health bashing—intolerance or negative feelings, words, or actions aimed at people who fail to meet our expectations of healthy attitudes and behaviours—indicates deficiencies in our psychological, social, or spiritual dimensions of health.

Prevention: The Key to Future Health

Prevention means taking action now to avoid becoming sick or less well later. Getting immunized against diseases such as polio, measles, mumps, and hepatitis, not smoking or chewing tobacco, practising safer sex, eating well, engaging in regular physical activity, and taking other preventive measures constitute **primary prevention**—actions designed to prevent health problems. **Secondary prevention** refers to the early recognition of a health problem and intervention to eliminate or reduce it before an

Primary prevention: Actions designed to stop problems before they start.

Secondary prevention: Intervention early in the development of a health problem to reduce symptoms or to halt its progression.

even more serious illness develops. Attending health education seminars in order to stop smoking is an example of secondary prevention. Another example is modifying one's dietary intake and physical activity levels in response to a blood-cholesterol or blood-glucose test.

Two-thirds of deaths in Canada are a result of cardiovascular diseases, cancer, type 2 diabetes, and respiratory diseases. These chronic diseases share common preventable risk factors: physical inactivity, poor dietary intake, and tobacco use. Further, these risk factors are influenced by income, employment, education, geographic isolation, and social exclusion. Common sense suggests that health promotion dollars should focus on the primary and secondary prevention of these and other lifestyle-related diseases. Instead, government money is primarily allocated for research and **tertiary prevention**—that is, treatment or rehabilitation efforts made after a person has become sick. (This is clearly a misnomer, since tertiary prevention is not really prevention but a response *after* illness has developed.) In addition, although the intent of tertiary prevention is to prevent the further development or progression of the disease (for example, chemotherapy and radiation therapy for individuals with cancer, or coronary bypass surgery for people with cardiovascular disease), it is more costly and less effective in promoting health than primary and secondary prevention.

SEX DIFFERENCES

Although much of male and female anatomy is identical, it's clear that many major medical differences exist. Many diseases—osteoporosis, arthritis, headaches, thyroid disease, lupus, and Alzheimer's disease, for example—are far more common in women than in men. Further, diseases may manifest differently in women than in men—for example, symptoms of a heart attack in women are more vague than in men. Finally, although women live longer than men, they do not necessarily have a better quality of life.

Sex bias has been identified as a serious weakness in medical research. In one study that reviewed medical journals in Canada and the United States, four factors reflecting bias were identified: androcentricity, overgeneralization, gender insensitivity, and double standards. *Androcentricity* refers to viewing the world from a male perspective. *Overgeneralization* occurs when a study explores issues for one sex and generalizes the findings to both sexes. (The same thing can be said for age bias—that is, conducting research on 20-year-olds and applying the results to all adults.) In the past, studies that examined the precise effects of a drug or treatment did not include women because researchers did not want to deal with potential issues related to hormonal fluctuations. *Sex insensitivity* means overlooking sex as an important variable. An example of sex insensitivity is research on symptoms of heart disease in men and women where the data from both sexes is analyzed in combination, with disregard for potential similarities and differences. When differences do not exist between men and women, the data can be collapsed and analyzed together; otherwise, sex should be a controlled variable. The term *double standards* refers to the "evaluation, treatment or measurement of the identical behaviours, traits or situations by different means." In 1996, a policy on clinical trials stated that if the product is likely to be used by women, then the testing must also be done on women. There has been increasing pressure placed on government to provide a more balanced approach to funding women's health programs. One example of increased activism is in the area of breast cancer. In Canada, one in nine women will be diagnosed with breast cancer, yet it was not until the mid-1990s that much research was conducted on the causes, treatments, and social and psychological concerns of women diagnosed with it.

Tertiary prevention: Treatment or rehabilitation efforts aimed at limiting the effects of a disease.

IMPROVING YOUR HEALTH

Benefits of Achieving Optimal Health

Figure 2c.2 provides an overview of the leading causes of death in Canada, and Figures 2c.3 to 2c.5 give estimated incidence and mortality rates for heart disease, stroke, and cancers in men and women. Heart disease and cancer continue to be the leading causes of death for both sexes.

As Figure 2c.3 shows, deaths from cardiovascular disease are declining among men and women. The Atlantic provinces have higher mortality rates than the western provinces, and these rates are consistent with the relative prevalence of smoking, high blood pressure, and obesity in these regions.

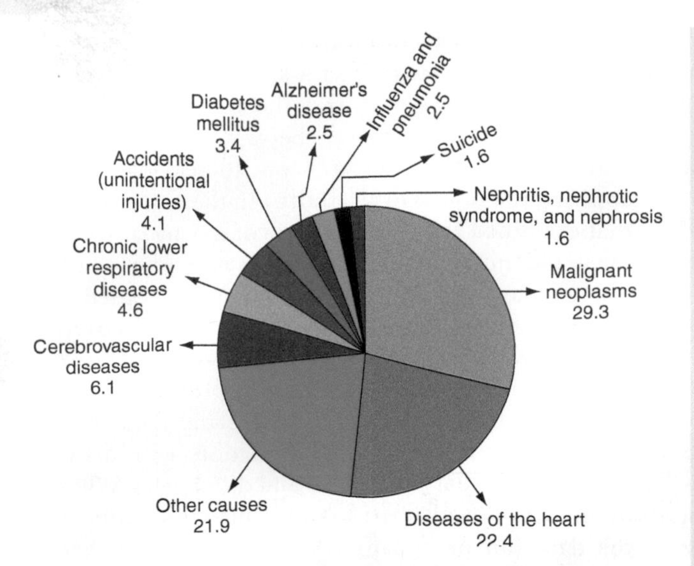

FIGURE 2c.2

Leading Causes of Death in Canada, 2005

Source: Adapted from Table 102-0561 "Leading causes of death, total population, by age group and sex, Canada, annual," Statistics Canada. Retrieved on July 20, 2009 from http://cansim2.statcan.gc.ca/cgi-win/cnsmcgi.pgm.

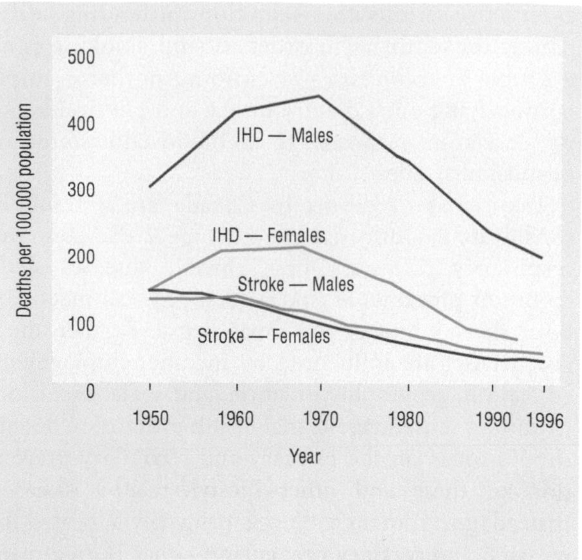

FIGURE 2c.3

Death Rates Due to Ischemic Heart Disease and Stroke, Canada, 1950 to 1996*

* Age-standardized to the 1991 Canadian population.

Source: "Death Rates due to Ischemic Heart Disease and Stroke, Canada, 1950–1996," adapted from the Statistics Canada publication "Health Indicators," Catalogue No. 82-221, 1999.

Figure 2c.4 provides estimated new cases and deaths from cancer for men. (The Canadian Cancer Society updates its estimates each year; see www.cancer.ca.) Incidence rates have declined for most forms of cancer, but there have been sizeable increases in the detection of prostate cancer through PSA testing. New cases of lung cancer have been declining since the 1980s, likely because of the decrease in smoking.

Figure 2c.5 shows estimated new cases and deaths from cancer for women. Similar to that for men, the incidence of new cancers in women has been relatively stable since the 1980s. Breast cancer is estimated to be the most common newly diagnosed cancer among women while the leading cause of cancer death is still expected to be lung cancer. The incidence of breast and lung cancer have been increasing among women since the 1970s. While prevention and control strategies are making an impact on death rates from breast cancer, the increasing number of women who smoke is related to the rates of lung cancer death.

While you cannot change your genetic history, and you may have little control over the medical services available in your area, you can influence your future health status by the attitudes and behaviours you choose today. Changing your lifestyle to improve your health status will reduce risk for cardiovascular disease, cancer, and other major diseases—as well as increasing your lifespan and improving your quality of life. Other equally important benefits include

- greater energy levels and increased capacity for and interest in having fun
- a stronger immune system, which enhances your ability to fight infections
- improved self-confidence, self-concept and self-esteem, and self-efficacy
- enhanced relationships with others due to better communication and "quality" time
- an improved ability to control and manage stress
- a reduced reliance on the health-care system
- improved cardiovascular functioning
- increased muscle tone, strength, flexibility, and endurance, which results in improved physical appearance, performance, and self-esteem
- a more positive outlook on life, fewer negative thoughts, and an ability to view life as challenging and to see negative events as an opportunity for growth
- improved environmental sensitivity, responsibility, and behaviours
- enhanced levels of spiritual health, awareness, and feelings of oneness with yourself, others, and the environment

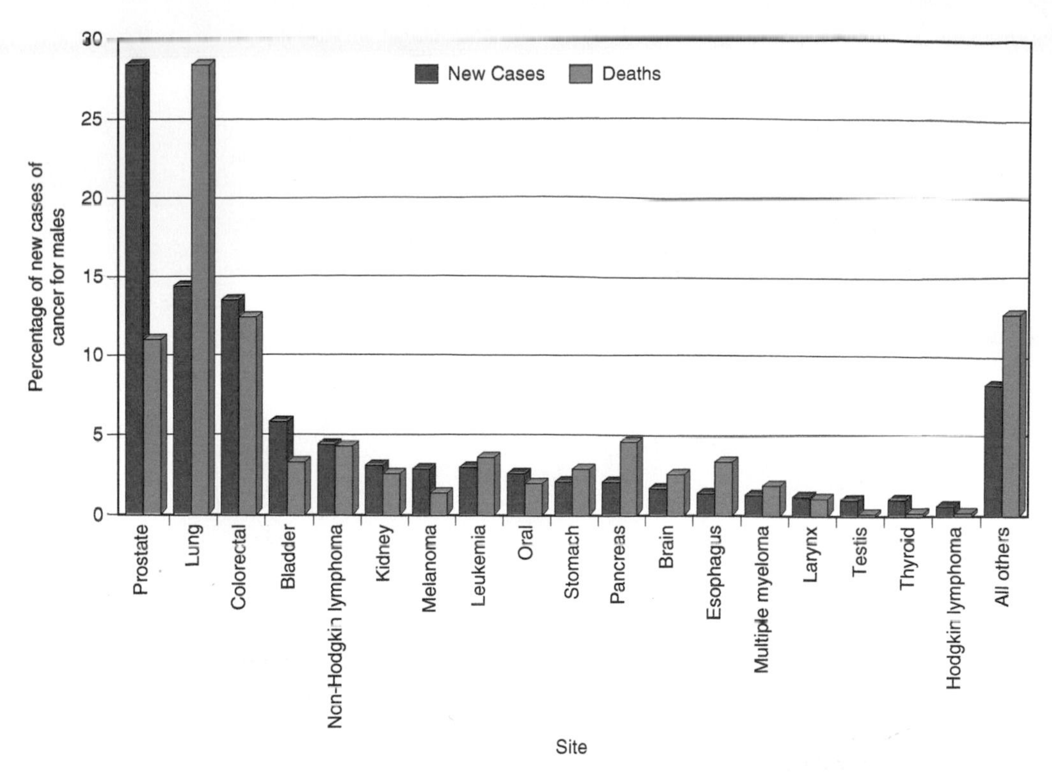

FIGURE 2c.4

Percentage Distribution of Estimated New Cases and Deaths for Selected Cancer Sites, Males, 2008

Source: Canadian Cancer Society/National Cancer Institute of Canada, *Canadian Cancer Statistics 2008*, a report produced by Canadian Cancer Society; National Cancer Institute of Canada; Statistics Canada; Provincial/Territorial Cancer Registries; Public Health Agency of Canada. Toronto: CCS/NCIC, 2008.

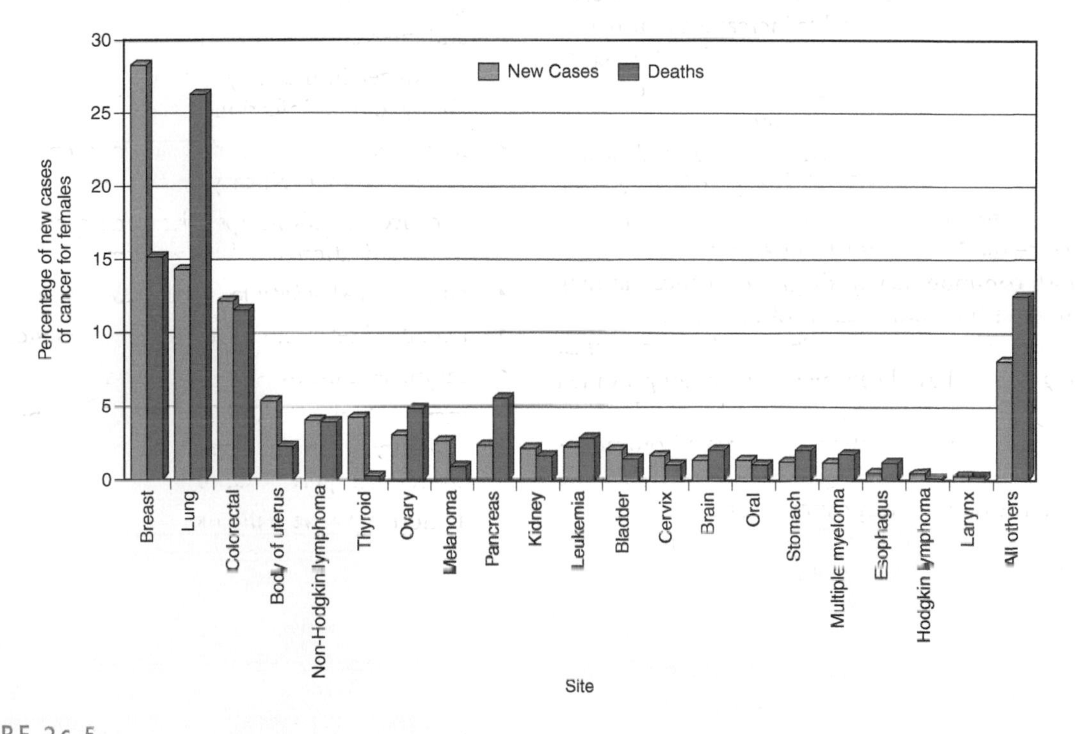

FIGURE 2c.5

Percentage Distribution of Estimated New Cases and Deaths for Selected Cancer Sites, Females, 2008

Source: Canadian Cancer Society/National Cancer Institute of Canada, *Canadian Cancer Statistics 2008*, a report produced by Canadian Cancer Society; National Cancer Institute of Canada; Statistics Canada; Provincial/Territorial Cancer Registries; Public Health Agency of Canada. Toronto: CCS/NCIC, 2008.

Percentage Distribution of Estimated New Cases and Deaths for Selected Cancer Sites, Males, [illegible]

Source: Canadian Cancer Society/National Cancer Institute of Canada: Canadian Cancer Statistics [illegible] produced by Canadian Cancer Society, National Cancer Institute of Canada, Statistics Canada, Provincial/Territorial Cancer Registries, Public Health Agency of Canada, Toronto, Canada, [illegible]

Percentage Distribution of Estimated New Cases and Deaths for Selected Cancer Sites, Females, [illegible]

Source: Canadian Cancer Society/National Cancer Institute of Canada: Canadian Cancer Statistics [illegible] produced by Canadian Cancer Society, National Cancer Institute of Canada, Statistics Canada, Provincial/Territorial Cancer Registries, Public Health Agency of Canada, Toronto, Canada, [illegible]

PART III: SYSTEM CONTROL AND COMMUNICATION AS THE FOUNDATION OF INDIVIDUAL HEALTH

*Posted on course website at http://www.pearsoncustom.com/can/uguelph_biohealth

CHAPTER 3A

THE CONTROL AND COMMUNICATION NETWORK

3a(i) Cell-Cell Communication

Taken from *Principles of Human Physiology*, Fourth Edition, by Cindy L. Stanfield

MECHANISMS OF INTERCELLULAR COMMUNICATION

Virtually all body functions require communication between cells. Seeing an apple requires communication between the cells in the eyes and the cells in the brain. Fighting an infection requires communication among several cell types in the blood. Growing and developing from an infant to an adult requires communication among cells throughout the body. There are hundreds of other possible examples. Remarkably, all the cells in the body use just a few mechanisms to communicate with one another. In relatively few instances, cells are physically linked by gap junctions; in most instances, cells communicate through chemical messengers.

Direct Communication Through Gap Junctions

Gap junctions link adjacent cells and are formed by plasma membrane proteins, called connexins, that form structures called connexons (Figure 3a(i).1). These connexons form channels that allow ions and small molecules to pass directly from one cell to another. The movement of ions through gap junctions electrically couples the cells, such that electrical signals in one cell are directly transmitted to the neighboring cells. For example, gap junctions found in heart muscle and the smooth muscle of other internal organs, such as the intestines and blood vessels, cause the muscle cells to contract as a unit; that is, the cells contract at the same time. The movement of small molecules through gap junctions metabolically couples the cells, such that one cell can provide necessary nutrients to other cells. For example, gap junctions allow nutrients to reach certain bone cells distant from the bloodstream. Gap junctions are also found in some glands and between some neurons in the brain and retina, where they function in communication.

Indirect Communication Through Chemical Messengers

Most often, cells communicate via chemical messengers (Figure 3a(i).1b), which are all *ligands,* molecules that bind to proteins reversibly. The body has hundreds of chemical messengers with a multitude of functions.

Communication through chemical messengers occurs when one cell releases a chemical into the interstitial fluid, usually by a process called secretion, and another cell, called the *target cell,* responds to the chemical messenger. The target cell, in essence, is the cell at which a message is "aimed." A target cell responds to the chemical messenger because it has certain proteins, called **receptors,** that specifically recognize and bind the messenger.

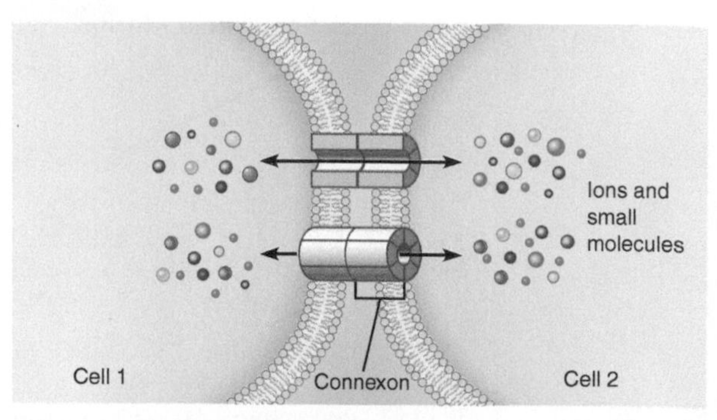

(a) Direct communication through gap junctions

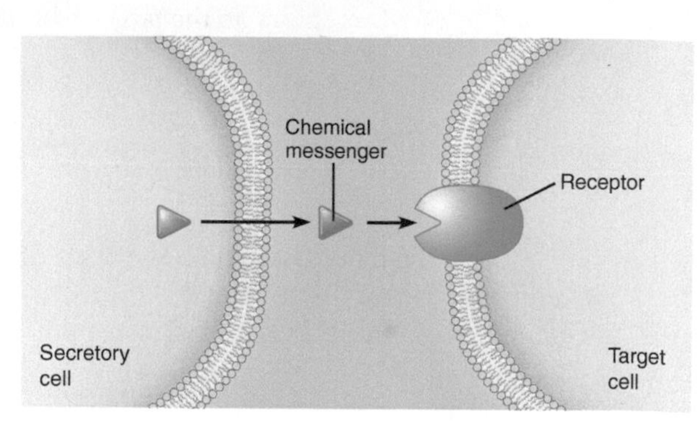

(b) Communication via chemical messengers

FIGURE 3a(i).1 Types of intercellular communication. (a) Direct communication through gap junctions. Gap junctions are composed of membrane protein structures called connexons that link the cytosols of two adjacent cells, allowing ions and small molecules to move between cells. (b) Communication via chemical messengers. After a secretory cell releases a messenger into the extracellular fluid, the messenger binds to receptors on target cells, triggering a response in the target cell.

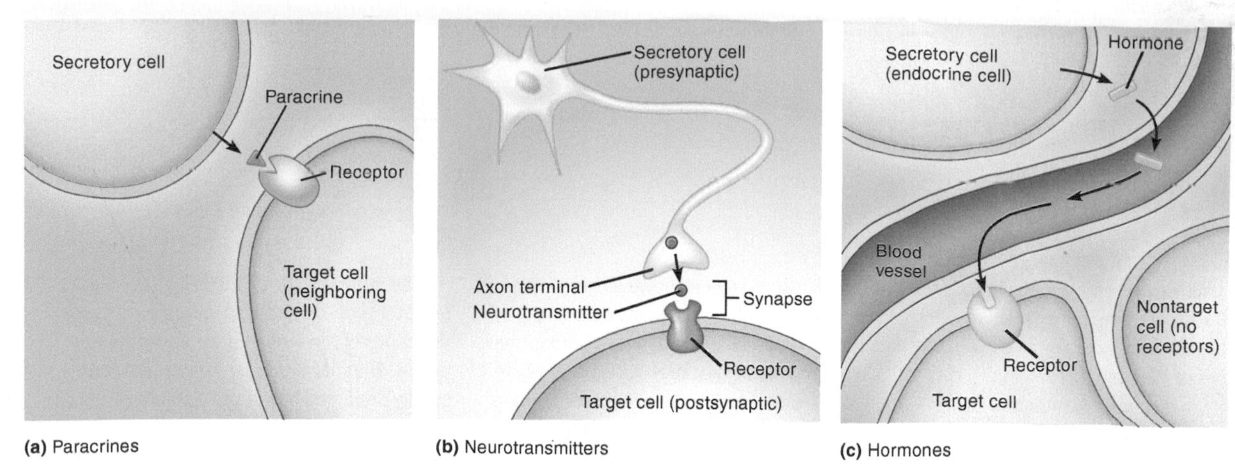

FIGURE 3a(i).2 **Functional classes of chemical messengers. (a) Paracrines are secreted by one cell and diffuse to a nearby target cell. (b) Neurotransmitters are secreted from neurons at functionally specialized structures called synapses. The axon terminal of a presynaptic cell releases the neurotransmitter, which then diffuses a very short distance to bind to receptors on a specific target cell, called the postsynaptic cell. (c) Hormones are secreted by endocrine cells into the interstitial fluid. Hormones then diffuse inkto the bloodstream for transport to target cells in the body. Target cells are identified by the presence of receptors for the specific hormone. Cells without receptors for the hormone cannot respond to the hormone's signal.**

The binding of messengers to receptors produces a response in the target cell through a variety of mechanisms referred to as **signal transduction**. Generally speaking, the strength of the target cell response increases as the number of bound receptors increases. The number of bound receptors depends on both the concentration of messenger in the interstitial fluid and the concentration of receptors on the target cell.

CHEMICAL MESSENGERS

Chemical messengers can be classified on the bases of their function and chemical structure. First we consider the functional classes of chemical messengers.

Functional Classification of Chemical Messengers

Although there are hundreds of chemical messengers, most can be classified into three main categories: (1) paracrines, (2) neurotransmitters, and (3) hormones (Figure 3a(i).2). When released into the interstitial fluid, each of these messenger categories transmits a signal by binding to receptors on a target cell, as described next.

Paracrines are chemicals that communicate with neighboring cells. The target cell must be close enough that once the paracrine is secreted into the extracellular fluid, it can reach the target cell by simple diffusion (Figure 3a(i).2a). Paracrines generally include *growth factors, clotting factors,* and *cytokines.* **Growth factors** are proteins that stimulate proliferation and differentiation of cells; they will not be covered further in this text. **Clotting factors** are proteins that stimulate formation of a blood clot. **Cytokines** are peptides, usually released from immune cells, that function in coordinating the body's defense against infections. Although most cytokines function as paracrines, others travel in the bloodstream to distant target cells and function more like hormones, described below.

An example of a paracrine messenger is *histamine,* a chemical that is important in allergic reactions and inflammation and is secreted by *mast cells* scattered throughout the body (**Discovery: Antihistamines**). During allergic reactions, histamine is responsible for the runny nose and red, watery eyes associated with that condition. In response to bacterial infections and various forms of tissue damage, the release of histamine by mast cells is part of a complex response called *inflammation,* which is characterized in part by redness and swelling. In inflammation, histamine increases blood flow to affected tissues (producing redness) and causes fluid to leak out of the blood vessels and into the tissue (producing swelling).

Autocrines are a subclass of paracrines that act on the same cell that secreted them. Thus the secretory cell is also the target cell. Often an autocrine regulates its own secretion.

Neurotransmitters are chemicals released into interstitial fluid from nervous system cells called *neurons.* Neurotransmitters are released from a specialized portion of the neuron called the *axon terminal*

DISCOVERY

Antihistamines

Histamine is a biogenic amine with paracrine and neurotransmitter functions. Once released, histamine acts on target cells by binding to one of three types of histamine receptors: H_1, H_2, or H_3 receptors. Histamines binding to H_1 receptors on target cells can produce several symptoms of allergic response, including constriction of the airways, increased fluid secretion in the airways, and dilation of the blood vessels. During severe allergic reactions, blood pressure may drop to levels so low that it can no longer move blood through the circulation adequately, resulting in anaphylactic shock. Also associated with anaphylactic shock is a swelling of the airways, which causes respiratory distress.

Treatment of allergic reactions and some ulcers often includes administration of *antihistamines*, which work by blocking H_1 or H_2 receptors on target cells. Classic H_1 receptor antagonists include diphenhydramine hydrochloride (Benadryl) and dimenhydrinate (Dramamine). When receptor antagonists are used to treat an ailment, however, they block receptors throughout the body, including those not involved in the ailment, thereby producing side effects. In the case of H_1 receptor antagonists, the predominant side effect is drowsiness caused by blockage of the H_1 receptors in the brain that are involved in mental alertness. Recently, H_1 receptor antagonists that do not access the brain have been developed to decrease sedative side effects; examples include loratidine (Claritin) and fexofenadine (Allegra).

Histamine binding to H_2 receptors stimulates acid secretion by the stomach, which may contribute to the production of *heartburn*, a burning sensation caused by acid irritation of the esophagus. Acid secretion also may produce gastric and intestinal ulcers, perforations of the linings of these organs. As a result, heartburn and some ulcers are treated with administration of H_2 receptor antagonists such as cimetidine (Tagamet) and rantidine (Zantac). Side effects associated with H_2 receptor antagonists include headache and drowsiness.

The more specific a drug is for a certain receptor type, the more specific the therapeutic actions of the drug and the fewer the side effects. Pharmaceutical companies are constantly designing new drugs to bind specifically to receptor subclasses for a certain messenger. In addition, drugs can be modified chemically to limit access to certain structures, again to eliminate unwanted side effects. The combined result is better treatments of ailments.

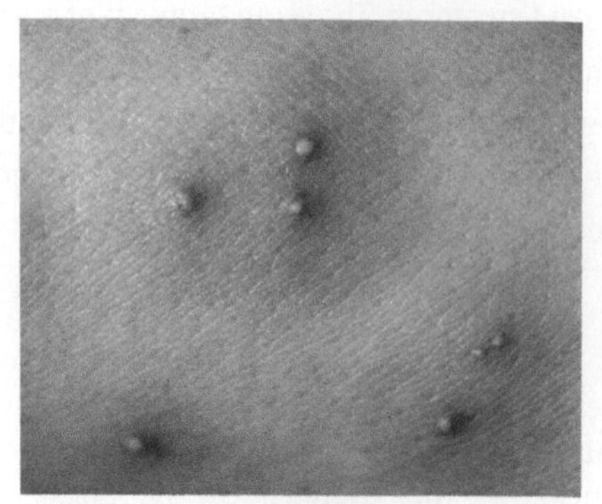

Histamine causes inflammation at insect bites.

(Figure 3a(i).2b), which is very close to the target cell. Because the juncture between the two cells is called a *synapse*, communication by neurotransmitters is often called *synaptic signaling*. The cell that releases the neurotransmitter is called the **presynaptic neuron,** whereas the target cell (which can be another neuron or a gland or muscle cell) is called the **postsynaptic cell.** Upon release from the presynaptic neuron, the neurotransmitter quickly diffuses over the short distance from the axon terminal and binds to receptors on the postsynaptic cell, triggering a response. Communication between a neuron and its target cell(s) is very specific because it is directed only to cells with which it has a synapse. An example of a neurotransmitter is *acetylcholine*, which is released by the neurons that trigger contraction of skeletal muscles.

Hormones are chemicals released from *endocrine glands* (or occasionally other types of tissue) into the interstitial fluid, where they can then diffuse into the blood (Figure 3a(i).2c). The hormone then travels in the blood to its target cells, which can be distant from the site of hormone release. The bloodstream distributes a hormone to virtually all cells of the body, but only cells possessing receptors specific for the hormone are able to respond and thus serve as its target cells. An example of a hormone is *insulin*, which is secreted by the pancreas and acts on target cells throughout the body to regulate energy metabolism.

A special class of hormones, called **neurohormones,** is released by a special class of neurons called *neurosecretory cells* through a mechanism similar to that of neurotransmitter release. Just like the "classical" hormones secreted by endocrine glands, neurohormones are released into the interstitial fluid and then diffuse into the blood, which distributes them to target cells throughout the body. An example of a neurohormone is *vasopressin*, or *ADH* (antidiuretic hormone), which is synthesized by neurosecretory cells originating in an area of the brain called the hypothalamus. Once vasopressin is released from the axon terminals of these neurosecretory cells, which are located in the posterior pituitary gland, it travels in the blood to its target cells. The primary target cells are located in the kidneys, where vasopressin affects the volume of urine that is excreted.

TABLE 3a(i).1 Functional Classification of Chemical Messengers

Class	Secretory cell type	Distance to target cell	Mode of transport to target cell	Chemical classification of messenger
Paracrine	(Several)	Short	Diffusion	Amines, peptides/proteins, eicosanoids
Neurotransmitter	Neuron	Short*	Diffusion	Amino acids, amines, peptides/proteins
Hormone	Endocrine	Long	Blood	Amines, steroids, peptides/proteins

*Even though neurotransmitters diffuse over only a short distance to the postsynaptic cell, some neurons are involved in long-distance communication because the neuron that releases the neurotransmitter is often long (up to 1 meter).

Some characteristics of the functional classes of chemical messengers are summarized in Table 3a(i).1.

It is important to realize that one chemical messenger may fit more than one of these functional classes. For example, serotonin is a neurotransmitter when released from neurons in certain regions of the brain, but it is a paracrine when released from platelets, cell fragments found in blood.

To learn how the different classes of chemical messengers work together, see **Understanding Exercise: Chemical Messengers of Exercise.**

Chemical Classification of Messengers

A messenger's chemical structure determines its mechanisms of synthesis, release, transport, and signal transduction. The most important chemical characteristic is whether the messenger can dissolve in water or cross the lipid bilayer in the plasma membrane of cells. **Lipophilic** (hydrophobic) molecules are lipid-soluble and, therefore, readily cross the plasma membrane—but they do not dissolve in water. Hydrophilic (or **lipophobic**) molecules are water-soluble and do not cross the plasma membrane.

In the following sections we discuss the five major classes of chemical messengers: (1) amino acids, (2) amines, (3) peptides/ proteins, (4) steroids, and (5) eicosanoids (Table 3a(i).2). Other chemical messengers, such as acetylcholine and nitric oxide, do not fit into any of these classes and are discussed in later chapters.

Amino Acid Messengers

Four amino acids are classified as chemical messengers because they function as neurotransmitters in the brain and spinal cord: *glutamate, aspartate, glycine,* and *gamma-aminobutyric acid (GABA).* Glutamate, aspartate, and glycine are among the 20 amino acids (alpha amino acids) that are used in protein synthesis, whereas GABA belongs to a different class of amino acids (gamma amino acids). Amino acids are lipophobic; therefore, they dissolve in water but do not cross plasma membranes.

Amine Messengers

Amines, which are chemical messengers derived from amino acids, are so named because they all possess an amine group (—NH_2) The amines include a group of compounds called **catecholamines,** which contain a *catechol* group (a six-carbon ring) and are derived from the amino acid tyrosine. Catecholamines include *dopamine, norepinephrine,* and *epinephrine.* Dopamine and norepinephrine function primarily as neurotransmitters, whereas epinephrine functions primarily as a hormone. Other amines include the neurotransmitter *serotonin,*

TABLE 3a(i).2 Chemical Classification of Messengers

Class	Chemical property	Location of receptors on target cell	Functional classification
Amino acids	Lipophobic	Plasma membrane	Neurotransmitters
Amines*	Lipophobic	Plasma membrane	Paracrines, neurotransmitters, hormones
Peptides/proteins	Lipophobic	Plasma membrane	Paracrines, neurotransmitters, hormones
Steroids	Lipophilic	Cytosol†	Hormones
Eicosanoids	Lipophilic	Cytosol	Paracrines

*One exception is the thyroid hormones, which, although amines, are lipophilic and have receptors in the nucleus of target cells.
†A few steroid hormones have receptors on the plasma membrane.

UNDERSTANDING EXERCISE

Chemical Messengers of Exercise

When a person exercises, she contracts *skeletal muscles*, muscles attached to bone or other connective tissue that allow voluntary movement of the body. Skeletal muscle contraction requires the action of all three functional classes of chemical messengers. The voluntary movements of exercise require neural signals from the brain and spinal cord to tell various muscles whether to contract and how strongly to contract. These signals come in the form of a neurotransmitter called acetylcholine. Remarkably, all of our body's muscle contractile activity is controlled by this one chemical—either it is released by the nervous system and causes the muscle to contract or it is not released and the muscle relaxes. The more acetylcholine that communicates with a given muscle cell, the more that muscle cell contracts.

Muscles cannot contract without energy, however. Thus a contracting muscle needs to receive an increased blood flow, bringing oxygen and nutrients to it in larger quantities. To increase blood flow, the heart needs to beat faster and stronger; likewise, the blood vessels supplying the muscles need to dilate (become larger in diameter). The heart receives neural signals as well as endocrine signals in the form of norepinephrine and epinephrine. It responds by beating faster and stronger. The blood vessels dilate primarily in response to endocrine and paracrine signals. Increases in the hormone epinephrine and the paracrine nitric oxide cause blood vessels to dilate. Thus epinephrine affects both the heart and the blood vessels during exercise. Hormones commonly have more than one type of target cell.

Dilation brings more blood to the muscle, but other chemical signals are necessary to ensure uptake of the required nutrients. For example, exercising muscles have enhanced glucose transport into the cells. The mechanism underlying this increase is not definitively established, but it requires increased glucose transporters expressed in the muscle cell membrane. Unlike most cell membrane glucose transporters, those expressed in exercising muscle are not dependent on insulin. Current theories suggest the involvement of paracrines such as calcium, nitric oxide, or bradykinin in this expression.

which is derived from tryptophan; the *thyroid hormones,* which are derived from tyrosine; and the paracrine *histamine,* which is derived from histidine. Most of the amines are lipophobic; therefore, they dissolve in water and do not cross plasma membranes. The thyroid hormones are an exception: They are lipophilic and thus do not dissolve in water, but they readily cross plasma membranes.

Peptide/Protein Messengers

Most chemical messengers are polypeptides, chains of amino acids linked together by peptide bonds. These messengers are classified as peptides or proteins based on their size, which varies considerably, from just two amino acids to more than a hundred amino acids. The term *peptide* generally refers to chains of fewer than 50 amino acids, whereas proteins are longer chains of amino acids. Polypeptides are lipophobic; therefore, they dissolve in water but cannot cross plasma membranes.

Steroid Messengers

Steroids are a class of compounds derived from *cholesterol.* All the body's steroid messengers function as hormones. Recall that cholesterol is a lipid with a distinctive four-ring structure. Because steroids are derived from cholesterol, which is lipophilic, they are also lipophilic; they readily cross plasma membranes and are insoluble in water.

Eicosanoid Messengers

Eicosanoids include a variety of paracrines that are produced by almost every cell in the body. Most eicosanoids are derivatives of arachidonic acid, a 20-carbon fatty acid that is found in various plasma membrane phospholipids. Because eicosanoids are lipids, they readily cross the plasma membrane and are insoluble in water. Eicosanoids include the following families of chemically related compounds: prostaglandins, leukotrienes, and thromboxanes.

Quick Test 3a(i).1

1. Name the three functional classes of messengers. Which messengers are transported in the blood to their target cells?
2. Name the five chemical classes of messengers. Which are lipophobic, and which are lipophilic?
3. Which chemical class of messengers is derived from cholesterol? To which functional class do these messengers belong?

Synthesis and Release of Chemical Messengers

The general synthetic pathways and mechanisms of release for chemical messengers are similar within a chemical class. In this section we examine the synthesis and release of each class of messenger.

Amino Acids

Although amino acids can be obtained from the diet, the four amino acids that function as neurotransmitters must be synthesized within the neuron that will secrete them.

Glutamate and aspartate are synthesized from glucose through a three-step series of reactions. First, glucose is catabolized to pyruvic acid by glycolysis; pyruvic acid is then converted to acetyl CoA, which then enters the Krebs cycle; and finally the amine groups are added to certain Krebs cycle intermediates to form glutamate or aspartate. Glycine is synthesized from a glycolytic intermediate, 3-phosphoglycerate, in a series of four reactions. GABA is synthesized from glutamate in a single reaction catalyzed by the enzyme *glutamic acid decarboxylase.*

Following their synthesis in the cytosol, amino acid neurotransmitters are transported into vesicles, where they are stored until they are released by exocytosis.

Amines

All amines are derived from amino acids, and all except thyroid hormones are synthesized in the cytosol by a series of enzyme-catalyzed reactions. Which amine is produced depends on the enzymes present in a given cell.

Figure 3a(i).3 shows the pathway for synthesis of the catecholamines, which are derived from the amino acid tyrosine. Note that in this pathway, dopamine is the precursor for norepinephrine, which in turn serves as the precursor for epinephrine. Because dopamine is a precursor for the other catecholamines, all catecholamine-secreting cells possess the two enzymes that catalyze its synthesis: *tyrosine* b-*hydroxylase* and *dopa decarboxylase.* Depending on which catecholamine it secretes, a cell may or may not possess enzymes for the remaining steps. Thus cells that secrete dopamine lack the enzymes necessary for the final two steps. Those that secrete norepinephrine and epinephrine contain the enzyme *dopamine* b-*hydroxylase,* whereas those that secrete epinephrine contain an additional enzyme, *phenylethanolamine N-methyl transferase (PNMT).*

Following synthesis, amines are packaged into cytosolic vesicles, where they are stored until their release is triggered. The synthesis of norepinephrine and epinephrine is actually completed within the vesicles, where dopamine β-hydroxylase and PNMT are located. Release occurs by exocytosis.

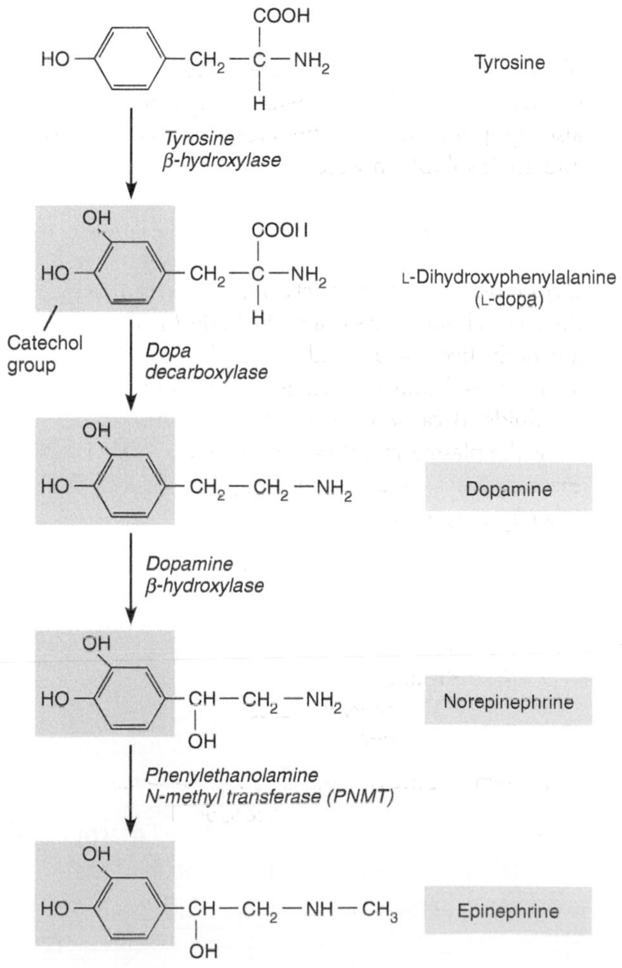

FIGURE 3a(i).3 Catecholamine synthesis. Catecholamines are synthesized from the amino acid tyrosine by a sequence of enzyme-catalyzed reactions in which one catecholamine functions as the precursor for the next. The names of catecholamines that function as messengers are highlighted.

Q *Which chemical group is removed from L-dopa to form dopamine?*

Peptides and Proteins

Peptides and proteins are synthesized in the same way as other proteins destined for secretion. Briefly, cytosolic mRNA serves as the template that codes for the amino acid sequence in the peptide or protein. Translation of this mRNA begins on ribosomes free in the cytosol. The subsequent steps, shown in Figure 3a(i).4a using a peptide for this example, are the following:

① Once translation starts, the ribosome attaches to the rough endoplasmic reticulum, where the rest of translation occurs. The polypeptide is formed inside the lumen of the rough endoplasmic reticulum, first as a *prepropeptide.*

② In the lumen of the endoplasmic reticulum, *proteolytic enzymes* cleave off some amino acids from the prepropeptide, yielding the *propeptide.*

③ In the smooth endoplasmic reticulum, the propeptide is packaged into transport vesicles.

④ The vesicles transport the propeptide to the Golgi apparatus.

⑤ In the Golgi apparatus, the propeptide is packaged into a secretory vesicle for storage until release is triggered. More amino acids are cleaved off by proteolytic enzymes in the Golgi apparatus or in the secretory vesicle to give the final product, a peptide.

⑥ Release occurs by exocytosis.

Typically, peptide fragments generated by proteolysis are released along with the primary messenger, and they may or may not exert their own biological effects. Figure 3a(i).4c shows a schematic example of the synthesis of a protein hormone—in this case, parathyroid hormone.

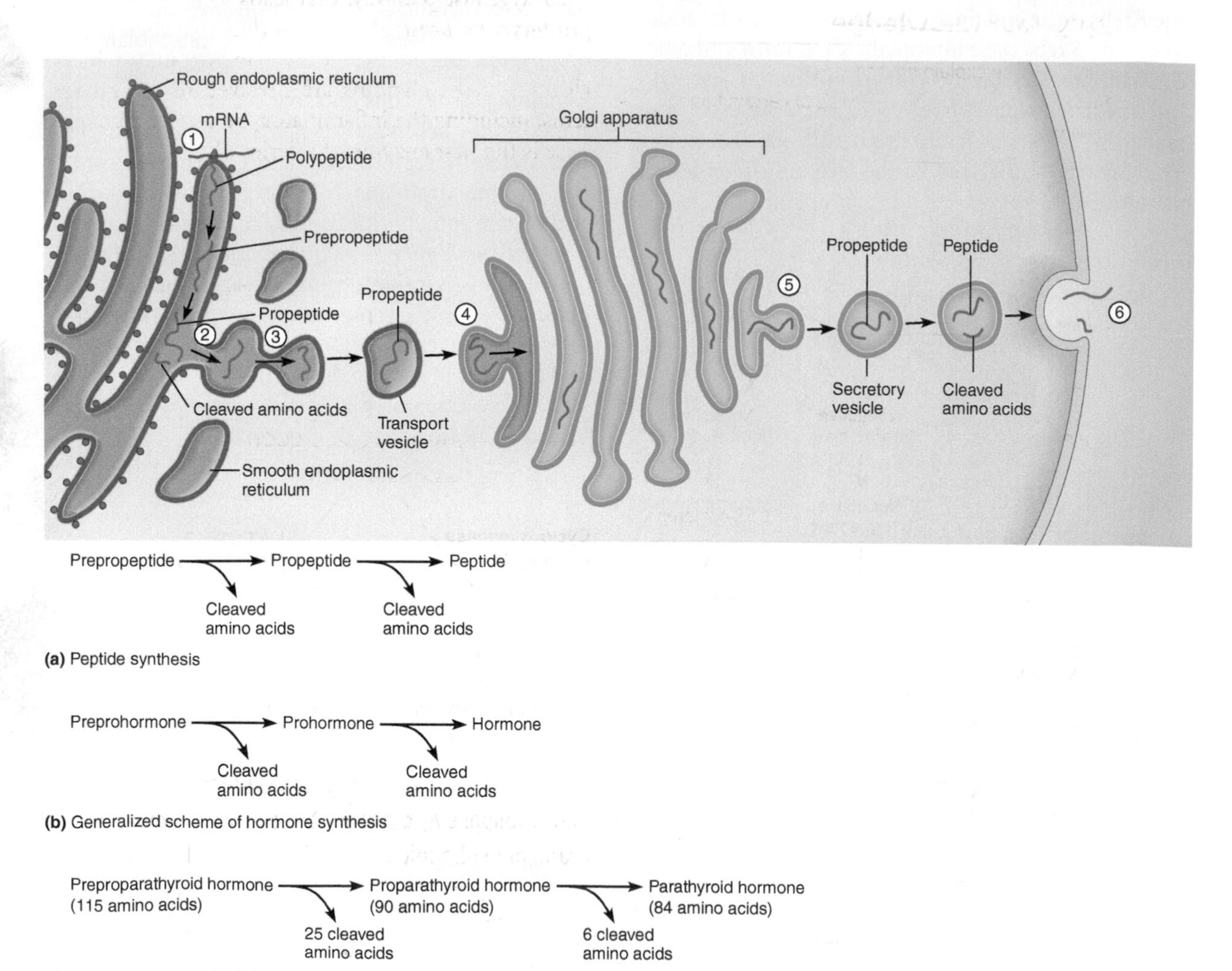

FIGURE 3a(i).4 **Peptide synthesis and release. (a) The steps of peptide synthesis. For a detailed description, see the text. (b) The general steps of peptide hormone synthesis. (c) Specific example of modification of preproparathyroid hormone, which contains 115 amino acids, to the active parathyroid hormone, which contains 84 amino acids.**

Steroids

Steroid messengers are synthesized from cholesterol in a series of reactions (Figure 3a(i).5) catalyzed by enzymes located in the smooth endoplasmic reticulum or mitochondria. As a result, the cholesterol molecule is modified slightly, but its basic ring structure remains intact, as does its lipophilic character. Consequently, all steroids are capable of crossing the plasma membrane. Because they are membrane-permeant, steroids cannot be stored prior to release and instead diffuse out of the cell into the interstitial fluid as soon as they are synthesized. Therefore, while cells that secrete peptides or amines can synthesize messengers in advance and store them in vesicles to be released on demand, steroid hormones are synthesized on demand and released immediately.

Apply Your Knowledge

Use Figure 3a(i).5 to explain how certain male sex hormones are required for the synthesis of certain female sex hormones.

Eicosanoids

Like steroids, eicosanoids are synthesized on demand and released immediately because they are lipophilic and able to pass through plasma membranes easily. The first step in eicosanoid synthesis (Figure 3a(i).6) involves an enzyme called *phospholipase A_2*, which is activated in response to chemical signals of various kinds (paracrines, hormones, neurotransmitters, and even foreign chemicals). When active, this enzyme catalyzes the release of arachidonic acid from membrane phospholipids. Once arachidonic acid is released from the membrane, the final product depends on the complement of enzymes present in the particular cell.

To become an eicosanoid, a molecule of arachidonic acid first binds with one of two enzymes: either *cyclooxygenase* or *lipoxygenase*. Cyclooxygenase is the first enzyme in a series of reactions, called the *cyclooxygenase pathway*, that leads to the synthesis of *prostacyclins, prostaglandins,* or *thromboxanes.* Prostacyclins and thromboxanes are important in blood clotting; prostaglandins are involved in several systems, including the inflammatory response. Lipoxygenase is the first enzyme of a series of reactions, called

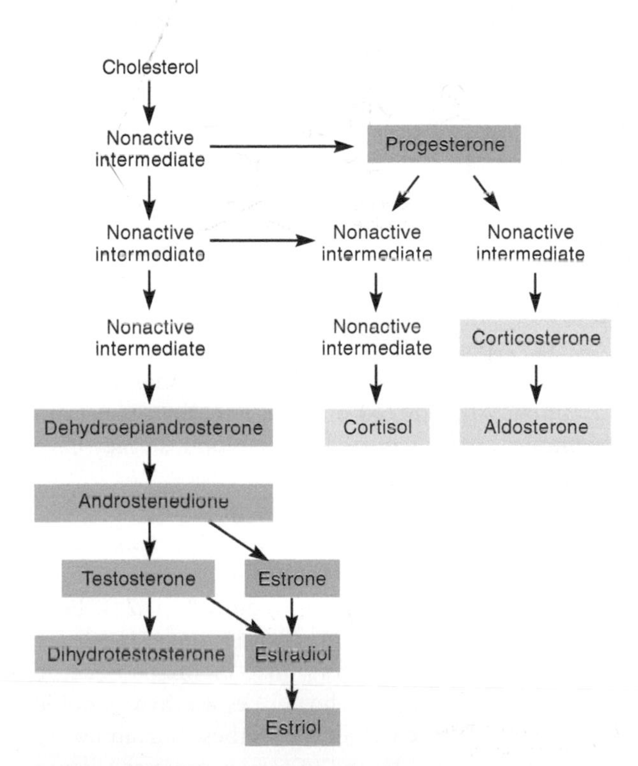

FIGURE 3a(i).5 Synthetic pathway for steroids. Each arrow indicates an enzyme-catalyzed reaction. Green boxes indicate hormones produced in the adrenal cortex; blue boxes indicate male sex hormones; orange boxes indicate female sex hormones.

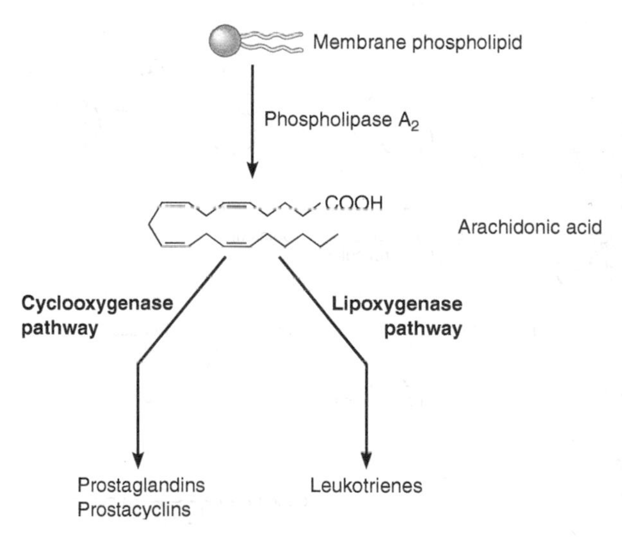

FIGURE 3a(i).6 Eicosanoid synthesis. Phospholipase A_2 catalyzes the conversion of a membrane phospholipid to arachidonic acid, the precursor for all eicosanoids. Arachidonic acid is converted into eicosanoids via two pathways: The cyclooxygenase-dependent pathway leads to the production of prostaglandins, prostacyclins, and thromboxanes, whereas the lipoxygenase-dependent pathway leads to the production of leukotrienes.

CLINICAL CONNECTIONS

From Aspirin to COX-2 Inhibitors

Aspirin is one of a number of nonsteroidal anti-inflammatory drugs (NSAIDs) that relieve pain by decreasing the production of certain prostaglandins (PG), eicosanoids that produce pain and inflammation. A critical enzyme in the synthesis of PGs is cyclooxygenase (COX). In the early 1990s, two forms of COX were identified: COX-1 and COX-2. COX-1, always present in the body, is generally associated with the synthesis of PGs necessary for maintaining homeostasis. In contrast, COX-2 is activated in the presence of chemicals released on tissue damage or infection and leads to production of PGs associated with pain and inflammation. Aspirin nonselectively inhibits the activity of both forms of COX; it is the inhibition of COX-2 that results in pain relief.

Although aspirin is used to treat pain, inflammation, and fever, its inhibition of COX-1 causes several side effects—some favorable, some not. Aspirin decreases the production of thromboxane A_2, a chemical involved in the formation of blood clots. However, at higher doses, aspirin also decreases the production of PGI_2 (prostacyclin), a chemical that inhibits the production of blood clots. Therefore, doctors frequently prescribe 82 mg of aspirin ("baby aspirin") to guard against the formation of blood clots that can trigger heart attack or stroke, whereas 350 mg of aspirin is generally used to treat pain and would actually promote formation of a blood clot. In addition, aspirin inhibits production of PGE_2 in the stomach, which indirectly protects the stomach lining from stomach acid. Thus major side effects of aspirin may include gastric ulcers and stomach bleeding.

In their search for safer pain relievers, pharmaceutical companies have developed drugs that selectively inhibit COX-2 to treat chronic pain and inflammatory diseases, such as arthritis. The chief advantages of COX-2 inhibitors (such as rofecoxib, also known as Vioxx, or celecoxib, also known as Celebrex) is that they do not inhibit production of PGE_2, so they cause less harm to the stomach lining than does aspirin. Unfortunately, COX-2 inhibitors produce serious side effects of their own. For reasons that are not understood, these drugs appear to increase the risk of heart attack and stroke in individuals who are already susceptible to cardiovascular disease. Alas, the quest for a perfect "aspirin" still eludes us.

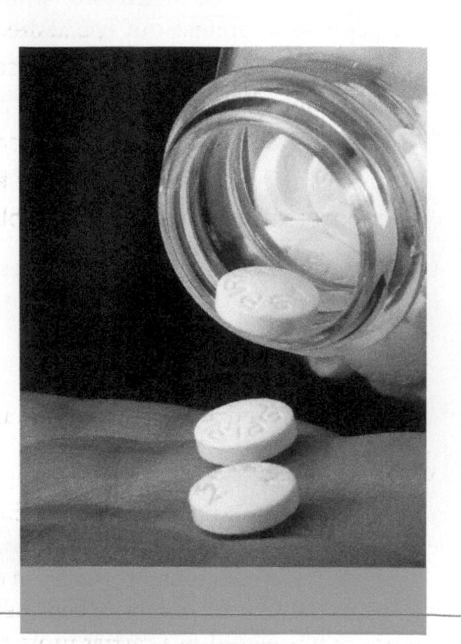

the *lipoxygenase pathway,* that leads to the synthesis of *leukotrienes,* which also contribute to the inflammatory response.

Because of the eicosanoids' role in inflammation, many anti-inflammatory drugs, such as aspirin, act by targeting enzymes involved in eicosanoid synthesis. By inhibiting the activity of the enzyme cyclooxygenase, aspirin decreases not only inflammation but also blood clotting. It is this latter effect of aspirin that has led physicians to prescribe low doses of aspirin to patients prone to a heart attack or stroke, which can be caused by blood clots in the coronary and cerebral arteries, respectively. (See **Clinical Connections: From Aspirin to COX-2 Inhibitors.**)

Transport of Messengers

Once released, a messenger must first reach and then bind to receptors on the target cell for the signal to be transmitted. In many instances, the messenger is released from a cell that is near the target cell, such that the messenger reaches the receptor by simple diffusion. This is true of paracrines and neurotransmitters. Typically these messengers are quickly degraded in the interstitial fluid and become inactive, minimizing the spread of their signaling. However, hormones are transported in the blood, so they have access to most cells in the body.

Hormones can be transported in the blood either in dissolved form or bound to *carrier proteins.* To be transported in dissolved form, the messenger must be a hydrophilic messenger (Figure 3a(i).7a). Peptides and amines (except thyroid hormones) are generally transported in this manner. Because steroids and the thyroid hormones are hydrophobic and do not dissolve well in blood, these hormones are largely transported bound to carrier proteins (Figure 3a(i).7b). Although most of the catecholamines that function as hormones are hydrophilic and are transported in dissolved form, some are bound to carrier proteins. Some carrier proteins are specific for a particular hormone; one example is *corticosteroid-binding globulin,* which transports the steroid hormone *cortisol.* Other carrier proteins—for example, *albumin*—

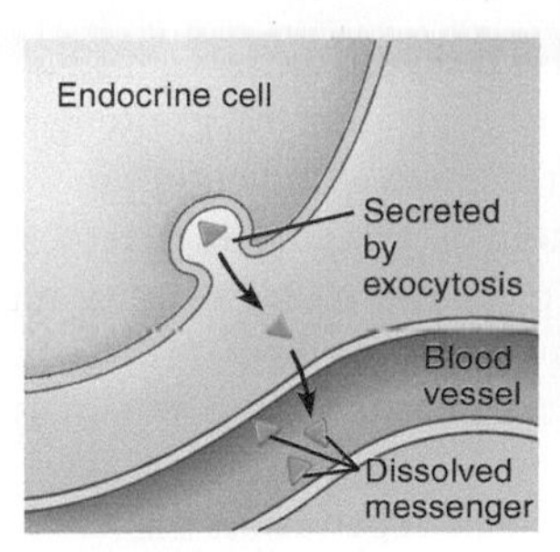

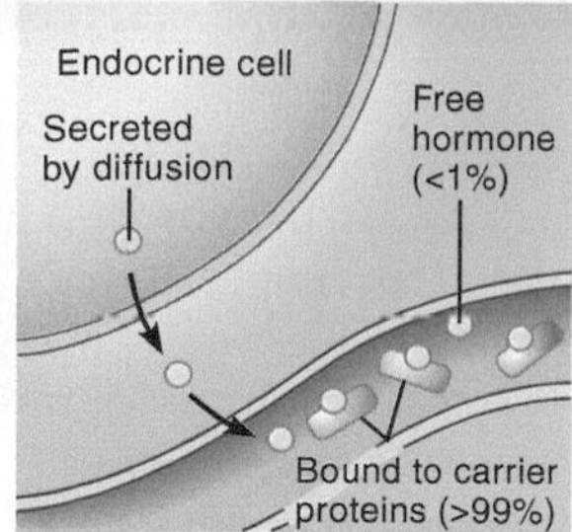

(a) Hydrophilic messenger **(b)** Hydrophobic messenger

FIGURE 3a(i).7 **Transport of messengers in blood. (a) Hydrophilic messengers are secreted by exocytosis, enter the bloodstream, and dissolve in the plasma. (b) Hydrophobic messengers are secreted by simple diffusion and then enter the bloodstream. Most of the messenger molecules are transported bound to carrier proteins. Only the small amount of free hormone in the plasma is immediately available for binding with target cell receptors.**

are not specific and can transport many different hormones.

Even though hydrophobic hormones are transported primarily in bound form, a certain fraction of the hormone molecules dissolve in plasma (generally less than 1%). For each such hormone, an equilibrium develops in the bloodstream between the amount of hormone that is bound to a carrier protein (Pr) in the form of a complex (H-Pr) and the amount of free hormone (H) that is dissolved in the plasma:

$$\text{H-Pr} \rightleftharpoons \text{H} + \text{Pr}$$

Only free hormone is available to bind to receptors on target cells. However, once the hormone binds, it is removed from the blood, and the equilibrium between bound and free hormone shifts to the right, causing more hormone to be released from the carrier proteins. Likewise, the secretion of hormones into the blood causes the equilibrium to be shifted to the left, such that more hormone binds to carrier proteins.

Once in the bloodstream, hormones will ultimately be degraded. How long a hormone persists in blood is measured in terms of **half-life**, the time it takes for half of the hormone in the blood to be degraded. Blood-borne messengers are generally degraded by the liver and excreted by the kidneys. Hormones that are present in dissolved form have relatively short half-lives, usually minutes. However, hormones that are bound to carrier proteins are protected from degradation and have longer half-lives, generally hours.

Quick Test 3a(i).2

1. Name the three catecholamines. Which amino acid is the precursor for catecholamines? Which catecholamine generally functions as a hormone?
2. Phospholipase A_2 causes the release of which fatty acid from membrane phospholipids? Which chemical class of messengers is produced from this fatty acid?
3. Which chemical class(es) of hormones is (are) transported in blood bound to carrier proteins? Does such binding generally *increase* or *decrease* the half-life of a hormone?

SIGNAL TRANSDUCTION MECHANISMS

Chemical messengers transmit their signals by binding to target cell receptors located either on the plasma membrane, in the cytosol, or in the nucleus. The location of the receptor depends on whether the messenger is lipophilic or lipophobic. In either case, binding of messenger to receptor either changes the activity of proteins (for example, enzymes) already present in the cell or stimulates the synthesis of new proteins. This section describes properties of receptors and the different signal transduction mechanisms that are set into motion by them.

Properties of Receptors

Receptors show *specificity* for the messenger; that is, they generally bind only one messenger or a class of messengers. Observe that in Figure 3a(i).8, messenger 1 can bind to receptor A but not to receptor B or C. Therefore, only cell A is a target cell for messenger 1. Likewise, cell C is the target cell for messenger 2. The binding between a messenger and a receptor is a brief, reversible chemical interaction similar to enzyme-substrate interactions. The strength of the binding between a messenger and its receptor is termed *affinity.*

A single messenger can often bind to more than one type of receptor, and these receptors may have different affinities for the messenger. For example, the catecholamine chemical messengers epinephrine and norepinephrine can both bind to *adrenergic* receptors (epinephrine is also called *adrenaline,* and norepinephrine is also called *noradrenaline*). Several different types of alpha (α) and beta (β) adrenergic receptors exist, including α_1, α_2, β_1, β_2, and β_3. α receptors have a greater affinity for norepinephrine than for epinephrine, which means that if norepinephrine and epinephrine are present in equal concentrations, a given

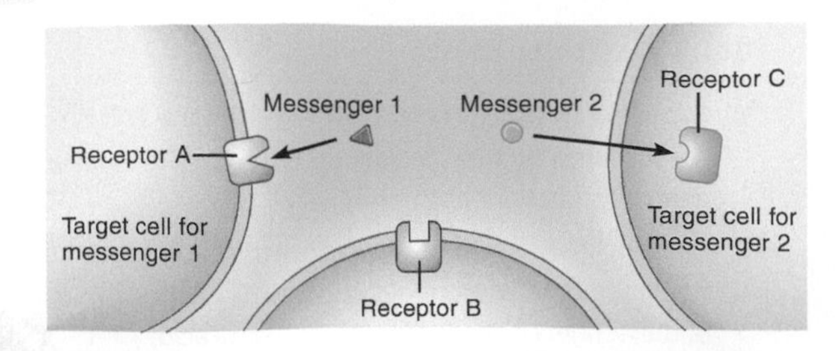

FIGURE 3a(i).8 Receptor specificity. Receptor A is specific for messenger 1, receptor C is specific for messenger 2, and neither messenger can bind to receptor B. Note that receptors can be located either on the plasma membrane (receptors A and B) or inside the cell (receptor C).

Q *If messenger 2 is to bind receptor C (located inside the target cell), it must cross the plasma membrane of the target cell. Which chemical property must messenger 2 possess to enable entry into the cell?*

α receptor is more likely to bind norepinephrine than epinephrine. β_2 receptors, by contrast, have a greater affinity for epinephrine than for norepinephrine. β_1 and β_3 receptors have approximately equal affinities for norepinephrine and epinephrine.

A single target cell may have receptors for more than one type of messenger. For example, skeletal muscle cells have receptors for both the neurotransmitter acetylcholine and the hormone insulin. Acetylcholine receptors are directly involved in stimulating muscle contraction, whereas insulin receptors are involved in stimulating glucose uptake and metabolism in the muscle cell.

The Relationship Between Receptor Binding and the Magnitude of the Target Cell Response

As a general rule, the magnitude of a target cell's response to a chemical messenger depends on three factors: (1) the messenger's concentration, (2) the number of receptors present, and (3) the affinity of the receptor for the messenger.

The response of a target cell generally increases as the concentration of messenger increases. This is a consequence of the fact that messengers usually exert their effects by binding reversibly to target cell receptors, as shown in the following reaction:

$$M + R \rightleftharpoons MR \longrightarrow \text{response}$$

where M is the messenger, R is the receptor, and M-R is the messenger-receptor complex. As messenger concentration increases, the reaction is driven to the right. The relationship between the concentration of messenger and the number of bound receptors is shown in Figure 3a(i).9. As the concentration of messenger increases, the proportion of bound receptors increases until all receptors have messengers bound to them (100% in Figure 3a(i).9), under which conditions the system is said to be 100% *saturated.*

The target cell's response also depends on the number of receptors it possesses. The more receptors there are (the higher their density), the more likely it is that a messenger will bind to a receptor (Figure 3a(i).10a). This means that at any given concentration of messenger, the number of bound receptors will be greater when more receptors are present, and the response will be greater.

The number of receptors that a target cell possesses can vary under different circumstances as a result of the synthesis of new receptors or turnover of old receptors. *Up-regulation,* an increase in the number of receptors compared to "normal" conditions, occurs when cells are exposed to low messenger concentrations for a prolonged period. By producing more receptors, target cells adapt to the relative lack of messenger by becoming more responsive to it. *Down-regulation,* a decrease in the number of receptors, occurs when messenger concentrations are higher than normal for a prolonged period. In this case, target cells adapt by producing fewer receptors and becoming less responsive to the messenger.

The target cell response also depends on the affinity of its receptors for the messenger. When a messenger is present at a given concentration, receptors with higher affinity are more likely to become bound than are

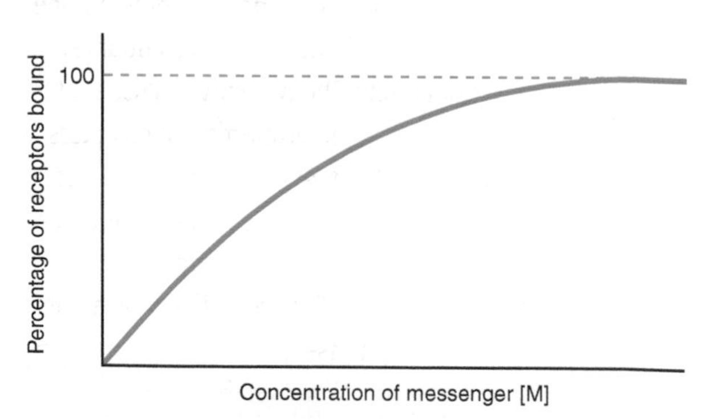

FIGURE 3a(i).9 Effect of messenger concentration on messenger-receptor binding. The proportion of receptors bound increases as the concentration of messenger increases. Because the amount of bound receptor determines the magnitude of target cell response, the y-axis could also have been labeled "target cell response."

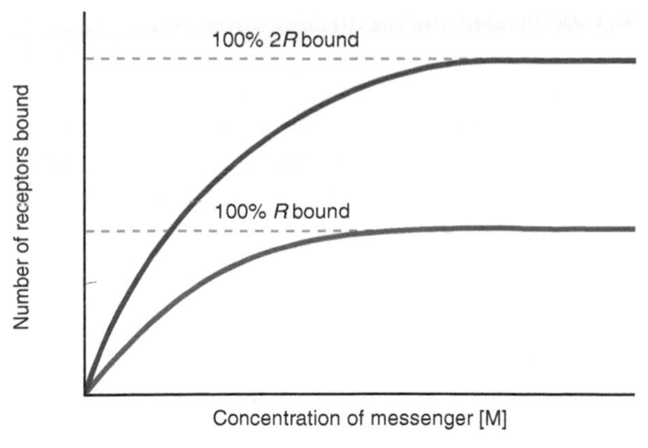

(a) Effects of receptor concentration

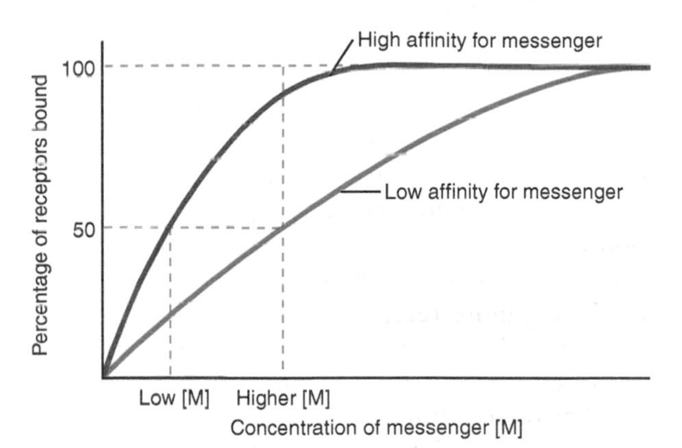

(b) Effects of receptor affinity

FIGURE 3a(i).10 **Effects of receptor concentration and affinity on messenger-receptor binding. (a) Effects of receptor density. The two curves illustrate the effects of doubling the concentration of a given receptor on a target cell. R refers to a given concentration of the receptor; 2R refers to twice that concentration of that receptor. When the receptor concentration doubles, the maximum number of receptors that can bind with messenger also doubles. (b) Effects of receptor affinity. The two curves illustrate the effects of receptor affinity on the proportion of receptors with messenger bound to them. At any concentration of messenger less than 100% saturation, a higher proportion of high-affinity receptors have bound messenger compared to low-affinity receptors. The high-affinity receptors reach saturation at a lower messenger concentration than do the low-affinity receptors. Note that the maximum number of sites that can be bound is independent of receptor affinity.**

receptors with lower affinity, as shown in Figure 3a(i).10b. Consequently, target cells possessing high-affinity receptors will respond more strongly to a given messenger, all else being equal.

Receptor Agonists and Antagonists

Although target cell responses are always triggered by receptor binding, it is not true that receptor binding always triggers a response. Among other things, it depends on the nature of the ligand that is binding to the receptors. Ligands that bind to receptors and produce a biological response are called **agonists,** whereas **antagonists** are ligands that bind to receptors but do not produce a response. Instead, antagonists may actually compete with agonists for the receptor, decreasing the likelihood that the binding of agonist to receptor will occur and bring about a response.

Apply Your Knowledge

Figure 3a(i).9 shows the effects of the concentration of messenger on the percentage of receptors bound. What would adding an antagonist to the extracellular fluid do to the percentage of receptors with messenger bound? Draw a graph depicting the percentage of receptors bound on the *y*-axis and the concentration of messenger on the *x*-axis. Draw three curves representing (1) no antagonist present, (2) low concentration of antagonist, and (3) high concentration of antagonist.

Some therapeutic and experimental drugs developed by pharmaceutical companies are artificial receptor agonists or antagonists (See **Discovery: Antihistamines**, p. 112). For example, under resting conditions, norepinephrine that is released from certain neurons binds to alpha receptors, causing constriction of blood vessels and an increase in blood pressure. The drug *phenylephrine* is an alpha agonist, and it exerts the same effects. However, the drug *phenoxybenzamine* is an alpha antagonist, and it prevents norepinephrine from binding to alpha receptors. Phenoxybenzamine has no effect itself, but by blocking the effect of norepinephrine, it causes blood pressure to decrease.

Signal Transduction Mechanisms for Responses Mediated by Intracellular Receptors

Receptors for lipophilic messengers are usually located in the cytosol or nucleus of target cells and are readily accessible because these messengers easily permeate the plasma membrane. The binding of the messenger to the receptor alters the synthesis of a specific protein (or proteins) by the mechanism depicted in Figure 3a(i).11, which shows the action of a lipophilic hormone.

(1a) If a receptor is located in the nucleus, then the hormone diffuses into the nucleus and binds to it, forming a hormone-receptor complex.

(1b) If a receptor is located in the cytosol, then the hormone binds to it there, forming a hormone-receptor complex that then enters the nucleus.

(2) Inside the nucleus, the complex binds to a certain region of DNA called the *hormone response element (HRE)*, which is located at the beginning of a specific gene.

(3) Binding of the complex to the HRE activates or deactivates the gene, which affects transcription of mRNA and ultimately increases or decreases synthesis of the protein coded by the gene. In this example, the gene is activated and mRNA synthesis is increased.

(4) The mRNA moves into the cytosol.

(5) The mRNA is translated by ribosomes to yield proteins.

Because changes in protein synthesis can take hours or even days, effects of lipophilic messengers are generally slow to develop. In addition, because these newly synthesized proteins often remain in the target cells long after the messenger is gone, the effects can persist a long time. For the few lipophilic messengers that have receptors in the plasma membrane, the effects are more rapid and are similar to those discussed next.

Signal Transduction Mechanisms for Responses Mediated by Membrane-Bound Receptors

Lipophobic messengers cannot permeate the plasma membrane to any significant degree. Thus their receptors are located on the plasma membrane, with the binding site facing the extracellular fluid. The receptors for these messengers fall into three general categories: channel-linked receptors, enzyme-linked receptors, and G protein–linked receptors. Responses produced at each of these receptor types are described next.

Channel-Linked Receptors

Because the lipid bilayer has virtually no permeability to ions, the ion permeability of the plasma membrane is determined by the presence of ion channels in it. These ion channels are generally specific, allowing only one type of ion or class of ions to pass through them. In addition, ion channels are proteins, most of which can be regulated between open and closed states.

Ion channels that open or close in response to the binding of a chemical to a receptor or to the channel are called **ligand-gated channels. Channel-linked receptors** are a type of ligand-gated channel in which the ligand is a messenger that binds to a receptor. These channels fall into two categories: fast channels, in which the receptor and channel are the same protein (as described next), and slow channels, in which the receptor and channel are separate proteins but are coupled together by a third type of protein, called a *G protein* (described shortly).

Fast ligand-gated channels are proteins that function as both receptors and ion channels. The binding of a messenger to the receptor/ion channel causes the channel to open, increasing the membrane's permeability for that specific ion. Open ion channels allow a

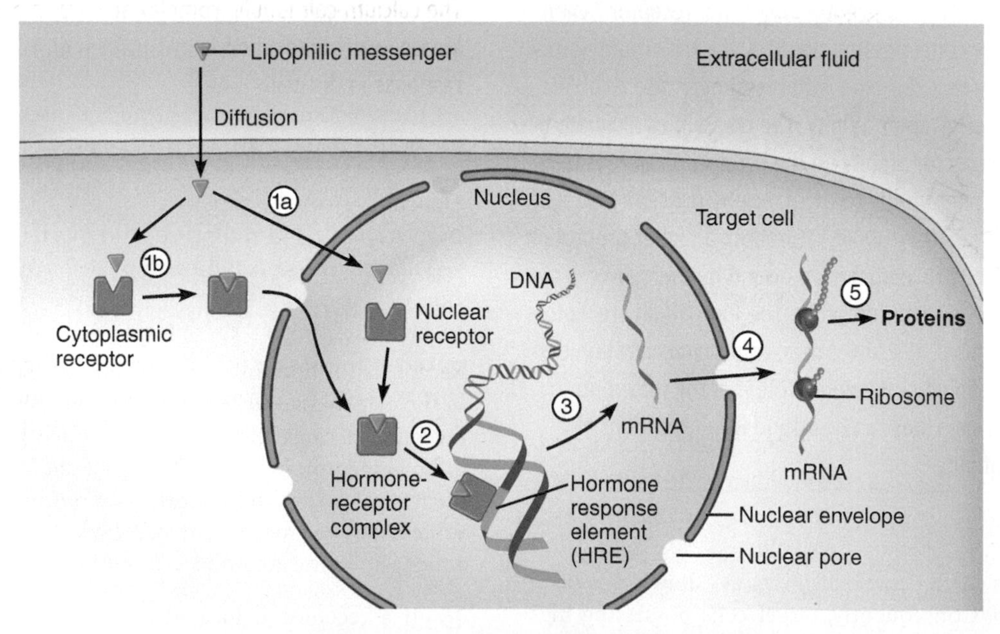

FIGURE 3a(i).11 **Actions of lipophilic hormones on the target cell. See the text for a detailed description.**

specific ion or class of ions to move across the plasma membrane down its electrochemical gradient. Ion movement into or out of the cell can have two different effects on the target cell: (1) Ions entering and leaving can change the electrical properties of the cell and (2) entering ions can interact with proteins inside the cell to induce a response such as muscle contraction, secretion, change in metabolism, or altered transport of a substance.

The opening of most ion channels causes effects by changing the electrical properties of the target cell (Figure 3a(i).12). Recall that a difference in potential exists across the plasma membrane at rest, such that the inside of the cell is negative relative to the outside. Ions that move through an open channel carry with them a charge that changes the membrane potential. For example, the neurotransmitter acetylcholine stimulates skeletal muscle contraction by binding to nicotinic cholinergic receptors on skeletal muscle cells, causing the opening of ion channels. Sodium ions move into the cell (potassium also moves out, but to a lesser degree), carrying positive charge into the muscle cell. Given that the receptor and ion channel are the same protein molecule, these changes in membrane potential begin rapidly, within a millisecond. Because the binding of messenger to receptor is brief, and the channel is open only while the messenger is bound, the change in membrane potential usually terminates in a few milliseconds.

In other cases, fast ligand-gated channels exert their effects by opening calcium channels (Figure 3a(i).13). When these channels open, calcium ions enter the cell.

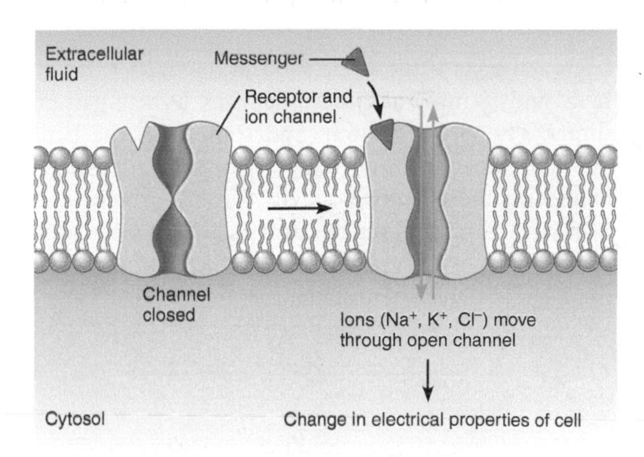

FIGURE 3a(i).12 Fast ligand-gated channels and how they change the electrical properties of cells. Binding of a messenger to the receptor/ channel opens the ion channel. The opening of most ion channels results in movement of ions into or out of the cell, which changes the electrical properties of the cell.

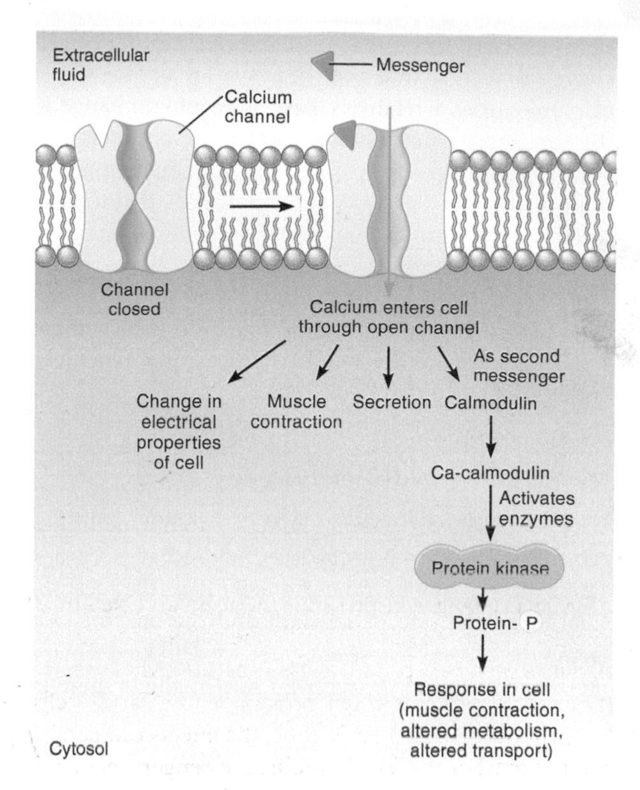

FIGURE 3a(i).13 Fast ligand-gated calcium channels. Binding of a messenger to the receptor/channel opens calcium channels, enabling calcium ions to enter the cell. Calcium entry will change the electrical properties of the cell, but calcium can also trigger a variety of responses, such as secretion of some product by exocytosis, muscle contraction, or change in activity of a protein. In the last instance, calcium acts as a second messenger, binding to the protein calmodulin to form a calcium-calmodulin complex. The calcium-calmodulin complex activates a protein kinase, which phosphorylates a protein that produces a response in the cell.

Depending on the target cell, this calcium can then trigger a variety of responses by interacting with intracellular proteins, including muscle contraction, secretion of a product by exocytosis, and functioning as a **second messenger**—an intracellular messenger produced by the binding of an extracellular messenger (the *first messenger*) to a receptor. As a second messenger, calcium binds to a cytosolic protein called **calmodulin.** The resultant calcium-calmodulin complex usually activates a protein kinase, an enzyme that catalyzes the phosphorylation of a protein, thereby altering its structure and function through covalent regulation.

Calcium is well suited for its role in intracellular signaling because it is normally present in very low concentrations in the cytosol (10^{-7} to 10^{-6} molar), as compared to 10^{-3} molar in extracellular fluid. The significance of this low cytosolic concentration of calcium is that entry into a cell of even a small quantity of calcium causes a relatively large percentage change in the concentration, which means that the system is sensitive. Intracellular calcium levels are maintained at their normal low levels by three processes that remove calcium ions from the cytosol: (1) active transport of calcium across the plasma membrane, (2) sequestration of calcium by binding with proteins in the cytosol, and (3) active transport of calcium into certain organelles, such as the smooth endoplasmic reticulum and mitochondria.

Enzyme-Linked Receptors

Certain receptor proteins, known as **enzyme-linked receptors,** function both as enzymes and as receptors. These are transmembrane proteins, with the receptor side facing the interstitial fluid and the enzyme side facing the cytosol. These enzymes are activated when a messenger binds to the receptor, which allows them to catalyze intracellular reactions.

Most enzyme-linked receptors are *tyrosine kinases,* which catalyze the addition of a phosphate group to the side chains of the amino acid tyrosine in certain locations in target proteins. The events occurring at tyrosine kinase receptors are as follows (Figure 3a(i).14):

① A messenger binds to the receptor, changing its conformation.

② The conformation change activates the tyrosine kinase.

③ The tyrosine kinase then catalyzes phosphorylation of an intracellular protein.

④ Phosphorylation of the protein changes its activity by covalent regulation, bringing about a response in the target cell.

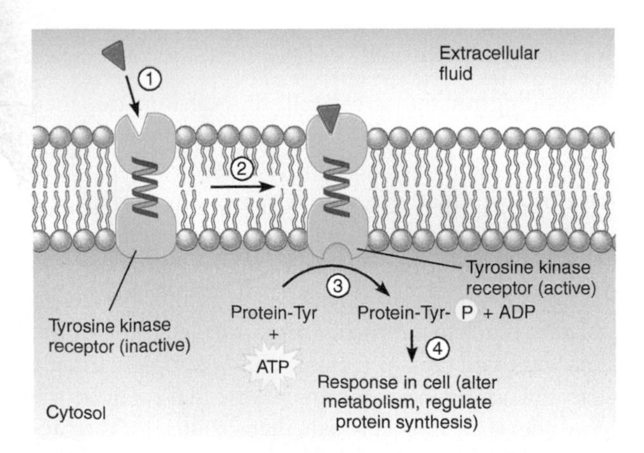

FIGURE 3a(i).14 **An enzyme-linked receptor. The enzyme-linked receptor depicted here is tyrosine kinase. See the text for a detailed description.**

A messenger that uses the tyrosine kinase signal transduction is the hormone insulin.

Other enzyme-linked receptors are *guanylate cyclases,* which catalyze the conversion of *GTP (guanosine triphosphate)* to the second messenger *cGMP (cyclic guanosine monophosphate)*. cGMP then activates a protein kinase, which catalyzes phosphorylation of a protein.

G Protein–Linked Receptors

G protein–linked receptors work by activating special membrane proteins called **G proteins.** See **Clinical Connections: Cholera and G Proteins,** p. 125, for an example of the significance of G proteins. G proteins are located on the intracellular side of the plasma membrane, where they function as links between the G protein–linked receptor and other proteins in the plasma membrane, called effectors. Effectors include ion channels and enzymes. G proteins, which get their name from their ability to bind guanosine nucleotides, have three subunits: alpha (α), beta (β), and gamma (γ) The guanosine binding site is in the alpha subunit. In its inactive state, a G protein binds GDP (guanosine diphosphate). When a messenger binds to the G protein–linked receptor, the G protein releases the GDP, binds a molecule of GTP (guanosine triphosphate), and becomes active, as shown in the following equation:

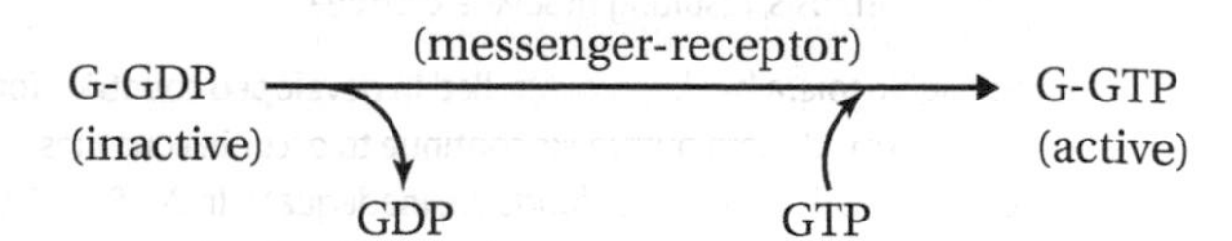

In its active state, the alpha subunit separates from the beta and gamma subunits, leaving a beta-gamma dimer. The alpha subunit, and sometimes the beta-gamma dimer, moves to the effector(s), causing a change in the effector's activity. The G protein does not stay active very long because it also functions as an enzyme that hydrolyzes the GTP, in the process returning itself to the inactive state:

$$\text{G-GTP} \xrightarrow{\text{GTPase}} \text{G-GDP} + P_i$$

G proteins are a diverse group, formed from at least 20 different alpha subunits, 5 beta subunits, and 13 gamma subunits. Functionally, G proteins can be classified into three basic types: (1) those that affect ion channels, (2) *stimulatory G proteins,* and (3) *inhibitory G proteins.* Stimulatory G proteins (G_s proteins) and inhibitory G proteins (G_i proteins) are associated with the activation

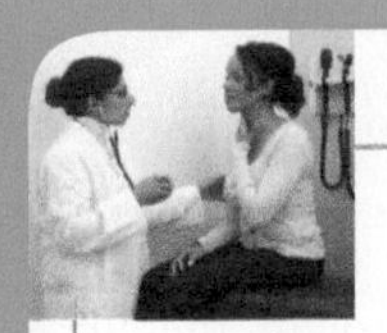

CLINICAL CONNECTIONS

Cholera and G Proteins

G proteins are susceptible to attack by several bacterial toxins, such as the toxin that causes cholera. Cholera, caused by infection with the bacterium *Vibrio cholerae,* is the leading cause of death among small children in developing countries. The primary sign of the disease is massive diarrhea, which can result in the loss of 15–20 liters of fluid from the body per day. The effects of cholera result from a toxin that *Vibrio cholerae* releases into the gut. The toxin acts on a G protein that overstimulates adenylate cyclase. Here is what happens (see the figure):

① Cholera toxin binds to a membrane *ganglioside* (phospholipid with carbohydrate residues attached) on secretory cells in the small intestine.

② A toxin subunit enters the cell, causing the sustained activation of a G protein.

③ This G protein activates adenyate cyclase.

④ Adenylate cyclase catalyzes the formation of cAMP.

⑤ cAMP activates protein kinases.

⑥ Phosphorylation of proteins enhances the secretion of chloride ions.

⑦ The flow of negatively charged chloride ions out of the cell causes positively charged sodium ions to follow them.

⑧ Water follows the electrolytes into the lumen of the small intestine by osmosis, resulting in severe diarrhea.

Although cholera has been controlled in developed countries for nearly a century, cholera outbreaks continue to occur in countries whose public health policies or funds are inadequate. In 2008–2009, a cholera epidemic hit Zimbabwe, with more than 30,000 individuals being infected and 1500 deaths occurring. Citizens of Zimbabwe, lacking sufficient treated water supplies, were getting drinking water from streams contaminated with sewage. *Vibrio cholerae* is generally transmitted through the feces of infected individuals.

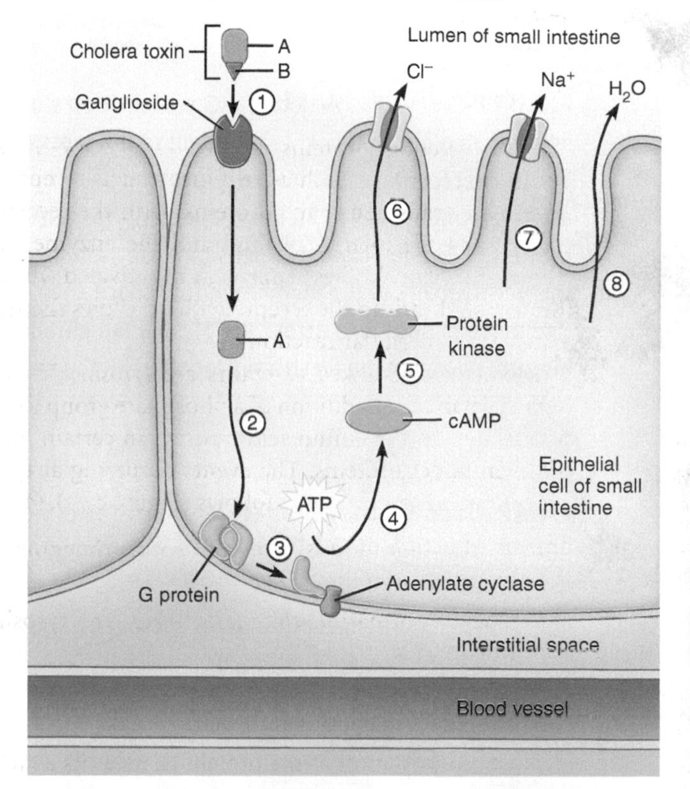

and inhibition, respectively, of enzymes, called **amplifier enzymes,** that catalyze the production of second messengers in the intracellular fluid. (There are other types of amplifier enzymes in cells, but those will not be covered in this text.) The functions of some different types of G proteins are discussed next.

Slow ligand-gated ion channels are regulated by G proteins, which cause the channels to open or close in response to a messenger binding to its receptor (Figure 3a(i).15). When the G protein is activated, the alpha subunit moves to the ion channel, causing a conformational change that causes it to open or close. These channels exert effects similar to those exerted by fast ligand-gated channels, but there are two important differences between these two classes of channels: (1) At fast ligand-gated channels, messenger binding to channel-linked receptors only *opens* the channel, so it increases the permeability of the target cell for the specific ion. By contrast, G protein–linked ion channels can be either *opened* or *closed* by messenger binding to the receptor. (2) Binding of a messenger to channel-linked receptors produces an immediate and brief (only a few milliseconds) response in the target cell. In contrast, G protein–linked ion channels are slow to open or close in response to receptor binding and stay open or closed for longer periods, often minutes.

G protein–regulated enzymes are associated with the production of second messengers in the cytosol. Five major second messengers account for most of the communication through G protein–regulated enzymes: (1) *cAMP* (cyclic adenosine monophosphate), (2) cGMP, (3) *inositol triphosphate,* (4) *diacylglycerol,* and (5) calcium. The second messenger systems described next are summarized in Table 3a(i).3.

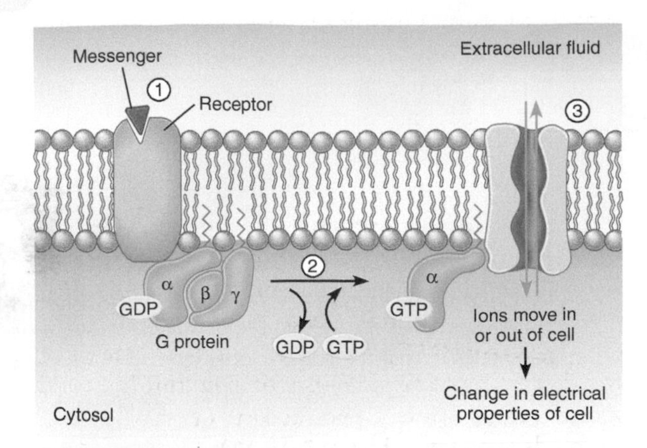

FIGURE 3a(i).15 **Action of a G protein on a slow ligand-gated ion channel. ① Binding of the messenger to the receptor activates the G protein. ② The alpha subunit moves to an ion channel in the membrane. ③ The ion channel opens or closes, changing the permeability of the membrane to a specific ion. The movement of ions across the plasma membrane is altered, changing the electrical properties of the cell.**

cAMP Second Messenger System The mechanisms of action of cAMP, the most common second messenger, are as follows (Figure 3a(i).16):

① The first messenger binds to the receptor, activating a G_s protein. (Some messengers inhibit the cAMP second messenger system by activating a G_i protein, not shown in the figure.)

② The G protein releases the alpha subunit, which binds to and activates the enzyme **adenylate cyclase.**

③ Adenylate cyclase catalyzes the conversion of ATP to cAMP.

④ cAMP activates *protein kinase A,* also called cAMP-dependent protein kinase.

⑤ The protein kinase catalyzes the transfer of a phosphate group from ATP to a protein, thereby altering the protein's activity.

⑥ Altered protein activity causes a response in the cell.

Termination of the actions of cAMP requires its degradation by the enzyme *cAMP phosphodiesterase.* For the actions of the phosphorylated protein to be terminated, the phosphate group must be removed from the protein by a chemical reaction. The enzymes that dephosphorylate a protein are called *phosphoprotein phosphatases.*

The concentration of cAMP in a cell is determined by the relative rates of synthesis and breakdown. When synthesis is faster than breakdown, the concentration rises. When breakdown exceeds synthesis, the concentration falls. Because intracellular levels of cAMP are determined by the rates of two competing enzymes (one that synthesizes it and one that breaks it down), the effects of stimulating one enzyme can be mimicked by inhibiting the other.

Apply Your Knowledge

Several drugs, including caffeine, inhibit the enzyme cAMP phosphodiesterase. What effect do these drugs have on cAMP levels? cAMP has many effects in the body, including increasing heart rate and strength of contraction. What effect does caffeine have on heart rate and strength of contraction? Explain.

TABLE 3a(i).3 Second Messenger Systems

Second messenger	Precursor	Amplifier enzyme	Usual action	Examples of first messengers in the system
Cyclic adenosine monophosphate (cAMP)	ATP	Adenylate cyclase	Activates protein kinase A	Epinephrine, vasopressin, ACTH, glucagon
Cyclic guanosine monophosphate (cGMP)	GTP	Guanylate cyclase	Activates protein kinase G	Atrial natriuretic peptide, endothelins
Diacylglycerol (DAG)	Inositol-4,5-biphosphate (PIP_2)	Phospholipase C	Activates protein kinase C	Angiotensin II, histamine, vasopressin
Inositol triphosphate (IP_3)	Inositol-4,5-biphosphate (PIP_2)	Phospholipase C	Stimulates calcium release from intracellular stores	Angiotensin II, histamine, vasopressin
Calcium*	None	None	Binds to calmodulin, then activates a protein kinase	Angiotensin II, histamine, vasopressin

*Calcium increases in the cytosol in response to opening of ion channels either in the plasma membrane or in certain organelles.

cGMP Second Messenger System We previously discussed cGMP as a product of an enzyme-linked receptor, guanylate cyclase. Guanylate cyclase is more commonly associated with G proteins, in which case the cGMP second messenger system is similar to cAMP but activates *protein kinase G,* also called cGMP-dependent protein kinase.

FIGURE 3a(i).16 **The cAMP second messenger system. See the text for a detailed description.**

Phosphatidylinositol Second Messenger System In the **phosphatidylinositol system,** a membrane phospholipid, *phosphatidylinositol-4,5-biphosphate* (PIP_2), undergoes an enzyme-catalyzed reaction that liberates two second messengers, **diacylglycerol (DAG)** and **inositol triphosphate** (IP_3); the latter stimulates release of the third second messenger, calcium. The action of this system proceeds as follows (Figure 3a(i).17):

① The messenger binds to its receptor, activating a G protein.

② The G protein releases the alpha subunit, which binds to and activates the enzyme *phospholipase C.*

③ Phospholipase C catalyzes the conversion of PIP_2 to DAG and IP_3, each of which functions as a second messenger.

④a DAG remains in the membrane and activates the enzyme *protein kinase C.*

⑤a Protein kinase C catalyzes the phosphorylation of a protein.

⑥a The phosphorylated protein brings about a response in the cell.

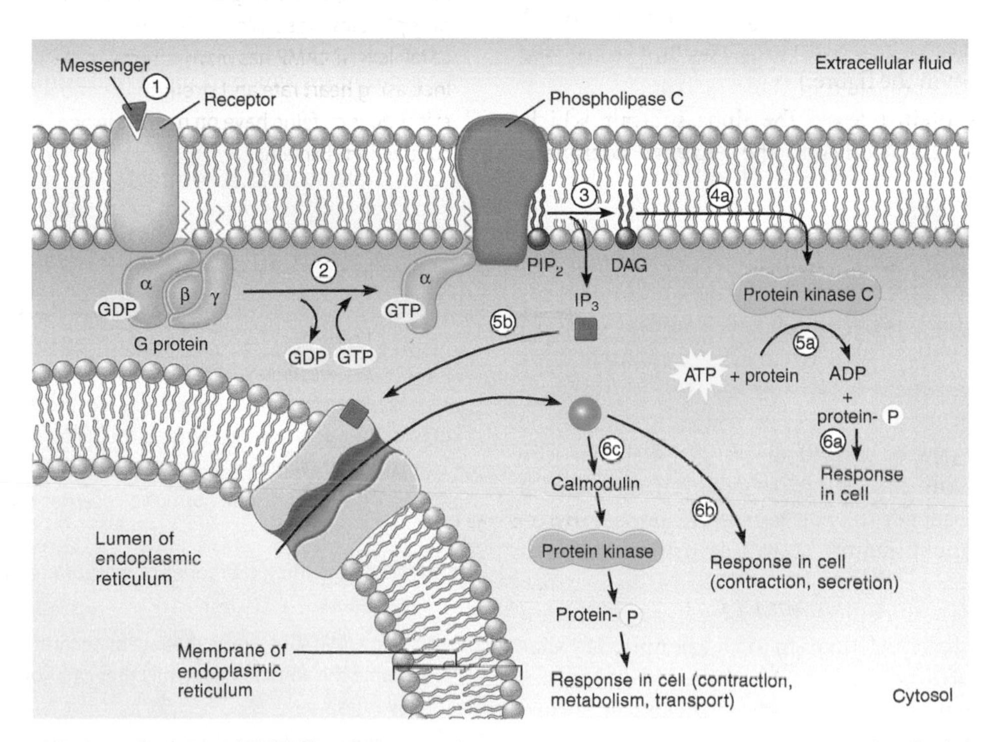

FIGURE 3a(i).17 **The phosphatidylinositol second messenger system. See the text for a detailed description.**

TABLE 3a(i).4 Signal Transduction Mechanisms for Selected Chemical Messengers

Messenger	Functional class	Chemical class	Signal transduction mechanism
Epinephrine	Hormone, neurotransmitter	Amine	G protein–coupled receptors
Thyroid hormones	Hormone	Amine (lipophilic)	Altered transcription of mRNA
Vasopressin (ADH)	Hormone, neurotransmitter	Peptide	G protein–coupled receptors
Insulin	Hormone, neurotransmitter	Peptide	Enzyme-linked receptors
Estrogen	Hormone	Steroid	Altered transcription of mRNA
Glutamate	Neurotransmitter	Amino acid	Channel-linked receptor, G protein–coupled receptors
Serotonin	Neurotransmitter, paracrine	Amine	Channel-linked receptor, G protein–coupled receptors
Prostaglandins	Paracrine	Eicosanoid	G proteins, unknown for many
Interleukins	Cytokine	Peptide	Enzyme-linked receptors
GABA	Neurotransmitter	Amino acid	Channel-linked receptor

At the same time,

(4b) IP_3 moves into the cytosol.

(5b) IP_3 triggers the release of calcium from the endoplasmic reticulum.

Depending on the cell, calcium then does one of two things:

(6b) It acts on proteins to stimulate contraction or secretion.

(6c) It acts as a second messenger by binding to calmodulin, activating a protein kinase that phosphorylates a protein that produces a response in the cell.

The signal transduction mechanisms for some selected chemical messengers in various functional and chemical classes are listed in Table 3a(i).4.

Signal Amplification in Chemical Messenger Systems

Given that some cells have simple signal transduction mechanisms such as the one-step activation of tyrosine kinase, one might wonder why second messenger systems are needed, when they ultimately have the same basic effect as tyrosine kinase—phosphorylation of a protein. The reason relates to one of the striking features of second messenger systems—the ability of small changes in the concentration of a chemical messenger to elicit marked responses in target cells, a phenomenon known as *signal amplification.*

Figure 3a(i).18 depicts how signal amplification works, using the cAMP system as an example. The diagram illustrates how a single activated receptor can activate several G proteins, each of which can in turn activate an adenylate cyclase. While active, each adenylate cyclase can generate hundreds of molecules of cAMP, each of which then activates a molecule of protein kinase A. Each protein kinase A molecule can then phosphorylate hundreds of target proteins. The net result is that a large number of end-product molecules can be regulated in response to the binding of a single ligand molecule to its receptor. In the example shown, one first messenger led to the phosphorylation of approximately 2,500,000 proteins.

The sequence of reactions shown in Figure 3a(i).18 is an example of a **cascade,** a series of sequential steps that progressively increase in magnitude, much as numerous tiny brooks, added together, can eventually become a major river. Cascades of one type or another are common in chemical messenger systems and account for much of the signal amplification that occurs.

Now that our discussion of the various aspects of chemical messengers is complete, see Table 3a(i).5 for a summary of the properties of chemical messengers. We turn next to a discussion of long-distance communication in the body.

Quick Test 3a(i).3

1. Where in the target cell are the receptors for lipophilic messengers located? What is the name of the regulatory region of DNA to which the hormone-receptor complex binds?
2. Name the three categories of membrane-bound receptors.
3. Name five substances that act as second messengers. Name the amplifier enzymes that catalyze their synthesis.

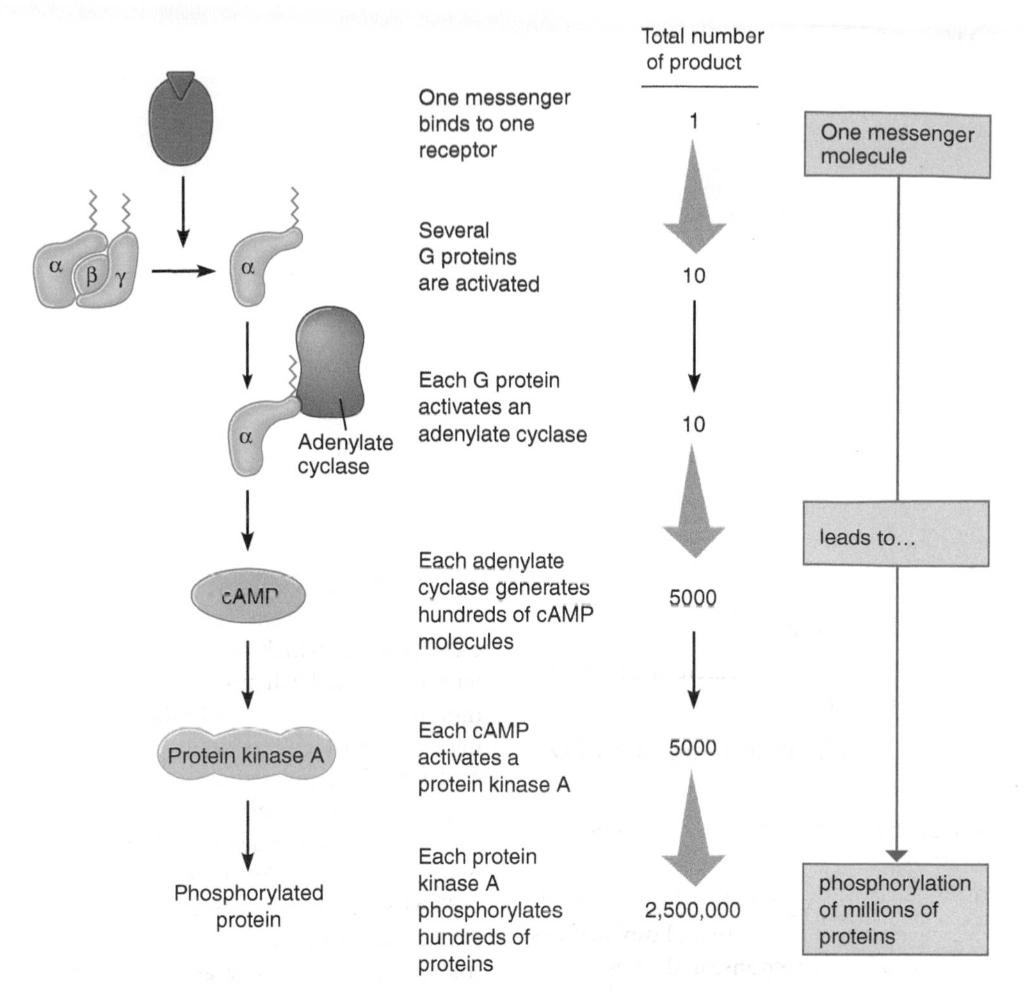

Total number of product
One messenger binds to one receptor
1
One messenger molecule
α
β
γ
α
Several G proteins are activated
10
Each G protein activates an adenylate cyclase
10
α
Adenylate cyclase
leads to...
cAMP
Each adenylate cyclase generates hundreds of cAMP molecules
5000
Protein kinase A
Each cAMP activates a protein kinase A
5000
Phosphorylated protein
Each protein kinase A phosphorylates hundreds of proteins
2,500,000
phosphorylation of millions of proteins

FIGURE 3a(i).18 **Signal amplification, in this case by the second messenger cAMP.**

TABLE 3a(i).5 Properties of Chemical Messengers

Property	Lipophobic messenger (hydrophilic)	Lipophilic messenger (hydrophobic)
Chemical classes	Amino acids, amines, peptides	Steroids, eicosanoids, thyroid hormones*
Storage in secretory cell	Secretory vesicles	None
Mechanism of secretion	Exocytosis	Diffusion
Transport in blood†	Dissolved	Bound to carrier protein
Location of receptor	Plasma membrane	Cytosol or nucleus
Signal transduction mechanism	Open/close ion channels‡ Activate membrane-bound enzymes G proteins and second messenger systems	Alter transcription of mRNA (alter protein synthesis)
Relative time to onset of response	Fast	Slow
Relative duration of response	Short	Long
Relative half-life	Short	Long

*Thyroid hormones are amines but are lipophilic.
†Refers to hormones and certain cytokines only.
‡Some of these effects are mediated by G proteins.

LONG-DISTANCE COMMUNICATION VIA THE NERVOUS AND ENDOCRINE SYSTEMS

To maintain homeostasis, it is crucial that cells in one region of the body be able to communicate with cells in distant regions. The body has two organ systems specialized for long-distance communication: the nervous system and the endocrine system.

The nervous system consists of neurons and supporting cells called *glial cells.* Neurons are capable of communicating long distances, first by transmitting electrical signals along the length of the cell (some of which are up to a meter long), and then by transmitting chemical signals through the release of a neurotransmitter from the axon terminal. The neurotransmitter then diffuses over a short distance to the target cell. The site where the axon terminal communicates with the target cell is called a synapse (Figure 3a(i).19). Because of the direct cell-to-cell communication of chemical signals at a synapse, the nervous system is often considered a "wired" system. (One exception involves the neurohormones, which travel via the bloodstream.) Communication in the nervous system generally involves the opening and closing of ion channels, which is very fast and generally of short duration. Signals transmitted by the nervous system travel quickly and are generally of short duration, making the system ideal for controlling movements and monitoring the world around us.

In contrast, the endocrine system lacks any direct anatomical link between secretory cell and target cell. Instead, the endocrine system communicates through chemical messengers called hormones, which travel via the bloodstream to virtually all cells in the body. Strictly speaking, hormones are secreted into the interstitial fluid and then diffuse into blood, but we often speak of the secretion of hormones into blood for the sake of simplicity. Hormones generally communicate by altering protein synthesis or activating G proteins, processes that are considerably slower than the electrical and chemical signals used by the nervous system. The relative slowness of the endocrine system and its ability to broadcast signals over wide areas are important in coordinating metabolic activities among organ systems. Various aspects of the nervous and endocrine systems are compared in Table 3a(i).6.

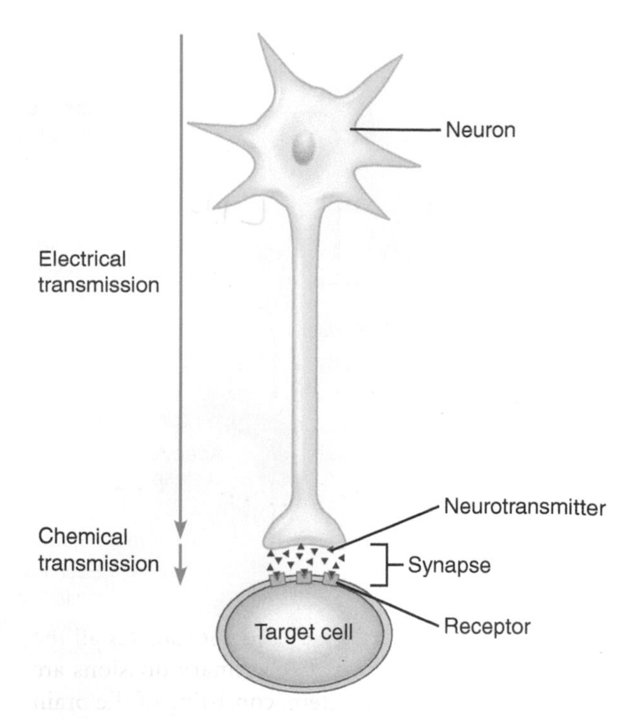

FIGURE 3a(i).19 Signal transmission in neurons. Neurons transmit both electrical signals within the cell and chemical signals between cells.

TABLE 3a(i).6 Characteristics of the Nervous and Endocrine Systems

Characteristic	Nervous system	Endocrine system
Secretory cell	Neuron	Endocrine cell
Target cell	Neuron, muscle, or gland	Most cell types in body
Messenger	Neurotransmitter	Hormone
Pathway for communication	Across synapse	Via bloodstream
Basis of specificity	Receptors on postsynaptic target cell	Receptors on target cells throughout body
Time to onset of effect	Immediate	Delayed
Duration of effect	Brief	Long

3a(ii) The Brain/Central Nervous System

Taken from *Biology of Humans: Concepts, Applications, and Issues*, Third Edition, by Judith Goodenough and Betty McGuire

CELLS OF THE NERVOUS SYSTEM

The *nervous system* integrates and coordinates all the body's varied activities. Its two primary divisions are (1) the central nervous system, consisting of the brain and spinal cord; and (2) the peripheral system, consisting of all the nervous tissue in the body outside the brain and spinal cord. Both these major divisions of the nervous system are composed of two types of specialized cells. **Neurons** (nerve cells) are excitable cells that generate and transmit messages. Outnumbering the neurons by about 10 to 1, **neuroglial cells** (also called glial cells) support and protect neurons.

Neuroglial Cells

The nervous system has several types of glial cells, each with different jobs to do. Some glial cells provide structural support for the neurons of the brain and spinal cord. Glial cells also provide a steady supply of chemicals, called nerve growth factors, that stimulate nerve growth. Without nerve growth factors, neurons die. Other glial cells form insulating sheaths around axons that, as described shortly, are the long projections extending from certain neurons. This sheath, called the myelin sheath, has several important functions that are also described shortly. Scientists now know that glial cells can communicate with one another and with neurons.

Neurons

The basic unit of the nervous system is the neuron, or nerve cell. Neurons, which are responsible for an amazing variety of functions, can be grouped into the three general categories depicted in Figure 3a(ii).1.

- **Sensory** (or afferent) **neurons** conduct information *toward* the brain and spinal cord. These neurons generally extend from sensory receptors, which are structures specialized to gather information about the conditions within and around our bodies.
- **Motor** (or efferent) **neurons** carry information *away from* the brain and spinal cord to an **effector**—either a muscle, which will contract, or a gland, which will secrete its product, as a response to information from a sensory or interneuron.
- Association neurons, commonly called **interneurons,** are located between sensory and motor neurons. They are found only within the brain and spinal cord, where they integrate and interpret the sensory signals, thereby "deciding" on the appropriate response. Interneurons are by far the most numerous nerve cells in the body; they account for more than 99% of the body's neurons.

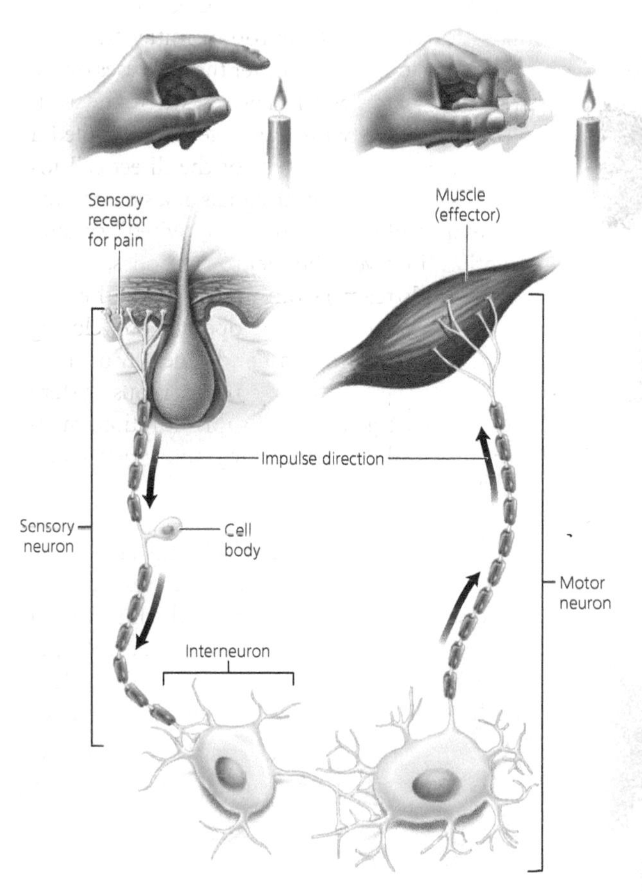

FIGURE 3a(ii).1 Neurons may be sensory neurons, interneurons, or motor neurons. This diagram traces the pathway of an impulse from a sensory receptor to an interneuron and from there to a motor neuron and its effector. Sensory receptors detect changes in the external or internal environment. An interneuron usually receives input from many sensory neurons, integrates that information, and if the input is appropriate, stimulates a motor neuron. The motor neuron then causes a muscle or a gland (an effector)

We can appreciate the specific roles of each type of neuron by considering the symptoms of a progressive disease called *amyotrophic lateral sclerosis (ALS)*, also known as Lou Gehrig's disease. In ALS, motor neurons throughout the brain and spinal cord die and stop sending messages to skeletal muscles. Without stimulation from motor neurons, the muscles gradually weaken, and the person loses control over arms, legs, and body. The cause of death is respiratory failure, because the muscles that control breathing (the diaphragm and rib muscles) eventually die. Sensory neurons and interneurons are not affected by ALS, so awareness and reasoning do not deteriorate.

STRUCTURE OF NEURONS

The shape of a typical neuron is specialized for communicating with other cells (Figure 3a(ii).2).

Axons and Dendrites

A neuron has many short, branching projections called **dendrites**, which provide a huge surface for receiving signals from other cells. Such signals travel toward an enlarged central region called the cell body, which has all the normal organelles, including a nucleus, for maintaining the cell. When a neuron responds to an incoming signal, it transmits its message along the **axon**, a single long extension of the neuron. The axon carries messages away from the cell body either to another neuron or to an effector, which can be a muscle or a gland. In some cases, the axon allows the neuron to communicate over very long distances. For example, a motor neuron that allows you to wiggle your big toe has its cell body in the spinal cord and its axon runs all the way to the muscles of your toe. The end of the axon has many branches specialized to release a chemical, called a neurotransmitter, that alters the activity of the effector. The axon is the *sending* portion of the neuron, whereas the dendrites and cell body are typically the *receiving* portions.

To appreciate the dimensions of a neuron, imagine a "typical" motor neuron, one that carries a message from the spinal cord to a muscle. Now picture the cell body of this neuron as being the size of a tennis ball. At that scale, the axon of this neuron would be about 1 mile (1.6 km) long and only about one-half inch (1.3 cm) in diameter. At the same scale, the dendrites—the shorter but more numerous projections of the neuron—would fill an average-sized living room.

A **nerve** is a bundle of parallel axons, dendrites, or both arising from many neurons. Each nerve is covered with connective tissue and, depending on the type of neurons it contains, can be classified as sensory, motor, or mixed (a mixed nerve is made up of both sensory and motor neurons).

Myelin Sheath

Most of the axons outside the brain and spinal cord, and some of those within, have an insulating outer layer called a **myelin sheath** (Figure 3a(ii).3), which increases the rate of conduction of a nerve impulse and helps its repair. The myelin sheath is composed of

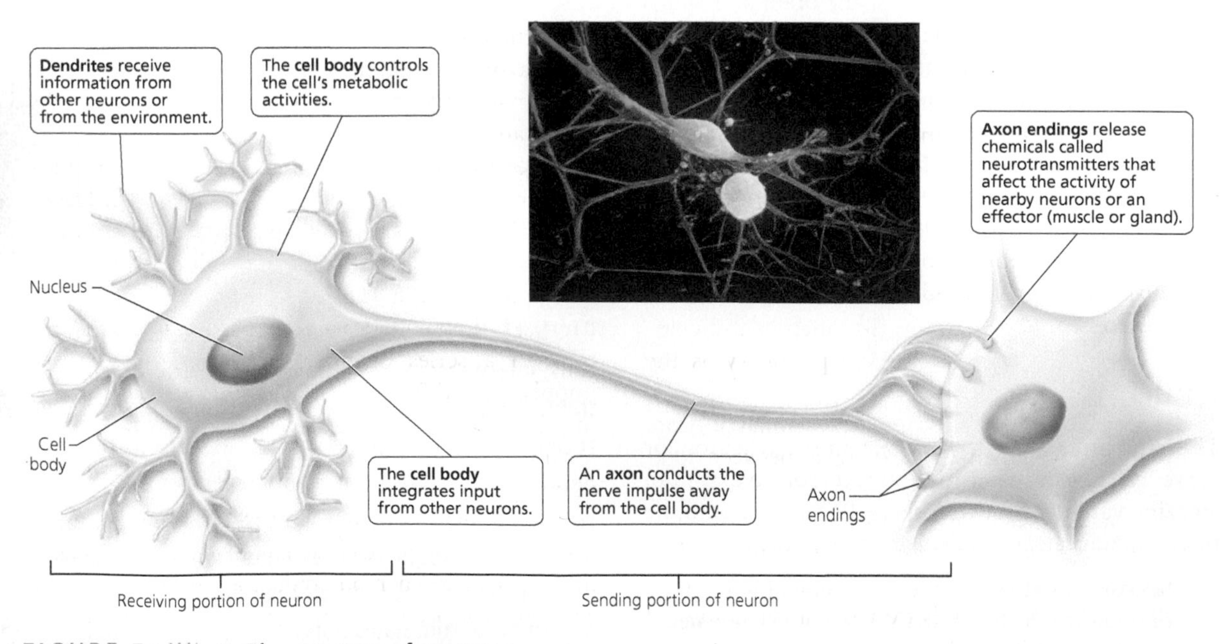

Dendrites receive information from other neurons or from the environment.
The cell body controls the cell's metabolic activities.
Axon endings release chemicals called neurotransmitters that affect the activity of nearby neurons or an effector (muscle or gland).
Nucleus
Cell body
The cell body integrates input from other neurons.
An axon conducts the nerve impulse away from the cell body.
Axon endings
Receiving portion of neuron
Sending portion of neuron

FIGURE 3a(ii).2 The structure of a neuron

Q *Long axons are myelinated, but short axons may not be. Why?*

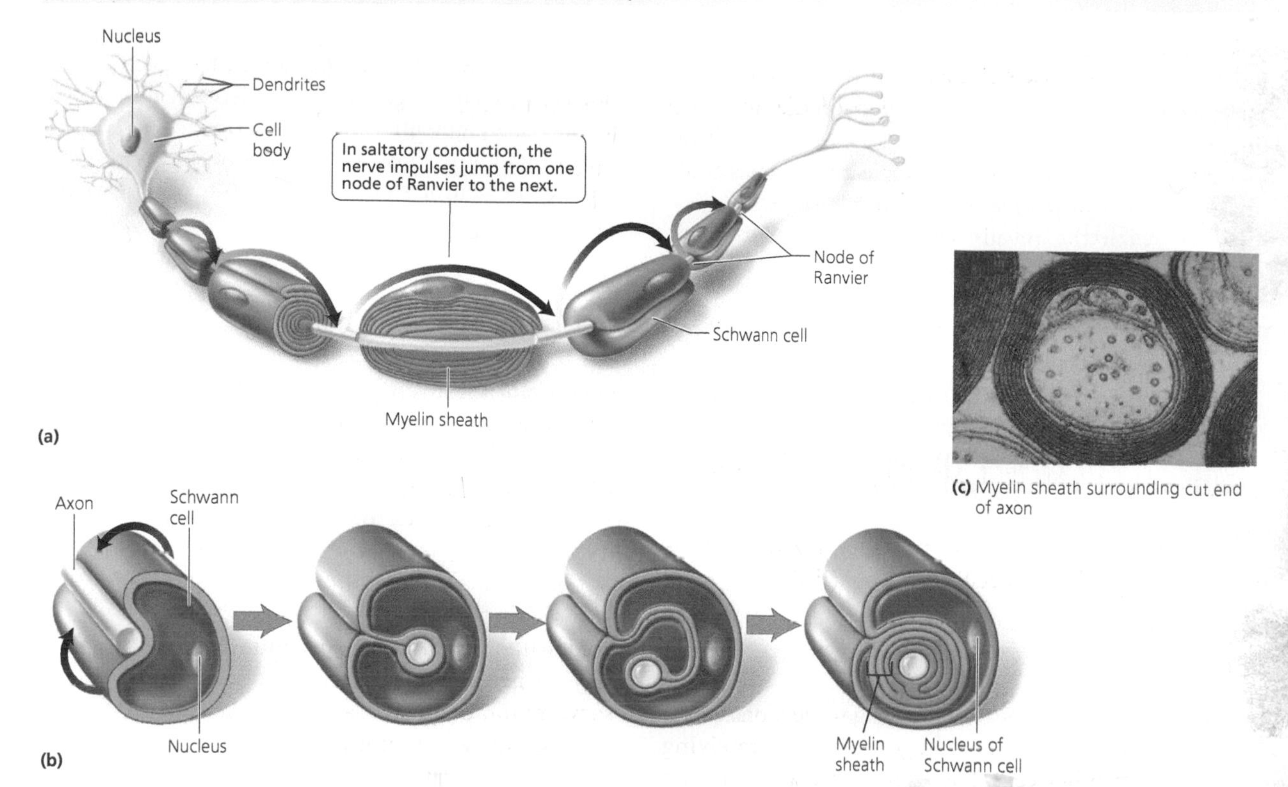

FIGURE 3a(ii).3 **The myelin sheath. (a) An axon protected by a myelin sheath. The Schwann cells that form the myelin sheath are separated by nodes of Ranvier–areas of exposed axon that allow for saltatory conduction. (b) The myelin sheath forms from multiple wrappings of Schwann cell plasma membranes. (c) An electron micrograph of the cut end of a myelinated axon.**

A *Saltatory conduction, which increases the speed of conduction, is possible only on myelinated axons. The increased speed is important when nerve impulses must travel long distances.*

the plasma membranes of glial cells. Outside of the brain and spinal cord, for example, glial cells known as **Schwann cells** form neurons' myelin sheaths. A Schwann cell plasma membrane wraps around the axon many times to provide a covering that looks somewhat like a jelly roll. This covering, the myelin sheath, serves as a kind of living electrical tape, insulating individual axons and preventing messages from short-circuiting between neurons. The myelin sheath is kept alive by the Schwann cell's nucleus and cytoplasm, which are squeezed to the periphery as the sheath forms.

A single Schwann cell encloses only a small portion, about 1 mm long, of an axon. The gaps between adjacent Schwann cells, where the axon is exposed to the extracellular environment, are called *nodes of Ranvier*. Their presence is crucial to how rapidly a neuron transmits messages. With the myelin sheath in place, a nerve impulse "jumps" successively from one node of Ranvier to the next in a type of transmission called **saltatory conduction** (*saltare*, to jump), which is up to 100 times faster than signal conduction would be on an unmyelinated axon of the same diameter. Not surprisingly, the axons responsible for conducting signals over long distances are typically myelinated.

To get a sense of how this "jumping" mode of transmission increases the speed at which a message travels, think of the different ways a ball can be moved down the court during a basketball game. When only seconds are left in the game, dribbling the ball the length of the court would take too much time. Passing the ball through a series of players is faster. Likewise, an impulse passed from one node to the next, as occurs in myelinated nerves, moves faster than one traveling uniformly along the full length of the axon, as occurs in unmyelinated nerves.

The myelin sheath also plays a role in helping to repair a neuron when a nerve is cut or crushed. When a neuron in the peripheral nervous system is cut, the part of the axon that has been separated from the cell body can no longer receive life-sustaining materials from the rest of the cell and begins to degenerate within a few minutes.

Once such degeneration occurs, the Schwann cells that wrapped the axon begin to remove all the axon fragments from inside the myelin sheath. Finally, the cut end of the axon begins "sprouting" from the cell body and regrows along the previous path, guided by the remaining myelin sheath.

The importance of the myelin sheath becomes dramatically clear in people with *multiple sclerosis*, a disease in which the myelin sheaths in the brain and spinal cord are progressively destroyed. The damaged regions of myelin become hardened scars called scleroses (hence the name of the disease) that interfere with the transmission of nerve impulses. Short-circuiting between normally unconnected conduction paths delays or blocks the signals going from one brain region to another. Depending on the part of the nervous system affected, the result can be paralysis or the loss of sensation, including loss of vision.

NERVE IMPULSES

The neuron membrane is specialized for communication. A nerve's message, which is called a nerve impulse or an action potential, is an electrochemical signal caused by sodium ions (Na^+) and potassium ions (K^+) crossing the neuron's membrane to enter and leave the cell.

Plasma Membrane of a Neuron

Like most living membranes, the plasma membrane of a neuron is selectively permeable; it allows some substances through but not others. The membrane contains many pores, called **ion channels,** that ions are able to pass through without using cellular energy (Figure 3a(ii).4). Each ion channel is designed to allow

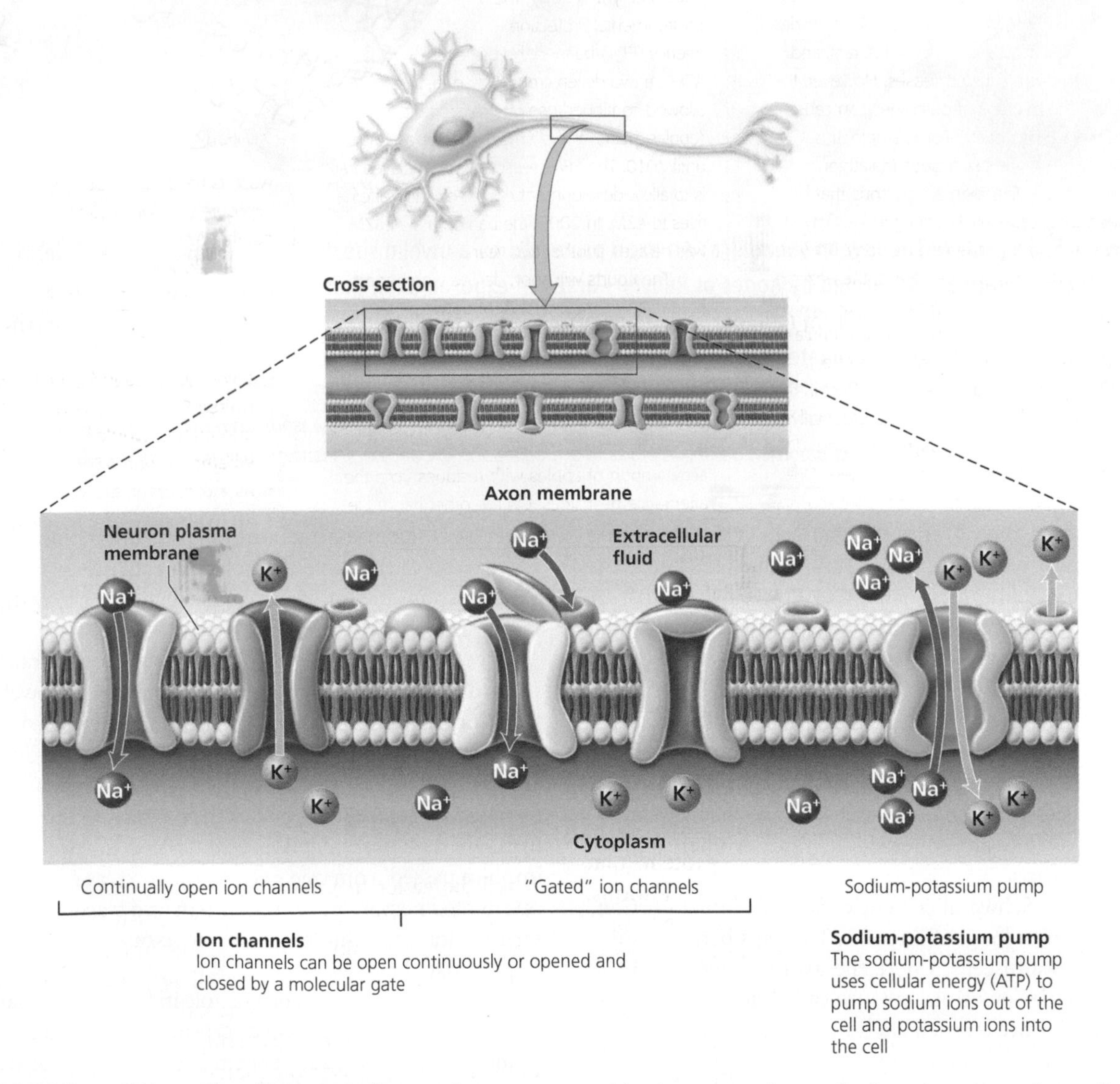
Cross section
Axon membrane
Neuron plasma membrane
Extracellular fluid
Cytoplasm
Na+
K+
Continually open ion channels
"Gated" ion channels
Sodium-potassium pump
Ion channels
Ion channels can be open continuously or opened and closed by a molecular gate
Sodium-potassium pump
The sodium-potassium pump uses cellular energy (ATP) to pump sodium ions out of the cell and potassium ions into the cell

FIGURE 3a(ii).4 The plasma membrane of a neuron provides two general ways for ions to enter or leave the cell: (1) diffusion through a channel or (2) active transport by the sodium-potassium pump

Ethical Issue

Pesticides and the Nervous System

Many of us are exposed each day to substances that can harm our nervous system. The exposure may occur because of our job, our lifestyle, the foods we eat, or the medications we use. The death of neurons can lead to irreversible loss of function. Some damage may take years to become apparent, but other effects are immediate.

Pesticides are chemicals for killing organisms that would otherwise damage crops and property. The use of pesticides increases crop production, preserves produce, and keeps our public lawns and gardens beautiful. Pesticides also reduce infestations of insects, rats, and mice that might cause diseases. However, the misuse and overuse of pesticides can cause illness and even death. For example, the organophosphate insecticides Malathion, Parathion, and Diazinon are poisons that kill insects by excessively boosting the activity at certain synapses in the insect's body. They work by inhibiting acetylcholinesterase, the enzyme that breaks down the neurotransmitter acetylcholine. As a result, acetylcholine accumulates in the synapses and has a continuous effect.

Because they have the same effect in the human body, these insecticides accidentally poison approximately 500,000 people around the world each year, primarily farm workers. One symptom of pesticide poisoning is muscle spasms (continuous involuntary contractions). The spasms occur because acetylcholine is the neurotransmitter that triggers contraction of voluntary muscles, such as those in the arms or legs. Death can occur if spasms occur in the muscles responsible for breathing.

Deciding whether to use pesticides usually requires balancing economic benefits with health risks. Currently, such a balancing act is occurring regarding the use of an organophosphate pesticide AZM (azinphos methyl). In 2001, the Environmental Protection Agency (EPA) banned the use of AZM on two dozen crops. However, it allowed continued use on orchard fruits (apples, pears, and cherries), berries, and nuts until 2010. The EPA's reason for the delayed ban is to allow development of cost-effective alternatives to AZM. In 2006, the ban on use of AZM was delayed another two years.

The courts will soon decide whether the potential health risks of AZM outweigh the potential economic benefits of continuing to use it. The EPA argues that the cost of quickly switching to other pesticides would be staggering. It could cost apple growers tens of millions of dollars. Furthermore, some other countries do not allow import of apples with residues from the alternative pesticides. On the other hand, the United Farm Workers argue that thousands of workers become seriously ill each year from exposure to AZM. Environmental groups point out that AZM is usually sprayed on crops from planes, allowing AZM to contaminate neighboring communities, rivers, and lakes.

Certain pesticides disrupt communication between neurons and muscles, which can be fatal.

Questions to Consider

- If you were the judge on the case of the United Farm Workers versus the EPA, what information would you use to decide whether to ban AZM?
- As a consumer, are you willing to pay more for foods if they are not sprayed with AZM?

only certain ions to pass through. For example, sodium channels allow the passage of only sodium ions, and potassium channels allow the passage of only potassium ions. In this way, ion channels function as molecular sieves. Some channels are permanently open. Others are regulated by a "gate"—a protein that changes shape in response to changing conditions, either opening the channel, which allows ions to pass through, or closing it, which prevents ions from crossing the membrane.

The cell membrane also contains **sodium-potassium pumps,** which are special proteins in the cell membrane that actively transport sodium and potassium ions across the membrane. These pumps use cellular energy in the form of ATP to move the ions against their concentration gradients. Each pump ejects sodium ions (Na^+) from within the cell while bringing in potassium ions (K^+; see Figure 3a(ii).4).

Resting Potential

It will be easier to understand the movement of ions during an action potential if we first consider a neuron that is not transmitting an action potential—that is, a neuron in its resting state. As we will see, however, *resting* is hardly the word to describe what is going on at this stage. The membrane of a resting neuron maintains a difference in the electrical charges near the two membrane surfaces (the surface facing inside the cell and the surface facing outside the cell), keeping the inside surface more negative than the outside one. This charge difference across the membrane, called the **resting potential,** results from the unequal distribution of ions across the membrane.

In a resting neuron, sodium and potassium ions are unequally distributed across the plasma membrane. There are more sodium ions outside the membrane than inside. Furthermore, there are more potassium ions inside than outside. Potassium ions tend to leak out because they are more concentrated inside the axon. (Recall that substances tend to move from an area of higher concentration to one of lower concentration.) To a lesser extent, sodium ions leak in. However, sodium-potassium pumps maintain the resting potential of a neuron by pumping out sodium ions while moving potassium ions back in. The cell also contains some negatively charged ions that are too large to pass through the membrane.

The result of this unequal distribution of ions is that the inner surface of a resting neuron's membrane is typically about 70 mV (millivolts) more negative than the outer surface. This voltage is the resting potential, and it is about 5% of the strength of a size AA flashlight battery.

Although the neuron's sodium-potassium pumps consume a lot of energy to maintain the resting potential, the energy is not wasted. The resting potential allows the neuron to respond more quickly than it could if the membrane were electrically neutral in its resting state. This situation is somewhat analogous to keeping your car's battery charged so that the car will start as soon as you turn the key.

Action Potential

Now we are ready to consider what happens when a neuron is stimulated—that is, when it receives some kind of excitatory signal. The **action potential,** or nerve impulse, resulting from such stimulation can be described briefly as a sudden reversal in the charge difference across the membrane, followed by the restoration of the original charge difference. Let's take a closer look at these two parts of a nerve impulse.

1. **Sodium ions (Na^+) enter the axon.** An excitatory stimulus causes the gates on sodium channels to open. Sodium ions then enter the neuron, and their positive charge begins to reduce the negative charge within. Reduction of the charge difference across the membrane is called *depolarization.* The action potential begins when membrane depolarization reaches a certain value called the **threshold.** When the threshold is reached, the gates on more sodium channels open. Enough sodium ions enter through the open gates to create a net positive charge in that region (about +30 mV), as shown in Figure 3a(ii).5.
2. **Potassium (K^+) ions leave the axon.** About halfway through the action potential, the gates on potassium channels open. Potassium ions now leave the cell. The exodus of potassium ions with their positive charge causes the interior of the neuron to become negative once again relative to the outside. The outward flow of potassium ions returns the membrane potential to close to its resting value. Restoration of the charge difference across the membrane is called *repolarization.*

As noted, at the end of an action potential, the charge distribution across the membrane returns to the resting potential. However, there are slightly more sodium ions and slightly fewer potassium ions inside the cell than before. This alteration is corrected by the sodium-potassium pump, which restores the original distribution of sodium and potassium ions. The action of the sodium-potassium pump is slow. Therefore, it does not contribute directly to the events of the action potential.

To summarize, the action potential is a reversal of the charge difference across the membrane caused by the inward flow of sodium ions, followed immediately by restoration of the original charge difference caused by the outward flow of potassium ions (Figure 3a(ii).6). These changes occur sequentially along the axon, like a wave rippling away from the cell body.

The action potential is described as a *wave* of changes that travels down the neuron's plasma membrane because the events just described do not occur simultaneously along the entire length of the axon. Instead, as sodium ions enter the cell at one location along the membrane, and the charge inside the membrane becomes less negative in that region of the cell, the change in charge causes the opening of the sodium channel gates in an adjacent part of the membrane. Due to this sequential opening of gates, the change in charge travels down the length of the axon. Once started, action potentials do not diminish—just like the last domino in a falling row falls with the same energy as the first. Moreover, the intensity of the nerve impulse does not vary with the strength of the stimulus that triggered it. If an action potential occurs at all, it is always of the same intensity as any other action potential. This "all-or-nothing" aspect of nerve cell conduction is similar to the firing of a gun in that the force of the bullet is not changed by how hard you pull the trigger.

Immediately after an action potential occurs, the neuron cannot be stimulated again for a brief instant called the **refractory period.** During the refractory period, the sodium channels are closed and cannot be reopened. Consequently, a new action potential cannot yet be generated. Because of the refractory period, a prolonged stimulus that is above threshold can cause only a series of discrete nerve impulses, not a single, larger, sustained impulse. For this reason, increasing

Resting Neuron
Plasma membrane is charged, with the inside negative relative to the outside.

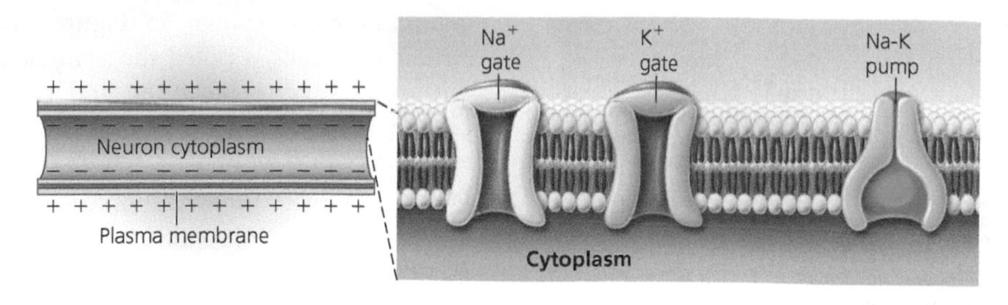
Na+ gate
K+ gate
Na-K pump
Neuron cytoplasm
Plasma membrane
Cytoplasm

Action Potential
The charge difference across the membrane reverses and then is restored.

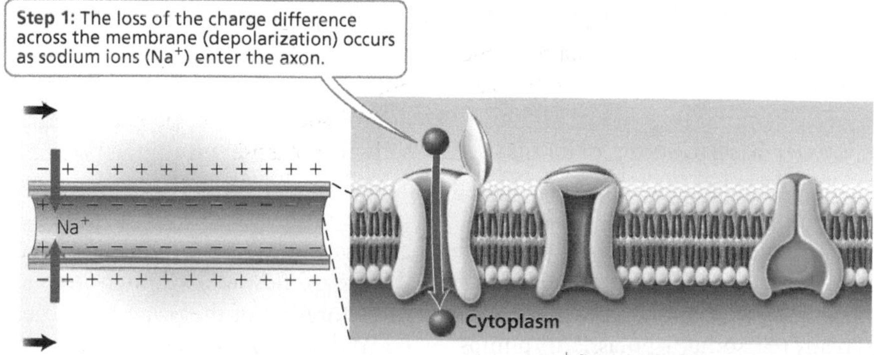
Step 1: The loss of the charge difference across the membrane (depolarization) occurs as sodium ions (Na+) enter the axon.
Na+
Cytoplasm
Na+ flows inward

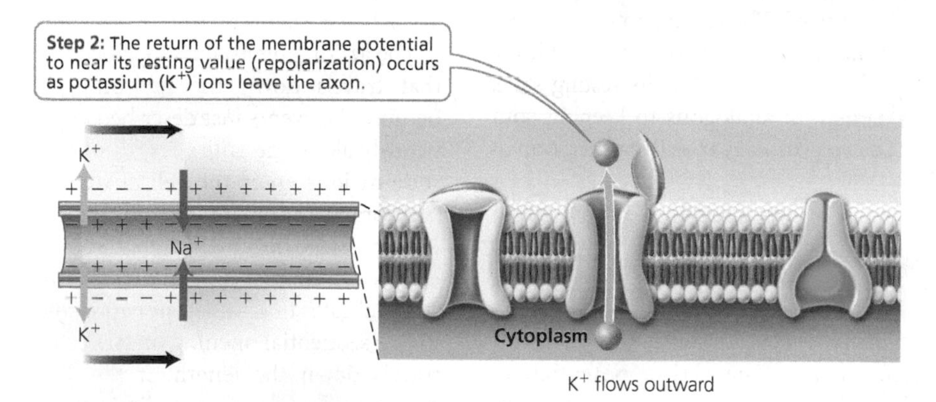
Step 2: The return of the membrane potential to near its resting value (repolarization) occurs as potassium (K+) ions leave the axon.
K+
Na+
K+
Cytoplasm
K+ flows outward

Restoration of Original Ion Distribution
The sodium-potassium pump restores the original distribution of ions.

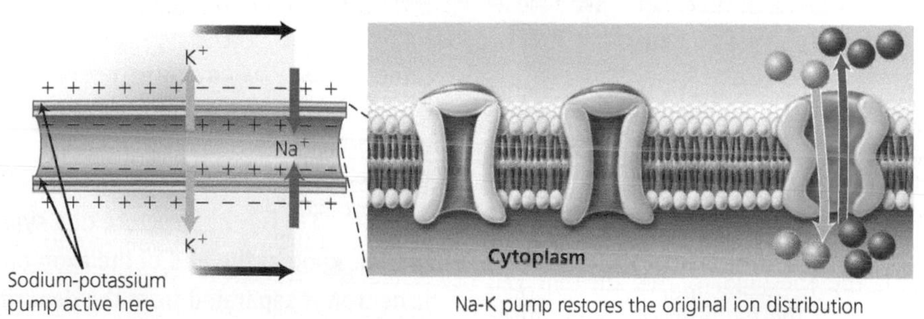
K+
Na+
K+
Sodium-potassium pump active here
Cytoplasm
Na-K pump restores the original ion distribution

FIGURE 3a(ii).5 **The resting state and the propagation of an action potential along an axon. The sequential opening and closing of sodium-channel gates and potassium-channel gates produces the action potential**

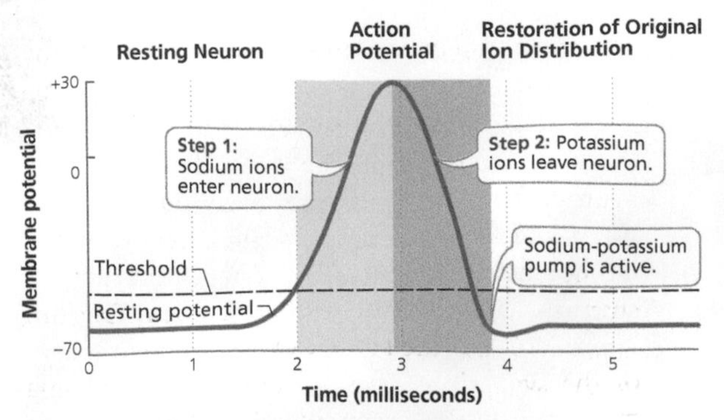

FIGURE 3a(ii).6 A graphic representation of an action potential. Voltage across the membrane can be measured by electrodes placed inside and outside the axon. The graph shows the changes in voltage that accompany an action potential.

the strength of a stimulus will increase the frequency of impulses. For example, the frequency of nerve impulses increases with the heat of an object touched. However, the frequency can increase only to a point. The inability of the sodium gates to open during the refractory period is also the reason that the nerve impulses cannot reverse and go backward toward the cell body.

stop and THINK

"Red tides" in the ocean are caused by proliferation of dinoflagellates. These single-celled marine algae contain a chemical called saxitoxin (STX), extremely small concentrations of which prevent sodium channels in mammalian neurons from opening. The clams, scallops, and mussels that consume the dinoflagellates are insensitive to the toxin, but the STX accumulates in their tissues. What effect would you expect STX to have on nerve transmission in humans who accidentally consume tainted shellfish?

SYNAPTIC TRANSMISSION

When a nerve impulse reaches the end of an axon, in almost all cases the message must be relayed to the adjacent cell across a small gap that the impulse cannot jump across. To transmit the message to the adjacent cell requires a brief change of the medium of communication from an electrochemical signal to a chemical signal. Therefore, when an action potential reaches the end of the axon, a chemical is released from the axon's tip. That chemical, called a **neurotransmitter,** diffuses across the gap and conveys the message to the adjacent cell.

The junction between a neuron and another cell is called a **synapse.** The structure of a synapse between two neurons is shown in Figure 3a(ii).7. The gap between the cells is called the *synaptic cleft.* Recall that the axon branches near the end of its length. Each branch ends with a small bulblike swelling called a *synaptic knob.* The neuron sending the message is the *presynaptic neuron* (meaning "before the synapse").

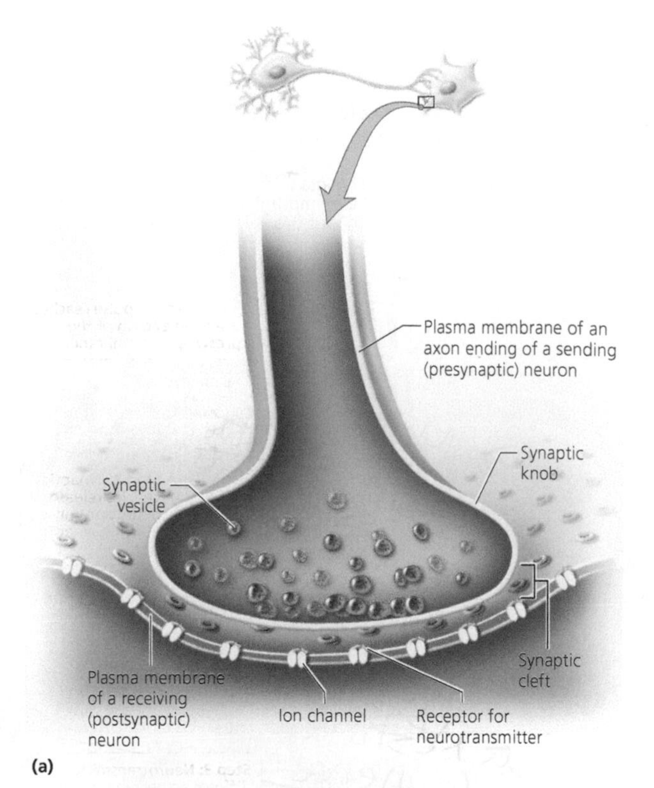

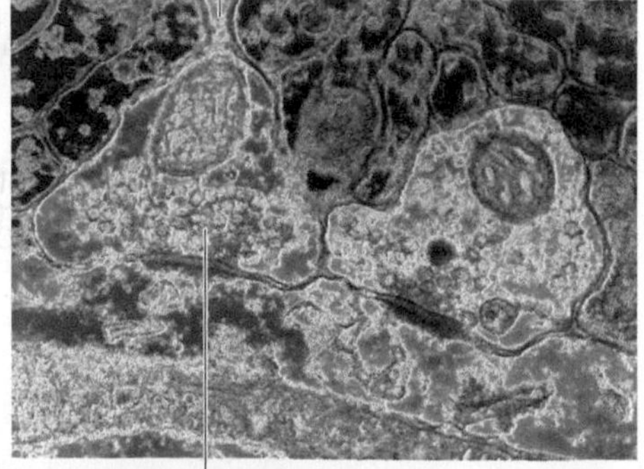

FIGURE 3a(ii).7 Structure of a synapse. (a) The synaptic knob at the end of the axon on the presynaptic neuron is separated from the dendrite or cell body of the postsynaptic neuron by a small gap called a synaptic cleft. Within the synaptic knob are small sacs, called synaptic vesicles, filled with neurotransmitter molecules. (b) An electron micrograph of a synapse.

The neuron receiving the message is the *postsynaptic neuron* ("after the synapse").

Release of the Neurotransmitter and the Opening of Ion Channels

Let's consider the events that occur in the synapse as the message is sent from one neuron to the next (Figure 3a(ii).8).

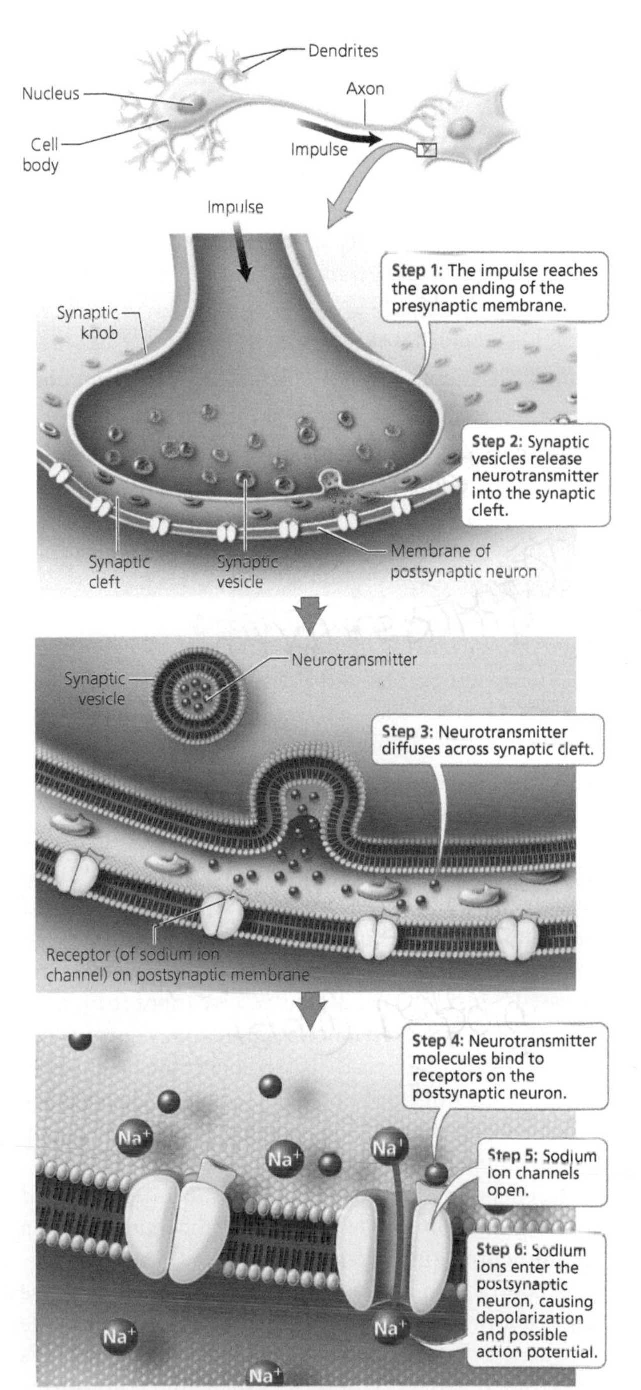

FIGURE 3a(ii).8 **Transmission across an excitatory synapse**

1. **The nerve impulse reaches the axon ending of the presynaptic neuron.**
2. **Synaptic knobs release packets of neurotransmitter.** Within the synaptic knobs of the presynaptic neuron, the neurotransmitter is contained in tiny sacs called *synaptic vesicles.* When a nerve impulse reaches the synaptic knob, the gates of calcium ion channels in the membrane there open. Calcium ions move into the knob, causing the membranes of the synaptic vesicles to fuse with the plasma membrane at the synaptic knob and to dump the enclosed neurotransmitter into the synaptic cleft.
3. **Neurotransmitter diffuses across the synaptic cleft.**
4. **Neurotransmitter binds with receptors on the membrane of the postsynaptic neuron.** A receptor is a protein that recognizes a particular neurotransmitter, much as a lock "recognizes" a key. The only cells a neurotransmitter can stimulate are cells that have receptors specific for that particular neurotransmitter. Thus, only certain neurons can be affected by a given neurotransmitter.
5. **When a neurotransmitter binds to its receptor, an ion channel is opened.** The binding of the neurotransmitter to a receptor causes the opening of an ion channel in the postsynaptic neuron. The response that is triggered as a result depends on the type of ion channel the receptor opens. It is the receptor that determines which ion channels will open and what the effect of a given neurotransmitter will be.

An *excitatory synapse* is one where the binding of the neurotransmitter to the receptor opens sodium channels, allowing sodium ions to enter and increasing the likelihood that an action potential will begin in the postsynaptic cell. In contrast, an *inhibitory synapse* is one where the binding of the neurotransmitter opens different ion channels, which decreases the likelihood that an action potential will be generated in the postsynaptic neuron. In this case, the cell's interior becomes more negatively charged than usual. As a result, the cell will require larger than usual amounts of an excitatory neurotransmitter in order to reach threshold.

Summation of Input from Excitatory and Inhibitory Synapses

A neuron may have as many as 10,000 synapses with other neurons at the same time (Figure 3a(ii).9). Some of these synapses will have excitatory effects on the postsynaptic membrane. Others will have inhibitory effects. The **summation** (combined effects) of excitatory and inhibitory effects on a neuron at any given moment determines whether an action potential is

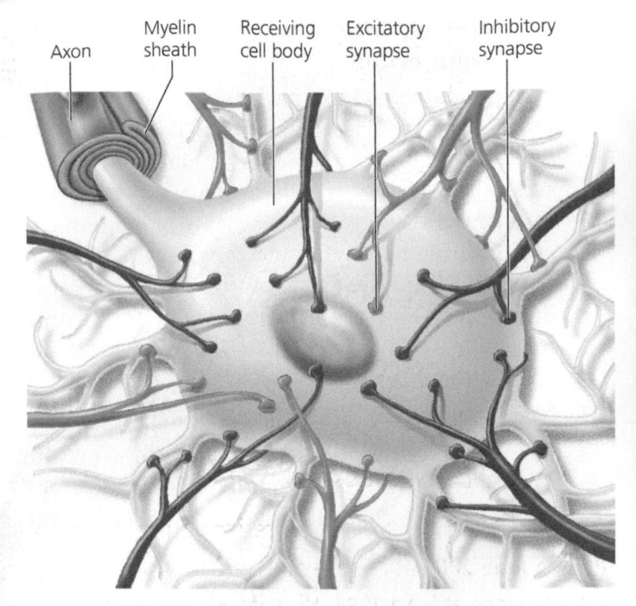

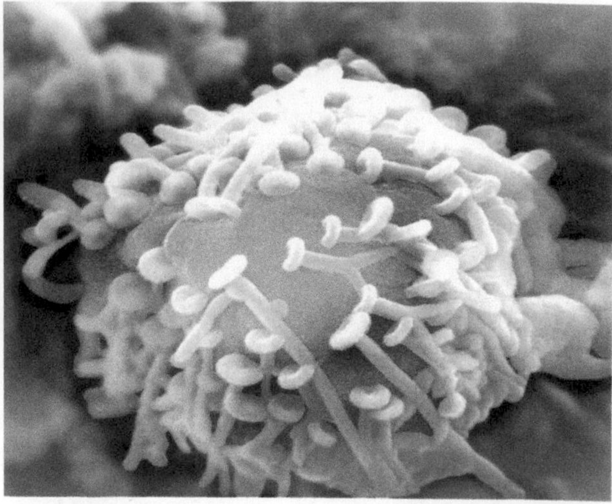

Figure 3a(ii).9 **A neuron may have as many as 10,000 synapses at which it receives input from other neurons. Some synapses have an excitatory effect on the membrane of the postsynaptic neuron and increase the likelihood that the neuron will fire. Other synapses have an inhibitory effect and reduce the likelihood that the postsynaptic neuron will fire. The net effect of all the synapses determines whether an action potential is generated in the postsynaptic neuron. (The shape of the synaptic knobs shown in this electron micrograph is distorted as a result of the preparation process.)**

generated. This integration of input from large numbers of different kinds of synapses gives the nervous system fine control over neuronal responses, just as having both an accelerator and a brake gives you finer control over the movement of a car.

Removal of Neurotransmitter

After being released into a synapse, neurotransmitters are quickly removed so their effects are temporary. If they were not removed, they would continue to excite or inhibit the postsynaptic membrane indefinitely. Depending on the neurotransmitter, disposal is accomplished in one of two ways. First, enzymes can deactivate a neurotransmitter. For example, the enzyme acetylcholinesterase removes the neurotransmitter **acetylcholine** from synapses where it has been released. Second, the neurotransmitter may be actively pumped back into the presynaptic knob. (See the Ethical Issue essay, *Pesticides and the Nervous System*.)

Roles of Different Neurotransmitters

As we have seen, neurotransmitters are the chemical means of communication within the nervous system. There are dozens of neurotransmitters, carrying messages among neurons and between neurons and muscles or glands. The activities of neurotransmitters produce our thoughts and feelings and enable us to interact appropriately with the world around us. Some neurotransmitters produce different effects on different types of cells.

Acetylcholine and norepinephrine are neurotransmitters that act in both the peripheral and the central nervous systems. Both have either excitatory or inhibitory effects, depending on where they are released. Most internal organs receive input from neurons that release acetylcholine *and* from neurons that release norepinephrine. Norepinephrine stimulates most organs but inhibits certain others. Whatever the effect of norepinephrine on any particular organ, acetylcholine will have the opposite effect.

Acetylcholine is also the neurotransmitter released at every neuromuscular junction (the junction of a motor neuron and a skeletal muscle cell), where it triggers contraction of voluntary (skeletal) muscles. We can see how important the nerve activation of muscle is whenever the interaction of nerve and muscle is interrupted. An example of such interruption is *myasthenia gravis*, an autoimmune disease in which the body's defense mechanisms attack the acetylcholine receptors at neuromuscular junctions. With any repeated movement, the amount of acetylcholine released with each nerve impulse decreases after the neurons have fired a few times in succession. The low number of acetylcholine receptors in people with myasthenia gravis makes such people extremely sensitive to even the slightest decline in acetylcholine availability. As a result, a person with myasthenia gravis has little muscle strength, and their repeated movements become feeble quite rapidly. Drugs that inhibit acetylcholinesterase are prescribed to prevent the breakdown of acetylcholine, elevating the level of acetylcholine in the neuromuscular junction.

About 50 neurotransmitters are used by the central nervous system for communication between the neurons in our brains. Why so many? One reason seems to be that different neurotransmitters are involved with different behavioral systems. Norepinephrine, for instance, is important in the regulation of mood, in the pleasure system of the brain, and in arousal. Norepinephrine is thought to produce an energizing "good" feeling. It is also thought to be essential in hunger, thirst, and the sex drive. Serotonin is thought to promote a generalized feeling of well-being. Dopamine helps regulate emotions. It is also used in pathways that control complex movements.

A change in the level of a neurotransmitter affects the behaviors controlled by neurons that communicate using that neurotransmitter. Neurotransmitter levels may change as a result of taking certain drugs. Changes in neurotransmitter levels also cause certain diseases.

FIGURE 3a(ii).10 **Former President Ronald Reagan died in June 2004 at the age of 93. He had Alzheimer's disease since at least 1994. His wife, Nancy Reagan, described Alzheimer's disease as "the long good-bye" because it robs people of their memories long before it takes their lives.**

Alzheimer's Disease and Acetylcholine

Alzheimer's disease is progressive and results in loss of memory, particularly for recent events, followed by sometimes severe personality changes (Figure 3a(ii).10). In Alzheimer's disease, the parts of the brain important in memory and intellectual functioning (hippocampus and cerebral cortex) lose large numbers of neurons. Some of the neurons in these regions use the neurotransmitter acetylcholine, which may decrease in level by as much as 90% in a person with Alzheimer's and possibly explains the loss of memory and mental capacity. In addition, a brain affected by Alzheimer's disease is pocked with clusters of proteins, some between the neurons (amyloid plaques) and others within the neurons (neurofibrillary tangles). The amyloid plaques and neurofibrillary tangles are the prime suspects for the cause of the death of acetylcholine-producing neurons.

In hypothesizing that the loss of acetylcholine is responsible for some of the Alzheimer's symptoms, researchers and physicians have attempted to treat Alzheimer's disease with drugs meant to raise or at least maintain acetylcholine levels. Although such drugs (Aricept, Exelon, and Reminyl) do improve the memory and intellectual ability of some people with Alzheimer's, they do not help in all cases. Moreover, any improvement is rapidly lost when a person stops taking the drugs.

Depression, Serotonin, Dopamine, and Norepinephrine

We all describe ourselves as feeling depressed at times. However, more than 19 million Americans experience depression that lasts for weeks, months, or years and interferes with their ability to function in daily life. This condition is considered *clinical depression*, and it can affect anyone. It is thought to be related in some way to insufficient levels of the neurotransmitter serotonin as well as of dopamine and norepinephrine. Signs of depression can include a loss of interest and pleasure in the activities and hobbies that were previously pleasurable; anxiety; sleep problems; decreased energy; and feelings of sadness, hopelessness, worthlessness, and guilt. Depression takes the joy out of life and complicates certain medical conditions such as heart disease, cancer, diabetes, epilepsy, and osteoporosis.

Many depressed people exhibit suicidal behavior or actually commit suicide (currently, the third-ranking cause of death for teenagers). Studies comparing the brains of people who committed suicide with those of people who died of other causes reveal structural and chemical differences. The brains of people who took their own lives indicate a problem in the production and activity of serotonin.

Depression can be treated successfully. Unfortunately, few of the millions of people suffering from depression recognize the symptoms and seek help. Antidepressant drugs affect the functioning of the neurotransmitters responsible for the problem: norepinephrine and serotonin. Older medications affected both neurotransmitters simultaneously. Newer ones, including Prozac, Zoloft, and Paxil, specifically affect serotonin functioning, increasing the level of serotonin in the synapse by reducing its rate of removal. Other antidepressants (such as Welbutrin) increase norepinephrine and dopamine functioning by reducing their rates of removal from the synapse.

what would you do?

Few people would question the justifiability of providing drugs that elevate neurotransmitter function to someone who is depressed or suicidal in order to help the person live a normal life. However, researchers believe that the levels of key neurotransmitters also affect personality traits, such as shyness or impulsiveness. If so, we may someday be able to design our own personalities. Should minor personality problems be treated with drugs? Should a personality "flaw" like shyness or impulsiveness be treated? What do you think?

Parkinson's Disease and Dopamine

Parkinson's disease is a progressive disorder that results from the death of dopamine-producing neurons deep in the brain's movement control center (Figure 3a(ii).11). A person with Parkinson's disease moves slowly, usually with a shuffling gait and a hunched posture, and may suffer from involuntary muscle contractions that further interfere with intended movements. The contractions may cause tremors (involuntary rhythmic shaking) of the hands or head, because of muscles alternately contracting and relaxing; or they may cause muscle rigidity, because of muscles contracting continuously. This muscle rigidity may cause sudden "freezing" in the middle of a movement.

As the dopamine-producing neurons in the brain's movement control center die, dopamine levels begin to fall. Initially, the symptoms are subtle and are often written off as part of the aging process. By the time the Parkinson's diagnosis is apparent, 80% of the neurons in this small area of the brain may already have died.

Attempts to treat Parkinson's disease have focused on replacing dopamine or helping the brain get by with the remaining dopamine. Unfortunately, swallowing pills containing dopamine does not help, because dopamine is prevented from reaching the brain by the blood–brain barrier. Instead, patients are given other substances that *can* reach the brain. The most common and effective treatment combines two drugs: L-dopa, an amino acid that the brain converts to dopamine, and carbidopa, which prevents dopamine from forming outside of the brain and causing undesirable side effects. However, this treatment does not stop the steady loss of dopamine-producing neurons, so it loses effectiveness as the disease progresses. Some patients are treated with drugs that enhance their levels of dopamine by inhibiting the enzyme that breaks down dopamine.

FIGURE 3a(ii).11 Actor Michael J. Fox and former heavyweight champion Muhammad Ali have Parkinson's disease, a progressive debilitating disease characterized by slowed movements, tremors, and muscle rigidity. The symptoms result from insufficient amounts of the neurotransmitter dopamine, caused by the death of dopamine-making nerve cells in a movement control center of the brain. The Michael J. Fox Foundation for Parkinson's Research (www.michaeljfox.org) funds research on the early diagnosis and treatment of Parkinson's disease.

Taken from *Biology of Humans: Concepts, Applications, and Issues*, Third Edition, by Judith Goodenough and Betty McGuire

ORGANIZATION OF THE NERVOUS SYSTEM

If you were to view the nervous system apart from the rest of the body, you would see a dense mass of neural tissue where the head should be, with a cord of neural tissue extending downward from it where the middle of the back should be. These structures are the brain and spinal cord, respectively, and they constitute the **central nervous system** (**CNS**; Figure 3a(ii).12), which integrates and coordinates all voluntary and involuntary nervous functions. Connected to the brain and spinal cord are many communication "cables"—the nerves that carry messages to and from the CNS. The nerves branch extensively, forming a vast network. Some of their cell bodies are grouped together in small clusters called **ganglia** (singular, *ganglion*). The nerves and ganglia are located outside of the CNS and make up the **peripheral nervous system (PNS)**. The PNS keeps the CNS in continuous contact with almost every part of the body.

The peripheral nervous system can be further subdivided on the basis of function into the somatic nervous system and the auto-nomic nervous system. The **somatic nervous system** consists of nerves that carry information to and from the CNS, resulting in sensations and voluntary movement. The **autonomic nervous system,** on the other hand, governs the involuntary, subconscious activities that keep the body functioning properly. The autonomic nervous system has two parts that generally produce opposite effects on the muscles or glands they control. One, the **sympathetic nervous system,** is in charge during stressful or emergency conditions. The other, the **parasympathetic nervous system,** adjusts bodily function so that energy is conserved during nonstressful times.

Although we have described the nervous system as having different parts and divisions, remember that all the parts function as a coordinated whole. Imagine for a moment that you are meditating in the park; your eyes are closed, and you are resting. While you are relaxing, the parasympathetic nervous system is ensuring that your life-sustaining bodily activities continue.

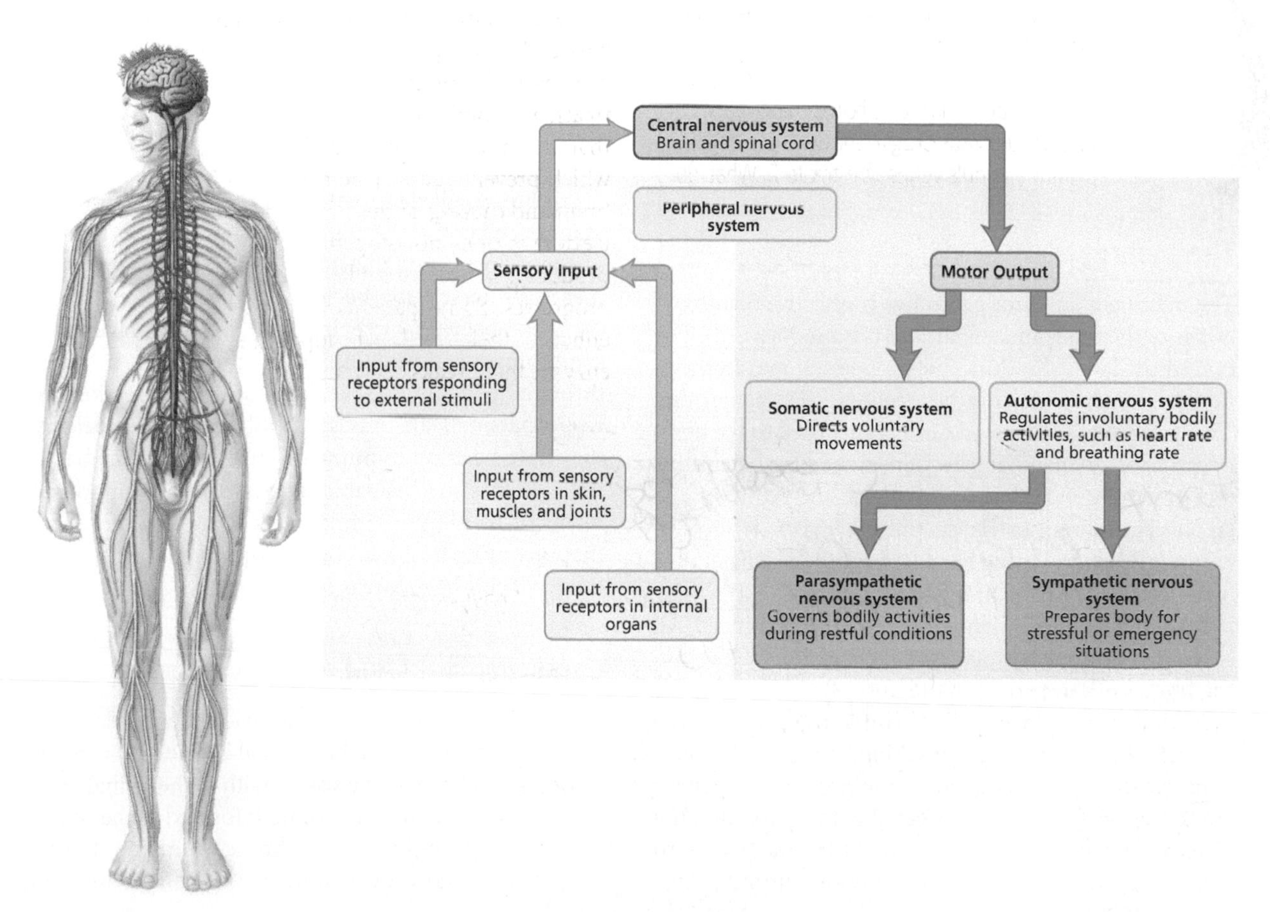

FIGURE 3a(ii).12 An overview of the nervous system. The various parts of the human nervous system have special functions but work together as an integrated whole.

Suddenly, someone grasps your hand. Sensory receptors in the skin (which are part of the somatic nervous system) respond to the pressure and warmth of the hand by sending messages over sensory nerves to the spinal cord. Neurons within the spinal cord relay the messages to the brain. The brain integrates incoming sensory information and "decides" on an appropriate response. For example, the brain may generate messages that cause your eyes to open. If the sight of the person holding your hand produces strong emotion, the sympathetic nervous system may speed up your heartbeat and perhaps even your breathing.

THE CENTRAL NERVOUS SYSTEM

The central nervous system includes the brain and spinal cord, which are made up of many closely packed neurons. Neurons are very fragile, and most cannot divide and produce new cells. Therefore, with few exceptions, a neuron that is damaged or dies cannot be replaced.

Protection of the Central Nervous System

The brain and spinal cord are protected by bony cases (the skull and vertebral column), membranes (the meninges), and a fluid cushion (cerebrospinal fluid).

The Meninges

The **meninges** are three protective connective tissue coverings of the brain and spinal cord (Figure 3a(ii).13). The outermost layer, the dura mater, is tough and leathery. Beneath the dura mater is the arachnoid (Latin, meaning "like a cobweb"). The arachnoid is anchored to the next-lower layer of meninges by thin, threadlike extensions that resemble a spider's web (hence the name of the layer). The innermost layer, the pia mater, is molded around the brain. Fitting like a leotard, the pia mater dips into every irregularity on the brain's surface.

Meningitis is an inflammation of the meninges. All cases of meningitis must be taken seriously because the infection can spread to the underlying nervous tissue and cause encephalitis (inflammation of the brain), which can be deadly. Many types of bacteria and certain viruses can cause meningitis. If bacteria are the cause, the person is treated with antibiotics. If a virus is the cause, treatment includes medicines to alleviate pain and fever while the body's immune system fights the virus.

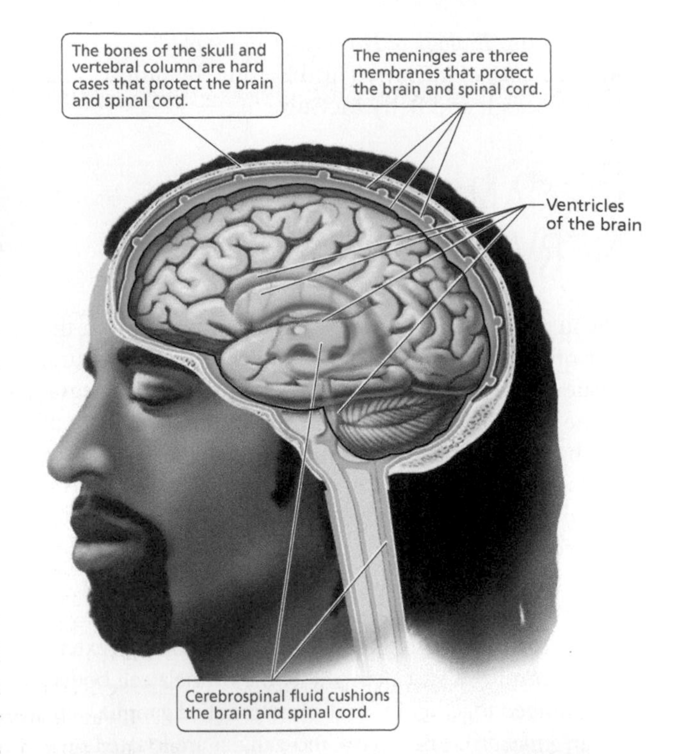
The bones of the skull and vertebral column are hard cases that protect the brain and spinal cord.
The meninges are three membranes that protect the brain and spinal cord.
Ventricles of the brain
Cerebrospinal fluid cushions the brain and spinal cord.

FIGURE 3a(ii).13 **The central nervous system is protected by the meninges, the cerebrospinal fluid, and the bones of the skull and vertebral column**

Freshmen college students housed in dormitories are at increased risk of getting bacterial meningitis because of their close living quarters. Part of the reason is the means by which the bacteria are spread. People can carry the bacteria in their throat without having any symptoms of illness and can spread the infection through coughing, sneezing, or intimate kissing. Upperclassmen are less susceptible, perhaps because they have built up immune defenses against the bacteria. Vaccines are available against most, but not all, forms of meningitis. Some colleges are now requiring that incoming freshmen be vaccinated against some of the most common forms of meningitis.

Cerebrospinal Fluid

The **cerebrospinal fluid** fills the space between layers of the me-ninges as well as the internal cavities of the brain, called *ventricles,* and the cavity within the spinal cord, called the *central canal.* This fluid is formed in the ventricles and circulates from them through the central canal. Eventually, cerebrospinal fluid is reabsorbed into the blood.

Health Issue

Brain Injury: A Silent Epidemic

Most of us take our brain for granted. We assume that this fragile control center is safe from harm, safely guarded by the thick bones of our skulls and cushioned by cerebrospinal fluid. The truth is that the brain is more vulnerable than we may think, and injuries to this vital organ are frighteningly common. Brain injury has been termed a "silent epidemic." It is silent because a brain injured person doesn't have visible physical symptoms. It is an epidemic because it is so common. One in every 220 people in the United States is suffering from a brain injury. A brain injury occurs every 16 seconds; a death from head injury occurs every 12 minutes.

Brain injuries are categorized as either acquired or traumatic. Acquired brain injury (ABI) is caused by a disruption in oxygen flow to the brain. Examples of ABIs include strokes and aneurysms, heart attacks, brain tumors, anoxia, meningitis, seizure disorders, and substance abuse. There is a strong correlation between substance abuse and acquired brain injury because alcohol and other substances are neurotoxins that cause damage to the brain with repeated use. Furthermore, substance abuse is associated with poor nutrition, which can cause dehydration and ultimately wastes brain cells.

Traumatic brain injury, or TBI, is caused by an external force. There are two types of TBI: open and closed. An open head injury is when the scalp is cut through and the skull is broken, damaging the brain underneath. A closed head injury happens when the head suddenly changes motion, forcing the brain to follow the movement, like when a car stops very suddenly. The brain is soft and jellylike, and it sits snugly within the skull. Sudden movement of the head can cause it to ricochet within the skull, damaging the millions of nerve fibers that run from one part of the brain to another. Also, the inside of the skull has many ridges and sharp edges that can cut or bruise the brain. Common causes of TBI include motor vehicle accidents, firearms, brawls, slip-and-fall accidents, and accidents related to sports such as skiing. Substance abuse is also associated with TBI, as the impairment caused by alcohol and drugs can lead to vehicular accidents and increase risk of falls and physical altercations. You can protect yourself against TBI by wearing a helmet when biking, skiing, or doing any other sport where a fall is likely. Since motor vehicle accidents cause nearly half of all head injuries, please buckle up!

TBI is getting a lot of attention recently because nearly two-thirds of injured U.S. soldiers sent from Iraq to Walter Reed Medical Center have been diagnosed with traumatic brain injury. That percentage, thought to be higher than in any other past U.S. conflict, is said to be due to improved armor that allows soldiers to survive injuries that previously would have been fatal.

To reduce your risk of traumatic brain injury always wear a helmet when cycling.

Also, compared to other wars, fewer firearms and more improvised explosive devices (IEDs) are being used in combat; the intense vibrations from these explosives cause the brain to move within the soldiers' skulls.

Regardless of cause, no two brain injuries are the same. The symptoms are diverse and vary widely due to severity and location of injury as well as the individual's functioning before the accident. Symptoms frequently include cognitive and emotional limitations, including difficulties with memory, attention, and reasoning; depression; anxiety; and impulse control and anger management issues. Physical impairments are common and can range from weakness on one side of the body to paralysis.

Cerebrospinal fluid has several important functions:

- **Shock absorption.** Just as an air bag protects the driver of a car by preventing impact with the steering wheel, the cerebrospinal fluid protects the brain by cushioning its impact with the skull during blows or other head trauma.
- **Support.** Because the brain floats in the cerebrospinal fluid, it is not crushed under its own weight.
- **Nourishment and waste removal.** The cerebrospinal fluid delivers nutrients and chemical messengers and removes waste products.

The brain is, indeed, protected by the skull, meninges, and cerebrospinal fluid. Nonetheless, 7 million brain injuries occur annually in the United States. We discuss brain injury further in the Health Issue essay, *Brain Injury: A Silent Epidemic.*

The Blood–brain Barrier

The CNS is also protected by the **blood–brain barrier,** a mechanism that selects the substances permitted to enter the cerebrospinal fluid from the blood. This barrier is formed by the tight junctions between the cells of the capillary walls that supply blood to the brain and spinal cord. Because the cells are held together much more tightly than are cells in capillaries in the rest of the body, substances in the blood are forced to pass through the cells of the capillaries instead of between the cells. Thus, the membranes of the capillary cells filter and adjust the composition of the filtrate by selecting the substances that can leave the blood. The plasma membranes of the capillary walls are largely lipid. So, lipid-soluble substances, including oxygen and carbon dioxide, can pass through easily. Certain drugs, including caffeine and alcohol, are lipid soluble, explaining why they can have a rapid effect on the brain. However, the blood–brain barrier prevents many potentially life-saving, infection-fighting, or tumor-suppressing drugs that are not lipid soluble from reaching brain tissue, which frustrates physicians.

Brain: Command Center

In a sense, your brain is more "you" than is any other part of your body, because it holds your emotions and the keys to your personality. Yet, if you were to look at your brain, you might not recognize it as yourself. The brain is the consistency of soft cheese and weighs less than 1600 g (3 lb), which is probably less than 3% of your body weight. Nevertheless, it is the origin of your secret thoughts and desires; it remembers your most embarrassing moment; and it keeps all your body systems functioning harmoniously while your conscious mind concentrates on other activities. Let's look at how its many circuits are organized to perform these amazing feats.

Cerebrum

The **cerebrum** is the largest and most prominent part of the brain (Figure 3a(ii).14). It is, quite literally, your "thinking cap." Accounting for 83% of the total brain weight, the cerebrum gives you most of your human characteristics.

The many ridges and grooves on the surface of the cerebrum make it appear wrinkled. Some furrows are deeper than others. The deepest indentation is in the center and runs from front to back. This groove, called the longitudinal fissure, separates the cerebrum into two hemispheres (Figure 3a(ii).15). Each hemisphere receives sensory information from and directs the movements of the opposite side of the body. In addition, the hemispheres process information in slightly

Q How do the left and right cerebral hemispheres communicate with one another?

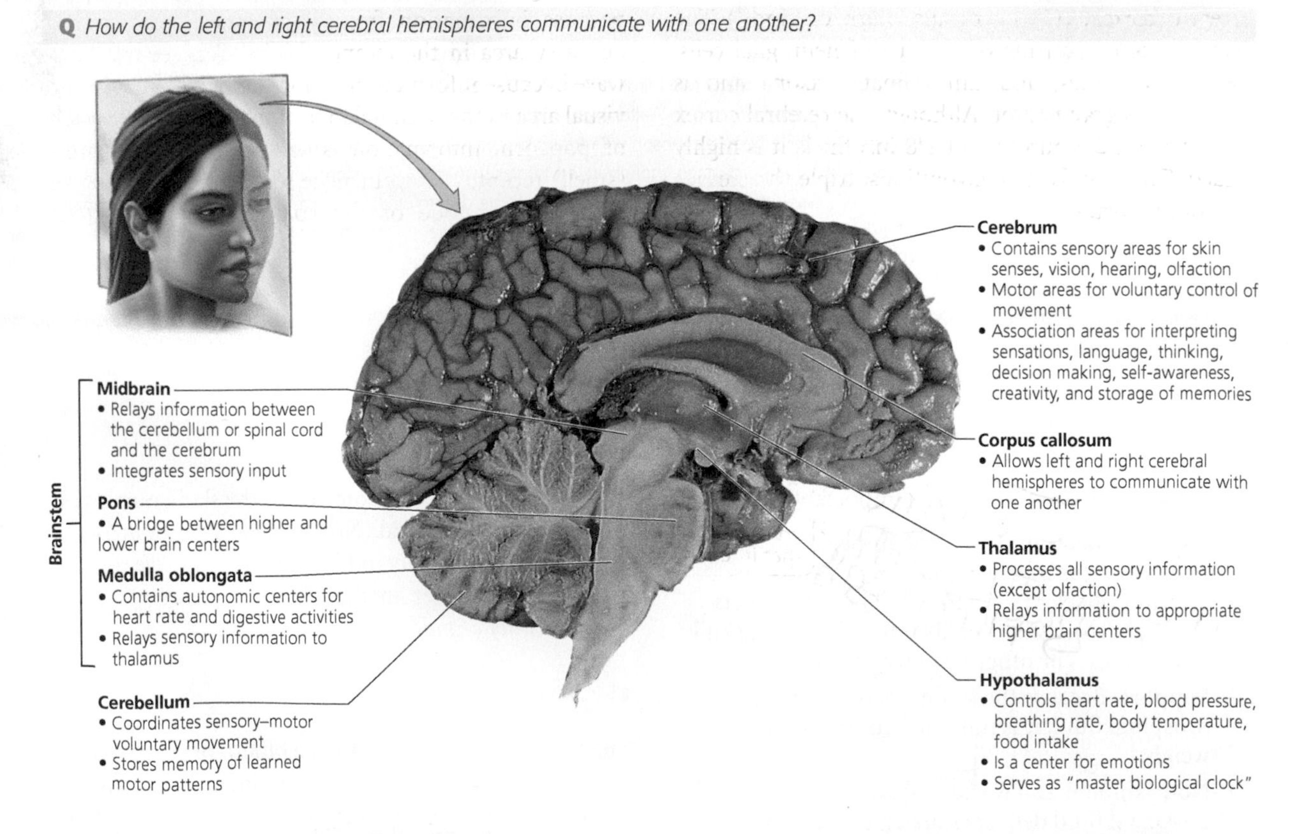
Cerebrum
• Contains sensory areas for skin senses, vision, hearing, olfaction
• Motor areas for voluntary control of movement
• Association areas for interpreting sensations, language, thinking, decision making, self-awareness, creativity, and storage of memories
Corpus callosum
• Allows left and right cerebral hemispheres to communicate with one another
Thalamus
• Processes all sensory information (except olfaction)
• Relays information to appropriate higher brain centers
Hypothalamus
• Controls heart rate, blood pressure, breathing rate, body temperature, food intake
• Is a center for emotions
• Serves as "master biological clock"
Brainstem
Midbrain
• Relays information between the cerebellum or spinal cord and the cerebrum
• Integrates sensory input
Pons
• A bridge between higher and lower brain centers
Medulla oblongata
• Contains autonomic centers for heart rate and digestive activities
• Relays sensory information to thalamus
Cerebellum
• Coordinates sensory–motor voluntary movement
• Stores memory of learned motor patterns

FIGURE 3a(ii).14 **A section through the brain from front to back, indicating the functions of selected structures**

A The corpus callosum

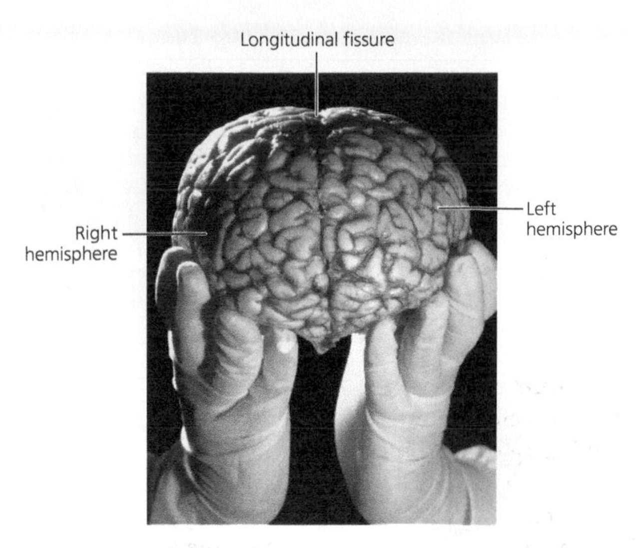

FIGURE 3a(ii).15 **A photograph of the human brain from the front, showing the left and right cerebral hemispheres**

different ways and are, therefore, specialized for slightly different mental functions.

The thin outer layer of each hemisphere is called the **cerebral cortex.** (*Cortex* means "bark or rind.") The cerebral cortex consists of billions of neuroglial cells, nerve cell bodies, and unmyelinated axons and is described as **gray matter.** Although the cerebral cortex is only about 2.5 mm (about 1/8 in.) thick, it is highly folded. These folds, or convolutions, triple the surface area of the cortex.

Beneath the cortex is the cerebral **white matter,** which appears white because it consists primarily of myelinated axons. Myelin sheaths increase the rate of conduction along axons and are, therefore, found on axons that conduct information over long distances. The axons of the cerebral white matter allow various regions of the brain to communicate with one another and with the spinal cord. A very important band of white matter, called the *corpus callosum,* connects the two cerebral hemispheres so they can communicate with one another (Figure 3a(ii).16).

Other grooves on the surface of the brain mark the boundaries of four lobes on each hemisphere: the *frontal, parietal, temporal,* and *occipital lobes* (Figure 3a(ii).17). Each of these lobes has its own specializations. Although the assignment of a specific function to a particular region of the cerebral cortex is imprecise, it is generally agreed that there are three types of functional areas: sensory, motor, and association.

Sensory Areas Our awareness of sensations depends on the sensory areas of the cerebral cortex. The various sensory receptors of the body send information to the cortex, where each sense is processed in a different region. If you stand on a street corner watching a parade go by, you hear the band play because information from your ears is sent to the auditory area in the temporal lobe. You see the flags wave because information from your eyes is sent to the visual area in the occipital lobe. When you catch a whiff of popcorn, information is sent from the olfactory (smell) receptors in your nose to the olfactory area in the temporal lobe of the cortex. As you eat that

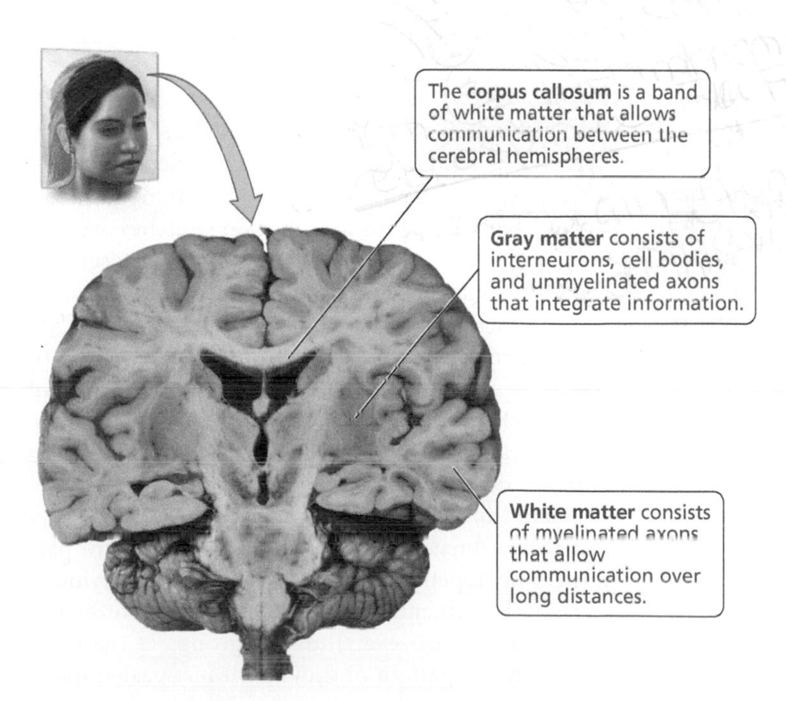

The corpus callosum is a band of white matter that allows communication between the cerebral hemispheres.
Gray matter consists of interneurons, cell bodies, and unmyelinated axons that integrate information.
White matter consists of myelinated axons that allow communication over long distances.

FIGURE 3a(ii).16 **A cross section through the brain, showing the gray matter (the cerebral cortex), white matter, and corpus callosum**

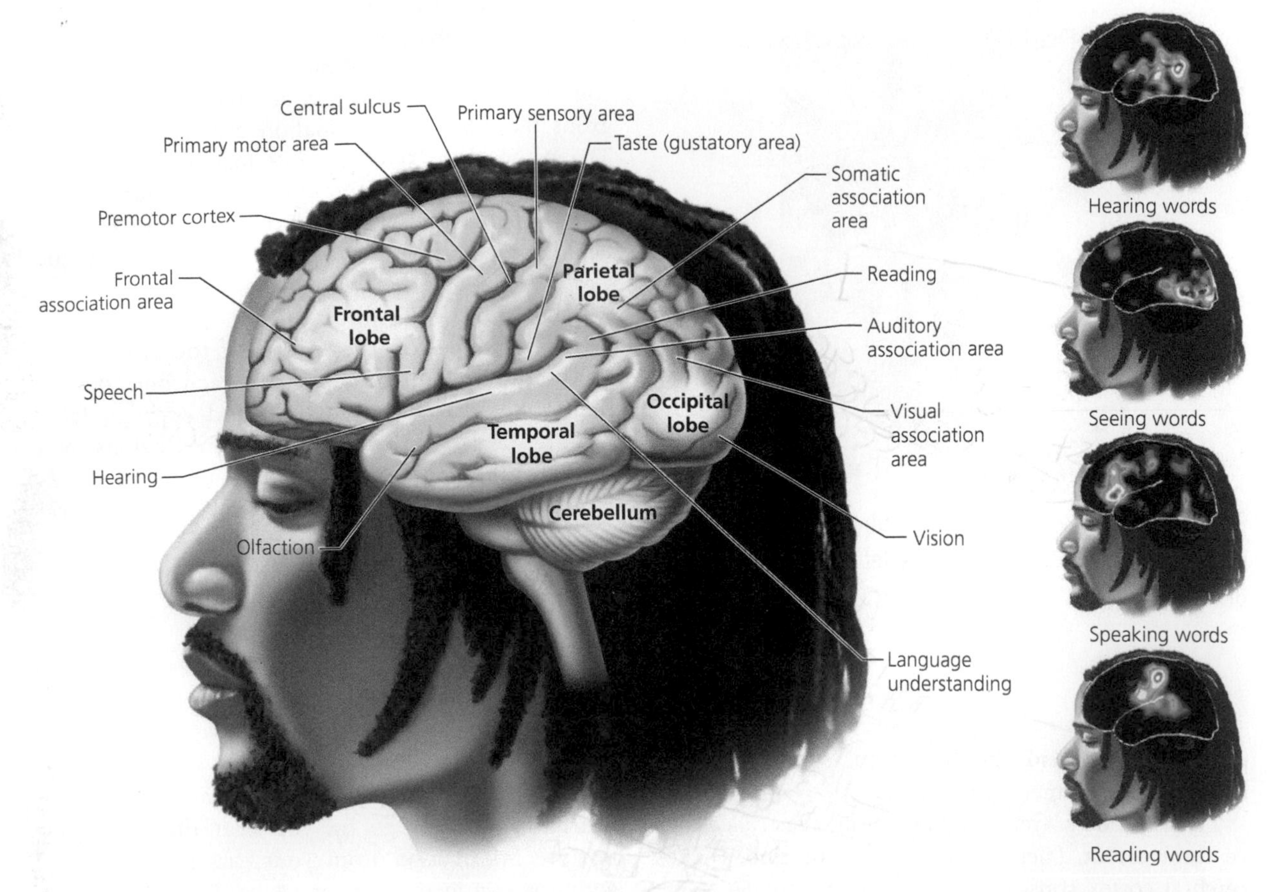

FIGURE 3a(ii).17 **The cerebral cortex. (a) The cerebral cortex has four lobes. Some of the functions associated with each lobe are indicated. (b) These PET scans of the brain show regions of increased blood flow during different mental activities. The increased flow of blood shows which region becomes active when the cerebrum is engaged in hearing words, seeing words, speaking words, and reading words. Notice the relation between active regions of the cerebral cortex during these tasks and the cortical areas for various language skills shown in part (a).**

popcorn, you know it is too salty because information from the taste receptors is sent to gustatory areas in the parietal lobe.

Still watching the parade, you know that you are standing in the hot sun and that your belt is too tight because information from touch, pain, and temperature receptors in the skin and from receptors in the joints and skeletal muscles is sent to the **primary somatosensory area.** This region forms a band in the parietal lobes that stretches over the cortex from ear to ear (Figure 3a(ii).18). Sensations from different parts of the body are represented in different regions of the primary somatosensory area (of the hemisphere on the opposite side of the body). The greater the degree of sensitivity, the greater the area of cortex devoted to that body part. Thus, your most sensitive body parts, such as the tongue, hands, face, and genitals, have more of the cortex devoted to them than do less sensitive areas, such as the forearm.

Motor Areas If you decide to join the parade, the **primary motor area** (Figure 3a(ii).18) of the cerebral cortex will send messages to your skeletal muscles. This motor area controls voluntary movement. It also forms a band in the frontal lobe that stretches over the cortex, just anterior to the primary somatosensory area. The motor area is organized in a manner similar to the somatosensory area. Each point on its surface corresponds to the movement of a different part of the body. The parts of the body we have finer control over, such as the tongue and fingers, have greater representation on the motor cortex than do regions with less dexterity, such as the trunk of the body.

Just in front of the motor cortex is the *premotor cortex.* It coordinates learned motor skills that are patterned or repetitive, such as typing or playing a musical instrument. The premotor cortex coordinates the movement of several muscle groups at the same time. When a pattern of movement is repeated many

Q *Our lips are more sensitive than is the skin on our forearm. We also have greater motor control of our lips than we do of our forearm. How is this difference in sensitivity and motor control represented on the cerebral cortex?*

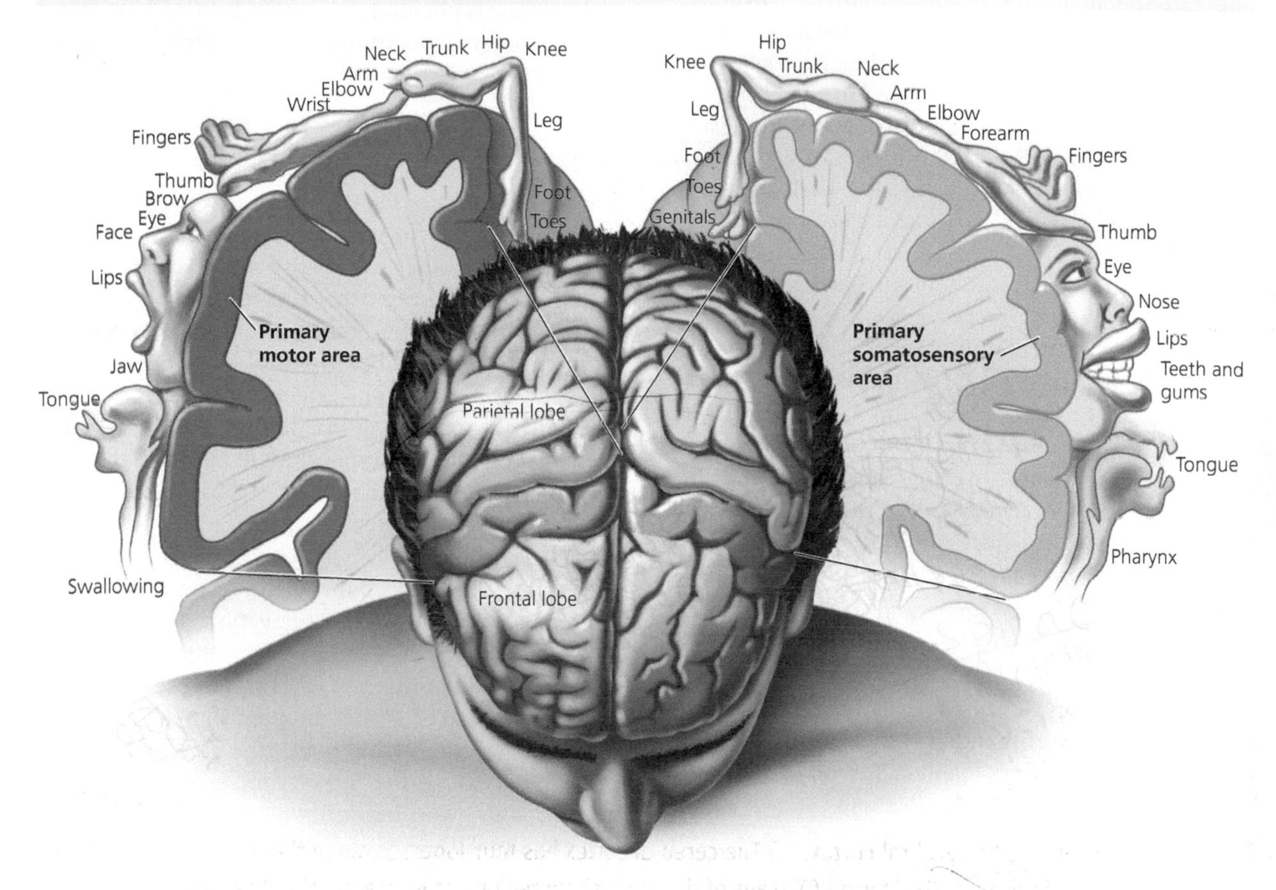

FIGURE 3a(ii).18 **The primary motor and the primary somatosensory regions of the cerebral cortex are organized in such a way that each location on their surface corresponds to a particular part of the body. The general arrangement is similar in the two regions.**

A *Areas with greater sensitivity and motor control have a proportionally larger area of representation on the cortex than do areas with less sensitivity and motor control, such as the forearm.*

times, the proper pattern of stimulation is stored in the premotor cortex. For example, as a guitar player practices playing a particular song many times, the pattern of stimulation needed to play that song is stored in the premotor cortex. Then, each time the song is played, the premotor cortex will stimulate the primary cortex in the pattern needed to play that song, without requiring the musician to think about where on the strings the fingers should be placed.

Association Areas Next to each primary sensory area is an association area. These communicate with the sensory and motor areas, and with other parts of the brain, to analyze and act on sensory input. In particular, each sensory association area communicates with the general interpretation area, to recognize what the sensory receptors are sensing. The general interpretation area assigns meaning to sensory information by integrating the input from sensory association areas with stored sensory memories. For example, on a dark night your eyes may detect a small, moving object. If the object then rubs against your legs and purrs, your general interpretation area will assist you in recognizing it as the neighbor's friendly cat. However, if the object turns away from you and raises its tail, you will recognize it as a skunk.

Once the sensory input has been interpreted, the information is sent to the most complicated of all association areas, the **prefrontal cortex**. This most anterior part of the frontal lobe predicts the consequences of various possible responses to the information it receives and decides which response will be best for you in your current situation. The prefrontal cortex enables us to reason, plan for the long term, and think about abstract concepts. It also plays a key rôle in determining our personality.

Thalamus

The cerebral hemispheres sit comfortably over the **thalamus** (see Figure 3a(ii).14). The thalamus is often described as the gateway to the cerebral cortex because all messages *to* the cerebral cortex must pass *through* the thalamus first. The thalamus functions in sensory experience, motor activity, stimulation of the cerebral cortex, and memory. Sensory input from every sense except smell and from all parts of the body is delivered to the thalamus. The thalamus sorts the information by function and relays it to appropriate regions of the cortex for processing. Some regions of the thalamus also integrate information from different sources rather than just relaying it. At the thalamic level of processing, you have a general impression of whether the sensation is pleasant or unpleasant. If you step on a tack, for instance, you may experience pain by the time the messages reach the thalamus; however, you will not know where you hurt until after the message is directed to the cerebral cortex.

Hypothalamus

Below the thalamus is the **hypothalamus** (*hypo*, under), a small region of the brain that is largely responsible for homeostasis—the body's maintenance of a stable environment for its cells. The hypothalamus, shown in Figure 3a(ii).14, coordinates the activities of the nervous and endocrine (hormonal) systems through its influence on the pituitary gland. The hypothalamus also influences blood pressure, heart rate, digestive activity, breathing rate, and many other vital physiological processes. It keeps body temperature near the set point, and it regulates hunger and thirst and therefore the intake of food. Moreover, because the hypothalamus receives input from the cerebral cortex, it can make your heart beat faster when you so much as see or think of something exciting or dangerous—a rattlesnake about to strike, for instance.

The hypothalamus is part of the limbic system (discussed later in this chapter), so it is also part of the circuitry for emotions. Specific regions of the hypothalamus play a role in the sex drive and in the perception of pain, pleasure, fear, and anger.

The hypothalamus also contains an area called the *suprachiasmatic nucleus,* often described as the body's "master biological clock." Day after day, many of the physiological processes within the body, affecting many physical abilities and even a person's mental sharpness, fluctuate so predictably that the variations are called biological rhythms and are described as being controlled by biological clocks. The suprachiasmatic nucleus synchronizes all these biological clocks and sets the timing for all the body's biological rhythms. Note that these fluctuations do not negate the concept of homeostasis; they simply remind us that the body's optimal internal state is not always the same. Instead, homeostasis is often rhythmic, so physiological processes fluctuate in a predictable manner.

Cerebellum

The **cerebellum** (see Figure 3a(ii).14) is the part of the brain responsible for sensory–motor coordination. It acts as an automatic pilot that produces smooth, well-timed voluntary movements and controls equilibrium and posture. Sensory information concerning the position of joints and the degree of tension in muscles and tendons is sent to the cerebellum from all parts of the body. By integrating this information with input from the eyes and the equilibrium receptors in the ears, the cerebellum knows the body's position and direction of movement at any given instant.

The coordination of sensory input and motor output by the cerebellum involves two important processes: comparison and prediction. During every move you make, the cerebellum continuously compares the actual position of each part of the body with where it *ought* to be at that moment (in relation to the intended movement) and makes the necessary corrections. Try to touch the tips of your two index fingers together above your head. You probably missed on the first attempt. However, the cerebellum makes the necessary corrections, and you will likely succeed on the next attempt. At the same time, the cerebellum calculates future positions of a body part during a movement. Then, just before that part reaches the intended position, the cerebellum sends messages to stop the movement at a specific point. Therefore, when you scratch an itch on your cheek, your hand stops before slapping your face!

Brain Stem

The brain stem consists of the medulla oblongata, the midbrain, and the pons. The **medulla oblongata** is often called simply the medulla (see Figure 3a(iii).14). This marvelous inch of nervous tissue contains reflex centers for some of life's most vital physiological functions—including the pace of the basic breathing

stop and THINK

Why would a brain tumor that destroyed the functioning of nerve cells in the medulla lead to death more quickly than a tumor of the same size on the cerebral cortex?

rhythm, the force and rate of heart contraction, and blood pressure. The medulla connects the spinal cord to the rest of the brain. Therefore, all sensory information going to the upper regions of the brain and all motor messages leaving the brain are carried by nerve pathways running through the medulla.

The **midbrain** processes information about sights and sounds and controls simple reflex responses to these stimuli. For example, when you hear an unexpected loud sound, your reflexive response is to turn your head and direct your eyes toward the source of the sound.

The **pons,** which means "bridge," connects lower portions of the CNS with higher brain structures. More specifically, it connects the spinal cord and cerebellum with the cerebrum, thalamus, and hypothalamus. In addition, the pons has a region that assists the medulla in regulating respiration.

Limbic System

The **limbic system** is a collective term for a group of structures that help to produce emotions and memory (Figure 3a(ii).19). The limbic system is defined on the basis of function rather than anatomy, and it includes parts of several brain regions and the neural pathways that connect them.

The limbic system is our emotional brain. It allows us to expe-rience countless emotions, including rage, pain, fear, sorrow, joy, and sexual pleasure. Emotions are important because they motivate behavior that will increase the chance of survival. Fear, for example, may have evolved to focus the mind on the threats in the environment so it can prepare the body to face them.

Connections between the cerebrum and the limbic system allow us to have *feelings* about *thoughts.* As a result, you may become excited at the thought of winning the lottery. Such connections also allow us to have thoughts about feelings, thus keeping us from responding to emotions, such as rage, in ways that would be unwise. The limbic system includes the hypothalamus, as Figure 3a(ii).19 shows. In addition, it is connected to lower brain centers, such as the medulla, that control the activity of internal organs. Therefore, we also have "gut" responses to emotions.

You wouldn't be you without your memories, and the limbic system plays a role in forming them. Memory, the storage and retrieval of information, takes place in two stages. The first is **short-term memory,** which holds a small amount of information for a few seconds or minutes, as when you look up a phone number and remember it only long enough to place the call. The second stage, **long-term memory,** stores seemingly limitless amounts of information for hours, days, or years. Not all short-term memories get consolidated into long-term memories, but when they do, the **hippocampus** plays an essential role. The amygdala, another part of the limbic system that functions in long-term memory, has widespread connections to sensory areas as well as to emotion centers. It associates memories gathered through different senses and links them to emotional states.

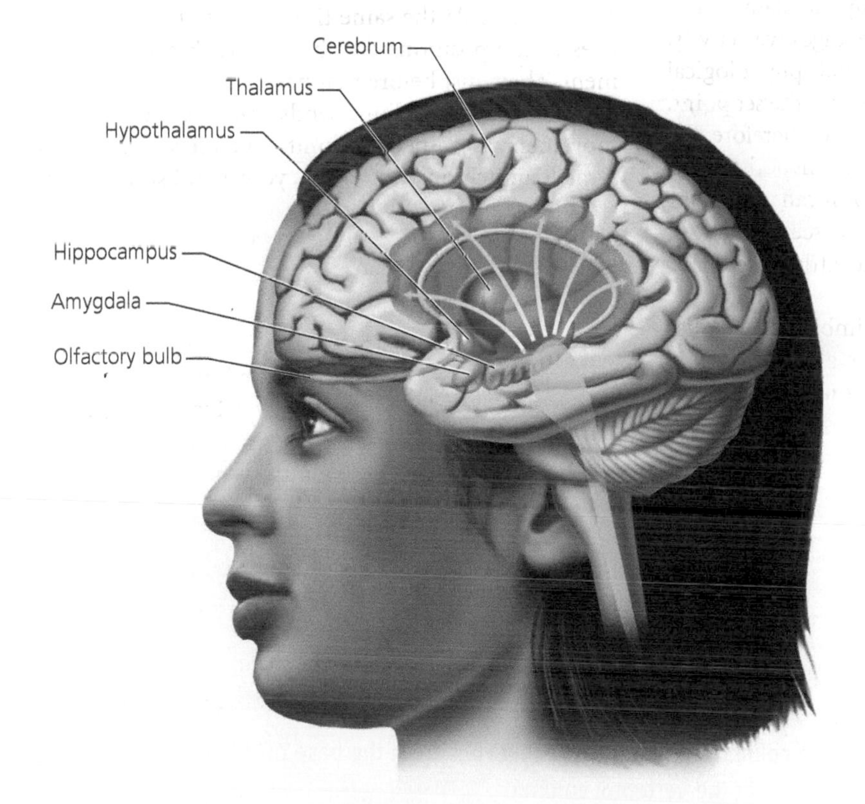

FIGURE 3a(ii).19 The limbic system and reticular activating system. The diagram shows the limbic system in purple as a three-dimensional structure within the brain, viewed from the left side. The reticular activating system is shown in green. Note the upward arrows.

The olfactory bulb transmits information about odors from the nose to the limbic system. Thus, the limbic system is a center where emotions, memory, and our sense of smell meet. As a result, we often have emotional responses to odors. The association between odor and emotion is the basis of aromatherapy as well as the perfume and scented candle industries. The interaction of emotion, sense of smell, and memory explains why odors can bring back memories. For example, the smell of cinnamon rolls may be pleasant because it reminds you of your grandmother baking special treats.

Reticular Activating System

The **reticular activating system** (RAS) is an extensive network of neurons that runs through the medulla and projects to the cerebral cortex (shown in Figure 3a(ii).19 in green). The RAS functions as a net, or filter, for sensory input. Our brain is constantly flooded with tremendous amounts of sensory information, about 100 million impulses each second, most of them trivial. The RAS filters out repetitive, familiar stimuli—the sound of street traffic, paper rustling, the coughing of the person next to you, or the pressure of clothing. However, infrequent or important stimuli pass through the RAS to the cerebral cortex and, therefore, reach our consciousness. Because of the RAS, you can fall asleep with the television on but wake up when someone whispers your name.

In addition, the RAS is an activating center. Unless inhibited by other brain regions, the RAS activates the cerebral cortex, keeping it alert and "awake." Consciousness occurs only while the RAS stimulates the cerebral cortex. When sleep centers in other regions of the brain inhibit activity in the RAS, we sleep. In essence, then, the cerebrum "sleeps" whenever it is not stimulated by the RAS. Sensory input to the RAS results in stimulation of the cerebral cortex and an increase in consciousness, which explains why it is usually easier to sleep in a dark, quiet room than in an airport terminal. Conscious activity in the cerebral cortex can also stimulate the RAS, which in turn will stimulate the cerebral cortex. Therefore, thinking about a problem may keep you awake all night.

stop and THINK

When a boxer is hit very hard in the jaw, his head–containing his medulla and RAS–is twisted sharply. Why might this twisting result in a knockout, in which the boxer loses consciousness?

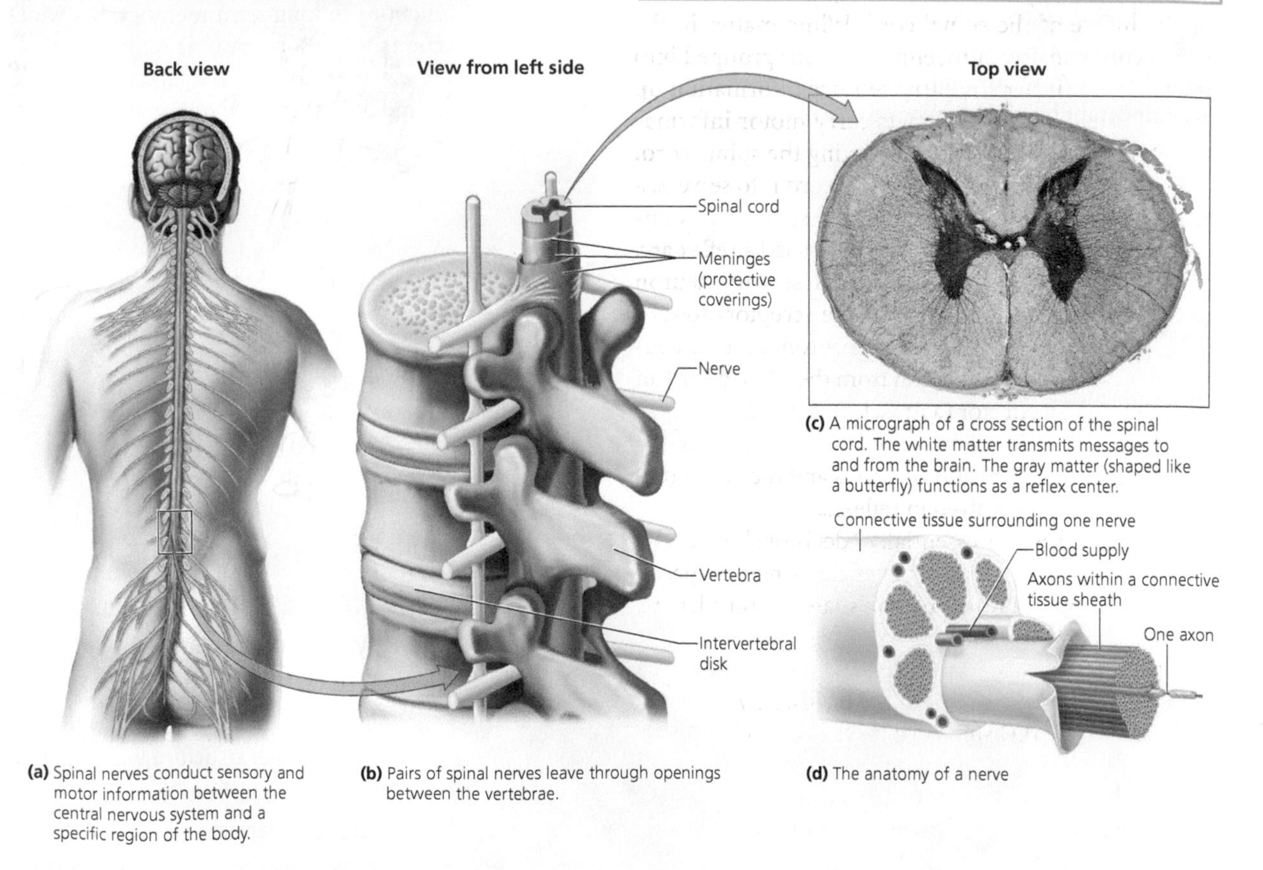

(a) Spinal nerves conduct sensory and motor information between the central nervous system and a specific region of the body.

(b) Pairs of spinal nerves leave through openings between the vertebrae.

(c) A micrograph of a cross section of the spinal cord. The white matter transmits messages to and from the brain. The gray matter (shaped like a butterfly) functions as a reflex center.

(d) The anatomy of a nerve

FIGURE 3a(ii).20 **The spinal cord is a column of neural tissue that runs from the base of the brain to just below the last rib. It is protected by the bones of the vertebral column**

Spinal Cord: Message Transmission and Reflex Center

The other major component of the central nervous system besides the brain is the spinal cord. The **spinal cord** is a tube of neural tissue that is continuous with the medulla at the base of the brain and extends about 45 cm (17 in.) to just below the last rib. For most of its length, the spinal cord is about the diameter of your little finger. It becomes slightly thicker in two regions, just below the neck and at the end of the cord, because of the large group of nerves connecting these regions of the cord with the arms and legs. The central canal, filled with cerebrospinal fluid, runs the length of the spinal cord.

The spinal cord is encased in and protected by the stacked bones of the vertebral column (Figure 3a(ii).20). Pairs of spinal nerves (considered part of the peripheral nervous system) extend from the spinal cord through openings between the vertebrae to serve different parts of the body. The vertebrae are separated by disks of cartilage that act as cushions.

The spinal cord has two functions: (1) to transmit messages to and from the brain and (2) to serve as a reflex center. The transmission of messages is performed primarily by white matter, found toward the outer surface of the spinal cord. White matter in the spinal cord consists of myelinated axons grouped into tracts. Ascending tracts carry sensory information up to the brain. Descending tracts carry motor information from the brain to a nerve leaving the spinal cord.

The second function of the spinal cord is to serve as a reflex center. A reflex is an automatic response to a stimulus, prewired in a circuit of neurons called a **reflex arc.** The circuit consists of a receptor, a sensory neuron (which brings information from the receptors toward the CNS), usually at least one interneuron, a motor neuron (which brings information from the CNS toward an effector), and an effector (a muscle or a gland). The gray matter, which is located in the central region of the spinal cord, houses the interneurons and the cell bodies of motor neurons involved in reflexes.

Spinal reflexes are essentially "decisions" made by the spinal cord. They are beneficial when a speedy reaction is important to a person's safety. Consider, for example, the withdrawal reflex. When you step on a piece of broken glass, impulses speed toward the spinal cord over sensory nerves (Figure 3a(iii).1). Within the gray matter of the spinal cord, the sensory neuron synapses with an interneuron. The interneuron, in turn, synapses with a motor neuron that sends a message to the appropriate muscle to contract and lift your foot off the glass.

While the spinal reflexes were removing the foot from the glass, pain messages from the cut foot were sent to the brain through ascending tracts in the spinal cord. However, it takes longer to get a message to the brain than it does to get one to the spinal cord, because the distance and number of synapses to be crossed are greater. Therefore, by the time pain messages reach the brain, you have already withdrawn your foot. Nonetheless, once the sensory information reaches the conscious brain, decisions can be made about how to care for the wound.

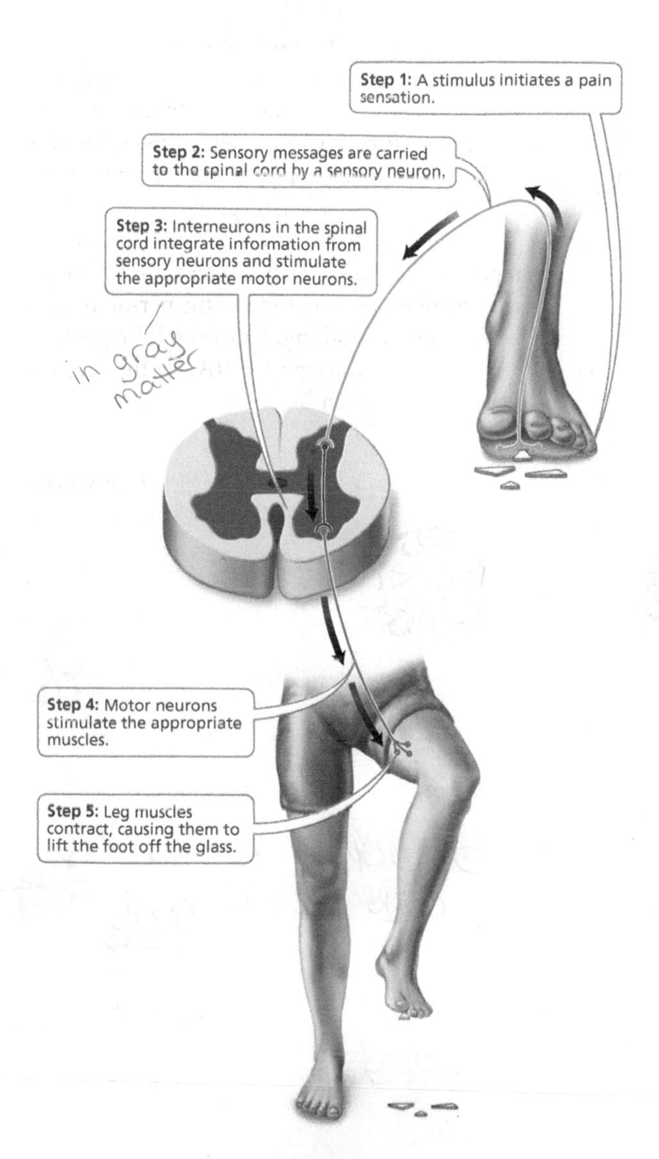

FIGURE 3a(iii).1 **A reflex arc consists of a sensory receptor, a sensory neuron, usually at least one interneuron, a motor neuron, and an effector**

3a(iii) The Peripheral Nervous System and the Senses

Taken from *Biology of Humans: Concepts, Applications, and Issues*, Third Edition, by Judith Goodenough and Betty McGuire

THE PERIPHERAL NERVOUS SYSTEM

The nerves and ganglia of the PNS carry information between the CNS and the rest of the body. The PNS consists of spinal nerves and cranial nerves.

The body has 31 pairs of **spinal nerves**, each of which originates in the spinal cord and services a specific region of the body. One member of each pair serves a part of the right side of the body, and the other serves the corresponding part of the left side. (Figure 3a(iii).2a).

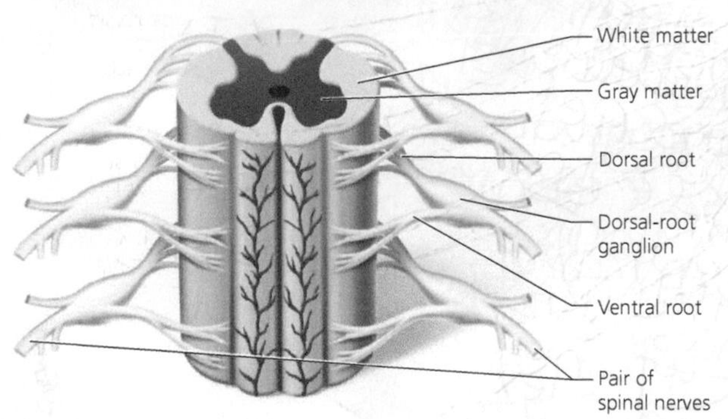

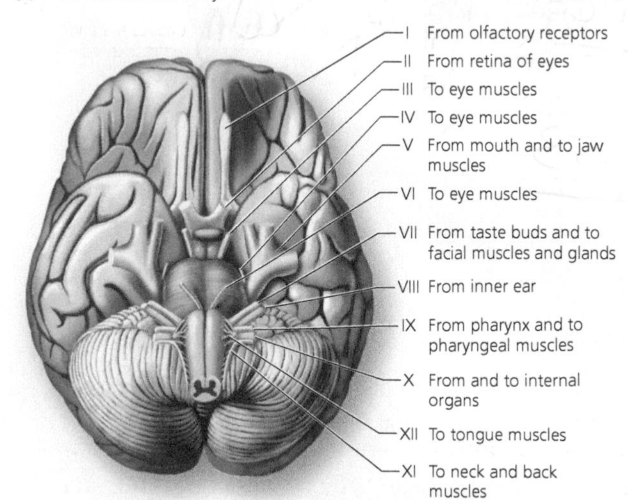

All spinal nerves carry both sensory and motor fibers. Fibers from the sensory neurons enter the spinal cord from the dorsal, or posterior, side, grouped into a bundle called the *dorsal root.* The cell bodies of these sensory neurons are located in a ganglion in the dorsal root. The axons of motor neurons leave the ventral (front side) of the spinal cord in a bundle called the *ventral root.* The cell bodies of motor neurons are located in the gray matter of the spinal cord. The dorsal and ventral roots join to form a single spinal nerve, which passes through the opening between the vertebrae.

The 12 pairs of **cranial nerves** (Figure 3a(iii).2b) arise from the brain and service the structures of the head and certain body parts, including the heart and diaphragm. Some cranial nerves carry only sensory fibers, others carry only motor fibers, and others carry both types of fibers.

Somatic Nervous System

The peripheral nervous system is subdivided into the somatic nervous system and the autonomic nervous system. The somatic nervous system carries sensory messages that tell us about the world around us and within us, and it controls movement. Sensory messages carried by somatic nerves result in conscious sensations, including light, sound, and touch. The somatic nervous system also controls our voluntary movements, allowing us to smile, stamp a foot, sing a lullaby, or frown as we sign a check.

Autonomic Nervous System

As part of the body's system of homeostasis, the autonomic nervous system automatically adjusts the functioning of our body organs so that the proper internal conditions are maintained and the body is able to meet the demands of the world around it. The somatic nervous system sends information about conditions within the body to the autonomic nervous system. The autonomic nervous system then makes the appropriate adjustments. Its activities alter digestive activity, open or close blood vessels to shunt blood to areas that need it most, and alter heart rate and breathing rate.

FIGURE 3a(iii).2 **(a) Spinal and (b) cranial nerves. The 12 pairs of cranial nerves can be seen in this view of the underside of the brain. Most cranial nerves service structures within the head, but some service organs lower in the body. The descriptions indicate whether the neuron carries sensory information (toward the brain) or motor information (away from the brain).**

Recall that the autonomic nervous system consists of two branches: the sympathetic and the parasympathetic nervous systems. The sympathetic nervous system gears the body to face an emergency or stressful situation, such as fear, rage, or vigorous exercise. Thus, the sympathetic nervous system prepares the body for fight or flight. In contrast, the parasympathetic nervous system adjusts body function so that energy is conserved during relaxation.

Both the parasympathetic and the sympathetic nervous systems send nerve fibers to most, but not all, internal organs (Figure 3a(iii).3). When both systems send nerves to a given organ, they have opposite, or antagonistic, effects on its function. If one system stimulates, the other system inhibits. The antagonistic effects are brought about by different neurotransmitters. Whereas sympathetic neurons release mostly norepinephrine at their target organs, parasympathetic neurons release acetylcholine at their target organs.

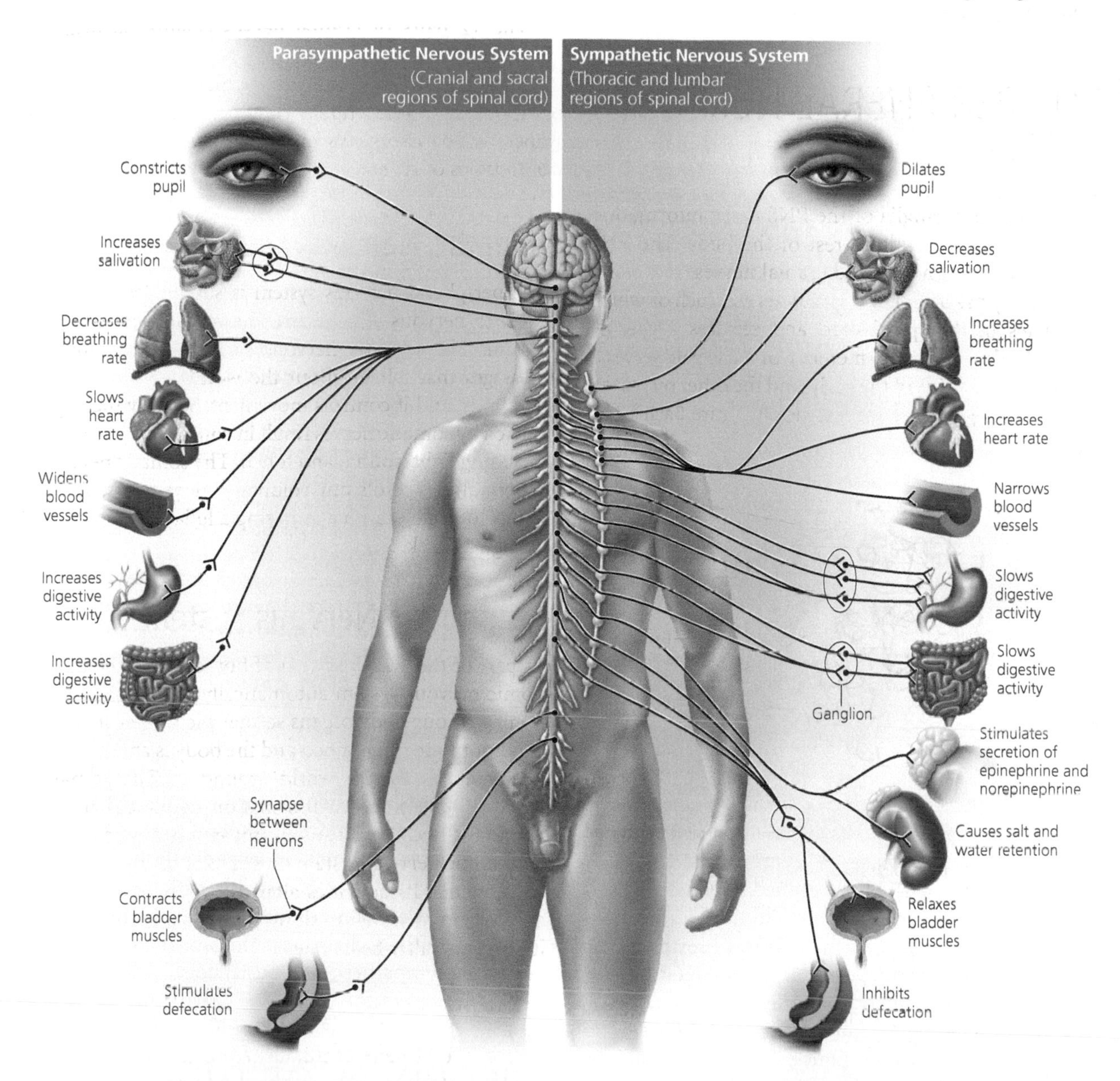

FIGURE 3a(iii).3 **Structure and function of the autonomic nervous system. Most organs are innervated by fibers from both the sympathetic and the parasympathetic nervous systems. When this dual innervation occurs, the two branches of the autonomic nervous system have opposite effects on the activity level of that organ. A chain of ganglia links the pathways of the sympathetic nervous system, which therefore usually acts as a unit, with all its effects occurring together. In contrast, the ganglia of the parasympathetic nervous system are each near the organ they service, so parasympathetic effects are more localized.**

Health Issue

To Sleep, Perchance to Dream

Not all sleep is the same. Indeed, each hour and a half during a typical night's sleep, you will cycle through a sequence of sleep stages. If the natural sleep pattern is disturbed, you may not feel well rested, even if you have "slept" for 8 hours. Stage 1 sleep occurs while you "drift off to sleep." During this period of transition from wakefulness to sleep, you become less aware of your surroundings, slowly tuning out lights and low-level noises (Figure **3a(iii).A**). Within the next few minutes, stage 2 sleep usually occurs. During stage 2 sleep, you are unaware of your surroundings. Muscle tension is lower than during wakefulness, and breathing and heart rate also decrease. More than half the night's sleeping time is spent in periods of stage 2 sleep.

Soon after entering stage 2, you sink even deeper into sleep—stages 3 and 4—and become increasingly difficult to awaken. After about 20 minutes of stage 4 sleep, you usually switch back to stage 3 followed by stage 2. Then, you begin an interval of paradoxical sleep, so named because the type of brain waves that occur are similar to those seen during alert mental activity. It would therefore seem that the brain is quite active at this time, and yet it is more difficult to awaken a person in paradoxical sleep than at any other stage. Paradoxical sleep is also called rapid eye movement (REM) sleep, because your eyes move rapidly behind closed eyelids during this stage. In REM sleep, your heart and breathing rate can be quite variable, but almost every skeletal muscle in your body, except for those of eyes and ears, is virtually paralyzed. This paralysis may keep us from hurting ourselves or others by acting out our dreams.

REM is the stage when dreams that have a storylike progression of events are apt to occur. About 80% of the people who are awakened during REM sleep and asked what was going on say they were dreaming. Only about 20% report that they were dreaming if awakened during other stages of sleep. Moreover, the dreams that occur outside of REM sleep are more likely to be a thought, an image, or an emotion than a story.

The function of REM sleep is not well understood, but it appears to be important for survival. Sleep researchers believe that REM sleep facilitates learning and memory consolidation. Other ideas are that REM is important for CNS development and for the maintenance of normal physiology.

The first bout of REM sleep usually occurs about 90 minutes after falling asleep and lasts about 10 minutes. The REM period of each successive cycle is a little longer. By morning, the interval of REM sleep may be about an hour long. As the bouts of REM lengthen, stages 3 and 4 are lost. So the second half of a night's sleep is not identical to the first half: there is much more REM in the second half. This is why taking several short catnaps does not provide the same quality of sleep as a single longer period of sleep, even if the total number of hours of sleep is identical.

How much sleep do we need to stay healthy? There's no set answer to this question. You need less sleep as you get older. A newborn sleeps 18 hours a day, young adults generally sleep 7 to 8 hours, and elderly people usually need only 4.5 to 6.5 hours. Sleep requirements also vary between individuals. A few people need as little as 3 hours of sleep a night. Others don't feel their best unless they get 10 hours or more. So, you need as much sleep as it takes to feel well and function efficiently the next day—and no more.

Unfortunately, millions of Americans cheat on sleep. Students pull "all-nighters" studying for exams. Many of them are holding down jobs as well. Parents juggle jobs and family. Workers cope with long shifts and long commutes. And when does *fun* fit into the schedule? People this busy may not have enough time for a good night's sleep.

After insufficient sleep, people usually can manage to get through the day as long as what they are doing is simple—walking, seeing, hearing. However, they have difficulty thinking clearly about complicated matters and reaching a rational decision. Their attention span is short, and their ability to learn is affected. Sleepy students often sit through class in a daze and sometimes nod off.

The sympathetic nervous system acts as a unified whole, bringing about all its effects at once. It is able to act in this way because its neurons are connected through a chain of ganglia. A unified response is exactly what is needed in an emergency. To meet a threat, the sympathetic nervous system increases breathing rate, heart rate, and blood pressure. It also increases the amount of glucose and oxygen delivered to body cells to fuel the response. In addition, it stimulates the adrenal glands to release two hormones, epinephrine and norepinephrine, into the bloodstream. These hormones back up and prolong the other effects of sympathetic stimulation. Lastly, the sympathetic nervous system inhibits digestive activity, because digesting the previous meal is hardly a priority during a crisis.

The effects of the parasympathetic nervous system occur more independently of one another. After the emergency, organ systems return to a relaxed state at their own pace. Organs can respond to the parasympathetic nervous system independently because the ganglia containing the parasympathetic neurons that stimulate each organ are located near the individual organs—not in a chain near the spinal cord, as they are in the sympathetic nervous system.

DISORDERS OF THE NERVOUS SYSTEM

Disorders of the nervous system vary tremendously in severity and impact on the body. Some disorders, such as a mild headache, are often more of a nuisance than

Sleep deprivation can be hazardous to health. Drowsiness is a major cause of industrial accidents and traffic fatalities. In a national poll, 20% of American drivers reported having fallen asleep at the wheel within the past year. Driving on Friday night is a greater risk than on Monday night, because so many drivers have been sleep deprived all week.

Ironically, because of the pressures of life, sleep does not always come easily—even when your body is sleep deprived. Tens of millions of Americans will lie awake tonight suffering from insomnia. This sleep disorder occurs in different patterns—difficulty falling asleep, waking up during the night, or waking up earlier than desired.

Here are some suggestions for what to do if you occasionally have trouble sleeping. Establish a regular bedtime and a regular waking time, but do not remain in bed if you cannot sleep. Relax before bedtime: read a book, watch television, take a warm shower—whatever helps you unwind. For at least 6 hours before bedtime, avoid caffeinated beverages, such as coffee, tea, and cola. Also, avoid drinking alcohol for 2 hours before bedtime. Establish a regular pattern of exercise, because mild exercise promotes sleep and reduces stress. However, do not exercise too close to bedtime. Lastly, avoid using sleeping pills, even those sold over the counter in the drugstore. At best, they decrease the amount of time it takes to fall asleep by only 10 to 20 minutes and lengthen the night's sleep by only 20 to 40 minutes. Sleeping pills decrease the user's REM sleep, and the REM sleep that does occur is not normal. Furthermore, people quickly become less sensitive to the effects of sleeping pills and as a result tend to increase the dosage to a dangerous level.

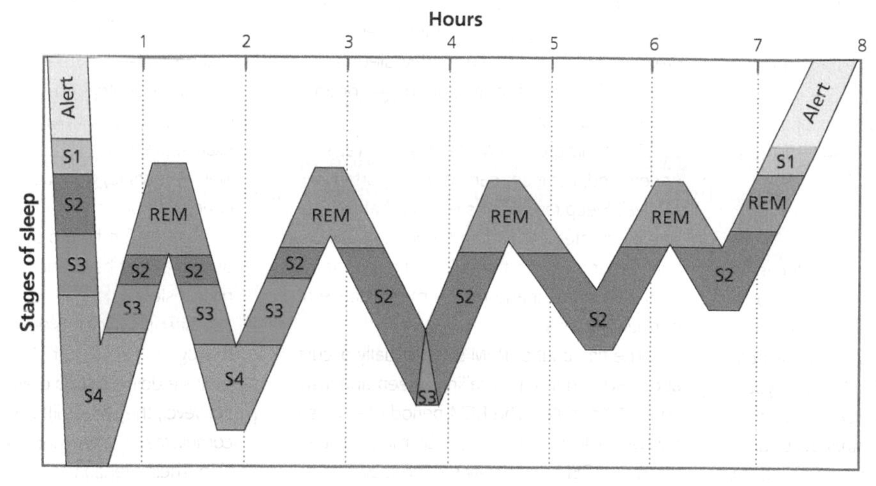

FIGURE 3a(iii).A During a good night's sleep, a person generally cycles through a sequence of sleep stages every 90 minutes.

a health problem. Others, such as insufficient sleep, can cause more problems than a person might expect (see the Health Issue essay, *To Sleep, Perchance to Dream*). Still other disorders, such as stroke, coma, and spinal cord injury, can have devastating effects on a person's well-being.

Headaches

Excessive exercise may make your muscles hurt. However, thinking too much cannot cause a headache. The brain has no pain receptors, so a headache is not a brainache. Headaches can occur for almost any reason: they can be caused by stress or by relaxation, by hunger or by eating the wrong food, or by too much or too little sleep. The most common type of headache is a *tension headache*, affecting some 60% to 80% of people who suffer from frequent headaches. In response to stress, most of us unconsciously contract the muscles of our head, face, and neck. Therefore, the pain of a tension headache is usually a dull, steady ache, often described as feeling like a tight band around the head. *Migraine headaches* are usually confined to one side of the head, often centered behind one eye. A migraine headache typically causes a throbbing pain that increases with each beat of the heart. It is sometimes called a sick headache because it may cause nausea and vomiting. Some migraine sufferers experience an aura, a group of sensory symptoms, different for different people, that occurs just before an attack. The aura may include visual disturbances (a blind spot, zigzag lines, flashing lights), auditory hallucinations, or numbness. Though the causes of migraine are not entirely understood, some researchers believe that migraines are set off by an imbalance in the brain's chemistry. Specifically, the level of one of the brain's chemical neurotransmitters, serotonin, is low. With too little serotonin, pain messages flood the brain.

what would you do?

In an experimental pain treatment for severe headaches, a tiny electrode is implanted in the skin and placed near the nerve responsible for the pain. The device, powered by a battery implanted near the collarbone, delivers continuous electric pulses intended to block the pain signals in the nerve and stop the pain. If you suffered from severely painful headaches, would you opt for this treatment? What criteria would you use to decide?

Strokes

A *stroke,* also called a cerebrovascular accident, is the death of nerve cells caused by an interruption of blood flow to a region of the brain. Neurons have a high demand for both oxygen and glucose. Therefore, when the blood supply to a portion of the brain is shut off, the affected neurons begin to die within minutes. The extent and location of the mental or physical impairment caused by a stroke depend on the region of the brain involved. If the left side of the brain is affected, the person may lose sensations in or the ability to move parts of the right side of his or her body because motor nerve pathways cross from one side of the brain to the other in the lower brain. Because the language centers are usually in the left hemisphere, the person may also have difficulty speaking. When the stroke damages the right rear of the brain, some people show what is called the neglect syndrome and behave as if the left side of things, even their own bodies, does not exist. The person may comb only the hair on the right side of the head or eat only the food on the right side of the plate.

Common causes of strokes include blood clots blocking a vessel, hemorrhage from the rupture of a blood vessel in one of the meninges, or the formation of fatty deposits that block a vessel. High blood pressure, heart disease, diabetes, smoking, obesity, and excessive alcohol intake increase the risk of stroke.

Coma

Although a comatose person seems to be asleep—with eyes closed and no recognizable speech—a coma is not deep sleep. A person in a *coma* is totally unresponsive to all sensory input and cannot be awakened. Although the cerebral cortex is most directly responsible for consciousness, damage to the cerebrum is rarely the cause of coma. Instead, coma is caused by trauma to neurons in regions of the brain responsible for stimulating the cerebrum, particularly those in the reticular activating system or thalamus. Coma can be caused by mechanical shock—as might be caused by a blow to the head—tumors, infections, drug overdose, or failure of the liver or kidney.

Spinal Cord Injury

The spinal cord is the pathway that allows the brain to communicate with the rest of the body. Therefore, damage to the spinal cord can impair sensation and motor control below the site of injury. The extent and location of the injury will determine how long these symptoms persist, as well as the degree of permanent damage. Depending on which nerve tracts are damaged, injury may result in paralysis, loss of sensation, or both. If the cord is completely severed, there is a complete loss of sensation and voluntary movement below the level of the cut.

Restoring the ability to function to people with spinal cord injuries is an active area of research. Some researchers are trying to reestablish neural connections by stimulating nerve growth through treatments with nerve growth factors. Others are exploring the potential use of stem cells for treatment. Stem cells retain the ability to develop into nerve cells, and they have been used successfully by researchers to restore some movement in laboratory mice with spinal cord injuries. Another approach to restoring the ability to move is to use computers to electronically stimulate specific muscles and muscle groups. The stimulation is delivered through wires that are either implanted under the skin or woven into the fabric of tight-fitting clothing. A small computer, usually worn at the wrist, directs the stimulation to the appropriate muscles. This technology has helped some people with a spinal cord injury to walk again. It has also helped some people by stimulating the diaphragm, a muscle important in breathing.

Taken from *Biology of Humans: Concepts, Applications, and Issues*, Third Edition, by Judith Goodenough and Betty McGuire

SENSORY RECEPTORS

Information about the external world and about the internal world of our bodies comes to us through our **sensory receptors,** structures that are specialized to detect and respond to changes in the environment, known as **stimuli,** by generating electrochemical messages. If a stimulus is strong enough, these messages eventually become nerve impulses (action potentials) that are then conducted to the brain.

Sensation is an awareness of a stimulus. Whether a sensation is experienced as sight, sound, or something else depends on which part of the brain receives the nerve impulses. For example, photoreceptors respond best to light, but they can also respond to pressure. Regardless of the stimulus, nerve impulses from photoreceptors go to the visual cortex of the brain, and we see light. This is why, if you press gently on your closed eyelids, you will have the sensation of seeing spots of light. The pressure stimulates photoreceptors, which send nerve impulses to the visual cortex, and you sense light.

We use the word *perception* to describe the conscious awareness of sensations. Perception occurs when the cerebral cortex integrates sensory input (Figure 3a(iii).4). For example, light reflected from a banana strikes the eye, stimulating some of the photoreceptors. The brain interprets the pattern of input from the photoreceptors, and we perceive a banana.

As we've seen, each type of sensory receptor responds best to one form of stimulus. The response of a sensory receptor is an electrochemical message (a change in the charge difference across plasma membrane) that varies in magnitude with the strength of the stimulus. For instance, the louder a sound, the larger the change in the charge difference across the membrane—up to a point. When the change reaches a critical level, called threshold level, an action potential (nerve impulse) is generated. Most types of sensory receptors gradually stop responding when they are continuously stimulated. This phenomenon is called **sensory adaptation.** As receptors adapt in this way, we become less aware of the stimulus. For example, the musty smell of an antique store may be obvious to a person who just walked in, but the salesclerk working in the store no longer notices it. Some receptors, such as those for pressure and touch, adapt quickly. For this reason, we quickly become unaware of the feeling of our clothing against our skin. (Adaptation can also occur in the central nervous system. The reticular activating system in the brain filters stimuli.) Other receptors adapt more slowly or not at all. For instance, the receptors in muscles and joints that report on the position of body parts never adapt. Their continuous input is essential for coordinated movement and balance.

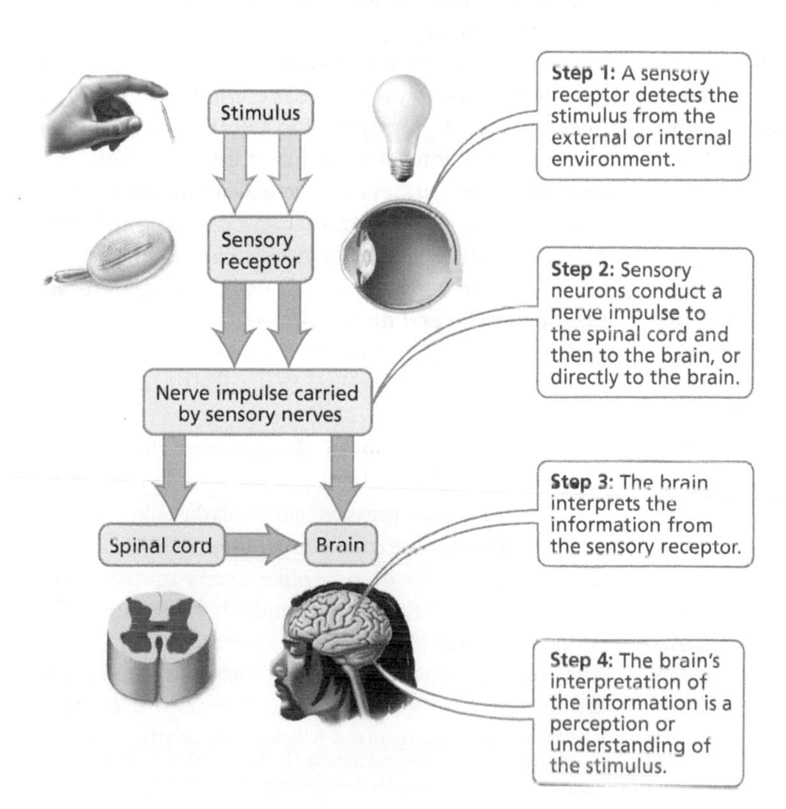

Stimulus
Sensory receptor
Nerve impulse carried by sensory nerves
Spinal cord
Brain
Step 1: A sensory receptor detects the stimulus from the external or internal environment.
Step 2: Sensory neurons conduct a nerve impulse to the spinal cord and then to the brain, or directly to the brain.
Step 3: The brain interprets the information from the sensory receptor.
Step 4: The brain's interpretation of the information is a perception or understanding of the stimulus.

FIGURE 3a(iii).4 **An overview of the steps involved in sensation and perception**

CLASSES OF RECEPTORS

Receptors are classified according to the stimulus they respond to. Several classes of receptors are traditionally recognized:

1. **Mechanoreceptors** are responsible for the sensations we describe as touch, pressure, hearing, and equilibrium. In addition, the body has mechanoreceptors that detect changes in blood pressure and others that indicate the body's position. Mechanoreceptors respond to distortions in the receptor itself or in nearby cells.
2. **Thermoreceptors** detect changes in temperature.
3. **Photoreceptors** detect changes in light intensity.
4. **Chemoreceptors** respond to chemicals. We describe the input from the chemoreceptors of the mouth as taste (gustation) and those from the nose as smell (olfaction). Other chemoreceptors monitor levels of specific substances such as carbon dioxide, oxygen, or glucose in our body fluids.
5. **Pain receptors** (or nociceptors) respond to very strong stimuli that usually result from physical or chemical damage to tissues. Pain receptors are sometimes classed with the chemo-receptors because they often respond to chemicals liberated by damaged tissue. These receptors are occasionally classed with the mechanoreceptors because they are stimulated by physical changes, such as swelling, in the damaged tissue.

We can sense stimuli both outside of our bodies and within them. Receptors located near the body surface respond to stimuli in the environment. We are usually aware of these stimuli. Other receptors are inside the body and monitor conditions there. Although we often are unaware of the activity of internal receptors, they play a vital role in maintaining homeostasis. In fact, they are key components of the feedback loops that regulate blood pressure, blood chemistry, and breathing rate. Internal receptors also cause us to feel pain, hunger, or thirst, thereby prompting us to attend to our body's needs.

The **general senses**—touch, pressure, vibration, temperature, body and limb position, and pain—arise from receptors in the skin, muscles, joints, bones, and internal organs. Although we are not usually aware of the general senses, they are important because they provide information about body position and help keep internal body conditions within the limits optimal for health. The **special senses** are vision, hearing, the sense of balance or equilibrium, smell, and taste. These are what usually come to mind when we think of "the senses," largely because we are so dependent on them for perceiving and understanding the world. The receptors of the special senses are located in the head. Most of them reside within specific structures.

THE GENERAL SENSES

The receptors for general senses are distributed throughout the body. Some monitor conditions within the body; others provide information about the world around us. Some of the receptors are free nerve endings; in other cases the nerve endings are encapsulated. *Free nerve endings,* the tips of dendrites of sensory neurons, are not protected by an accessory structure. In contrast, an *encapsulated nerve ending* is one in which a connective tissue capsule encloses and protects the tips of the dendrites of sensory neurons (Figure 3a(iii).5).

Touch, Pressure, and Vibration

As noted earlier, mechanoreceptors respond to touch and pressure— to any stimulus that stretches, compresses, or twists the receptor membrane. Throughout life, we actively use touch as a way of learning about the world and of communicating with one another. The messages we get from pressure can be equally important. Some pressure receptors inform us of the need to loosen our belt after a big meal. Other pressure receptors monitor internal conditions, including blood pressure.

Light touch, as when the cat's tail brushes your legs, is de-tected by several types of receptors. For example, free nerve endings wrapped around the base of the fine hairs on the skin detect any bending of those hairs. Free nerve endings and the special cells they end on (Merkel cells) form *Merkel disks.* When compressed, Merkel cells stimulate the free nerve endings in the associated Merkel disks to tell us that something has touched us. Merkel disks are found on both the hairy and hairless parts of the skin. *Meissner's corpuscles* are encapsulated nerve endings that tell us exactly where we have been touched. They are common on the hairless, very sensitive areas of skin, such as the lips, nipples, and fingertips.

The sensation of pressure generally lasts longer than does touch and is felt over a larger area. *Pacinian corpuscles,* which consist of onionlike layers of tissue surrounding a nerve ending, respond when pressure is first applied and therefore are important in sensing vibration. They are scattered in the deeper layers of skin and the underlying tissue. *Ruffini corpuscles* are encapsulated endings that respond to continuous pressure.

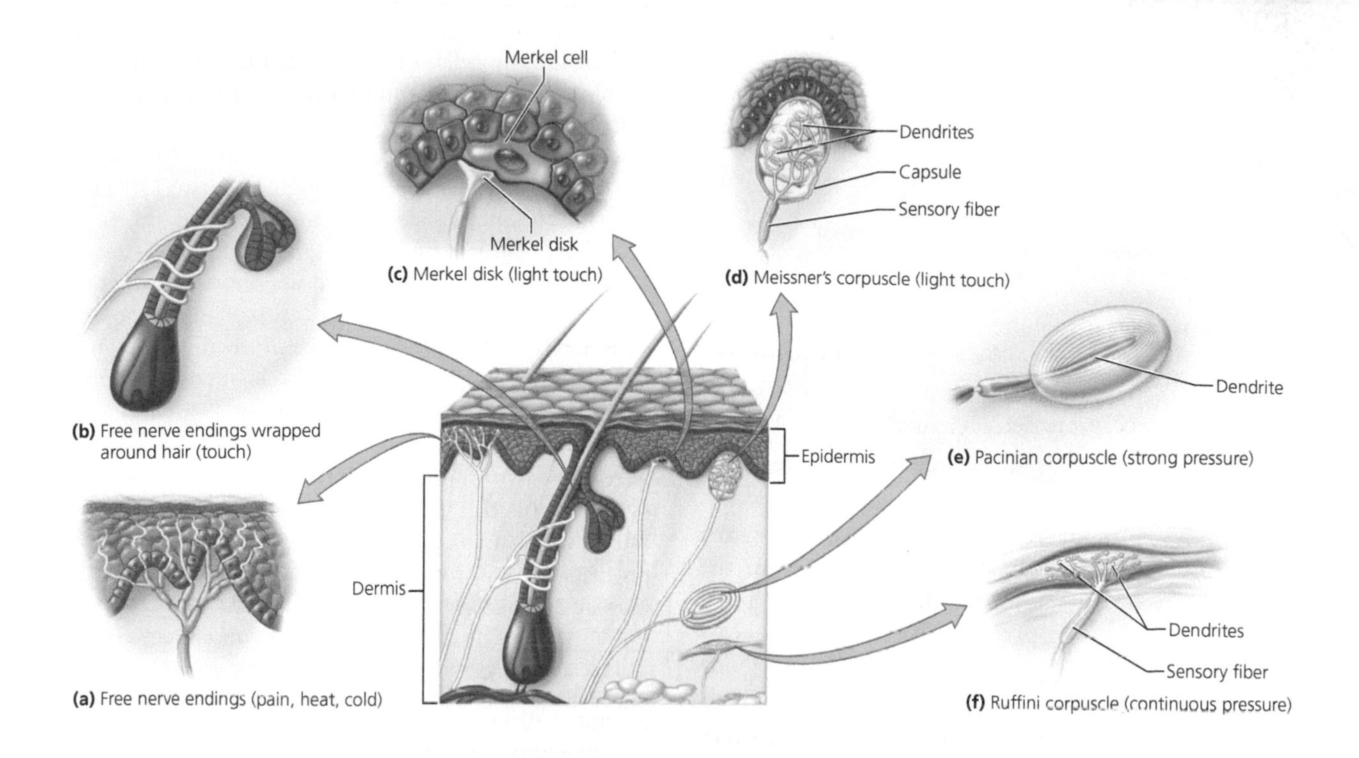

FIGURE 3a(iii).5 **General sense receptors of the skin allow us to feel touch, pressure, temperature, and pain**

Temperature Change

Thermoreceptors respond to changes in temperature. In humans, thermoreceptors are specialized free nerve endings found just below the surface of the skin. One kind responds to cold and another responds to warmth. They are widely distributed throughout the body but are especially numerous around the lips and mouth. You may have noticed that the sensation of hot or cold fades rapidly. This fading occurs because thermoreceptors are very active when temperature is changing but adapt rapidly when temperature is stable. As a result, the water in a hot tub may feel scalding at first, but very soon it feels comfortably warm.

Body and Limb Position

Whether you are at rest or in motion, the brain "knows" the location of all your body parts. It continuously scans the signals from muscles and joints to check body alignment and coordinate balance and movement. **Muscle spindles**—specialized muscle fibers wrapped in sensory nerve endings—monitor the length of a skeletal muscle. **Golgi tendon organs**—highly branched nerve fibers located in tendons (connective tissue bands that connect muscles to bones)—measure the degree of muscle tension. The brain combines information from muscle spindles and Golgi tendon organs with information from the inner ear (as we see shortly) to coordinate our movements.

Pain

The receptors for pain are free nerve endings found in almost every tissue of the body. When tissue is damaged, cells release chemicals that alert the free nerve endings of the injury. The stimulated sen-sory neurons then carry the message to the brain, where it is interpreted as pain. Aspirin and ibuprofen reduce pain by interfering with the production of one of the released chemicals. Any stimulus strong enough to damage tissues, including heat, cold, touch, and pressure, can cause pain.

Many of our internal organs also have pain receptors. However, pain originating in an internal organ is sometimes perceived as pain in an uninjured region of the skin (Figure 3a(iii).6). This phenomenon is called **referred pain.** For example, the pain of a heart attack is often experienced as pain in the left arm. This pain probably occurs because sensory neurons from the internal organ and those from a particular region of the skin communicate with the same neurons in the spinal cord. Because the message is delivered to the brain by the same neurons, the brain interprets the input as coming from the skin.

Q *If you had pain caused by a kidney stone, where would you experience the pain?*

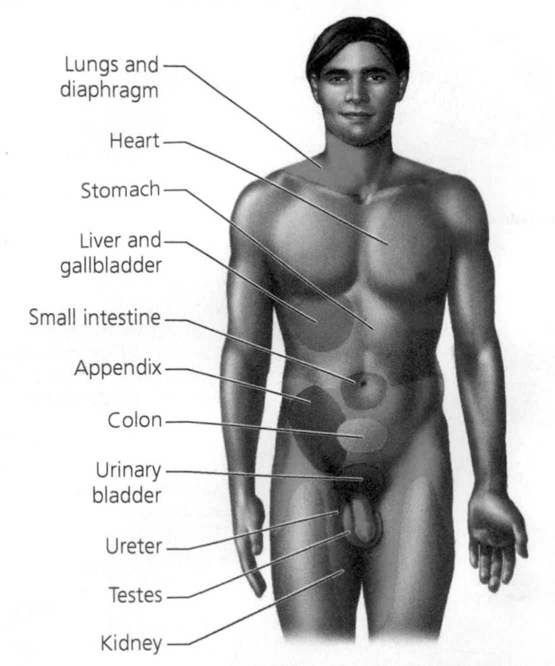

FIGURE 3a(iii).6 **Referred pain. Pain from certain internal organs is sensed as originating in particular regions of the skin.**

A *The lower body trunk and inner thigh.*

Pain is an important mechanism that warns the body and protects it from further injury. For example, pain usually prevents a person with a broken leg from causing additional damage by moving the limb. Nonetheless, few of us appreciate the value of pain while we are experiencing it. Furthermore, pain that persists long after the warning is needed can be debilitating.

3a(iv) The Endocrine System

Taken from *Biology of Humans: Concepts, Applications, and Issues*, Third Edition, by Judith Goodenough and Betty McGuire

FUNCTIONS AND MECHANISMS OF HORMONES

Our bodies contain two types of glands: exocrine glands and endocrine glands. **Endocrine glands** (Figure 3a(iv).1) are made of secretory cells that release their products, called hormones. Hormones move from the cells that produced them to the fluid just outside the cells, where they diffuse directly into the bloodstream. The **endocrine system** consists of endocrine glands and of organs that contain some endocrine tissue; these organs have other functions besides hormone secretion (Figure 3a(iv).2). The major endocrine glands are the pituitary gland, thyroid gland, parathyroid glands, adrenal glands, and pineal gland. Organs with some endocrine tissue include the hypothalamus, thymus, pancreas, ovaries, testes, heart, and placenta. Organs of the digestive and urinary systems, such as the stomach, small intestine, and kidneys, also have endocrine tissue.

Our discussion focuses on the major endocrine glands. As we describe individual glands, keep in mind that the main function of the endocrine system—like that of the nervous system—is to regulate and coordinate other body systems and thereby maintain homeostasis. Recall also that whereas the nervous system is our rapid system of internal communication, the endocrine system is our more leisurely system, often coordinating and regulating longer-term processes such as growth, development, and reproduction.

We also examine three organs with endocrine tissue: hypothalamus, thymus, and pancreas. The other organs containing endocrine tissue are discussed in the chapters that cover the organs' other functions.

Q *Look closely at the structure of the endocrine gland. How does it differ from the structure of an exocrine gland, such as an oil gland?*

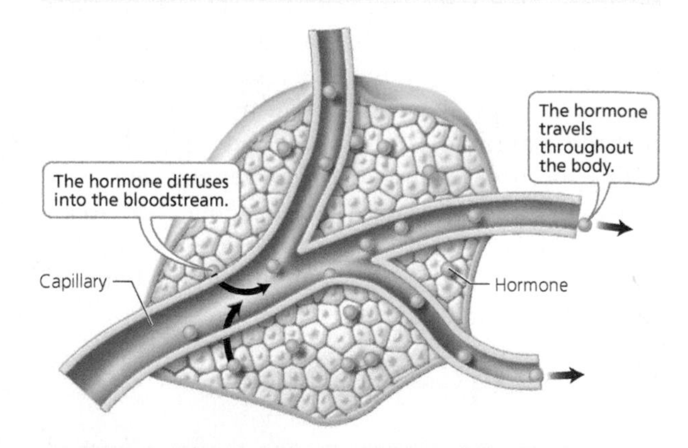

FIGURE 3a(iv).1 **An endocrine gland. Endocrine glands release their products, called hormones, into the fluid just outside cells. The hormones then diffuse into the bloodstream to be transported throughout the body.**

A *Endocrine glands lack ducts. Rather than secreting their products into ducts that open to a surface, endocrine glands secrete hormones to the fluid just outside their cells, and from there the hormone moves into the bloodstream.*

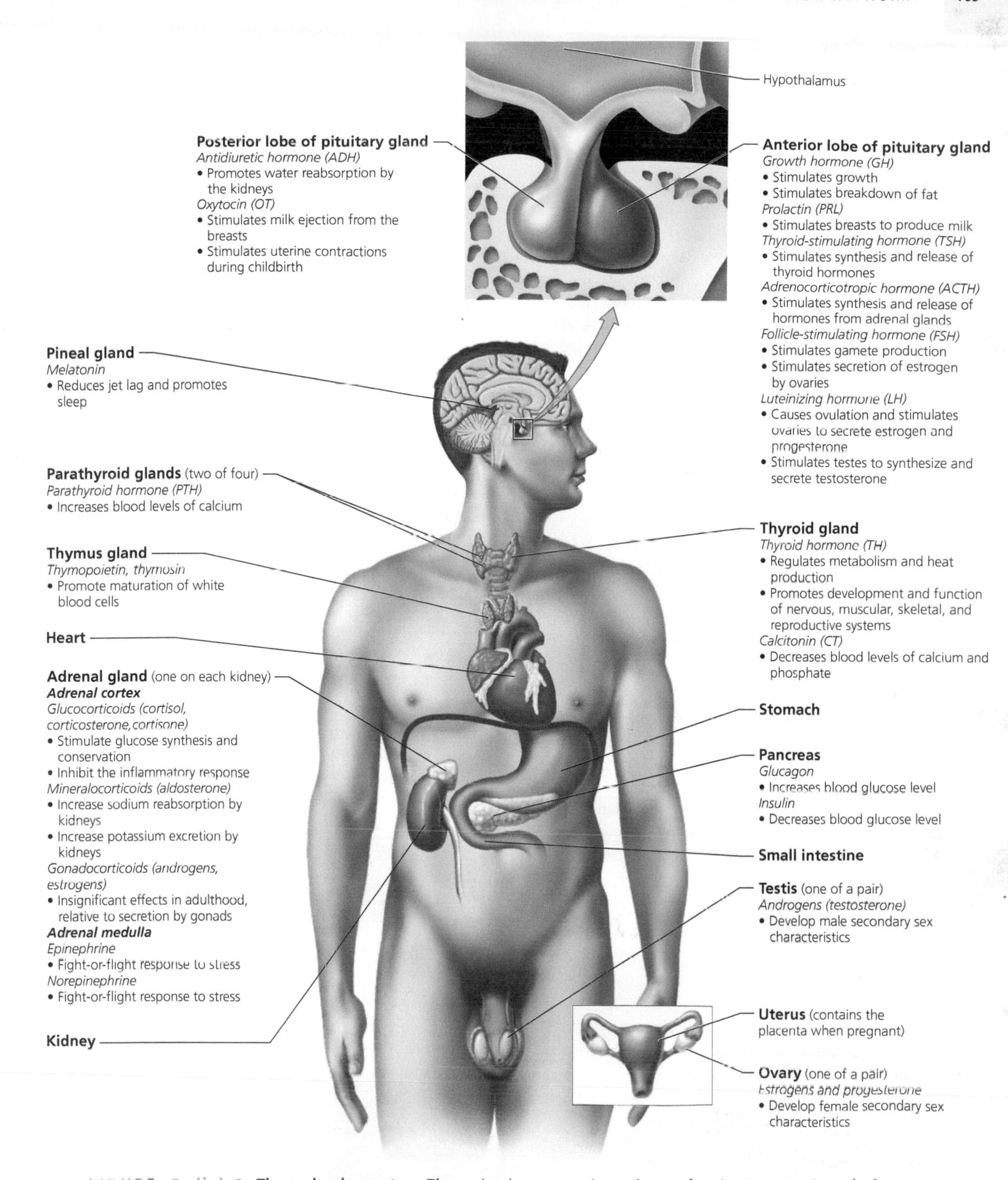
Hypothalamus
Posterior lobe of pituitary gland
Antidiuretic hormone (ADH)
• Promotes water reabsorption by the kidneys
Oxytocin (OT)
• Stimulates milk ejection from the breasts
• Stimulates uterine contractions during childbirth
Anterior lobe of pituitary gland
Growth hormone (GH)
• Stimulates growth
• Stimulates breakdown of fat
Prolactin (PRL)
• Stimulates breasts to produce milk
Thyroid-stimulating hormone (TSH)
• Stimulates synthesis and release of thyroid hormones
Adrenocorticotropic hormone (ACTH)
• Stimulates synthesis and release of hormones from adrenal glands
Follicle-stimulating hormone (FSH)
• Stimulates gamete production
• Stimulates secretion of estrogen by ovaries
Luteinizing hormone (LH)
• Causes ovulation and stimulates ovaries to secrete estrogen and progesterone
• Stimulates testes to synthesize and secrete testosterone
Pineal gland
Melatonin
• Reduces jet lag and promotes sleep
Parathyroid glands (two of four)
Parathyroid hormone (PTH)
• Increases blood levels of calcium
Thymus gland
Thymopoietin, thymosin
• Promote maturation of white blood cells
Heart
Adrenal gland (one on each kidney)
Adrenal cortex
Glucocorticoids (cortisol, corticosterone, cortisone)
• Stimulate glucose synthesis and conservation
• Inhibit the inflammatory response
Mineralocorticoids (aldosterone)
• Increase sodium reabsorption by kidneys
• Increase potassium excretion by kidneys
Gonadocorticoids (androgens, estrogens)
• Insignificant effects in adulthood, relative to secretion by gonads
Adrenal medulla
Epinephrine
• Fight-or-flight response to stress
Norepinephrine
• Fight-or-flight response to stress
Kidney
Thyroid gland
Thyroid hormone (TH)
• Regulates metabolism and heat production
• Promotes development and function of nervous, muscular, skeletal, and reproductive systems
Calcitonin (CT)
• Decreases blood levels of calcium and phosphate
Stomach
Pancreas
Glucagon
• Increases blood glucose level
Insulin
• Decreases blood glucose level
Small intestine
Testis (one of a pair)
Androgens (testosterone)
• Develop male secondary sex characteristics
Uterus (contains the placenta when pregnant)
Ovary (one of a pair)
Estrogens and progesterone
• Develop female secondary sex characteristics

FIGURE 3a(iv).2 The endocrine system. The endocrine system is made up of endocrine glands and of organs that contain some endocrine tissue. Here, the hormones and their functions are listed under the endocrine gland or organ that produces them. (Note that hormones secreted by organs for which hormone secretion is a secondary function—the heart, stomach, small intestine, kidneys, testes, ovaries, and uterus with placenta—are discussed in chapters that cover the organs' other functions.)

Hormones as Chemical Messengers

Hormones are the chemical messengers of the endocrine system. They are released in very small amounts by the cells of endocrine glands and tissues and enter the bloodstream to travel throughout the body. Although hormones come into contact with virtually all cells, most affect only a particular type of cell, called a **target cell.** Target cells have *receptors,* protein molecules that recognize and bind to specific hormones. Once a hormone binds to its specific receptor, this hormone–receptor complex begins to exert its effects on the cell. Because cells other than target cells lack the correct receptors, they are unaffected by the hormone.

The mechanisms by which hormones influence target cells depend on the chemical makeup of the hormone. Hormones are classified as being either lipid soluble or water soluble. **Lipid-soluble hormones** include **steroid hormones,** a group of closely related hormones derived from cholesterol. The ovaries, testes, and adrenal glands are the main organs that secrete steroid hormones. Lipid-soluble hormones move easily through any cell's plasma membrane because it is a lipid bilayer (see Figure 3a(iv).3). Once inside a target cell, a steroid hormone combines with receptor molecules in the cytoplasm (only target cells have the proper receptors for a given hormone). This hormone–receptor complex then moves into the nucleus of the cell, where it attaches to DNA and activates certain genes. Ultimately, such activation leads the target cell to synthesize specific proteins. These proteins may include enzymes that stimulate or inhibit particular metabolic pathways.

Water-soluble hormones, such as protein or peptide hormones, cannot pass through the lipid bilayer of the plasma membrane and therefore cannot enter target cells themselves. Instead, the hormone—which in this situation is called the **first messenger**—binds to a recep-

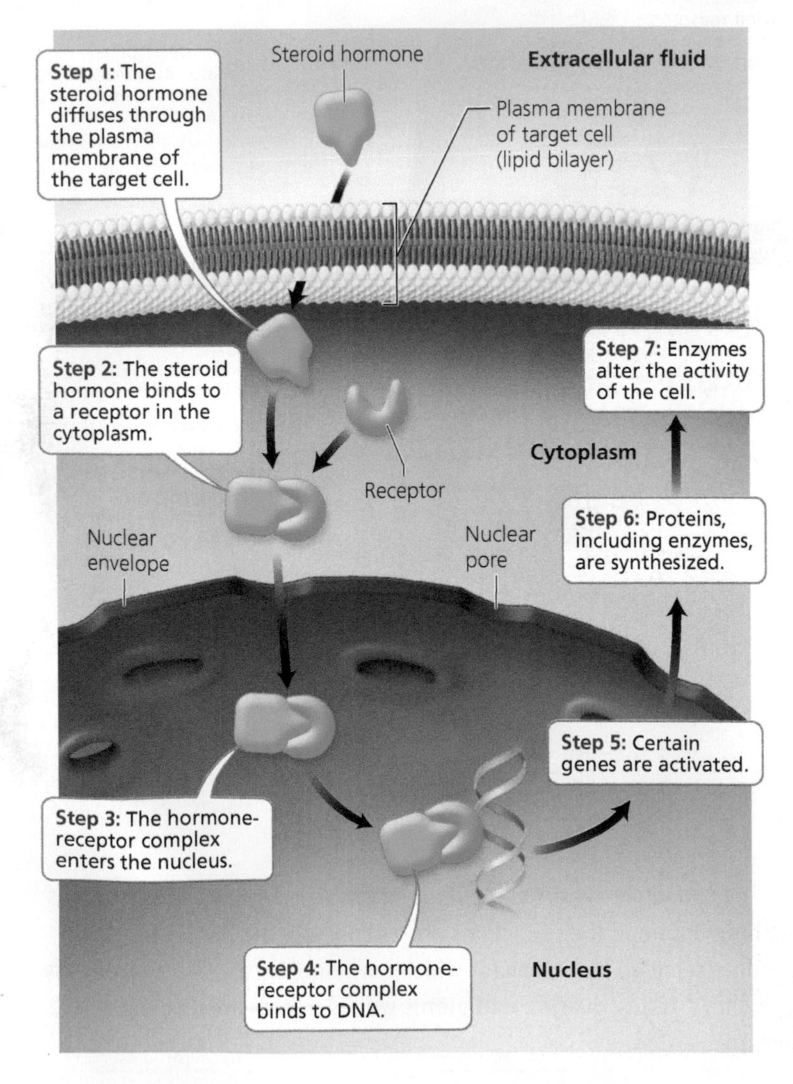
Step 1: The steroid hormone diffuses through the plasma membrane of the target cell.
Steroid hormone
Extracellular fluid
Plasma membrane of target cell (lipid bilayer)
Step 2: The steroid hormone binds to a receptor in the cytoplasm.
Step 7: Enzymes alter the activity of the cell.
Cytoplasm
Receptor
Nuclear envelope
Nuclear pore
Step 6: Proteins, including enzymes, are synthesized.
Step 5: Certain genes are activated.
Step 3: The hormone-receptor complex enters the nucleus.
Step 4: The hormone-receptor complex binds to DNA.
Nucleus

FIGURE 3a(iv).3 Mode of action of lipid-soluble (steroid) hormones

tor on the plasma membrane of the target cell. This binding activates a molecule—called the second messenger—in the cytoplasm. **Second messengers** are molecules within the cell that influence the activity of enzymes, and ultimately the activity of the cell, to produce the effect of the hormone. Cyclic adenosine monophosphate (cAMP) is a common second messenger (illustrated in Figure 3a(iv).4). As an example of how cAMP functions in its role as a second messenger, we consider the effects of the water-soluble hormone epinephrine on a liver cell. Binding of epinephrine to a receptor on the plasma membrane of a liver cell (the target cell) prompts the conversion of ATP to cAMP within the cell. Cyclic adenosine monophosphate then activates an enzyme within the cell (a protein kinase), which in turn activates another enzyme, and so on. The end result of this enzyme cascade is the activation of an enzyme that catalyzes the breakdown of glycogen to glucose within the liver cell. Thus, whereas lipid-soluble hormones stimulate the synthesis of proteins by a cell, water-soluble hormones like epinephrine activate proteins that are already present in the cell.

Feedback Mechanisms and Secretion of Hormones

Now that we have seen how hormones work at the cellular level, let's turn our attention to the factors that stimulate and regulate the release of hormones from endocrine glands. Stimuli that cause endocrine glands to manufacture and release hormones include other hormones, signals from the nervous system, and changes in the levels of certain ions (such as calcium, Ca^{2+}) or nutrients (such as glucose) in the blood.

Recall that homeostasis keeps the body's internal environment relatively constant. Such constancy most often is achieved through **negative feedback mechanisms,** which are homeostatic mechanisms in which the outcome of a process feeds back to the system,

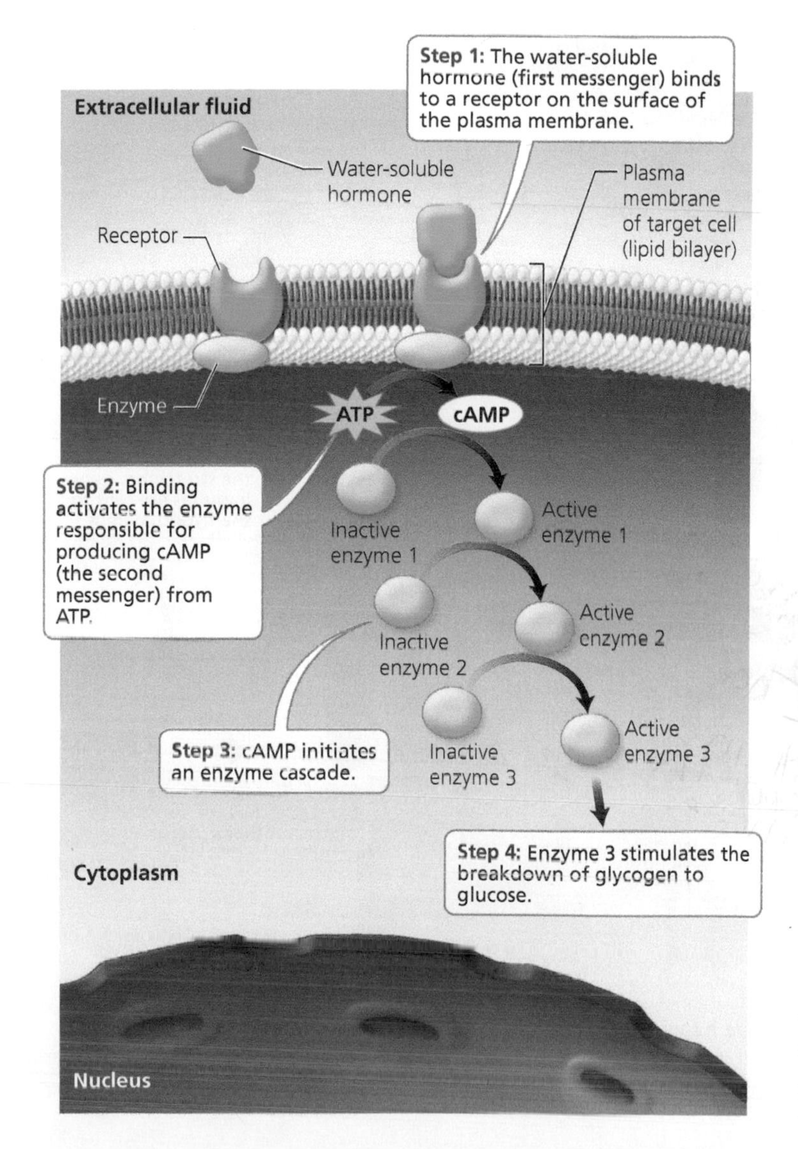
Step 1: The water-soluble hormone (first messenger) binds to a receptor on the surface of the plasma membrane.
Extracellular fluid
Water-soluble hormone
Plasma membrane of target cell (lipid bilayer)
Receptor
Enzyme
ATP
cAMP
Step 2: Binding activates the enzyme responsible for producing cAMP (the second messenger) from ATP.
Inactive enzyme 1
Active enzyme 1
Inactive enzyme 2
Active enzyme 2
Inactive enzyme 3
Active enzyme 3
Step 3: cAMP initiates an enzyme cascade.
Step 4: Enzyme 3 stimulates the breakdown of glycogen to glucose.
Cytoplasm
Nucleus

FIGURE 3a(iv).4 Mode of action of some water-soluble hormones: the second messenger system of cAMP

shutting the process down. Negative feedback mechanisms regulate the secretion of some hormones. Typically, a gland releases a hormone, and then rising blood levels of that hormone inhibit its further release. In an alternative form of negative feedback, some endocrine glands are sensitive to the particular condition they regulate rather than to the level of the hormone they produce. For example, the pancreas secretes the hormone insulin in response to high levels of glucose in the blood. Insulin prompts the liver to store glucose, which in turn causes the blood level of glucose to decline. The pancreas senses the low glucose in the blood and stops secreting insulin.

Secretion of hormones is sometimes regulated by **positive feedback mechanisms,** in which the outcome of a process feeds back to the system and stimulates the process to continue. For example, during childbirth, the pituitary gland releases the hormone oxytocin (OT), which stimulates the uterus to contract. Uterine contractions then stimulate release of more oxytocin, which stimulates even more contractions (Figure 3a(iv).5). The feedback is described as positive because it acts to stimulate, rather than to inhibit, the release of oxytocin. Eventually, some change breaks the positive feedback cycle. In the case of childbirth, expulsion of the baby and placenta terminates the feedback cycle. When we discuss the various glands and their hormones in the sections that follow, we also describe the feedback mechanisms by which they are regulated.

Sometimes the nervous system overrides the controls of the endocrine system. During times of severe stress, for example, the nervous system overrides the mechanism controlling the release of the hormone insulin. Recall that the level of insulin in the blood is controlled by a negative feedback system. Because of this negative feedback system, levels of glucose in the blood are normally maintained within a relatively narrow range. However, under conditions of severe stress, such as those associated with strong emotional reactions, heavy bleeding, or starvation, the nervous system permits

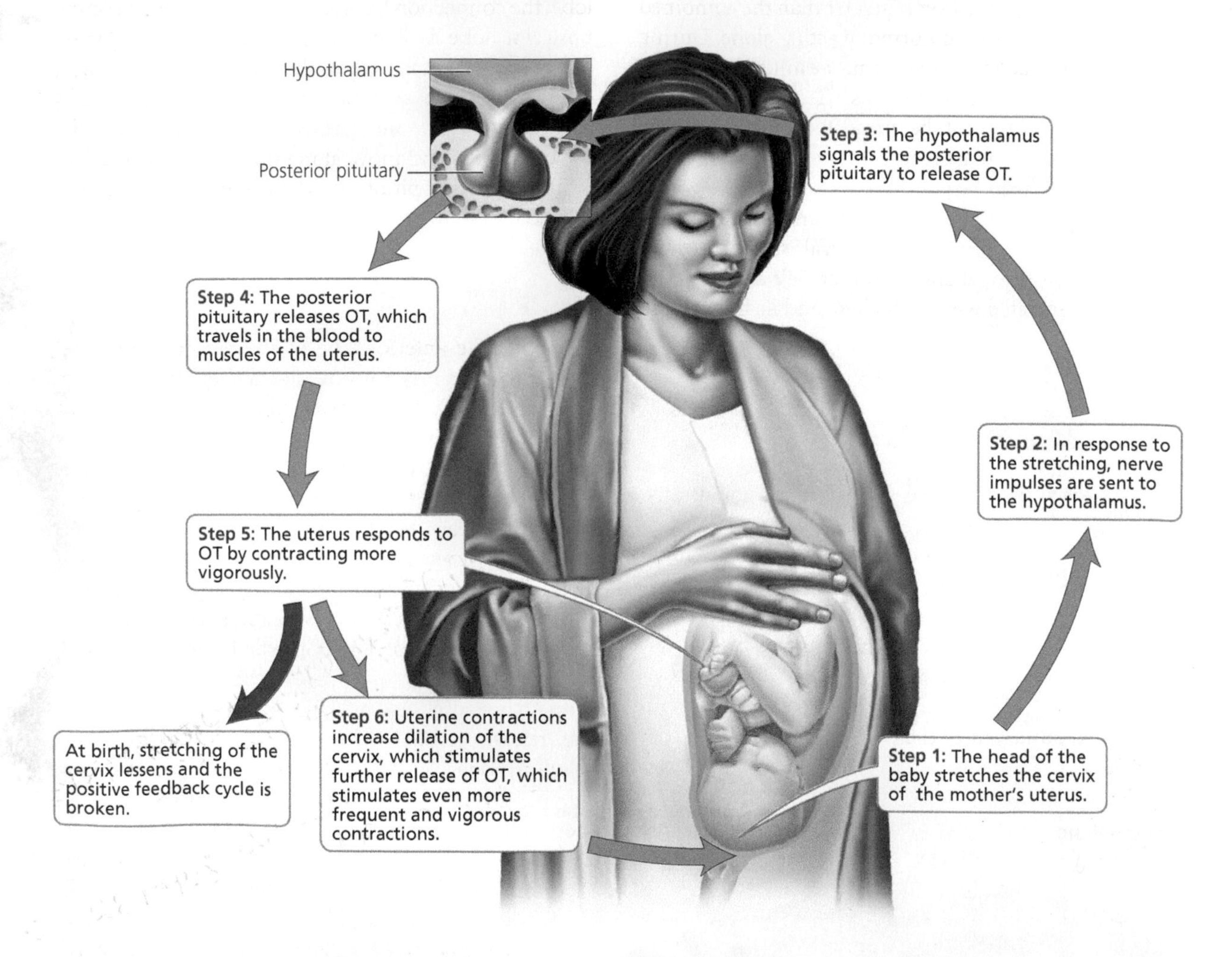

FIGURE 3a(iv).5 The positive feedback cycle by which OT stimulates uterine contractions during childbirth

levels of blood glucose to rise much higher than normal. This response gives cells access to the large amounts of energy they need for coping with the stressful situation.

Interactions between Hormones

Interactions between hormones may be antagonistic, synergistic, or permissive. When the effect of one hormone opposes that of another hormone, the interaction is described as *antagonistic.* For an example of an antagonistic interaction, consider glucagon and insulin, two hormones secreted by the pancreas. Whereas glucagon increases the level of glucose in the blood, insulin decreases the level of glucose in the blood. During *synergistic* interactions, the response of a tissue to a combination of two hormones is much greater than its response to either individual hormone. For example, epinephrine (from the adrenal glands) and glucagon both prompt the liver to release glucose to the blood. When the two hormones act together, the amount of glucose released by the liver is greater than the combined amount released by each hormone acting alone. During *permissive* interactions, one hormone must be present for another hormone to exert its effects. For example, thyroid hormone must be present for the hormone aldosterone to stimulate reabsorption of sodium within the tubules of the kidneys.

Next we look at the individual endocrine glands, describing the location and general structure, hormones, and hormonal effects of each. We also consider disorders associated with each gland and its hormones.

PITUITARY GLAND

The **pituitary gland** is the size of a pea and is suspended from the base of the brain by a short stalk (see Figure 3a(iv).2). The stalk connects the pituitary gland to the **hypothalamus,** the area of the brain that regulates physiological responses like body temperature, sleeping, and water balance. The pituitary gland consists of two lobes, the anterior lobe and the posterior lobe. These lobes differ in size and in their relationship with the hypothalamus; the two lobes release different hormones.

The anterior lobe is the larger one. A network of capillaries runs from the base of the hypothalamus through the stalk of the pituitary. The capillaries connect to veins that lead into more capillaries in the anterior lobe of the pituitary gland (Figure 3a(iv).6). This circulatory connection allows hormones of the hypothalamus to control the secretion of hormones from the anterior lobe of the pituitary. Nerve cells in the hypothalamus synthesize and secrete hormones that travel by way of the bloodstream to the anterior lobe, where they stimulate or inhibit hormone secretion. Substances produced by the hypothalamus that stimulate hormone secretion by the anterior pituitary are called **releasing hormones.** Those that inhibit hormone secretion by the anterior pituitary are called **inhibiting hormones.** The anterior pituitary responds to releasing and inhibiting hormones from the hypothalamus by modifying its own synthesis and secretion of six hormones. These hormones are growth hormone (GH), prolactin (PRL), thyroid-stimulating hormone (TSH), adrenocorticotropic hormone (ACTH), follicle-stimulating hormone (FSH), and luteinizing hormone (LH).

The posterior lobe of the pituitary is very small, just larger than the head of a pin. It consists of neural tissue that releases hormones. In contrast to the *circulatory* connection between the hypothalamus and the anterior lobe, the connection between the hypothalamus and the posterior lobe is a *neural* one. As shown in Figure 3a(iv).6, nerve cells from the hypothalamus project directly into the posterior lobe. Oxytocin (OT) and antidiuretic hormone (ADH) are produced by the hypothalamus and move along the axons of nerve cells to the posterior pituitary, where they are stored and released.

Anterior Lobe

As noted, the anterior lobe of the pituitary produces and secretes six major hormones. We begin with **growth hormone (GH),** the primary function of which is to stimulate growth through increases in cell size and rates of cell division. The target cells of GH are quite diverse. Cells of bone, muscle, and cartilage are most susceptible to GH, but cells of other tissues are affected as well. Growth hormone also plays a role in glucose conservation by making fats more available as a source of fuel.

Two hormones of the hypothalamus regulate the synthesis and release of GH. Growth hormone-releasing hormone (GHRH) stimulates the release of GH. Growth hormone-inhibiting hormone (GHIH) inhibits the release of GH. Through the actions of these two hormones, levels of GH in the body are normally maintained within an appropriate range. However, excesses or deficiencies of the hormone can dramatically affect growth. For example, abnormally high production of GH in childhood, when the bones are still capable of growing in length, results in *gigantism,* a condition characterized by rapid growth and eventual attainment of heights up to 8 or 9 feet (Figure 3a(iv).7).

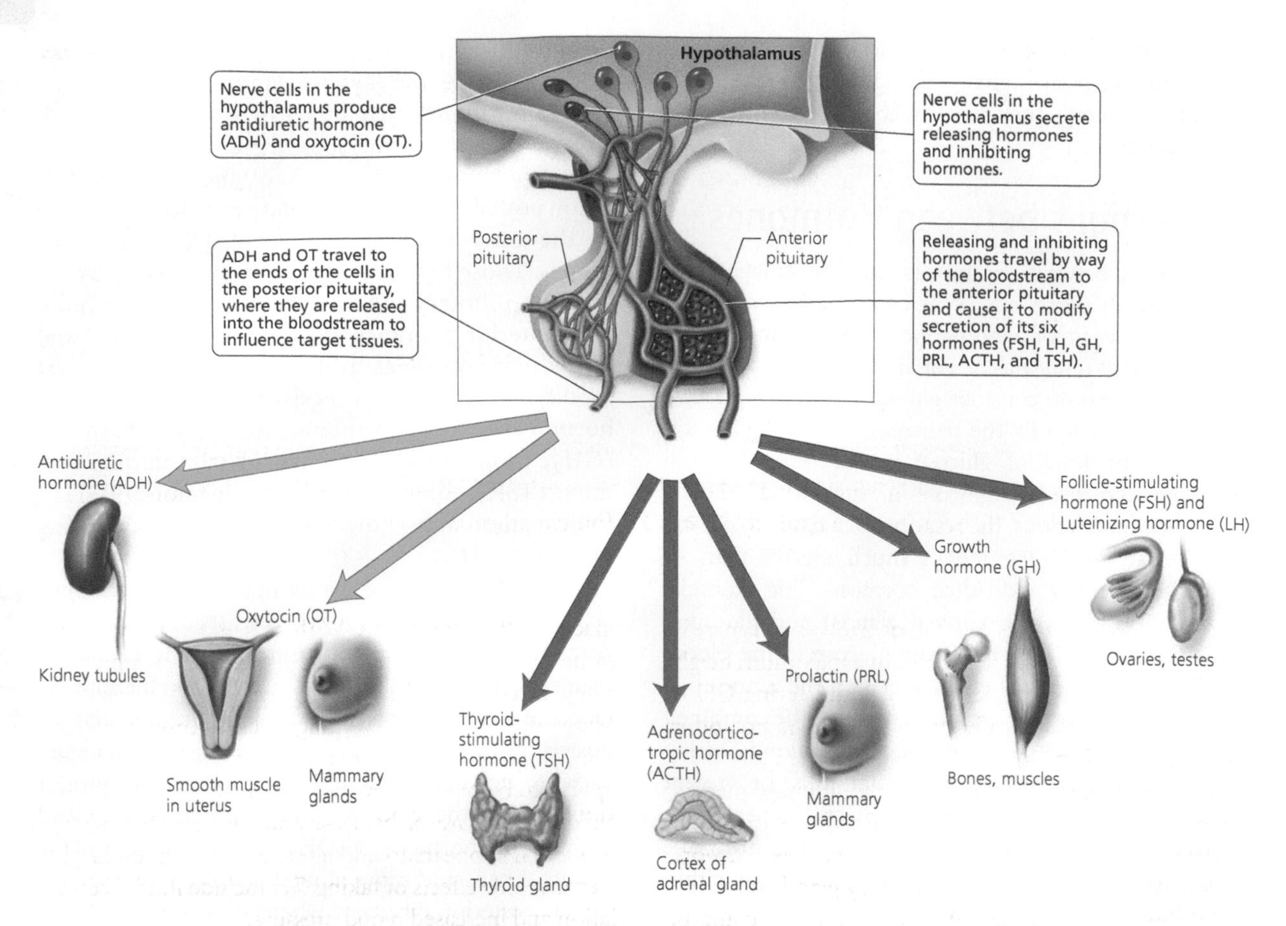
Hypothalamus
Nerve cells in the hypothalamus produce antidiuretic hormone (ADH) and oxytocin (OT).
Nerve cells in the hypothalamus secrete releasing hormones and inhibiting hormones.
Posterior pituitary
Anterior pituitary
ADH and OT travel to the ends of the cells in the posterior pituitary, where they are released into the bloodstream to influence target tissues.
Releasing and inhibiting hormones travel by way of the bloodstream to the anterior pituitary and cause it to modify secretion of its six hormones (FSH, LH, GH, PRL, ACTH, and TSH).
Antidiuretic hormone (ADH)
Kidney tubules
Oxytocin (OT)
Smooth muscle in uterus
Mammary glands
Thyroid-stimulating hormone (TSH)
Thyroid gland
Adrenocortico-tropic hormone (ACTH)
Cortex of adrenal gland
Prolactin (PRL)
Mammary glands
Growth hormone (GH)
Bones, muscles
Follicle-stimulating hormone (FSH) and Luteinizing hormone (LH)
Ovaries, testes

FIGURE 3a(iv).6 The two lobes of the pituitary gland and the hormones they secrete

Increased production of GH in adulthood, when the bones can thicken but not lengthen, causes acromegaly (literally, "enlarged extremities"). *Acromegaly* is characterized by enlargement of the tongue and a gradual thickening of the bones of the hands, feet, and face (Figure 3a(iv).8). Both conditions are associated with decreased life expectancy. The excesses of GH that cause such conditions as gigantism and acromegaly may be caused by a tumor of the anterior pituitary. Tumors can be treated with surgery, radiation, or drugs that reduce GH secretion and tumor size. Insufficient production of

FIGURE 3a(iv).7 Robert Wadlow, a pituitary giant, was born in 1918 at a normal size but developed a pituitary tumor as a young child. The tumor caused increased production of GH. Robert never stopped growing until his death at 22 years of age, by which time he had reached a height of 8 feet 11 inches.

(a) Age 9

(b) Age 16

(c) Age 33

(d) Age 52

FIGURE 3a(iv).8 **Acromegaly. Excess secretion of GH in adulthood, when the bones can thicken but not lengthen, causes acromegaly, a gradual thickening of the bones of the hands, feet, and face. The disorder was not apparent in this female at ages 9 or 16, but it became apparent by age 33. The symptoms were even more obvious at age 52.**

GH in childhood results in *pituitary dwarfism.* Typically, pituitary dwarfs are sterile and attain a maximum height of about 4 feet (Figure 3a(iv).9). Administering GH in childhood can treat pituitary dwarfism but not other forms of dwarfism.

In the past, the use of GH for the treatment of medical conditions (such as pituitary dwarfism) was extremely limited because GH was scarce, given that the hormone had to be extracted from the pituitary glands of cadavers. Beginning in the late 1970s, however, GH could be made in the laboratory. With this greater availability came research on its potential uses in the treatment of aging in adults and below-average height in children. Many aspects of normal aging, such as thinning of the skin, decreased muscle mass, and increased body fat, appear to be reversed by the administration of GH. For children who are of below-average height, administration of GH appears to add a few inches of adult height. Negative side effects of taking GH include fluid accumulation and increased blood pressure.

what would you do?

A recent review of studies in which children of below-average height were administered GH concluded that such therapy could yield an additional 2 inches of adult height. Opponents of this use of GH believe it is wrong to give a powerful and potentially harmful hormone to children who are basically healthy. Rather than administering GH to such children, opponents suggest working to increase societal acceptance of persons who are short. Opponents also point out that GH therapy has negative side effects and is expensive (the average yearly cost of GH therapy is $20,000, and some children remain on therapy for 10 or more years). Do you think that GH should be used to "treat" below-average height in children? What would you do if you were the parent of a healthy child who was destined to be very short? What if your child were a pituitary dwarf; would you approve the use of GH then?

FIGURE 3a(iv).9 **Pituitary dwarfism is caused by insufficient GH in childhood**

Prolactin (PRL), another hormone secreted by the anterior lobe of the pituitary gland, stimulates the mammary glands to produce milk. (Oxytocin, a hormone secreted from the posterior pituitary, causes the ducts of the mammary glands to eject milk, as discussed later in the chapter.) PRL interferes with female sex hormones, which explains why most mothers fail to have regular menstrual cycles while nursing their newborn. (Lactation should not, however, be relied upon as a method for birth control, because the suppression of female hormones and ovulation lessens as mothers breast-feed their growing infants less frequently.)

Growth of a pituitary tumor may cause excess secretion of PRL, which may cause infertility in females, along with production of milk when birth has not occurred. In males, PRL appears to be involved in the production of mature sperm in the testes, but its precise role is not yet clear. Nevertheless, production of too much PRL, as might occur with a pituitary tumor, can cause sterility and impotence in men. Some hormones from the hypothalamus stimulate and others inhibit production and secretion of PRL.

The remaining hormones produced by the anterior lobe of the pituitary gland influence other endocrine glands. A hormone produced by one endocrine gland or organ that influences another endocrine gland is called a **tropic hormone.** Two such hormones secreted by the anterior lobe of the pituitary are thyroid-stimulating hormone and adrenocorticotropic hormone. **Thyroid-stimulating hormone** (TSH) acts on the thyroid gland in the neck to stimulate synthesis and release of thyroid hormones. **Adrenocorticotropic hormone** (ACTH), also called corticotropin, controls the synthesis and secretion of glucocorticoid hormones from the outer portion (cortex) of the adrenal glands (see Figure 3a(iv).2).

Two other tropic hormones secreted by the anterior lobe of the pituitary gland influence the gonads (ovaries in the female and testes in the male). **Follicle-stimulating hormone** (FSH) promotes development of egg cells and secretion of the hormone estrogen from the ovaries in females. **Luteinizing hormone** (LH) causes ovulation, the release of a future egg cell by the ovary in females. LH also stimulates the ovaries to secrete estrogen and progesterone. These two hormones prepare the uterus for implantation of a fertilized ovum and the breasts for production of milk. In males, FSH promotes maturation of sperm, while LH stimulates cells within the testes to produce and secrete the hormone testosterone.

Posterior Lobe

The posterior pituitary does not produce any hormones of its own. However, neurons of the hypothalamus manufacture antidiuretic hormone and oxytocin. These hormones travel down the nerve cells into the posterior pituitary, where they are stored and released.

The main function of **antidiuretic hormone** (ADH) is to conserve body water by decreasing urine output. ADH accomplishes this task by prompting the kidneys to remove water from the fluid destined to become urine. The water is then returned to the blood. Alcohol temporarily inhibits secretion of ADH, causing increased urination following alcohol consumption. The increased output of urine causes dehydration and the resultant headache and dry mouth typical of many hangovers. ADH is also called vasopressin. This name comes from its role in constricting blood vessels and raising blood pressure, particularly during times of severe blood loss.

A deficiency of ADH may result from damage to either the posterior pituitary or the area of the hypothalamus responsible for the hormone's manufacture. Such a deficiency results in *diabetes insipidus,* a condition characterized by excessive urine production and resultant dehydration. Mild cases may not require treatment. Severe cases may cause extreme fluid loss, and death through dehydration can result. Treatment usually includes administration of synthetic ADH in a nasal spray. Diabetes insipidus (*diabetes,* overflow; *insipidus,* tasteless) should not be confused with *diabetes mellitus* (*mel,* honey). The latter is a condition in which large amounts of glucose are lost in the urine as a result of an insulin deficiency. Both conditions, however, are characterized by increased production of urine. (We discuss diabetes mellitus later, when we discuss the hormones of the pancreas.)

Oxytocin (OT) is the second hormone produced in the hypothalamus and released by the posterior pituitary. The name *oxytocin* (*oxy,* quick; *tokos,* childbirth) reveals one of its two main functions, stimulating the uterine contractions of childbirth. As described earlier, the control of OT during labor is an example of a positive feedback mechanism (see Figure 3a(iv).5). Pitocin is a synthetic form of OT sometimes administered to induce and speed labor.

stop and THINK

Women who have just given birth are often encouraged to nurse their babies as soon as possible after delivery. How might an infant's suckling promote completion of, and recovery from, the birth process? Consider that the placenta (afterbirth) must still be expelled after the birth of the baby and that the uterus must return to an approximation of its prepregnancy form.

The second major function of oxytocin is to stimulate milk ejection from the mammary glands. Milk ejection occurs in response to the sucking stimulus of an infant (Figure 3a(iv).10). Recall that prolactin secreted by the anterior pituitary stimulates the mammary glands to produce, but not to eject, milk. Men also secrete OT, and there is some evidence that this hormone facilitates the transport of sperm in the male reproductive tract.

THYROID GLAND

The **thyroid gland** is a shield-shaped, deep red structure in the front of the neck, as shown in Figure 3a(iv).11a. (The color stems from its prodigious blood supply.) Within the thyroid are small, spherical chambers called follicles (Figure 3a(iv).11b). Cells line the walls of the follicles and produce thyroglobulin, the substance from which thyroxine (T_4) and triiodothyronine (T_3) are made. These two very similar hormones have different numbers of iodine molecules; as indicated by their abbreviations, thyroxine has four iodine molecules and triiodothyronine has three. Thyroxine is usually produced in greater quantity than triiodothyronine, and most thyroxine is eventually converted to triiodothyronine. Because these two hormones are so similar, we will simply refer to them as **thyroid hormone** (TH). Other endocrine cells in the thyroid, called parafollicular cells (because they occur near the follicles), secrete the hormone calcitonin (Figure 3a(iv).11b).

Nearly all body cells are target cells for TH. Therefore, it is not surprising that the hormone has broad effects. TH regulates the body's metabolic rate and production of heat. It also maintains blood pressure and promotes normal development and functioning of several organ systems. TH affects cellular metabolism by

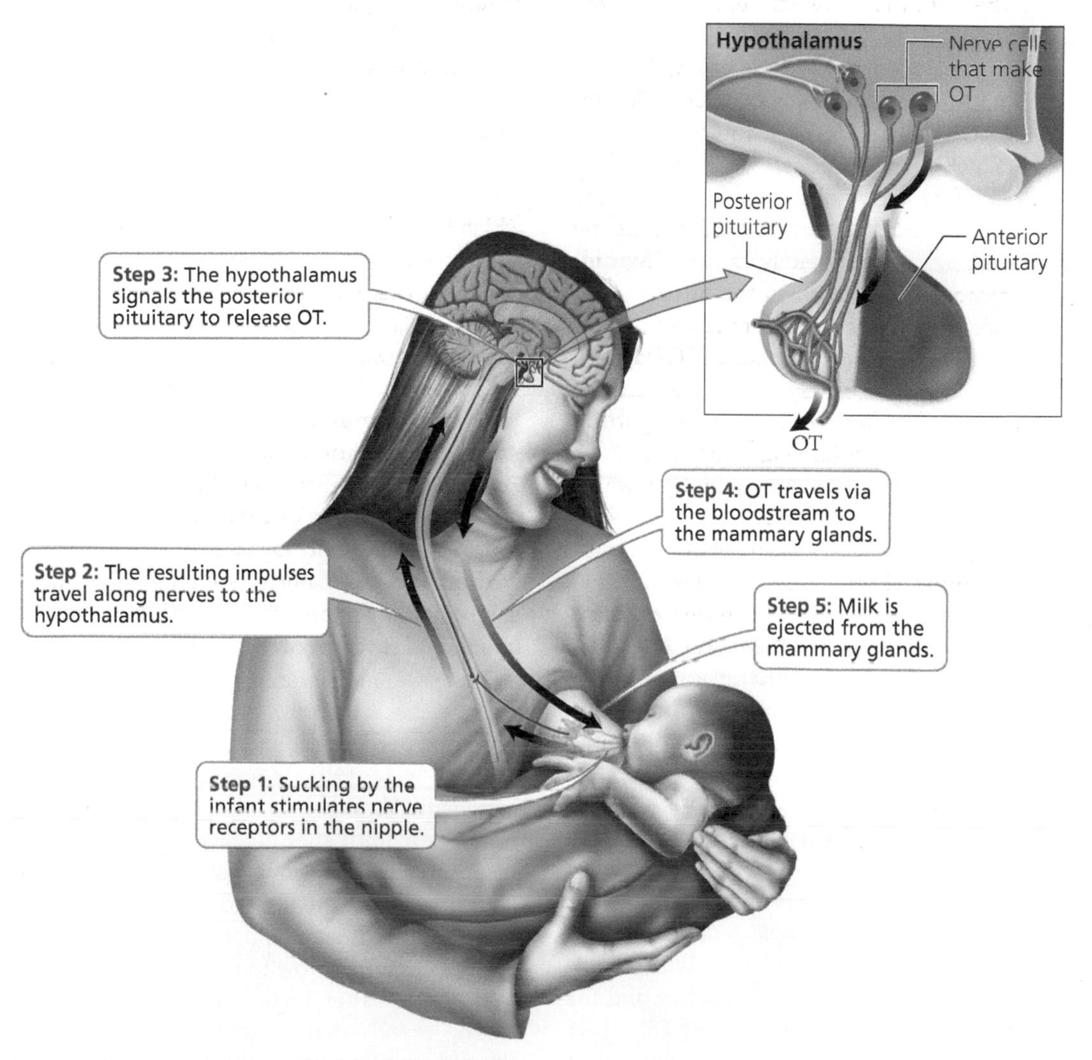
Hypothalamus
Nerve cells that make OT
Posterior pituitary
Anterior pituitary
OT
Step 3: The hypothalamus signals the posterior pituitary to release OT.
Step 4: OT travels via the bloodstream to the mammary glands.
Step 2: The resulting impulses travel along nerves to the hypothalamus.
Step 5: Milk is ejected from the mammary glands.
Step 1: Sucking by the infant stimulates nerve receptors in the nipple.

FIGURE 3a(iv).10 **The steps by which OT stimulates milk ejection from the mammary glands**

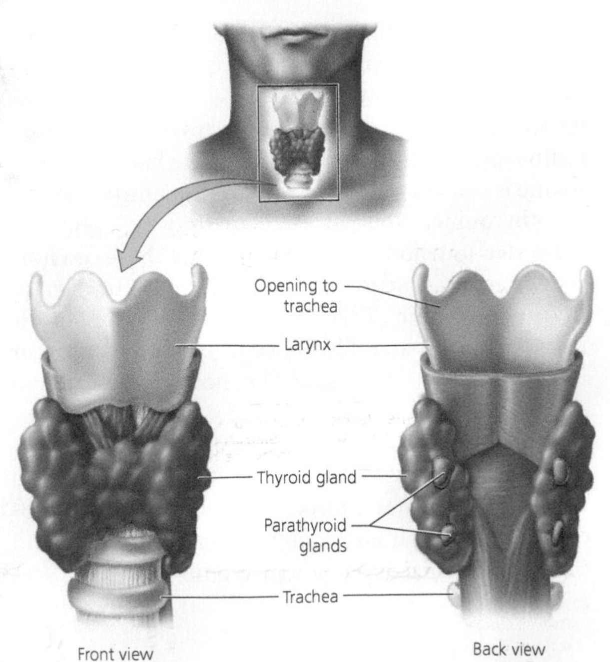

(a) The thyroid gland lies over the trachea, just below the larynx.

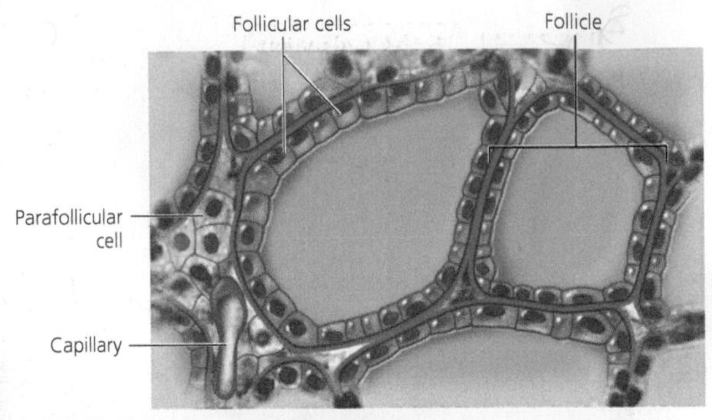

(b) Diagram showing structure of thyroid tissue. Note the follicular cells that produce the precursor to thyroid hormone and the parafollicular cells that produce calcitonin.

FIGURE 3a(iv).11 Location and structure of the thyroid gland and parathyroid glands

(a) Simple goiter

(b) Cretinism

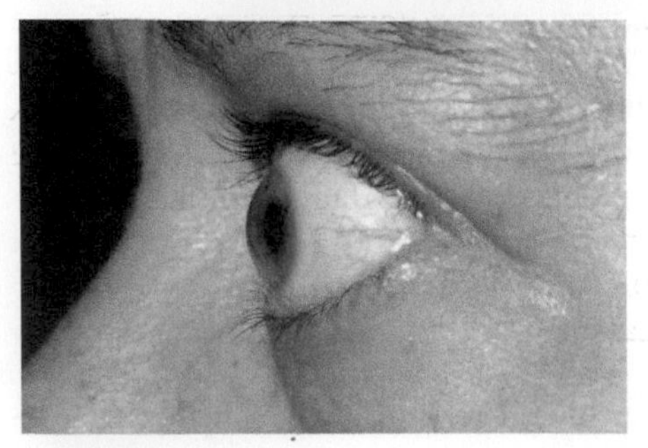

(c) Exophthalmos

FIGURE 3a(iv).12 Disorders of the thyroid gland

stimulating protein synthesis, the breakdown of lipids, and the use of glucose for production of ATP. The pituitary gland and hypothalamus control the release of TH. Falling levels of TH in the blood prompt the hypothalamus to secrete a releasing hormone. The releasing hormone stimulates the anterior pituitary to secrete TSH, which, in turn, causes the thyroid to release more TH.

Iodine is needed for production of TH. A diet deficient in iodine can produce a *simple goiter*, that is, an enlarged thyroid gland (Figure 3a(iv).12a). When intake of iodine is inadequate, the level of TH is low, and the low level of TH in turn triggers secretion of TSH. TSH stimulates the thyroid gland to increase production of thyroglobulin. The lack of iodine prevents formation of TH from the accumulating thyroglobulin. In response to continued low levels of TH, the pituitary continues to release increasing amounts of TSH, which cause the thyroid to enlarge in a futile effort to filter more iodine from the blood. In the past, goiters were quite common, especially in parts of the Midwestern United States (dubbed the Goiter Belt), where iodine-poor soil and little access to iodine-rich shellfish led to diets deficient in iodine. The incidence of goiter in the United States dramatically decreased once iodine was added to most table salt beginning in the 1920s. Simple goiter can be treated by iodine supplements or administration of TH.

Undersecretion of TH during fetal development or infancy causes *cretinism*, a condition characterized by dwarfism and delayed mental and sexual development (Figure 3a(iv).12b). If a pregnant woman produces sufficient TH, many of the symptoms of cretinism do not appear until after birth, when the deficient infant begins to rely solely on its own malfunctioning thyroid gland to supply the needed hormones. Oral doses of TH can prevent cretinism, so most infants in industrialized nations are now tested for proper thyroid function shortly after birth. In the United States, such testing reveals that incomplete development of the thyroid gland occurs in about 1 in every 3,000 births. Undersecretion of TH in adulthood causes *myxedema*, a condition in which fluid accumulates in facial tissues. Other symptoms of TH undersecretion include decreases in alertness, body temperature, and heart rate. Oral administration of TH can prevent and treat these symptoms.

Oversecretion of TH causes *Graves' disease,* an autoimmune disorder in which a person's own immune system produces Y-shaped proteins called antibodies that in this case mimic the action of TSH. The antibodies stimulate the thyroid gland, causing it to enlarge and overproduce its hormones. Symptoms of Graves' disease include increased metabolic rate and heart rate, accompanied by sweating, nervousness, and weight loss. Many patients with Graves' disease also have *exophthalmos,* protruding eyes caused by the swelling of tissues in the eye orbits (Figure 3a(iv).12c). Graves' disease may be treated with drugs that block synthesis of thyroid hormones. Alternatively, thyroid tissue may be reduced through surgery or the administration of radioactive iodine. Because the thyroid gland accumulates iodine, ingestion of radioactive iodine (usually administered in capsules) selectively destroys thyroid tissue.

The **calcitonin (CT)** secreted by the parafollicular cells of the thyroid helps regulate the concentration of calcium in the blood to ensure the proper functioning of muscle cells and neurons. Calcium ions bind to the protein troponin, leading to changes in other muscle proteins and eventually causing muscle contraction. In addition, calcium causes the release of neurotransmitters into the synaptic cleft and therefore is critical in the transmission of messages from one neuron to the next. When the level of calcium in the blood is high, CT stimulates the absorption of calcium by bone and inhibits the breakdown of bone, thereby lowering the level of calcium in the blood. CT also lowers blood calcium by stimulating an initial increase in the excretion of calcium in the urine. When the level of calcium in the blood is low, the parathyroid glands, which we discuss next, are prompted to release their hormone.

PARATHYROID GLANDS

The **parathyroid glands** are four small, round masses at the back of the thyroid gland (Figure 3a(iv).11a, back view). These glands secrete **parathyroid hormone (PTH),** also called *parathormone.* As mentioned earlier, CT from the thyroid gland lowers the level of calcium in the blood. In contrast, PTH increases levels of calcium in the blood. Low levels of calcium in the blood stimulate the parathyroid glands to secrete PTH, which causes calcium to move from bone and urine into the blood. PTH exerts its effects by stimulating (1) bone-destroying cells called osteoclasts that release calcium from bone into the blood, (2) the removal of calcium from the urine and its return to the blood, and (3) the rate at which calcium is absorbed into the blood from the gastrointestinal tract. PTH also inhibits bone-forming cells called osteoblasts and thereby reduces the rate at which calcium is deposited in bone. The feedback system by which CT and PTH together regulate levels of calcium in the blood is summarized in Figure 3a(iv).13.

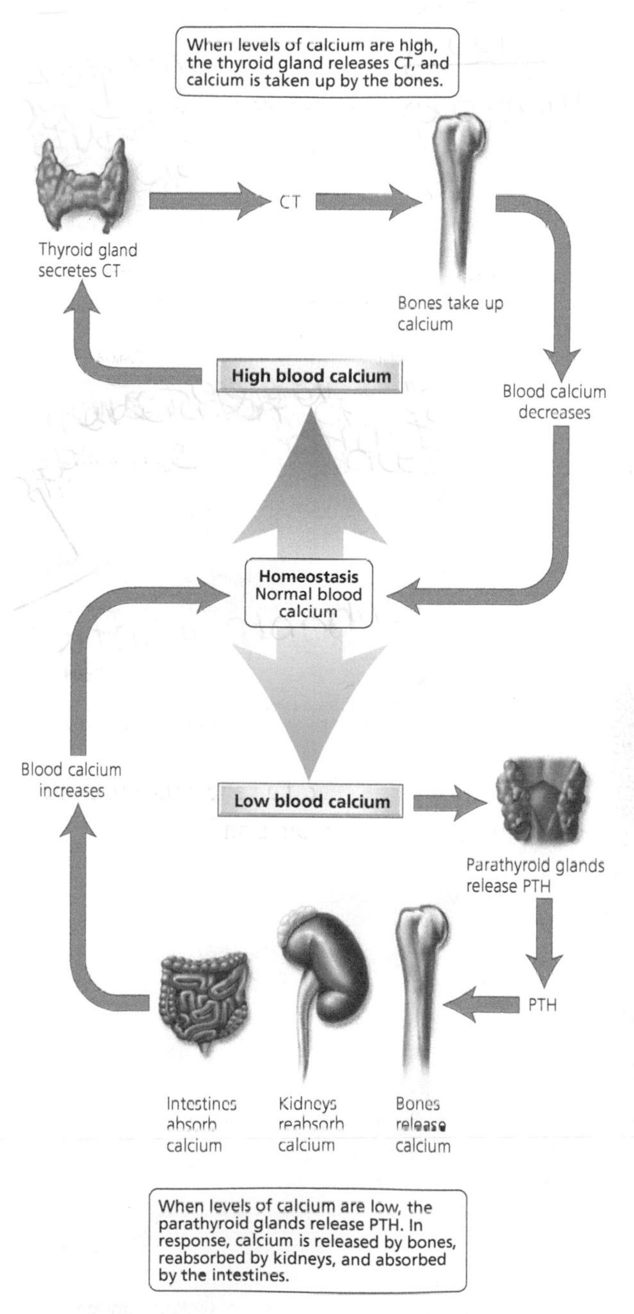

FIGURE 3a(iv).13 **Regulation of calcium levels in the blood by CT from the thyroid gland (top) and by PTH from the parathyroid glands (bottom)**

Surgery on the neck or thyroid gland may damage the parathyroid glands. The resultant decrease in PTH causes decreased blood calcium that in turn produces nervousness and irritability (low calcium is associated with hyperexcitability of the membranes of neurons) and muscle spasms (recall that calcium is also important in muscle contraction). In severe cases, death may result from spasms of the larynx and paralysis of the respiratory system. PTH is difficult to purify, so deficiencies are not usually treated by administering the hormone. Instead, calcium is given either in tablet form or through increased dietary intake.

A tumor of the parathyroid gland can cause excess secretion of PTH. Oversecretion of PTH pulls calcium from bone tissue, causing increased blood calcium and weakened bones. High levels of calcium in the blood may lead to kidney stones, calcium deposits in other soft tissue, and decreased activity of the nervous system.

stop and THINK

High blood pressure can signal abnormal aldosterone secretion. Would high blood pressure be associated with the undersecretion or oversecretion of aldosterone?

ADRENAL GLANDS

The body's two **adrenal glands** (*ad,* upon; *renal,* kidney), each about the size of an almond, are located at the tops of the kidneys. Each adrenal gland has an outer and an inner region. The outer region of the gland, the **adrenal cortex,** secretes more than 20 different lipid-soluble (steroid) hormones, generally divided into three groups: the gonadocorticoids, mineralocorticoids, and glucocorticoids (Figure 3a(iv).14). The inner region, called the **adrenal medulla,** secretes two water-soluble hormones, epinephrine (also known as adrenaline) and norepinephrine (also known as noradrenaline).

Adrenal Cortex

The **gonadocorticoids** are male and female sex hormones known as **androgens** and **estrogens.** In both males and females, the adrenal cortex secretes both androgens and estrogens. However, in normal adult males, androgen secretion by the testes far surpasses that by the adrenal cortex. Thus, the effects of adrenal androgens in adult males are probably insignificant. In females, the ovaries and placenta also produce estrogen, although during menopause, the ovaries decrease secretion of estrogen and eventually stop secreting it.

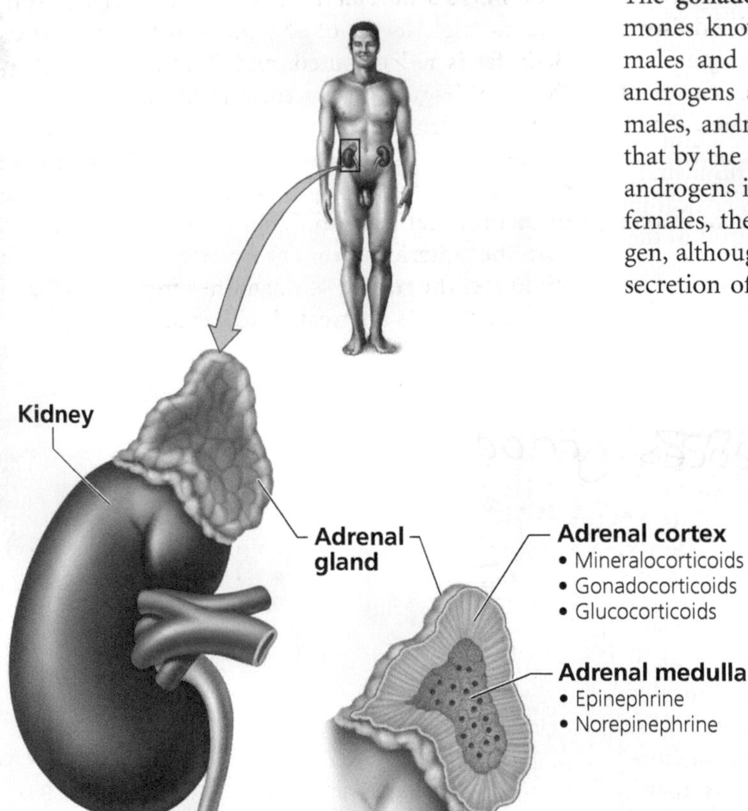

(a) Each adrenal gland sits on top of a kidney.

(b) A section through the adrenal gland reveals two regions, the outer adrenal cortex and the inner adrenal medulla. These regions secrete different hormones.

FIGURE 3a(iv).14 **Location and structure of an adrenal gland**

The gonadocorticoids from the adrenal cortex may somewhat alleviate the effects of decreased ovarian estrogen in menopausal women. One option for menopausal women suffering from estrogen deficiency is hormone therapy. The advantages and disadvantages of this therapy are considered in the Health Issue essay, *Is It Hot in Here, or Is It Me? Hormone Therapy and Menopause.*

The **mineralocorticoids** secreted by the adrenal cortex affect mineral homeostasis and water balance. The primary mineralocorticoid is **aldosterone,** a hormone that acts on cells of the kidneys to increase reabsorption of sodium ions (Na^+) into the blood. This reabsorption prevents depletion of Na^+ and increases water retention. Aldosterone also acts on kidney cells to promote the excretion of potassium ions (K^+) in urine. *Addison's disease* is a disorder caused by the undersecretion of aldosterone and the glucocorticoid cortisol (see the following discussion). This disease appears to be an autoimmune disorder in which the body's own immune system perceives cells of the adrenal cortex as foreign and destroys them. The resulting deficiency of adrenal hormones causes weight loss, fatigue, electrolyte imbalance, poor appetite, and poor resistance to stress. A peculiar bronzing of the skin also is associated with Addison's disease (Figure 3a(iv).15). Recall that the pituitary gland secretes ACTH, which stimulates the cortex of the adrenal glands to secrete its hormones. Thus, Addison's disease can also be caused by inadequate secretion of ACTH by the pituitary. Regardless of its cause, Addison's disease can be treated with hormone tablets.

The **glucocorticoids** are hormones secreted by the adrenal cortex that affect glucose levels. Glucocorticoids act on the liver to promote the conversion of fat and protein to intermediate substances that are ultimately converted into glucose. The glucocorticoids also act on adipose tissue to prompt the breakdown of fats to fatty acids that are released into the bloodstream, where they are available for use by the body's cells. Glucocorticoids further conserve glucose by inhibiting its uptake by muscle and fat tissue.

Glucocorticoids also inhibit the inflammatory response; such inhibition can be beneficial when the body is faced with the swelling and intense irritation associated with skin rashes such as that caused by poison ivy. One way glucocorticoids inhibit inflammation is by slowing the movement of white blood cells to the site of injury. Another way is by reducing the likelihood that other cells will release chemicals that promote inflammation. Unfortunately, these activities of glucocorticoids inhibit wound healing. Steroid creams containing synthetic glucocorticoids are therefore intended to be applied only to the surface of the skin and to be used for superficial rashes only. These creams should not be applied to open wounds. Some examples of glucocorticoids are cortisol, corticosterone, and cortisone.

Cushing's syndrome results from prolonged exposure to high levels of the glucocorticoid cortisol. Body fat is redistributed, and fluid accumulates in the face (Figure 3a(iv).16). Additional symptoms include fatigue, high blood pressure, and elevated glucose levels. A tumor on either the adrenal cortex or the anterior pituitary may cause the oversecretion of cortisol that leads to Cushing's syndrome. (Recall that the anterior pituitary secretes ACTH, which stimulates the release of hormones from the adrenal cortex.) Tumors are treated with radiation, drugs, or

FIGURE 3a(iv).15 John F. Kennedy suffered from Addison's disease, which is caused by undersecretion of cortisone and aldosterone from the adrenal cortex. JFK's complexion showed the peculiar bronzing of the skin characteristic of Addison's disease.

Health Issue

Is It Hot in Here, or Is It Me? Hormone Therapy and Menopause

Many endocrine disorders are characterized by little or no secretion of certain hormones. Cretinism, for example, is caused by the undersecretion of thyroid hormone during fetal development or infancy. In other cases, hormone secretion declines as part of the normal aging process. Estrogen, a hormone produced primarily by the ovaries, is secreted in decreasing amounts beginning when women are about age 30. This decrease eventually leads into menopause, the termination of ovulation and menstruation. Menopause usually occurs when women are between 45 and 55 years of age. Undersecretion of hormones, whether caused by malfunctioning glands or normal aging, often is treated with hormone replacement therapy (HRT). In HRT, the deficient hormone is replaced using injections, pills, patches, or creams. Today, HRT is commonly called hormone therapy.

Hormone therapy has had many successes, but it is not without controversy, particularly when it is used to treat normal declines in hormone levels. As mentioned, levels of ovarian hormones decline as women age; menopause is the ultimate result. Some women face a host of uncomfortable symptoms in conjunction with the eventual end of ovulation and menstruation. Such symptoms include hot flashes, night sweats, vaginal dryness, stress incontinence (involuntary loss of small amounts of urine when laughing, coughing, or sneezing), heightened mood swings, and memory loss. Symptoms may last only a few months or a few years. Declining estrogen levels also have been linked to increased risk of osteoporosis (increased bone loss leading to increased risk of fracture). For many years doctors administered ovarian hormones to millions of women at or past menopause to treat these effects. For women who naturally entered menopause, doctors prescribed estrogen and progestin (a form of progesterone). This combination was used because of the increased risk of uterine cancer associated with using estrogen alone. For women who entered menopause because their uterus had been surgically removed (this surgical procedure is known as a hysterectomy), doctors prescribed estrogen alone.

In recent years, there has been a significant research effort to evaluate the benefits and risks of hormone therapy for the treatment of menopause. Both estrogen therapy and the combination estrogen and progestin therapy have some benefits; they relieve hot flashes and night sweats, and slow the loss of bone. Hormone therapy involving estrogen plus progestin also seems to reduce the risk of colorectal cancer. There are also risks associated with these therapies. Both therapies are associated with increased risk of blood clots and stroke. Therapy involving estrogen plus progestin is also associated with increased risk of heart attack and breast cancer.

In view of the risks of hormone therapies, many physicians are now urging women to consider other ways available to stave off osteoporosis. These physicians urge women to avoid smoking, to eat a diet rich in calcium and vitamin D, and to exercise regularly. Nonhormonal drugs may be better and safer for preventing bone fractures. Some alternative practitioners advise getting estrogen from dietary sources such as yams and soybeans. These foods are certainly weaker sources than prescription estrogen and may reduce the risks.

surgery. Cushing's syndrome also may result from glucocorticoid hormone treatment for asthma, lupus, or rheumatoid arthritis. Treatment in medically induced cases of Cushing's syndrome typically entails a gradual reduction of the glucocorticoid dose, ideally to the lowest level necessary to control the existing disorder without prompting adverse affects.

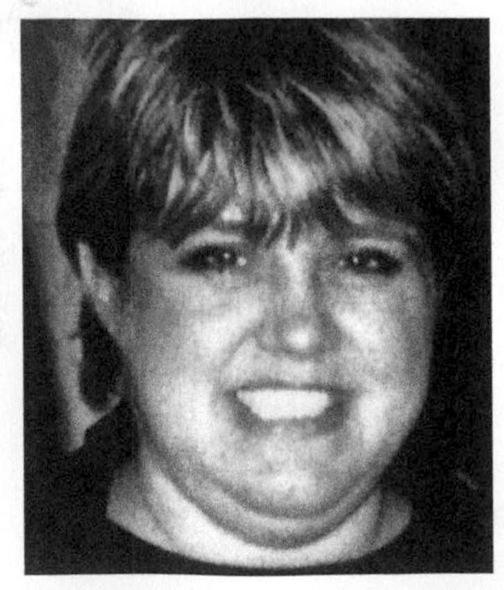

(a) Patient diagnosed with Cushing's syndrome

(b) Same patient after treatment

FIGURE 3a(iv).16 **Cushing's syndrome. Prolonged exposure to cortisol causes fluid to accumulate in the face. Most often, Cushing's syndrome is caused by the administration of cortisol for allergies or inflammation.**

Adrenal Medulla

As introduced earlier, the adrenal medulla produces **epinephrine** and **norepinephrine.** These hormones are critical in the **fight-or-flight response,** the reaction by the body's sympathetic nervous system to emergencies. Imagine that you are walking home alone late at night and a stranger suddenly steps toward you from the bushes. Impulses received by your hypothalamus are sent by neurons to your adrenal medulla. These impulses cause cells in your adrenal medulla to increase output of epinephrine and norepinephrine. In response to these hormones, your heart rate, respiratory rate, and blood glucose levels rise. Blood vessels associated with the digestive tract constrict because digestion is not of prime importance during times of extreme stress. Vessels associated with skeletal and cardiac muscles dilate, allowing more blood, glucose, and oxygen to reach them. These substances also reach your brain in greater amounts, leading to the increased mental alertness needed for fleeing or fighting.

In contrast to the near instantaneous response of the sympathetic nervous system to a perceived threat, the hormonal response takes about 30 seconds to mount. This is because epinephrine and norepinephrine must be released by the adrenal medulla, travel in the bloodstream to all cells, bind to receptors on their target cells, and initiate changes in those cells. Even after the danger has passed, we feel the changes brought on by these hormones for a few additional minutes. Epinephrine and norepinephrine thus augment and prolong the response of the sympathetic nervous system to stress. The more leisurely onset and conclusion of the effects of epinephrine and norepinephrine highlight the differences between neural and hormonal systems of internal communication. We explore further how our bodies react to stress in the Health Issue essay, *Hormones and Our Response to Stress.*

PANCREAS

The **pancreas** is located in the abdomen just behind the stomach (Figure 3a(iv).17); it contains both endocrine and exocrine cells. The endocrine cells occur in small clusters called **pancreatic islets** (or islets of Langerhans). These clusters contain three types of hormone-producing cells. One type produces the hormone glucagon; a

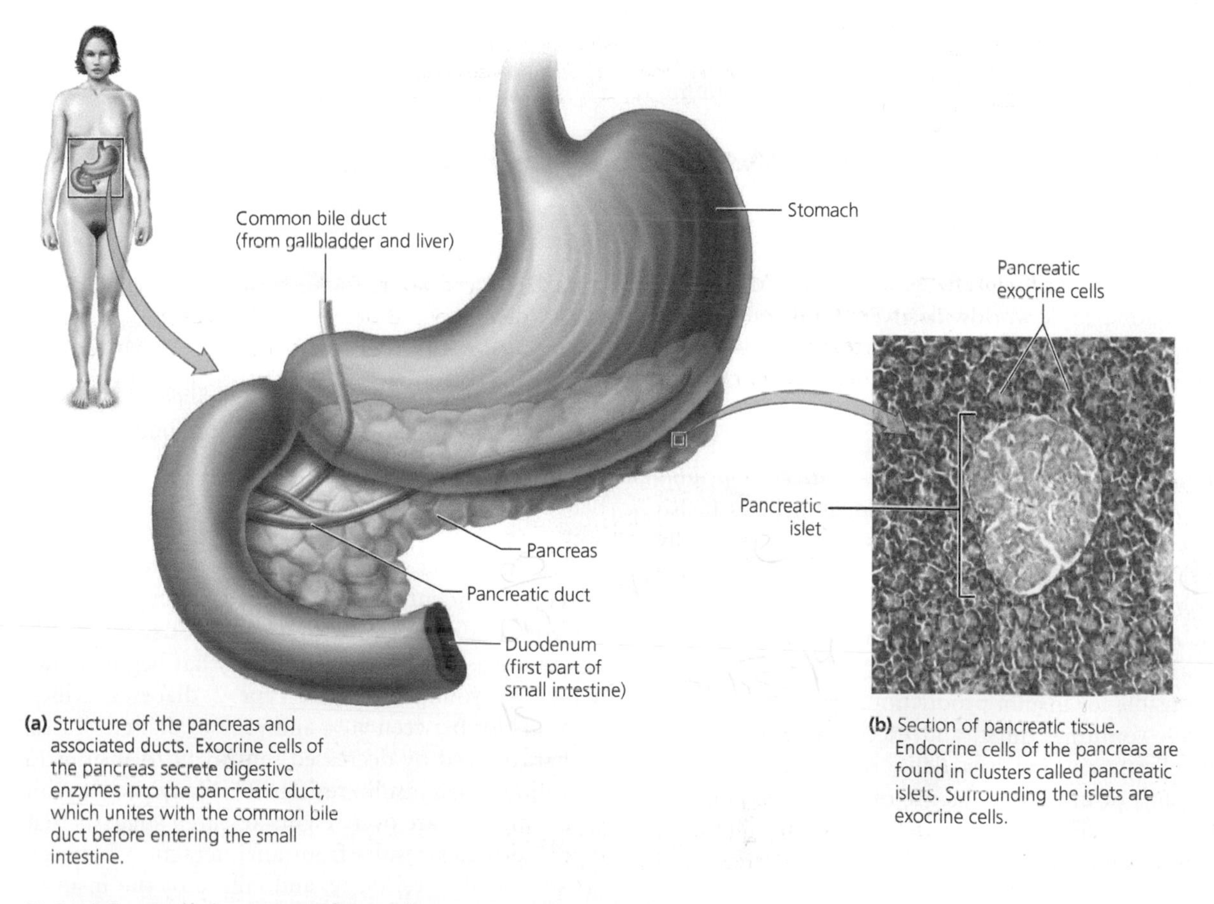

(a) Structure of the pancreas and associated ducts. Exocrine cells of the pancreas secrete digestive enzymes into the pancreatic duct, which unites with the common bile duct before entering the small intestine.

(b) Section of pancreatic tissue. Endocrine cells of the pancreas are found in clusters called pancreatic islets. Surrounding the islets are exocrine cells.

FIGURE 3a(iv).17 **Location and structure of the pancreas**

second produces the hormone insulin; and a third produces the hormone somatostatin. Somatostatin is also secreted by the digestive tract, where it inhibits secretions of the stomach and small intestine, and by the hypothalamus, where it inhibits secretion of growth hormone. The somatostatin secreted by the pancreas may regulate the secretion of glucagon and insulin. However, the precise function of pancreatic somatostatin is not well understood, so we focus on glucagon and insulin.

Between meals, as the level of blood sugar declines, the pancreas secretes glucagon. **Glucagon** increases the level of blood sugar. It does so by prompting cells of the liver to increase conversion of glycogen (the storage polysaccharide in animals) to glucose (a simple sugar, or monosaccharide). Glucagon also stimulates the liver to form glucose from lactic acid and amino acids. The liver releases the resultant glucose molecules into the bloodstream, causing a rise in blood sugar level.

After a meal, as the level of blood sugar rises with the absorption of sugars from the digestive tract, the pancreas secretes insulin. In contrast to glucagon, **insulin** decreases glucose in the blood; insulin and glucagon thus have opposite or antagonistic effects. Insulin decreases blood glucose in several ways. First, insulin stimulates transport of glucose into muscle cells, white blood cells, and connective tissue cells. Second, insulin inhibits the breakdown of glycogen to glucose. Third, insulin prevents conversion of amino and fatty acids to glucose. As a result of these actions, insulin promotes protein synthesis, fat storage, and the use of glucose for energy. Figure 3a(iv).18 summarizes the regulation of glucose in the blood by insulin and glucagon.

Insulin has dramatic effects on health. More than 120 million people worldwide, over 15 million of them in the United States, suffer from *diabetes mellitus,* a group of metabolic disorders characterized by an abnormally high level of glucose in the blood. There are several types of diabetes mellitus; we focus on type 1 and type 2 diabetes mellitus. *Type 1 diabetes mellitus* used to be known as insulin-dependent diabetes. It also was called juvenile-onset diabetes, because it usually develops in people younger than 25 years of age. In this autoimmune disorder, which represents about 5% to 10% of all diagnosed cases of diabetes, a person's own immune system attacks the cells of the pancreas responsible for insulin production. Symptoms include nausea, vomiting, thirst, and excessive urine production. Treatment involves daily, sometimes multiple, injections of insulin or the use of an insulin pump (a relatively small device that delivers the insulin at an infusion site, often on the abdomen). Exercise and careful monitoring of diet and blood glucose levels also are essential.

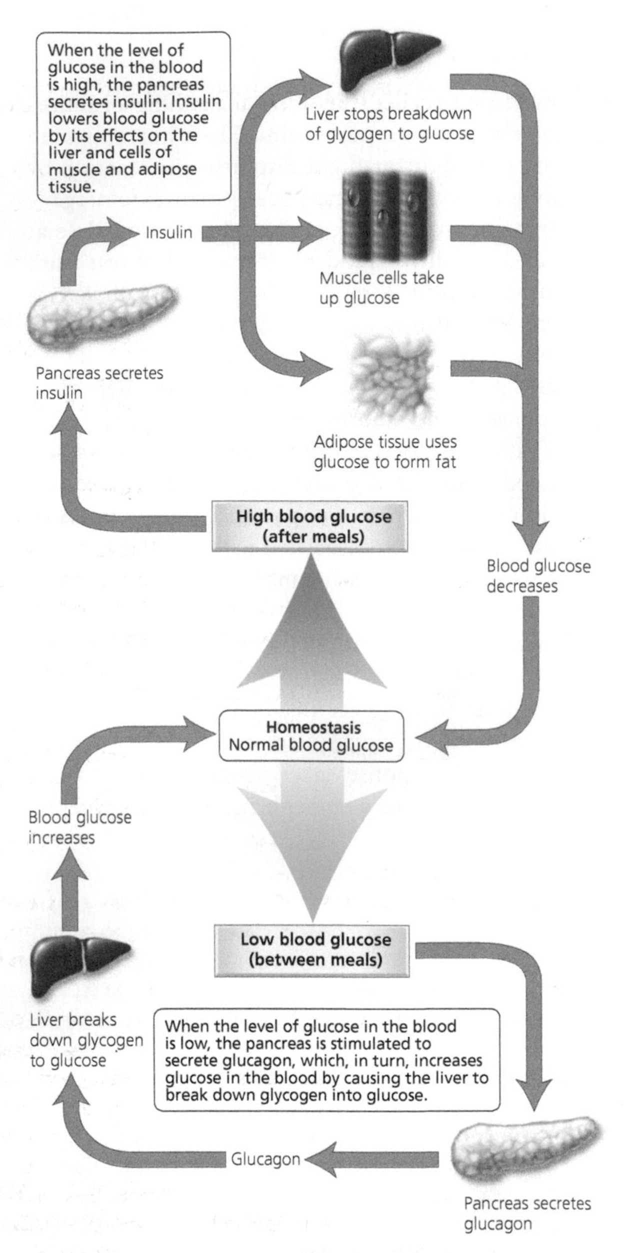

FIGURE 3a(iv).18 **Regulation of glucose level in the blood by insulin (top) and glucagon (bottom), both of which are secreted by the pancreas**

Type 2 diabetes mellitus used to be known as non-insulin-dependent diabetes. It was formerly called adult-onset diabetes as well, because it usually develops after age 40, although it recently has begun showing up in younger people. Type 2 diabetes, which accounts for between 90% and 95% of diabetes cases, is characterized by decreased sensitivity to insulin (a condition called insulin resistance). Many people with type 2 diabetes are overweight. Research suggests that type 2 diabetes results from an interaction between obesity, insulin resistance, and failure of the insulin-producing cells of the pancreas to fully compensate for

Health Issue

Hormones and Our Response to Stress

Stress can be defined broadly as mental or physical tension. Rarely does a day go by that we are not subjected to stress. Awaiting the start of an exam, some personal performance, or an interview can be stressful. Our bodies usually can deal with everyday stresses and maintain the relative constancy of our internal environment. Sometimes, however, stress is extreme in its intensity and duration, and our coping mechanisms prove inadequate. At such times, stress triggers the hypothalamus to initiate the general adaptation syndrome (GAS), a series of physiological adjustments made by our bodies in response to extreme stress.

The GAS has three phases: alarm, resistance, and exhaustion. The alarm phase is popularly known as the fight-or-flight response. Recall that the fight-or-flight response is initiated by epinephrine from the adrenal medulla. The response immediately funnels huge amounts of glucose and oxygen to the organs most critical in responding to danger.

Sometimes the adjustments of the alarm phase are sufficient to end or escape whatever is causing the stress. At other times, stress is so intense and long lasting that the individual enters the resistance phase. Changes wrought by the resistance phase are more long term than are those of the alarm phase. Also, rather than being stimulated by nerve impulses from the hypothalamus, the resistance phase is initiated by the release of hormones from the hypothalamus. The released hormones stimulate the anterior pituitary to secrete several more hormones. In turn, some of these newly secreted hormones stimulate other glands to secrete their hormones. Glucocorticoids from the adrenal cortex are the main hormones of the resistance phase. Two primary effects of glucocorticoids are to mobilize the body's protein and fat reserves and to conserve glucose for use by cells of the nervous system. The hormones of the resistance phase also result in conservation of body fluids.

The resistance phase is sustained by the body's fat reserves. This phase may last for weeks or months, but it cannot go on indefinitely. Sooner or later, lipid reserves are exhausted and structural proteins must be broken down to meet energy demands. Eventually, organs are unable to meet the heavy demands of the resistance phase, and they begin to fail. This is the exhaustion phase. Without immediate attention, death may result from collapse of one or more organ systems.

Stress, especially when it is prolonged and uncontrollable, can dramatically affect our health. It depresses wound healing, increases our susceptibility to infections, and leads to disorders such as hypertension, irritable bowel syndrome, and asthma. Some studies have shown that stress puts people at greater risk for developing chronic diseases. Overall, prolonged stress appears to shorten the life span.

Given the connection between stress and health, it is important to reduce some of the stress in our lives. Commonly used means to alleviate the effects of stress include regular exercise and relaxation techniques. A specialized relaxation technique is biofeedback, a procedure that can be used to help a person recognize the symptoms of stress and learn how to control them. During a stress biofeedback session, a health care professional connects a patient to a machine that monitors one or more physiological indicators of stress, such as heart rate or muscle tension (Figure 3a(iv).A). The health care worker then discusses a stressful situation with the patient. The machine gives off signals when the conversation makes the patient exhibit physiological symptoms that indicate experience of stress. For example, increased tension in muscles might elicit a clicking sound from the machine. The patient can use the clicking sound as a signal of stress, and then practice decreasing the muscle tension that prompted the clicks through deep breathing and relaxation. Eventually, patients are able to recognize and cope with signs of stress without the help of the machine.

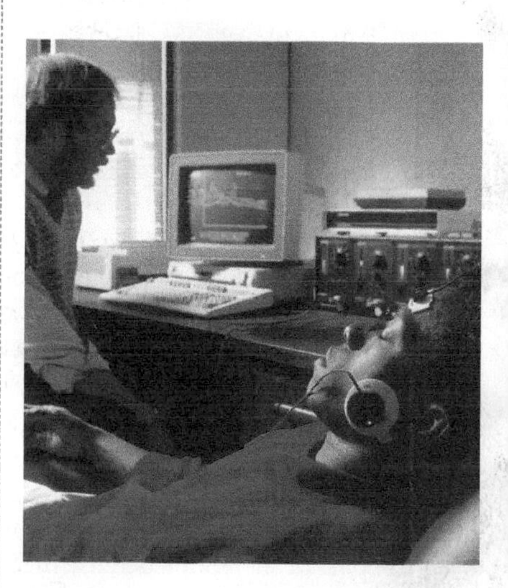

FIGURE 3a(iv).A Biofeedback is one way that people can learn to recognize the symptoms of stress and how to cope with them.

the decreased sensitivity to insulin. The link between these factors may be certain fatty acids released by adipose tissue. These fatty acids induce insulin resistance in cells and impair the function of insulin-producing cells of the pancreas. Treatment typically involves dietary restrictions, exercise (which increases the sensitivity of body cells to insulin), and weight loss. Oral medications that increase insulin sensitivity or production also may be given. About 40% of people with type 2 diabetes need insulin injections. (This was one reason for dropping the name non-insulin-dependent diabetes.)

Diabetes has serious complications. Diabetics are at increased risk for blindness, kidney disease, heart disease, high blood pressure, and atherosclerosis (buildup of fatty deposits in the arteries). Many diabetics suffer from gum disease and from damage to their nervous system that may include impotence and loss of sensation. Poor circulation and problems with nerves in the lower legs may make amputation of the lower limbs necessary. Indeed, more than half of lower limb amputations in the United States are done in people with diabetes. Given these serious complications, it is important to diagnose and treat diabetes early and, of course, to prevent it when possible (type 2 diabetes can be prevented or delayed; type 1 diabetes cannot be actively prevented at this time). The risk factors for type 2 diabetes include obesity, high blood pressure, having a parent or sibling with diabetes, and a history of gestational diabetes (a form of diabetes mellitus that develops in some women during pregnancy). The risk factors for type 1 diabetes are not so clearly defined, although development of this disease has genetic, autoimmune, and environmental components.

Too much insulin sometimes results from a tumor of the pancreas. More typically, however, a diabetic person mistakenly injects too much insulin. The result is depressed levels of glucose in the blood. Initial symptoms of low blood glucose include anxiety, sweating, hunger, weakness, and disorientation. Because brain cells fail to function properly when starved of glucose, the initial symptoms may be followed by convulsions and unconsciousness. The consequences associated with severe depletion of blood glucose are known collectively as *insulin shock.* Insulin shock can prove fatal unless blood sugar levels are raised.

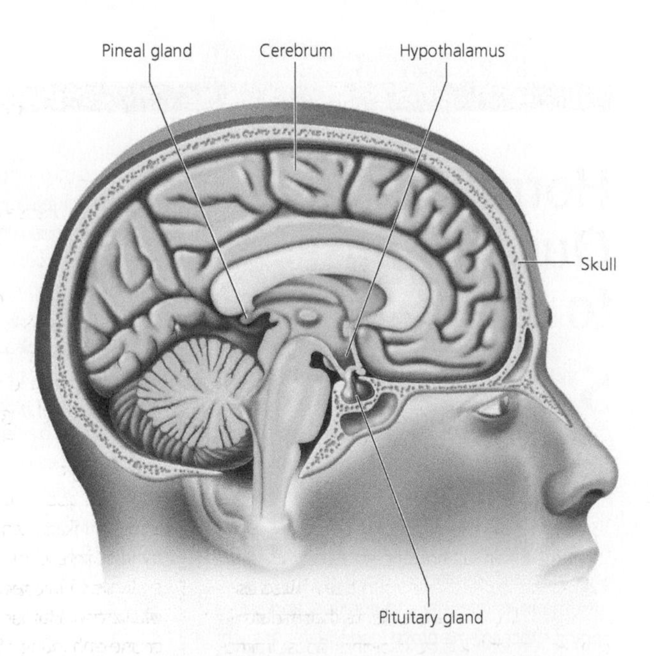

FIGURE 3a(iv).19 The pineal gland. Located near the center of the brain, the pineal gland secretes the hormone melatonin.

THYMUS GLAND

The **thymus gland** lies just behind the breastbone, on top of the heart (see Figure 3a(iv).2). It is more prominent in infants and children than in adults because it decreases in size as we age. The hormones it secretes, such as **thymopoietin** and **thymosin,** promote the maturation of white blood cells called T lymphocytes. Precursor cells from the bone marrow travel by way of the bloodstream to the thymus gland where they mature into T lymphocytes, also known as T cells, to become part of the body's defense mechanisms.

PINEAL GLAND

The **pineal gland** is a tiny gland at the center of the brain (Figure 3a(iv).19). Its secretory cells produce the hormone **melatonin.** Levels of circulating melatonin are greater at night than during daylight hours, because of input the pineal gland receives from visual pathways. Neurons of the retina, stimulated by light entering the eye, send impulses to the hypothalamus and ultimately the pineal gland, where they inhibit secretion of melatonin.

Research in the past few decades has suggested diverse roles for melatonin. Melatonin may inhibit production of the pigment melanin by melanocytes of the skin, as it does in some nonhuman animals. Melatonin may also influence daily rhythms. Sleep and, for some people, seasonal changes in mood appear to be influenced by melatonin. Melatonin also may slow the aging process. The possible links between melatonin and sleep, daily rhythms, and aging have led to widespread over-the-counter purchasing of melatonin, a situation described as "melatonin mania." We examine the promise and possible risks of taking melatonin in the Health Issue essay, *Melatonin: Miracle Supplement or Potent Drug Misused by Millions?*

One disorder associated with too much melatonin is *seasonal affective disorder (SAD).* This form of depression is associated with winter, when short day length and a decreased exposure to light results in overproduction of melatonin. Too much melatonin causes symptoms such as lethargy, long periods of sleep, low spirits, and a craving for carbohydrates. The symptoms usually appear around October and end about April in the Northern Hemisphere. Three-quarters of persons who suffer from SAD are female. Treatment of SAD often includes repeated exposure to very bright light for about an hour each day. The intense light inhibits melatonin production.

LOCALLY ACTING CHEMICAL MESSENGERS

Now that we have surveyed the endocrine glands and their hormones, let's consider another group of chemical messengers—those that act locally. Once secreted by a cell, these **local signaling molecules** act near the

Health Issue

Melatonin: Miracle Supplement or Potent Drug Misused by Millions?

Melatonin, a hormone secreted by the pineal gland, has often been billed as a wonder drug. There are claims that melatonin can reduce jet lag, cure insomnia, boost immunity, and slow the aging process. In addition, melatonin is apparently well tolerated. But which, if any, of these claims are well supported by scientific evidence? And even if melatonin can be helpful under certain circumstances, should this potent hormone be sold as an over-the-counter dietary supplement to self-prescribing consumers?

The claim that melatonin helps to alleviate jet lag is well supported by scientific evidence. Studies have shown that melatonin taken by mouth on the day of travel and continued for several days has the following effects in about half the people who take it to fight jet lag: (1) reduced fatigue during the day; (2) reduced time to fall asleep at night; and (3) more rapid development of a normal sleep pattern. Such benefits are usually most evident during eastward travel that crosses more than four time zones. For people who are not traveling, but who toss and turn and watch the clock on the nightstand at home, there is some evidence that melatonin can bring sleep. Research, beginning in the 1980s and continuing today, has shown that melatonin reduces the time it takes to fall asleep and may lengthen the time that people stay asleep. Although most agree that melatonin can be an effective sleep aid, scientists debate the precise mechanism by which melatonin produces its soporific effect.

What about the claims that melatonin can be used to boost immunity? Recall that the thymus gland, responsible for the production of infection-fighting white blood cells called T lymphocytes, is largest in infants and young children and shrinks as we age. Old mice also show shrinkage of the thymus. Such shrinkage can be reversed in geriatric mice by injections of melatonin. Indeed, the immune systems of injected animals showed signs of revitalization. Human trials on the potential immune-enhancing effects of melatonin in cancer patients are now under way. Although some promising results have been reported, there is insufficient evidence at present to support the claim that melatonin effectively boosts the human immune system.

Melatonin may slow aging through its effective scavenging of free radicals, molecular fragments that contain an unpaired electron. Free radicals have been implicated in many chronic diseases of old age, such as cancer and heart disease. Substances, such as melatonin, that destroy free radicals are called antioxidants. Free radicals are normally generated by some cells of the body for the purpose of destroying bacteria and old cells. Environmental agents such as drugs, toxins, and radiation also generate free radicals. What evidence is there to support melatonin as an effective antioxidant? Although numerous studies with other animals have supported the antioxidant properties of melatonin, well-designed studies with humans are lacking.

Should consumers hoping to cure jet lag or insomnia or to boost immunity and slow aging be gobbling down melatonin pills and lozenges purchased at health food stores? At present, melatonin is sold as a dietary supplement in the United States and thus is not subject to intense scrutiny by the Food and Drug Administration. This lack of intense scrutiny raises questions about the strength and purity of the final marketed product. Additionally, researchers are still investigating the benefits of melatonin. For these reasons, some people in the medical profession caution consumers to wait until melatonin is further scrutinized and the research results are in. Others argue, however, that melatonin is probably safe for most people but that certain groups should avoid it until additional information is available. For example, pregnant and nursing women should avoid melatonin (the effects of high doses on fetuses or infants are unknown), as should children (who normally produce melatonin in large amounts). People with autoimmune disorders or cancers of the immune system should also avoid melatonin, because it may stimulate the immune system and worsen these conditions. Finally, people taking other medications should consult their physician before taking melatonin. Such consultation should help people avoid dangerous drug interactions.

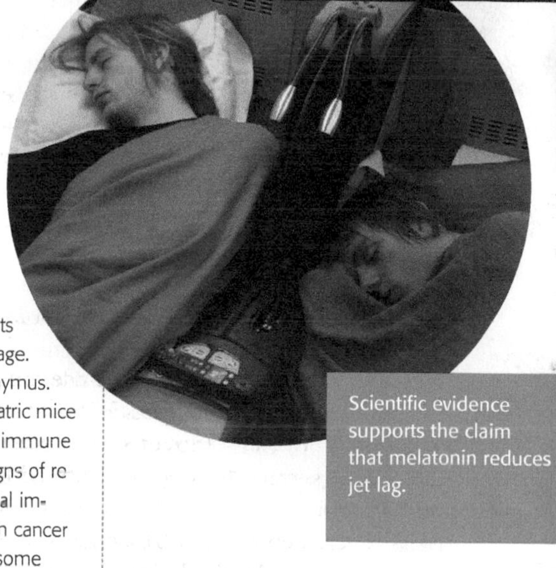

Scientific evidence supports the claim that melatonin reduces jet lag.

site of their release, on adjacent target cells, within seconds or milliseconds. Communication via local signaling molecules occurs much more rapidly than the communication carried out by hormones, which travel to distant sites within the body (recall that the flight-or-fight response may take 30 seconds to initiate physiological changes). Neurotransmitters are examples of chemicals that rapidly convey messages from one cell (a neuron) to a neighboring cell (often another neuron). Prostaglandins, growth factors, and nitric oxide (NO) are other examples of local signaling molecules.

Prostaglandins are lipid molecules continually released by the plasma membranes of most cells. Different types of cells secrete different prostaglandins. At least 16 different prostaglandin molecules function within the human body. These molecules have remarkably diverse effects, influencing blood clotting, regulation of body temperature, diameter of airways to the lungs, and the body's inflammatory response. Prostaglandins also affect the reproductive system. Menstrual cramps are thought to be caused by prostaglandins released by cells of the uterine lining. These prostaglandins act on the smooth muscle of the uterus, causing muscle contractions and cramping. Anti-inflammatory drugs, such as aspirin and ibuprofen, inhibit the synthesis of prostaglandins and thus may lessen the discomfort of menstrual cramps. Prostaglandins also are found in semen. Once in the female reproductive tract, prostaglandins in semen cause the smooth muscles of the uterus to contract, perhaps helping the sperm continue their journey.

Other chemical messenger molecules, called **growth factors,** are peptides or proteins that, when present in the fluid outside target cells, stimulate those cells to grow, develop, and multiply. For example, one growth factor causes precursor cells in the bone marrow to proliferate and differentiate into particular white blood cells. Another growth factor prompts endothelial cells to proliferate and organize into tubes that eventually form blood vessels.

The gas **nitric oxide (NO)** functions in the cellular communication that leads to the dilation of blood vessels. Basically, endothelial cells of the inner lining of blood vessels make and release NO, which signals the smooth muscles in the surrounding (middle) layer to relax, allowing the vessel to dilate. NO aids in peristalsis, the rhythmic waves of smooth muscle contraction and relaxation that push food along the digestive tract. NO also functions as a neurotransmitter, carrying messages from one neuron to the next. Histamine is another local signaling molecule.

3a(v) The Local Support & Defense Sytem

→ spelling mistake!

Taken from *Biology of Humans: Concepts, Applications, and Issues*, Third Edition, by Judith Goodenough and Betty McGuire

THE BODY'S DEFENSE SYSTEM

Your body generally defends you against anything that it does not recognize as being part of or belonging inside you. Common targets of your defense system include organisms that cause disease or infection and body cells that have turned cancerous.

The bacteria, viruses, protozoans, fungi, parasitic worms, and prions (infectious proteins) that cause disease are called **pathogens.** Note that this term does not apply to most of the microorganisms we encounter. Many bacteria, for example, are actually beneficial. They flavor our cheese, help rid the planet of corpses through decomposition, and help keep other, potentially harmful bacteria in check within our bodies. Indeed, certain bacteria are essential because they decompose dead material, thereby recycling nutrients to support new life.

Cancerous cells also threaten our well-being. A cancer cell was once a normal body cell; but because of changes in its genes, it can no longer regulate its cell division. If left unchecked, these renegade cells can multiply until they take over the body, upsetting its balance, choking its pathways, and ultimately causing great pain and sometimes death.

THREE LINES OF DEFENSE

The body has three strategies for defending against foreign organisms and molecules or cancer cells:

1. **Keep the foreign organisms or molecules out of the body in the first place.** This is accomplished by the first line of defense—*chemical and physical surface barriers.*
2. **Attack *any* foreign organism or molecule or cancer cell inside the body.** The second line of defense consists of *internal cellular and chemical defenses* that become active if the surface barriers are penetrated.
3. **Destroy a *specific* type of foreign organism or molecule or cancer cell inside the body.** The third line of defense is the *immune response,* which destroys *specific* targets, usually disease-causing organisms, and remembers those targets so that a quick response can be mounted if that target enters the body again.

Thus, the first and second lines of defense consist of nonspecific mechanisms that are effective against *any* foreign organisms or substances. The third line of defense, the immune response, is a specific mechanism of defense. The three lines of defense against pathogens are summarized in Figure 3a(v).1.

First Line of Defense: Physical and Chemical Barriers

The skin and mucous membranes that form the first line of defense are physical barriers that help keep foreign substances from entering the body (Figure 3a(v).2). In addition, they produce several protective chemicals.

Physical Barriers

Like a suit of armor, unbroken skin helps shield the body from pathogens by providing a barrier to foreign substances. A layer of dead cells forms the tough outer layer of skin. These cells are filled with the fibrous protein keratin, which waterproofs the skin and makes it resistant to the disruptive toxins (poisons) and enzymes of most would-be invaders. Some of the strength of this barrier results from the tight connections binding the cells together. What is more, the dead cells are continuously shed and replaced, at the rate of about a million cells every 40 minutes. As dead cells flake off, they take with them any microbes that have somehow managed to latch on. Another physical barrier, the mucous membranes lining the digestive and respiratory passages, produces sticky mucus that traps many microbes and prevents them from fully entering the body. The cells of the mucous membranes of the upper respiratory airways have cilia—short, hairlike structures that beat constantly. This beating moves the contaminated mucus to the throat. We eliminate the mucus in the throat by swallowing, coughing, or sneezing.

Chemical Barriers

The skin also provides chemical protection against invaders. Sweat and oil produced by glands in the skin wash away microbes. Moreover, the acidity of the secretions slows bacterial growth, and the oils contain chemicals that kill some bacteria.

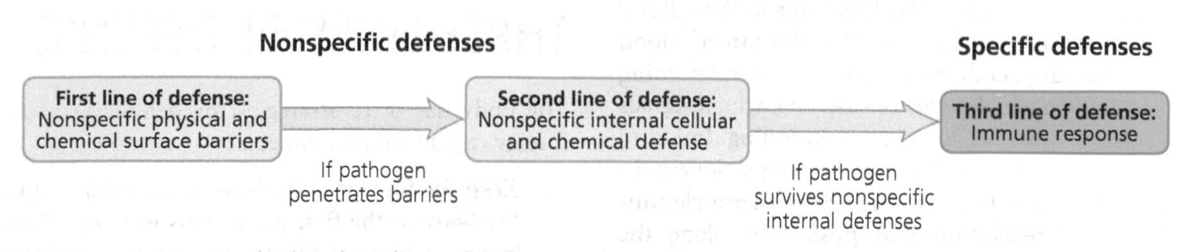
Nonspecific defenses
Specific defenses
First line of defense: Nonspecific physical and chemical surface barriers
Second line of defense: Nonspecific internal cellular and chemical defense
Third line of defense: Immune response
If pathogen penetrates barriers
If pathogen survives nonspecific internal defenses

FIGURE 3a(v).1 The body's three lines of defense against pathogens

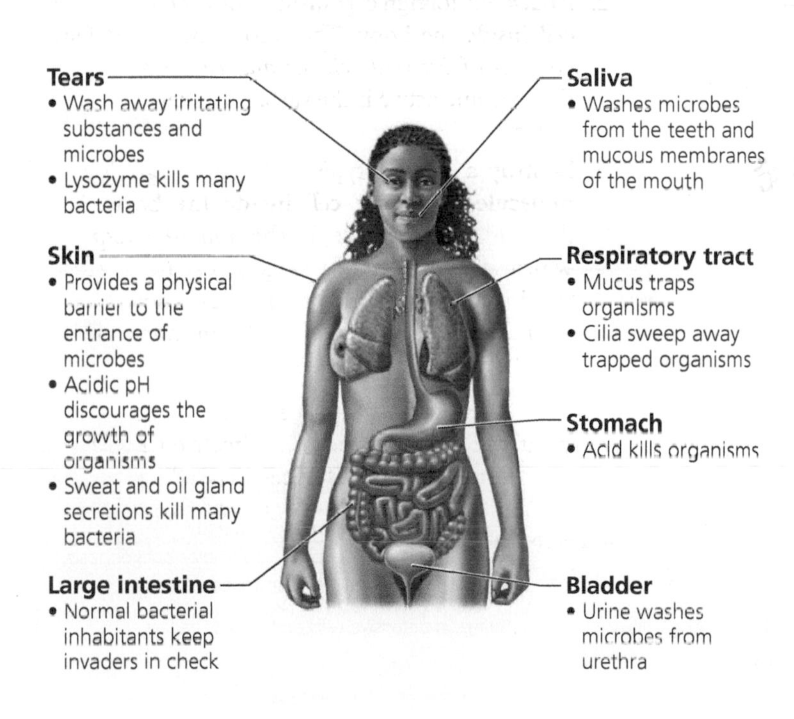
Tears
• Wash away irritating substances and microbes
• Lysozyme kills many bacteria
Skin
• Provides a physical barrier to the entrance of microbes
• Acidic pH discourages the growth of organisms
• Sweat and oil gland secretions kill many bacteria
Large intestine
• Normal bacterial inhabitants keep invaders in check
Saliva
• Washes microbes from the teeth and mucous membranes of the mouth
Respiratory tract
• Mucus traps organisms
• Cilia sweep away trapped organisms
Stomach
• Acid kills organisms
Bladder
• Urine washes microbes from urethra

FIGURE 3a(v).2 The body's first line of defense consists of physical and chemical barriers that serve as nonspecific defenses against *any* threats to our well-being. Collectively, they prevent many invading organisms and substances from entering the body, or confine them to a local region, kill them, remove them, or slow their growth.

Other chemical barriers include the lining of the stomach, which produces hydrochloric acid and protein-digesting enzymes that destroy many pathogens. Beneficial bacteria in a woman's vagina create an acidic environment that discourages the growth of some pathogens. The acidity of urine slows bacterial growth. (Urine also works as a physical barrier, flushing microbes from the lower urinary tract.) Saliva and tears contain an enzyme called *lysozyme* that kills some bacteria by disrupting their cell walls.

> **stop and THINK**
> Harmful bacteria within the digestive system often cause diarrhea. How might this be a protective response of the body?

Second Line of Defense: Defensive Cells and Proteins, Inflammation, and Fever

The second line of defense consists of nonspecific internal defenses against any pathogen that breaks through the physical and chemical barriers and enters the body. This second line of defense includes defensive cells and proteins, inflammation, and fever (see Table 3a(v).1).

Defensive Cells

Specialized "scavenger" cells called **phagocytes** (*phage*, to eat; *cyte*, cell) engulf pathogens, damaged tissue, or dead cells by the process of phagocytosis. This class of white blood cells serves not only as the front-line soldiers in the body's internal defense system but also as janitors that clean up debris. When a phagocyte encounters a foreign particle, cytoplasmic extensions flow from the phagocytic cell, bind to the particle, and pull it inside the cell. Once inside the cell, the particle is enclosed within a membrane-bound vesicle and quickly destroyed by digestive enzymes.

The body has several types of phagocytes. One type, *neutrophils*, arrives at the site of attack before the other types of white blood cells and immediately begins to consume the pathogens, especially bacteria, by phagocytosis. Other white blood cells (monocytes) leave the vessels of the circulatory system and enter the tissue fluids, where they develop into large **macrophages** (*macro*, big; *phage*, to eat). Macrophages have hearty and less discriminating appetites than neutrophils do, and they attack and consume virtually anything that is not recognized as belonging in the body—including viruses, bacteria, and damaged tissue (Figure 3a(v).3).

A second type of white blood cell, *eosinophils*, attacks pathogens that are too large to be consumed by phagocytosis, such as parasitic worms. Eosinophils get close to the parasite and discharge enzymes that destroy the organism. Macrophages then remove the debris.

Natural Killer Cells

A third type of white blood cell, called **natural killer (NK) cells,** roams the body in search of abnormal cells and quickly orchestrates their death. In a sense, NK cells function as the body's police walking a beat. They are not seeking a specific villain. Instead, they respond to any suspicious character, including a cell whose cell membrane has been altered by the addition of proteins that are unfamiliar to the NK cell. The prime targets of NK cells are cancerous cells and cells infected with viruses. Cancerous cells routinely form but are quickly destroyed by NK cells and prevented from spreading (Figure 3a(v).4).

TABLE 3a(v).1 The Second Line of Defense–Nonspecific Internal Defenses

Defense	Example	Function
Defensive cells	Phagocytic cells such as neutrophils and macrophages	Engulf invading organisms
	Eosinophils	Kill parasites
	Natural killer cells	Kill many invading organisms and cancer cells
Defensive proteins	Interferons	Slow the spread of viruses in the body
	Complement system	Stimulates histamine release; promotes phagocytosis; kills bacteria; enhances inflammation
Inflammation	Widening of blood vessels and increased capillary permeability, leading to redness, heat, swelling, and pain	Brings in defensive cells and speeds healing
Fever	Abnormally high body temperature	Slows the growth of bacteria; speeds up body defenses

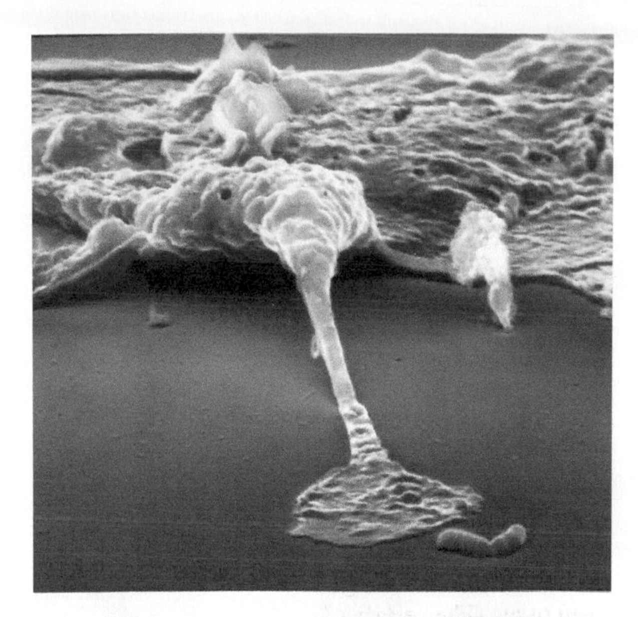

FIGURE 3a(v).3 **A macrophage ingesting a bacterium (the rod-shaped structure). The bacterium will be pulled inside the cell within a membrane-bound vesicle and quickly killed.**

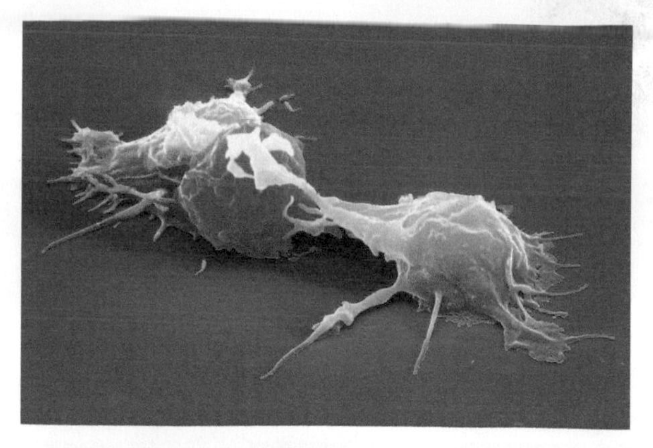

FIGURE 3a(v).4 **Natural killer cells (shown in orange) attacking a leukemia cell (shown in red). NK cells patrol the body, bumping and touching other cells as they go. When NK cells contact a cell with an altered cell surface, such as a cancer cell or a virus-infected cell, a series of events is immediately initiated. The NK cell attaches to the target cell and releases proteins that create pores in the target cell, making the membrane leaky and causing the cell to burst.**

As soon as it touches a cell with an abnormal surface, the NK cell attaches to the abnormal cell and delivers a "kiss of death" in the form of proteins that create many pores in the target cell. The pores make the target cell "leaky," so that it can no longer maintain a constant internal environment and eventually bursts.

Defensive Proteins

The second line of defense also includes defensive proteins. We will discuss two types of defensive proteins: interferons, which slow viral reproduction, and the complement system, which assists other defensive mechanisms.

Interferons A cell that has been infected with a virus can do little to help itself. But cells infected with a virus can help cells that are not yet infected. Before certain virally infected cells die, they secrete small proteins called **interferons** that act to slow the spread of viruses already in the body. As the name implies, interferons interfere with viral activity.

Interferons mount a two-pronged attack. First, they help rid the body of virus-infected cells by attracting macrophages and NK cells that destroy the infected cells immediately. Second, interferons protect cells that are not yet infected with the virus. When released, an interferon diffuses to neighboring cells and stimulates them to produce proteins that prevent viruses from replicating in those cells. Because viruses cause disease by replicating inside body cells, preventing replication curbs the disease. Interferon helps protect uninfected cells from *all* strains of viruses, not just the one responsible for the initial infection.

Pharmaceutical preparations of interferon have been shown to be effective against certain cancers and viral infections. Interferons inhibit cell division of cancer cells. For instance, interferon is often successful in combating a rare form of leukemia (hairy cell leukemia) and Kaposi's sarcoma, a form of cancer that often occurs in people with AIDS. Interferon has also been approved for treating the hepatitis C virus, which can cause cirrhosis of the liver and liver cancer; the human papillomavirus (HPV), which causes genital warts and cervical cancer; and the herpes virus, which causes genital herpes.

Complement System The **complement system,** or simply *complement,* is a group of at least 20 proteins whose activities enhance, or complement, the body's other defense mechanisms. Until these proteins are activated by infection, they circulate in the blood in an inactive state. Once activated, these proteins enhance both nonspecific and specific defense mechanisms. The effects of complement include the following:

- **Destruction of pathogen** Complement can act *directly*, by punching holes in a target cell's membrane (Figure 3a(v).5), so that the cell is no longer able to maintain a constant internal environment. Just as when NK cells secrete proteins that make a target cell's membrane leaky, water enters the cell, causing it to burst.

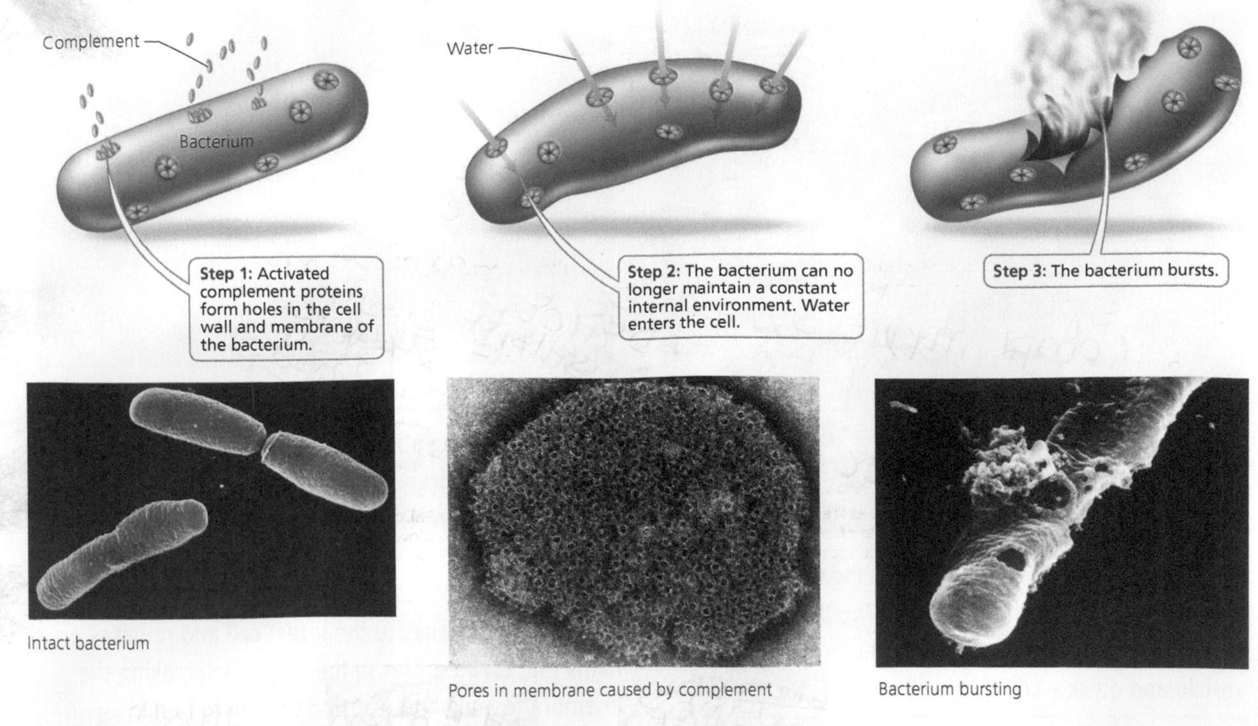
Complement
Bacterium
Water
Step 1: Activated complement proteins form holes in the cell wall and membrane of the bacterium.
Step 2: The bacterium can no longer maintain a constant internal environment. Water enters the cell.
Step 3: The bacterium bursts.
Intact bacterium
Pores in membrane caused by complement
Bacterium bursting

FIGURE 3a(v).5 **Complement has a direct destructive effect on pathogens**

- **Enhancement of phagocytosis** Complement enhances phagocytosis in two ways. First, complement proteins attract macrophages and neutrophils to the site of infection to remove the foreign cells. Second, one of the complement proteins binds to the surface of the microbe, making it easier for macrophages and neutrophils to "get a grip" on the intruder and devour it.
- **Stimulation of inflammation** Complement also causes blood vessels to widen and become more permeable. These changes provide increased blood flow to the area and increased access for white blood cells.

Inflammation

When body tissues are injured or damaged, a series of events called the **inflammatory response** or reaction occurs. This response destroys invaders and helps repair and restore damaged tissue. The four cardinal signs of inflammation that occur at the site of a wound are redness, heat (or warmth), swelling, and pain. These signs announce that certain cells and chemicals have combined efforts to contain infection, clean up the damaged area, and heal the wound. Let's consider the causes of the cardinal signs and how they are related to the benefits of inflammation.

- **Redness** Redness occurs because blood vessels dilate (widen) in the damaged area, causing blood flow in this area to increase. The dilation is caused by **histamine,** a substance that is also released during allergic reactions (discussed later in the chapter). Histamine is released by small, mobile connective tissue cells called **mast cells** in response to chemicals from damaged cells.

  The increased blood flow to the site of injury delivers phagocytes, blood-clotting proteins, and defensive proteins, including complement and antibodies. At the same time, the increased blood flow washes away dead cells and toxins produced by the invading microbes.
- **Heat** The increased blood flow also elevates the temperature in the area of injury. The elevated temperature increases the metabolic rate of the body cells in the region and speeds healing. Heat also increases the activities of phagocytic cells and other defensive cells.
- **Swelling** The injured area swells because histamine also makes capillaries more permeable, or leakier, than usual. Fluid seeps into the tissues from the bloodstream, bringing with it many beneficial substances. Blood-clotting factors enter the injured area and begin to wall off the region, thereby helping to protect surrounding areas from

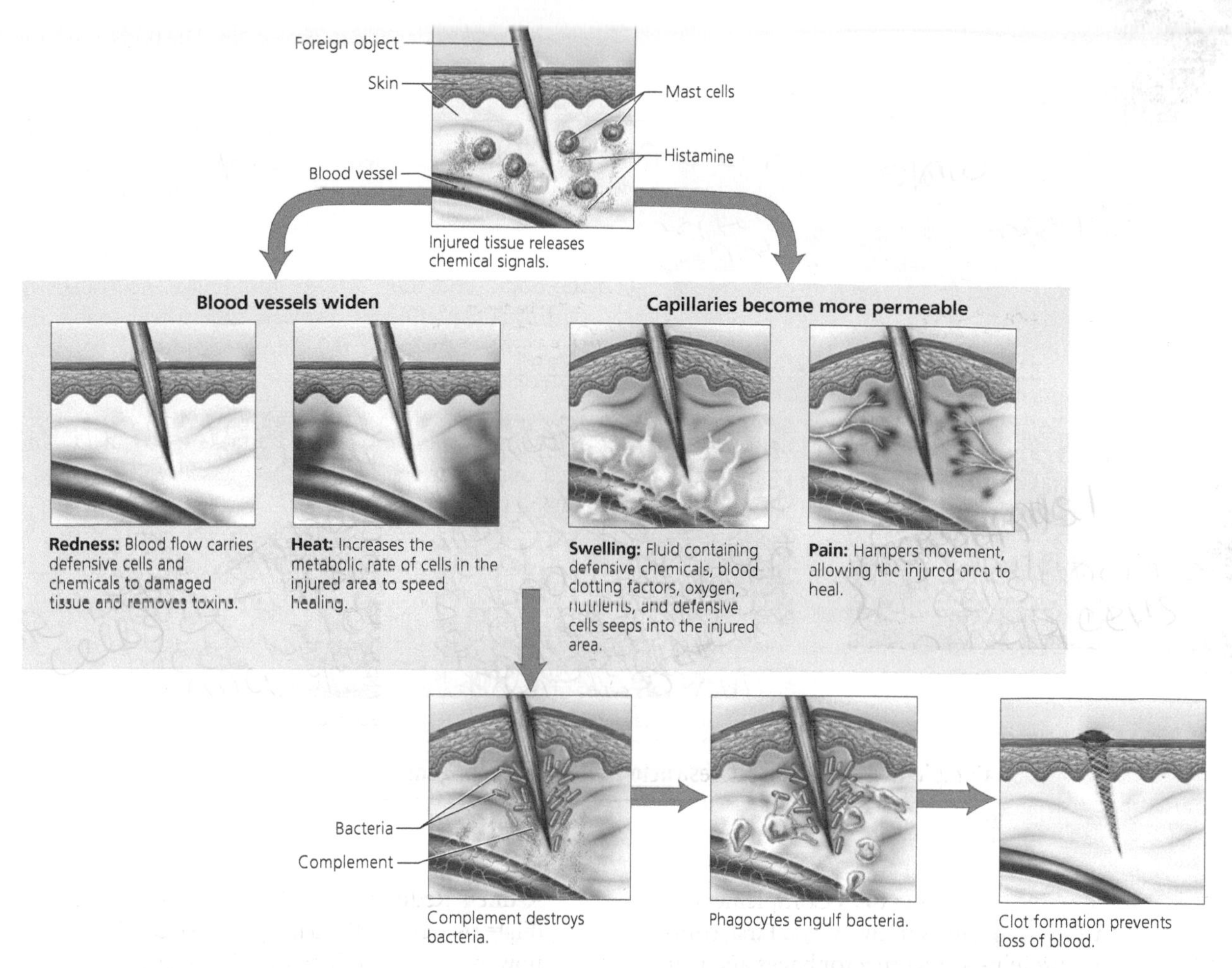
Foreign object
Skin
Mast cells
Histamine
Blood vessel
Injured tissue releases chemical signals.
Blood vessels widen
Capillaries become more permeable
Redness: Blood flow carries defensive cells and chemicals to damaged tissue and removes toxins.
Heat: Increases the metabolic rate of cells in the injured area to speed healing.
Swelling: Fluid containing defensive chemicals, blood clotting factors, oxygen, nutrients, and defensive cells seeps into the injured area.
Pain: Hampers movement, allowing the injured area to heal.
Bacteria
Complement
Complement destroys bacteria.
Phagocytes engulf bacteria.
Clot formation prevents loss of blood.

FIGURE 3a(v).6 **The inflammatory response is a general response to tissue injury or invasion by foreign microbes. It serves to defend against pathogens and to clear the injured area of pathogens and dead body cells, allowing repair and healing to occur. The four cardinal signs of inflammation are redness, heat, swelling, and pain.**

injury and preventing excessive loss of blood. The seepage also increases the oxygen and nutrient supply to the cells. If the injured area is a joint, swelling can hamper movement, an effect that might seem to be an inconvenience, but it permits the injured joint to rest and recover.

- **Pain** There are several causes for the pain in an inflamed area. For example, the excessive fluid that has leaked into the tissue presses on nerves and contributes to the sensation of pain. Some soreness might be caused by bacterial toxins, which can kill body cells. Injured cells also release pain-causing chemicals, such as prostaglandins. Pain usually causes a person to protect the area to avoid additional injury.

Because of the wider blood vessels and increased capillary permeability that bring about the inflammatory response, phagocytes begin to swarm to the injured site, attracted by chemicals released when tissue is damaged. Within minutes, the neutrophils squeeze through capillary walls into the fluid around cells and begin engulfing pathogens, toxins, and dead body cells. Soon macrophages arrive and continue the body's counterattack for the long term. Macrophages are also important in cleaning debris, such as dead body cells, from the damaged area. As the recovery from infection continues, dead cells, including microbes, body tissue cells, and phagocytes, may begin to ooze from the wound as pus (Figure 3a(v).6).

Fever

A *fever* is an abnormally high body temperature (Figure 3a(v).7). Fevers are caused by *pyrogens* (*pyro*, fire; *gen*, producer), chemicals that raise the "thermostat" in the brain (the hypothalamus) to a higher set point. Bacteria

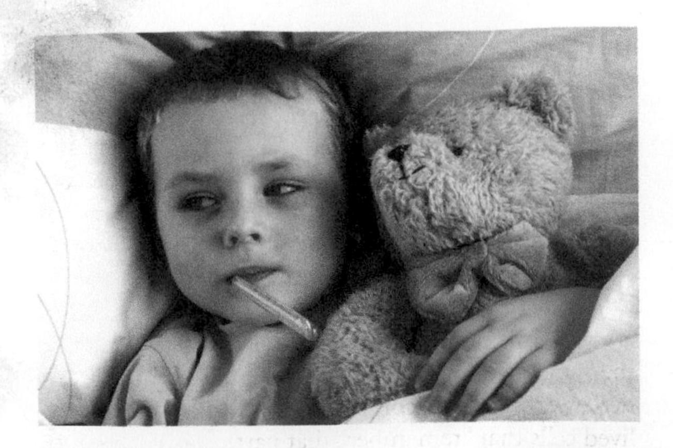

FIGURE 3a(v).7 **Although a fever might make us feel uncomfortable, it can help the body fight disease.**

release toxins that sometimes act as pyrogens. It is interesting to note, however, that the body produces its own pyrogens as part of its defensive strategy. Regardless of the source, pyrogens have the same effect on the hypothalamus, raising the set point so that physiological responses, such as shivering, are initiated to raise body temperature. Thus, we have the chills while the fever is rising. When the set point is lowered, the fever breaks and physiological responses such as perspiring reduce the body temperature until it reaches the new set point.

A mild or moderate fever helps the body fight bacterial infections by slowing the growth of bacteria and stimulating body defense responses. Bacterial growth is slowed because a mild fever causes the liver and spleen to remove iron from the blood, and many bacteria require iron to reproduce. Fever also increases the metabolic rate of body cells; the higher rate speeds up defensive responses and repair processes. On the other hand, a very high fever (over 105°F, or 40.6°C) is dangerous. It can inactivate enzymes needed for biochemical reactions within body cells.

Third Line of Defense: Immune Response

When the body's first and second lines of defense fail to stop a pathogen, the body's specific defenses respond and target the particular pathogen, cancer cell, or foreign molecule that has entered the body. The third line of defense, the **immune system,** provides the specific responses and memory. The organs of the lymphatic system are important components of the immune system because they produce the various cells responsible for immunity. The immune system is not an organ system in an anatomical sense. Instead, the immune system is defined by its *function:* recognizing and destroying specific pathogens or foreign molecules. The body's specific defenses working together are called an *immune response.*

There are several important characteristics of an immune response. First, an immune response is directed at a particular pathogen. For example, the immune system of a child infected with measles recognizes the measles virus as a foreign substance (not belonging in the body) and then acts to immobilize, neutralize, or destroy it. An effective immune system will enable the child to recover from the illness. Second, the immune system has memory. If the same child is again exposed to the same pathogen years later, the immune system remembers the pathogen and attacks it so quickly and vigorously that she will not become ill with measles a second time.

DISTINGUISHING SELF FROM NONSELF

To defend against a foreign organism or molecule, the body must be able distinguish it from a body cell and recognize it as foreign. This ability depends on the fact that each cell in your body has special molecules embedded in the plasma membrane that label the cell as *self.* These molecules serve as flags declaring the cell as a "friend." The molecules are called **MHC markers,** named for the major histocompatibility complex genes that code for them. The self labels on your cells are different from those of any other person (except an identical twin) as well as from those of other organisms, including pathogens. The immune system uses these labels to distinguish between what is part of your body and what is not (Figure 3a(v).8). It doesn't attack cells that are recognized as self.

A nonself substance or organism that triggers an immune response is called an **antigen.** Because an antigen is not recognized as belonging in the body, the immune system directs an attack against it. Typically, antigens are large molecules, such as proteins, polysaccharides, or nucleic acids. Often, antigens are found on the surface of an invader—embedded in the plasma membrane of an unwelcome bacterial cell, for instance, or part of the protein coat of a virus. However, pieces of invaders and chemicals secreted by invaders, such as bacterial toxins, can also serve as antigens. Each antigen is recognized by its shape.

Certain white blood cells, called lymphocytes, are responsible for both the specificity and the memory of the immune response. There are two principal types of lymphocytes: **B lymphocytes,** or more simply *B cells,* and **T lymphocytes,** or *T cells.* Both types form in the bone marrow, but they mature in different organs of

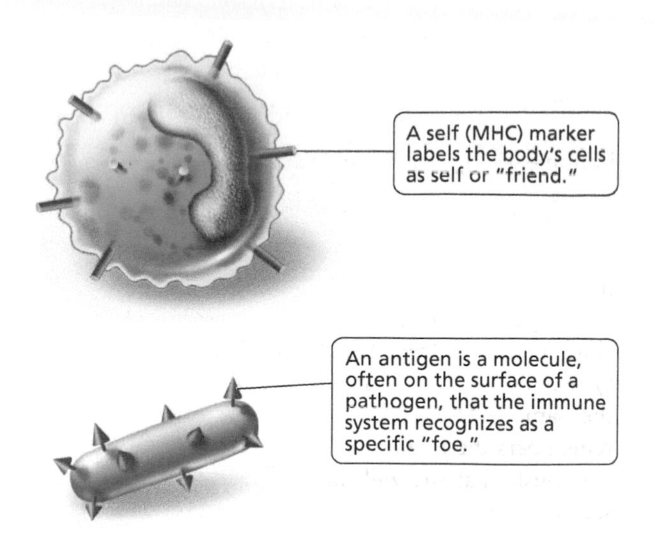

A self (MHC) marker labels the body's cells as self or "friend."
An antigen is a molecule, often on the surface of a pathogen, that the immune system recognizes as a specific "foe."

FIGURE 3a(v).8 **All nucleated cells in the body have molecular MHC markers on their surface that label them as self. Foreign substances, including potential disease-causing organisms, have molecules on their surfaces that are not recognized as belonging in the body. Foreign molecules that are capable of triggering an immune response are called antigens.**

the body. It is thought that B cells mature in the bone marrow. The T cells, on the other hand, mature in the thymus gland, which overlies the heart.

As the T lymphocytes mature, they develop the ability to distinguish between cells that belong in the body and those that do not. The T cells must be able to recognize the specific MHC self markers of that person and *not* respond vigorously to cells bearing that MHC self marker. If T cells do respond to cells with those self markers, they are destroyed. Once they are mature, T lymphocytes circulate through the body, bumping into other cells and checking to be sure those cells have the correct self (MHC) marker. Cells with proper MHC markers are passed by.

In addition, both T and B lymphocytes, as they mature, are programmed to recognize one particular type of antigen. This recognition is the basis of the specificity of the immune response. Each lymphocyte develops its own particular receptors—molecules having a unique shape—on its surface. Thousands of *identical* receptor molecules pepper the surface of each lymphocyte, and they are unlike the receptor molecules on other lymphocytes. When an antigen fits into a lymphocyte's receptors, much like a key into a lock, the body's defenses target that particular antigen. Due to the tremendous diversity of receptor molecules, each type occurring on a different lymphocyte, a few of the billions of lymphocytes in your body are able to respond to each of the thousands of different antigens that you will be exposed to in your lifetime.

When an antigen is detected, B cells and T cells bearing receptors able to respond to that particular invader are stimulated to divide repeatedly, forming two lines of cells. One line of descendant cells is made up of **effector cells,** which carry out the attack on the enemy. Effector cells generally live for only a few days. Thus, after the invader has been eliminated from the body, the number of effector cells declines. The other line of descendant cells is composed of **memory cells,** long-lived cells that "remember" that particular invader and mount a rapid, intense response to it if it should ever appear again. The quick response of memory cells is the mechanism that prevents you from getting ill from the same pathogen twice.

ANTIBODY-MEDIATED RESPONSES AND CELL-MEDIATED RESPONSES

An analogy can be made between the body's immune defenses and a nation's military defense system. The military has scouts who look for invaders. If an invader is found, the scout alerts the commander of the military forces and provides an exact description of the villain. The scout must also provide the appropriate password so that the commander knows he or she is not a spy planting misinformation. The body also has scouts, called macrophages, that are part of the nonspecific defenses. Macrophages roam the tissues, looking for any invader. The cells that act as the immune system's commander are a subset of T cells called helper T cells. When properly alerted, helper T cells call out the body's specific defensive forces, and the immune responses begin.

A nation's military may have two (or more) branches. For example, it may consist of an army and a navy. Specialized to respond in slightly different ways to enemy invasion, each branch is armed with certain types of weapons. Either branch can be activated to combat a particular threat, say little green people with purple hair. The navy may be called into action if the enemy is encountered at sea, whereas the army will come to the defense if the enemy is on land.

The body, similarly, has two types of specific defenses. These specific defenses recognize the same antigens and destroy the same invaders, but they do so in different ways.

- *Antibody-mediated immune responses* defend primarily against antigens found traveling freely in intercellular and other body fluids—for example, toxins or extracellular pathogens such as bacteria or free viruses. The warriors of this branch of immune defense are the effector B cells (also called plasma cells), and their weapons are Y-shaped proteins called *antibodies*, which neutralize and remove potential threats from the body. Antibodies are programmed to recognize and bind to the antigen posing the threat; they help eliminate the antigen from the body. We discuss how this works in greater detail later in the chapter.

- *Cell-mediated immune responses* protect against cellular pathogens or abnormal cells, including body cells that have become infected with viruses or other pathogens and cancer cells. The lymphocytes responsible for cell-mediated immune responses are a type of T cell called cytotoxic T cell (discussed at greater length later in the chapter). Once activated, cytotoxic T cells quickly destroy the cellular pathogen, infected body cells, or cancerous cells by causing them to burst.

Now that the various defenders have been introduced, let's see how they work together to produce your body's highly effective immune response. Table 3a(v).2 summarizes the functions of the cells participating in the immune response, and Table 3a(v).3 summarizes the steps in the immune response.

STEPS OF IMMUNE RESPONSE

Although the cell-mediated immune response and the antibody-mediated immune response use different mechanisms to defend against pathogens or foreign molecules (nonself), the general steps in these responses are the same (Figure 3a(v).9).

Q *Why are helper T cells critical to the immune response?*

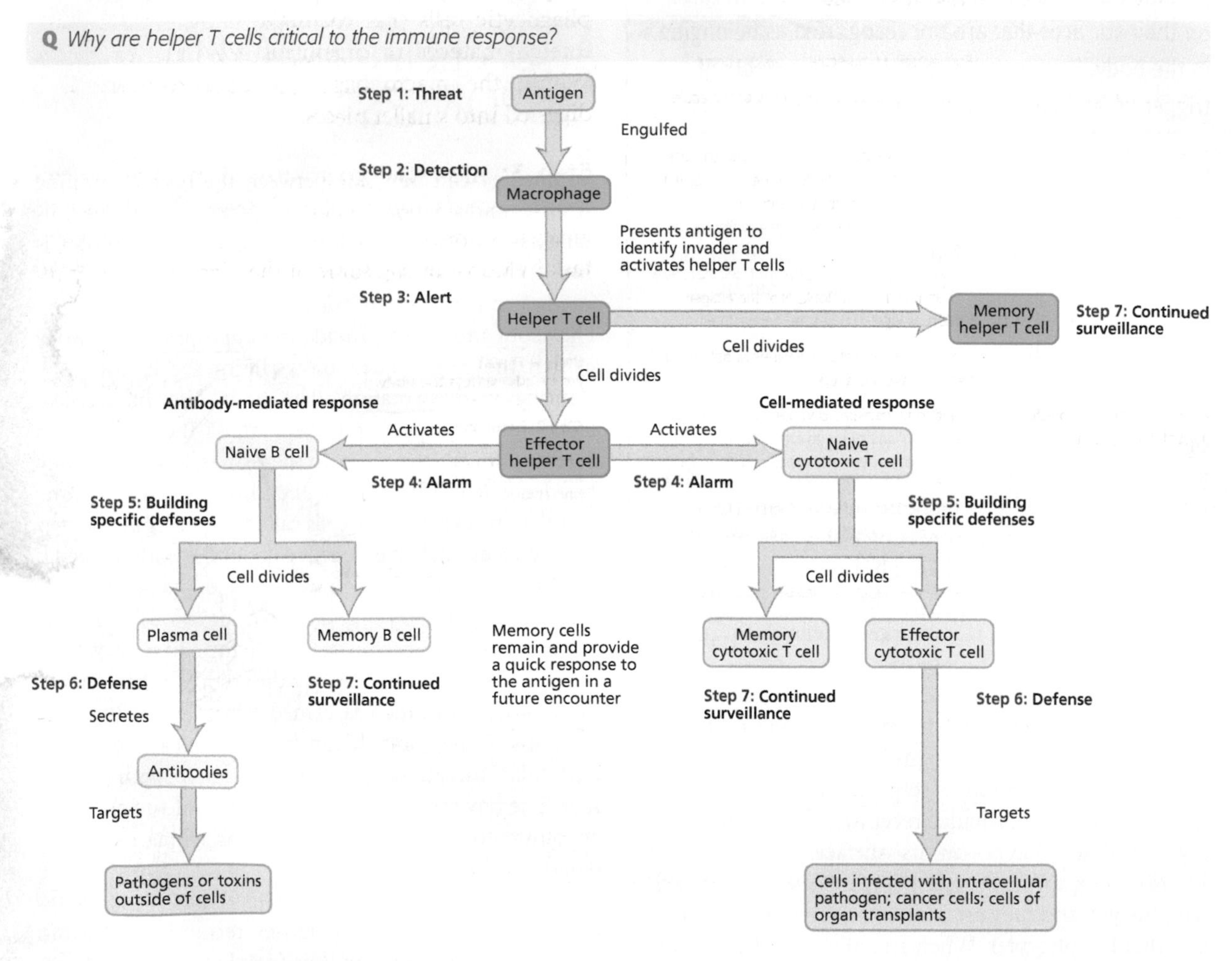

FIGURE 3a(v).9 **An overview of the immune response**

A *Helper T cells activate both naive cytotoxic T cells and naive B cells. Thus, helper T cells turn on both the cell-mediated and the antibody-mediated immune responses.*

TABLE 3a(v).2 Cells Involved in the Immune Response

Cell	Functions	Cell	Functions
Macrophage	**An antigen-presenting cell** • Engulfs and digests pathogen or invader • Places a piece of digested antigen on its plasma membrane • Presents the antigen to a helper T cell • Activates the helper T cell	Suppressor T cell	**The "off" switch for both lines of immune responses** Suppresses the activity of the B cells and T cells after the foreign cell or molecule has been successfully destroyed
T Cells		*B Cells*	**Involved in antibody-mediated responses** When activated by helper T cell, it divides to form plasma cells and memory cells
Helper T cell	**The "on" switch for both lines of immune response** • After activation by macrophage, it divides, forming effector helper T cells and memory helper T cells • Helper T cells activate B cells and T cells	Plasma cell	**Effector in antibody-mediated response** Secretes antibodies specific to extracellular antigens, such as toxins, bacteria, and free viruses
Cytotoxic T cell (effector T cell)	**Responsible for cell-mediated immune responses** • When activated by helper T cells, it divides to form effector cytotoxic T cells and memory cytotoxic T cells • Destroys cellular targets, such as infected body cells, bacteria, and cancer cells	*Memory Cells*	**Responsible for memory of immune system** • Generated by B cells or any type of T cell during an immune response • Enable quick and efficient response on subsequent exposures of the antigen • May live for years

TABLE 3a(v).3 Steps in the Immune Response

Step	Description
Step 1: Threat	Foreign cell or molecule enters the body
Step 2: Detection	Macrophage detects foreign cell or molecule and engulfs it
Step 3: Alert	• Macrophage puts antigen from the pathogen on its surface and finds the helper T cell with correct receptors for that antigen • Macrophage presents antigen to the helper T cell • Macrophage alerts the helper T cell that there is an invader that "looks like" the antigen • Macrophage activates the helper T cell
Step 4: Alarm	Helper T cell activates both lines of defense to fight that specific antigen
Step 5: Building specific defenses (clonal selection)	• Antibody-mediated defense—B cells are activated and divide to form plasma cells that secrete antibodies specific to the antigen • Cell-mediated defense—T cells divide to form cytotoxic T cells that attack cells with the specific antigen
Step 6: Defense	• Antibody-mediated defense—antibodies specific to antigen eliminate the antigen • Cell-mediated defense—cytotoxic T cells cause cells with the antigen to burst
Step 7: Continued surveillance	Memory cells formed when helper T cells, cytotoxic T cells, and B cells were activated remain to provide swift response if the antigen is detected again
Step 8: Withdrawal of forces	Once the antigen has been destroyed, suppressor T cells shut down the immune response to that antigen

Step 1: Threat The immune response begins when a molecule or organism (an antigen) lacking the self (MHC) marker manages to evade the first two lines of defense and enters the body (Figure 3a(v).10).

Step 2: Detection Recall that macrophages are phagocytic cells that roam the body, engulfing any foreign material or organisms they may encounter. Within the macrophage, the engulfed material is digested into smaller pieces.

Step 3: Alert The macrophage then alerts the immune system's commander, a helper T cell, that an antigen is present. The macrophage accomplishes this task by transporting some of the digested pieces to its

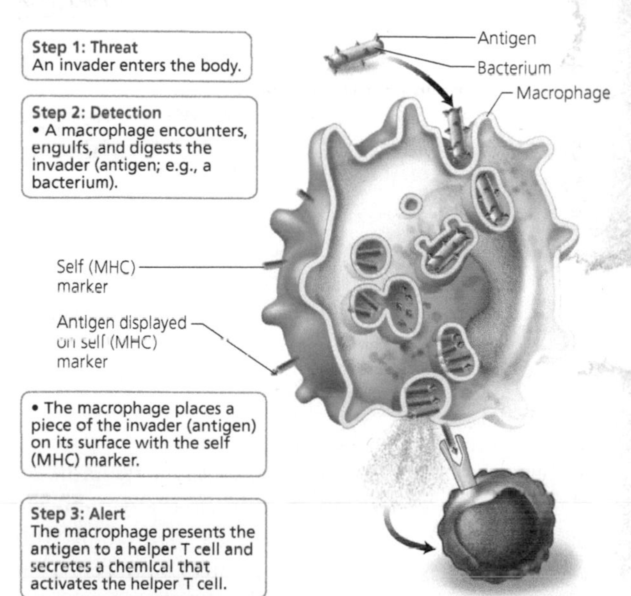

Step 1: Threat
An invader enters the body.
Step 2: Detection
• A macrophage encounters, engulfs, and digests the invader (antigen; e.g., a bacterium).
Self (MHC) marker
Antigen displayed on self (MHC) marker
• The macrophage places a piece of the invader (antigen) on its surface with the self (MHC) marker.
Step 3: Alert
The macrophage presents the antigen to a helper T cell and secretes a chemical that activates the helper T cell.
Antigen
Bacterium
Macrophage

FIGURE 3a(v).10 A macrophage is an important antigen-presenting cell. It presents the antigen, which is attached to a self (MHC) marker, to a helper T cell, and activates the helper T cell.

own surface, where they bind to the MHC self markers on the macrophage membrane. The self marker acts as a secret password that identifies the macrophage as a "friend." On the other hand, the antigen bound to the self markers function as a kind of wanted poster, telling the lymphocytes that there is an invader and revealing how the invader can be identified. The displayed antigens trigger the immune response. Thus, the macrophage is an important type of **antigen-presenting cell (APC).** (B cells and dendritic cells—cells with long extensions found in lymph nodes—are two other kinds of antigen-presenting cells.)

The macrophage presents the antigen to a **helper T cell,** the kind of T cell that serves as the main switch for the entire immune response. However, the macrophage must alert the *right* kind of helper T cell—a helper T cell bearing receptors that recognize the specific antigen being presented. These specific helper T cells constitute only a tiny fraction of the entire T cell population. Finding the right helper T cell is like looking for a needle in a haystack. The macrophage wanders through the body until it literally bumps into an appropriate helper T cell. The encounter most likely occurs in one of the lymph nodes, because these bean-shaped structures contain huge numbers of lymphocytes of all kinds. When the antigen-presenting macrophage meets the appropriate helper T cell and binds to it, the macrophage secretes a chemical that activates the helper T cell.

Step 4: Alarm Within hours, an activated helper T cell begins to secrete its own chemical messages. The helper T cell's message calls into active duty the appropriate B cells and T cells—those with the ability to bind to the particular antigen that triggered the response.

Step 5: Building Specific Defenses When the appropriate "naive"[1] B cells or T cells are activated, they begin to divide repeatedly. The result is a clone (a population of genetically identical cells) that is specialized to protect against the particular target antigen.

The process by which this highly specialized clone is produced, called **clonal selection,** underlies the entire immune response. We have seen that each lymphocyte is equipped to recognize an antigen of a specific shape. Any antigen that enters the body will be recognized by only a few lymphocytes at most. By binding to the receptors on a lymphocyte's surface, an antigen *selects* a lymphocyte that was preprogrammed during its maturation with receptors able to recognize that particular antigen. That particular lymphocyte is then stimulated to divide and produces a clone of millions of identical cells able to recognize that same antigen (Figure 3a(v).11).

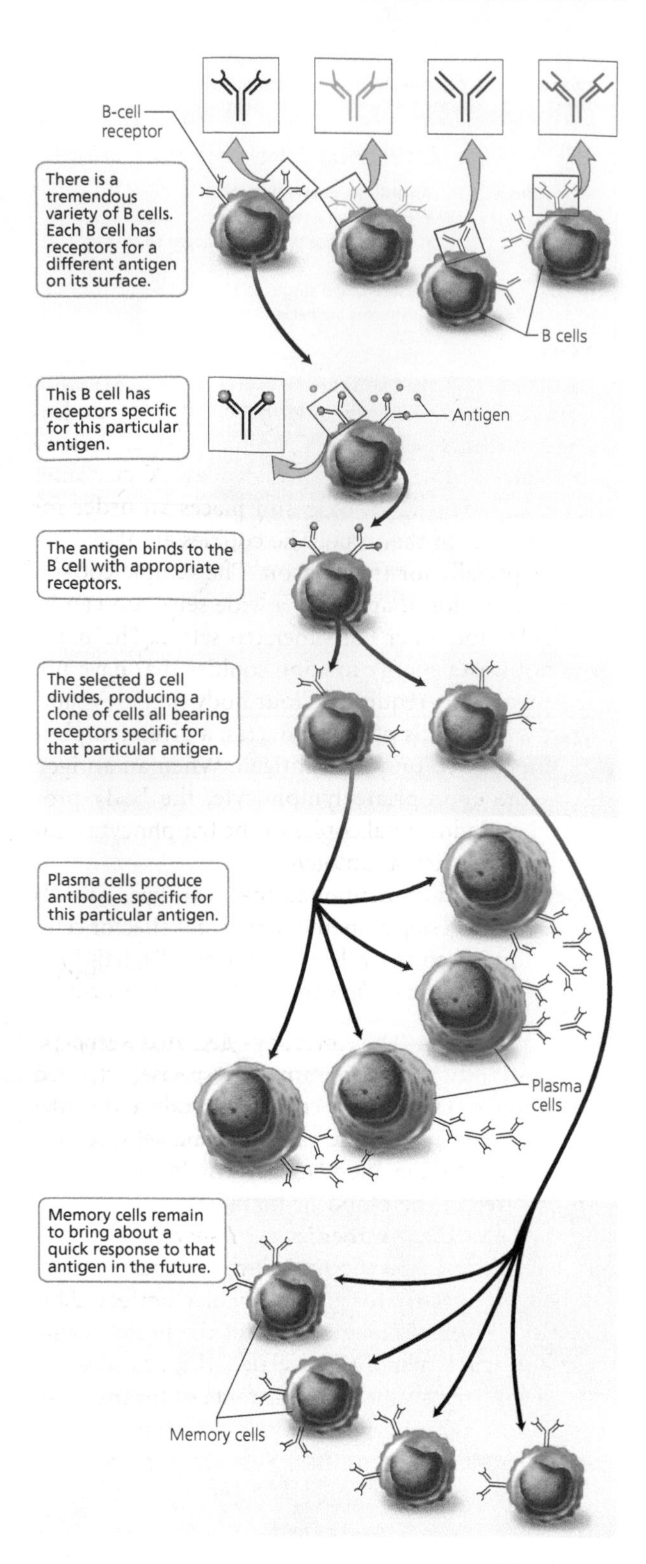

FIGURE 3a(v).11 **Clonal selection is the process by which an immune response to a specific antigen becomes amplified. This figure shows clonal selection of B cells, but a similar process occurs with T cells.**

[1] A "naive" cell is one that has been preprogrammed to respond to a particular antigen but has not been previously activated to respond.

stop and THINK

A primary target of HIV, the human immunodeficiency virus that leads to AIDS, is the helper T cell. Why does the virus's preference for the helper T cell impair the immune system more than if another type of lymphocyte were targeted?

The following analogy may be helpful for understanding clonal selection. Consider a small bakery with only sample cookies on display. A customer chooses a particular cookie and places an order for many cookies of that type. The cookies are then prepared especially for that person. The sample cookies do not take a lot of space, so a wide selection can be on display for other customers to select. The baker does not waste energy making cookies that have not been specifically requested. Your body prepares samples of many kinds of lymphocytes; a given lymphocyte responds to only one antigen. When an antigen selects the appropriate lymphocyte, the body produces many additional copies of the lymphocyte chosen by that particular antigen.

We have already mentioned that two types of cells are produced in step 5: memory cells and effector cells. Before turning to the role of memory cells, let's look more closely at exactly *how* the effector cells protect us.

Step 6: Defense—The Antibody-Mediated Response

In the **antibody-mediated immune response,** activated B cells divide. The effector cells they produce through clonal selection, which are called **plasma cells,** secrete antibodies into the bloodstream to defend against antigens free in the blood or bound to a cell surface (Figure 3a(v).12). **Antibodies** are Y-shaped proteins that recognize a specific antigen by its shape. Each antibody is specific for one particular antigen. The specificity results from the shape of the proteins that form the tips of the Y (Figure 3a(v).13). Because of their shapes, the antibody and antigen fit together like a lock and a key. Each antibody can bind to two identical antigens, one at the tip of each arm on the Y.

Antibodies can bind only to antigens that are free in body fluids or attached to the surface of a cell. Their main targets are toxins and extracellular microbes, including bacteria, fungi, and protozoans. Antibodies help defend against these pathogens in several ways that can be remembered with the acronym PLAN.

- **Precipitation:** The antigen–antibody binding causes antigens to clump together and precipitate (settle out of solution), enhancing phagocytosis by making the antigens easier for phagocytic cells to capture and engulf.

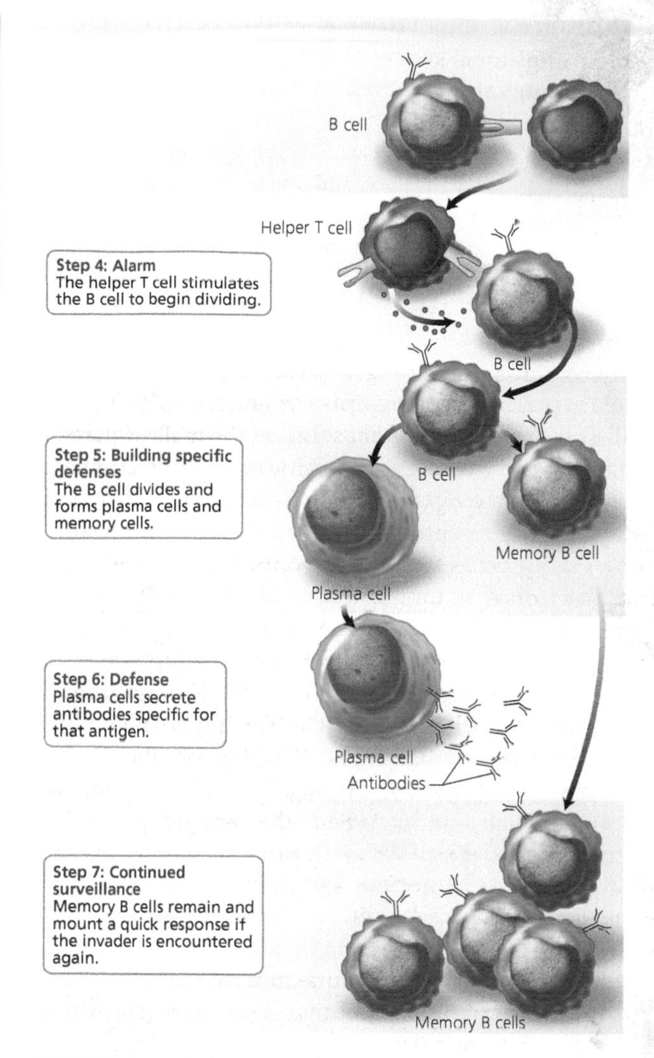

FIGURE 3a(v).12 Antibody-mediated immune response

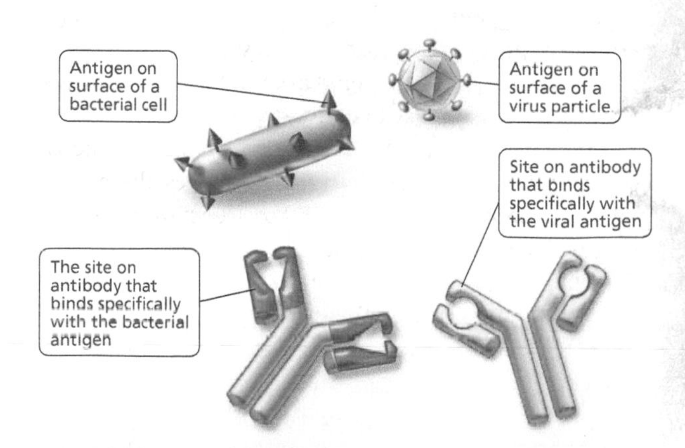

FIGURE 3a(v).13 An antibody is a Y-shaped protein designed to recognize an antigen having a specific shape. The recognition of a specific antigen occurs due to the shape of the tips of the Y in the antibody molecule.

- **Lysis** (bursting): Certain antibodies activate the complement system, which then pokes holes through the membrane of the target cell and causes it to burst.
- **Attraction of phagocytes:** Antibodies also attract phagocytic cells to the area. Phagocytes then engulf and destroy the foreign material.
- **Neutralization:** Antibodies bind to toxins and viruses, neutralizing them and preventing them from causing harm.

There are five classes of antibodies, each with a special role to play in protecting against invaders. Antibodies are also called **immunoglobulins** (Ig), and each class is designated with a letter: IgG, IgA, IgM, IgD, and IgE. As you can see in Table 3a(v).4, the antibodies of some classes exist as single Y-shaped molecules (monomers), in one class they exist as two attached molecules (dimers), and in one class they exist as five attached molecules (pentamers) radiating outward like the spokes of a wheel.

Step 6: Defense—The Cell-Mediated Response The **cytotoxic T cells** are the effector T cells responsible for the **cell-mediated immune response,** which destroys antigen-bearing cells. Each cytotoxic T cell is programmed to recognize a particular antigen bound to MHC markers on the surface of a cellular pathogen, an infected or cancerous body cell, or on cells of a tissue or organ transplant. A cytotoxic T cell becomes activated to destroy a target cell when two events occur simultaneously, as shown in Figure 3a(v).14. First, the cytotoxic T cell must encounter an antigen-presenting cell, such as a macrophage. Second, a helper T cell must release a chemical to activate the cytotoxic T cell. When activated, the cytotoxic T cell divides, producing memory cells and effector cytotoxic T cells.

An effector cytotoxic T cell releases chemicals called **perforins,** which cause holes to form in the target cell membrane. The holes are large enough to allow some of the cell's contents to leave the cell so that the cell disintegrates. The cytotoxic T cell then detaches from the target cell and seeks another cell having the same type of antigen.

stop and THINK

Rejection of an organ transplant occurs when the recipient's immune system attacks and destroys the cells of the transplanted organ. Why would this attack occur? Which branch of the immune system would be most involved?

Step 7: Continued Surveillance The first time an antigen enters the body, only a few lymphocytes can recognize it. Those lymphocytes must be located and stimulated to divide in order to produce an army of lymphocytes ready to eliminate that particular antigen. As a result, the primary response, the one that occurs during the body's first encounter with a particular antigen, is relatively slow. A lapse of several days occurs before the antibody concentration begins to rise, and the concentration does not peak until 1 to 2 weeks after the initial exposure to the antigen (Figure 3a(v).15).

TABLE 3a(v).4 Classes of Antibodies

Class	Structure	Location	Characteristics	Protective Functions
IgG	Monomer	Blood, lymph, and intestines	Most abundant of all antibodies in body; involved in primary and secondary immune responses; can pass through placenta from mother to fetus and provides passive immune protection to fetus and newborn	Enhances phagocytosis; neutralizes toxins; triggers complement system
IgA	Dimer or monomer	Present in tears, saliva, and mucus as well in secretions of gastrointestinal system and excretory systems; present in breast milk	Levels decrease during stress, raising susceptibility to infection	Prevents pathogens from attaching to epithelial cells of surface lining
IgM	Pentamer	Attached to B cell, where it acts as a receptor for antigens; free in blood and lymph	First Ig class released by plasma cell during primary response	Powerful agglutinating agent (10 antigen-binding sites); activates complement
IgD	Monomer	Surface of many B cells; blood and lymph	Life span of about 3 days	Thought to be involved in recognition of antigen and in activating B cells
IgE	Monomer	Secreted by plasma cells in skin, mucous membranes of gastrointestinal and respiratory systems	Become bound to surface of mast cells and basophils	Involved in allergic reactions by triggering release of histamine and other chemicals from mast cells or basophils

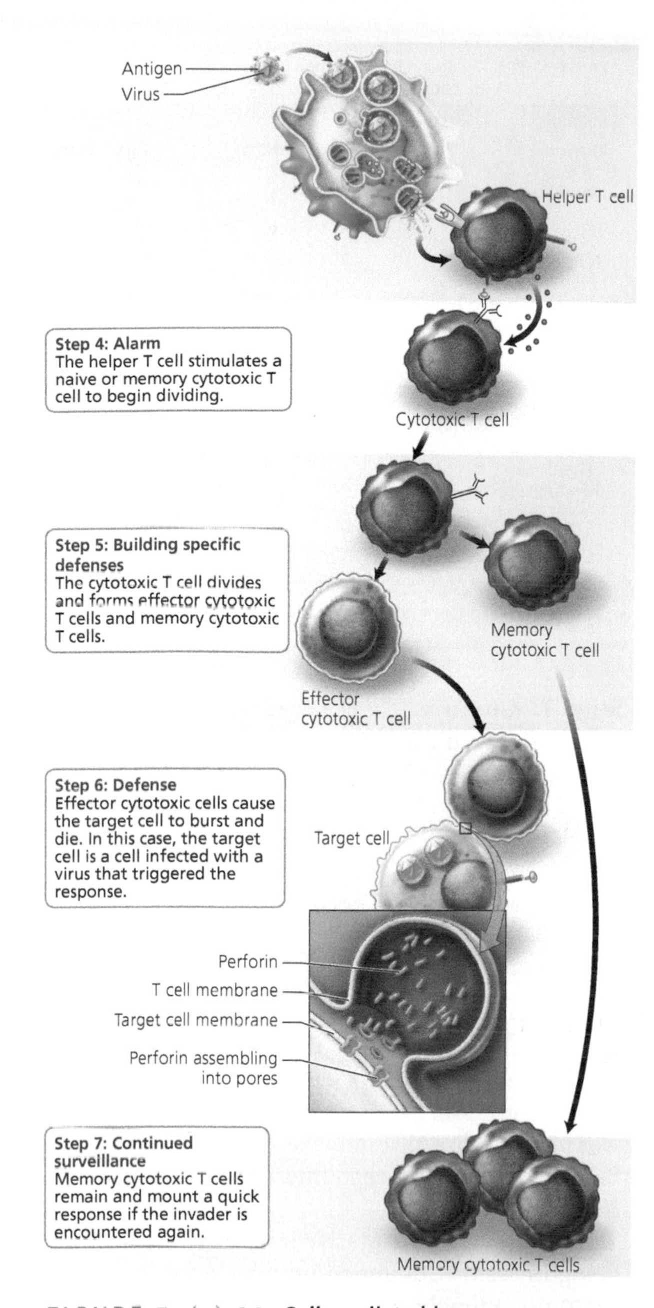

Antigen
Virus
Helper T cell
Step 4: Alarm
The helper T cell stimulates a naive or memory cytotoxic T cell to begin dividing.
Cytotoxic T cell
Step 5: Building specific defenses
The cytotoxic T cell divides and forms effector cytotoxic T cells and memory cytotoxic T cells.
Memory cytotoxic T cell
Effector cytotoxic T cell
Step 6: Defense
Effector cytotoxic cells cause the target cell to burst and die. In this case, the target cell is a cell infected with a virus that triggered the response.
Target cell
Perforin
T cell membrane
Target cell membrane
Perforin assembling into pores
Step 7: Continued surveillance
Memory cytotoxic T cells remain and mount a quick response if the invader is encountered again.
Memory cytotoxic T cells

FIGURE 3a(v).14 **Cell-mediated immune response**

Following subsequent exposure to the antigen, the *secondary response* is strong and swift. Recall that when naive B cells and T cells were stimulated to divide, not only did they produce effector cells that actively defended against the invader, but they also produced memory cells. These memory B cells, memory cytotoxic T cells, and memory helper T cells live for years or even decades. As a result, the number of lymphocytes programmed to respond to that particular antigen is much greater than it was before the first exposure. When the antigen is encountered again, each of those memory cells divides and produces new effector cells and memory cells specific for that antigen. Therefore, the number of effector cells rises quickly during the secondary response, and within 2 or 3 days reaches a higher peak than it did during the primary response.

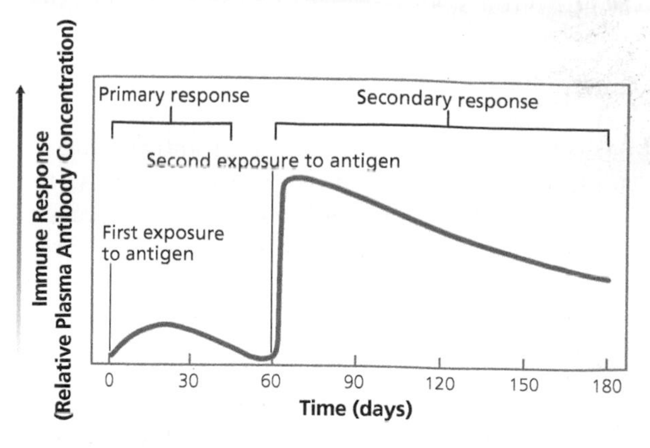

Immune Response
(Relative Plasma Antibody Concentration)
Primary response
Secondary response
Second exposure to antigen
First exposure to antigen
0
30
60
90
120
150
180
Time (days)

FIGURE 3a(v).15 **The primary and secondary immune responses. In the primary response, which occurs after the first exposure to an antigen, there is a delay of several days before the concentration of circulating antibodies begins to increase. It takes 1 to 2 weeks for the antibody concentration to peak because the few lymphocytes programmed to recognize that particular antigen must be located and activated. (The T cells show a similar pattern of response.) The secondary response following a subsequent exposure to an antigen is swifter and stronger than the primary response. The difference is due to the long-lived memory cells produced during the primary response; these are a larger pool of lymphocytes programmed to respond to that particular antigen.**

Step 8: Withdrawal of Forces As the immune system begins to conquer the invading organism and the level of antigens declines, another type of T cell, the **suppressor T cell,** releases chemicals that dampen the activity of both B cells and T cells. Suppressor T cells turn off the immune response when the antigen no longer poses a threat. This may be a mechanism that prevents the immune system from overreacting and harming healthy body cells.

ACTIVE AND PASSIVE IMMUNITY

There are two types of immunity: In **active immunity** the body actively defends itself by producing memory B cells and T cells following exposure to an antigen. Active immunity happens naturally whenever a person gets an infection. Fortunately, active immunity can also develop through *vaccination* (also known as immunization), a procedure that introduces a harmless form of an antigen into the body to stimulate immune responses against that antigen. Today, some vaccines, such as the vaccine for hepatitis B, are prepared using bacteria that are genetically modified to produce a protein from the pathogen. Since only the protein (antigen) is injected, rather than the actual virus, the vaccine can't cause disease. In some kinds of vaccination—whooping cough and typhoid fever, for instance—the microbe is killed before the vaccine is prepared. Other vaccines must be made from live organisms in order to be effective. In these cases, the microbes are first weakened so that they can no longer cause disease. The microbes are weakened by transferring them repeatedly in tissue culture, which allows unpredictable mutations to occur. Still other vaccines, including the one against smallpox, are prepared from microbes that cause related but milder diseases.

Because it leads to the production of memory cells, active immunity—occurring naturally or via vaccination—is relatively long-lived. The first dose of a vaccine causes the primary immune response, and antibodies and some memory cells are generated. In certain cases, especially when inactivated antigens are used in the vaccine, the immune system may "forget" its encounter with the antigen after a time. A booster is administered periodically to make sure the immune system does not forget. The booster results in a secondary immune response and enough memory cells to provide for a quick response should a potent form of that pathogen ever be encountered.

Vaccinations have saved millions of lives. In fact, they have been so effective in preventing diseases such as whooping cough and tetanus that many people mistakenly think those diseases have been eliminated. However, most of the diseases that vaccines prevent still exist, so vaccinations are still important. Children should be immunized (given vaccines) on a recommended schedule, as shown in Table 3a(v).5.

Although adverse reactions to vaccines are possible, the risk of being harmed by a vaccine is much lower than the risk associated with the disease that it prevents. For example, a severe paralytic illness called Guillain-Barré syndrome may develop in one or two people out of a million receiving the influenza (flu) vaccine. But the flu kills tens of thousands of unvaccinated people each year. In most cases, a reaction to a vaccine is mild: warmth, redness, and tenderness at the site of injection.

TABLE 3a(v).5 Childhood Immunization Schedule Recommended by CDC, 2008

Vaccine	Age (months)	Age (years)
Hepatitis B	Birth–18	
Rotavirus	2, 4, 6	
Diphtheria, tetanus, pertussis (DtaP)	2, 4, 6, 15–18	4–6, 11–12
Haemophilus influenzae, type B	2, 4, 6, 12–15	
Pneumococcal	2, 4, 6, 12–15	
Inactivated poliovirus	2, 4, 6–18	4–6
Measles, mumps, rubella (MMR)	12–15	4–6
Varicella (chicken pox)	12–15	4–6
Hepatitis A	12–23	
Meningococcal		11–12
Human papillomavirus (HPV)		11–12 (years)

Passive immunity is protection that results when a person receives antibodies produced by another person or animal. For instance, some antibodies produced by a pregnant woman can cross the placenta and give the growing fetus some immunity. These maternal antibodies remain in the infant's body for as long 3 months after birth, at which point the infant is old enough to produce its own antibodies. Antibodies in breast milk also provide passive immunity to nursing infants, especially against pathogens that might enter through the intestinal lining. The mother's antibodies are a temporary yet critical blanket of protection, because most of the pathogens that would otherwise threaten the health of a newborn have already been encountered by the mother's immune system.

People can acquire passive immunity medically by being injected with antibodies produced in another person or animal. In this case, passive immunity is a good news–bad news situation. The good news is that the effects are immediate. Gamma globulin, for example, is a preparation of antibodies used to protect people who have been exposed to diseases such as hepatitis B or who are already infected with the microbes that cause tetanus, measles, or diphtheria. Gamma globulin is often given to travelers before they visit a country where viral hepatitis is common. The bad news is that the protection is short-lived. The borrowed antibodies circulate for 3 to 5 weeks before being destroyed in the recipient's body. Because the recipient's immune system was not stimulated to produce memory cells, protection disappears with the antibodies.

stop and THINK

The viruses that cause influenza (the flu) mutate rapidly, so the antigens in the protein coat continually change. Why does this characteristic make it difficult to develop a flu vaccine that will be effective for several consecutive years?

what would you do?

There is now a vaccine against the human papillomavirus, a sexually transmitted virus that is also the most important cause of cervical cancer. Health officials recommend the vaccine for girls 11 or 12 years of age, but it can be given to girls as young as 9 years and to women as old as 26 years. Some social conservatives fear that use of this vaccine will encourage vaccinated teenagers to be sexually active. If you were (or are) a parent, would you have your daughter vaccinated? Why or why not?

MONOCLONAL ANTIBODIES

Suppose you wanted to determine whether a particular antigen was present in a solution, tissue, or even somewhere in the body. An antibody specific for that antigen would be just the tool you would need. Because of its specificity, any such antibody would go directly to the target antigen. If a label (such as a radioactive tag or a molecule that fluoresces) were attached to the antibody, the antibody could reveal the location of the antigen. You can see that for a test of this kind, it is desirable to have a supply of identical antibodies that react with a specific antigen. Groups of identical antibodies that bind to one specific antigen are called **monoclonal antibodies.**

Monoclonal antibodies have many uses. Home pregnancy tests contain monoclonal antibodies produced to react with a hormone (human chorionic gonadotropin) secreted by membranes associated with the developing embryo. Monoclonal antibodies have also proved useful in screening for certain diseases, including Legionnaire's disease, hepatitis, certain sexually transmitted diseases, and certain cancers, including those of the lung and prostate. Some monoclonal antibodies are also used in cancer treatment. The radioactive material or chemical treatment to combat the cancer is attached to a monoclonal antibody that targets the tumor cells but has little effect on healthy cells.

PROBLEMS OF THE IMMUNE SYSTEM

The immune system protects us against myriad threats from agents not recognized as belonging in the body. However, sometimes the defenses are misguided. In autoimmune disease, the body's own cells are attacked. Allergies result when the immune system protects us against substances that are not harmful. Tissue rejection following organ transplant is also caused by the immune system (see the Health Issue essay, *Rejection of Organ Transplants*).

Autoimmune Disorders

Autoimmune disorders occur when the immune system fails to distinguish between self and nonself and attacks the tissues or organs of the body. If the immune system can be called the body's military defense, then autoimmune disease is the equivalent of "friendly fire."

As we have seen, during their development, lymphocytes are programmed to attack a specific foreign antigen while still tolerating self antigens. Lymphocytes that do not learn to make this distinction are usually destroyed. Unfortunately, some lymphocytes that are primed to attack self antigens escape destruction. These cells are like time bombs ready to attack the body's own cells at the first provocation. For example, if these renegade lymphocytes are activated by a virus or bacterium, they may direct their attack against healthy body cells as well as the invading organism.

Autoimmune disorders are often classified as organ-specific or non-organ-specific. As the name implies, organ-specific autoimmune disorders are directed against a single organ. Organ-specific autoimmune disorders are usually caused by T cells that have gone awry. The thyroid gland, for example, is attacked in *Hashimoto's thyroiditis.* In contrast, non-organ-specific autoimmune disorders are generally caused by antibodies produced by B cells gone awry and tend to have effects throughout the body. In *systemic lupus erythematosus*, for instance, connective tissue is attacked. Since connective tissue can be found throughout the body, almost any organ can be affected. Lupus can cause skin lesions or rashes, especially a butterfly-shaped rash centered on the nose and spreading to both cheeks (Figure 3a(v).16). It may affect the heart (pericarditis), joints (arthritis), kidneys (nephritis), or nervous system (seizures).

A number of autoimmune disorders occur because portions of disease-causing organisms resemble proteins found on normal body cells. If the immune system

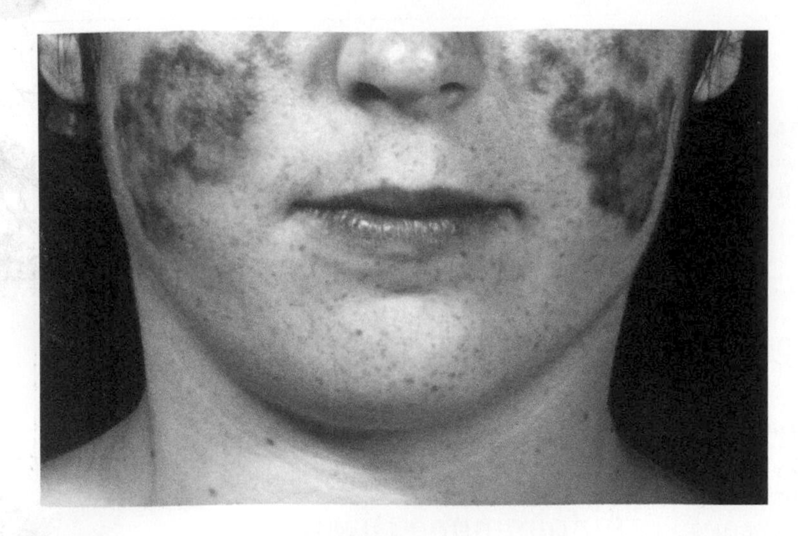

FIGURE 3a(v).16 **In autoimmune diseases, the body's lymphocytes attack the body's own cells. One example is lupus erythematosus, in which lymphocytes attack connective tissue throughout the body. The butterfly rash shown here is characteristic of lupus.**

mistakes the body's antigens for the foreign antigens, it may attack them. For instance, the body's attack on certain streptococcal bacteria that cause a sore throat may result in the production of antibodies that target not only the streptococcal bacteria but also similar molecules that are found in the valves of the heart and joints. The result is an autoimmune disorder known as *rheumatic fever*.

Health Issue

Rejection of Organ Transplants

Each year, tens of thousands of people receive a gift of life in the form of a transplanted kidney, heart, lungs, liver, or pancreas. Although these transplants seem almost commonplace today, they have been performed for only about 30 years. Before organ transplants could be successful, physicians had to learn how to prevent the effector T cells of the immune system from attacking and killing the transplanted tissue because it lacked appropriate self markers. When transplanted tissue is killed by the host's immune system, we say that the transplant has been rejected.

The success of a transplant depends on the similarity between the host and transplanted tissues. The most successful transplants are those in which tissue is taken from one part of a person's body and transplanted to another part. In cases of severe burns, for example, healthy skin from elsewhere on the body can replace badly burned areas of skin.

Another way to increase the likelihood that a transplant will be accepted is to use cells from the person's body to grow the transplant in a laboratory. Today, it is possible to grow some organs, urinary bladders for instance, in the laboratory. Cells are taken from the defective organ and grown in tissue culture. When there are enough cells, they are placed on a 3-D model of the organ. Then the cell-covered mold is incubated until the new organ is formed.

Because identical twins are nearly genetically identical, their cells have the same self markers, and organs can be transplanted from one twin to another with little fear of tissue rejection. But few of us have an identical twin. The next best source for tissue for a transplant, and the most common, is a person whose cell surface markers closely match those of the host. Usually the transplanted tissue comes from a person who has recently died. The donor is usually brain-dead, but his or her heart is kept beating by life-support equipment. Some organs—primarily kidneys—can be harvested from someone who has died and whose heart has stopped beating. In some cases, living people can donate organs; one of two healthy kidneys can be donated to a needy recipient, as can sections of liver.

The odds in favor of a successful transplant are always improving, and so the waiting list of patients in need of an organ from a suitable donor has outpaced the supply. Some researchers believe that in the future, organs from nonhuman animals may fill the gap between the supply of organs and the demand. So far, however, attempts to transplant animal organs into people have failed. The biggest obstacle is hyperacute rejection. Within minutes to hours after transplant, the animal organ dies because its blood supply is choked off by the human immune system.

Other dangers may remain, even if the rejection problem is solved. Animals carry infectious agents that are harmless to their hosts but that might "jump species" and then gain the ability to spread from the transplant recipient to another person. If that were possible, we would have to ask whether it is ethical to expose a third party to risk.

Questions to Consider

- **If you are a tissue match for someone who needs a kidney or a bone marrow transplant, how would you decide whether to be a donor?**
- **Do you think that family members who are a tissue match should be obligated to donate a kidney or bone marrow?**
- **Do you think that people should be able to buy a kidney or bone marrow from a suitable donor?**

TABLE 3a(v).6 Common Allergies

Type of Allergic Response	Common Causes	Location of Reactive Mast Cells	Symptoms
Hay fever (allergic rhinitis)	Pollen, mold spores, animal dander (bits of skin and hair), feces of dust mites	Lining of nasal cavity	Sneezing, nasal congestion
Asthma	Pollen, mold spores, animal dander	Airways of lower respiratory tract	Difficulty breathing
Food allergy	Chicken, eggs, fish, milk, nuts (especially peanuts), shellfish, soybeans, and wheat	Lining of digestive system	Nausea, vomiting, abdominal cramps, and diarrhea
Hives	Foods (especially shellfish, strawberries, chocolate, nuts, and tomatoes); insect bites; certain drugs (especially penicillin and aspirin); chemicals such as food additives, dyes, and cosmetics	Skin	Patches of skin become red and swollen
Anaphylactic shock	Insect stings (especially from bees, wasps, hornets, yellow jackets, fire ants); medicines (especially penicillin and tetracycline); certain foods (especially eggs, seafood, nuts, and grains)	Throughout the body	Widening of blood vessels, causing blood to pool in capillaries and resulting in dizziness, nausea, diarrhea, unconsciousness, and sometimes death

Treatment of autoimmune disorders is usually two pronged. First, any deficiencies caused by the disorder are corrected. Second, drugs are administered to depress the immune system.

Allergies

An **allergy** is an overreaction by the immune system to an antigen, in this case called an *allergen*. The immune response in an allergy is considered an overreaction because the allergen itself usually is not harmful to the body (Table 3a(v).6). The most common allergy is hay fever—which, by the way, is not caused by hay and does not cause a fever. *Hay fever* is more correctly known as *allergic rhinitis* (*rhino*, nose; *–itis*, inflammation of). The symptoms of hay fever—sneezing and nasal congestion—occur when an allergen is inhaled, triggering an immune response in the respiratory system. Mucous membranes of the eyes may also respond, causing red, watery eyes. Common causes of hay fever include pollen, mold spores, animal dander, and the feces of dust mites—microscopic creatures that are found throughout your home (Figure 3a(v).17). The same allergens, however, can trigger asthma. During an asthma attack, the small airways in the lung (bronchioles) constrict, making breathing difficult. In food allergies, the immune response occurs in the digestive system and may cause nausea, vomiting, abdominal cramps, and diarrhea. Food allergies can also cause hives, a skin condition in which patches of skin temporarily become red and swollen.

An immediate allergic response begins when a person is exposed to an allergen and a primary immune response is launched (Figure 3a(v).18). Soon, plasma cells churn out the antibody IgE, which binds to either basophils or mast cells. In subsequent exposures to that allergen, the allergen binds to IgE antibodies on the surface of basophils or mast cells and causes granules within the cells to release their contents: histamine.

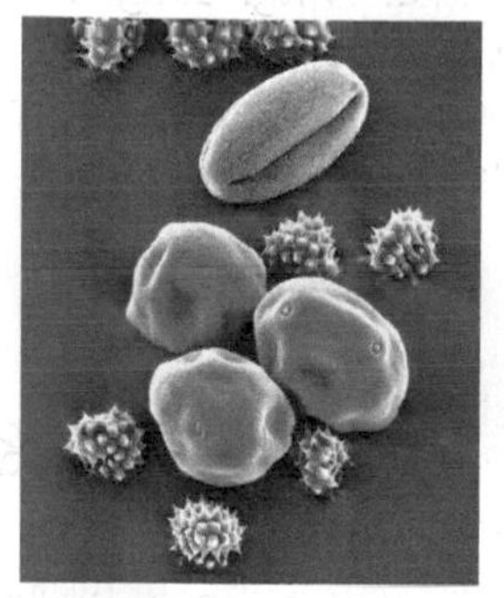

Pollen grains

Dust mite

FIGURE 3a(v).17 Common causes of allergies are pollen grains and the feces of dust mites, such as the mite shown here.

Histamine then causes the swelling, redness, and other symptoms of an allergic response. The blood vessels widen, slowing blood flow and causing redness. At the same time, the blood vessels become leaky, allowing fluid to flow from the vessels into spaces between tissue cells, swelling the tissues. Histamine also causes the release of large amounts of mucus, so the nose begins to run. In addition, histamine can cause smooth muscles of internal organs to contract. Thus, if the allergen is in the respiratory system, histamine can trigger an asthma attack by causing the air tubules to contract. If the allergen moves from the area where it entered the body, these effects can be widespread. The result can be anaphylactic shock.

Anaphylactic shock is an extreme allergic reaction that occurs within minutes after exposure to the substance a person is allergic to. It can cause pooling of blood in capillaries, which leads to dizziness, nausea, and sometimes unconsciousness as well as extreme difficulty in breathing. Anaphylactic shock can be fatal, but most people survive. Allergies that are common triggers of anaphylactic shock include certain foods; medicines, including antibiotics such as penicillin; and insect stings, especially stings from bees, wasps, yellow jackets, and hornets.

People with allergies often know which substances cause their problems. When the culprits are not known, doctors can identify them using a crude but effective technique in which small amounts of suspected allergens are injected into the skin. If the person is allergic to one of the suspected allergens, a red welt will form at the site of injection.

If you know you have an allergy, the simplest way to avoid the miseries of an allergic reaction is to avoid exposure to the substances that cause problems. During pollen season, spend as much time as possible indoors, using an air conditioner to filter pollen out of the incoming air. Unfortunately, spores from molds growing in air conditioners and humidifiers are also common triggers of allergies. Some common allergy-causing foods, for instance, strawberries or shellfish, may be easy to avoid. Others, such as peanut oil, can show up in some unlikely dishes, including stew, chili, baked goods, or meat patties.

Certain drugs may reduce allergy symptoms. As their name implies, antihistamines block the effects of histamine. Antihistamines are most effective if they are taken before the allergic reaction begins. Unfortunately, allergies tend to become less susceptible to antihistamines over time, and most antihistamines cause drowsiness, which can impair performance on the job or in school and can make driving a car extremely hazardous.

Some allergies can be treated by gradually desensitizing the person to the offending allergens. Allergy shots containing gradually increasing amounts of a known allergen are injected into the person's bloodstream. During this treatment, the allergen causes the production of another class of antibodies—IgG. Afterward, when the allergen enters the body, IgG antibodies bind to it and prevent it from binding to IgE antibodies on mast cells and triggering an allergic reaction.

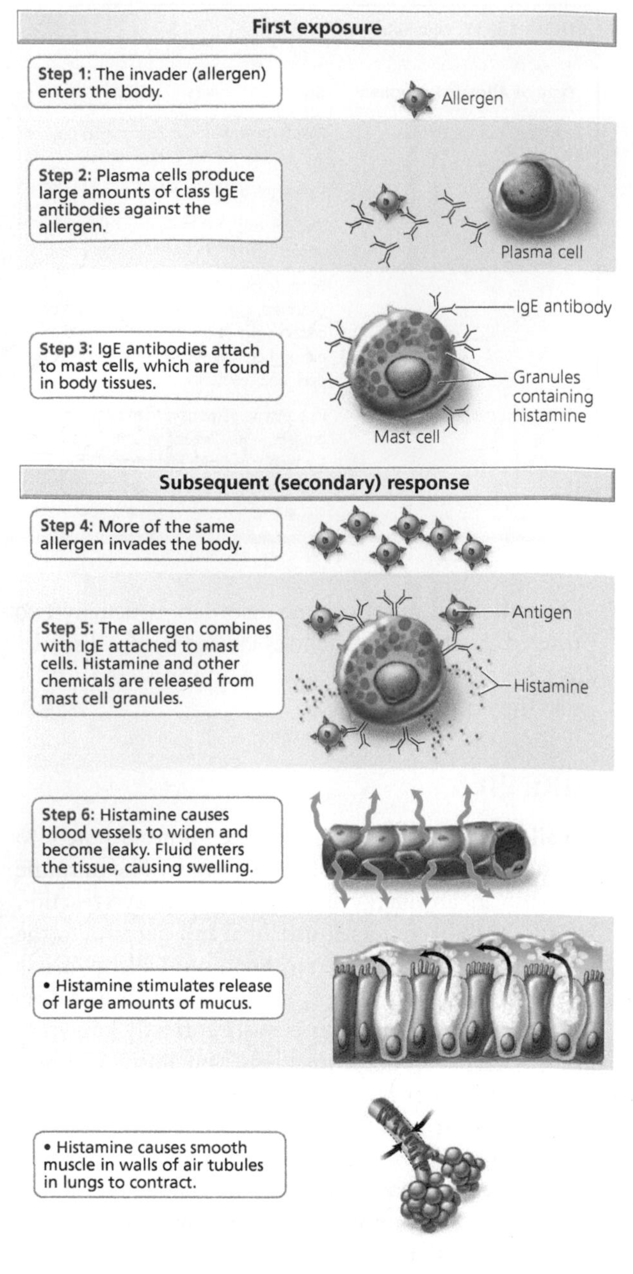

First exposure
Step 1: The invader (allergen) enters the body.
Allergen
Step 2: Plasma cells produce large amounts of class IgE antibodies against the allergen.
Plasma cell
IgE antibody
Step 3: IgE antibodies attach to mast cells, which are found in body tissues.
Granules containing histamine
Mast cell
Subsequent (secondary) response
Step 4: More of the same allergen invades the body.
Antigen
Step 5: The allergen combines with IgE attached to mast cells. Histamine and other chemicals are released from mast cell granules.
Histamine
Step 6: Histamine causes blood vessels to widen and become leaky. Fluid enters the tissue, causing swelling.
• Histamine stimulates release of large amounts of mucus.
• Histamine causes smooth muscle in walls of air tubules in lungs to contract.

FIGURE 3a(v).18 Steps in an allergic reaction

CHAPTER 3B

SELECT PHYSIOLOGICAL SYSTEMS

3b(i) The Cardiovascular & Lymphatic Systems

Taken from *Biology of Humans: Concepts, Applications, and Issues*, Third Edition, by Judith Goodenough and Betty McGuire

FUNCTIONS OF BLOOD

Blood is sometimes referred to as the river of life. The comparison is apt because, like many a river, blood serves as a transportation system. It carries vital materials to all the cells of the body and carries away the wastes that cells produce. But blood does more than passively move its cargo. Its white blood cells help protect us against disease-causing organisms, and its clotting mechanisms help protect us from excessive blood loss when a vessel is damaged. In addition, buffers in the blood help regulate the acid–base balance of body fluids. Blood also helps regulate body temperature by absorbing heat produced in metabolically active regions and distributing it to cooler regions and to the skin, where the heat is dissipated. So the diverse functions of blood can be grouped into three categories: transportation, protection, and regulation.

COMPOSITION OF BLOOD

Blood *is* thicker than water. The reason for the difference is that blood contains cells suspended in its watery fluid. In fact, a single drop of blood contains more than 250 million blood cells. You may recall that blood is classified as a connective tissue because it contains cellular elements suspended in a matrix. The liquid matrix is called plasma, and the cellular elements are collectively called the formed elements (Figure 3b(i).1).

Plasma

Plasma is a straw-colored liquid that makes up about 55% of blood. Plasma serves as the medium in which materials are transported by the blood. Almost every substance that is transported by the blood is dissolved in the plasma. These include nutrients (such as simple sugars, amino acids, lipids, and vitamins), ions (such as sodium, potassium, and chloride), dissolved gases (including carbon dioxide, nitrogen, and a small amount of oxygen), and every hormone. In addition to transporting materials to the cells, the plasma carries away cellular wastes. For example, urea from protein breakdown and uric acid from nucleic acid breakdown are carried to the kidneys, where they can be removed from the body. Blood also transports carbon dioxide from the cells where it is produced to the lungs for release. Indeed, if wastes were not removed the cells would die.

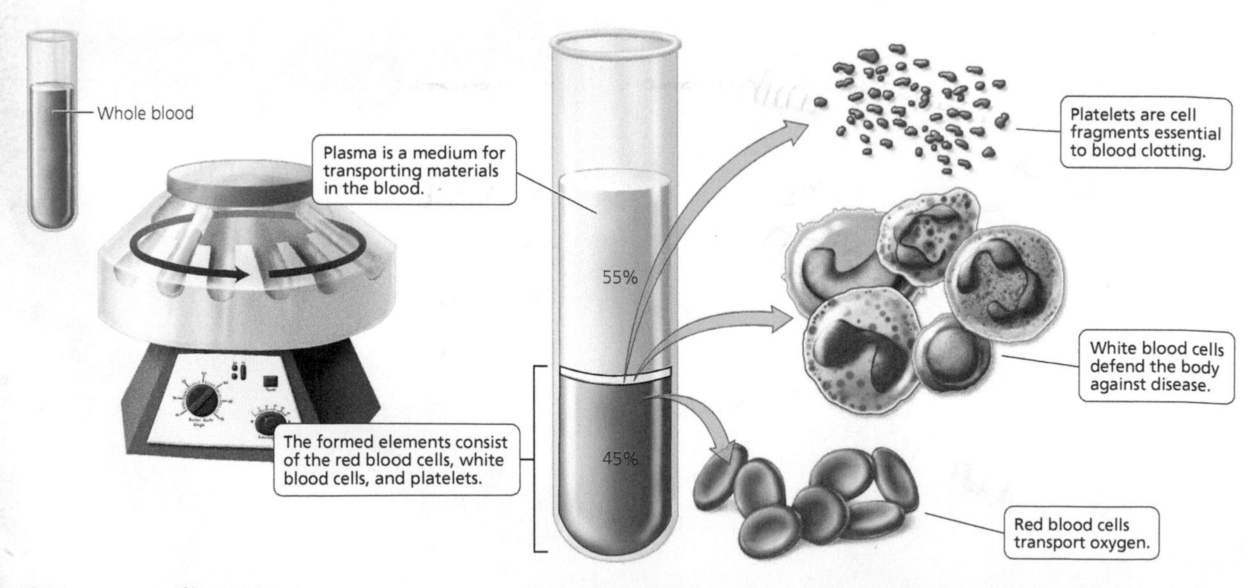

FIGURE 3b(i).1 Blood can be separated into its major components when it is placed in a test tube with a substance that prevents coagulation and then spun in a centrifuge. Whole blood consists of a straw-colored liquid, called plasma, in which cellular elements, called formed elements, are suspended. After separation, the uppermost layer in the test tube consists of plasma. The formed elements are found in two layers below the plasma. Just below the plasma is a thin layer consisting of platelets and white blood cells (leukocytes). The red blood cells (erythrocytes) are packed at the bottom of the test tube.

Despite the amount and variety of substances transported by the blood, most of the dissolved substances (solutes) in the blood are **plasma proteins,** which make up 7% to 8% of plasma. Plasma proteins help balance water flow between the blood and the cells. You may recall that water moves by osmosis across biological membranes from an area of lesser solute concentration to an area of greater solute concentration. Without the plasma proteins, water would be drawn out of the blood by the proteins in cells. As a result, fluid would accumulate in the tissues, causing swelling.

Most of the 50 or so types of plasma proteins fall into one of three general categories: albumins, globulins, and clotting proteins. The albumins make up more than half of the plasma proteins. They are most important in the blood's water-balancing ability. The globulins have a variety of functions. Some globulins transport lipids, including fats and some cholesterol, as well as fat-soluble vitamins. Other globulins are antibodies, which provide protection against many diseases. An example of the third category of plasma protein, the clotting proteins, is fibrinogen, whose role we discuss later in the chapter.

Formed Elements

Among the substances transported by the plasma are the **formed elements**—platelets, white blood cells, and red blood cells. These cell fragments and cells perform some of the key functions of the blood. Descriptions and functions of the formed elements of the blood are summarized in Table 3b(i).1.

Red bone marrow, a porous connective tissue that fills the cavities within many bones, is the birthplace and nursery for the formed elements. Its spongelike framework supports fat cells, but in addition it supports the undifferentiated cells called blood **stem cells** that divide and give rise to all the formed elements (Figure 3b(i).2).

Platelets

Platelets, sometimes called thrombocytes (*thromb,* clot; *cyte,* cell), are essential to blood clotting. They are actually fragments of larger cells called megakaryocytes and are formed in the red bone marrow when megakaryocytes break apart. The fragments are released into the blood at the astounding rate of about

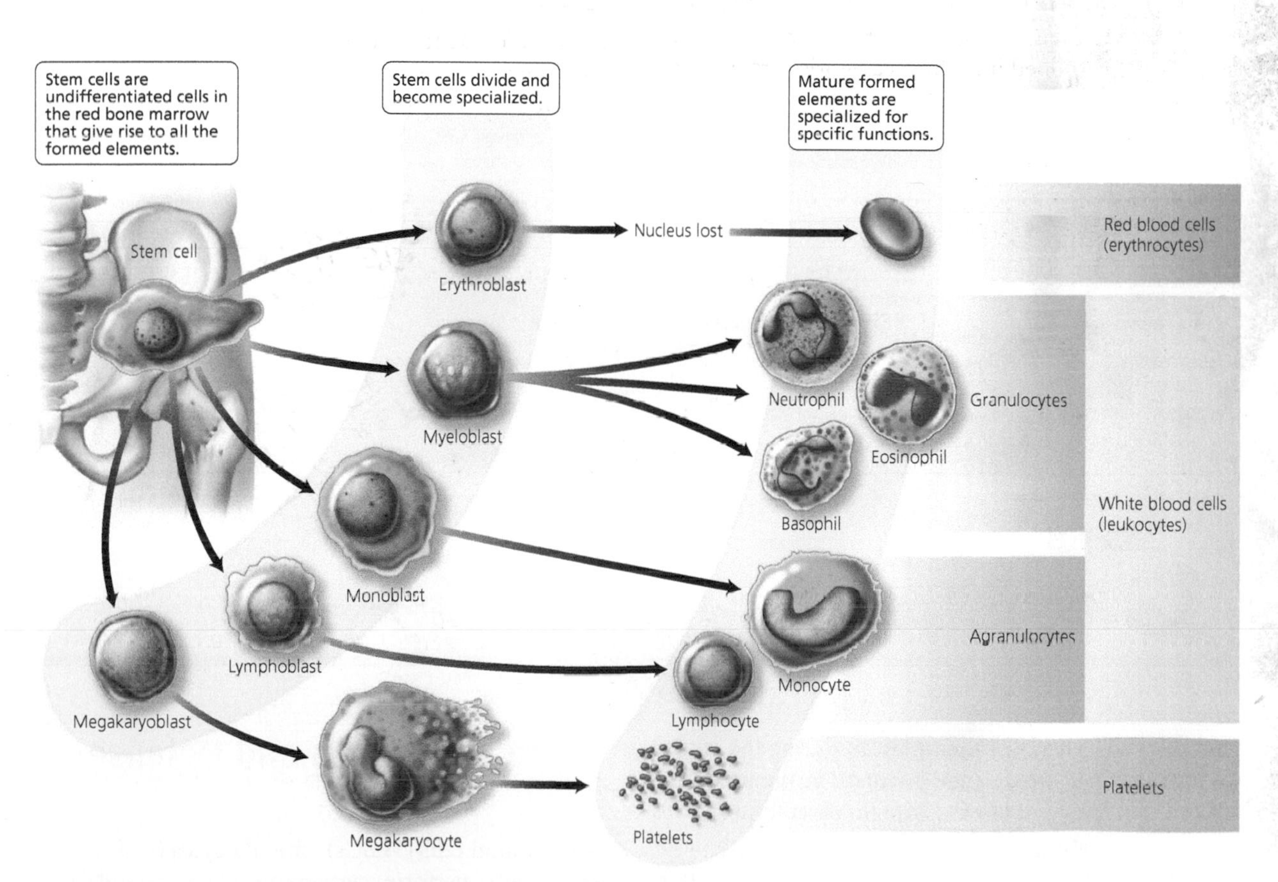

FIGURE 3b(i).2 **All formed elements originate in the red bone marrow from an undifferentiated cell called a stem cell. Stem cells divide and differentiate, giving rise to the various types of blood cells**

TABLE 3b(i).1 The Formed Elements of Blood

Type of Formed Element	Cell Function	Description	No. of Cells/mm³	Life Span
Platelets	Play role in blood clotting	Fragments of a megakaryocyte; small, purple-stained granules in cytoplasm	250,000–500,000	5–10 days
White Blood Cells (WBCs; leukocytes)				
Granulocytes				
Neutrophils	Consume bacteria by phagocytosis	Multilobed nucleus, clear-staining cytoplasm, inconspicuous granules	3000–7000	6–72 hours
Eosinophils	Consume antibody–antigen complex by phagocytosis; attack parasitic worms	Large, pink-staining granules in cytoplasm, bilobed nucleus	100–400	8–12 days
Basophils	Release histamine, which attracts white blood cells to the site of inflammation and widens blood vessels	Large, purple-staining cytoplasmic granules; bilobed nucleus	20–50	3–72 hours
Agranulocytes				
Monocytes	Give rise to macrophages, which consume bacteria, dead cells, and cell parts by phagocytosis	Gray-blue cytoplasm with no granules; U-shaped nucleus	100–700	Several months
Lymphocytes	Attack damaged or diseased cells, or disease-causing organisms; produce antibodies	Round nucleus that almost fills the cell	1500–3000	Many years
Red Blood Cells (RBCs; erythrocytes)	Transport oxygen and carbon dioxide	Biconcave disk, no nucleus	4–6 million	About 120 days

200 billion a day. They then mature during the course of a week, after which they circulate in the blood for about 5 to 10 days. Platelets contain several substances important in stopping the loss of blood through damaged blood vessels. This vital function of platelets is considered later in the chapter.

White Blood Cells and Defense against Disease

White blood cells (WBCs), or **leukocytes** (*leuk–*, white; *–cyte*, cell), perform certain mundane housekeeping duties—such as removing wastes, toxins, and damaged or abnormal cells—but they also serve as warriors in the body's fight against disease. Although leukocytes represent less than 1% of whole blood, we simply could not live without them. We would succumb to the microbes that surround us. Because the number of white blood cells increases when the body responds to microbes, white blood cell counts are often used as an index of infection.

Like the other formed elements, white blood cells are produced in the red bone marrow.[1] Unlike platelets and red blood cells, however, white blood cells are nucleated. Moreover, although they circulate in the bloodstream, they are not confined there. By squeezing between neighboring cells that form the walls of blood vessels, white blood cells can leave the circulatory system and move to a site of infection, tissue damage, or inflammation (Figure 3b(i).3). Having slipped out of the capillary into the fluid bathing the cells, white blood cells roam through the tissue spaces. Chemicals released by invading microbes or damaged cells attract the white blood cells and cause them to gather in areas of tissue damage or infection. Certain types of white blood cells may then engulf the "offender" in a process called **phagocytosis** (*phago–*, to eat; *–cyt–*, cell. Our consideration of white blood cells in this chapter is brief.

There are two groups of white blood cells. **Granulocytes** have granules in their cytoplasm. The granules are actually sacs containing chemicals that are used as weapons to destroy invading pathogens, especially bacteria. **Agranulocytes** lack cytoplasmic granules or have very small granules. These two groups include a total of five types of white blood cells.

Granulocytes

All white blood cells are colorless, and thus they are often stained so that they are visible under a microscope. Depending on the color of the granules after they have been stained for microscopic study, the granulocytes are classified as neutrophils, eosinophils, or basophils. Neutrophils have small granules that don't stain with either acidic red stain eosin or with a basic blue stain. The granules in eosinophils pick up a pink color from the stain eosin. Basophils have purple-staining granules (see Table 3b(i).1).

- **Neutrophils,** the most abundant of all white blood cells, are the blood cell soldiers on the front lines. Arriving at the site of infection before the other types of white blood cells, neutrophils immediately begin to engulf microbes by phagocytosis, thus curbing the spread of the infection. After engulfing a dozen or so bacteria, a neutrophil dies. But even in death it helps the body's defense by releasing chemicals that attract more neutrophils to the scene. Dead neutrophils, along with bacteria and cellular debris, make up pus, the yellowish liquid we usually associate with infection.

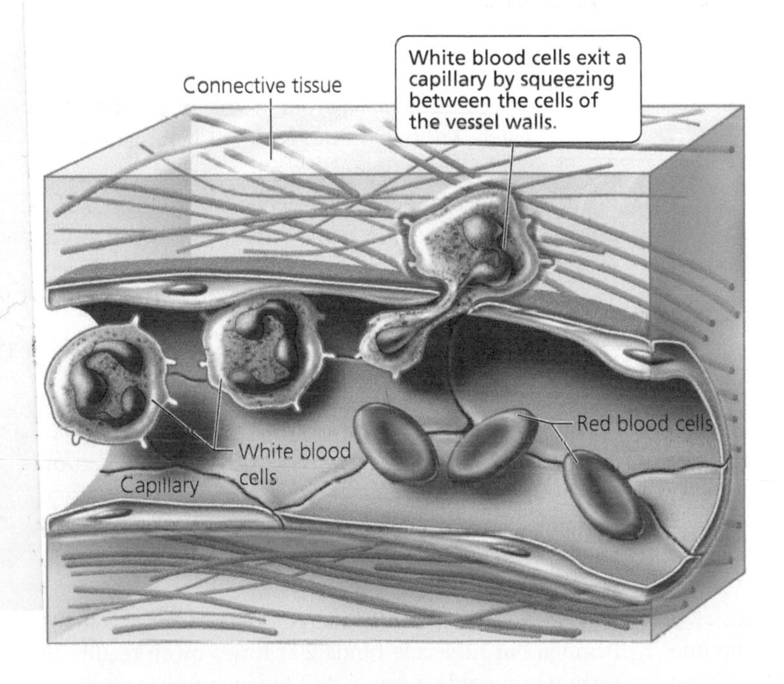
Connective tissue
White blood cells exit a capillary by squeezing between the cells of the vessel walls.
Red blood cells
White blood cells
Capillary

FIGURE 3b(i).3 **White blood cells can squeeze between the cells that form the wall of a capillary. They then enter the fluid surrounding body cells and, attracted by chemicals released by microbes or damaged cells, gather at the site of infection or injury.**

[1]One type, the lymphocytes, also may be produced in the lymph nodes and other lymphoid tissues.

- **Eosinophils** contain substances that are important in the body's defense against parasitic worms, such as tapeworms and hookworms. They also lessen the severity of allergies by engulfing antibody–antigen complexes and inactivating inflammatory chemicals.
- **Basophils** release histamine, a chemical that attracts other white blood cells to the site of infection and causes blood vessels to dilate (widen), thereby increasing blood flow to the affected area. They also play a role in some allergic reactions.

Agranulocytes

The agranulocytes, which lack visible granules in the cytoplasm, are classified as monocytes or lymphocytes.

- **Monocytes,** the largest of all formed elements, leave the bloodstream and enter various tissues, where they develop into macrophages. Macrophages are phagocytic cells that engulf invading microbes, dead cells, and cellular debris.
- **Lymphocytes** are classified into two types: B lymphocytes and T lymphocytes. The *B lymphocytes* give rise to plasma cells, which, in turn, produce antibodies. *Antibodies* are proteins that recognize specific molecules—called *antigens*—on the surface of invading microbes or other foreign cells. After recognizing the foreign cell by its antigens, the antibodies help prevent it from harming the body. There are several types of *T lymphocytes,* specialized white blood cells that play roles in the body's defense mechanisms.

Red Blood Cells and Transport of Oxygen

Red blood cells (RBCs), also called **erythrocytes** (*erythro–*, red; *–cyt–*, cell), pick up oxygen in the lungs and ferry it to all the cells of the body. Red blood cells also carry about 23% of the blood's total carbon dioxide, a metabolic waste product. They are by far the most numerous cells in the blood. Indeed, they number 4–6 million/mm^3 of blood and constitute approximately 45% of the total blood volume.

Red Blood Cells and Hemoglobin

The shape of red blood cells, as shown in Figure 3b(i).4, is marvelously suited to their function of picking up and transporting oxygen. Red blood cells are quite small, and each is shaped like a biconcave disk—a flattened disk indented on each side. This shape maximizes the surface area of the cell. Because of the greater surface area, oxygen can enter the red blood cell more rapidly than if the disk did not have an indent. A red blood cell is unusually flexible and thus able to squeeze through capillaries (the smallest blood vessels, those in which gas exchange occurs), even those with a diameter much smaller than red blood cells. Each red blood cell is packed with **hemoglobin,** the oxygen-binding pigment that is responsible for the cells' red color. As a red blood cell matures in the red bone marrow, it loses its nucleus and most organelles. Thus, it is scarcely more than a sack of hemoglobin molecules. Each red blood cell is packed with approximately 280 million molecules of hemoglobin. As can be seen in Figure 3b(i).5, each hemoglobin molecule is made up of four subunits. Each subunit consists of a polypeptide chain and a heme group. The heme group includes an iron ion that actually binds to the oxygen. Therefore, each hemoglobin molecule can carry up to four molecules of oxygen. The compound formed when hemoglobin binds with oxygen is called, logically enough, *oxyhemoglobin.* Body cells use the oxygen to boost the amount of energy extracted from food molecules in cellular respiration. As oxygen is used, carbon dioxide is produced. Most of the carbon dioxide travels to the lungs dissolved in plasma, but some of it binds to hemoglobin (at a site other than that where the iron atom binds oxygen).

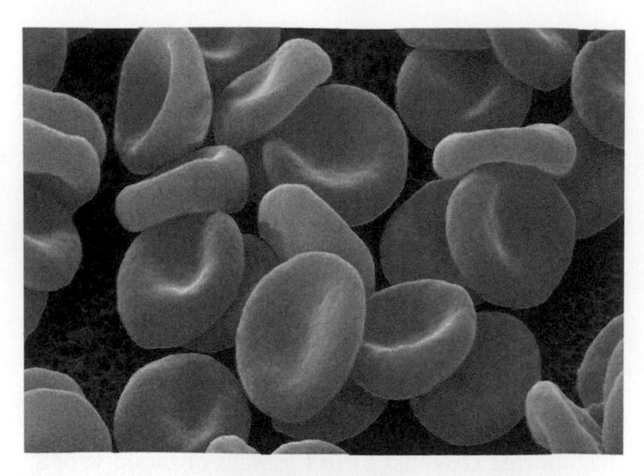

FIGURE 3b(i).4 **Red blood cells serve to ferry oxygen from the lungs to the needy tissues. Each red blood cell is packed with the oxygen-binding pigment hemoglobin. A red blood cell is a small disk that is indented on both sides. This design maximizes the surface area for gas exchange.**

As wonderfully adapted as it is for carrying oxygen, the hemoglobin molecule binds 200 times more readily to carbon monoxide, a product of the incomplete combustion of any carbon-containing fuel. In other words, if concentrations of carbon monoxide and oxygen were identical in inhaled air, for every 1 molecule of hemoglo-

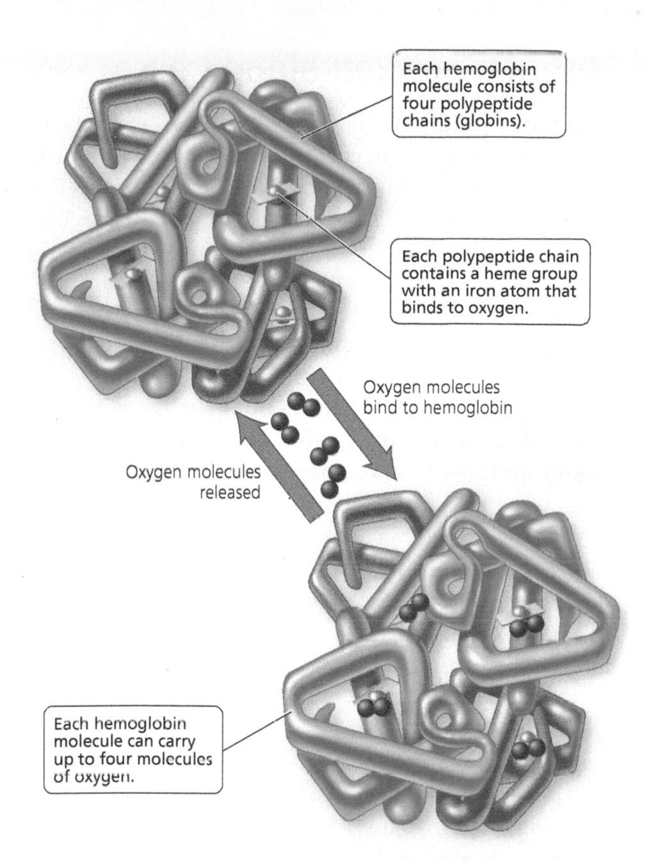
Each hemoglobin molecule consists of four polypeptide chains (globins).
Each polypeptide chain contains a heme group with an iron atom that binds to oxygen.
Oxygen molecules bind to hemoglobin
Oxygen molecules released
Each hemoglobin molecule can carry up to four molecules of oxygen.

FIGURE 3b(i).5 **The structure of hemoglobin, the pigment in red blood cells that transports oxygen from the lungs to the cells**

bin that binds to oxygen molecules, 200 molecules of hemoglobin would bind to carbon monoxide molecules. This is the reason carbon monoxide can be deadly. When carbon monoxide binds to the oxygen-binding sites on hemoglobin, it blocks oxygen from binding to it, preventing the blood from carrying life-giving oxygen to the cells. Carbon monoxide is a particularly insidious poison because it is odorless and tasteless. Its primary source is automobile exhaust, but it can also come from indoor sources, including improperly vented heaters and leaky chimneys. Thus, indoor carbon monoxide detectors can save lives.

Life Cycle of Red Blood Cells

The creation of a red blood cell, which takes about 6 days, entails many changes in the cell's activities and structure. First, the very immature cell becomes a factory for hemoglobin molecules. And as noted earlier, after the cell is packed with hemoglobin, its nucleus is pushed out. Then a structural metamorphosis occurs, culminating in a mature red blood cell with a typical biconcave shape. Once this change in shape takes place, the cell leaves the bone marrow and enters the bloodstream. Red marrow produces roughly 2 million red blood cells a second, throughout the life of an individual, for a cumulative total of more than half a ton in a lifetime.

A red blood cell lives for only about 120 days. During that time, it travels through approximately 100 km (62 mi) of blood vessels, being bent, bumped, and squeezed along the way. Its life span is probably limited by the lack of a nucleus that would otherwise maintain it and direct needed repairs. Without a nucleus, for instance, protein synthesis needed to replace key enzymes cannot take place, so the cell becomes increasingly rigid and fragile.

The liver and spleen are the "graveyards" where worn-out red blood cells are removed from circulation. The old, inflexible red blood cells tend to become stuck in the tiny circulatory channels of these organs. Macrophages then engulf and destroy the dying cells. The demolished cells release their hemoglobin, which the liver degrades into its protein (globin) component and heme. The protein is digested to amino acids, which can be used to make other proteins. The iron from the heme is salvaged and sent to the red marrow for recycling.

The remaining part of the heme is degraded to a yellow pigment, called *bilirubin,* which is excreted by the liver in bile. Bile is released into the small intestine, where it assists in the digestion of fats. It is then carried along the digestive system to the large intestine with undigested food and becomes a component of feces. The color of feces is partly due to bilirubin that has been broken down by intestinal bacteria.

Products formed by the chemical breakdown of heme also create the yellowish tinge in a bruise that is healing. A bruise, or black-and-blue mark, results when tiny blood vessels or capillaries are ruptured and blood leaks into the surrounding tissue. As the tissues use up the oxygen, the blood becomes darker and, viewed through the overlying tissue, looks black or blue. Gradually, the red blood cells degenerate, releasing hemoglobin. The breakdown products of hemoglobin then make the bruise appear yellowish.

A negative feedback mechanism regulates red blood cell production according to the needs of the body, especially the need for oxygen (Figure 3b(i).6). Most of

stop and THINK

Hepatitis is an inflammation of the liver that can be caused by certain viruses or exposure to certain drugs. It impairs the liver's ability to handle bilirubin properly. A symptom of hepatitis is jaundice, a condition in which the skin develops a yellow tone. Why does hepatitis cause jaundice?

the time, red blood cell production matches red blood cell destruction. However, there are circumstances—blood loss, for instance—that trigger a homeostatic mechanism that speeds up the rate of red blood cell production. This mechanism is initiated by a decrease in the oxygen supply to the body's cells. Certain cells in the kidney sense the reduced oxygen, and they respond by producing the hormone **erythropoietin.** Erythropoietin then travels to the red marrow, where it steps up both the division rate of stem cells and the maturation rate of immature red blood cells. When maximally stimulated by erythropoietin, the red marrow can increase red blood cell production tenfold—to 20 million cells per second! The resulting increase in red blood cell numbers is soon adequate to meet the oxygen needs of body cells. The increased oxygen-carrying capacity of the blood then inhibits erythropoietin production.

BLOOD CELL DISORDERS

Disorders of red and white blood cells have many different causes. The problems associated with each disorder depend on the type of blood cells affected, because red and white blood cells have different functions.

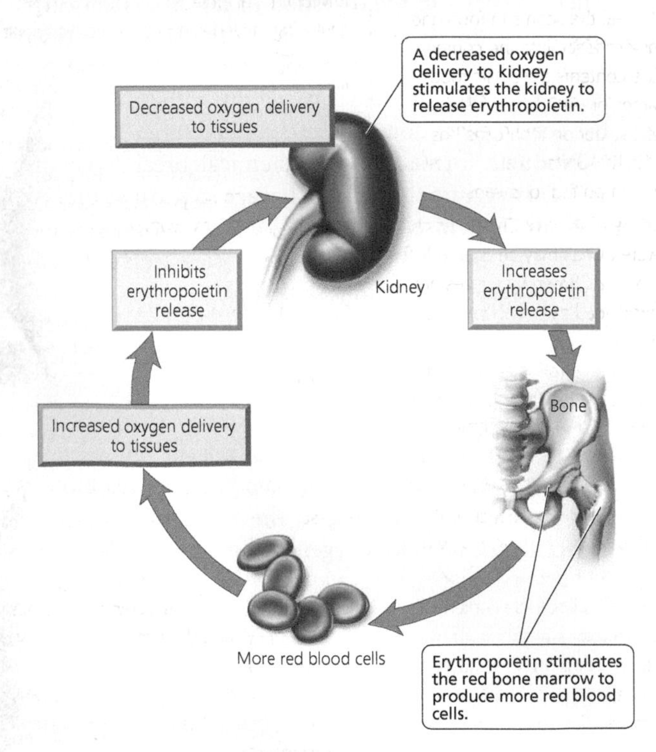
A decreased oxygen delivery to kidney stimulates the kidney to release erythropoietin.
Decreased oxygen delivery to tissues
Inhibits erythropoietin release
Kidney
Increases erythropoietin release
Bone
Increased oxygen delivery to tissues
More red blood cells
Erythropoietin stimulates the red bone marrow to produce more red blood cells.

FIGURE 3b(i).6 **The production of red blood cells is regulated by a negative feedback relationship between the oxygen-carrying capacity of the blood and the production of erythropoietin.**

Disorders of Red Blood Cells

Anemia, a condition in which the blood's ability to carry oxygen is reduced, can result from too little hemoglobin, too few red blood cells, or both. The symptoms of anemia include fatigue, headaches, dizziness, paleness, and breathlessness. In addition, an anemic person's heart often beats faster to compensate for the blood's decreased ability to carry oxygen. The accelerated pumping can cause heart palpitations—the uncomfortable awareness of one's own heartbeat. Although anemia is not usually life threatening, it can affect the quality of life because lack of energy and low levels of productive activity often go hand in hand.

Worldwide, the most common cause of anemia is an insufficiency of iron in the body, which leads to inadequate hemoglobin production. *Iron-deficiency anemia* can be caused by a diet that contains too little iron, by an inability to absorb iron from the digestive system, or from blood loss, such as might occur because of menstrual flow or peptic ulcers. Treatment for iron-deficiency anemia includes dealing with the cause of the iron depletion, as well as restoring iron levels to normal by eating foods that are rich in iron—such as meat, leafy green vegetables, and fortified cereals—or by taking pills that contain iron.

Blood loss will obviously lower red blood cell counts, but so will any condition that causes the destruction of red blood cells at an amount that exceeds the production of red blood cells. For example, in hemolytic anemias, red blood cells are ruptured because of infections, defects in the membranes of red blood cells, transfusion of mismatched blood, or hemoglobin abnormalities. *Sickle-cell anemia* is an example of a hemolytic anemia caused by abnormal hemoglobins. This abnormal hemoglobin (hemoglobin S) causes the red blood cells to become deformed to a crescent (or sickle) shape when the blood's oxygen content is low. The misshapen cells are fragile and rupture easily, clogging small blood vessels and promoting clot formation. These events prevent oxygen-laden blood from reaching the tissues and can cause episodes of extreme pain.

Red blood cell numbers also drop when the production of red blood cells is halted or impaired, as occurs in *pernicious anemia.* The production of red blood cells depends on a supply of vitamin B_{12}. The small intestine absorbs vitamin B_{12} from the diet with the aid of a chemical called intrinsic factor, which is produced by the stomach lining. People with pernicious anemia do not produce intrinsic factor and are therefore unable to absorb vitamin B_{12}. They are treated with injections of B_{12}. Lead poisoning can also cause anemia. (See the Environmental Issue essay, *Lead Poisoning.*)

Environmental Issue

Lead Poisoning

What do children in old buildings in America today have in common with the ancient upper-class Romans? Lead poisoning. Today, some children are poisoned by the lead in paint chips that they unintentionally ingest as aging paint peels (or, in very young children, when they chew or bite objects that have been treated with lead paint). Centuries ago, Romans were poisoned by lead in their eating and drinking vessels.

The types of cells that are most sensitive to lead are nerve cells and the bone marrow cells that give rise to red blood cells. The best-known effects of lead on human health are probably those on the nervous system—mental retardation, lowered IQs, reading disabilities, irritability, hyperactivity, and even death. However, the effects of lead on the blood, including anemia and changes in blood enzymes, can also be devastating. Indeed, a blood test is the only way to positively diagnose lead poisoning.

Lead launches a two-pronged attack on the blood's ability to carry oxygen. First, it interferes with the absorption of iron from the digestive system. Second, it inhibits one of the essential enzymes leading to hemoglobin synthesis.

As our example of ancient Romans suggests, lead has been a common pollutant for centuries, encountered in a surprising number of substances. The major causes of lead poisoning in the United States are as follows:

1. **House paint** Although lead has not been added to house paint for years, this remains the most prevalent cause of poisoning. Young children tend to put almost anything they find into their mouths, and lead-containing paint chips are no exception. Although most cases of lead poisoning occur in children of poor families living in big cities, lead poisoning can also affect the affluent and those living in the country or suburbs. The entire family—adults, children, and even pets—can be exposed to lead during the renovation of old homes. For example, lead dust is created as lead paint is sanded from surfaces. That dust can then be inhaled and absorbed into the bloodstream.
2. **Drinking water** One out of every five Americans drinks tap water containing excess levels of lead, according to Environmental Protection Agency estimates. Most of these people are unaware that their drinking water is contaminated with lead because the water still tastes and smells normal. Lead leaches into the water from sources within the homes—copper pipes that contain lead solder, lead connectors in the plumbing, or fancy faucets made of brass or bronze. The leaching process is hastened by heat, acidity, and soft water.
3. **Air and soil pollution** The primary source of lead in the atmosphere has been leaded gasoline. As early as the 1920s, tetraethyl lead was added to motor fuel because it slowed combustion and therefore reduced engine knock and wear. Tiny particles of lead are released into the atmosphere when leaded fuel is burned. Thus, as the use of leaded motor fuel increased, so did the concentration of atmospheric lead. (Leaded gasoline is no longer sold in the United States for use in automobiles, although it is permissible in farm equipment, race cars, and other off-road vehicles.)
4. **Lead solder on food cans** The lead in the solder used to seal the seams in food and beverage cans can leach into the contents, especially if the contents are acidic foods such as tomatoes or citrus juices. Although the use of lead solder on food cans has been banned in the United States, it is still found on some imported food cans.
5. **Lead-containing dishware** China, ceramic, and earthenware dishes may be coated with lead-containing glaze. When the glazes are not properly fired, lead can leach into the food or beverage contained in the dish. Lead is most likely to leach into foods or beverages that are hot or acidic. Thus, it is probably best to avoid daily use of a ceramic mug for coffee or tea. Wine should not be stored in lead crystal decanters, and if a wine bottle is sealed with a lead foil capsule, clean the rim of the bottle before removing the cork.
6. **Fruits and vegetables grown on lead-contaminated soil** Soil can be contaminated by lead from the atmosphere or by leakage from lead-containing solid wastes, such as lead batteries in automobiles that are dumped into landfills. Important sources of atmospheric lead are the combustion of lead motor fuel, the smelting of ores and other industrial processes, and the incineration of refuse. Fruits and vegetables can then incorporate the lead or be coated in lead dust. When the contaminated food is eaten, the lead is absorbed into the bloodstream.

Children often put objects into their mouths. They may unintentionally ingest lead paint chips if the object has been treated with lead.

Although it is true that blood levels of lead are at an all-time low in the United States, the lead problem has not been eliminated. In 2008 the Environmental Protection Agency (EPA) proposed tightening the federal limits for lead in the air. An important problem now is deciding who should be financially responsible for keeping us safe. China's safety standards are not as high as those in the United States. Recently, the paint on children's toys imported from China contained lead. Some people blame the companies that imported the toys. In turn, some of those companies blame the failure of federal agencies to protect us.

Questions to Consider

In 2008 San Diego, California, wrestled with establishing lead-safe apartments and workplaces. The city has about 310,000 buildings built before 1979 that contain lead paint, and the average cost of lead reduction is $704 for each housing unit.

- **Who do you think should bear the financial responsibility of removing lead paint from old apartment buildings? The residents? The landlords? The city? The federal government?**
- **Do you think the residents of buildings with lead paint should be compensated for any lead-related health problems they experience? If so, who do you think should pay—the landlords? The original contractors? The government?**

what would you do?

Blood doping is a practice that boosts red blood cell numbers and, therefore, the blood's ability to carry oxygen. In one method, blood is drawn from the body and stored, prompting the body temporarily to boost its production of red blood cells. The stored blood is then returned to the body. Some athletes who compete in aerobic events, such as swimming or cycling, have used blood doping to increase their endurance and speed. Although blood doping is considered unethical and is prohibited in Olympic competition, it is difficult to detect. One sign is an exceptionally high number of red blood cells; another is the presence in the urine of a hormone (erythropoietin) that stimulates red blood cell production; but tests can detect only about 50% of the athletes who practice blood doping. Considering the large percentage of blood-doped athletes who will escape detection even if they are tested, do you think that those who are caught should be punished?

Disorders of White Blood Cells

Infectious mononucleosis ("mono") is a viral disease of the lymphocytes. It is caused by the Epstein-Barr virus, which is common in humans but usually asymptomatic. In mononucleosis, the infection causes an increase in lymphocytes that have an atypical appearance. Because mono often is spread from person to person by oral contact, it is sometimes called the kissing disease; however, it can also be spread by sharing eating utensils or drinking glasses. Mono is most common among teenagers and young adults, particularly those living in dormitories. It often strikes at stressful times, such as during final exams, when immune resistance is low.

The initial symptoms of mono are similar to those of influenza: fever, chills, headache, sore throat, and an overwhelming sense of being ill. Within a few days, the lymph node (commonly called "glands") in the neck, armpits, and groin become painfully swollen. There is no treatment, so mono must simply run its course. The major symptoms generally subside within a few weeks, but fatigue may linger for several months or longer.

Leukemia is a cancer of the white blood cells that causes their uncontrolled multiplication, so that their number increases greatly. These cancerous cells—all descendants of a single abnormal cell—remain immature and are therefore unable to defend the body against infectious organisms. Because they divide more rapidly than do normal cells, the abnormal cells "take over" the bone marrow, preventing the development of all normal blood cells, including red blood cells, white blood cells, and platelets.

Symptoms of leukemia generally result either from the insufficient number of normal blood components or from the invasion of organs by abnormal white blood cells. The increased number of white blood cells crowds out the other formed elements. Insufficient numbers of platelets lead to inadequate clotting, which causes gum bleeding and frequent bruising. Reduced levels of red blood cells lead to anemia, which in turn causes chronic fatigue, breathlessness, and pallor. Because their white blood cells do not function properly, leukemia patients may suffer from repeated respiratory or throat infections, herpes, or skin infections. Also, bone tenderness may be experienced because the immature white blood cells pack the red marrow. Headaches, another symptom of leukemia, may be caused by anemia or by the effects of abnormal white blood cells in the brain.

Treatment of leukemia usually includes radiation therapy and chemotherapy to kill the rapidly dividing cells. In addition, transfusions of red blood cells and platelets may be given to alleviate anemia and prevent excessive bleeding. Today, many patients with acute leukemia are cured with bone marrow transplants. Someone, most often a family member whose tissue type closely matches that of the patient, must be located and agree to serve as a donor. Then the bone marrow in the leukemia patient must be destroyed by irradiation and drugs. Next, the donor's bone marrow is given to the patient intravenously, just like a blood transfusion. The marrow cells find their way to the patient's marrow and begin to grow. Treatment with stem cells from umbilical cord blood seems to be as effective as bone marrow transplant in helping some patients with leukemia go into remission (the signs and symptoms of leukemia go away).

BLOOD TYPES

Human blood is classified into different **blood types,** depending on the presence or absence of certain molecules, mostly proteins, on the surface of a person's red blood cells. Each of your body cells is labeled as "self" (that is, as belonging to your body) by proteins on its surface. If a cell that lacks these self markers enters the body, the body's defense system recognizes that the foreign cell is "nonself" and does not belong. The foreign cell will have different proteins on its surface. To the body's defense system, these proteins are antigens, identifying the cell as foreign and marking it for destruction. As was mentioned earlier, one way the body attacks the foreign cell is by producing proteins called antibodies that specifically target the antigen on the foreign cell's surface. Let's consider the role of antigens and antibodies in blood types and transfusions.

ABO Blood Types

When asked about your blood type, you are probably used to responding by indicating one of the types in the ABO series: A, B, AB, or O. Red blood cells with only the antigen A on their surface are type A. When only the B antigen is on the red blood cell surface, the blood is type B. Blood with both A and B antigens on the red blood cell surface is designated type AB. When neither A nor B antigens are present, the blood is type O.

Normally, a person's plasma contains antibodies against those antigens that are not on his or her own red blood cells. Thus, individuals with type A blood have antibodies against the B antigen (anti-B antibodies[2]), and those with type B blood have antibodies against A (anti-A antibodies). Because individuals with type AB blood have both antigens on their red blood cells, they have neither antibody. Those with type O blood have neither antigen, so they have both anti-A and anti-B antibodies in their plasma.

In a typical test for blood type, technicians mix a drop of a person's blood with a solution containing anti-A antibodies and mix another drop of the blood with a solution containing anti-B antibodies. If clumping occurs in one of the mixtures, it means the antigen corresponding to the antibody in that mixture is present (Figure 3b(i).7).

Similarly, when a person is given a blood transfusion with donor blood containing foreign antigens, the antibodies in the recipient's blood will cause the donor's cells to clump, or **agglutinate.** This clumping of the donor's cells is damaging and perhaps even fatal. The clumped cells can get stuck in small blood vessels and block blood flow to body cells. Or they may break open, releasing their cargo of hemoglobin. The hemoglobin then clogs the filtering system in the kidneys, causing death.

Q What blood type will agglutinate to each serum when mixed separately with sera containing anti-A, anti-B, and anti-Rh antibodies?

It is important to be sure that the blood types of a donor and recipient are compatible, which means that the recipient's blood does not contain antibodies to antigens on the red blood cells of the donor. The plasma of the donor's blood may contain antibodies

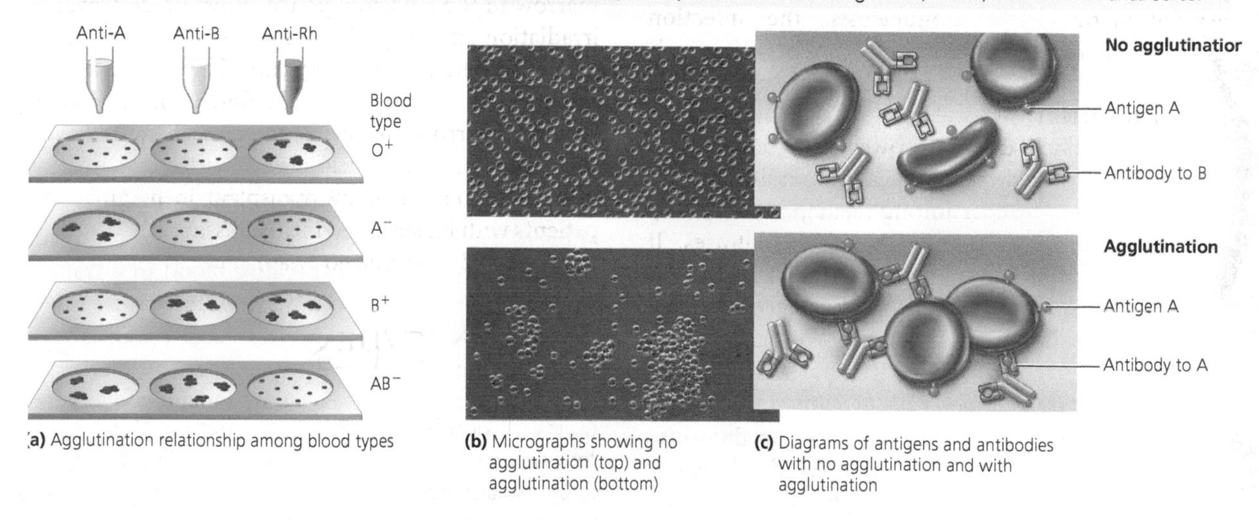

(a) Agglutination relationship among blood types

(b) Micrographs showing no agglutination (top) and agglutination (bottom)

(c) Diagrams of antigens and antibodies with no agglutination and with agglutination

FIGURE 3b(i).7 **Blood is typed by mixing it with serum known to contain antibodies specific for a certain antigen. If blood containing that antigen is mixed with the serum, the blood will agglutinate (clump). Thus, one drop of blood is mixed with serum containing anti-A and another drop with serum containing anti-B. A third drop of blood is mixed with serum containing antibodies to Rh. Agglutination in response to an antibody reveals the presence of the antigen.**

A AB+

[2]It is not certain why these antibodies form without exposure to red blood cells bearing the foreign antigen. It may be that either the bacteria that invade our bodies or the foods we eat contain a small amount of A and B antigens, enough to stimulate antibody production.

TABLE 3b(i).2 Transfusion Relationships among Blood Types

Blood Types	Antigens on Red Blood Cells	Antibodies in Plasma	Blood Types (RBCs) That Can Be Received in Transfusions	Incidence of Blood Type in United States
A	A	Anti-B	A, O	Caucasian, 40% African American, 27% Asian, 28% Native American, 8%
B	B	Anti-A	B, O	Caucasian, 10% African American, 20% Asian, 27% Native American, 1%
AB	A and B	None	A, B, AB, O	Caucasian, 5% African American, 4% Asian, 5% Native American, 0%
O	None	Anti-A, Anti-B	O	Caucasian, 45% African American, 49% Asian, 40% Native American, 91%

against antigens on the recipient's red blood cells, but these will be diluted as they enter the recipient's circulation. Therefore, the donor's antibodies are not a major problem. The questions to ask in this case are (1) what, if any, antigens are on the donor's cells and (2) what, if any, antibodies are in the recipient's blood. For example, if a person with blood type A is given a transfusion of blood type B or of type AB, the naturally occurring anti-B antibodies in the recipient's blood will cause the donor's red blood cells to clump because they have the B antigen. The transfusion relationships among blood types in the ABO series are shown in Table 3b(i).2.

Rh Factor

The A and B antigens are not the only important antigens found on the surface of red blood cells. The presence or absence of an **Rh factor** is also an important component of blood type. The name Rh comes from the beginning of the name of the rhesus monkey, in which an Rh antigen was first discovered. People who have the Rh antigens on their red blood cells are considered Rh-positive (Rh^+). When Rh antigens are missing from the red blood cell surface, the individual is considered Rh-negative (Rh^-).

An Rh-negative person will not form anti-Rh antibodies unless he or she has been exposed to the Rh antigen. For this reason, an Rh-negative individual should be given only Rh-negative blood in a transfusion. If he or she is mistakenly given Rh-positive blood, it will stimulate the production of anti-Rh antibodies. A transfusion reaction will not occur after the first such transfusion, because it takes time for the body to start making anti-Rh antibodies. After a second transfusion of Rh-positive blood, however, the antibodies in the recipient's plasma will react with the antigens on the red blood cells of the donated blood. This reaction may lead to the death of the patient.

The Rh factor can also have medical importance for pregnancies in which the mother is Rh-negative and the fetus is Rh-positive, a situation that may occur if the father is Rh-positive (see Figure 3b(i).8). Ordinarily, the maternal and fetal blood supplies do not mix during pregnancy. However, as a result of blood vessel damage, some mixing may occur during a miscarriage or delivery. If the baby's red blood cells, which bear Rh antigens, accidentally pass into the mother's bloodstream, she will

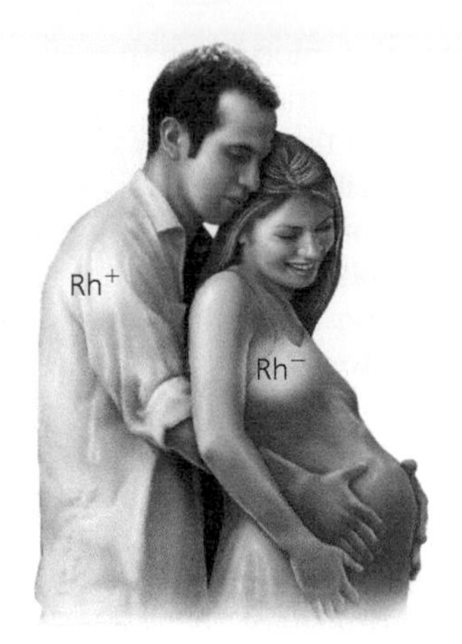

An Rh^+ man and an Rh^- woman could have an Rh^+ baby.

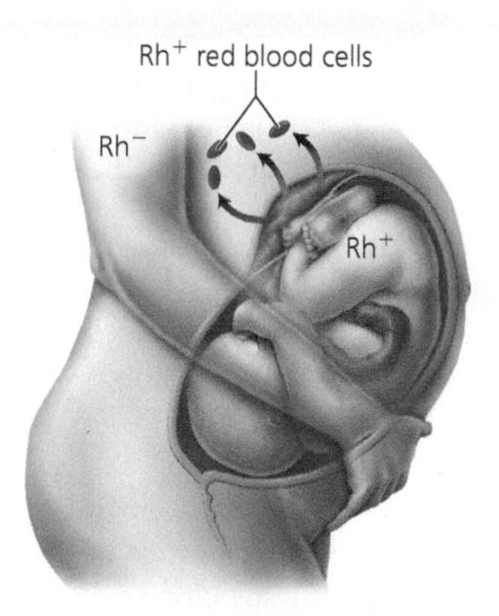

First pregnancy: At birth some of the Rh^+ blood of the fetus may enter the mother's circulation.

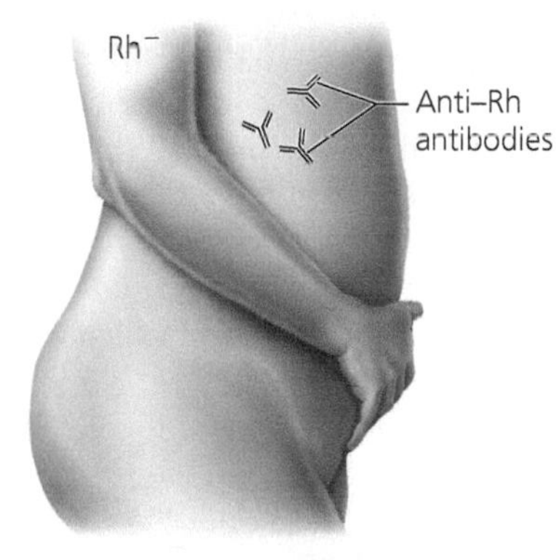

After delivery: The mother forms anti-Rh antibodies over the next few months.

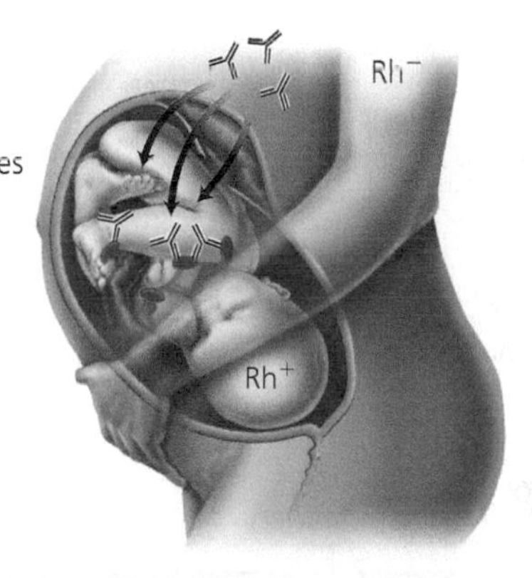

Second pregnancy with an Rh^+ fetus: anti-Rh antibodies may pass into the fetus's blood, causing its blood cells to burst.

FIGURE 3b(i).8 **Rh incompatibility can result when an Rh-negative (Rh^-) woman is pregnant with an Rh-positive (Rh^+) baby if the woman has been previously exposed to Rh^+ blood.**

produce anti-Rh antibodies. There are usually no ill effects associated with the first introduction of the Rh antigen. However, if antibodies are present in the maternal blood from a previous pregnancy with an Rh-positive child or from a transfusion of Rh-positive blood, the anti-Rh antibodies may pass into the blood of the fetus during a subsequent pregnancy. This transfer can occur because anti-Rh antibodies, unlike red blood cells, can cross the placenta (a structure that forms during pregnancy to allow the exchange of selected substances between the maternal and fetal circulatory systems). These anti-Rh antibodies may destroy the fetus's red blood cells. As a result, the child may be stillborn or very anemic at birth. This condition is called *hemolytic disease of the newborn.*

The incidence of hemolytic disease of the newborn has decreased in recent years due to the development of a means of destroying any Rh-positive fetal cells in an Rh-negative mother's blood supply before they can stimulate the mother's cells to produce her own anti-Rh antibodies. The Rh-positive cells are killed by injecting RhoGAM, a serum containing antibodies against the Rh antigens, at about the seventh month of pregnancy and shortly after delivery if the baby is Rh-positive. Rh antigens are thus prevented from being "set" in the memory of the mother's immune system. The injected antibodies disappear after a few months. Therefore, no antibodies linger to affect the fetus in a subsequent pregnancy.

Blood Donation

We have seen that blood is indeed a life-saving fluid, and someone in the United States or Canada needs donated blood every two seconds. If you are a healthy person at least 17 years old (16 years in some states), weigh at least 110 lbs, and are willing to spend 10 to 20 minutes, you may be eligible to give the gift of life. When you donate you may feel a slight twinge as the needle is inserted, but the procedure is generally painless. Each donation is a pint of blood. The donated plasma is replaced within hours, and the cells are replaced within weeks. The donated blood can be separated into its components: red blood cells to increase the oxygen-carrying capacity of the recipient's blood, platelets to help the recipient's blood clot, and plasma to help the recipient control bleeding.

BLOOD CLOTTING

When a blood vessel is cut, several responses are triggered to stop the bleeding. To understand the process of clotting, imagine how you might respond if the garden hose you are using springs a leak. Your initial response might be to squeeze the hose in hopes of stopping the water flow. Likewise, the body's immediate response to blood vessel injury is for the vessel to constrict (squeeze shut).

The next response is to plug the hole (Figure 3b(i).9). Your thumb might do the job on your garden hose; in an injured blood vessel, platelets form a plug that seals the leak. The *platelet plug* is formed when platelets cling to cables of collagen, a protein fiber on the torn blood vessel surface. When the platelets attach to collagen, they swell, form many cellular extensions, and stick together. Platelets also produce a chemical that attracts other platelets to the wound and makes them stick together even more. Aspirin prevents the formation of this chemical and, therefore, inhibits clot formation. For this reason, a daily dose of aspirin is sometimes prescribed to prevent the formation of blood clots that could block blood vessels nourishing heart tissue and thus cause the death of heart cells (a heart attack). It is also why aspirin can cause excessive bleeding.

The next stage in stopping blood loss through a damaged blood vessel is the formation of the clot itself. There are more than 30 steps in the process of clot formation, but here we will describe only the key events. Clot formation begins when clotting factors are released from injured tissue and from platelets. At the site of the wound, the clotting factors convert an inactive blood protein to **prothrombin activator**[3], which then converts **prothrombin,** a plasma protein produced by the liver, to an active form, **thrombin.** Thrombin then causes a remarkable change in another plasma protein produced by the liver, **fibrinogen.** The altered fibrinogen forms long strands of **fibrin,** a protein that makes a web that traps blood cells and forms a clot. The clot is a barrier that prevents additional blood loss through the wound in the vessel.

If even one of the many factors needed for clotting is lacking, the process can be slowed or completely blocked. Vitamin K is needed for the liver to synthesize prothrombin and three other clotting factors. Thus, without vitamin K, clotting does not occur. We have two sources of vitamin K. One is our diet. Vitamin K is found in leafy green vegetables, tomatoes, and vegetable oils. The second source is bacteria living in our intestines and producing vitamin K, some of which we

stop and THINK

Thromboplastin, a chemical important in initiating clot formation, is released from both damaged tissue and activated platelets. How does this fact explain why a scrape, which causes a great deal of tissue damage, generally stops bleeding more quickly than a clean cut, such as a paper cut or one that might occur with a razor blade?

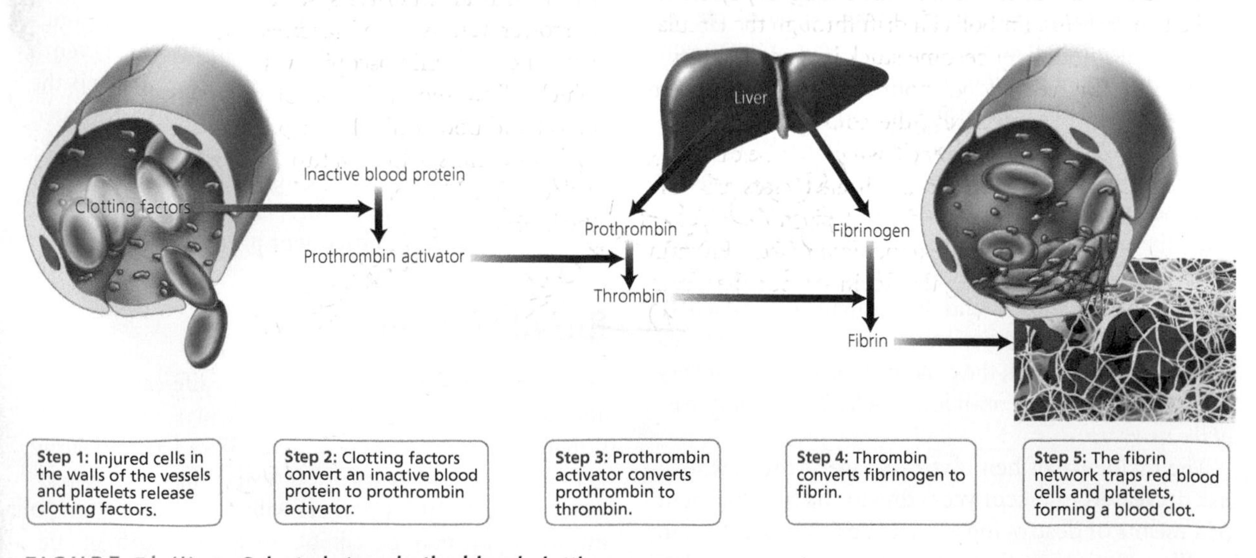

Clotting factors
Inactive blood protein
Prothrombin activator
Liver
Prothrombin
Thrombin
Fibrinogen
Fibrin
Step 1: Injured cells in the walls of the vessels and platelets release clotting factors.
Step 2: Clotting factors convert an inactive blood protein to prothrombin activator.
Step 3: Prothrombin activator converts prothrombin to thrombin.
Step 4: Thrombin converts fibrinogen to fibrin.
Step 5: The fibrin network traps red blood cells and platelets, forming a blood clot.

FIGURE 3b(i).9 **Selected steps in the blood-clotting process**

[3]Prothrombin activator is an enzyme called prothrombinase.

absorb for our own use. Vitamin K is used rapidly by body tissues, so both sources are needed for proper blood clotting. Antibiotic treatment for serious bacterial infections can kill gastrointestinal bacteria and lead to a vitamin K deficiency in as few as 2 days.

Hemophilia is an inherited condition in which the affected person bleeds excessively owing to a fault in one of the genes involved in producing clotting factors. As noted earlier, there are many steps in the clotting process, and so there are many clotting factors. Although a loss of any of the clotting factors could cause hemophilia, the two most common types of hemophilia are caused by insufficient amounts of clotting factors VIII or IX. Because of the way hemophilia is inherited, the condition usually occurs in males. Symptoms appear when the affected child first becomes physically active. Crawling, for instance, causes bruises on the elbows and knees, and cuts tend to bleed longer than is normal. Excessive internal bleeding can damage nerves or, when it occurs in joints, permanently cripple the hemophiliac.

Treatment for hemophilia involves restoring the missing clotting factor. Bleeding episodes can be controlled with repeated transfusions of fresh plasma or with injections of concentrated clotting factor. Concentrated clotting factor is made by combining the plasma donations of many people. In fact, each injection requires 2000 to 5000 individual donations. Fortunately, two of the clotting factors (factors VIII and IX) are now being manufactured using recombinant DNA technology.

The failure of blood to clot can shorten the life of a person with hemophilia. But in people without hemophilia, the formation of unnecessary blood clots can have much more immediate health consequences because clots can disrupt blood flow. A blood clot lodged in an unbroken blood vessel is called a *thrombus.* A blood clot that drifts through the circulatory system is called an *embolus.* Emboli can drift through the circulatory system until they become stuck in a narrow vessel. When the tiny vessels that nourish the heart or brain become clogged with a clot, the consequences can be severe—a stroke or heart attack, which can be disabling or even fatal. After a wound has healed, clots are normally dissolved by an enzyme called **plasmin,** which is formed from an inactive protein, *plasminogen.* Plasmin dissolves clots by digesting the fibrin strands that form the framework of the clot.

stop and THINK

Heparin is a drug that inactivates thrombin. It is sometimes administered to patients for the purpose of inhibiting the clotting response. How would heparin act to achieve these ends?

CARDIOVASCULAR SYSTEM

The **cardiovascular system** consists of the **heart**—a muscular pump that contracts rhythmically and provides the force that moves the blood—and the blood vessels—a system of tubules through which blood flows (Figure 3b(i).10). The blood delivers a continuous supply of oxygen and nutrients to the cells of the body and carries away metabolic waste products so that they cannot poison the cells.

Why is the cardiovascular system so critical to survival? It is the body's transportation network, similar in some ways to the highways within a country. Our bodies are too large and complex for diffusion alone to distribute materials efficiently. The cardiovascular system provides a means for distributing vital chemicals from one part of the body to another quickly enough to sustain life. The cardiovascular system is more than just a passive system of pipelines, however. The heart rate and the diameter of certain blood vessels are continually being adjusted in prompt response to the body's changing needs.

BLOOD VESSELS

Once every minute, or about 1440 times each day, the blood moves through a life-sustaining circuit. The circuit of blood vessels is extensive. Indeed, if all the vessels in an average adult's body were placed end to end, they would stretch about 100,000 km (60,000 mi), long enough to circle the Earth's equator more than twice!

The blood vessels do not form a single long tube. Instead, they are arranged in branching networks. With each circuit through the body, blood is carried away from the heart in *arteries,* which branch to give rise to narrower vessels called *arterioles.* Arterioles lead into networks of microscopic vessels called *capillaries,* which allow the exchange of materials between the blood and body cells. The capillaries eventually merge to form *venules,* which in turn join to form larger tubes called *veins.* The venules and veins return the blood to the heart.

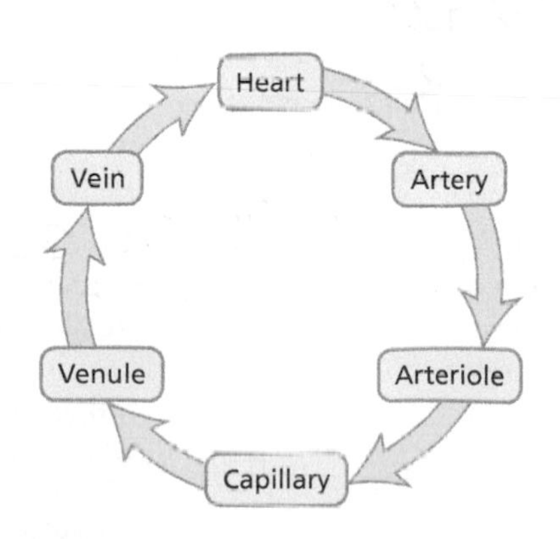

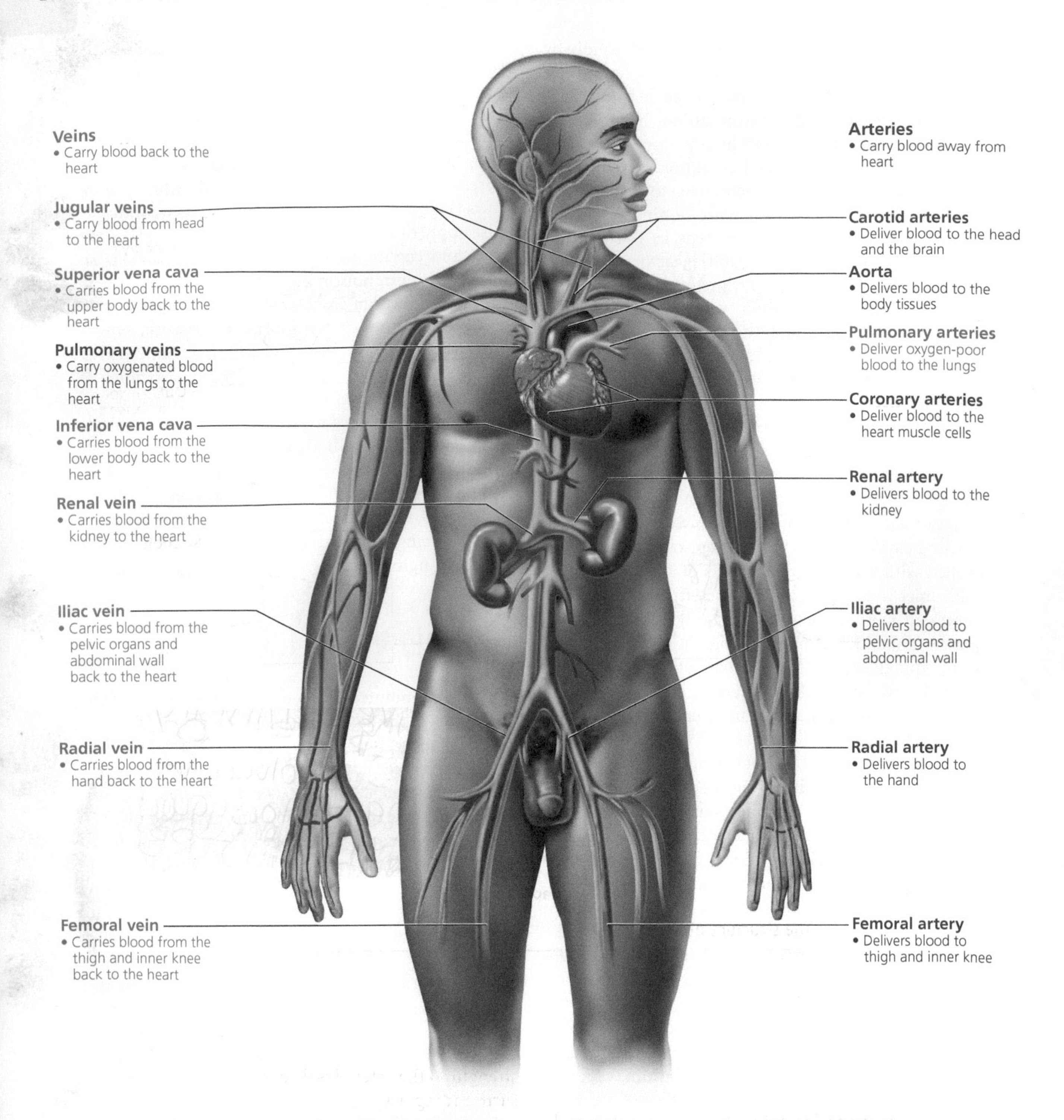
Veins
• Carry blood back to the heart
Jugular veins
• Carry blood from head to the heart
Superior vena cava
• Carries blood from the upper body back to the heart
Pulmonary veins
• Carry oxygenated blood from the lungs to the heart
Inferior vena cava
• Carries blood from the lower body back to the heart
Renal vein
• Carries blood from the kidney to the heart
Iliac vein
• Carries blood from the pelvic organs and abdominal wall back to the heart
Radial vein
• Carries blood from the hand back to the heart
Femoral vein
• Carries blood from the thigh and inner knee back to the heart
Arteries
• Carry blood away from heart
Carotid arteries
• Deliver blood to the head and the brain
Aorta
• Delivers blood to the body tissues
Pulmonary arteries
• Deliver oxygen-poor blood to the lungs
Coronary arteries
• Deliver blood to the heart muscle cells
Renal artery
• Delivers blood to the kidney
Iliac artery
• Delivers blood to pelvic organs and abdominal wall
Radial artery
• Delivers blood to the hand
Femoral artery
• Delivers blood to thigh and inner knee

FIGURE 3b(i).10 **A diagrammatic view of the cardiovascular system (heart and blood vessels). Throughout this chapter, red indicates blood that is high in oxygen. Blue indicates blood that is low in oxygen**

All blood vessels share some common features, but each type also has its own traits and is marvelously adapted for its specific function (Figure 3b(i).11). The hollow interior of a blood vessel, through which the blood flows, is called the *lumen*. The inner lining that comes into contact with the blood flowing through the lumen is composed of simple squamous epithelium (flattened, tight-fitting cells). This lining, called the endothelium, provides a smooth surface that minimizes friction so that the blood flows easily. The lumen and endothelium are characteristic of all blood vessels.

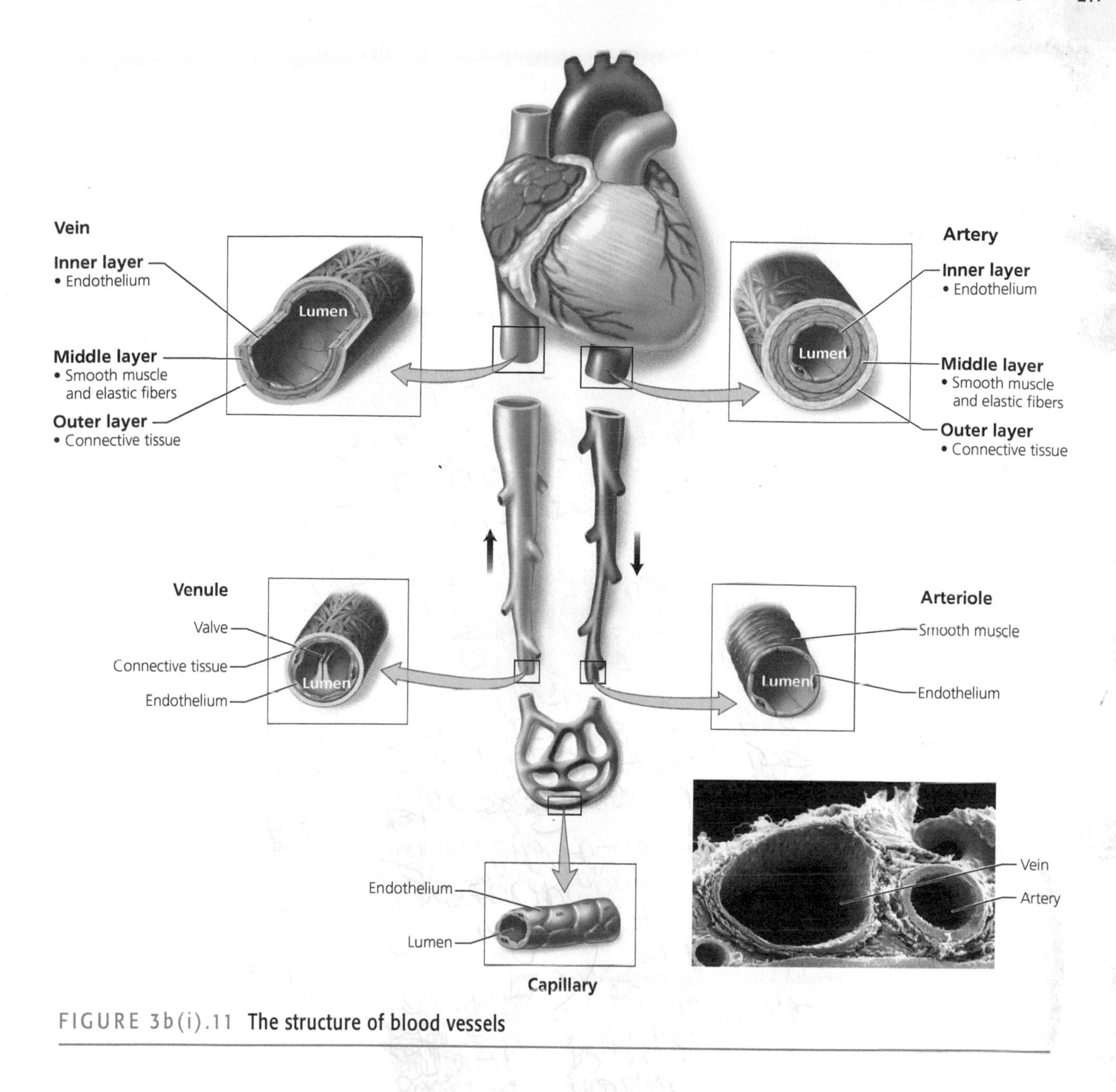

FIGURE 3b(i).11 The structure of blood vessels

Arteries

Arteries are muscular tubes that transport blood *away* from the heart, delivering it rapidly to the body tissues. As noted, the innermost layer of an arterial wall is the endothelium. Immediately outside the endothelium is a middle layer that contains elastic fibers and circular layers of smooth muscle (Figure 3b(i).12). The elastic fibers allow an artery to stretch and then return to its original shape. The smooth muscle enables the artery to contract. The outer layer of an arterial wall is a sheath of connective tissue that contains elastic fibers and collagen. This layer adds strength to the arterial wall and anchors the artery to surrounding tissue.

The elastic fibers in the middle layer of an artery have two important functions: (1) They help the artery tolerate the pressure shock caused by blood surging into it when the heart contracts; and (2) they help maintain a relatively even pressure within the artery, despite large changes in the volume of blood passing through it. Consider, for instance, what happens when the heart contracts and sends blood into the **aorta,** the body's main artery. Each beat of the heart causes 70 ml (about one-fourth cup) of blood to pound against the wall of the aorta like a tidal wave. A rigid pipe could not withstand the repeated pressure surges, but the elastic walls of the artery stretch with each wave of blood and return to their original size when the surge has moved past; this results in a continuous stream of blood rather than intermittent waves.

The alternate expansion and recoil of arteries create a pressure wave, called a **pulse,** that moves along the arteries with each heartbeat. Thus, the pulse rate is the same as the heart rate. You can feel the pulse by slightly compressing with your fingers any artery that lies near the body's surface, such as the one at the wrist or the one under the angle of the jaw.

As previously mentioned, the middle layer of an artery wall also contains smooth muscle that enables the artery to contract. When this circular muscle contracts and the diameter of the lumen becomes narrower, a process called *vasoconstriction,* blood flow through the artery is reduced. On the other hand, when the smooth muscle relaxes and the arterial lumen increases in diameter, a process called *vasodilation,* blood flow through the artery increases. The smooth muscle is best developed in small- to medium-sized arteries. These arteries serve to regulate the distribution of blood, adjusting flow to suit the needs of the body.

We see the importance of the strength of an artery wall when it becomes weakened, as might occur due to disease, inflammation, injury, or a birth defect. When the arterial wall becomes weakened, the pressure of the blood flowing through the weakened area may cause the wall to swell outward like a balloon, forming an *aneurysm.* Most aneurysms do not cause symptoms, but the condition can be threatening just the same. The primary risk is that the aneurysm will burst, causing blood loss. The tissues serviced by that vessel will then be deprived of oxygen and nutrients, a situation that can be fatal. Even if the aneurysm does not rupture, it can cause the formation of life-threatening blood clots. A clot can break free from the site of formation and float through the circulatory system until it lodges in a small vessel, where it can block blood flow and cause tissue death beyond that point. In some cases, an aneurysm can be repaired surgically. The risk of blood clots and aneurysms is exacerbated by the nicotine in tobacco products. (See the Health Issue essay, *Cardiovascular Disease and Cigarette Smoking.*)

The smallest arteries, called **arterioles,** are barely visible to the unaided eye. Their walls have the same three layers found in arteries; but the middle layer is primarily smooth muscle with only a few elastic fibers, and the outer layer is much thinner.

Arterioles have two extremely important regulatory roles. First, they are the prime controllers of blood pressure, which is the pressure of blood against the vessel walls. When the muscle in arteriole walls contracts, blood pressure increases. The greater the number of arterioles contracted, the higher the blood pressure. Relaxation of arteriole walls lowers blood pressure. Second, they serve as gatekeepers to the capillary networks. A capillary network can be open or closed, depending on whether the smooth muscle in the walls of the arteriole leading to it allows blood through. In this way, arterioles can regulate the amount of blood sent to cells based on those cell's immediate needs. Arterioles are constantly responding to input from hormones, the nervous system, and local conditions, modifying blood pressure and flow to meet the body's changing needs.

Capillaries

Capillaries are microscopic blood vessels that connect arterioles and venules. The capillaries are well suited to their primary function: the exchange of materials between the blood and the body cells (Figure 3b(i).12). Capillary walls are only one cell layer thick, and so substances move easily between the blood and the fluid surrounding the cells outside the capillary. The plasma membrane of the capillary's endothelial cells is an effective and selective barrier that determines which substances can cross. Some substances that cross the capillary walls do not pass *through* the endothelial cells. Instead, these substances filter through small slits *between* adjacent endothelial cells. The slits between the cells are just large enough for some fluids and small dissolved molecules to pass through.

The design of the capillary networks allows blood flow through capillaries to be adjusted to deliver the necessary amount of oxygen and nutrients to meet the needs of particular regions of the body. The network of capillaries servicing a particular area is called a **capillary bed** (Figure 3b(i).13). The number of capillaries in a bed generally ranges from 10 to 100, depending on the type of tissue. A ring of smooth muscle called a **precapillary sphincter** surrounds the capillary where it branches off the arteriole and regulates blood flow into it.

The precapillary sphincters act as valves that open and close the capillary beds. Contraction of the precapillary sphincter squeezes the opening to the capillary shut. For instance, while you are resting on the beach after finishing a picnic lunch, the capillary beds servicing the digestive organs will be open, and nutrients from the food will be absorbed. If you dive into the water and start swimming, the capillary beds of the digestive organs will close down, and those in the skeletal muscles will open.

Collectively, the capillaries provide a tremendous surface area for the rapid exchange of materials between body and blood. Capillary beds bring capil-

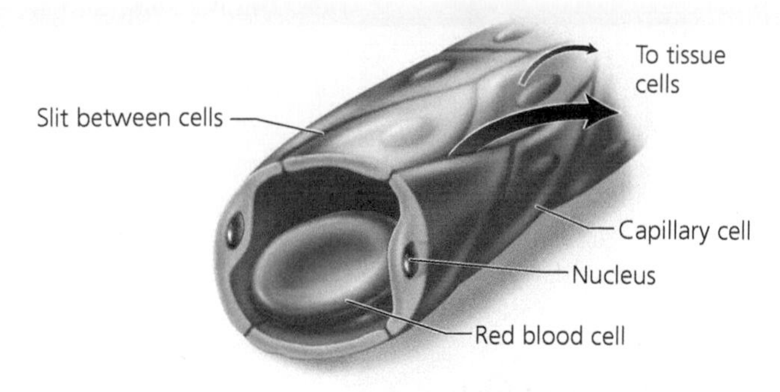

(a) Substances are exchanged between the blood and tissue fluid across the plasma membrane of the capillary or through slits between capillary cells.

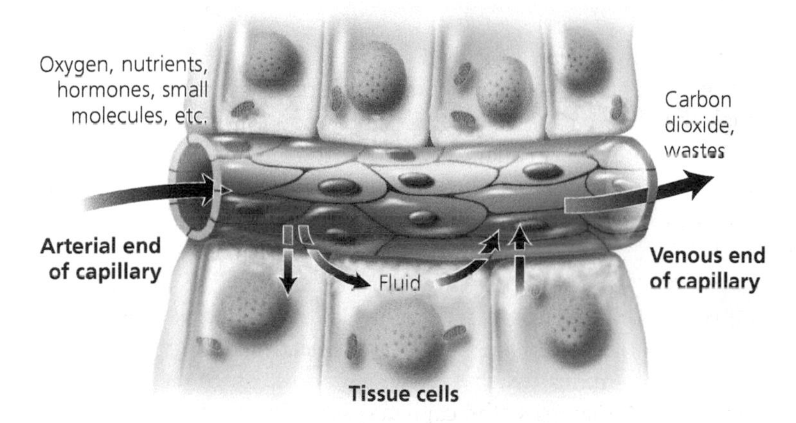

(b) At the arterial end of a capillary, blood pressure forces fluid out of the capillary to the fluid surrounding tissue cells. At the venous end, fluid is drawn back into the capillary by osmotic pressure.

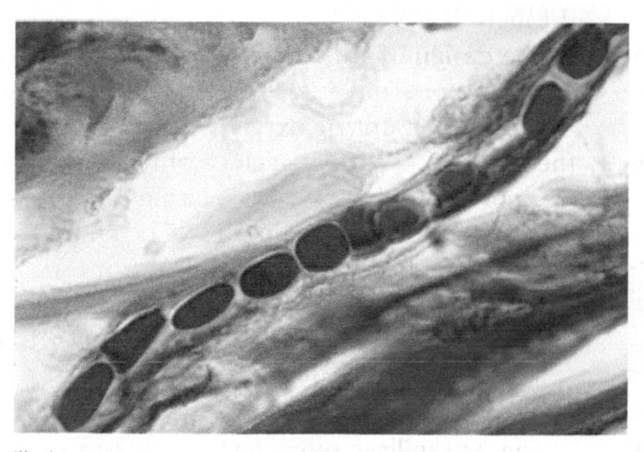

(c) Capillaries are so narrow that red blood cells must travel through them in single file.

FIGURE 3b(i).12 **Capillaries are the sites where materials are exchanged between the blood and the body cells**

laries very close to nearly every cell. Your fingernails provide windows that allow you to appreciate the efficiency with which capillary networks reach all parts of the body. You may have noticed that the tissue beneath a fingernail normally has a pink tinge. The color results from blood flowing through numerous capillaries there. Gentle pressure on the nail causes the tissue to turn white as the blood is pushed from those capillaries.

A capillary is so narrow that red blood cells must squeeze through single file. Despite their size, there are so many capillaries that their *combined* cross-sectional area is enormous, much greater than that of the arteries or veins. Because of the large cross-sectional area of the capillaries, the blood flows much more slowly through them than through the arteries or veins. The slower rate of flow in the capillaries provides more time for the exchange of materials (Figure 3b(i).14).

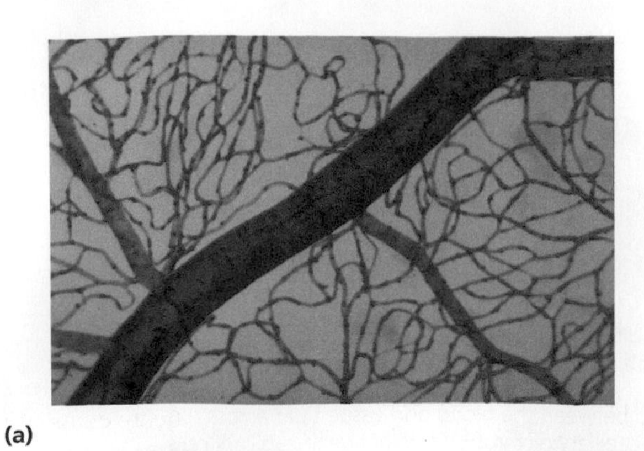

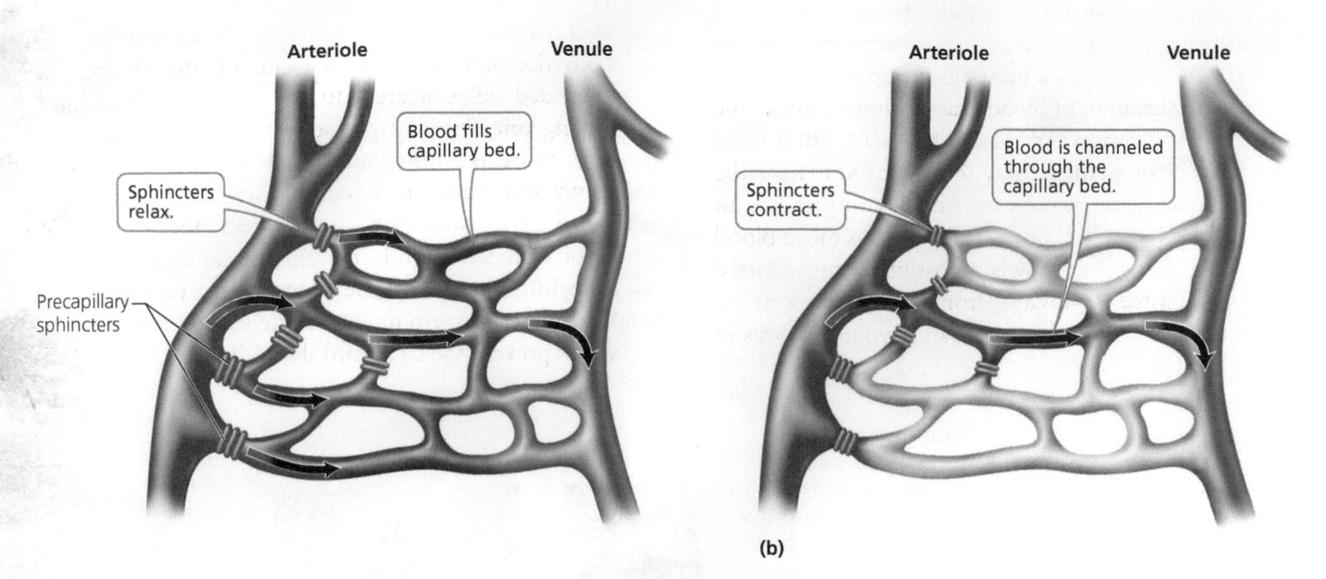

FIGURE 3b(i).13 (a) A capillary bed is a network of capillaries. (b) The entrance to each capillary (the arterial side) is guarded by a ring of muscle called a precapillary sphincter. Blood flow through a capillary bed is regulated according to the body's metabolic needs.

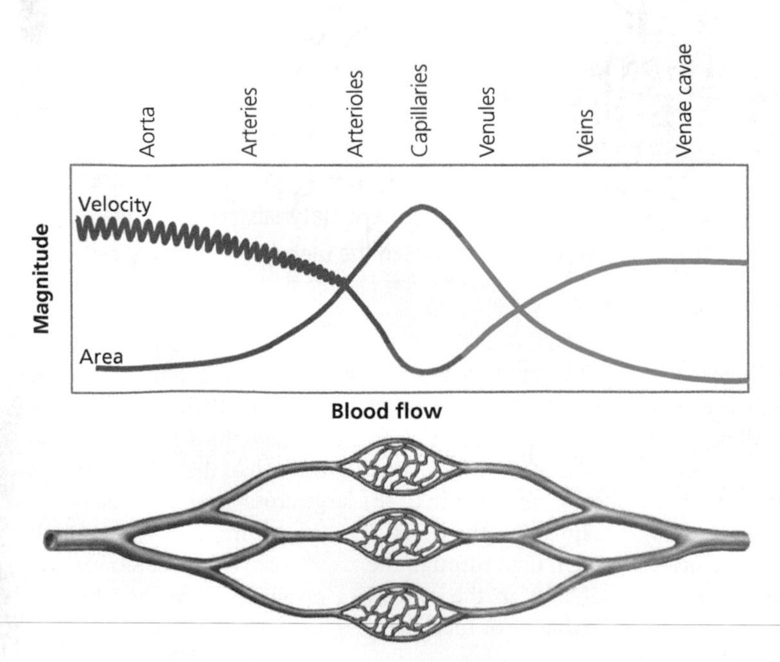

FIGURE 3b(i).14 The capillaries are so numerous that their total cross-sectional area is much greater than that of arteries or veins. Thus, blood pressure drops and blood flows more slowly as it passes through a capillary bed. The slower rate of flow allows time for the exchange of materials between the blood and the tissues.

Veins

After the capillary bed, capillaries merge to form the smallest kind of vein, a **venule.** Venules then join to form larger veins. **Veins** are blood vessels that return the blood to the heart.

Although veins share some structural features with arteries, there are also some important differences. The walls of veins have the same three layers found in arterial walls, but the walls of veins are thinner and the lumens of veins are larger than those of arteries of equal size (see Figure 3b(i).11). The thin walls and large lumens allow veins to hold a large volume of blood. Indeed, veins serve as blood reservoirs, holding up to 65% of the body's total blood supply.

The same amount of blood that is pumped out of the heart must be conducted back to the heart, but it must be moved through the veins without assistance from the high pressure generated by the heart's contractions. In the head and neck, of course, gravity helps move blood toward the heart. But how is it possible to move blood against the force of gravity—from the foot back to the heart, for instance (unless, by chance, your foot was in your mouth)?

Three mechanisms move blood from lower parts of the body toward the heart:

1. **Valves in veins prevent backflow of blood.** Veins often contain valves that act as one-way turnstiles, allowing blood to move toward the heart but preventing it from flowing backward. These valves are pockets of connective tissue projecting from the lining of the vein, as shown in Figure 3b(i).15a.

   A simple experiment can demonstrate the effectiveness of venous valves. Allow your hand to hang by your side until the veins on the back of your hand become distended. Place two fingertips from the other hand at the end of one of the distended veins nearest to the knuckles. Then, leaving one fingertip pressed on the end of the vein, move the other toward the wrist, pressing firmly and squeezing the blood from the vein. Lift the fingertip near the knuckle and notice that blood immediately fills the vein. Repeat the procedure, but this time lift the fingertip near the wrist. You will see the vein remains flattened, because the valves prevent the backward flow of blood.

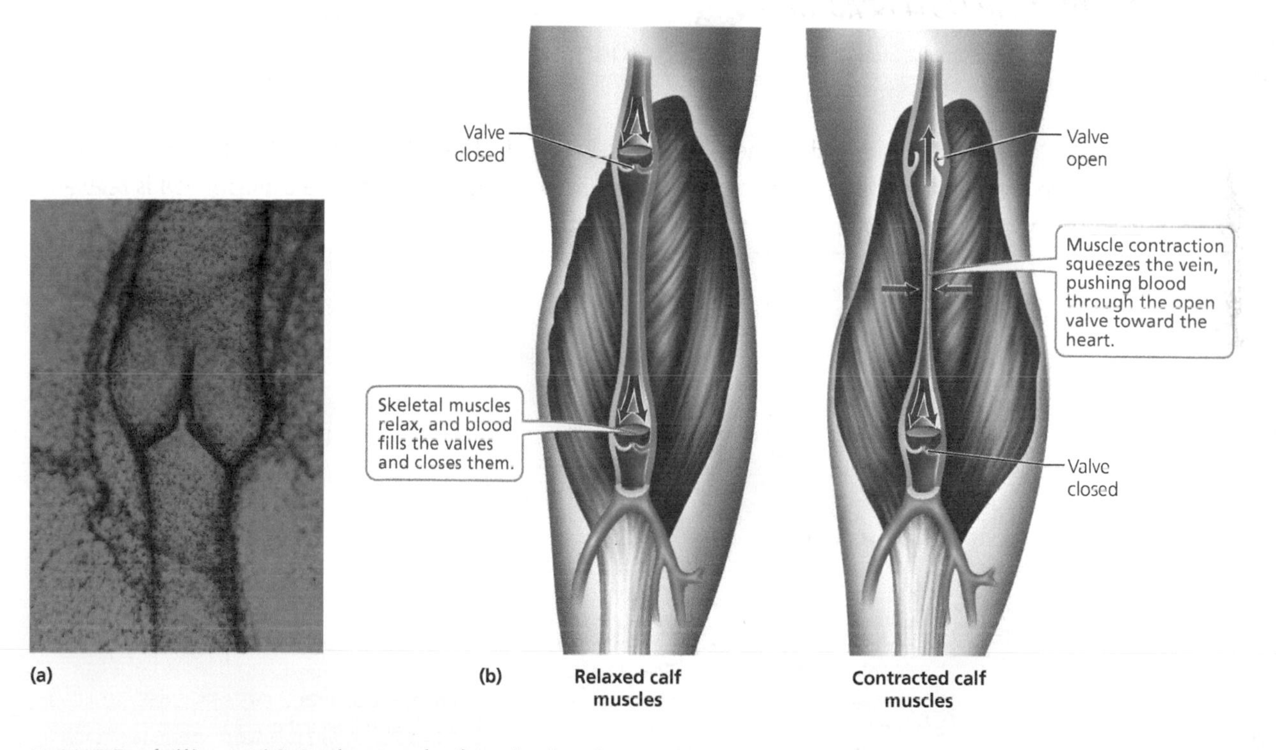
Valve closed
Skeletal muscles relax, and blood fills the valves and closes them.
Valve open
Muscle contraction squeezes the vein, pushing blood through the open valve toward the heart.
Valve closed
(a)
(b)
Relaxed calf muscles
Contracted calf muscles

FIGURE 3b(i).15 (a) A micrograph of a vein showing a valve. (b) Pocketlike valves on the inner surface of veins assist the return of blood to the heart against gravity by preventing backflow.

Health Issue

Cardiovascular Disease and Cigarette Smoking

When we think about the hazards of tobacco smoke, lung cancer generally leaps to mind. But the increased risk of cardiovascular (heart and blood vessel) disease is even more significant. Each year, cardiovascular disease kills many more people than does lung cancer, and smokers have a twofold to threefold increase in the risk of heart disease (Figure **3b(i).A**). The American Heart Association estimates that about 25% of all fatal heart attacks are caused by cigarette smoke. This translates to roughly 200,000 heart attacks a year in the United States that could have been prevented by not smoking.

Nicotine and carbon monoxide in cigarette smoke stress the heart and blood vessels in many ways. Nicotine makes the heart beat faster and constricts blood vessels, raising blood pressure. In addition, nicotine makes platelets, the cell fragments responsible for blood clotting, stick together, increasing the risk of forming abnormal blood clots. The resulting clots may break loose from the site where they form and travel through the bloodstream until they lodge in a small vessel and block the blood flow. These blockages may result in a heart attack or stroke.

The amount of carbon monoxide in cigarette smoke is 1600 ppm (parts per million), which greatly exceeds the 10 ppm considered dangerous in industry. Furthermore, carbon monoxide from smoking a cigarette lingers in the bloodstream for up to 6 hours. You may recall that carbon monoxide is a poison that prevents red blood cells from transporting oxygen. In fact, carbon monoxide from smoking a cigarette lowers the oxygen-carrying capacity of the blood by about 12%, reducing oxygen delivery to every part of the body, including the brain and heart. Thus, the heart must work harder to deliver oxygen to the cells. The diminished oxygen supply to the brain can impair judgment, vision, and attentiveness to sounds. For these reasons, smoking can be hazardous for drivers.

A less immediate but no less important way that smoking leads to cardiovascular disease is by increasing atherosclerosis, a condition in which lipid deposits, primarily composed of cholesterol, form in the walls of blood vessels and restrict the flow of blood. Smoking influences atherosclerosis in two ways. One is by decreasing the levels of protective cholesterol-transport particles, called HDLs, that carry cholesterol to the liver, perhaps even removing cholesterol from cells, so that it can be eliminated from the body. With fewer HDLs, more cholesterol begins to clog the arteries. A second way that smoking promotes cholesterol deposits is by raising blood pressure. The elevated blood pressure causes rapid, turbulent blood flow that damages the walls of the arteries, making them more susceptible to cholesterol deposit. The cholesterol deposits cause inflammation, which leads to atherosclerosis. The narrowing of blood vessels caused by atherosclerosis leads to starvation of tissue downstream and an increase in blood pressure. When atherosclerotic deposits form in the arteries that supply blood to the heart, as they often do, the blood supply to the heart may be reduced or shut down completely, causing heart cells to die.

The cardiovascular system benefits from quitting smoking within five years. In regard to heart disease, 61% of the full benefit of quitting smoking is gained within 5 years. And, 42% of the full benefit of reduced risk of stroke is gained within 5 years.

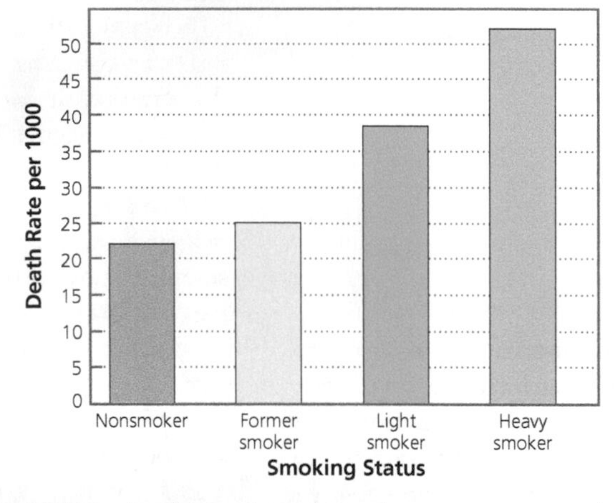

FIGURE 3b(i).A Death rates due to heart disease among nonsmokers and smokers. Notice that the death rate from heart disease increases with the number of cigarettes smoked per day. People who smoke over a pack per day (heavy smokers) have more than twice the risk of death due to heart disease than do people who have never smoked. In any case, a smoker who successfully quits is much less likely to die of heart disease than if the smoking habit continues.

2. **Contraction of skeletal muscle squeezes veins.** Virtually every time a skeletal muscle contracts, it squeezes nearby veins. This pressure pushes blood past the valves toward the heart. The mechanism propelling the blood is similar to the one that causes toothpaste to squirt out of the uncapped end of the tube regardless of where the tube is squeezed; valves in veins ensure that blood flows in only one direction. When skeletal muscles relax, any blood that moves backward fills the valves. As the valves fill with blood, they extend further into the lumen of the vein, closing the vein and preventing the flow of blood from reversing direction (Figure 3b(i).15b). Thus, the skeletal muscles are always squeezing the veins and driving blood toward the heart.
3. **Breathing causes pressure changes that move blood toward the heart.** The thoracic (chest) cavity increases in size when we inhale. The expansion reduces pressure within the thoracic cavity and at the same time increases pressure in the abdominal cavity. Blood naturally moves toward regions of lower pressure. Thus, the reduced pressure in the thoracic cavity that comes with each breath pulls blood back toward the heart. In addition, the increased pressure in the abdominal cavity squeezes veins, also forcing blood back toward the heart.

stop and THINK

If an artery is cut, blood is lost in rapid spurts. In contrast, blood loss through a cut vein has an even flow. What accounts for these differences?

HEART

The heart is about the size of a fist, but it is an incredible muscular pump that generates the force needed to circulate blood. It beats about 72 times a minute, every hour of every day—although this rate varies with age, physical fitness, and current physical exertion. To appreciate the work done by the heart, alternately clench and relax a fist 70 times a minute. How many minutes does it take before the muscles of your hand are too tired to continue? In contrast, the healthy heart does not fatigue. It beats more than 100,000 times each day, which adds up to about 2 billion beats over a lifetime. The volume of blood pumped by the heart is equally remarkable. It pumps slightly less than 5 liters (10 pt) of blood a minute through its chambers, which adds up to more than 9400 liters (2500 gal) per day.

The heart has three layers, each one contributing to the heart's ability to function as a pump. The wall of the heart, called the **myocardium,** is mostly cardiac muscle tissue. The myocardium's contractions are responsible for the heart's incredible pumping action. The **endocardium** is a thin lining in the cavities of the heart. By reducing friction, the endocardium's smooth surface lessens the resistance to blood flow through the heart. The **pericardium** is a thick, fibrous sac that holds the heart in the center of the chest (thoracic) cavity and slides over the surface of the heart without hampering its movements, even when they are vigorous.

Although the heart appears to be a single structure, it actually has two halves, with the right and left halves functioning as two separate pumps. As we will see shortly, the right side of the heart pumps blood to the lungs, where it picks up oxygen. The left side pumps the blood to the body cells. The two pumps are physically separated by a partition called a **septum.** Each half of the heart consists of two chambers: an upper chamber, called an **atrium** (plural, atria), and a lower chamber, called a **ventricle** (Figure 3b(i).16). The two atria function as receiving chambers for the blood returning to the heart. The two ventricles function as the main pumps of the heart. Contraction of the ventricles forces blood out of the heart under great pressure. When we think about the work of the heart, we are in fact thinking about the work of the ventricles. It should not be surprising, then, that the ventricles are much larger chambers than the atria and have thicker, more muscular walls.

Two pairs of valves ensure that the blood flows in only one direction through the heart. The first pair is the **atrioventricular (AV) valves,** each leading from an atrium to a ventricle, as shown in Figure 3b(i).17. The AV valves are connective tissue flaps, called cusps, anchored to the wall of the ventricle by strings of connective tissue called the *chordae tendineae*—the heartstrings. These strings prevent the AV valves from flapping back into the atria under the pressure developed when the ventricles contract. The AV valve on the right side of the heart has three flaps and is called the *tricuspid valve.* The AV valve on the left side of the heart has two flaps and is called the *bicuspid,* or *mitral, valve.*

Each of the second pair of valves, the **semilunar valves,** is located between a ventricle and its connecting artery—either the aorta or the pulmonary artery. The cusps of the semilunar valves are small pockets of tissue attached to the inner wall of the respective artery. When the pressure in the arteries becomes greater than the pressure in the ventricles, these valves fill with blood in a manner similar to a parachute filling with air. In this way, the semilunar valves prevent the backflow of blood into the ventricles from the aorta or pulmonary artery.

Q *When the ventricles contract, which valves would open and which valves would close?*

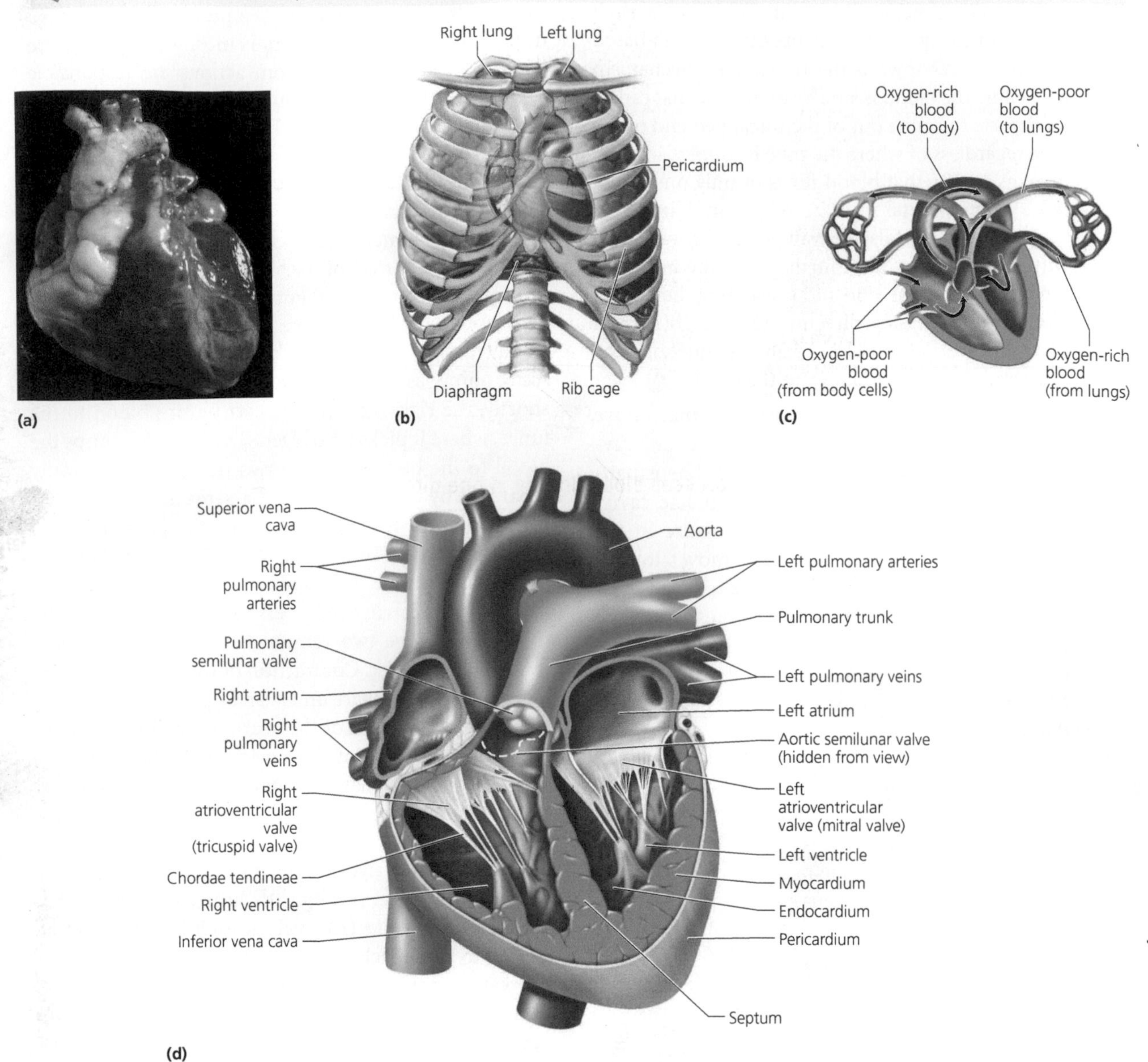

FIGURE 3b(i).16 **(a) The human heart. (b) The heart is located in the thoracic (chest) cavity. (c) Blood flows through the heart from the atria to the ventricles. (d) This diagram of a human heart shows the four chambers, the major vessels connecting to the heart, and the two pairs of heart valves.**

A *The semilunar valves would open and the AV valves would close.*

Two Circuits of Blood Flow

As we mentioned, the left and right sides of the heart function as two separate pumps, each circulating the blood through a different route, as shown in Figure 3b(i).18. Note that in both circuits the blood moves through the arteries, arterioles, capillaries, and venules before returning to the heart via the veins. The right side of the heart pumps blood through the **pulmonary circuit,** which transports blood to and from the lungs. The left side of the heart pumps blood through the **systemic circuit,** which transports blood to and from body tissues. This arrangement prevents oxygenated blood (blood rich in oxygen) from mixing with blood that is low in oxygen.

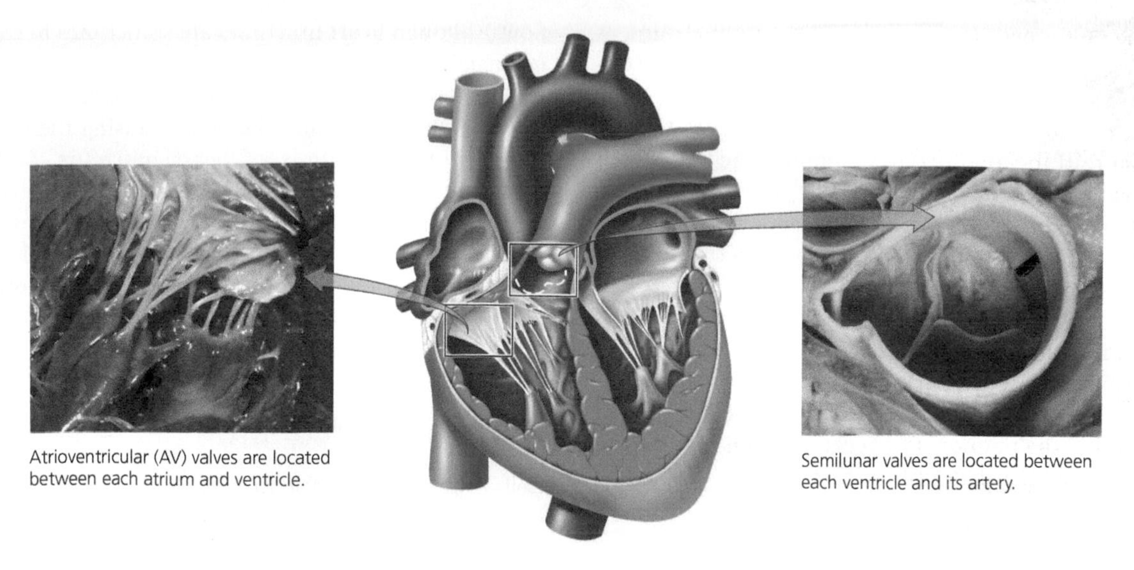

Atrioventricular (AV) valves are located between each atrium and ventricle.
Semilunar valves are located between each ventricle and its artery.

FIGURE 3b(i).17 The valves of the heart keep blood flowing in one direction

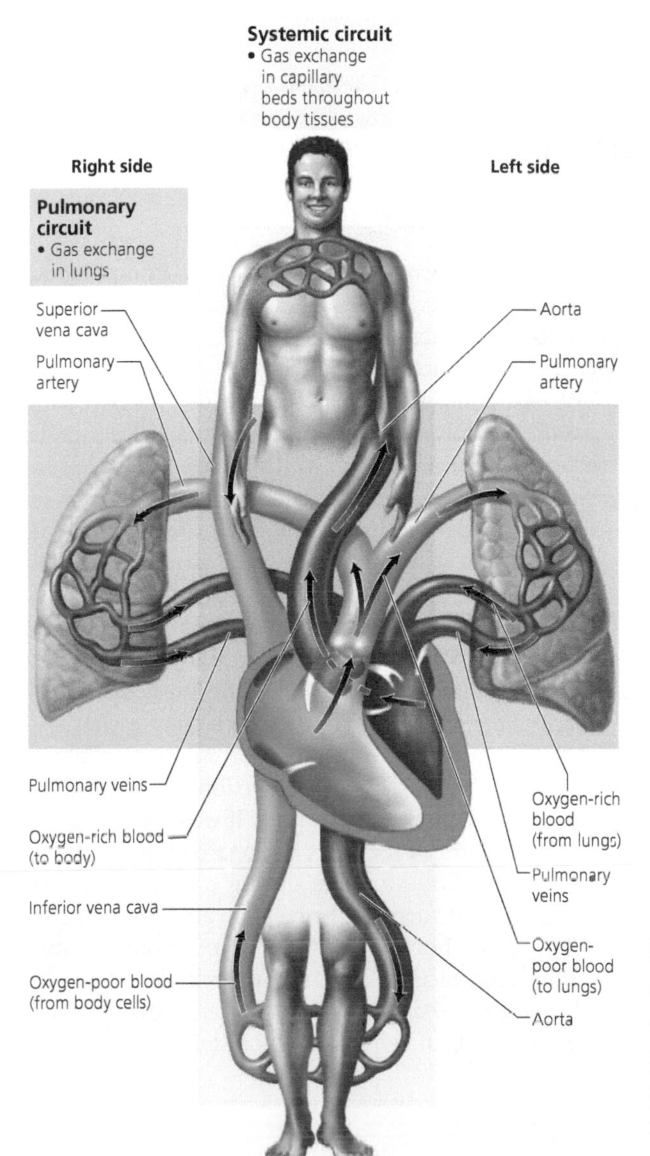

FIGURE 3b(i).18 Circuits of blood flow. The right side of the heart pumps blood through the pulmonary circuit, which carries blood to and from the lungs. The left side of the heart pumps blood through the systemic circuit, which conducts blood to and from the body tissues.

The pulmonary circuit begins in the right atrium, as veins re-turn oxygen-poor blood from the systemic circuit. (You can trace the flow of blood through the heart in the pulmonary and systemic circuits in Figure 3b(i).18 as you read the following description.) The blood then moves from the right atrium to the right ventricle. Contraction of the right ventricle pumps poorly oxygenated blood to the lungs through the pulmonary trunk (main pulmonary artery), which divides to form the left and right *pulmonary arteries.* In the lungs, oxygen diffuses into the blood, and carbon dioxide diffuses out. The now oxygen-rich blood is delivered to the left atrium through four *pulmonary veins,* two from each lung. (Note that the pulmonary circulation is an *exception* to the general rule that arteries carry oxygen-rich blood and veins carry oxygen-poor blood. Exactly the opposite is true of vessels in the pulmonary circulation.) The pathway of blood pumped through the pulmonary circuit by the right side of the heart is

Right atrium ⟶ AV valve (tricuspid) ⟶
Right ventricle ⟶ Pulmonary semilunar valve ⟶
Pulmonary trunk ⟶ Pulmonary arteries ⟶
Lungs ⟶ Pulmonary veins ⟶ Left atrium

The systemic circuit begins when oxygen-rich blood enters the left atrium (see Figure 3b(i).18). Blood then flows to the left ventricle. When the left ventricle contracts, oxygenated blood is pushed through the largest artery in the body, the aorta. The aorta arches over the top of the heart and gives rise to the smaller arteries that eventually feed the capillary beds of the body tissues. The venous system collects the oxygen-depleted blood and eventually culminates in veins that return the blood to the right atrium. These veins are the *superior vena cava,* which delivers blood from regions above the heart, and the *inferior vena cava,* which returns blood from regions below the heart. Thus, the pathway of blood through the systemic circuit pumped by the left side of the heart is

Left atrium ⟶ AV (bicuspid or mitral) valve ⟶
Left ventricle ⟶ Aortic semilunar valve ⟶
Aorta ⟶ Body tissues ⟶ Inferior vena cava or
superior vena cava ⟶ Right atrium

The familiar sounds of the heart, which are often described as "lub-dup," are associated with the closing of the valves. The first heart sound ("lub") is produced by the turbulent blood flow when the AV valves snap shut as the ventricles begin to contract. The higher-pitched second heart sound ("dup") is produced by the turbulent blood flow when closure of the semilunar valves and the beginning of ventricular relaxation occur.

Heart murmurs, which are swooshing heart sounds other than lub-dup, are created by disturbed blood flow. Although heart murmurs are sometimes heard in normal, healthy people, they can also indicate a heart problem. For instance, malfunctioning valves often disturb blood flow through the heart, causing the swishing or gurgling sounds of heart murmurs. Several conditions can cause valves to malfunction. In some cases, thickening of the valves narrows the opening and impedes blood flow. In other cases, the valves do not close properly and, therefore, allow the backflow of blood. In either case, the heart is strained because it must work harder to move the blood.

Coronary Circulation

Cells of the heart muscle themselves obtain little nourishment from blood flowing through the heart's chambers. Instead, an extensive network of vessels, known as the **coronary circulation,** services the tissues of the heart. The first two arteries that branch off the aorta are the **coronary arteries** (Figure 3b(i).19). These arteries give rise to numerous branches, ensuring that the heart receives a rich supply of oxygen and nutrients. After passing through the capillary beds that nourish the heart tissue, blood enters cardiac veins and eventually flows into the right atrium.

Cardiac Cycle

Although the two sides of the heart pump blood through different circuits, they work in tandem. The two atria contract simultaneously, and then the two ventricles contract simultaneously.

We see, then, that a heartbeat is not a single event. Each beat involves contraction, which is called **systole** (*sis*-to-lee) and relaxation, which is called **diastole** (di-*as*-to-lee). All the events associated with the flow of blood through the heart chambers during a single heartbeat are collectively called the **cardiac cycle,** as illustrated in Figure 3b(i).20. First, all chambers relax (diastole) and blood passes through the atria and enters the ventricles. When the ventricles are about 70% filled, the atria contract (atrial systole) and push their contents into the ventricles. The atria then relax (atrial diastole) and the ventricles begin their contraction phase (ventricular systole). Upon completion of this contraction, the whole heart again relaxes. If we were to add the contraction time of the heart during a day and compare it with the relaxation time during a day, the heart's workday might turn out to be equivalent to yours. In 24 hours, the heart spends a total of about 8 hours working (contracting) and 16 hours relaxing. However, unlike your workday, the heart's day is divided into repeating cycles of work and relaxation.

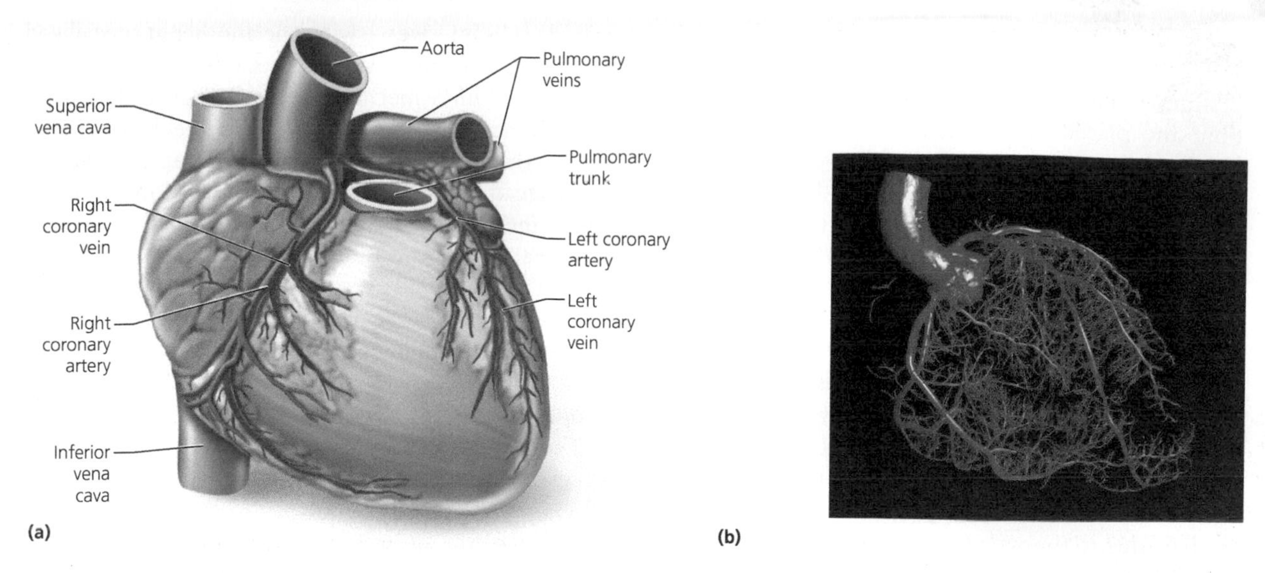

FIGURE 3b(i).19 Coronary circulation. (a) The coronary vessels deliver a rich supply of oxygen and nutrients to the heart muscle cells and remove the metabolic wastes. (b) This cast of the coronary blood vessels reveals the complexity of the coronary circuit.

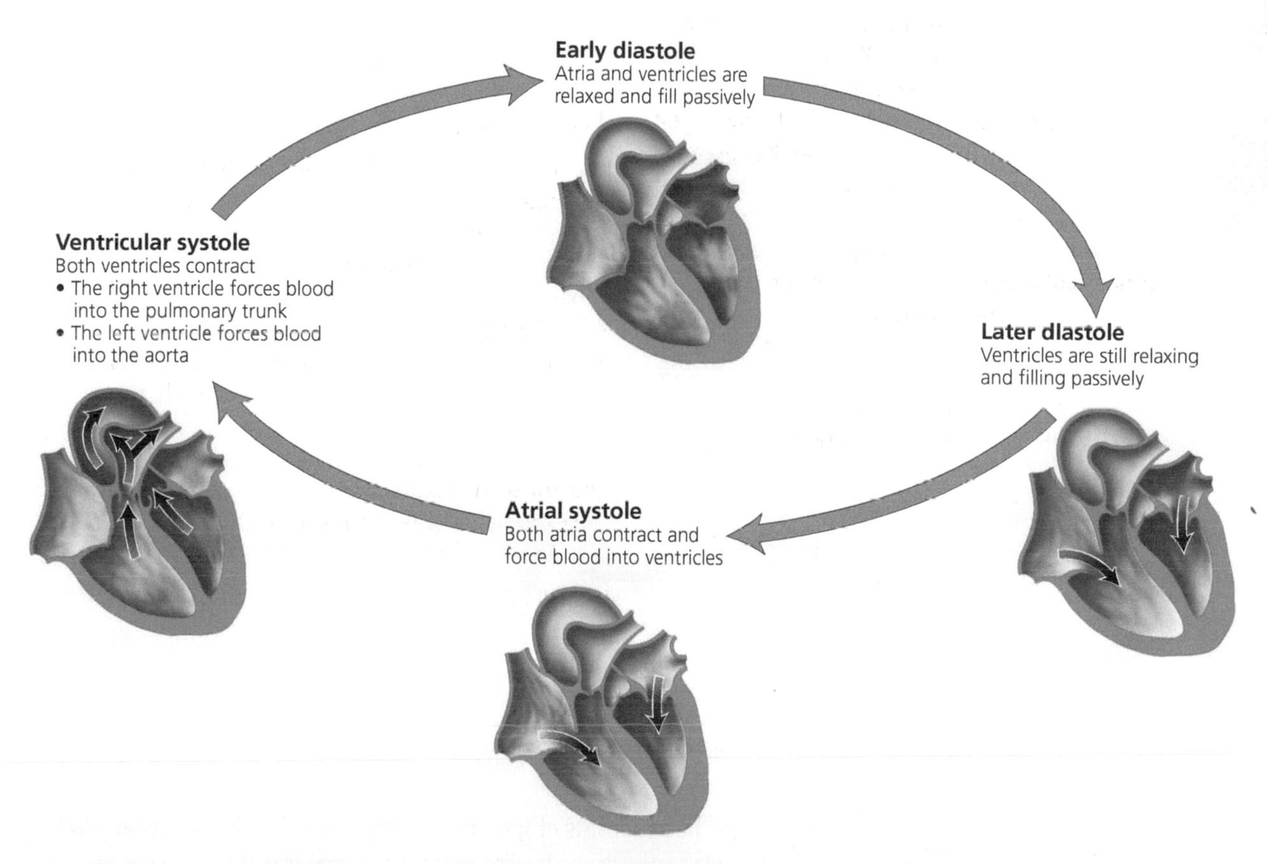

FIGURE 3b(i).20 The cardiac cycle—all of the events associated with the flow of blood through the heart during each heartbeat. The atria contract together and the ventricles contract together. Red indicates blood high in oxygen. Blue indicates blood low in oxygen.

Internal Conduction System

If a human heart is removed, as in a transplant operation, and placed in a dish, it will continue to beat, keeping a lonely and useless rhythm until its tissues die. In fact, if a few cardiac muscle cells are grown in the laboratory, they, too, will beat on their own, each twitch a reminder of the critical role the intact organ plays. Clearly, then, the heart muscle does not require outside stimulation to beat. Instead, the tendency is intrinsic, within the heart muscle itself.

Another remarkable observation has been made of heart muscle cells grown in a laboratory dish. Although isolated heart cells twitch independently of each other, if two cells should touch, they will begin beating in unison. This, too, is an inherent property of the cells, but it is partly due to the type of connections between heart muscle cells. The cell membranes of adjacent cardiac muscle cells interweave with one another at specialized junctions called intercalated disks. Cell junctions in the *intercalated disks* mechanically and electrically couple the connected cells. Adjacent cells are held together so tightly that they do not rip apart during contraction but instead transmit the pull of contraction from one cell to the next. At the same time, the junctions permit electrical communication between adjacent cells, allowing the electrical events responsible for contraction to spread rapidly over the heart by passing from cell to cell. Yet even though heart cells contract automatically, they still need some outside control to contract at the proper rate.

The tempo of the heartbeat is set by a cluster of specialized cardiac muscle cells, called the **sinoatrial (SA) node,** located in the right atrium near the junction of the superior vena cava (Figure 3b(i).21). Because the SA node sends out the impulses that

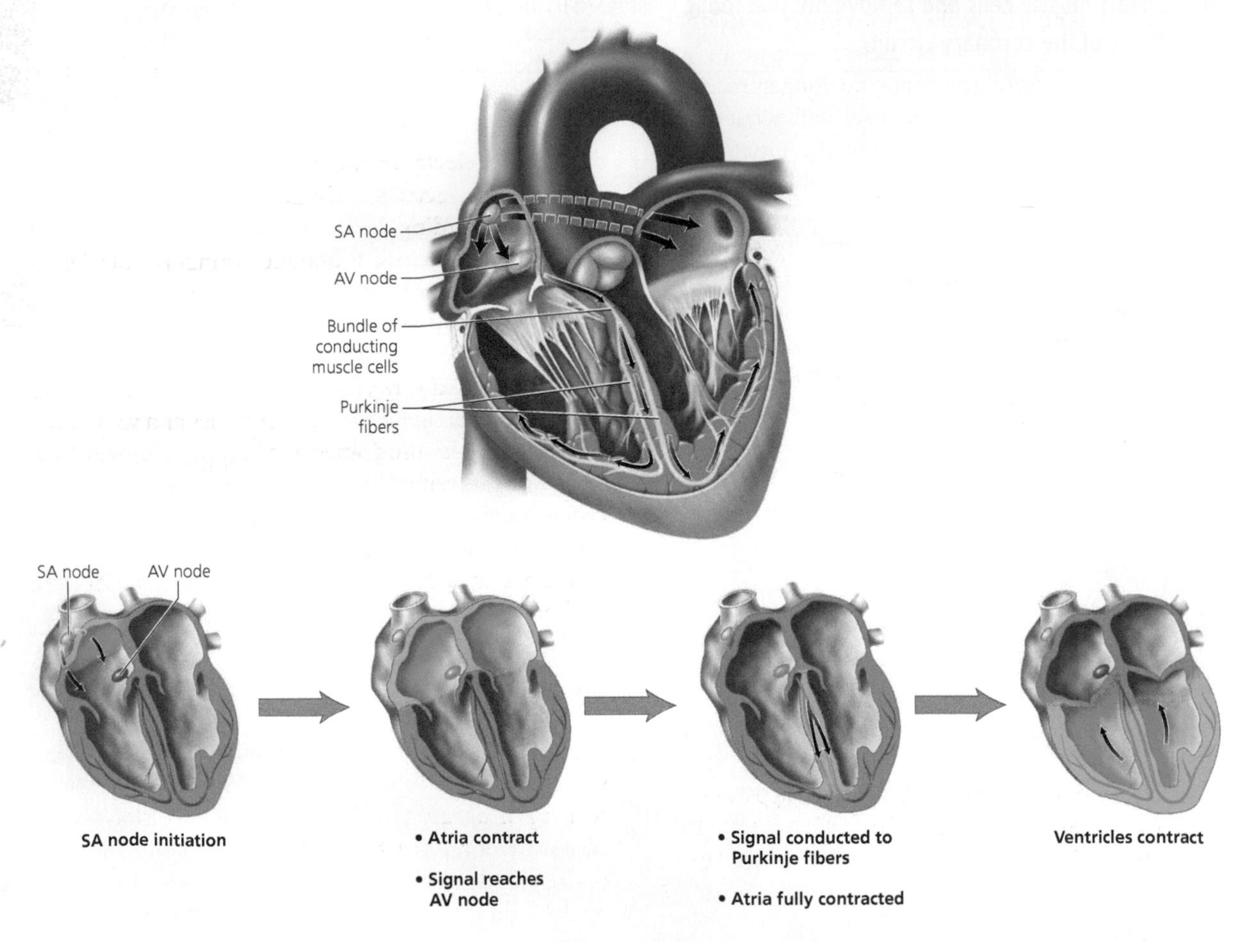

FIGURE 3b(i).21 The conduction system of the heart consists of specialized cardiac muscle cells that speed electrical signals through the heart. The sinoatrial (SA) node serves as the heart's internal pacemaker that determines the heart rate. Electrical signals from the SA node spread through the walls of the atria, causing them to contract. The signals then stimulate the atrioventricular (AV) node, which in turn sends the signals along the AV bundle to its forks and finally to the many Purkinje fibers that penetrate the ventricular walls. The Purkinje fibers distribute the signals to the walls of the ventricles, causing them to contract. Electrical activity is indicated by the color green in the bottom row of drawings.

initiate each heartbeat, it is often referred to as the **pacemaker.** About 70 to 80 times a minute, the SA node sends out an electrical signal that spreads through the muscle cells of the atria, causing them to contract. The signal reaches another cluster of specialized muscle cells called the **atrioventricular (AV) node,** located in the partition between the two atria, and stimulates it. The AV node then relays the stimulus by means of a bundle of specialized muscle fibers, called the *atrioventricular bundle,* that runs along the wall between the ventricles. The bundle forks into right and left branches and then divides into many other specialized cardiac muscle cells, called *Purkinje fibers,* that penetrate the walls of the ventricles. The rapid spread of the impulse through the ventricles ensures that they contract smoothly.

When the heart's conduction system is faulty, cells may begin to contract independently. Such cellular independence can result in rapid, irregular contractions of the ventricles, called *ventricular fibrillation,* which render the ventricles useless as pumps and stop circulation. With the brain no longer receiving the blood it needs to function, death will occur unless an effective heartbeat is restored quickly. A method for stopping ventricular fibrillation is to subject the heart to an electric shock; in many cases, the SA node will once again begin to function normally. Although costly, an implantable defibrillator (a device that electrically shocks the heart) can provide a life-saving "jump start" when needed.

Problems with the conduction system of the heart can sometimes be treated with an artificial pacemaker, a small device implanted just below the skin that monitors the heart rate and rhythm and responds to abnormalities if they occur. For instance, if the heart rate becomes too slow, the pacemaker will send an electrical stimulus to the heart through an electrode.

The pace or rhythm of the heartbeat changes constantly in response to activity or excitement. The autonomic nervous system and certain hormones make the necessary adjustments so that the heart rate suits the body's needs. During times of stress, the sympathetic nervous system increases the rate and force of heart contractions. As part of this response, the adrenal medulla produces the hormone epinephrine, which can prolong the sympathetic nervous system's effects. In contrast, when restful conditions prevail, the parasympathetic nervous system dampens heart activity, in keeping with the body's more modest metabolic needs.

what would you do?

In a heart transplant operation, a person's diseased heart is replaced with a healthy heart from a person who recently died. Not surprisingly, there are thousands more people in need of a heart transplant than there are donor hearts available. An artificial heart, AbioCor, is now approved by the Food and Drug Administration. To qualify as a recipient, a person must have a 70% chance of dying within the next 30 days. (AbioCor II will begin clinical trials in 2008, and patients will not have to be as close to death to qualify as a recipient.) Some recipients of AbioCor have died within a day of receiving the artificial heart. Most lived several months. As of 2008, the longest living recipient survived for 17 months. If you were in need of a transplant, would you volunteer to participate in the testing of an artificial heart? What criteria would you use to decide?

Electrocardiogram

The electrical events that spread through the heart with each heartbeat actually travel throughout the body, because body fluids are good conductors. Electrodes placed on the body surface can detect these electrical events, transmitting them so that they cause deflections (movements) in the tracing made by a recording device. An **electrocardiogram** (**ECG** or **EKG**) is an image of the electrical activities of the heart, generated by such a recording device.

A typical ECG consists of three distinguishable deflection waves, as shown in Figure 3b(i).22). The first wave, called the P wave, accompanies the spread of the electrical signal over the atria and the atrial contraction that follows. The next wave, the QRS wave, reflects the spread of the electrical signal over the ventricles and ventricular contraction. The third wave, the T wave, represents the return of the ventricles to the electrical state that preceded contraction (ventricular repolarization). Because the pattern and timing of these waves are remarkably consistent in a healthy heart, abnormal patterns can indicate heart problems.

Blood Pressure

We hear a lot about blood pressure, usually when someone worries about having a high blood pressure reading or brags about having a low one. **Blood pressure** is the force exerted by the blood against the walls of the blood vessels. When the ventricles contract, they push blood into the arteries under great pressure. This pressure is the driving force that moves blood through the body, but it also pushes outward against vessel walls. Ideally, a person's blood pressure should be great enough to circulate the blood but not so great that it stresses the blood vessels and the heart, as we see later in the chapter. Many factors influence blood pressure, including gender, age, time of day, physical activity, stress, and lifestyle.

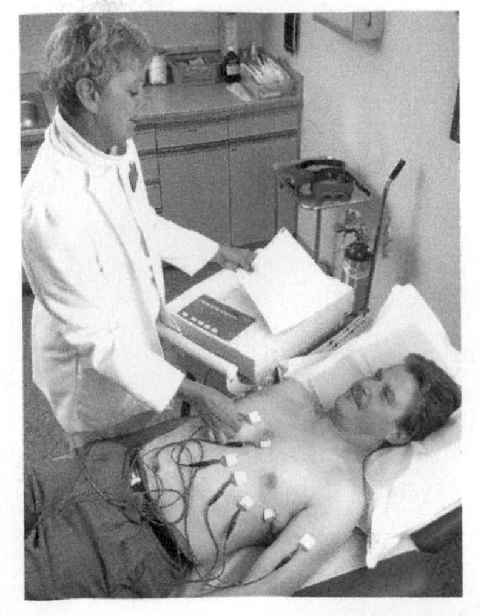

(a)

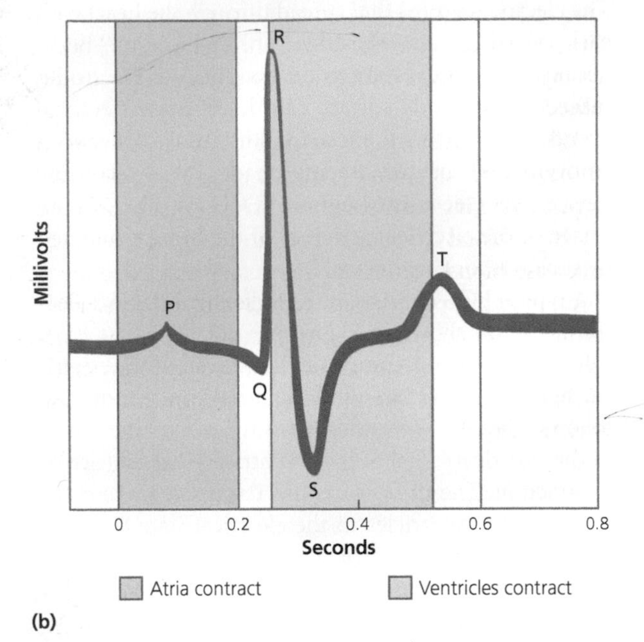

(b)

FIGURE 3b(i).22 (a) A person having an electrocardiogram (ECG) recorded. (b) The electrical activity that accompanies each heartbeat can be visualized in an ECG tracing. The P wave is generated as the electrical signals from the SA node spread across the atria and cause them to contract. The QRS wave represents the spread of the signal through the ventricles and ventricular contraction. The T wave occurs as the ventricles recover and return to the electrical state that preceded contraction.

Blood pressure in the arteries varies predictably during each heartbeat. It is highest during the contraction of the ventricles (ventricular systole), when blood is being forced into the arteries. In a typical, healthy adult, the optimal **systolic pressure,** the highest pressure in the artery during each heartbeat, is 110–120 mm of mercury (mm Hg).[1] Blood pressure is lowest when the ventricles are relaxing (diastole). In a healthy adult, the optimal lowest pressure, or **diastolic pressure,** is 70–80 mm Hg. A person's blood pressure is usually expressed as two values—the systolic followed by the diastolic. For instance, optimal adult blood pressure is said to be less than 120/80. (Do you know what your blood pressure is?)

Blood pressure is measured with a device called a *sphygmomanometer* (sfig-mo-mah-nom'-e-ter), which consists of an inflatable cuff that wraps around the upper arm and is attached to a device that can measure the pressure within the cuff. Figure 3b(i).23 shows how a manually operated sphygmomanometer uses the easily measured pressure of the air pumped into the cuff to measure the blood pressure in the brachial artery (which runs along the inner surface of the arm).

CARDIOVASCULAR DISEASE

Cardiovascular disease is the single biggest killer of men and women in the United States. It affects slightly more men than women because, until menopause, women receive some natural protection from cardiovascular disease through the action of the sex hormone estrogen. Ironically, although slightly fewer women than men have heart attacks, women who do have heart attacks are twice as likely to die within the following weeks as are men. Because heart attacks are commonly thought of as a male problem, women and their physicians often fail to recognize the symptoms, thus delaying treatments that could be lifesaving. (See the Health Issue essay, *The Cardiovascular Benefits of Exercise.*)

High Blood Pressure

High blood pressure, or *hypertension,* is often called the silent killer. It is *silent* because it does not produce any telltale symptoms. It is a *killer* because it can cause fatal problems, usually involving the heart, brain, blood vessels, or kidneys. Hypertension damages the heart in a number of ways, primarily by causing the heart to work harder to keep the blood moving. In response, the heart muscle thickens, and the heart enlarges. The enlarged heart works less efficiently and has difficulty keeping up with the body's needs. At the same time, the increased workload increases the heart's need for oxygen and nutrients. If these cannot be delivered rapidly enough, a heart attack can result.

[1]Pressure is measured as the height to which that pressure could push a column of mercury (Hg).

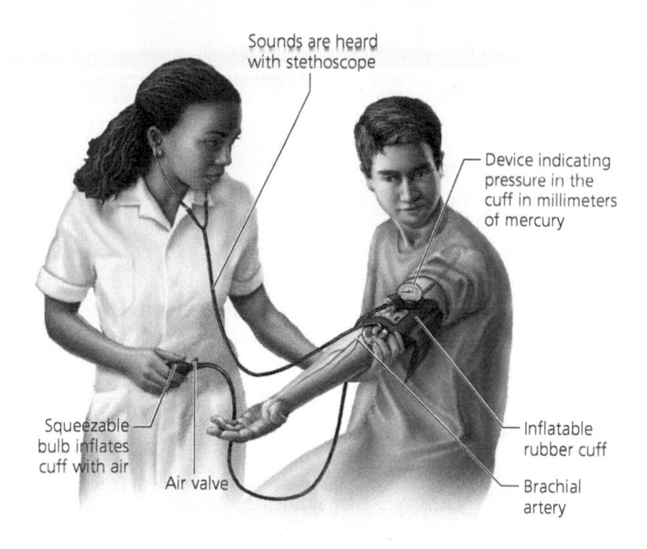

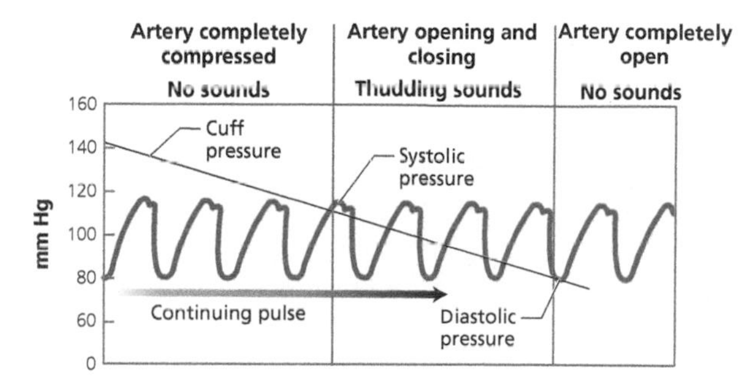

FIGURE 3b(i).23 Blood pressure is measured with a sphygmomanometer, which consists of an inflatable cuff and a means of measuring the pressure within the cuff. The cuff is placed around the upper arm and inflated so that it compresses the brachial artery. The pressure in the cuff is slowly released, and as it descends it reaches a point where blood is able to spurt through the constricted artery only at the moments of highest blood pressure. This pressure, at which "tapping" sounds are first heard, is the systolic pressure, the blood pressure when the heart is contracting. As the pressure in the cuff continues to drop, a point is reached where the sounds disappear. The blood is now flowing continuously through the brachial artery. The pressure in the cuff when the sounds first disappear is the diastolic pressure, the blood pressure when the heart is relaxing.

High blood pressure can also damage the kidneys, reducing the blood flow through them. In response, the kidneys make matters worse by secreting renin, a chemical that leads to further increases in blood pressure in an ever-escalating cycle.

Although about 90% of the cases of hypertension have no *known* cause, many contributing factors have been identified. When a cause can be identified, the kidneys are sometimes to blame. If kidneys have an impaired ability to handle sodium, the resulting fluid retention increases blood pressure by increasing blood volume. In other cases of hypertension, the sympathetic nervous system reacts too strongly to stress, constricting the blood vessels and increasing heart rate. Thus, more blood per minute is pumped through vessels that provide a greater resistance to flow.

Most physicians agree that a blood pressure of 160/90 is high and should be treated (see Figure 3b(i).24). But uncertainty clouds the treatment issue when the person's diastolic pressure is between 80 and 89, the higher end of normal. Although drug treatment may help in borderline cases, it usually must be continued for life. A diagnosis of high blood pressure may influence other aspects of a person's life, such as life insurance premiums. So, sometimes, only lifestyle changes are recommended for high normal values of blood pressure.

When the diagnosis of hypertension is clear, one or more of various kinds of drugs can be prescribed, each type combating a different mechanism that contributes to high blood pressure. The diuretics, for instance, decrease blood volume by increasing the excretion of sodium and fluids, thereby reducing blood pressure by reducing blood volume. Other drugs cause the blood vessels to dilate (become wider), reducing hypertension in instances where is it caused by overly constricted vessels.

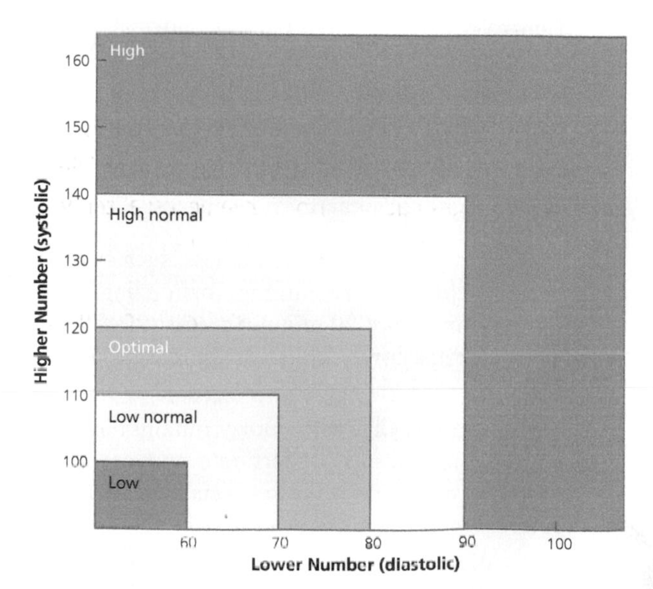

FIGURE 3b(i).24 Values of blood pressure in adults

Health Issue

The Cardiovascular Benefits of Exercise

What would you say if you were told there is a simple way to reduce your risk of heart attack, stroke, diabetes, and cancer while controlling your weight, strengthening your bones, relieving anxiety and tension, and improving your memory? "Impossible!" you might say. "What's the catch?" There is none. This key to life is regular aerobic exercise that uses large muscle groups rhythmically and continuously and elevates heart rate and breathing rate for at least 15 to 20 minutes.

Although exercise has many beneficial effects on the body, here we will consider only the benefits to the cardiovascular system. Exercise benefits the heart by making it a more efficient pump, thus reducing its workload. A well-exercised heart beats more slowly than the heart of a sedentary person—during both exercise and rest. The lower heart rate gives the heart more time to rest between beats. Yet at the same time, the well-exercised heart pumps more blood with each beat.

Exercise also increases the oxygen supply to the heart muscle by widening the coronary arteries, thereby increasing blood flow to the heart. Moreover, because the capillary beds within the heart muscle become more extensive with regular exercise, oxygen and nutrients can be delivered to the heart cells and wastes can be removed more quickly.

Furthermore, exercise helps to ensure continuous blood flow to the heart. One way it accomplishes this benefit is by increasing the body's ability to dissolve blood clots that can lead to heart attacks or strokes. Exercise stimulates the release of a natural enzyme that prevents blood clotting and remains effective for as long as $1\frac{1}{2}$ hours after you stop exercising. Besides this, exercise stimulates the development of collateral circulation, that is, additional blood vessels that provide alternative pathways for blood flow. As a result, blood flows continuously through the heart, even if one vessel becomes blocked.

Exercise affects the blood in ways that allow more oxygen to be delivered to the cells. The amount of hemoglobin, the oxygen-binding protein in red blood cells, increases. In addition, the blood volume and the numbers of red blood cells increase.

Exercise lowers the risk of coronary artery disease by lowering blood pressure and by shifting the balance of lipids in the blood. High-density lipoproteins (HDLs), which are the "good" form of cholesterol-carrying particles that remove cholesterol from the arterial walls, increase with exercise.

To reap cardiovascular benefits, you must exercise hard enough, long enough, and often enough. The exercise must be vigorous enough to elevate your heart rate to the so-called target zone, which is between 70% and 85% of your maximal attainable heart rate. The target zone can be determined by subtracting your age in years from 222 beats per minute. The exercise must continue for at least 20 minutes and be performed at least 3 days a week, with no more than 2 days between sessions.

Doing *something* active on a regular basis can improve your quality of life. Moderate activity helps you feel better emotionally and physically. The difference has been likened to traveling first class instead of coach.

A number of changes in lifestyle are recommended to treat or prevent hypertension.

1. **Control weight.** Maintaining normal body weight can help control blood pressure. Many overweight people with high blood pressure benefit from shedding just a few extra pounds. The best way to lose weight is to eat a moderate, balanced diet; reduce fat intake; and increase physical activity.
2. **Exercise regularly.** Aerobic exercise, such as brisk walking, jogging, swimming, or cycling, performed for at least 20 minutes at least three times a week, helps lower blood pressure and keep it low.
3. **Do not smoke.** Cigarette smoke contains nicotine, a drug that increases heart rate and constricts blood vessels; both of those effects increase blood pressure.
4. **Limit dietary salt.** Some people with hypertension can lower their blood pressure by lowering the amount of salt in their diet. Salt can affect fluid retention and, therefore, blood volume.

Atherosclerosis

Atherosclerosis (*ather-*, yellow, fatty deposit; *sclerosis*, a hardening) is a buildup of fatty substances in the walls of arteries, fueled by an inflammatory response. In some cases, the deposits narrow the artery (Figure 3b(i).25). Such narrowing causes problems because it reduces blood flow through the vessel, choking off the vital supply of oxygen and nutrients to the tissues served by that vessel. But contrary to the beliefs held just a few years ago, atherosclerosis is more than just a plumbing problem, akin to a clog in a passive pipeline.

The inflammatory response thought to cause atherosclerosis is the same process that wards off infection when you scrape your knee. In this case, it begins with an injury to the wall of an artery. The injury may be caused by some kind of bloodborne irritant (such as the chemicals inhaled in cigarette smoke), by cholesterol deposits in the artery lining, or by infection. Perhaps the excessively rapid or turbulent blood flow caused by high blood pressure can also produce such arterial damage. The damaged cells begin to pick up low-density lipoproteins (LDLs), the so-called bad

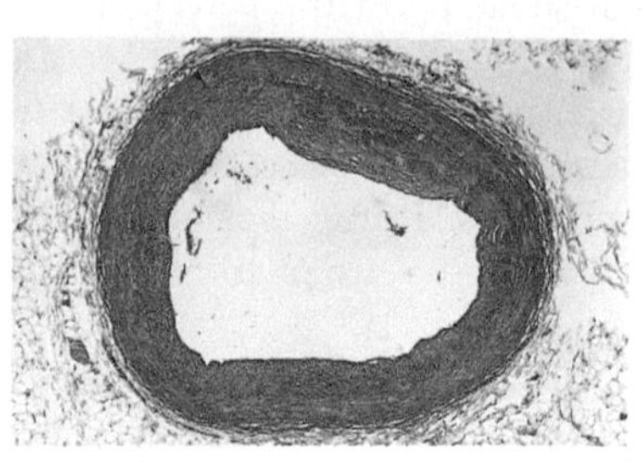

(a) A normal artery

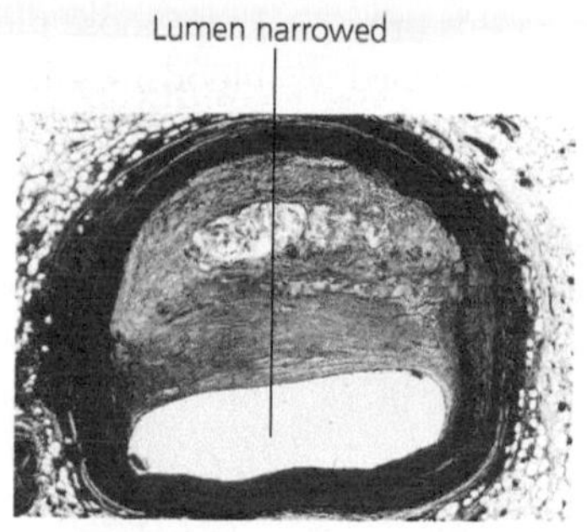

(b) An artery partially obstructed with plaque

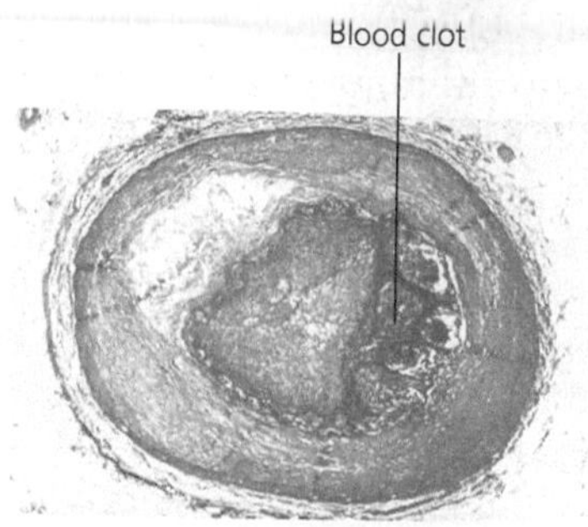

(c) An artery completely obstructed with plaque and a blood clot

FIGURE 3b(i).25 **Atherosclerosis, a low-level inflammatory response in the wall of an artery, is associated with the formation of fat-filled plaques. Plaque can obstruct blood flow through the artery, thus depriving the cells that would be fed life-sustaining blood by the artery. Plaque can also rupture, causing a blood clot to form. The clot may then completely clog the vessel and cause the death of tissue downstream.**

form of cholesterol. This accumulation of LDLs is most likely to occur when the LDL concentration in the blood is high. The LDLs undergo chemical changes that stimulate the cells of the arterial lining to enlist the body's defense responses: inflammatory chemicals and defense cells. Growth factors produced by defense cells stimulate smooth muscle cells in the arterial wall to divide, thereby thickening the wall. Other defense cells engulf LDLs, become enlarged, and form fatty streaks on the arterial lining. As these defense cells continue to scavenge lipids, the fatty streak increases in size and forms plaque, a bumpy, fatty layer in the artery wall. The plaque can bulge into the artery channel, blocking the blood flow, or it can expand outward into the artery wall. Although the plaque has a fibrous cap that initially keeps pieces from breaking away, the fat-filled cells secrete inflammatory substances that weaken the cap. A small break in the cap can allow the plaque to rupture, which triggers the formation of a blood clot. In any case, restriction of the blood flow can starve and kill the cells lying downstream. Such an occurrence in the heart (leading to a heart attack) or brain (leading to a stroke) can be fatal. Because plaques do not necessarily bulge into the artery and cause symptoms of atherosclerosis before they rupture, heart attacks often occur in patients without previous symptoms.

There are several approaches to treating atherosclerosis. A healthy lifestyle promotes healthy arteries, so control your weight, engage in regular aerobic exercise, and eat a heart-healthy diet. Medications to treat atherosclerosis include drugs to lower blood pressure, drugs to reduce blood cholesterol levels, and drugs to prevent unwanted blood clot formation. Some physicians recommend a daily dose of a low-strength aspirin, because aspirin reduces the risk of blood clot formation.

stop and THINK

C-reactive protein (CRP) is an inflammatory chemical released by injured cells in the artery lining. Why might CRP prove to be a better predictor of atherosclerosis than blood cholesterol level?

Coronary Artery Disease

Coronary artery disease is a condition in which the fatty deposits associated with atherosclerosis form within coronary arteries, the arteries that nourish the heart muscle. Coronary artery disease is the underlying cause of the vast majority of heart attacks.

A temporary shortage of oxygen to the heart is accompanied by angina pectoris—chest pain, usually experienced in the center of the chest or slightly to the left. The name *angina* comes from the Latin word *angere*, meaning "to strangle." The name is apt, since the pain of angina is often described as suffocating, viselike, or choking. Typically, the pain begins during physical exertion or emotional stress, when the demands on the heart are increased and the blood flow to the heart muscle can no longer meet the needs. The pain stops after a period of rest. Angina serves as a warning that part of the heart is receiving insufficient blood through the coronary arteries, but it does not cause permanent damage to the heart. The warning should be taken seriously, however, because each year up to 15% of those people who have angina later die from a heart attack.

Although coronary artery disease is usually diagnosed from the symptoms of angina and a physical examination, a procedure called *coronary angiography* may be used to spot areas in the coronary arteries that have become narrowed by atherosclerosis. In this procedure, a contrast dye that is visible in x-rays is released in the heart, allowing the coronary vessels to be seen on film. A catheter (a slender, flexible tube) is inserted into an artery in the arm or leg and then threaded through the blood vessels until it reaches the heart. The dye is then squirted into the openings of the coronary arteries, and its movement through the arteries is recorded in a series of high-speed x-rays.

Coronary artery disease can be treated with medicines or with surgery. Among the medicines commonly used are some that dilate (widen) blood vessels, such as nitroglycerin. Certain other drugs specifically dilate only the coronary arteries. Wider blood vessels make it easier for the heart to pump blood through the circuit. When the coronary arteries dilate, more blood is delivered to the heart muscle. Also used are drugs that dampen the heart's response to stimulation from the sympathetic nervous system, thus decreasing its need for oxygen.

Two surgical operations for treating coronary artery disease are balloon angioplasty and coronary artery bypass. In *angioplasty,* the channel of an artery narrowed by soft, fatty plaque is widened by inflating a tough, plastic balloon inside the artery (Figure 3b(i).26). First the tiny, uninflated balloon is attached to the end of a catheter and inserted through an artery in the arm or upper thigh. It is then pushed to the blocked spot in a coronary artery; high-speed x-rays are used to track its progress. After it reaches the blockage, the balloon is inflated under pressure, stretching the artery and pressing the soft plaque against the wall to widen the lumen.

After angioplasty, physicians commonly insert a metal-mesh tube called a stent into the treated arteries. The stent prevents the arteries from collapsing and keeps loose pieces of plaque from being swept into the bloodstream. Although stents boost the percentage of arteries that stay open, they sometimes trigger an inflammatory response, and some arteries become clogged again, even with a stent in place. One kind of stent slowly releases sirolimus, a drug that blocks cell division, preventing scar tissue from forming and blocking the artery again.

A *coronary bypass* is a procedure in which a segment of a leg vein is removed and grafted so that it provides an alternate pathway that bypasses a point of obstruction between the aorta and a coronary artery (Figure 3b(i).27).

stop and **THINK**

In a coronary bypass operation, why is it important for the surgeon to insert the grafted vein in the correct orientation? What would happen if the piece of vein were inserted backward?

Heart Attack

In a heart attack, technically known as a *myocardial infarction,* a part of the heart muscle dies because of an insufficient blood supply. (*Myocardial* refers to heart muscle; *infarct* refers to dead tissue.) Heart muscle cells begin to die if they are cut off from their essential blood supply for more than 2 hours. Depending on the extent of damage, the effects of a heart attack can spread quickly throughout the body: as a result of a

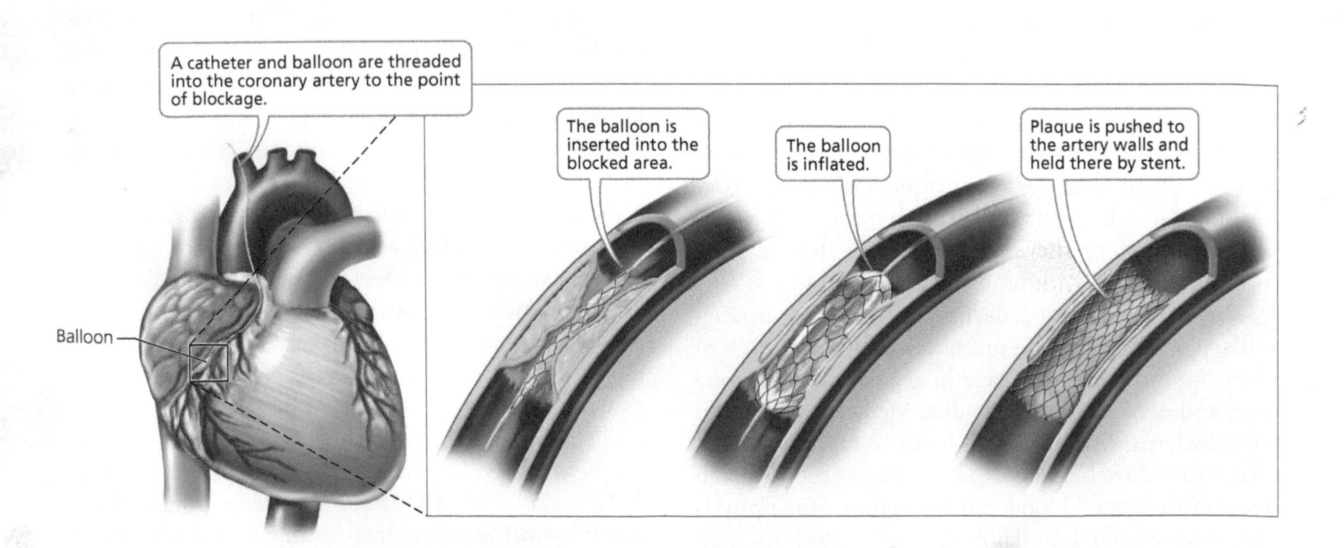
A catheter and balloon are threaded into the coronary artery to the point of blockage.
Balloon
The balloon is inserted into the blocked area.
The balloon is inflated.
Plaque is pushed to the artery walls and held there by stent.

FIGURE 3b(i).26 **Balloon angioplasty opens a partially blocked artery**

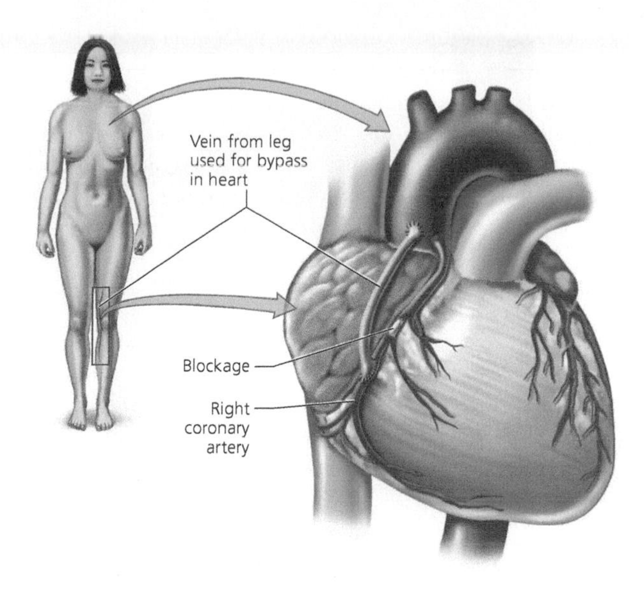

FIGURE 3b(i).27 **In coronary bypass surgery, a section of a leg vein is removed. One end of the vein is attached to the heart's main artery, the aorta, and the other to a coronary artery, bypassing the obstructed region. The grafted vein provides a pathway through which blood can reach the previously deprived region of heart muscle.**

heart attack, the brain receives insufficient oxygen; the lungs fill with fluid; and the kidneys fail. Within a short time, white blood cells swarm in to remove the damaged heart tissue. Then—if the individual survives—over the next 8 weeks or so, scar tissue replaces the dead cardiac muscle (Figure 3b(i).28). Because scar tissue cannot contract, part of the heart permanently loses its pumping ability.

Heart attacks can be caused in many ways. The most common type of heart attack is a coronary thrombosis, which means the attack is caused by a blood clot blocking a coronary artery. Coronary thrombosis is unlikely to happen unless the artery already contains plaques of atherosclerosis, as occurs in coronary artery disease. In some instances, the blood clot is formed elsewhere in the body but is swept along in the bloodstream until it lodges in a coronary artery. In other instances of heart attacks, the blockage is temporary, caused by constriction of a coronary artery, called a coronary artery spasm.

Chest pain is a common indication that a heart attack is in progress, especially in men. Unlike angina, the pain is not necessarily brought on by activity, and it doesn't go away with rest. In some cases, the victim feels a severe, crushing pain that begins in the center of the chest and often spreads down the inside of one or both arms (most commonly the left one) as well as up to the neck and shoulders. Although the pain is usually severe enough to cause the victim to stop whatever he or she is doing, it is not always so strong that it is recognized as a sign of heart attack. A heart attack may also cause nausea and dizziness, which can prompt the victim to interpret the symptoms as an upset stomach. Oddly, persons who experience severe pain may be the lucky ones, because they are more likely to realize they are having a heart attack and seek immediate help. Doubt about the cause of the symptoms is unfortunate because it often delays treatment, and treatment within the first few hours after a heart attack can make the difference between life and death.

If a large enough section of heart muscle is damaged by a heart attack, the heart may not be able to continue pumping blood to the lungs and the rest of the body at an adequate rate. A condition in which the heart is no longer an efficient pump is known as *heart failure.* Symptoms of heart failure include shortness of breath, fatigue, weakness, and fluid accumulation in the lungs or limbs. Although the heart can never be restored to

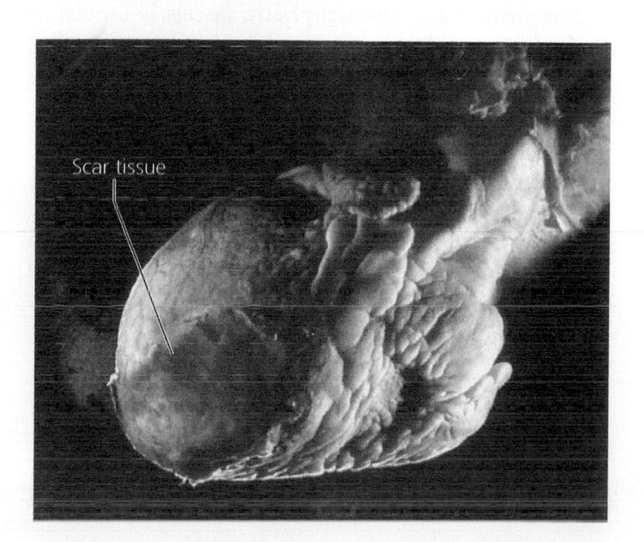

FIGURE 3b(i).28 **The ravages of a prior heart attack are visible as scar tissue at the bottom of this lifeless heart. Scar tissue replaced cardiac muscle when the blood supply to the heart muscle was shut down. Because scar tissue cannot contract, that part of the life-sustaining pump becomes ineffective.**

its former health, the symptoms of heart failure can be treated with drugs. For instance, digitalis can increase the strength of heart contractions, and diuretics reduce fluid accumulation, thus lessening the heart's workload. Other drugs relax constricted arteries, thereby reducing resistance to blood flow and lowering the blood pressure. Together, these drugs help a weakened heart pump more efficiently.

Sometimes, drugs and bypass surgery cannot halt progressive heart failure. In this case, heart transplant surgery may provide hope for some patients, but generally only for those younger than 80 years of age. First, a donor heart must be found whose tissue is an acceptable match with that of the recipient. During transplant surgery, a heart-lung machine takes over the circulation while the weakened heart is removed, and the new heart is sewn in place. The patient is then treated with drugs that lessen the chances of organ rejection.

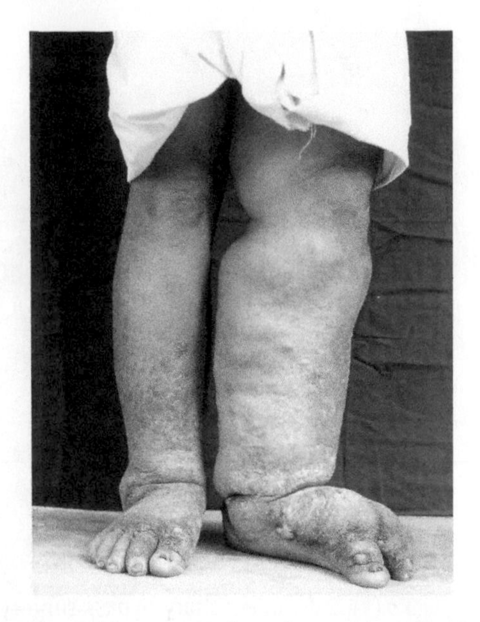

FIGURE 3b(i).29 The leg of a person with elephantiasis. In this condition, parasitic worms plug lymphatic vessels and prevent the return of fluid from the tissues to the circulatory system.

LYMPHATIC SYSTEM

The **lymphatic system** consists of **lymph,** which is a fluid identical to interstitial fluid (the fluid that bathes all the cells of the body); of **lymphatic vessels** through which the lymph flows; and of various lymphoid tissues and organs scattered throughout the body.

The functions of the lymphatic system are as diverse as they are essential to life:

1. **Return excess interstitial fluid to the bloodstream.** The lymphatic system maintains blood volume by returning excess interstitial fluid to the bloodstream. Only 85% to 90% of the fluid that leaves the blood capillaries and bathes the body tissues as interstitial fluid is reabsorbed by the capillaries. The rest of that fluid (as much as 3 liters a day) is absorbed by the lymphatic system and then returned to the circulatory system. This job is important. If the surplus interstitial fluid were not drained, it would cause the tissue to swell; the volume of blood would drop to potentially fatal levels; and the blood would become too viscous (thick) for the heart to pump.

   A dramatic example of the importance of returning fluid to the blood is provided by *elephantiasis,* a condition in which parasitic worms block lymphatic vessels (Figure 3b(i).29). The blockage can cause a substantial buildup of fluid in the affected body region, followed by the growth of connective tissue. Elephantiasis is so named because it results in massive swelling and the darkening and thickening of the skin in the affected region, making the region resemble the skin of an elephant. Elephantiasis is a tropical disease that is transmitted by mosquitoes.
2. **Transport products of fat digestion from the small intestine to the bloodstream.** The products of fat digestion are too large to be absorbed into the capillaries in the small intestine. Instead, these products enter a lymphatic vessel, called a lacteal, and travel in the lymphatic system to be returned to the blood circulatory system.
3. **Help defend against disease-causing organisms.** The lymphatic system helps protect against disease and cancer.

The structure of the lymphatic vessels is central to their ability to absorb the interstitial fluid not carried away by capillaries. The extra fluid enters a branching network of microscopic tubules, called *lymphatic capillaries,* that penetrate between the cells and the capillaries in almost every tissue of the body (except teeth, bones, bone marrow, and the central nervous system; Figure 3b(i).30). The lymphatic capillaries differ from the blood capillaries in two ways. First, unlike blood capillaries, which form continuous networks, lymphatic capillaries end blindly, like the fingers of a glove. In essence, lymphatic capillaries serve as drainage tubes. Fluid enters at the "fingertips" and moves through the system in only one direction. Second, lymphatic capillaries are much more permeable than blood capillaries, a feature that is crucial to their

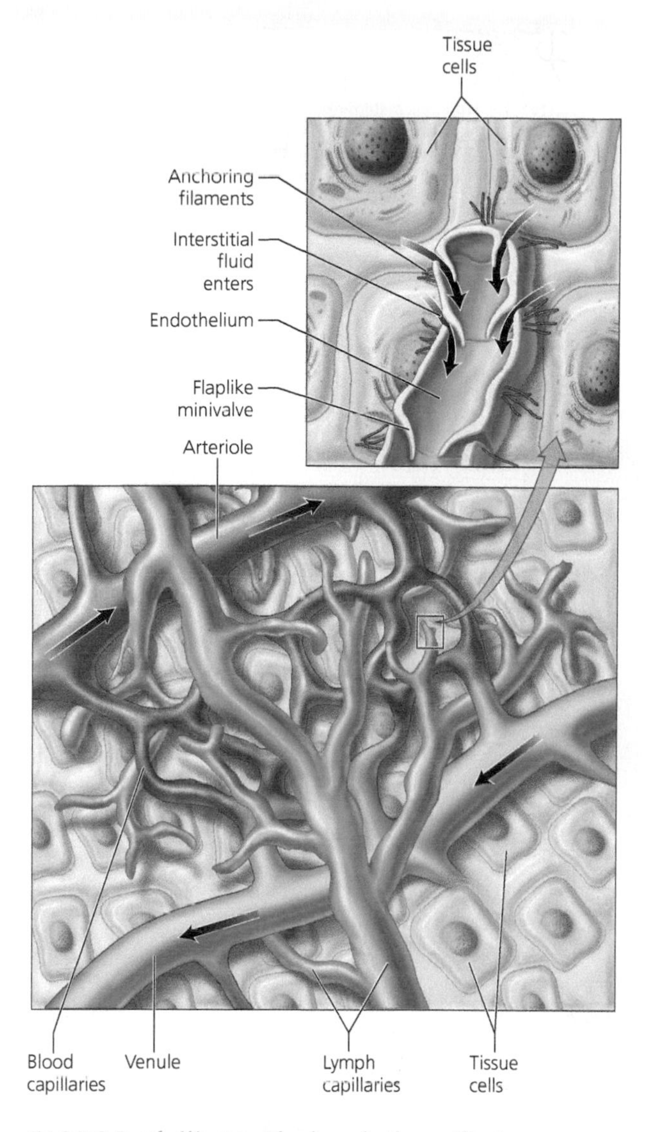

FIGURE 3b(i).30 **The lymphatic capillaries are microscopic, blind-ended tubules through which surplus tissue fluid enters the lymphatic system to be returned to the bloodstream.**

ability to absorb the digestive products of fats as well as excess interstitial fluid. The lymphatic capillaries drain into larger lymphatic vessels, which merge into progressively larger tubes with thicker walls. Lymph is eventually returned to the blood through one of two large ducts that join with the large veins at the base of the neck.

With no pump to drive it, lymph flows slowly through the lymphatic vessels, propelled by the same forces that move blood through the veins. That is, the contractions of nearby skeletal muscles compress the lymphatic vessels, pushing the lymph along. One-way valves similar to those in veins prevent backflow. And as with the flow of blood back to the heart from the lower part of the body, pressure changes in the thorax (chest cavity) that accompany breathing also help pull the lymph upward from the lower body. Gravity assists the flow from the upper body.

The lymphatic vessels are studded with **lymph nodes,** small bean-shaped structures that cleanse the lymph as it slowly filters through. The lymph nodes contain macrophages and lymphocytes, white blood cells that play an essential role in the body's defense system. Macrophages engulf bacteria, cancer cells, and other debris, clearing them from the lymph. Lymphocytes serve as the surveillance squad of the immune system. They are continuously on the lookout for specific disease-causing invaders. When lymphocytes detect bacteria or viruses, the lymphocytes are stimulated to divide. The increased number of lymphocytes causes the lymph nodes to swell. Thus, swollen and painful lymph nodes (commonly called "glands") are a symptom of infection.

Besides the lymph nodes, there are several other *lymphoid organs* (Figure 3b(i).31). Among these are the *tonsils,* which form a ring around the entrance to the throat, where they help protect against disease organisms that are inhaled or swallowed. The **thymus gland,** located in the chest, is another lymphoid organ. It plays its part during early childhood by helping the maturation of certain lymphocytes that protect us from specific disease-causing organisms. On the left side of the abdominal region is the largest lymphoid organ, the **spleen.** Besides containing a reservoir of lymphocytes, the spleen clears the blood of old and damaged red blood cells and platelets. Finally, isolated clusters of lymph nodules along the small intestine, known as *Peyer's patches,* keep bacteria from breaching the intestinal wall. The *red bone marrow,* where white blood cells and other formed elements are produced, is a lymphoid organ found in the ends of long bones, ribs, sternum, and vertebrae.

stop and THINK

Cancer cells that break loose from their original site in a process called metastasis have easy access to the highly permeable lymphatic capillaries. The lymphatic vessels then provide a route by which the cancer cells may spread to nearly every part of the body. Why are the lymph nodes often examined to determine whether cancer has spread? Why are the lymph nodes near the original cancer site often removed?

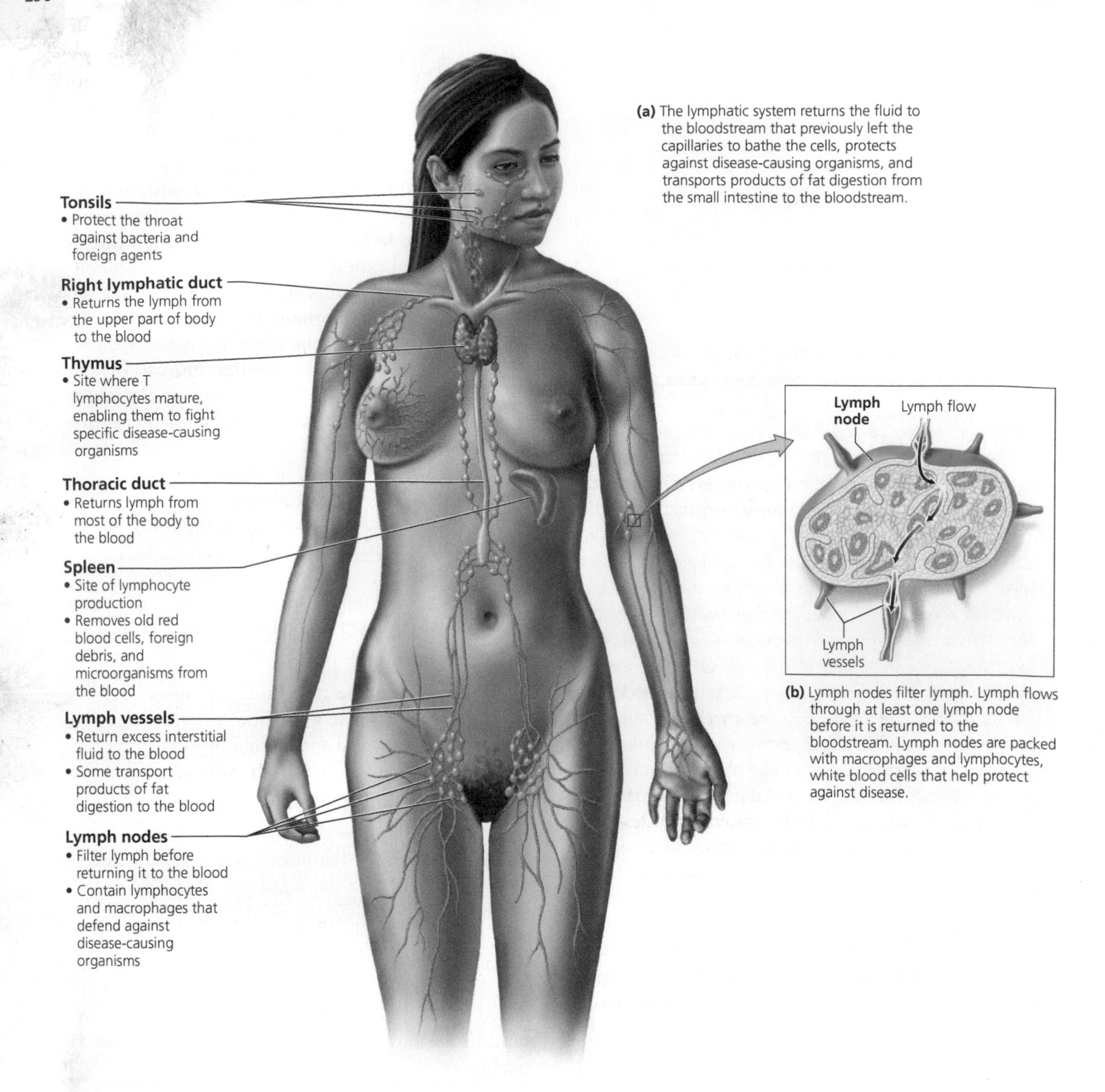
(a) The lymphatic system returns the fluid to the bloodstream that previously left the capillaries to bathe the cells, protects against disease-causing organisms, and transports products of fat digestion from the small intestine to the bloodstream.
Tonsils
• Protect the throat against bacteria and foreign agents
Right lymphatic duct
• Returns the lymph from the upper part of body to the blood
Thymus
• Site where T lymphocytes mature, enabling them to fight specific disease-causing organisms
Thoracic duct
• Returns lymph from most of the body to the blood
Spleen
• Site of lymphocyte production
• Removes old red blood cells, foreign debris, and microorganisms from the blood
Lymph vessels
• Return excess interstitial fluid to the blood
• Some transport products of fat digestion to the blood
Lymph nodes
• Filter lymph before returning it to the blood
• Contain lymphocytes and macrophages that defend against disease-causing organisms
Lymph node
Lymph flow
Lymph vessels
(b) Lymph nodes filter lymph. Lymph flows through at least one lymph node before it is returned to the bloodstream. Lymph nodes are packed with macrophages and lymphocytes, white blood cells that help protect against disease.

FIGURE 3b(i).31 The lymphatic system is a system of lymphatic vessels containing a clear fluid, called lymph, and various lymphatic tissues and organs located throughout the body. Green indicates lymphatic vessels and nodes

3b(ii) The Digestive System

Taken from *Biology of Humans: Concepts, Applications, and Issues*, Third Edition, by Judith Goodenough and Betty McGuire

There is some truth to the saying, "You are what you eat." Rest assured, however, that no matter how many hamburgers you eat, you will never become one. Instead, the hamburger becomes *you.* This transformation is largely due to the activities of the digestive system. Like an assembly line in reverse, the digestive system takes the food we eat and breaks the complex organic molecules into their chemical subunits. The subunits are molecules small enough to be absorbed into the bloodstream and delivered to body cells, where they either provide fuel for growth and repair of the body or they provide energy for daily activities. Imagine that you just ate a cheeseburger on a bun. The starch in the bun may fuel a jump for joy; the protein in the beef may be used to build muscle; and the fat in the cheese may become myelin sheaths that insulate nerve fibers. The digestive system breaks food into molecules small enough to be absorbed and delivered to the cells that use them. Table 3b(ii).1 identifies the structures of the digestive system and describes their roles in both mechanical and chemical digestion. You can refer to the table as you read about each of the digestive structures below.

The **digestive system** consists of a long, hollow tube, called the **gastrointestinal (GI) tract,** into which various accessory glands release their secretions (Figure 3b(ii).1). The GI tract begins at the mouth and continues to the esophagus, stomach, small intestine, and large intestine. The hollow area of the tube through which food and fluids travel is called the *lumen.* Along most of its length, the walls of the GI tract have four basic layers.

- **Mucosa.** The innermost layer of the GI tract is the moist, mucus-secreting layer called the **mucosa.** The mucus helps lubricate the lumen, allowing food to slide through easily. Mucus also helps protect the cells in the lining of the GI tract from rough substances in the food and from digestive enzymes. In some regions of the digestive system, cells in the mucosa also secrete digestive enzymes. In addition, the mucosae in some parts of the digestive tract are highly folded, which increases the surface area for absorption.
- **Submucosa.** The next layer, the **submucosa,** consists of connective tissue containing blood vessels, lymph vessels, and nerves. The blood supply maintains the cells of the digestive system and, in some regions, picks up and transports the products of digestion. The nerves are important in coordinating the contractions of the next layer.
- **Muscularis.** The next layer, the **muscularis,** is responsible for movement of materials through the GI tract and for mixing ingested materials with digestive secretions. In most sections of the GI tract, the muscularis is a double layer of smooth muscle. (The stomach, as you will read later, is an exception; it has three layers of muscle.) In the inner, "circular" layer of muscle, the muscle cells encircle the tube, causing a constriction when they contract. In the outer, longitudinal layer, the muscle cells are arranged parallel to the GI tract. Longitudinal muscles shorten the GI tract when they contract. The

TABLE 3b(ii).1 Review of Structures of the Digestive System

Structure	Description/Functions	Mechanical Digestion	Chemical Digestion
Mouth	Receives food; contains teeth and tongue; tongue manipulates food and monitors quality	Teeth tear and crush food into smaller pieces	Digestion of carbohydrates begins
Pharynx	Area that both food and air pass through	None	None
Esophagus	Tube that transports food from mouth to stomach	None	None
Stomach	J-shaped muscular sac for food storage	Churning of stomach mixes food with gastric juice, creating liquid chyme	Protein digestion begins
Small intestine	Long tube where digestion is completed and nutrients are absorbed	Segmental contractions mix food with intestinal enzymes, pancreatic enzymes, and bile	Carbohydrate, protein, and fat digestion completed
Large intestine	Final tubular region of GI tract; absorbs water and ions; houses bacteria; forms and expels feces	None	Some digestion is carried out by bacteria
Anus	Terminal outlet of digestive tract	None	None

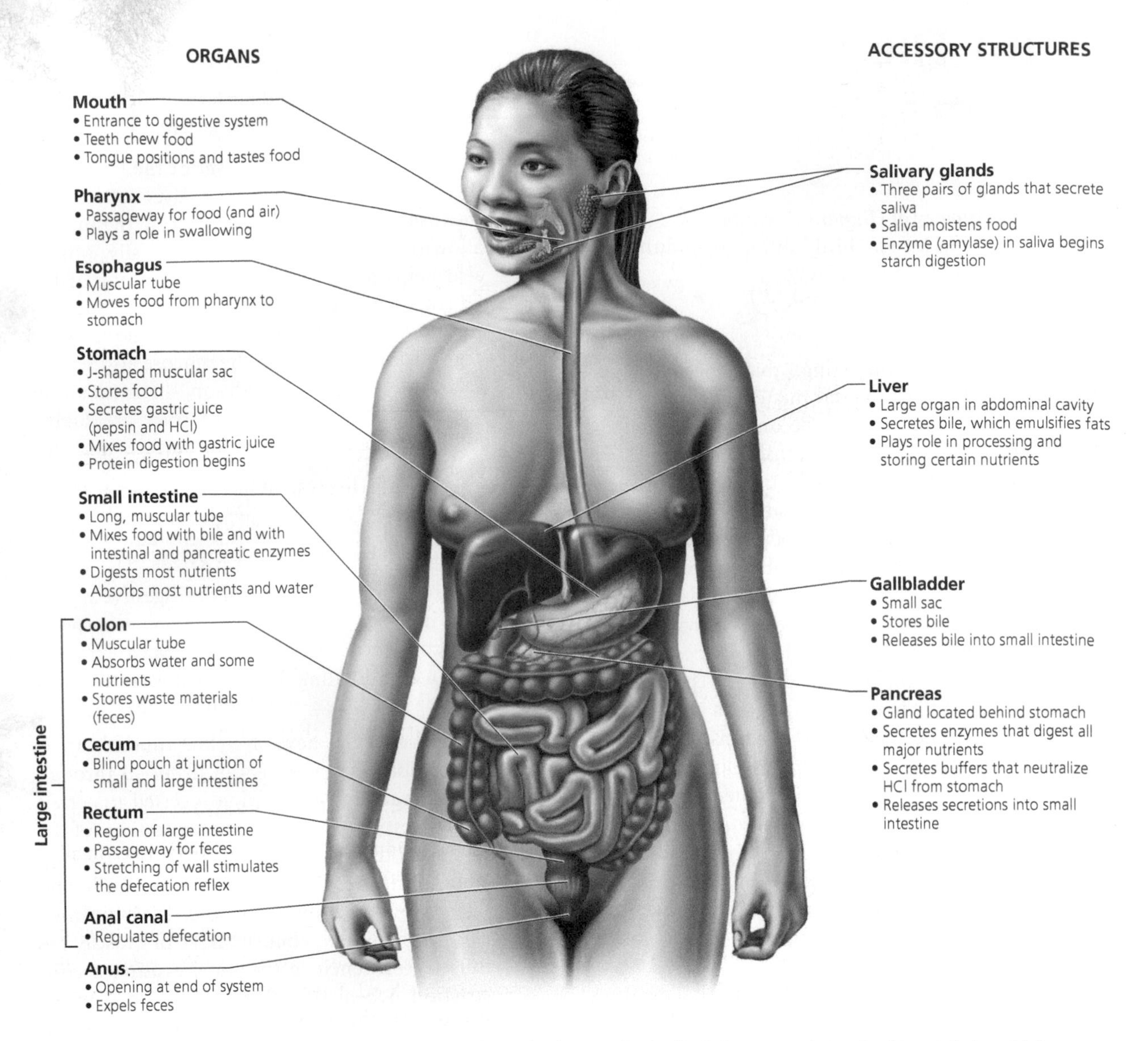
ORGANS
Mouth
• Entrance to digestive system
• Teeth chew food
• Tongue positions and tastes food
Pharynx
• Passageway for food (and air)
• Plays a role in swallowing
Esophagus
• Muscular tube
• Moves food from pharynx to stomach
Stomach
• J-shaped muscular sac
• Stores food
• Secretes gastric juice (pepsin and HCl)
• Mixes food with gastric juice
• Protein digestion begins
Small intestine
• Long, muscular tube
• Mixes food with bile and with intestinal and pancreatic enzymes
• Digests most nutrients
• Absorbs most nutrients and water
Large intestine
Colon
• Muscular tube
• Absorbs water and some nutrients
• Stores waste materials (feces)
Cecum
• Blind pouch at junction of small and large intestines
Rectum
• Region of large intestine
• Passageway for feces
• Stretching of wall stimulates the defecation reflex
Anal canal
• Regulates defecation
Anus
• Opening at end of system
• Expels feces
ACCESSORY STRUCTURES
Salivary glands
• Three pairs of glands that secrete saliva
• Saliva moistens food
• Enzyme (amylase) in saliva begins starch digestion
Liver
• Large organ in abdominal cavity
• Secretes bile, which emulsifies fats
• Plays role in processing and storing certain nutrients
Gallbladder
• Small sac
• Stores bile
• Releases bile into small intestine
Pancreas
• Gland located behind stomach
• Secretes enzymes that digest all major nutrients
• Secretes buffers that neutralize HCl from stomach
• Releases secretions into small intestine

FIGURE 3b(ii).1 **The digestive system consists of a long tube, called the gastrointestinal tract, into which accessory structures release their secretions.**

muscle layers churn the food until it is liquefied, mix the resulting liquid with enzymes, and propel the food along the GI tract in a process called peristalsis, which is discussed later in this chapter. Local muscle contractions in random regions of the GI tract, especially in the small intestine, are called segmental contractions. Segmental contractions mix intestinal contents—food and digestive juices (fluids containing enzymes and other fluids that aid in digestion). Segmental contractions also assist absorption of digested food by moving intestinal contents over the intestinal wall.

- **Serosa.** The **serosa,** a thin layer of epithelial tissue supported by connective tissue, wraps around the GI tract. It secretes a fluid that lubricates the outside of the GI tract to reduce friction with contacting surfaces of the intestine and other abdominal organs. (Figure 3b(ii).2).

Regions of the GI tract are specialized to process food in particular ways. One aspect of that processing is *mechanical digestion,* the physical breaking of food into smaller pieces, and another is *chemical digestion,* the breaking of chemical bonds so that complex molecules are taken apart into smaller subunits. Chemical

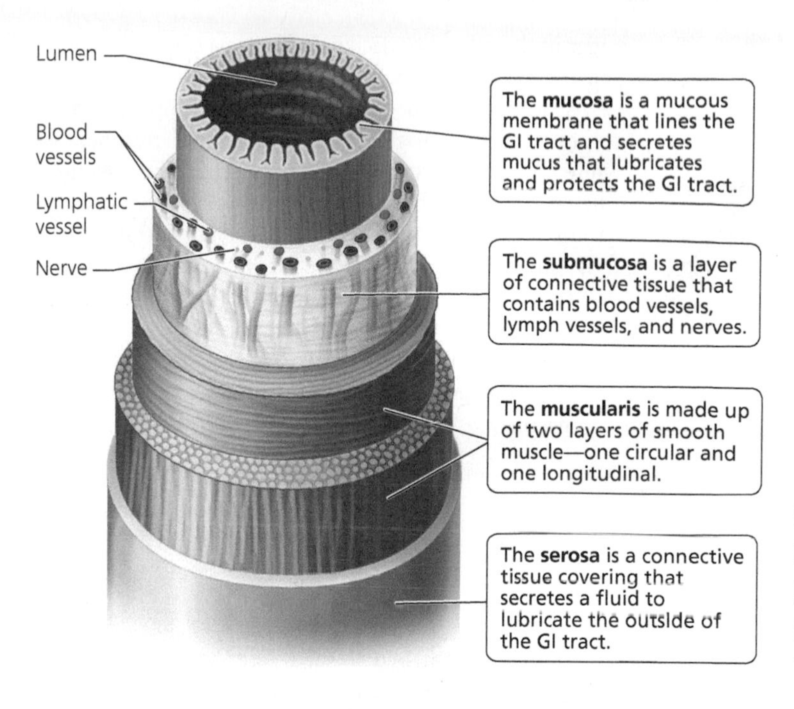

Lumen
Blood vessels
Lymphatic vessel
Nerve
The **mucosa** is a mucous membrane that lines the GI tract and secretes mucus that lubricates and protects the GI tract.
The **submucosa** is a layer of connective tissue that contains blood vessels, lymph vessels, and nerves.
The **muscularis** is made up of two layers of smooth muscle—one circular and one longitudinal.
The **serosa** is a connective tissue covering that secretes a fluid to lubricate the outside of the GI tract.

FIGURE 3b(ii).2 **Along most of its length, the wall of the GI tract has four basic layers: the mucosa, the submucosa, the muscularis, and the serosa.**

digestion produces molecules that can be absorbed into the bloodstream and used by the cells. Next we trace the path food travels along the GI tract to see how it is processed and absorbed.

SPECIALIZED COMPARTMENTS FOR FOOD PROCESSING

As food moves along the GI tract, it passes through the mouth, pharynx, esophagus, stomach, small intestine, and large intestine. The salivary glands, liver, and pancreas add secretions along the way. Most nutrients are absorbed from the small intestine. Additional water is absorbed in the large intestine. Undigested and indigestible materials pass out the anus.

Mouth

The entryway to the digestive system and the first stop on food's journey through it is the *mouth,* also called the oral cavity. The roof of the mouth is called the *palate.* The region of the palate closest to the front of the mouth, the hard palate, is reinforced with bone. Toward the back of the mouth is the soft palate, which consists only of muscle and prevents food from entering the nose during swallowing. The mouth serves several functions: (1) it begins mechanical and, to some extent, chemical digestion; (2) it monitors food quality; and (3) it moistens and manipulates food so that it can be swallowed. The teeth, salivary glands, and tongue all contribute to these functions.

Teeth and Mechanical Digestion

As we chew, our teeth break solid foods into smaller fragments that are easier to swallow and digest. The sharp, chisel-like incisors in the front of the mouth (see Figure 3b(ii).3a) slice the food as we bite into it. At the same time, the pointed canines to the sides of the incisors tear the food. Then the food is ground, crushed, and pulverized by the premolars and molars, which lie along the sides of the mouth.

Teeth are alive. In the center of each tooth is the pulp, which contains the tooth's life-support systems—blood vessels that nourish the tooth and nerves that sense heat, cold, pressure, and pain (Figure 3b(ii).3b). Surrounding the pulp is a hard, bonelike substance, called dentin. The crown of the tooth (the part visible above the gum line) is covered with enamel, a nonliving material that is hardened with calcium salts. The root of the tooth (the part below the gum line) is covered with a calcified, yet living and sensitive connective tissue called cementum. The roots of the teeth fit into sockets in the jawbone. Blood vessels and nerves reach the pulp through a tiny tunnel through the root, called the root canal.

Tooth decay is caused by acid produced by bacteria living in the mouth (Figure 3b(ii).4). When you eat, food particles become trapped between the teeth, in the small spaces where the teeth meet the gums, and in the hollows of molars. Bacteria in the mouth are nourished by the

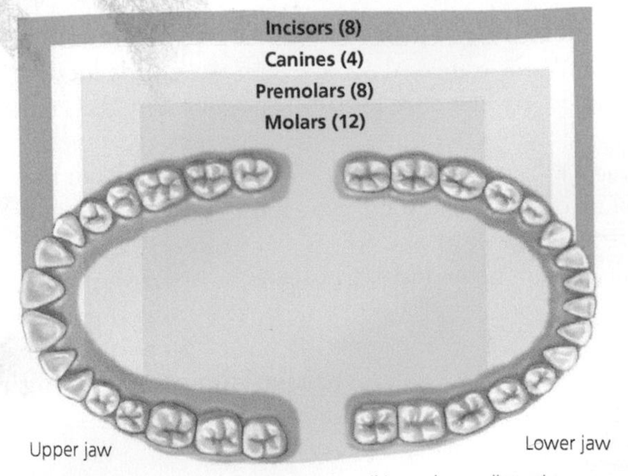

(a) The teeth slice, tear, and grind food until it can be swallowed.

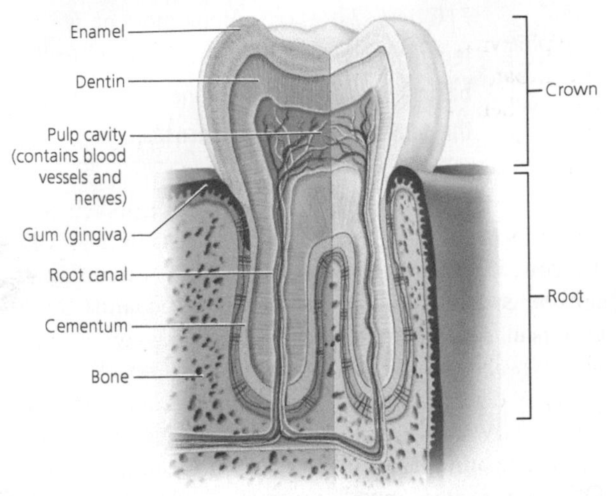

(b) The structure of the human tooth is suited for its function of breaking food into smaller pieces.

FIGURE 3b(ii).3 **Adult human teeth**

sugar in these food particles. As bacteria digest the sugar, acid is produced that erodes the enamel and causes a cavity to form. Blood vessels in the pulp widen in response to this erosion, allowing greater numbers of white bloods cells to reach the area and fight infection. The widened blood vessels may press on nerves, causing a toothache. When the enamel has been penetrated, bacteria can invade the softer dentin beneath. If a dentist does not fill the cavity, the bacteria can infect the pulp. *Plaque,* an invisible film of bacteria, mucus, and food particles, promotes tooth decay because it holds the acid against the enamel. Daily brushing and flossing helps remove plaque, reducing the chance of tooth decay.

what would you do?

For the past 50 years, some communities whose water is not naturally fluoridated have added low doses of fluoride to the public water supply to reduce tooth decay. Nearly 98% of Americans have, or have had, tooth decay. Over 6 million teeth are removed each year. Proponents of fluoridation point out that the incidence of tooth decay has declined after the addition of fluoride to drinking water. Opponents of the practice argue that (1) fluoridation of the water supply is a form of forced medication; (2) the dosage cannot be properly controlled because of differences in people's body weight and the amount of water people consume; and (3) excessive fluoride intake causes teeth to become brown and mottled. If you had to vote on fluoridation of your public water supply, what additional information would you want before voting? How would you vote at present?

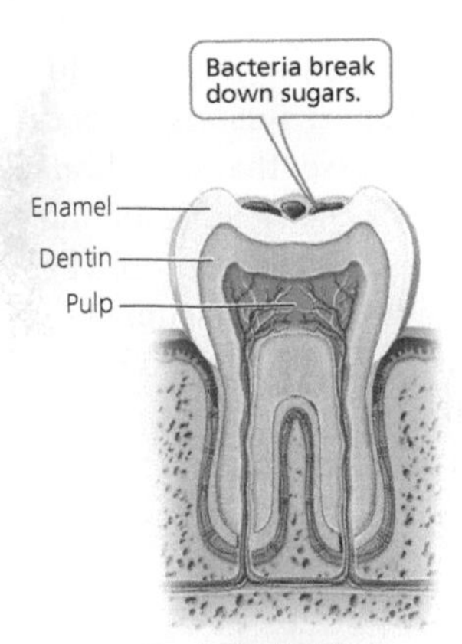

Step 1: Tooth decay is caused by acid produced when bacteria living on the tooth surface break down sugars in food particles adhered to teeth.

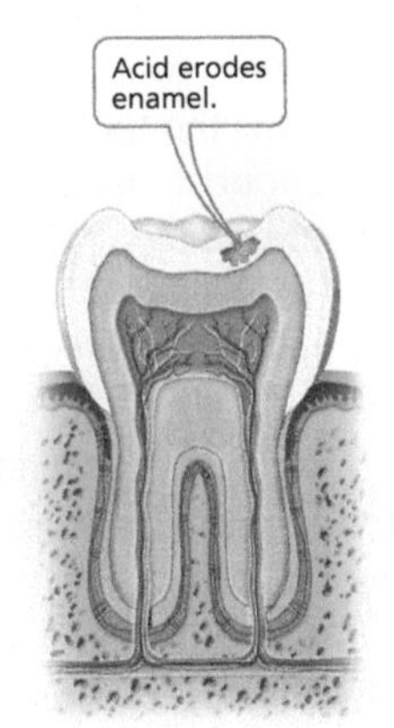

Step 2: The acid erodes the tooth's enamel, causing a cavity to form.

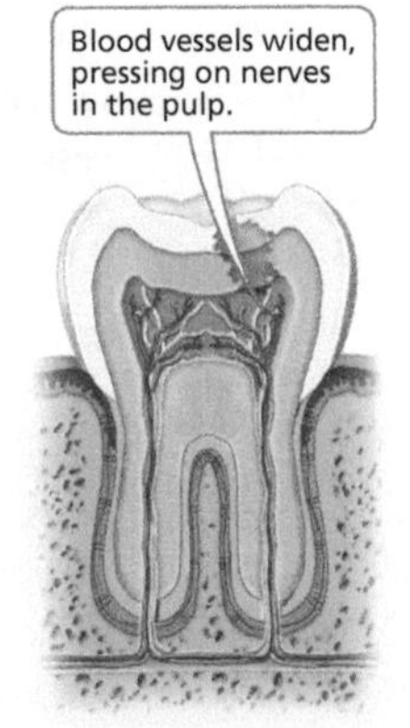

Step 3: The body responds by widening blood vessels in the pulp, to increase delivery of white blood cells to fight the infection. When widened blood vessels press on nerves within the pulp, a toothache results.

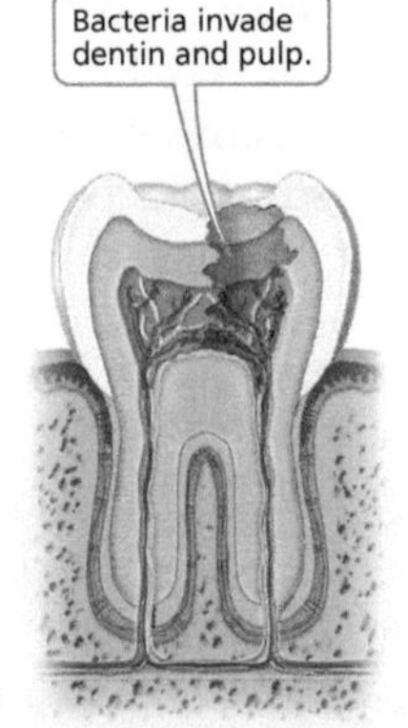

Step 4: Bacteria can then infect the softer dentin beneath the enamel and later the pulp at the heart of the tooth.

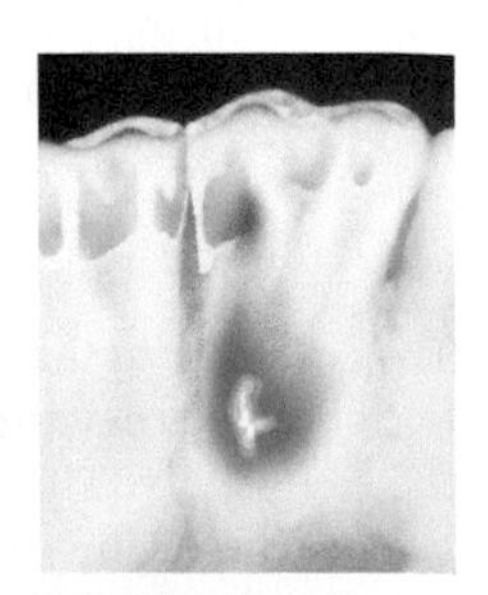

A dental cavity can be seen as an orange area in this artificially colored x-ray of teeth.

FIGURE 3b(ii).4 **The development of a dental cavity**

Gum disease, which affects two of three middle-aged people in the United States, is a major cause of tooth loss in adults. *Gingivitis* (*gingiv–*, the gums; *–itis*, inflammation of), an early stage of gum disease, occurs when plaque that has formed along the gum line causes the gums to become inflamed and swollen. The swollen gums can bleed and do not fit as tightly around the teeth as they should. The pocket that forms between the tooth and the gum traps additional plaque. The bacteria in the plaque can then attack the bone and soft tissues around the tooth, a condition called *periodontitis* (*peri–*, around; *dont,* teeth; *–itis,* inflammation of). As the tooth's bony socket and the tissues that hold the tooth in place are eroded, the tooth becomes loose.

Salivary Glands and Chemical Digestion

Three pairs of salivary glands—the sublingual (below the tongue), submandibular (below the jaw), and parotid (in front of the ears)—release their secretions, collectively called **saliva,** into the mouth (Figure 3b(ii).5). As we chew, food is mixed with saliva. Water in saliva moistens food, and mucus binds food particles together, making it easier for the food to pass through the GI tract.

Saliva also contains an enzyme, called **salivary amylase,** that begins to chemically digest starches into shorter chains of sugar. You will notice the result of salivary amylase activity if you chew a piece of bread for several minutes: The bread will begin to taste sweet. Try it.

Tongue: Taste and Food Manipulation

The tongue is a large skeletal muscle studded with taste buds. Our ability to control the position and movement of the tongue is critical to both speech and the manipulation of food within the mouth. Once food molecules are dissolved in saliva, the chemicals in the food can stimulate receptors in taste buds located primarily on the tongue. Information from the taste buds, along with input from the olfactory receptors in the nose, helps us to monitor the quality of food. For instance, spoiled or poisonous food usually tastes and smells bad, so we can spit it out before swallowing. The tongue moves food to position it for crushing and grinding by the teeth, to mix it with saliva, and to shape it into a small, soft mass, called a *bolus,* that is easily swallowed. The tongue also initiates swallowing by pushing the bolus to the back of the mouth.

Pharynx

The **pharynx,** which is the passageway commonly called the throat, is shared by the respiratory and digestive systems. When we swallow, food is pushed from the mouth, through the pharynx, and into the **esophagus,** the tube that connects the pharynx to the stomach.

Swallowing consists of a voluntary component followed by an involuntary one. When a person begins to swallow, the tongue pushes the bolus of softened and moistened food into the pharynx (Figure 3b(ii).6). Once food is in the pharynx, it is too late to change one's mind about swallowing. Sensory receptors in the wall of the pharynx detect the presence of food and stimulate the involuntary swallowing reflex. Reflex movements of the soft palate prevent food from entering the nasal cavities. Other involuntary muscle contractions push the larynx (the voice box, commonly called the Adam's apple) upward. The movement of the larynx causes a cartilaginous flap called the *epiglottis* to move, covering the opening to the airways of the respiratory system (the glottis). The movement of the epiglottis prevents food from entering the airways. Instead, food is pushed into the esophagus.

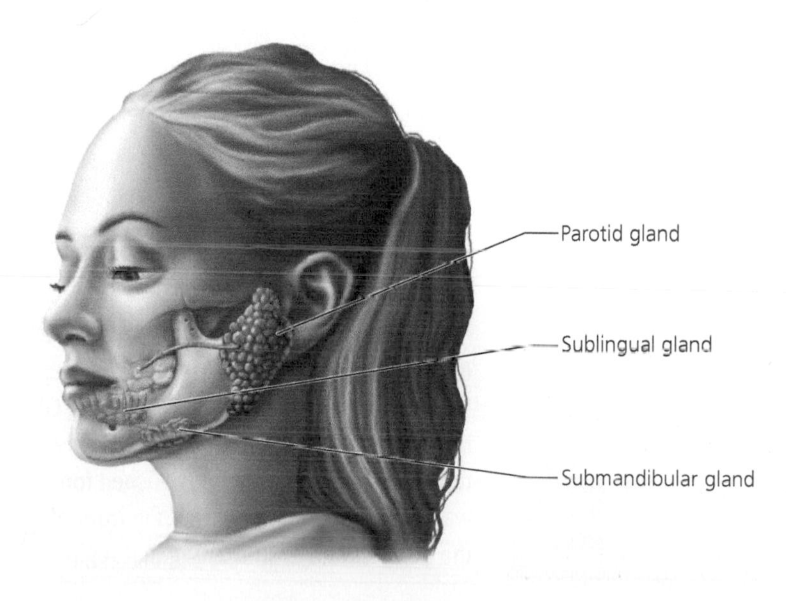

FIGURE 3b(ii).5 **Three pairs of salivary glands release their secretions into the mouth. These secretions, collectively called saliva, make food easier to swallow, dissolve substances so they can be tasted, and begin the chemical digestion of starch.**

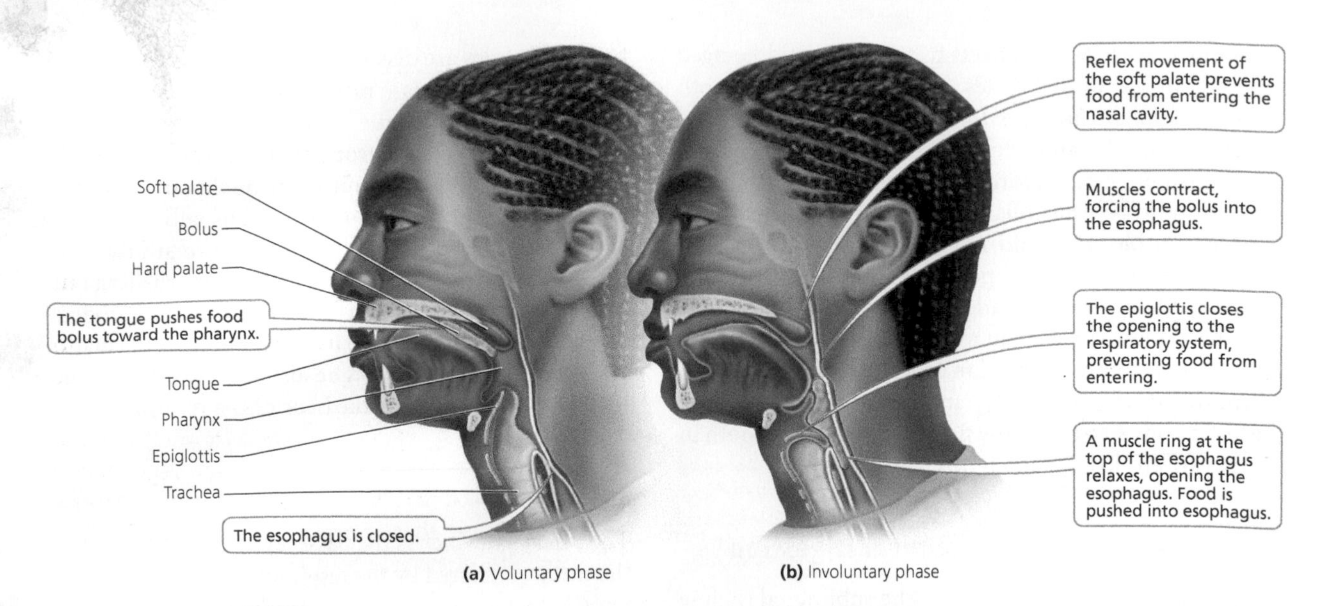

Soft palate
Bolus
Hard palate
The tongue pushes food bolus toward the pharynx.
Tongue
Pharynx
Epiglottis
Trachea
The esophagus is closed.
Reflex movement of the soft palate prevents food from entering the nasal cavity.
Muscles contract, forcing the bolus into the esophagus.
The epiglottis closes the opening to the respiratory system, preventing food from entering.
A muscle ring at the top of the esophagus relaxes, opening the esophagus. Food is pushed into esophagus.
(a) Voluntary phase
(b) Involuntary phase

FIGURE 3b(ii).6 **Swallowing consists of (a) voluntary and (b) involuntary phases**

Esophagus

The esophagus is a muscular tube that conducts food from the pharynx to the stomach. Food is moved along the esophagus and all the rest of the GI tract by rhythmic waves of muscle contraction called **peristalsis.** In the esophagus, small intestine, and large intestine, peristalsis is produced by the two layers of muscle in the muscularis. The muscles of the inner layer circle the tube, causing a constriction when they contract. The muscles in the outer layer run lengthwise, causing a shortening of the region where they contract. The presence of food stretches the walls in one region of the tube, and this triggers the contraction of circular muscles in the region of the tube immediately behind the food mass. When these circular muscles contract, that region of the tube pinches inward, pushing food forward. The food then stretches the next adjacent region of the tube, again stimulating contraction of circular muscles behind it. At the same time, longitudinal muscles in front of the food contract, shortening this region and widening its walls to receive the food. We see, then, that gravity is not important in moving food along the digestive tract. It is possible, therefore, to swallow while standing on your head or in the weightless conditions of outer space (Figure 3b(ii).7).

Stomach

The **stomach** is a muscular sac that is well designed to carry out its three important functions: (1) storing food and regulating the release of food to the small

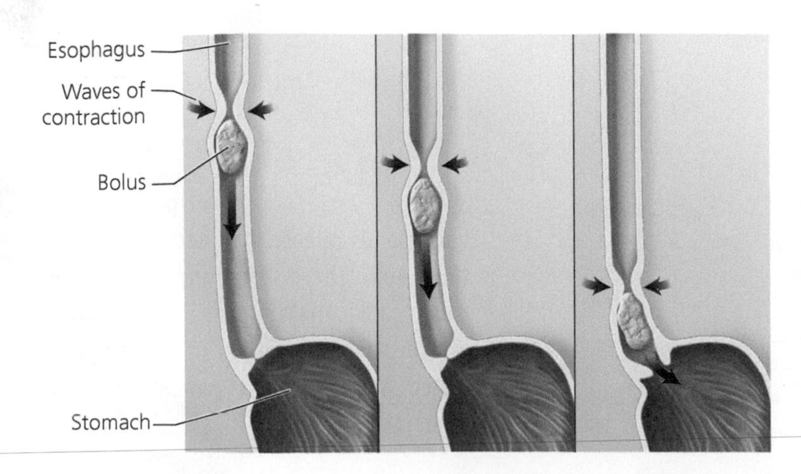

Esophagus
Waves of contraction
Bolus
Stomach

FIGURE 3b(ii).7 **Peristalsis is a wave of muscle contraction that pushes food along the esophagus and the entire remaining GI tract. When circular muscles contract, the tube is narrowed and food is pushed forward. The longitudinal muscles in front of the bolus contract, shortening that region.**

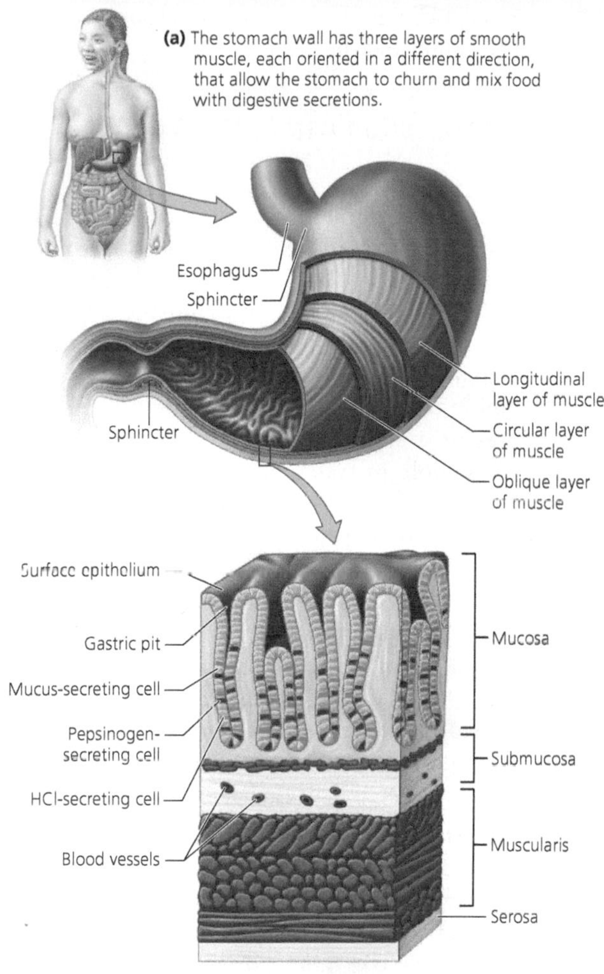

(a) The stomach wall has three layers of smooth muscle, each oriented in a different direction, that allow the stomach to churn and mix food with digestive secretions.

(b) Gastric glands in the wall of the stomach produce gastric juice, a mixture of hydrochloric acid and pepsin.

(c) The holes seen in this electron micrograph are the gastric pits, openings in the stomach wall through which gastric glands release their secretions.

FIGURE 3b(ii).8 **The structure of the stomach is well suited to its functions of churning food with digestive secretions, storing food, and beginning protein digestion.**

intestine, (2) liquefying food, and (3) carrying out the initial chemical digestion of proteins. The structure of the stomach is shown in Figure 3b(ii).8.

Storage of Food and Regulation of the Release of Food to the Small Intestine

Like any good storage compartment, the stomach is expandable and has openings that can close to seal the contents within as well as open for filling and emptying. When empty, the stomach is a small, J-shaped sac that can hold only about 50 ml (a quarter of a cup) without stretching. However, the wall of the empty stomach has folds that can spread out, allowing the stomach to expand as it fills. When fully expanded, as after a large meal, the stomach can hold several liters of food.

Bands of circular muscle called sphincters guard the openings at each end of the stomach and regulate the release of food to the small intestine. Contraction of a sphincter closes the opening, and relaxation of a sphincter allows material to pass through.

Liquefaction of Food

Food is generally stored and processed within the stomach for 2 to 6 hours. The stomach wall has three layers of smooth muscle, each oriented in a different direction. The coordinated contractions of these layers twist, knead, and compress the stomach contents, physically breaking food into smaller pieces. This additional mechanical digestion occurs as the food is churned and mixed with secretions produced by the glands of the stomach until it is a soupy mixture called **chyme.**

Initial Chemical Digestion of Proteins

Chemical digestion in the stomach is limited to the initial breakdown of proteins. The lining of the stomach has millions of gastric pits, within which are **gastric glands** containing several types of secretory cells. Certain secretory cells produce hydrochloric acid (HCl), which kills most of the bacteria swallowed with food or drink. Hydrochloric acid also breaks down the connective tissue of meat and activates pepsinogen, which is secreted by other cells in the gastric glands. Once activated by HCl, pepsinogen becomes **pepsin,** a protein-digesting enzyme. When the mixture of pepsin and HCl, called *gastric juice,* is released into the stomach, the pepsin begins the chemical digestion of the protein in food. Still other cells within the gastric glands secrete mucus, which helps protect the stomach wall from the action of gastric juice. Although not related to the digestive function of the stomach, a very important material secreted by the gastric glands is *intrinsic factor,* a protein necessary for the absorption of vitamin B_{12} from the small intestine.

The stomach wall is composed of the same materials that gastric juice is able to attack, so various protections are in place to keep the stomach from digesting itself. One, mentioned previously, is the presence of mucus.

Mucus forms a thick, protective coat that prevents gastric juice from reaching the cells of the stomach wall. The alkalinity of mucus helps to neutralize the HCl. Another protection is that pepsin is produced in an inactive form (pepsinogen) that cannot digest the cells that produce it. In addition, neural and hormonal reflexes regulate the production of gastric juice so that little is released unless food is present to absorb and dilute it. Finally, if the stomach lining is damaged, it is quickly repaired. The high rate of cell division in the stomach lining replaces a half million cells every minute. As a result, you have a new stomach lining every 3 days!

Very little absorption of food and other ingested materials occurs in the stomach because food simply has not been broken down into molecules small enough to be absorbed. Notable exceptions are alcohol and aspirin. The absorption of alcohol from the stomach is the reason its effects can be felt very quickly, especially if there is no food present to dilute it. The absorption of aspirin can cause bleeding of the wall of the stomach, which is the reason aspirin should be avoided by people who have stomach ulcers (see the Health Issue essay, *Heartburn and Peptic Ulcers—Those Burning Sensations*).

Small Intestine

The next region of the digestive tract, the **small intestine,** has two major functions: chemical digestion and absorption. As food moves along this twisted tube, it passes through three specialized regions: the duodenum, the jejunum, and the ileum. Chyme from the stomach enters the **duodenum,** the first region of the small intestine, in squirts, so that only a small amount enters the small intestine at one time. Digestive juices also enter the duodenum from the pancreas and liver. However, most chemical digestion and absorption occur in the *jejunum* and the *ileum.*

Chemical Digestion within the Small Intestine

Within the small intestine, a battery of enzymes completes the chemical digestion of virtually all the carbohydrates, proteins, fats, and nucleic acids in food. Although both the small intestine and the pancreas contribute enzymes, most of the digestion that occurs in the small intestine is actually performed by pancreatic enzymes (Table 3b(ii).2).

Fats present a special digestive challenge because they are insoluble in water. You have observed this when the oil (a fat) quickly separates from the vinegar (a water solution) in your salad dressing. In water, droplets of fat tend to coalesce into large globules. This poses a problem for digestion because lipase, the enzyme that chemically breaks down fats, is soluble in water and not in fats. As a result, lipase can work only at the surface of a fat globule. Large fat globules have less combined surface area than do smaller droplets, so their digestion by lipase proceeds more slowly.

Bile, a mixture of water, ions, cholesterol, bile pigments, and bile salts, plays an important role in the digestion of fats. The bile salts emulsify fats; that is, they keep fats separated into small droplets that disperse in liquid. This separation exposes a larger combined surface area to lipase, making the digestion and absorption of fats faster and more complete. Bile is produced by the liver, is stored in the gallbladder, and acts in the small intestine.

We have more to say about the pancreas, liver, and gallbladder shortly.

TABLE 3b(ii).2 Major Digestive Enzymes

Site of Production	Enzyme	Site of Action	Substrate and Products
Salivary glands	Salivary amylase	Mouth	Polysaccharides into shorter molecules
Stomach	Pepsin	Stomach	Proteins into protein fragments (polypeptides)
Pancreas	Trypsin	Small intestine	Proteins and polypeptides into smaller fragments
	Chymotrypsin	Small intestine	Proteins and polypeptides into smaller fragments
	Amylase	Small intestine	Polysaccharides into disaccharides
	Carboxypeptidase	Small intestine	Polypeptides into amino acids
	Lipase	Small intestine	Triglycerides (fats) into fatty acids and glycerol
	Nucleases (deoxyribonuclease and ribonuclease)	Small intestine	DNA or RNA into nucleotides
Small intestine	Maltase	Small intestine	Maltose into glucose units
	Sucrase	Small intestine	Sucrose into glucose and fructose
	Lactase	Small intestine	Lactose into glucose and galactose
	Aminopeptidase	Small intestine	Peptides into amino acids

Structure of the Small Intestine

The small intestine, the primary site of absorption in the digestive system, is extremely effective at its task because it is long and has several structural specializations that vastly increase its surface area (Figure 3b(ii).9). First, the entire lining of the small intestine is pleated, like an accordion, into circular folds. These circular folds increase the surface area for absorption and cause chyme to flow through the small intestine in a spiral pattern. The spiral flow helps mix the chyme with digestive enzymes and increases its contact with the absorptive surfaces. Covering the entire lining surface are tiny 1-mm projections called **villi** (singular, villus). The villi give the lining a velvety appearance and, like the pile on a bath towel, increase the absorptive surface. Indeed, the villi increase the surface area of the small intestine tenfold. In addition, the absorptive epithelial cells covering the surface of each villus contain thousands of microscopic projections, called *microvilli*, that increase the surface area of the small intestine by another 20 times. The microvilli form a fuzzy surface, known as a *brush border*. The circular folds, villi, and microvilli create a surface area of 300 to 600 m^2—greater than the size of a tennis court!

The core of each villus is penetrated by a network of capillaries and a **lacteal,** which is a lymphatic vessel. As substances are absorbed from the small intestine, they cross only two cell layers: the epithelial cells of the villi and the wall of either a capillary or a lacteal. Most materials enter the epithelial cells by active transport, facilitated diffusion, or simple diffusion (Figure 3b(ii).10). Monosaccharides, amino acids, water, ions, vitamins, and minerals diffuse across the capillary wall into the bloodstream and are delivered to body cells. The products of fat digestion, glycerol and fatty acids,

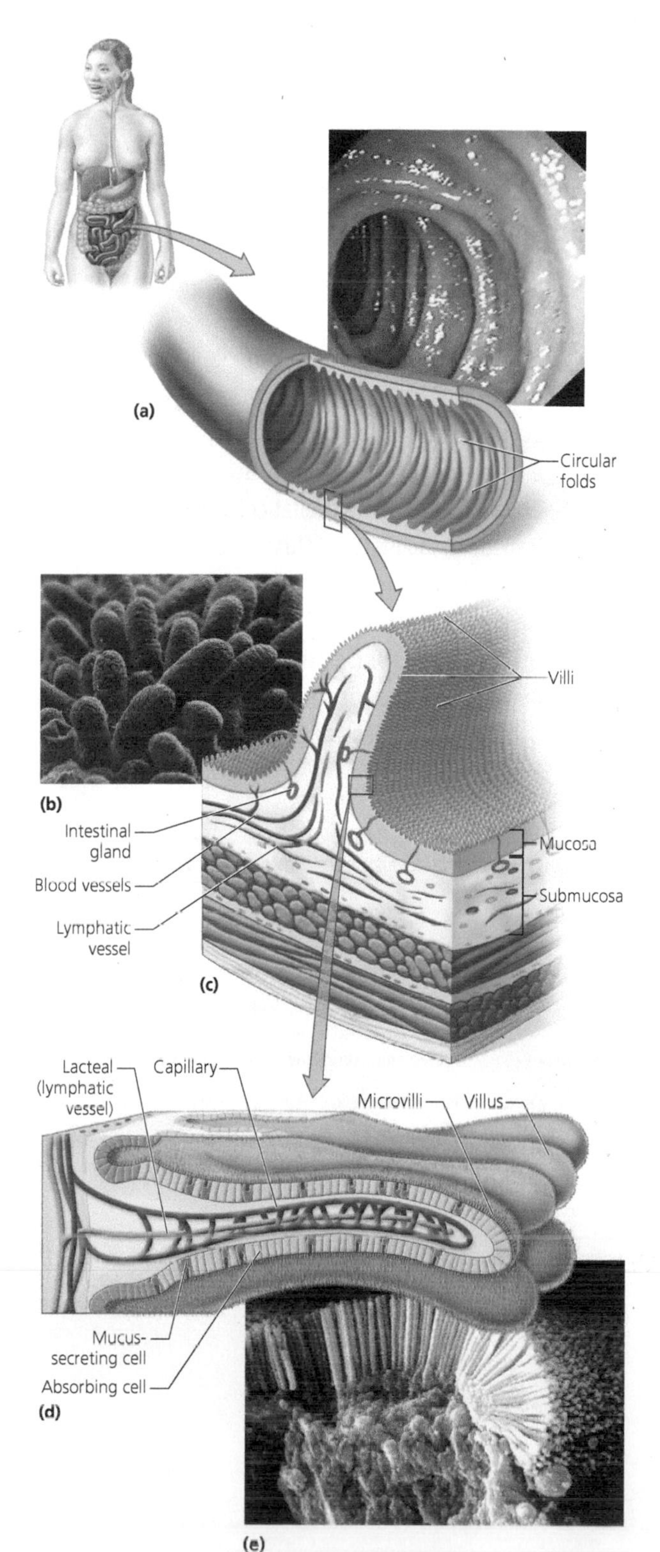

Q *List three structural adaptations of the small intestine that increase its surface area for absorption of digested nutrients.*

FIGURE 3b(ii).9 The small intestine is specialized for the absorption of nutrients by structural modifications that increase its surface area. (a) Its wall contains accordion-like pleats called circular folds. (b) This electron micrograph shows the intestinal villi, the numerous fingerlike projections on the intestinal lining (the mucosa in part c). (d) The surface of each villus bristles with thousands of microscopic projections (of cell membranes) called microvilli. In the center of each villus, a network of blood capillaries, which carries away absorbed products of protein and carbohydrate digestion as well as ions and water, surrounds a lacteal (a small vessel of the lymphatic system) that carries away the absorbed products of fat digestion. (e) An electron micrograph of the microvilli that cover each villus.

A *Circular folds, villi, and microvilli.*

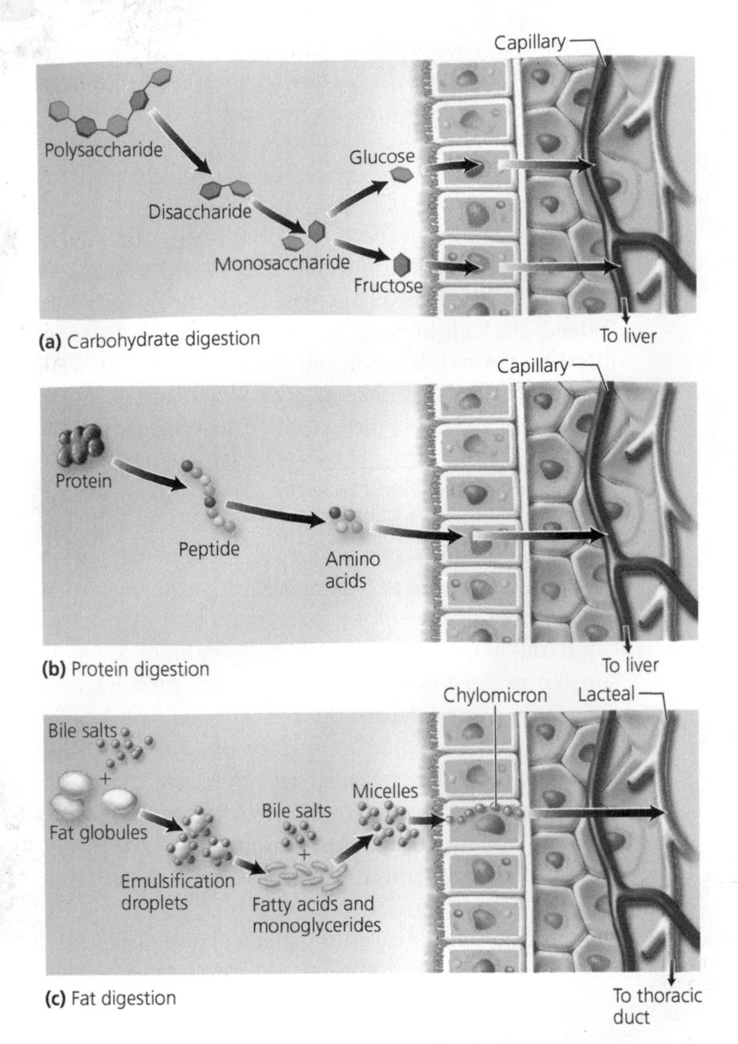

FIGURE 3b(ii).10 **The small intestine is the primary site for chemical digestion and absorption. The digestive products, such as monosaccharides, amino acids, fatty acids, and glycerol, enter absorptive epithelial cells of villi by active transport, facilitated diffusion, or diffusion. Monosaccharides and amino acids, along with water, ions, and vitamins, then enter the capillaries within the villus and are carried to body cells by the bloodstream. The products of fat digestion diffuse into the lacteal within the villus.**

combine with bile salts in the small intestine, creating particles called *micelles* (pronounced my-*cells*). When a micelle contacts an epithelial cell of a villus, the products of fat digestion easily diffuse into the cell. Within an epithelial cell, the glycerol and fatty acids are reassembled into triglycerides, mixed with cholesterol and phospholipids, and coated with special proteins, thus becoming part of a complex known as a *chylomicron.* The protein coating makes the fat soluble in water, allowing it to be transported throughout the body. The chylomicrons leave the epithelial cell by exocytosis. Chylomicrons are too large to pass through capillary walls. However, they easily diffuse into the more porous lacteal and enter the lymphatic system, which carries them to the bloodstream.

Accessory Organs: Pancreas, Liver, and Gallbladder

The pancreas, liver, and gallbladder are not part of the GI tract. However, they play vital roles in digestion by releasing their secretions into the small intestine. The functions of the secretions of the accessory organs are summarized in Table 3b(ii).3.

TABLE 3b(ii).3 Review of Accessory Structures of the Digestive System

Structure	Secretions/Functions	Site of Action of Chemical Secretions
Salivary glands (sublingual, submandibular, parotid)	Secrete saliva, a liquid that moistens food and contains an enzyme (amylase) for digesting carbohydrates	Mouth
Pancreas	Digestive secretions include bicarbonate ions that neutralize acidic chyme and enzymes that digest carbohydrates, proteins, fats, and nucleic acids	Small intestine
Liver	Digestive function is to produce bile, a liquid that emulsifies fats, making chemical digestion easier and facilitating absorption	Small intestine
Gallbladder	Stores bile and releases it into small intestine	Small intestine

Pancreas

The **pancreas** is an accessory organ that lies behind the stomach, extending toward the person's left from the small intestine. Pancreatic juice drains from the pancreas into the pancreatic duct, which fuses with the common bile duct from the liver just before entering the duodenum of the small intestine (Figure 3b(ii).11). In addition to enzymes, pancreatic juice contains water and ions, including bicarbonate ions that are important in neutralizing the acid in chyme when it emerges from the stomach. Neutralization is essential for optimal enzyme activity in the small intestine.

Collectively, the pancreatic enzymes and intestinal enzymes break nutrients into their component building blocks: proteins to amino acids, carbohydrates to monosaccharides, and triglycerides (a type of lipid) to fatty acids and glycerol.

Liver

The nutrient-laden blood from the capillaries in the villi travels through the hepatic portal vein to the **liver**, the largest internal organ in the body, which has a variety of metabolic and regulatory roles. A portal system consists of the blood vessels that link two capillary beds. The hepatic portal system delivers blood from a capillary bed in the small intestine to a second capillary bed in the liver (Figure 3b(ii).12).

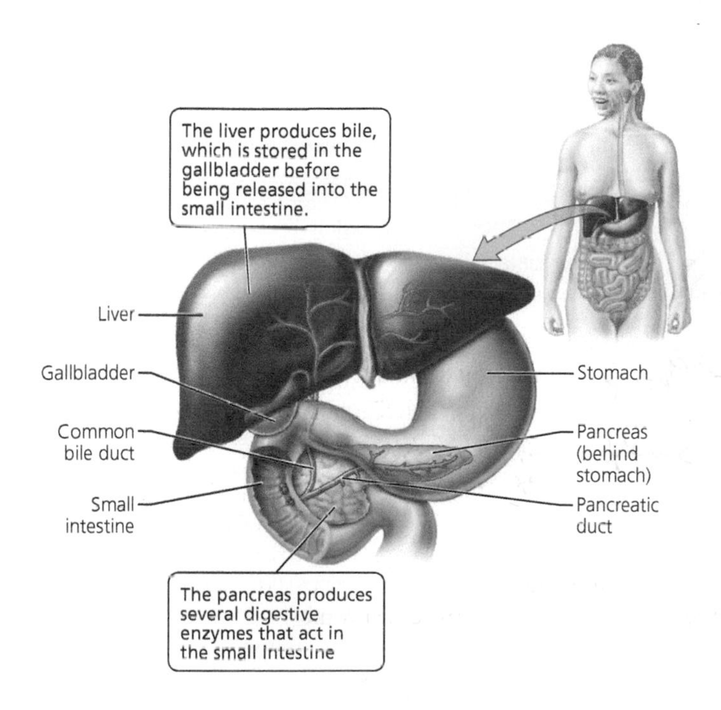

FIGURE 3b(ii).11 The pancreas, liver, and gallbladder are accessory organs of the digestive system

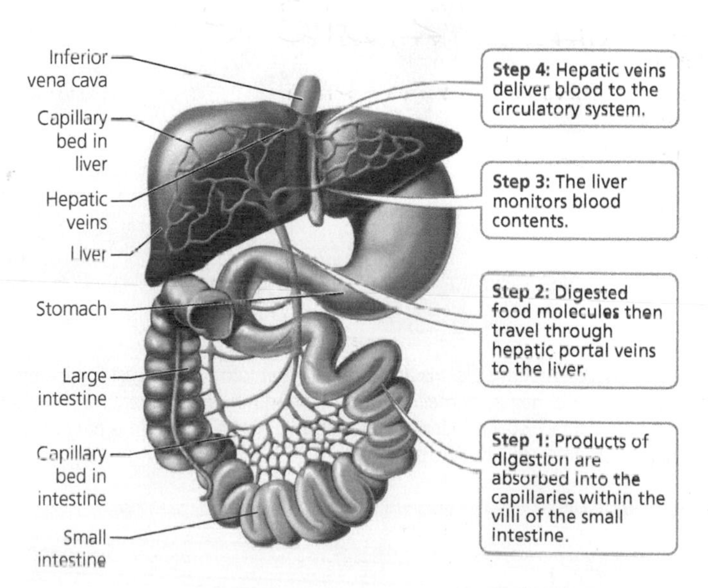

Inferior vena cava
Capillary bed in liver
Hepatic veins
Liver
Stomach
Large intestine
Capillary bed in intestine
Small intestine
Step 4: Hepatic veins deliver blood to the circulatory system.
Step 3: The liver monitors blood contents.
Step 2: Digested food molecules then travel through hepatic portal veins to the liver.
Step 1: Products of digestion are absorbed into the capillaries within the villi of the small intestine.

Q *Where are the two capillary beds in the hepatic portal system? What does the liver do in this system?*

FIGURE 3b(ii).12 A portal system transports blood from one capillary bed to another. In the hepatic portal system the hepatic portal vein carries blood from the capillary network of the villi of the small intestine to the capillary beds of the liver. The liver monitors blood content and processes nutrients before they are delivered to the bloodstream.

A *The small intestine and the liver. The liver monitors and adjusts blood content.*

Health Issue

Heartburn and Peptic Ulcers—Those Burning Sensations

Heartburn is a burning sensation behind the breastbone that occurs when acidic gastric juice backs up into the esophagus. At least 30% of all Americans suffer from heartburn on a monthly basis and 10% on a daily basis. Heartburn occurs when the pressure of the stomach contents overwhelms the sphincter at the lower end of the esophagus. In some people, this sphincter is weak and unable to keep stomach contents out of the esophagus. A person with a normal esophageal sphincter will experience heartburn when the stomach contents exert a greater pressure than usual against the sphincter, as might occur after a large meal, during pregnancy, when lying down, or when constipated. Acidic foods, such as tomatoes and citrus fruits, and spicy, fatty, or caffeine-containing products can aggravate the problem by causing the sphincter to relax and open. Tight clothing also worsens heartburn, because it compresses the stomach, increasing the pressure against the sphincter.

There are several treatments for heartburn. Antacids will provide temporary relief. Unfortunately, long-term use of certain antacids can have undesirable side effects. The fizzing bicarbonate types are high in sodium and should be avoided by people with high blood pressure. Others are high in calcium, which might promote the formation of kidney stones and stimulate the production of stomach acid. Newer medications, such as Tagamet, Zantac, Pepcid, Axid, Prilosec, and Nexium, decrease the production of stomach acid, which as we have seen is required at normal levels.

People who have chronic heartburn—at least one attack per week—have an increased risk of developing cancer of the esophagus. The risk increases with the frequency of attacks and the number of years of experiencing heartburn. Those who have one attack per week have a risk eight times higher than normal. Esophageal cancer is particularly aggressive and has become more common in recent years. It is detected using a test called endoscopy, in which a thin, lighted tube is snaked down the throat. A more recently developed means of detecting potentially harmful changes in the esophagus is the PillCam ESO. The patient swallows a camera that is about the size of a vitamin pill. As the camera moves through the esophagus, it takes thousands of pictures and sends them to a small recording device worn by the patient.

At some point in their lives, nearly 13% of Americans experience a failure of the mechanisms that protect the stomach and duodenum from their acidic contents, so that the lining of some region in the GI tract becomes eroded. The resulting sore resembles a canker sore of the mouth and is called a peptic ulcer (Figure 3b(ii).A). Although a peptic ulcer may form in the esophagus or the stomach, the most common site is the duodenum of the small intestine. Ulcers are usually between 10 and 25 mm (0.33 and 1 in.) in diameter and may occur singly or in multiple locations.

The symptoms of an ulcer are variable. A common symptom is abdominal pain, which can be quite severe. Vomiting, loss of appetite, bloating, indigestion, and heartburn are other common symptoms. However, some people with ulcers, especially those who are taking nonsteroidal anti-inflammatory drugs (NSAIDs), have no pain. Unfortunately, the degree of pain is a poor indicator of the severity of ulceration. Often, people with no symptoms are unaware of their ulcers until serious complications develop. Gastric juice can erode the lining of the GI tract until it bleeds. In some cases, the ulcer can eat a hole completely through the wall of the GI tract (a condition called perforated ulcer). Recurrent ulcers can cause scar tissue to form, which may narrow or block the lower end of the stomach or duodenum.

Although acidic gastric juice is the direct cause of peptic ulcers, factors that interfere with the mechanisms that normally protect the lining of the GI tract from the acid are considered to be the real causes. For example, NSAIDs, which include aspirin, ibuprofen, and naproxen, can cause ulcers because they slow the production of chemicals called prostaglandins, which normally help protect the lining of the GI tract from damage by acid.

The leading cause of peptic ulcers, however, is an infection with the bacterium *Helicobacter pylori*. More than 80% of persons with ulcers in the stomach or duodenum are infected with *H. pylori*. This bacterium produces an alkaline compound that neutralizes the stomach acid. These corkscrew-shaped bacteria live in the layer of mucus that protects the lining of the GI tract. Here, the bacteria attract body defense cells—specifically, macrophages and neutrophils—that cause inflammation leading to ulcer formation. Toxic chemicals produced by the bacteria also contribute to ulcers.

H. pylori infections may last for years. These bacteria affect more than a billion people throughout the world and approximately 50% of the people in the United States who are over 60 years of age. For some reason, however, only about 10% to 15% of those who are infected actually develop peptic ulcers. Besides ulcers, an *H. pylori* infection is a risk factor for esophageal and stomach cancer. However, it may soon be possible to vaccinate children against this bacterium, thereby reducing the risk of both peptic ulcers and stomach cancer.

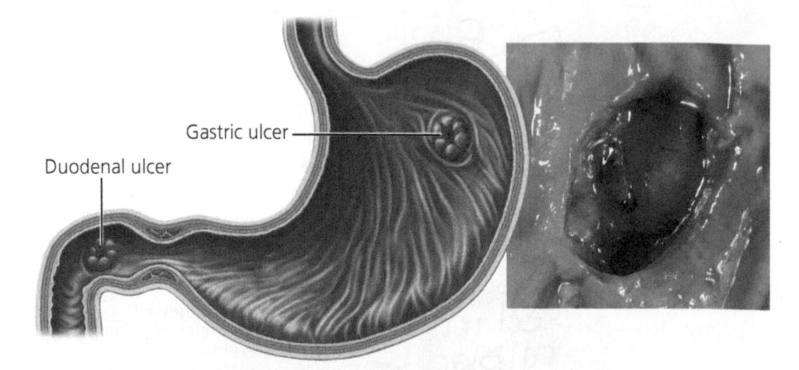

FIGURE 3b(ii).A A peptic ulcer is an open sore that forms when gastric juice erodes the lining of the esophagus, stomach, or, most commonly, the duodenum. The ulcer shown in this stomach wall is bleeding. The most common symptom is abdominal pain that occurs when the stomach is empty.

We have already seen that the liver's primary role in digestion is to produce bile. One of its other roles is to control the glucose level of the blood, either removing excess glucose and storing it as glycogen or breaking down glycogen to raise blood glucose levels. Thus, the liver keeps the glucose levels of the blood within the proper range. The liver also packages lipids with protein carrier molecules to form lipoproteins, which transport lipids in the blood. After the liver adjusts the blood composition, the blood is returned to the general circulation through the hepatic veins. In addition, the liver stores iron and vitamins A, D, E, K, B_{12}, and folate.

The liver also removes poisonous substances, including lead, mercury, and pesticides, from the blood and in some cases breaks them down into less harmful chemicals. What's more, the liver converts the breakdown products of amino acids into urea, which can then be excreted by the kidney. These are but a few of the approximately 500 functions of the liver.

Considering the liver's many vital functions, it is no surprise that diseases of the liver can be serious and life threatening. Cirrhosis is a condition in which the liver becomes fatty and gradually deteriorates, its cells eventually being replaced by scar tissue.

Hepatitis is inflammation of the liver. It is most commonly caused by one of six viruses, designated as A, B, C, D, E, and G. Although all the hepatitis viruses attack the liver and destroy liver cells, there are differences in their means of transmission and their symptoms, as well as their severity. All forms of hepatitis do have one symptom in common: healthy liver cells remove bilirubin, a yellowish pigment produced by the breakdown of red blood cells, from the bloodstream and use it to make bile. Liver cells injured by hepatitis viruses stop filtering bilirubin from the blood. The accumulating bilirubin is deposited in the skin and the whites of the eyes, giving them a yellowish tint. This condition, called jaundice, is characteristic of any disease that damages the liver.

Currently, about 4 million people in the United States have hepatitis C, and most of them have no idea that they are infected. For years, the disease has spread silently because it has no outward warning signs or very mild symptoms—vague fatigue, or flu-like muscle and joint pain. It is spread primarily through contaminated blood. Hundreds of thousands of intravenous drug users have been infected by sharing contaminated needles. Hepatitis C can also be spread through contaminated needles used in body piercing or tattooing. Before there was a way to test for the virus, many people became infected when they received transfusions with contaminated blood.

Gallbladder

After it is produced by the liver, bile is stored, modified, and concentrated in a muscular, pear-shaped sac called the **gallbladder.** When chyme enters the small intestine, a hormone causes the gallbladder to contract, squirting bile through the common bile duct into the duodenum of the small intestine.

Bile is rich in cholesterol. Sometimes, if the balance of dissolved substances in bile becomes upset, a tiny crystalline particle precipitates out of solution. Cholesterol and other substances can then build up around the particle to form a *gallstone* (Figure 3b(ii).13). Many

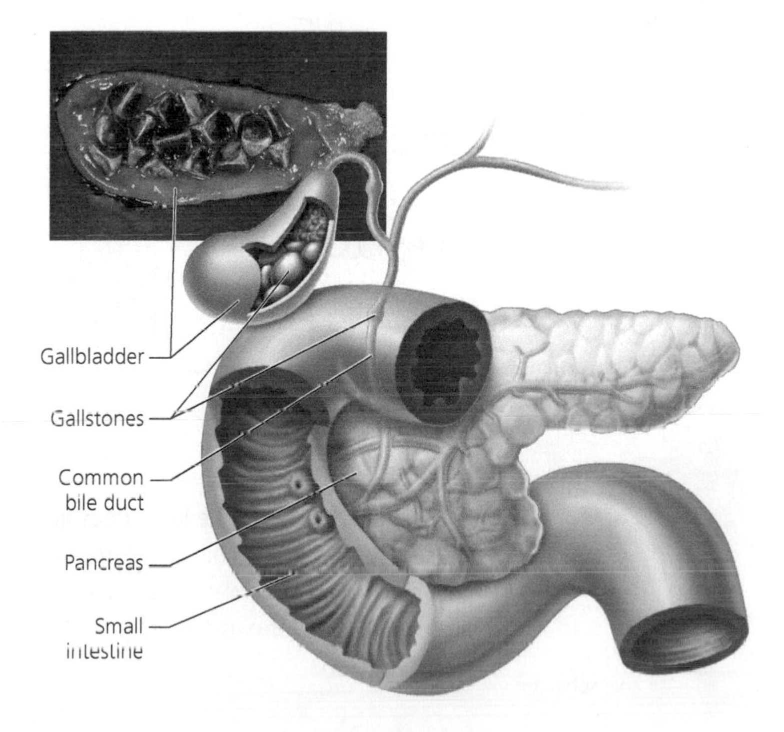

FIGURE 3b(ii).13 Gallstones consist primarily of cholesterol that has precipitated from bile during storage in the gallbladder. A gallstone can intermittently or continuously block the ducts that drain bile into the small intestine. The photograph shows a gallbladder and several gallstones.

people develop several gallstones, which can cause problems if they block the flow of bile and may necessitate surgical removal of the gallbladder.

Large Intestine

Now that we have discussed the accessory organs that assist digestion and absorption in the small intestine, we go back to following the movement of ingested substances through the GI tract. The material that was not absorbed in the small intestine moves into the final major structure of the digestive system, the **large intestine.** The principal functions of the large intestine are (1) to absorb most of the water remaining in the indigestible food residue, thereby adjusting the consistency of the waste material, or feces; (2) to store the feces; and (3) to eliminate them from the body. The large intestine is home to many types of bacteria, some of which produce vitamins that may be absorbed for use by the body.

Regions of the Large Intestine

The large intestine has four regions: the cecum, colon, rectum, and anal canal, as shown in Figure 3b(ii).14. The **cecum** is a pouch that hangs below the junction of the small and large intestines. Extending from the cecum is another slender, wormlike pouch, called the **appendix.** The appendix has no digestive function. Some scientists believe the appendix plays a role in the immune system, which protects the body against disease.

Each year, about 1 in 500 people develops *appendicitis,* inflammation of the appendix. Appendicitis is usually caused by an infection that arises in the appendix after it becomes blocked by a piece of hardened stool from the cecum, food, or a tumor. After the blockage occurs, bacteria that are normally present in the appendix can multiply and cause an infection. At first, appendicitis is usually experienced as vague bloating, indigestion, and a mild pain in the region of the navel (bellybutton). As the condition worsens, the pain becomes more severe and is localized in the region of the appendix, the lower right abdomen. The pain is typically accompanied by fever, nausea, and vomiting. When appendicitis is diagnosed, antibiotics are administered and the infected appendix is surgically removed. Untreated infection in the appendix usually causes the appendix to rupture, allowing its infected contents to spill into the abdominal cavity. Spillage from the appendix generally leads to infection and inflammation throughout the abdomen (a condition called peritonitis), which is potentially fatal.

The largest region of the large intestine, the **colon,** is composed of the ascending colon on the right side of the abdomen, the transverse colon across the top of the abdominal cavity, and the descending colon on the left side (see Figure 3b(ii).14). Although much of the water that is originally in chyme is absorbed in the small intestine, the material entering the colon is still quite liquid. The colon absorbs 90% of the remaining water and sodium and potassium ions. The material left in the large intestine after passing through the colon is called feces and consists primarily of undigested food, sloughed-off epithelial cells, water, and millions of bacteria. The brown color of feces comes from bile pigments.

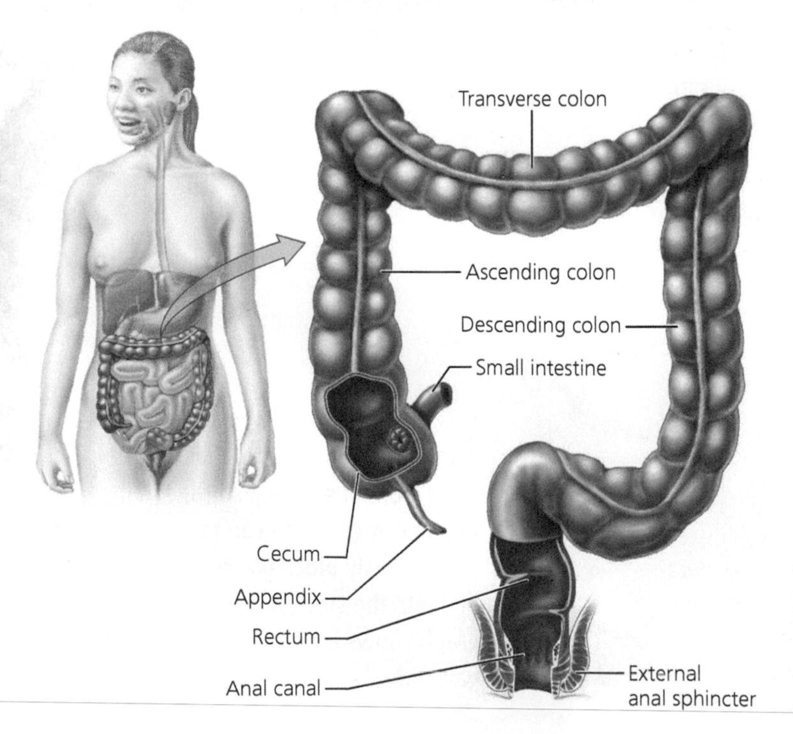

FIGURE 3b(ii).14 The large intestine consists of the cecum, colon, rectum, and anal canal. It absorbs water from undigested material, forming the feces, and houses bacteria.

stop and THINK

Certain foods–beans, for instance–are notorious for producing intestinal gas. Beans contain large amounts of certain short-chain carbohydrates that our bodies are unable to digest. How is the nutritional content of beans related to flatulence?

The bacteria in the colon are not normally disease causing and, in fact, are beneficial. Intestinal bacteria produce several vitamins that we are unable to produce on our own, including vitamin K and some of the B vitamins. Some of these vitamins are then absorbed from the colon for our own use. There are roughly 50 species of bacteria, including the well-known *Escherichia coli* (*E. coli*) that live in the healthy colon. Bacteria are nourished by undigested food and by material that we are unable to digest, including certain components of plant cells. When the intestinal bacteria use the undigested and indigestible food for their own nutrition, their metabolic processes liberate gas that sometimes has a foul odor. Although most of the gas is absorbed through the intestinal walls, the remaining gas can produce some embarrassing moments when released as flatus.

People who are *lactose intolerant* lack the enzyme lactase, which is normally produced by and acts in the small intestine. Lactase breaks down lactose, the primary sugar in milk, into its component monosaccharides. Without lactase, then, lactose moves intact into the colon, where it provides a nutritional bonanza for the bacteria living there. As a result, when people who are lactose intolerant consume milk products, the intestinal bacteria ferment the lactose and produce the gases carbon dioxide and methane that, in turn, produces bloating, gas, and abdominal discomfort. Although lactose intolerance is common in adults, it is not dangerous. Problems can usually be avoided by swallowing capsules or tablets of lactase or by modifying the diet to avoid dairy products.

Periodic peristaltic contractions move material through the large intestine, but these contractions are slower than the contractions in the small intestine. Slower contractions allow for adequate water absorption as material moves through the large intestine. Eventually, the feces are pushed into the **rectum,** stretching the rectal wall and initiating the *defecation reflex.* Nerve impulses from the stretch receptors in the rectal wall travel to the spinal cord, which sends motor impulses back to the rectal wall, stimulating muscles there to contract and propel the feces into the **anal canal.** Two rings of muscles, called sphincters, must relax to allow *defecation,* the expulsion of feces. The internal sphincter relaxes automatically as part of the defecation reflex. The external sphincter is under voluntary control, allowing the person to decide whether to defecate. Conscious contraction of the abdominal muscles can increase abdominal pressure and help expel the feces.

Disorders of the Colon

The water absorption that occurs in the colon adjusts the consistency of feces. When material passes through the colon too rapidly, as might occur when colon contractions are stimulated by toxins from microorganisms or by excess food or alcoholic drink, too little water is absorbed. As a result, the feces are very liquid. This condition, which results in frequent loose stools, is called *diarrhea.* Persistent diarrhea can be dangerous, especially in an infant or young child, because it can lead to dehydration. Diarrhea is a major cause of death worldwide.

On the other hand, if material passes through the colon too slowly, too much water is absorbed, resulting in infrequent, hard stools—a condition called *constipation.* People who are constipated may need to strain during bowel movements. Straining increases pressure within veins in the rectum and anus, causing them to stretch and enlarge. The wall of the large intestine also experiences great pressure during a strained bowel movement. Then, like the inner tube of an old tire, the weaker spots in the intestinal wall can begin to bulge outward, forming small outpouchings called diverticula (singular, diverticulum; Figure 3b(ii).15). Diverticula are very common in people older than age 50. When diverticula do not cause problems or symptoms, the condition is called *diverticulosis.* But if the diverticula become infected with bacteria and inflamed, the condition is then called *diverticulitis,* which can cause abrupt, cramping abdominal pain, a change in bowel habits, fever, and rectal bleeding. Diverticulitis can be treated by changing the diet (increasing fiber, avoiding nuts), taking drugs that reduce muscle spasms, or having surgery.

stop and THINK

Stimulant laxatives enhance peristalsis in the large intestine but do not affect the small intestine. Some people with eating disorders use laxatives to speed the movement of food through the digestive system, thinking that the calories in the food will not be absorbed. Are they correct in their thinking? After purging in this way, the person may weigh less on the bathroom scale. What accounts for the weight loss? Could laxative use help a person lose body fat?

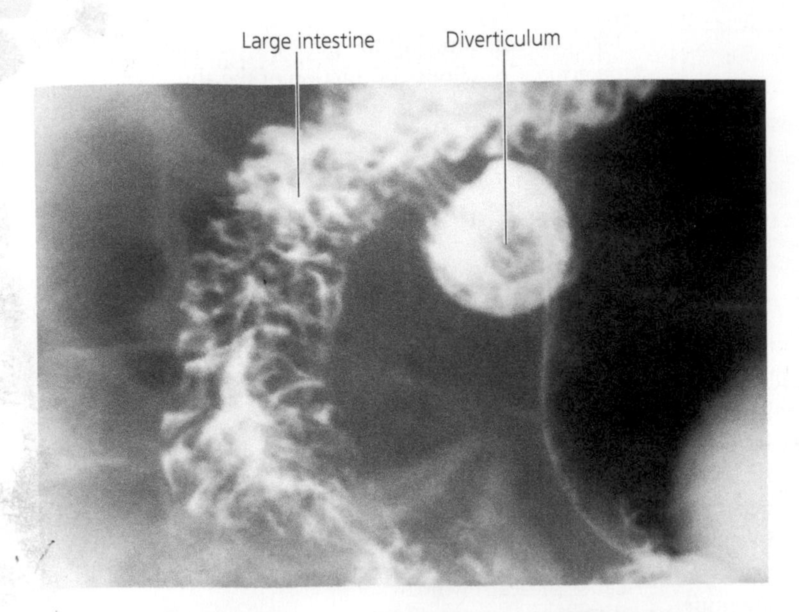

FIGURE 3b(ii).15 **A diverticulum is a small pouch that forms in the wall of the large intestine and is usually caused by repeated straining during bowel movements. A high-fiber diet results in softer, bulkier stools that are easier to pass, thus making it less likely that diverticula will form.**

Cancers of the colon or rectum are common and can be deadly. *Colorectal cancer* is the second leading cause of cancer deaths. Early detection and treatment cut the risk of death dramatically.

Colorectal cancer begins with a small, noncancerous growth called a polyp. If the polyp continues to grow, genetic mutations accumulate in them that can transform a cell into a cancerous tumor. Polyps may take as long as 10 years to grow and turn cancerous, generally allowing plenty of time for detection. Sometimes polyps bleed, so one sign of colorectal polyps and perhaps cancer is blood in the stool. However, the blood is not usually visible and must be detected with a diagnostic test. Because many polyps do not bleed, screening methods that allow a direct view of the wall of the rectum and colon are generally more effective. A long, flexible fiber-optic tube is threaded through the first third of the colon in a procedure known as a sigmoidoscopy, or through the entire colon in a procedure called a colonoscopy. If a polyp is detected, it can be removed and biopsied to determine whether it is cancerous.

NERVES AND HORMONES IN DIGESTION

As we have seen, ingested material moves along the GI tract, stopping for specific kinds of treatment along the way. For digestion to occur, enzymes must be present in the right place at the right time. However, because the body is composed of many of the same substances found in food, digestive enzymes should not be released until food is present (otherwise the enzymes might start digesting the digestive system). Both nerves and hormones play a role in orchestrating the release of digestive secretions, timing the release of each to the presence of food at each stop.

Food spends little time in the mouth; so to be effective, saliva must be secreted quickly. Because nervous stimulation is faster than hormonal stimulation, it is not surprising to learn that the nervous system controls salivation. Some saliva is released before food even enters the mouth, which may begin to "water" simply at the *thought* of food—and certainly begins at the sight or smell of food. The major trigger for salivation, however, is the presence of food in the mouth—its flavor and pressure. Salivary juices continue to flow for some time after the food is swallowed, helping to rinse out the mouth.

While food is still being chewed, neural reflexes stimulate the stomach lining to begin secreting gastric juice and mucus. Distention of the stomach by swallowed food, along with the presence of partially digested proteins, stimulates cells in the stomach lining to release the hormone *gastrin*. Gastrin enters the bloodstream and circulates throughout the body and back to the stomach, where it increases the production of gastric juice.

The presence of acidic chyme in the small intestine, which triggers local nerve reflexes, is the most important stimulus for the release of enzymes from both the small intestine and the pancreas, as well as bile from the gallbladder. Acid chyme also causes the small intestine to release several hormones that, in turn, are responsible for the release of digestive enzymes and bile. For instance, one hormone, *vasoactive intestinal peptide*, is released from the small intestine into the bloodstream and is carried back to the small intestine, where it causes the release of intestinal juices. At the same time, the small intestine releases a second hormone, *secretin*, which stimulates the release of sodium bicarbonate from the pancreas into the small intestine to help neutralize the acidity of chyme. A third hormone from the small intestine is *cholecystokinin,* which causes the pancreas to release its digestive enzymes and causes the gallbladder to contract and release bile. The neural and hormonal controls of the digestive system are summarized in Tables 3b(ii).4 and 3b(ii).5, respectively.

TABLE 3b(ii).4 Examples of Neural Controls on Digestive Activity

Stimulus	Effect
Sight of food, thought of food, presence of food in mouth	Release of saliva from salivary glands
Chewing food	Release of gastric juice (enzymes from stomach and HCl) and mucus from cells of stomach lining
Presence of acidic chyme in small intestine	Release of enzymes from small intestine and pancreas into the small intestine; release of bile from gallbladder into small intestine; increased motility in small intestine

TABLE 3b(ii).5 Examples of Hormonal Control on Digestive Activity

Hormone	Stimulus	Origin	Target	Effects
Gastrin	Distention of stomach by food; presence of partially digested proteins in stomach	Stomach	Stomach	Release of gastric juice (enzymes from stomach and HCl)
Vasoactive intestinal peptide	Presence of acidic chyme in small intestine	Small intestine	Small intestine	Release of enzymes from small intestine
Secretin	Presence of acidic chyme in small intestine	Small intestine	Pancreas	Release of sodium bicarbonate from pancreas into small intestine to neutralize acidic chyme
Cholecystokinin	Arrival of chyme-containing lipids	Small intestine	Pancreas Gall bladder	Release of enzymes from pancreas Contraction of gallbladder and release of bile

PART IV: HOMEOSTASIS, ALLOSTASIS AND STRESS

Chapter 4a: What is Stress?

Chapter 4b: Homeostasis, Allostasis and Allostatic Load*

Chapter 4c: Physiological Complexity and Health*

*Posted on course website at http://www.pearsoncustom.com/can/uguelph_biohealth

CHAPTER 4A

WHAT IS STRESS?

Taken from *Health: The Basics*, Fifth Canadian Edition, by Rebecca J. Donatelle and Angela M. Thompson

Stress: it's hard to live with and it's almost impossible to live without. We are bombarded by a host of subtle and not-so-subtle internal and external factors that may lead us to feel stressed from the moment we wake until we finally fall asleep. Even during our sleep, noise, temperature changes, and other activities can lead to a stress response. Rarely does a day go by without someone you know talking about being under stress—from homework, part-time or full-time job responsibilities, financial pressures, relationship demands, volunteer-related responsibilities, technology, or other problems. Despite our best efforts to ignore it, stress-inducing factors cannot be run from, hidden from, or wished away. For some people, these factors provide the stimulus for growth and higher levels of achievement. Yet for others, they increase the likelihood of dysfunctional or abnormal behaviours or illness.

Stress in itself is neither positive nor negative. Rather, it is our reactions to it that can be described as positive or negative. Whether we are aware of it or not, our reactions to stress can become the habits that lead us either to health-enhancing personal growth or to debilitation in the form of migraines, substance misuse and abuse, circulatory disorders, asthma, gastrointestinal problems, and hypertension (high blood pressure). In addition, our responses to stress can lead to psychological and social problems, including dysfunctional relationships. In this chapter, we explore why and how these reactions take place and how we may be able to control them and channel our efforts more effectively such that our health and wellness is not compromised.

WHAT IS STRESS?

Many things that have contributed to making you who you are also influence how you respond to potentially stress-inducing events in your life. Stress responses—such as breaking out in a cold sweat before asking someone to go out on a date, becoming anxious or irritated around people who speak too slowly or drive too cautiously, feeling nervous when meeting new people, a racing heart rate when you are called upon to make a response in class, feeling edgy or pumped when it is time to play a game—are all unique by-products of past experiences. Your family, friends, environmental conditions, general health status, drug use, personality, and support systems influence how you respond to a given event.

Stress means different things to different people. Often, we think of **stress** as an externally imposed factor that threatens or makes a demand on our minds and bodies. If your hard-nosed instructor tells you that you have to do a 10-page paper in the next week, that's an external stressor. However, most stress is actually self-imposed and is usually the result of an internal state of emotional tension that occurs in response to the various demands of living. Stress may manifest itself in physiological and psychological responses to the demands placed upon us, and many researchers define stress as these responses. Most current definitions state that stress is the mental and physical response of our bodies to the various demands or expectations in our lives. It is our thoughts about the situation we are in that are the critical factor; if we decide the demands of the situation outweigh the skills we have, then we are likely to judge he situation as stressful and react with a stress response.

A **stressor** is any physical, social, or mental event or condition that forces our minds and bodies to react or adjust. Stressors may be tangible, such as an angry parent or a disgruntled roommate, or intangible, such as the mixed emotions associated with meeting your significant other's parents for the first time. Adjustment is our attempt to cope with a given situation. As we try to adjust to the various stressors in our lives, strain may develop. Strain is the wear and tear our bodies and minds sustain during the process of adjusting to or resisting a stressor.

Most of our daily activities involve situations or events that may elicit a stress response. Positive stress, or stress that results from generally positive situations, is called **eustress**. Getting married, starting school, beginning a career, developing new friendships, and learning a new physical skill can lead to eustress. **Distress**, or negative stress, is caused by things such as financial problems, injury or illness, the death of a loved one, trouble at work, academic difficulties, the unexpected ending of a relationship, and not being sure of your purpose in life. Both types of stress provide an opportunity for personal growth and can lead to personal satisfaction.

Although the mind and body each react to eustress and distress, most of us only worry about our reactions to distress. We cannot prevent distress; like eustress, it is simply a part of life. However, we can learn to recognize the events likely to cause stress and to anticipate our reactions to them by learning to practise prestress coping skills and develop post-stress management techniques. Developing these skills depends on our understanding of the major components of stress.

The Mind–Body Connection: Physical Responses

Although much has been written about the negative effects of stress, researchers have only recently begun to untangle the complex web of physical and emotional interactions that actually cause the body to wear down over time. As a result, stress is often described generically as a "disease of prolonged arousal" that often leads to other negative health effects. Nearly all systems of the body become potential targets for this onslaught, and the long-term effects may be devastating.

Much of the initial impetus for studying the health effects of stress came from prospective observations. Specifically, researchers in the Framingham Study noted that highly stressed individuals were significantly more likely to experience cardiovascular diseases. Monkeys exposed to high levels of unpredictable stressors in studies also showed significantly increased levels of disease and mortality. In a study of susceptibility to cold viruses, subjects who reported recent high levels of stressors were much more likely to catch a cold after inhaling large doses of a cold virus through their nose than their counterparts who reported fewer stressors. While the battle over the legitimacy of these observations continues to be waged in research labs, the correlation of too much stress over long periods of time to selected ailments has gained credibility. What do repeated experiences of the stress response actually do to the body? Why are health and wellness experts concerned about repeated responses or reactions to stress? What are the short- and long-term health implications of the stress response?

Stress is a positive factor in life when it creates opportunities for personal growth and satisfaction rather than psychological or physiological wear and tear.

Stress and Impaired Immunity

Although the health effects of prolonged stress responses provide dramatic evidence of the direct and indirect impact of stress on body organs, researchers continue to seek more definitive answers about the exact physiological and psychological mechanisms that lead to specific diseases. The science of **psychoneuroimmunology (PNI)** analyzes the relationship between the mind's response to stress and the functioning of the immune system.

Much of the preliminary PNI data on stress and immune functioning focused on the hypothesis that during periods of prolonged stress elevated levels of adrenal hormones, including cortisol, destroy or reduce the ability of the white blood cells known as "natural killer T cells." Killer T cells aid in the immune response, and when they are suppressed the body is less effective at combatting illnesses. In addition to killer T suppression, many other body processes are disrupted and overall disease-fighting capacity is reduced. Although several studies have supported the hypothesis of a relationship between increased stress levels and greater risk of disease in times of grief, social disruption, poor mood, and so forth, there is still much to be learned about possible mediating factors. Other studies have shown no increased risk for disease among people suffering from prolonged arousal by stressors. These conflicting findings also emphasize the need to further examine the relationships of physical and mental health and wellness to stressors, stress responses, and coping mechanisms.

Stress: Our mental and physical responses to the demands placed upon us.

Stressor: A physical, social, or mental event or condition that forces us to adjust to it.

Eustress: Stress perceived as "good" because it results in positive change.

Distress: Stress perceived as "bad" because it potentially results in negative change.

Psychoneuroimmunology (PNI): Science that focuses on the relationship between the mind's response to stress and the functioning of the immune system.

THE GENERAL ADAPTATION SYNDROME

Every living organism attempts to achieve a state of balance known as **homeostasis**. In homeostasis, all physiological and psychological systems function smoothly, and equilibrium is maintained. When a stress is perceived, the mind and body adjust with an **adaptive response**, or an attempt to restore homeostasis. This adaptive response varies in intensity and physical manifestation from person to person and from stressor to stressor. Further, this response can vary within an individual from time to time, even in reaction to the same stressor.

The physiological and psychological responses to stress follow a pattern first recognized in 1936 by Hans Selye. The three-stage response to stress is called the **general adaptation syndrome (GAS)**. The phases of the GAS are alarm, resistance, and exhaustion (see Figure 4a.1).

Alarm Phase

During the alarm phase, a stressor disturbs homeostasis. The brain subconsciously perceives the stressor and prepares the body either to fight or to run away, a response sometimes called the "fight or flight response." The subconscious perceptions and appraisal of the stressor stimulate the areas in the brain responsible for emotions. Emotional stimulation, in turn, starts the physical reactions that we associate with stress (see Figure 4a.2). This entire process usually takes only a few seconds.

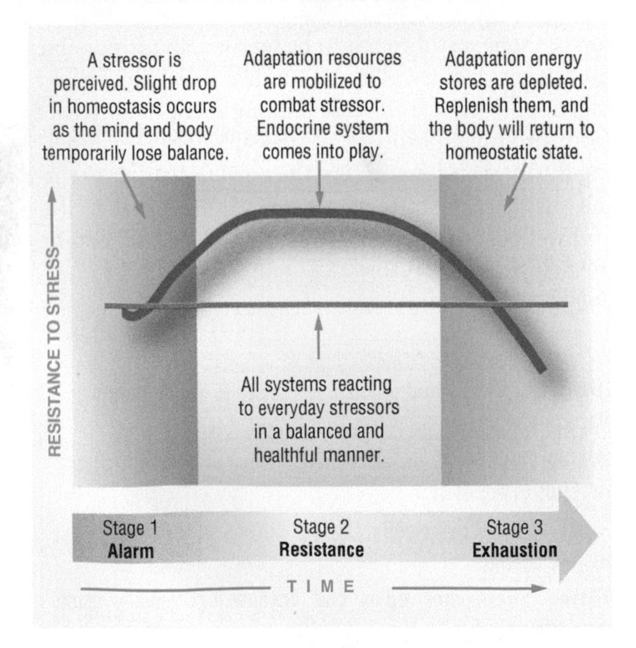

FIGURE 4a.1
The General Adaptation Syndrome

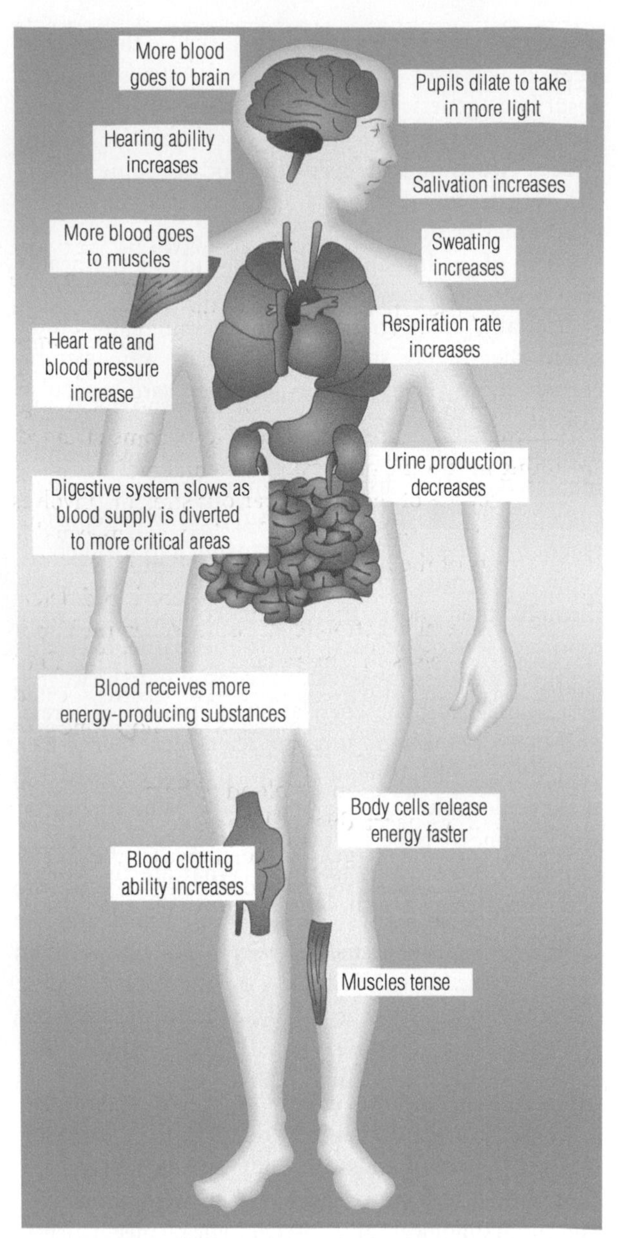

FIGURE 4a.2
The General Adaptation Syndrome: Alarm Phase

When the mind perceives a stressor (either real or imaginary), such as a potential attacker, the cerebral cortex, the region of the brain that interprets the nature of an event, is called to attention. If the cerebral cortex consciously or unconsciously perceives a threat, it triggers an instantaneous **autonomic nervous system (ANS)** response that prepares the body for action (that is, fight or flight). The ANS is the portion of the central nervous system that regulates bodily functions that we do not normally consciously control, such as heart rate, breathing, and glandular function. When we are stressed, the rate of these bodily functions increases dramatically to give us the physical strength to protect ourselves against an attack, or to mobilize internal forces. The ANS has two branches. One branch, the **sympathetic nervous system (SNS)**, energizes the body for either fight or flight by signalling the release of several stress hormones that increase heart and breathing rates, as well as many other responses. The other branch, the **parasympathetic nervous system (PNS)**, slows all the systems stimulated by the stress response. In other words, the PNS works in opposition to the SNS and attempts to restore homeostasis. In a healthy person, these two systems work together to maintain balance or homeostasis. Long-term stress can cause this balance to become strained, resulting in chronic physical and mental problems.

The response of the SNS to various stressors involves a complex series of biochemical exchanges between different parts of the body. The **hypothalamus**, a section of the brain, functions as the control centre and determines the overall reaction to stressors. When the hypothalamus perceives that extra energy is needed to fight or flee a stressor, it stimulates the adrenal glands, located near the top of the kidneys, to release the hormone **epinephrine**, also called adrenaline.

Epinephrine causes more blood to be pumped with each beat of the heart, dilates the alveoli (air sacs in the lungs) to increase oxygen intake, increases the rate of breathing, stimulates the liver to release more glucose (which fuels muscular contractions), and dilates the pupils to improve visual sensitivity. The body is then poised to act immediately. As epinephrine secretion increases, blood is diverted away from the digestive system, which can cause nausea and cramping if it occurs shortly after eating. Further, epinephrine dries nasal and salivary tissues, resulting in a dry mouth.

The stress response of the alarm phase also leads to longer-term reactions to stress. The hypothalamus triggers the pituitary gland, which in turn releases another powerful hormone, **adrenocorticotrophic hormone (ACTH)**. ACTH signals the adrenal glands to release **cortisol**, a hormone that facilitates the release of stored nutrients to meet energy demands. Finally, other parts of the brain and body release endorphins, the body's naturally occurring opiates, which relieve pain that may be caused by a stressor or the body's response to the stressor.

Resistance Phase

The resistance phase of the GAS begins almost immediately after the alarm phase kicks in. In this phase, the body has reacted to the stressor and adjusted in a way that begins to allow the system to return to homeostasis. As the sympathetic nervous system is working to energize the body via the hormonal action of epinephrine, norepinephrine, cortisol, and other hormones, the parasympathetic nervous system is working to keep these energy levels under control and attempting to return the body to a normal level of functioning.

Exhaustion Phase

In the exhaustion phase of the GAS, the physiological and psychological energy used to respond to a stressor (that is, the fight or flight impulse) has been depleted. Short-term response to stress would probably not deplete all a person's energy reserves, but chronic stressors may create continuous states of alarm and resistance. When a person no longer has the adaptation energy stores for responding to a distressor, burnout and serious illness may result.

what do you THINK?

How do you typically react to stressors? What happens to your body? To your mind? Do your responses cause you discomfort? Can you control your responses?

SOURCES OF STRESS

Eustress and distress have many sources, including psychosocial factors, such as change, pressure, inconsistent goals and behaviours, conflict, overload, and

Homeostasis: A balanced physical and mental state in which all the body's systems function smoothly.

Adaptive response: Form of adjustment in which the mind and body attempt to restore homeostasis.

General adaptation syndrome (GAS): The pattern followed by our physiological and psychological responses to stress, consisting of the alarm, resistance, and exhaustion phases.

Autonomic nervous system (ANS): The portion of the central nervous system that regulates bodily functions and is not normally consciously controlled.

Sympathetic nervous system (SNS): Branch of the ANS responsible for stimulating the stress response.

Parasympathetic nervous system (PNS): Part of the ANS responsible for slowing systems stimulated by the SNS.

Hypothalamus: A section of the brain that controls the SNS and directs the stress response.

Epinephrine: Also called adrenaline, a hormone that stimulates body systems.

Adrenocorticotrophic hormone (ACTH): A pituitary hormone that stimulates the adrenal glands to secrete cortisol.

Cortisol: Hormone released by the adrenal glands that facilitates the release of stored nutrients to meet energy demands.

burnout; environmental stressors, such as natural and human-made disasters; and self-imposed stressors including factors related to self-concept.

Psychosocial Sources of Stress

As you learned in the previous chapter, psychosocial health refers to the social, mental, emotional, and spiritual dimensions of health. These components combined define how we perceive our lives, relate to one another, and react to stress. Many psychosocial factors in our daily lives cause us to feel stressed. Our interactions with others, the subtle and not-so-subtle expectations we have for ourselves and others, the expectations others have for us, and the social conditions we work, play, and live in force us to adjust and readjust continually. Some of these stressors present real threats to our mental or physical well-being; others cause us to worry about things that may never happen. Still other stressors result from otherwise good psychosocial events—being around someone you are attracted to, meeting new friends, moving to a new and better apartment, celebrating a win or successful paper or exam.

Change

There is the potential to experience stress any time there is change, whether good or bad, in your normal daily routine. The more changes you experience and the more adjustments you must make as a result, the greater the stress response may be. In 1967, Holmes and Rahe analyzed the social readjustments experienced by more than 5000 patients, noting which events seemed to occur just before the onset of disease. They determined that certain events (positive and negative) were predictive of increased risk for illness. They called their scale for predicting stress overload and the likelihood of illness the Social Readjustment Rating Scale (SRRS). The SRRS has since been modified for certain groups, including university or college-aged students. Although many other factors must be considered, it is generally believed that the more stressors you have, the more likely you are to experience negative effects on your health and wellness and the more important it is to address your behaviours or situations before health problems occur. (See the Rate Yourself box.)

While Holmes and Rahe focused on such major sources of stress as a death in the family, psychologists such as Richard Lazarus focused on petty annoyances, irritations, and frustrations—collectively referred to as hassles—as sources of stress. Minor hassles—losing your keys, having the grocery bag rip on the way to the door, slipping and falling in front of everyone as you walk to your seat in class, finding that you went through a whole afternoon with a big chunk of spinach stuck in your front teeth—may seem unimportant, but Lazarus's research found that the cumulative effects of these minor hassles may be harmful in the long run.

Pressure

Pressure occurs when we feel forced to speed up, slow down, intensify, or shift the direction of our behaviours to meet a higher standard of performance. Pressures can be based on our personal goals and expectations or on a concern about what others may think of us. Pressure can also come from outside influences. Among the most significant and consistent of these are seemingly relentless demands from society that we look a certain way, compete in all that we do, and be all that we can be. The forces that push us to attempt to shape our bodies into an image that may not even be physiologically realistic for us or to compete for the best grades, the nicest cars, the most attractive partners, and the highest paying jobs create a lot of pressure to be the personification of success. Being pressured into doing something we do not want to do (for example, being pressured to go to a movie or party because everyone else is going, when you really need and want to be studying) can also be a source of frustration.

Inconsistent Goals and Behaviours

For many of us, negative stress effects are magnified when there is a conflict between our goals (what we value or hope to obtain in life) and our behaviours. For instance, you want good grades and your family expects them, yet you party and procrastinate throughout the term, spending very little time studying. Thus, your behaviours are inconsistent with your goals. On the other hand, if you choose to use your time well, study hard, and are committed to your school work, your goals and behaviours are congruent and you will not experience this kind of negative stress. Thwarted goals may lead to frustration, and frustration has been shown to be a significant disrupter of homeostasis (see Figure 4a.3).

Determining whether our behaviours are consistent with the goals we want to reach is an essential component of our efforts to maintain a balance in our lives. If we consciously strive to attain our goals in a very direct manner, our chances of success are greatly improved. If we deviate from the plan, or if we act in a manner that is inconsistent with our goals, significant stress may result that makes achieving our goals impossible, and they may then become negative sources of stress.

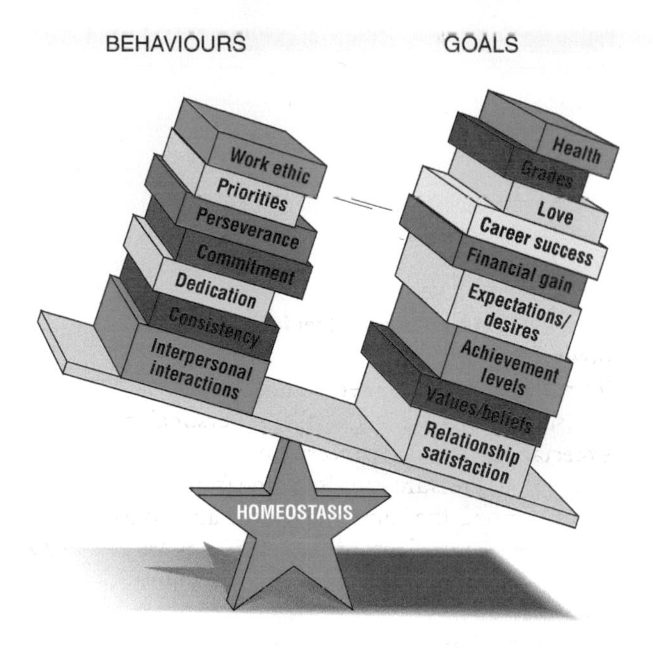

FIGURE 4a.3
Homeostatic Balance Requires Actions Related to Goals and Values

Conflict

Of all life's difficulties, **conflict** is probably the most common. Conflict occurs when we are forced to make challenging decisions concerning two or more competing motives, behaviours, or impulses, or when we are forced to face two incompatible demands, opportunities, needs, or goals. What if your best friends choose to smoke marijuana and you don't want to, yet you fear rejection? Such conflicts occur every day for most of us. Worrying about the alternatives, fretting, stewing, and becoming overly anxious are common responses when conflict occurs.

Overload

Overload occurs when we experience excessive time pressure, excessive responsibility, lack of support, or excessive expectations of ourselves and those around us. Have you ever felt that you had so many responsibilities that you could not possibly begin to fulfill them all? Have you longed for a weekend when you could just curl up and read a good book or take time out with friends and not feel guilty? These feelings typically occur when a person has been under continuous pressure for some time and as a result experiences overload. Students who are overloaded may experience anxiety about tests and assignments, poor self-concept, thoughts about dropping classes or dropping out of school, and other problems. In severe cases, in which they are unable to see any solutions to their problems, students may suffer from depression or resort to overeating or consuming alcohol or drugs.

> **try it NOW!**
> Write it down! Journal writing is a great way to cleanse the mind, release emotions, and draft strategies for resolution. The next time an event or situation activates your stress response, identify the emotions that accompany it and then list several options to bring closure to the event. You might also consider journaling a little every day—write about the good things that happened as well as the challenges and your feelings associated with each.

Burnout

People who regularly feel overload, frustration, and disappointment may eventually experience **burnout,** a state of physical and mental exhaustion caused by an excessive and continuous response to stress. People involved in the helping professions, such as teaching, social work, drug counselling, nursing, and psychology, appear to experience high levels of burnout, as do police officers, firefighters, and air-traffic controllers, who work in high-pressure, dangerous jobs.

Other Forms of Psychosocial Stress

Other forms of psychosocial stress include problems with adaptation (difficulty in adapting to life's changes), frustration (the thwarting or inhibiting of natural or desired behaviours or goals), overcrowding (the presence of too many people in one's space), discrimination (the unfavourable actions taken against people based on prejudices concerning race, ethnicity, religion, social status, gender, sex, sexual orientation, lifestyle, national origin, or physical characteristics), and socioeconomic events (inflation, unemployment, or poverty). People of different ethnic backgrounds and individuals who are homosexual may face disproportionately heavy impacts from these sources of stress.

Conflict: Simultaneous existence of incompatible demands, opportunities, needs, or goals.

Overload: A condition in which we feel pressured by constant and overwhelming demands made upon us.

Burnout: Physical and mental exhaustion as a result of the continuous experience of overload.

RATE YOURSELF

How Stressed Are You?

Each of us reacts differently to life's little challenges. Faced with a long line at the bank, most of us will get heated up for a few seconds before we shrug and move on. But for others—the one in five of us whom researchers call *hot reactors*—such incidents are an assault on good health. That's why rating your stress requires you to tally your life's stressors (Part One) and to figure out whether you are particularly susceptible to stress (Part Two). (As university or college students, you should consider your job as being a student.) You can then read the interpretation and make efforts to manage your stress response more effectively in the future.

PART ONE

The Stress in Your Life

How often are the following potentially stressful situations a part of your daily life?

1. Never
2. Rarely
3. Sometimes
4. Often
5. All the time

I work long hours.	1 2 3 4 5
There are signs my job is not secure.	1 2 3 4 5
Doing a good job goes unnoticed.	1 2 3 4 5
It takes all my energy just to make it through the day.	1 2 3 4 5
There are severe arguments at home.	1 2 3 4 5
A family member is seriously ill.	1 2 3 4 5
I am having problems with child care.	1 2 3 4 5
I do not have enough time for fun.	1 2 3 4 5
I am on a diet.	1 2 3 4 5
My family and friends count on me to solve their problems.	1 2 3 4 5
I'm expected to keep up a certain standard of living.	1 2 3 5 5
My neighbourhood is crowded or dangerous.	1 2 3 4 5
My home is a mess.	1 2 3 4 5
I cannot pay my bills on time.	1 2 3 4 5
I cannot save money.	1 2 3 4 5

Your Total Score

Below 38: You have a lower-stress life.

38 and above: You have a high-stress life.

PART TWO

Your Stress Susceptibility

Try to imagine how you would react in these situations:

1. You have been waiting 20 minutes for a table in a crowded restaurant, and the host seats a party that arrived after you. You feel your anger rise as your face gets hot and your heart beats faster.

   True or False

2. Your sister calls you out of the blue and starts to tell you how much you mean to her. Uncomfortable, you change the subject without expressing what you feel.

   True or False

3. You come home to find the kitchen looking like a disaster area and your partner (or roommate) lounging in front of the TV. You tense up and can not seem to shake your anger.

   True or False

4. Faced with a public-speaking event (such as a class presentation), you get keyed up and lose sleep for a day or more, worrying about how you will do.

   True or False

5. On Thursday, your repair shop promises to fix your car in time for a weekend trip. As the hours go by, you become increasingly worried that something will go wrong and your trip will have to be cancelled.

   True or False

Two or Fewer True: You are a Cool Reactor, someone who tends to roll with the punches when a situation is out of your control.

Three or More True: You are a Hot Reactor, someone who responds to mildly stressful situations with a "fight-or-flight" adrenaline rush that drives up blood pressure and can lead to heart rhythm disturbances, accelerated clotting, and damaged blood vessel linings. Some hot reactors can seem cool as a cucumber on the outside, but inside their bodies are silently killing them.

WHAT YOUR SCORES MEAN

Combine the results from Parts One and Two to get your total stress rating.

Lower-Stress Life/Cool Reactor

Whatever your problems, stress is not one of them. Even when stressful events do occur—and they will—your health is not likely to suffer.

Lower-Stress Life/Hot Reactor

You are not under stress—at least for now. Though you tend to overreact to problems, you have wisely managed your life to avoid the big stressors. Before you honk at the guy who cuts you off in rush-hour traffic, remember that getting angry can destroy thousands of heart muscle cells within minutes. Robert S. Eliot, author of *From Stress to Strength,* says hot reactors have no choice but to calm themselves down with rational thought. Ponder the fact that the only thing you will hasten by reacting is a decline in health. "You have to stop trying to change the world," Eliot advises, "and learn to change your response to it."

High-Stress Life/Cool Reactor

You are under stress, but only you know if it is hurting. Even if you normally thrive with a full plate of challenges, now you might be biting off more than you can chew. Note any increase in headaches, backaches, or insomnia; that is your body telling you to lighten your load. If your job is the main source of stress, think about reducing your hours. If that is not possible, find a way to make your job more enjoyable, and stress will become manageable.

High-Stress Life/Hot Reactor

You are in the danger zone. Make an extra effort to engage in physical activity, get enough sleep, and keep your family and friends close. Unfortunately, even being physically active and physically fit does little to protect you if your body is in perpetual stress mode. To survive, you may need to make major changes—walking away from a life-destroying job or relationship, perhaps—as well as to develop a whole new approach to life's hourly obstacles. Such effort will be rewarded, too. In one experiment, 77 percent of hot reactors were able to cool down—lower their blood pressure and cholesterol levels—by training themselves to stay calm.

Source: Reprinted by permission of the Health Publishing Group, a division of Time Publishing Ventures, Inc., from "How Stressed Are You?" *Health* (October 1994): 47. Researched by Lora Elise Ma. © 1994.

Environmental Stress

Environmental stress results from events occurring in our physical environment. Environmental stressors include natural disasters, such as floods, earthquakes, hurricanes, tornadoes, hail storms, blizzards, ice storms, and forest fires, and industrial disasters, such as chemical spills, accidents at nuclear power plants, and explosions. Often as damaging as one-time disasters are **background distressors**, such as noise, air, and water pollution or heat, humidity, cold, and windchills—although we may be unaware of them, and their effects may not become apparent for decades. As with other distressors, our bodies respond to environmental distressors with the GAS. People who cannot escape background distressors may exist in a constant resistance phase, which may also contribute to the development of stress-related disorders.

Moderate and vigorous intensity aerobic exercise is an effective stress management tool.

Self-Imposed Stress

Self-Concept and Stress

How we feel about ourselves, our attitudes toward others, and our perceptions and interpretations of the stressors in our lives are part of the psychological component of stress. Also included are the defence or coping mechanisms we have learned to use in various situations in response to stress.

The psychological system that governs our stress responses is called the **cognitive stress system**. It recognizes stressors; evaluates them on the basis of self-concept, past experiences, and emotions; and makes decisions about how to best cope with them. Our sensory organs serve as input channels for information reaching the brain. From that point on, attention to the problem, memory, reasoning, and problem solving processes are organized in various parts of the brain before we respond to the stressor. Because learning and memory involve the changing of various proteins in brain neurons, the emotions we experience during the stress response also "tickle" the memory-storage neurons and contribute to our responses. Behaviourally, we respond to the stressor in ways consistent with our memories of similar situations.

Self-esteem is closely related to the emotions engendered by past experiences. People with low self-esteem are more likely to feel helpless anger, an emotion experienced by people who have not learned to express anger in appropriate ways. People with helpless anger have usually learned that they are wrong to feel angry; therefore, instead of expressing their anger in healthy

Background distressors: Environmental stressors, such as heat, humidity, noise, etc. that result in the GAS even though we may be unaware of them.

Cognitive stress system: The psychological system that governs our emotional responses to stress.

BUILDING COMMUNICATION SKILLS

Expressing Anger Effectively

Expressing anger constructively is an important skill involved in learning to cope with intimate relationships, family interactions, and other stressful situations. Suggestions for constructively expressing anger are included in this textbox.

1. *Determine the reason behind your anger.* Is it due to a real event (for example, someone you trusted is spreading malicious gossip) or to a perception you have about a situation (friends are avoiding you, so you think someone may be gossiping)?
2. *Do not let your anger build.* When you become angry, take control, and decide what actions you need to take. Try not to act rashly, and do not stew for too long. Employ the 24–48 hour rule. Allow 24 hours to pass; if you are still angry, take action to manage the situation. If more than 48 hours pass and you do not do anything, let it go; it was not that important to you.
3. *If you decide to confront a person, select an appropriate time and place for the meeting.* Do not attack your target unexpectedly or in the presence of others: the person may become defensive. Give the person a general idea of what you want to discuss ahead of time and choose the appropriate time and location together.
4. *Stick to the main reason for your anger.* Bringing up a whole list of things that have made you angry over the last year will complicate the issue and make the other person want to create his or her own list of wrongs that you have committed. Plan in advance which issue you want to discuss. Be careful of using all inclusive statements such as "You always . . . " or "You never . . . ."
5. *Attack the problem rather than the person.* ("It made me angry that we had to leave early" instead of "You made me angry because you made us leave early.") Do not get into a battle over personal characteristics. Use "I" statements to communicate resentment or disappointment ("I feel angry that we had to leave the party so early"). "You" statements often put people on the defensive.
6. *Listen carefully to what the other person has to say.* Do not interrupt; give the other person a chance to speak. Listen rather than planning what you are going to say next. If the other person starts wandering from the issue, gently bring him or her back to the point. If the other person attacks you personally, stay in control and do not allow yourself to fight back.
7. *Treat the other person with respect.* Even though you may say the right things, your gestures and body language can reveal that you do not value what the other person has to say, that you are hostile, or that you are losing patience. Drumming your fingers, sighing, or rolling your eyes while the other person is talking often increases friction. Remember, communication is 90 percent non-verbal.
8. *Recognize when to quit.* Sometimes even the best-laid plans go awry. No matter what you do, the problem may appear impossible to resolve. In such situations, knowing when to quit, either temporarily or permanently, is a key factor in controlling anger and the stress that results from it. Agree to disagree. Nobody has to "win" the argument.
9. *When it is over, let it be over.* After you have done all that you can do, let go of your anger. Do not dwell in the past. Acknowledge your right to be angry, recognize it for what it was, and move on.

ways, they turn it inward. They "swallow" their anger in food, alcohol, or other drugs, or act in other self-destructive ways. See the Building Communication Skills box for a series of questions concerning expressing your anger effectively.

Self-esteem significantly affects various disease processes. People with low self-esteem create a self-imposed distressor that can impair the immune system's ability to combat disease. Some researchers believe that chronic distress can depress the immune system and thus increase the symptoms of such diseases as acquired immune deficiency syndrome (AIDS), herpes, multiple sclerosis, and Epstein-Barr syndrome.

Personality Types and Hardiness

A person's personality may contribute to the kind and degree of self-imposed stress he or she experiences. The coronary-disease-prone personality was first described by physicians Friedman and Rosenman in their book *Type A Behavior and Your Heart*. Although their work is now considered controversial, it is the basis for much current research.

Friedman and Rosenman identified two stress-related personality types: Type A and Type B. Type A personalities are hard-driving, competitive, anxious, time-driven, impatient, angry, and perfectionistic. Type B personalities are relaxed and non-competitive. According to Rosenman and Friedman, people with Type A characteristics are more prone to heart attacks than their Type B counterparts.

Researchers today believe that more needs to be discovered about Type A and Type B personalities before we can say that all people with a Type A personality will have greater risks for heart disease than those with a predominantly Type B personality. First

SKILLS FOR BEHAVIOUR CHANGE

Taming Technostress

Cellphones that ring or vibrate constantly with incoming calls or text messages; email lists that grow on your computer desktop like an out-of-control fungus; laptop computers that somehow end up in your luggage when you go on vacation; voice message systems that do not allow you to talk to a live person; and slow, slow, slow downloading of information. Can you feel your heart rate speeding up just thinking about these situations? On campuses across the country, students, faculty, and administrators are using electronic organizers, the internet, and other forms of technology. Email, the World Wide Web, and personal digital assistants (PDAs) are no longer flashy new tools but are now as commonplace as the backpack. Unfortunately, many people feel frustrated and distressed in their struggle to adapt to increasingly complex technology. As many as 85 percent of us have at least some level of discomfort around technology. If you are like millions of people today, you find that technology is often a daily terrorizer that raises your blood pressure, frustrates you, and prevents you from ever really getting away from it all. In short, you may be a victim of stressors that previous generations only dreamed (or had nightmares) about. Known as "technostress," this problem is defined as "personal stress generated by reliance on technological devices . . . a panicky feeling when they fail, and a state of near-constant stimulation, or being perpetually 'plugged in.'" When technostress grabs you, it may interact with other forms of stress to create a synergistic, never-ending form of stimulation that keeps your stress response reverberating all day.

Part of the problem, ironically, is that technology enables us to be productive. Because it encourages polyphasic activity, or "multitasking," people are forced to juggle multiple thoughts and actions at the same time, such as driving and talking on cellphones or checking handheld devices for appointments. People who multitask, however, are actually less efficient than those who focus on one project at a time. Moreover, there is clear evidence that multitasking contributes to auto accidents and other harmful consequences, including short-term memory loss. What is less clear is what happens to someone who is always plugged in. What are the symptoms of technology overload? It evokes typical stress responses by increasing heart rate and blood pressure and causing irritability and memory disturbances. Over time, many stressed-out people lose the ability to relax and find that they feel nervous and anxious when they are supposed to be having fun. Headaches, stomach and digestive problems, skin irritations, frequent colds, difficulty in wound healing, lack of sleep, ulcers, and other problems may result. Other red flags include gaps in your attentiveness and changes in your ability to concentrate. One study indicates that chronic stress may even thicken the waistline. Authors Michelle Weil and Larry Rosen describe *technosis,* a syndrome in which people get so immersed in technology that they risk losing their own identity. If you answer yes to questions such as, "Do you rely on preprogrammed systems to contact others?", "Do you feel stressed if you haven't checked your email within the last couple of hours?", or "Are you lost without your cellphone or PDA?" you may be too dependent on technology.

TIPS FOR FIGHTING TECHNOSTRESS

- *Enjoy the natural environment.* Take some time away from all forms of technology. Try to find a place that has few people and little noise—that usually means outdoors.
- *Become aware of what you are doing.* Log the time you spend on email, voice mail, etc. Set up a schedule to limit your use of technology. For example, spend no more than an hour per day answering emails or interacting on Facebook or MSN.
- *Give yourself more time for everything you do.* If you are surfing the web for resources for a term paper, start early rather than the night before the paper is due.
- *Manage the telephone—do not let it manage you.* Rather than interrupting what you are doing to answer, screen calls with an answering machine or caller ID. Get rid of call waiting, which forces you to juggle multiple calls, and subscribe to a voice mail service that takes messages when you are on the phone.
- *Set "time out" periods when you do not answer the phone, listen to the stereo, use the computer, or watch TV.* Switch off email notification systems so you are not notified of an incoming message during these periods.
- *Take regular breaks.* Even when working, take a short break every hour; get up, walk around, stretch, do deep breathing, get a glass of water, use the washroom, etc.
- *If you are working on the computer, look away from the screen and focus on something far away every 30 minutes.* Stretch your shoulders and neck hourly as you work. Play soft background music to help you relax.
- *When working on the computer, focus on one task at a time.* If you are working on a paper, close your email and instant messaging so that you can focus on your paper and not feel pressured to respond because "you've got mail" or someone has logged on to instant messaging.
- *Resist the urge to buy the newest and fastest technology.* Such purchases not only cause financial stress but also add to stress levels with the typical glitches that occur when installing and adjusting to new technology.
- *Do not take laptops, hand-held devices, or other technological gadgets on vacation.* If you must, take a cellphone for emergencies, turn it and your voice messaging system off, and use the phone only in true emergencies.
- *Back up materials on your computer at regular intervals.* Writing a term paper only to lose it during a power outage will send you into hyperstress very quickly.

- *Expect technological change.* The only constant with technology is improvement and change. No matter how at ease you are with your current computer, cellphone, PDA, etc., at some point you will need to move on to a new one.

Sources: D. Zielinski, "Techno-stressed?," *Presentations* 18.2 (2004): 28–34; L. D. Rosen and M. M. Weil, *TechnoStress: Coping with Technology @Work@Home@Play* (New York: John Wiley & Sons, 1997). Copyright © 1997. Material used by permission of John Wiley & Sons; M. Weil and L. Rosen, "Technostress: Are You a Victim of Technosis?" Retrieved 2004 from www.technostress.com/tstechnosis.htm; Yale University, "Stress May Cause Excess Abdominal Fat in Otherwise Slender Women, Study Conducted at Yale Shows," *ScienceDaily,* November 23, 2000; MayoClinic.com, "Are You a Slave to the Telephone?" Retrieved on November 1, 2000, from www.mayoclinic.com; S. Shellenbarger, "Multitasking Makes You Stupid: Studies Show Pitfalls of Doing Too Much at Once," *Wall Street Journal,* February 27, 2003: D1.

of all, most people are not one personality type or the other all the time. Second, there are many other unexplained variables that must be explored, such as why some Type A personalities seem to thrive in stress-filled environments. Now labelled Type C personalities, these individuals appear to succeed more often than Type B personalities and have good health even while displaying Type A patterns of behaviour.

Critics of the supposed links between these personality types and risk of disease argue that attempts to explain ill health by means of personal behavioural patterns have so far been crude. For example, Ragland and Brand contend that the Type A personality may be more complex than previously described. These researchers identified a "toxic core" in some Type A personalities. People with this toxic core are angry, distrustful of others, and have above-average levels of cynicism. Generally, people who are angry and hostile also have below-average levels of social support and other increased risks for ill health. It may be this toxic core rather than the hard-driving nature of the Type A personality that makes people more prone to self-imposed stress and its consequences.

Psychological hardiness has been identified as a characteristic that helps some people cope with the self-imposed stress associated with Type A behaviours. Psychologically hardy people are characterized by control, commitment, challenge, choices, and connectedness (sometimes called the "Type C personality"). People with a sense of control take control of their actions and are able to accept responsibility for their behaviours. People with a sense of commitment have good self-esteem and understand their purpose in life. These individuals choose to commit themselves to the things that matter to them and say no when the situation is not of personal importance. People with a sense of challenge see changes or struggles in life as stimulating opportunities for personal growth. Psychologically hardy people also make lifestyle choices that enhance their health, such as eating well, being physically active regularly, getting adequate sleep, developing meaningful relationships, making time for themselves, and so on. Finally, these individuals are connected to others in meaningful ways. This connectedness provides a level of social support that is health enhancing.

Modification of the Type A personality is possible when particular "learned" behaviours are modified. For example, some people with a Type A personality are able to reduce their hurried behaviours and become more tolerant, more patient, and better-humoured. Unfortunately, many people do not decide to modify their Type A habits until after they have become ill or suffered a heart attack or other circulatory system distress. Prevention of heart and circulatory disorders resulting from stress entails recognizing and changing dangerous behaviours before damage is done.

Self-Efficacy and Control

Whether people are able to cope successfully with stressful situations often depends on their level of self-efficacy, or belief in their skills and performance abilities. If people have been successful in mastering similar problems in the past, they are more likely to believe in their own effectiveness in future situations. Similarly, people who have repeatedly tried and failed may lack confidence in their abilities to deal with life's problems. In some cases, this insecurity may prevent them from even trying to cope.

In addition, people who believe they lack control in a situation may become easily frustrated and give up quickly. Those who feel they have little to no personal control over their life and what happens to them tend to have an external locus of control (that is a belief that an outside power—fate or destiny—controls one's life) and a low level of self-efficacy. People who are confident that their behaviours will influence the ultimate outcome of life's events tend to have an internal locus of control (that is, the belief that one is in control of one's own life). People who feel that they have limited control over their lives tend to have higher levels of stress.

> **what do you THINK?**
> What type of personality do you think you have? Do you think it is possible to change your personality type? Why or why not? Which of the Type C personality traits do you already possess? Which ones do you lack? What are you willing to do to become more like a Type C personality? Why?

Taken from *An Introduction to Health Psychology*, Second Edition, by Val Morrison and Paul Bennett

STRESS AND IMMUNE FUNCTION DYSREGULATION

Declines or alterations in immune function have frequently been associated with the experience of stressful life events (e.g. Ader 2001; Dantzer and Kelley 1989; Glaser and Kiecolt-Glaser 2005; Salovey *et al.* 2000). The immune system is the body's defence against disease. It operates by producing certain types of cell that operate against foreign organisms (e.g. bacteria, poisons, viruses, parasites) and abnormal cells (e.g. cancer cells) in the blood and lymphatic systems. These potential threats to the body are known as antigens, and their threat can be met by either a general first line of defence, or a more specifically targeted defence. Immune cells are white blood cells of two major types, lymphocytes and phagocytes, which can be found in the lymphatic system, in the lymph nodes, spleen and in the blood circulation. The second of these, phagocytes, are attracted to sites of infection due to tissue releasing chemical messengers, and when they reach their destination they destroy abnormal cells or antigens by engulfing and consuming them. They provide what is known as 'non-specific immunity' in that they offer a first general line of defence. Lymphocytes on the other hand offer 'specific immunity'. This involves 'cell-mediated immunity' via lymphocyte action (triggered by a subtype of phagocytes, a macrophage) where lymphocytes consist of T cells made in the thymus (CD4+ T cells or helper T cells, and CD8+ cells or cytoxic T cells) and also 'humoral-mediated immunity' involving B cells (memory and plasma cells). B cells label invading antigens in order to identify them for destruction and also 'remember' the antigen to enable early detection of future attacks. Their plasma produces antibodies, which remain in the blood circulation until the germ or disease is no longer present.

Natural killer (NK) cells also occur in body plasma and slow down the growth of abnormal cells (in cancer, for example) so that other immune responses can form an attack. As with phagocyte action, the NK cells provide non-specific immunity in that they defend against a wide variety of antigens, whereas the specific immunity provided by B and T cells is to specific antigens that they have been sensitised to (see Table 4a.1 for a summary of T and B cell roles). Each type of cell, NK, B and T, interact and help one another in the fight against infection or the growth of abnormal cells.

The immune system is also affected by the workings of the sympathetic nervous system and the endocrine responses described earlier; for example, the HPA system causes the release of hormones such as cortisol from the adrenal glands, and these hormones are thought to stimulate the immune system. Unfortunately, cortisol appears to damage T and B cells and increase a person's susceptibility to infection, not decrease it. It is now generally accepted that there is communication both within and between the neuroendocrine and immune systems, with the brain providing an immuno-regulatory role (e.g. Blalock 1994).

What is important to health psychologists is that studies have found a link between the proliferation of

Table 4a.1 Specific immunity and cell types

Humoral immunity: B cells	Cell-mediated immunity: T cells
Operate in the bloodstream	Operate at level of the cell
Work by releasing antibodies, which then destroy the antigen	Include memory, killer, helper (CD4+) and suppressor T cells
Include memory cells	Mature in the thymus and not the bone marrow as other white blood cells do

B, T and NK cells and the subjective experience of stress; in other words, they have shown that psychological stress interferes with the workings of our body. One early study by Kiecolt-Glaser *et al.* (1984) found a significant reduction in NK cell activity among students prior to important end-of-term exams compared with those tested in mid-term. In addition, those students who reported feelings of loneliness plus a high number of recent stressful life events showed significantly less NK cell activity at both times than those students who were low in life events and low in loneliness. This evidence was simultaneously being confirmed elsewhere, but it took a long time for the findings of such experimental studies to be accepted, because these findings necessitated a paradigm shift from where the body was thought to operate independently of the mind to acceptance of the fact that psychological factors could influence immunocompetence (i.e. the degree to which our immune system functions effectively). Since the late 1970s, work in the area of psychoneuroimmunology (the study of how psychosocial factors interact with the central and peripheral nervous system and the immune system) has gone from strength to strength, with improvements in technologies leading to even greater developments in the twenty-first century (compare the classic reviews of Herbert and Cohen 1993 and Cohen and Herbert 1996, with more recent work, e.g. Vedhara *et al.* 2001; reviews, e.g. Vingerhoets and Perski 2000, and textbooks, e.g. Ader 2007).

Age and Immune Function

It is generally accepted that immune function declines with age. This is sometimes referred to as 'immunosenescence' whereby the innate system of an immediate immune response to invading germs, and also the slower-acting immune resistance response, declines (Gomez *et al.* 2005). There is evidence, from animal and human studies, suggesting that NK cell function becomes less efficient even though they are increased in number in older people, and that pro-inflammatory cytokine activity is also increased. The importance of these findings lies in the fact that they place older people at greater risk of severe reactions to infections, as seen in the figures for deaths from influenza for example, or in the complications of inflammation following wounds or surgery and slower healing. Additionally, Graham *et al.* (2006), following a review of the current evidence, have suggested that in young adults stress can mimic the effects of aging, and in older adults, stress can exaggerate the effects of aging on immune competence. While this is a relatively under-researched area as yet, studies of caregivers are certainly pointing to significant associations.

STRESS AND CARDIOVASCULAR REACTIVITY

There is also a reasonably consistent body of psychobiological evidence showing that stress can cause alterations in physiological responses, in some people more than others. This 'reactivity hypothesis' first proposed by Krantz and Manuck (1984) describes how genetic or environmental factors combine to influence a person's vulnerability to a physiological response following stress and negative emotion that is likely to be detrimental to their health, particularly their arterial health implicated in heart disease. Reactivity, for example periods of elevated heart rate or blood pressure, is seen in both laboratory settings where individuals are exposed to acute or repeated stress, such as mental arithmetic tasks or public speaking, and in real-life settings where people face occupational challenge or marital conflict, for example. Whether or not this CVR (cardiovascular reactivity) is related to the development of disease, or indeed disease progression, is something of great interest to psychobiologists and psychologists alike (e.g. Johnston 2007; Linden *et al.* 2003) although evidence is mixed, as seen in a subsequent section where we review the role of stress in cardiovascular disease.

Evidence of the influence of psychological stress upon immune function, or upon cardiovascular reactivity has provided scientists with the opportunity to assess 'objective' indices of the stress response alongside, and in relation to, subjective stress reports. For example, Burns, V. *et al.* (2003) examined the effects of minor and major life events on the antibody response to influenza vaccination among a sample of undergraduate students. Students were followed up over five months and results found that participants with low antibody levels at five months reported having experienced significantly more life events in the intervening time following vaccination. Although a relatively small-scale study, if replicated in larger studies, such findings would have implications for the long-term success of vaccination programmes. Evidence of physiological correlates of occupational stress have also been reported, for example Clays *et al.* (2007) found that the ambulatory blood pressure at work, home and even while asleep, was significantly higher in workers with high job strain than in those with lower strain. Students are often used as participants in this area of research due to the 'occupational hazard' of exposure to potentially stressful patterns of assessment and examinations. Chandrashekara *et al.* (2007), for example, found that medical students with high anxiety and poorer emotional adaptability about end-of-term exams showed lower levels of an inflammatory cytokine (tumor necrosis factor alpha—TNF-a) than students with lower anxiety and greater emotional adaptability. The effect was not seen for mid-term exams, similar to that reported in the 1984 study of Kiecolt-Glaser *et al.* mentioned above. Such situation-specific responses contrasts with other findings where exposure to non-academic stressors contributed to a delayed *increase* in circulating cytokine levels (Steptoe *et al.* 2001). More research on these responses is warranted, particularly studies which contrast stressor types and contexts, as well as consider other individual difference variables that may contribute to stress reactivity. In terms of the implications of such findings for psychological intervention, there is some evidence that immune conditioning effects can be achieved (see Miller and Cohen 2001 for a metaanalytic review of 85 studies of psychological interventions and immune functioning) whereby individuals can be 'trained' using classical or operant conditioning procedures to alter immune response to threat. However further work, including better controlled studies that also address potential mediators of any shown effects, is needed.

It should therefore have become clear during the course of this chapter that stress is not a unitary process but a highly complex one. The experience of stress is, to varying degrees, dependent on stimulus events (acute or chronic, physical or psychological), on internal representations of events, including a person's appraisals and emotional responses, and on the nature and extent of physiological and behavioural activation that follows. Stress indisputably has a strong psychological component, and furthermore stress responses change over time as a person adjusts (or not) to their situation. Given all the evidence reviewed above, it is hardly surprising that measuring stress is complex, and some of these complexities are described in issues below.

The final challenge in the domain of stress research is that of establishing causality between stressful events and illness, ideally via immune or other physiological pathways. The concluding section of this chapter therefore describes some of the evidence that stress is associated with the development of illness.

THE STRESS AND ILLNESS LINK

The workings of the nervous, respiratory, digestive, cardiovascular and immunological systems were described in some detail and the reader was introduced to common diseases associated with these bodily systems. This final section takes a closer look at the role of stress in activating these systems with resulting implications for the development of illness. First, however, it is worth knowing that there are different ways of viewing the relationship between stress and illness.

The Direct Route

As described above, stress can produce physiological changes that may lead to the development of illness, particularly in instances where the stress is chronic rather than brief (Cacioppo *et al.* 1998; Johnston 2007; Smith *et al.* 2003). However, there is so much individual variation in responding to stressors that the direct route is complex (e.g. Esterling *et al.* 1996; Vedhara *et al.* 1999). The mixed evidence for direct effects of stress on the development of specific diseases is reviewed below.

The Indirect Routes

- People, by virtue of their behavioural responses to stress such as smoking, eating habits and drinking, predispose themselves to disease. Such behaviour may serve coping functions.
- People, by virtue of certain personality traits, predispose themselves to disease by the manner in which they respond to stress.
- People experiencing stress are more likely to use health services than people who are not under stress. Stress can produce symptoms such as anxiety, fatigue, insomnia and shakiness, which people seek treatment for but which are not in themselves illnesses.

However, we should bear in mind a quote of Sapolsky's throughout the reading of the next sections: 'everything bad in human health now is not caused by stress, nor is it in our power to cure ourselves of our worst medical nightmares merely by reducing stress and thinking healthy thoughts full of courage and spirit and love. Would it were so. And shame on those who sell this view' (1994).

There is a moderate relationship between stress and illness and this is best illustrated by selectively reviewing the evidence, as we do below. We can of course only address a selected few of the many illnesses that have been found to have an association with stress.

Stress and the Common Cold

Cohen and his colleagues (Cohen *et al.* 1993a, 1993b; Cohen *et al.* 1998) have conducted a series of experiments where volunteers submitted themselves to artificial exposure to respiratory rhinoviruses of the common cold (using nasal drops mainly). Participants then remained in a controlled environment for varying lengths of time while researchers waited to see whether colds or infections develop more often among those who received viral drops than among the control subjects, who received saline drops. Volunteers who had reported more chronic negative life events, perceived stress, negative affect and poor coping responses prior to the experiment were more likely to develop signs of respiratory infection and subsequent colds than both control subjects and experimental subjects with low-level life stress. Perceived stress and negative affect predicted infection rates, whereas negative life events did not predict infection itself but predicted the probability of illness among those who became infected. These associations persisted when health behaviour such as smoking and alcohol consumption or personality variable such as self-esteem and introversion–extroversion were controlled for. Similarly, Stone *et al.* (1993) found a similar dose–response relationship between the number of stressful life events experienced prior to the introduction of a rhinovirus and the subsequent presentation of cold symptoms.

Although the results relating to stress and susceptibility to influenza have been inconsistent and predominantly lab-based using artificially induced viruses, the work of Cohen's research group, summarised in their 1998 paper, provides convincing evidence of a relationship between chronic stress (as opposed to severity) and the common cold. They controlled for other potential influences such as mood and smoking behaviour and hoped to identify a physiological or immunological pathway that mediated the stress–colds relationship, but they failed to find one despite taking many careful neuroendocrine and immune function measures (Leventhal *et al.* 1998). More recent work has, however, supported chronic stress–immune response—cold and influenza association (Marsland *et al.* 2002; Takkouche *et al.* 2001). This latter study importantly also considered the naturally acquired common cold. They carried out a one-year prospective cohort study among the faculty and staff of a Spanish university (N = 1,149) and found that the occurrence of stressful life events, perceived stress, positive and negative affect were all related to the occurrence of common cold.

There is still some way to go before full understanding of how stress operates and, in particular, how it operates in real-life environments. This has been achieved to some extent in studies of real-life stress and cardiovascular reactivity, although reactivity in itself is not 'disease', but a risk factor (Johnston 2007). We return to this work in the next section.

Prospective studies with clinical populations facing 'natural' stressors will inevitably improve our understanding of the stress–immune function–illness link. While some evidence exists that stress-mediated physiological changes play a role in the initial onset of disease among healthy individuals (such as coronary heart disease), there is more evidence that stress experienced by 'ill' individuals can affect further progression of their symptoms or disease. We review some of this evidence below.

STRESS AND CORONARY HEART DISEASE

Coronary heart disease (CHD) is a disease of the **cardiovascular** system that develops over time in response to a range of factors, such as family history and lifestyle factors (e.g. smoking and diet). The cause of CHD is a gradual narrowing of blood vessels that supply the heart. In situations of acute stress, activation of the sympathetic nervous system causes increased cardiac output and the blood vessels to constrict, thus restricting blood flow, so blood pressure increases. This can cause damage to the artery walls, a process that is contributed to further by stress-induced adrenaline and noradrenaline output. If blood pressure remains raised for prolonged periods of time, a person is said to have hypertension, a contributory factor in CHD.

Repeated or chronic stress also activates the sympathetic nervous system's release of fatty acids into the bloodstream, which, if not utilised for energy expenditure, are metabolised by the liver into cholesterol. A build-up of cholesterol is highly implicated in the 'furring up' of arteries or atheroma (the laying down of fatty plaques on artery walls), and a key feature of heart disease is this atherosclerosis. Furthermore, the release of catecholamines during the stress process also increases the stickiness of blood platelets (thrombocytes), which elevates the risk of a clot forming or thrombosis as they adhere to the artery walls with the fatty plaques, thus making the 'passageway' narrower for blood to flow through. Inflammatory processes, involving proinflammatory cytokines such as IL-6 (interleukin-6), are also implicated in this process. If reduced blood flow causes a clot to form, it could then travel through a person's arteries until it becomes so big as to form a blockage (occlusion) and depending on whether it blocks an artery to the brain or to the

cardiovascular pertaining to the heart and blood vessels.

heart, this will lead to either a stroke or a heart attack—both major causes of mortality worldwide.

In terms of CHD, stress does appear to contribute to various related conditions, such as hypertension, elevated serum lipids (fats in the blood) and smoking behaviour, an acknowledged risk factor (e.g. Ming *et al.* 2004). Cardiovascular reactivity during acute stress (i.e. the extent to which a stressor produces cardiac arousal such as increased heart rate or blood pressure) has been implicated in various disease processes, such as the extent and progression of carotid artery atherosclerosis, and the emergence of coronary heart disease itself (Smith *et al.* 2003). Experimental studies of reactivity in response to aversive or rewarding stimuli have speculated that the individuals who responded to aversive tasks with sizeable heart-rate and blood-pressure increases (high reactives) but who showed no difference from controls in subjective ratings of the tasks, had greater activation of the hypothalamic system and neuroendocrine responses such as those described earlier. Indeed, high-reactive participants showed larger noradrenaline increases in response to both types of task than low-reactive participants and larger cortisol increases to the aversive task but not to the reward task (Lovallo *et al.* 1990). This highlights the importance of considering the type of task. Also important is finding whether effects persist outwith the artificial laboratory setting. This has been achieved, for example, by Johnston and colleagues (Johnston 2007) who found that laboratory-based reactivity was reflected in similar increases in heart rate reactivity when individuals were exposed to the real-life stressor of public speaking.

What this section points to is a need to distinguish between chronic stress and its role in potentiating certain risk behaviours which provide the 'indirect' link with chronic manifestations of CHD, e.g. smoking and arterial disease; and acute stress events which appear implicated in the potentiating of acute coronary events, such as heart attacks (Johnston 2002, 2007; Strike and Steptoe 2005).

Speculation as to the role of stress in the development of actual disease has abounded for many years; for example, Rosch (1994), in an editorial in the journal *Stress Medicine*, pointed to the importance of distinguishing between causal factors and contributing factors when considering disease, arguing that the 'true cause' of any disease is biomedical and that behavioural or social factors such as smoking or stress are not 'true' causes but contributors. This conclusion seems to have been challenged through research developments over the past decade or more, in that the evidence of causality in relation to acute coronary events and to CHD does seem to implicate stress reactivity and also negative emotions (depression primarily). We know from many years of research that the mind and body interact, and if into this we add individual 'risk' or 'protective' behaviours, we can begin to understand the complexity of influences upon disease processes such as those subsumed under the broad heading of 'heart disease'.

STRESS AND BOWEL DISEASE

Two diseases of the bowel have been investigated in terms of their association with the experience of stress. In both, stress is examined as an exacerbating factor rather than one involved in the aetiology of the condition. First, *irritable bowel syndrome* is a disorder of the lower large intestine characterised by abdominal pain and prolonged periods of either diarrhoea or constipation, although no organic disease is identifiable. Naliboff *et al.* (1998) note that during stressful episodes, the reactivity of the gut is greater and symptoms such as bloatedness, pain or diarrhoea increase. A second bowel disease is *inflammatory bowel disease* (IBD), which can be subdivided into Crohn's disease (CD) and ulcerative colitis (UC). These diseases are both typified by pain and diarrhoea, which worsen and improve in an alternating and disruptive manner. UC is typified by inflammation of the lower colon, whereas CD can occur anywhere in the gastrointestinal tract and is seen as inflammation of the outer intestinal wall. Both diseases, as with IBS, were originally thought to be psychosomatic; however, evidence that stress plays a role in their aetiology is limited, although stress may exacerbate the condition, being associated with symptom 'flare-ups' (Searle and Bennett 2001). This is also reported by Duffy *et al.* (1991) who examined exposure to stressful events among 124 individuals and found that over a period of six months, those exposed to stress showed a two- to fourfold increase in clinical disease episodes compared with those participants who did not report stressful incidents. When the authors distinguished between disease-related and disease-unrelated events (on the basis of patient report), the relationship between stress and illness was clearest when the reported events were health-related but not necessarily IBD-specific. When the authors examined the issue of time lag between event and disease activity (i.e. a stressful event preceding disease activity), they found instead that concurrent relationships were strongest. Furthermore, their results showed that disease activity was predictive of subsequent levels of stress. Such bidirectional relationships between variables makes the disentangling of issues of cause and effect difficult.

In addition, individual variation in stress-responsivity/reactivity may explain mixed research findings. Illustrating this point, Dancey *et al.* (1998) used repeated measures of daily stress and daily symptomatology obtained from thirty-one IBS patients to examine the associations between stress and symptoms over time and found that only in half of the sample was an association evident between stress and the onset or exacerbation of symptoms.

IN THE SPOTLIGHT

Can stress prevent your wounds healing?

Janice Kiecolt-Glaser and Ronald Glaser have spent many years researching the mind–body relationship, in particular the relationship between the experience of stress and immune function. While this chapter has presented evidence of the physiological pathways underlying stress responses, you may not have stopped to consider how stress might affect you, not just in terms of potentially increasing your risk of diseases such as heart disease but in terms of more day-to-day health challenges, such as wounds received while participating in sporting activities. The Glasers have shown in many studies of elderly carers of people with Alzheimer's disease that healing of experimentally induced tissue wounds took significantly longer among carers than among healthy age-matched control participants. However, this may in part be due to coexisting ageing processes, so further studies have explored whether similar effects can be found in younger samples. Vedhara and colleagues in Bristol (2003) examined the healing rates of foot ulcers among sixty adults with Type 2 diabetes. They found that healing was reduced in those who had shown high anxiety, depression or stress. Importantly, similar effects of stress have been found on the healing rates of otherwise healthy students who are given a small experimental skin wound at two different times, one during the summer holiday, the other prior to sitting exams. The wound inflicted before exams took on average three days longer to heal, and this was reflected by decreases in immunological status (Marucha *et al.* 1998). Broadbent *et al.* (2003) have confirmed the impairing effects of high stress and worry levels on wound healing where wounds were not experimental but real, i.e. participants were recovering from hernia surgery.

Why do all these findings matter? Think of your own stress levels; think of your likelihood of becoming wounded in sport or other activity; or of the potential to be facing surgery in the future. Think of current concern about MRSA (methicillin-resistant *Staphylococcus aureus*) and *C difficile* infections in hospitals and in the community. Effectively dealing with your own stress is important, not only in keeping you healthy but also in helping you to heal and recover when and if you become ill or injured or require surgery.

PART V: LIFESTYLE FACTORS AND HEALTH

Chapter 5a: Physical Activity and Exercise

Chapter 5b: Diet, Natural Health Products and Nutrition

Chapter 5c: Therapeutic, Performance Enhancement and Recreational Drugs

Chapter 5d: Stress Management

Chapter 5e: Achieving the Balance of Psychological Health

Chapter 5f: Preventing and Fighting Disease

CHAPTER 5a

PHYSICAL ACTIVITY AND EXERCISE

Taken from *Health: The Basics,* Fifth Canadian Edition, by Rebecca J. Donatelle and Angela M. Thompson

Regular physical activity results in a wide range of physical, social, and mental health benefits. These health benefits are a result of an increased energy expenditure that relates to an overall improvement in the quality and quantity of life. Regular physical activity reduces the likelihood of coronary artery disease, high blood pressure, type 2 diabetes, obesity, and other chronic diseases. Further, regular physical activity helps to control stress, increases self-esteem, and contributes to that "feel-good" feeling. Thus, it is no wonder that physical activity is often viewed as the key to health and considered a tool for disease prevention.

Most Canadians are aware of the health benefits of physical activity and that they should be more physically active, yet almost half the population is considered physically inactive—that is, expends less than 3 kcal/kg/day in physical activity. Even more disturbing is that only 21 percent of Canadian teenagers are sufficiently physically active to meet the international physical activity recommendations for optimal growth and development, with boys twice as likely to obtain the recommendations as girls (27 versus 14 percent). At all ages, men are more active than women. Further, children are more active than adolescents, and adolescents are more active than adults. Research also indicates that your physical activity level as a child and adolescent influences your attitudes and behaviours toward your physical activity as an adult. If your physical activity experiences as a child or adolescent were negative, don't despair! Your years at university or college provide an excellent opportunity to make a break with the past and develop positive physical activity attitudes and behaviours that can increase the quality and quantity of your life. Keep in mind that changes in physical activity level are not uncommon, with most people regularly cycling through more and less physically active times. For example over a 10-year span, 26.8 percent of Canadians over the age of 12 became more physically active while 21.5 percent became less active.

what do you THINK?

Why do the physical activity levels of Canadians, on average, change from year to year or decade to decade? Check out the facts online at the Canadian Fitness and Lifestyle Research Institute (www.cflri.ca) and Statistics Canada (www.statcan.ca).

PHYSICAL ACTIVITY FOR HEALTH, FITNESS, AND PERFORMANCE

Physical activity refers to all body movements produced by skeletal muscles resulting in energy expenditure. Walking, swimming, gardening, and housework are examples of physical activity. Physical activities can vary by intensity. For example, walking to class typically requires little effort, while walking up hill is more intense. There are three general categories of physical activity defined by the purpose for which they are done: physical activity for health, physical activity for fitness, and physical activity for performance.

what do you THINK?

Have you had your physical fitness assessed recently? Which components of your physical fitness would you like to improve? What exercises will you do to improve this component of your physical fitness?

Physical Activity for Health

Canadian researchers Warburton, Nicol, and Bredin concluded from their review of the research on physical activity and health that "there is irrefutable evidence of the effectiveness of regular physical activity in the primary and secondary prevention of several chronic diseases (e.g., cardiovascular disease, diabetes, cancer, hypertension, obesity, depression and osteoporosis and premature death)" (801). Furthermore, the risk of breast cancer in women 40 years of age and younger is significantly reduced when they participated in regular physical activity (four or more hours accumulated over a week) beginning in adolescence and continuing into adulthood.

Just adding more physical activity to your day can benefit your health. In fact, if *all* Canadians followed the physical activity recommendations in Canada's Physical Activity Guide for Healthy Living (CPAG), about one-third of deaths related to coronary heart disease, one-quarter of deaths related to stroke and osteoporosis, one-fifth of deaths related to colon cancer, high blood pressure, and type 2 diabetes, and one-seventh of deaths related to breast cancer could be prevented. Unfortunately, few Cana-

Physical activity: Body movements produced by skeletal muscles resulting in energy expenditure.

Reduced risk of chronic disease and improved quality of life are among the many benefits of regular physical activity for people of all ages and capabilities.

dians are aware of CPAG (that is, 20.7 percent) and even fewer (that is, 5.5 percent) actually follow the recommendations.

A physically active lifestyle might include choices such as walking or cycling to school, parking further away from your destination, taking movement breaks while studying, or taking the stairs instead of the elevator. You can also choose to be more physically active in your leisure or "down" time by dancing, playing Frisbee, or walking your dog. Every little bit helps, so get out of your seat and move more, more often. For additional information on putting together a physical activity program, download or view CPAG at www.phac-aspc.gc.ca/pau-uap/paguide/index.html.

Physical Activity for Fitness

Exercise refers to a particular kind of physical activity. Although all exercise is physical activity, not all physical activity would be considered exercise. For example, walking from your car to class is physical activity, whereas going for a brisk 30-minute walk is exercise. **Exercise** is defined as planned, structured, and repetitive bodily movements done to improve or maintain one or more components of physical fitness, such as cardiorespiratory endurance, muscular strength and endurance, or flexibility. **Physical fitness** refers to a set of attributes that are either health- or performance-related. The health-related attributes—cardiorespiratory endurance, muscular strength and endurance, and flexibility—allow you to perform moderate- to vigorous-intensity physical activity on a regular basis without undue fatigue and with energy left over to handle physical or mental emergencies.

To become physically fit, you will need to do more than simply make physically active lifestyle choices. You will need to do particular exercises for a particular length of time, at a specific intensity, and for a certain number of times each week. Specific to cardiorespiratory endurance exercises, the Public Health Agency of Canada, along with the Canadian Society for Exercise Physiology, recommends 60 minutes of light-effort physical activity or exercise every day to maintain or improve your health. Physical activities of a light effort—for example, light walking, easy gardening—result in the body feeling warm and a slight increase in breathing rate. As the intensity of your physical activity increases to a moderate level—where you are feeling warmer and have a noticeable increase in breathing rate—you can exercise for 30 minutes, four days a week. Examples of moderate-intensity physical activities include brisk walking, cycling, dancing, etc. Further, if the intensity of your exercise increases to a vigorous effort, you can exercise for 20 to 30 minutes, three days per week. Vigorous-intensity physical activities make you quite warm and breathing quite quickly, as you would while jogging, or playing basketball. In other words, the intensity of your exercise dictates the length and frequency of your exercise sessions. Further, your exercise can be accumulated in 10-minute time periods.

Some people have physical limitations that might be viewed as preventing them from being able to get the exercise recommended for them to achieve and/or maintain physical fitness. In fact, these individuals can and should be physically active and, in particular, should exercise to obtain the health-related benefits. For example, a woman with arthritis in her knee and hip joints might not be able to play soccer, but she can participate in water exercises, since the water may help relieve the stress on her joints. Similarly, a man who uses a wheelchair may not be able to jog, but he can meet the exercise recommendations by playing wheelchair basketball or rugby.

what do you THINK?

What type of physical fitness training do you think Canadian triathlete Simon Whitfield completes? How would his training and approach to exercise compare to yours? Which of the key aspects of physical fitness would you like to improve or develop? What types of physical activities (exercises) could you do to improve these key aspects?

It is important for all people, including those with disabilities, to develop optimal levels of physical fitness to participate in physical activities they enjoy—including competitive sports.

Physical Activity for Performance

People who participate in athletics use physical activity to improve their performance. As such, specific exercises are undertaken to increase power, agility, speed, coordination, and the other performance-related attributes of physical fitness. Plyometrics are often used in training to improve performance. Plyometrics are exercises that contract muscles in a certain order to increase power. An example is doing push-ups with a hand-clap between each one. In addition to developing power, plyometrics help to improve body control and the speed at which you change directions.

Although many recreational exercisers use interval training to improve their speed as well as their cardiorespiratory fitness, performance training is safest for individuals who already have a high level of physical fitness. Generally, those who engage in performance training will achieve a higher level of physical fitness, but careful monitoring of one's training plan is essential, since there is an increased risk of injury and overtraining.

BENEFITS OF REGULAR PHYSICAL ACTIVITY

Improved Cardiorespiratory Endurance

A regular program of moderately intense aerobic physical activity improves the efficiency of your cardiovascular and respiratory systems: it enables the heart to pump more blood with each stroke, thus lowering resting heart rate; it improves the body's capacity to take in and distribute oxygen to working muscles; and it strengthens the muscles responsible for respiration.

Reduced Risk of Heart Disease

Your heart is a muscle made up of highly specialized tissue. Because muscles become stronger and more efficient with use, regular physical activity of sufficient intensity strengthens the heart, enabling it to pump more blood with each beat. This increased efficiency means that your heart requires fewer beats per minute to circulate blood throughout your body to maintain function. In this way, a stronger, more efficient heart is better able to meet the demands of life.

Prevention of Hypertension

Hypertension is the medical term for chronic high blood pressure. It is a cardiovascular disease itself and, in addition, increases the risk of coronary heart disease and stroke. Hypertension causes the heart to work harder with each beat because of increased resistance due to less pliable arterial walls.

Regular moderate-intensity physical activity lowers systolic and diastolic blood pressure by about 10 mmHg in people with mild to moderate hypertension. Regular physical activity can also reduce systolic and diastolic blood pressure in people with normal blood pressure.

Improved Blood Lipid and Lipoprotein Profile

Lipids are fats that circulate in the bloodstream and are stored in various places in your body. A high level of blood lipids (cholesterol and triglycerides) increases risk of coronary heart disease. Risk increases for heart

Exercise: Planned, structured, and repetitive bodily movements done to improve or maintain one or more components of physical fitness.

Physical fitness: A set of attributes that are either health- or performance-related.

RATE YOURSELF

How Physically Fit Are You?

EVALUATING YOUR AEROBIC FITNESS: THE MODIFIED CANADIAN AEROBIC FITNESS TEST (MCAFT)

In this test endorsed by the Canadian Society for Exercise Physiology (CSEP), you complete one or more 3-minute sessions of stepping on double 20.3 cm steps at a predetermined pace based on your age and sex. Heart rate is measured 5 to 10 seconds after each 3 minutes of stepping. Depending upon your heart rate, you will proceed to the next step or terminate the test. Your final exercising heart rate, along with your age and sex, are used to determine your aerobic fitness score, which is then compared to the established health benefit zone. For complete details, refer to MyHealthLab.

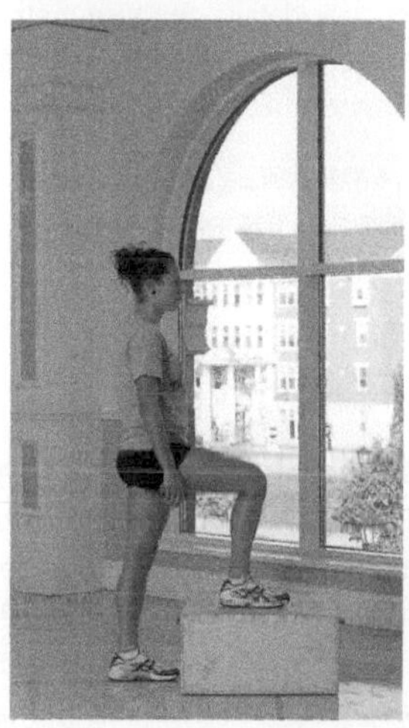

An alternative to the two-step approach in the mCAFT, is using a single step; participants step up onto a 40.6-cm (18") box or step completely with one foot (a), then the other (b), and then step down with one foot (c) and then other (d) to measure their cardiorespiratory endurance.

EVALUATING YOUR MUSCULAR STRENGTH AND ENDURANCE

A number of tests are proposed by the CSEP for determining these parameters of physical fitness. The most commonly used tests are partial curl-ups and push-ups. Other tests include grip strength and vertical jump.

Female push-up.

Male push-up.

Partial curl-up.

Trunk flexibility is usually evaluated using the sit and reach test.

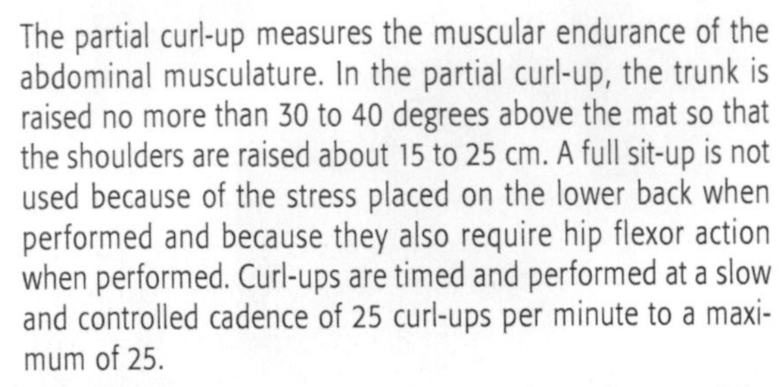

The partial curl-up measures the muscular endurance of the abdominal musculature. In the partial curl-up, the trunk is raised no more than 30 to 40 degrees above the mat so that the shoulders are raised about 15 to 25 cm. A full sit-up is not used because of the stress placed on the lower back when performed and because they also require hip flexor action when performed. Curl-ups are timed and performed at a slow and controlled cadence of 25 curl-ups per minute to a maximum of 25.

Push-ups provide a measure of the muscular endurance of the upper body, including the shoulders, arms, and chest. There is no time or ceiling limit for the measurement of push-ups.

Complete instructions for these two tests, as well as the tests for grip strength and vertical jump and the applicable health benefit zones, are included in MyHealthLab.

EVALUATING YOUR FLEXIBILITY

The most commonly used test to measure flexibility is the sit and reach test or trunk forward flexion. Another test endorsed by CSEP is back extension. The sit and reach test measures the ability of the back to flex, which involves the muscles of the lower back and of the back of the legs (that is, hamstrings). Complete details on how to perform this test as well as the back extension test, along with the normative tables, are presented in MyHealthLab.

EVALUATING YOUR BODY COMPOSITION

Your body composition can be measured in a number of ways. One method involves determining your Body Mass Index (BMI) from your height and weight. Although widely used in population studies as an indicator of overweight and obesity, BMI does not actually provide a measure of fatness. Waist circumference is a simple measure that provides a relatively valid measure of abdominal fatness. Sum of five skinfolds is the final measurement of body composition advocated by the CSEP. Skinfold measurements provide an indication of subcutaneous fat (that is, fat that lies directly below the skin). Five measurements (triceps, biceps, subscapular, iliac crest, and medial calf) are taken, totalled, and compared to the health benefit zones. Complete details on these methods of body composition assessment, as well as the health benefits zones, are included in MyHealthLab.

Source: Adapted from: The Canadian Physical Activity, Fitness, and Lifestyle Approach Protocol (CPAFLA). Retrieved on August 28, 2008 from www.csep.ca.

disease because the heart has to work harder with each beat as a result of the reduced blood flow caused by the narrowing of the arteries that occurs with high blood fats as they "build up" on the artery walls. Regular aerobic exercise reduces low-density lipoproteins (LDLs—"bad cholesterol"), total cholesterol, and triglycerides (a blood fat), thus reducing plaque build-up in the arteries while increasing high-density lipoproteins (HDLs—"good cholesterol"). Higher HDL levels are associated with lower risk for coronary artery disease because they remove some of the "bad cholesterol," thus reducing fatty plaque accumulation from coronary artery walls and easing the work effort of the heart.

Improved Bone Health

Osteoarthritis is a nonfatal but incurable disease characterized by degeneration of joint cartilage and irritation of surrounding bone and soft tissues. Affecting 1 in 10 Canadians, osteoarthritis is the most prevalent chronic joint condition in Canada. Women are afflicted more frequently than men. Supervised walking and weight-loss programs can improve physical capacity while reducing knee-joint osteoarthritis symptoms.

A common affliction for the older population is osteoporosis, a disease characterized by low bone mass and deterioration of bone tissue, which increases

try it NOW!

Boost daily physical activity with small changes. For example, when you have a choice between the elevator and stairs, choose the stairs. Walking up a few flights of stairs each day can be beneficial to your health. Walking stairs helps strengthen your legs, gets your heart beating a little faster, and contributes to your daily physical activity level.

Another place to easily add a little more daily physical activity is to park your car a little further from your destination—whether that is in a mall parking lot or when you park for school or work.

fracture risk. Although men and women are both negatively affected by osteoporosis, the prevalence is greater in women. Weight-bearing and strength-building physical activities are recommended to maintain bone health and to prevent osteoporotic fractures. Bone, like other human tissues, responds to the demands placed upon it (the overload principle), and unless the mechanical stresses placed on bone by a particular physical activity exceed the level of stress the bone has adapted to, bone mass and structure will not adapt. Women (and men) have much to gain by remaining physically active as they age—bone mass levels have been found to be significantly higher among physically active women than among those who are sedentary. However, it appears that the full bone-related benefits of physical activity can be achieved only with sufficient hormone levels (estrogen in women, testosterone in men) and adequate calcium, vitamin D, and total calorie intakes.

Improved Weight Management

For many people, the desire to lose weight is the main reason for their physical activity. Physical activity has a direct positive effect on metabolic rate and keeps it elevated for a few hours following vigorous physical activities. As previously noted, research suggests that 60 minutes of moderate intensity physical activity each day should help in maintaining body weight. An effective method for losing weight should combine regular endurance-type physical activities with a moderate decrease (about 500 calories per day) in dietary intake. Decreasing daily caloric intake beyond this may decrease metabolic rate by as much as 20 percent, making short- and long-term weight loss more difficult.

Improved Health and Life Span

Prevention of Type 2 Diabetes

Diabetes is a complex metabolic disorder that affects many Canadians. It is believed that a healthy dietary intake combined with sufficient physical activity could prevent many of the current cases of type 2 diabetes. A recent large epidemiological study found that for every 2000 calories of energy expended during leisure-time physical activities, the incidence of diabetes was reduced by 24 percent. Perhaps the most encouraging finding was that the protective effect of physical activity was greatest among individuals at the highest risk.

Increased Longevity

Experts have long debated the relationship between physical activity and longevity. For decades, most research failed to show an increase in life expectancy through physical activity alone. Then, a classic prospective study of the Harvard alumni of more than 30 years reported that inactive men were at a greater risk of premature death from all causes than men who engaged in regular physical activity. How much physical activity was required to produce this effect? Inactive men who included a brisk 30- to 60-minute walk each day experienced the most significant increases in their life expectancies.

Improved Immunity to Disease

Will regular physical activity improve your immunity? Research suggests that regular moderate-intensity physical activity makes people less susceptible to disease, but that this potential benefit depends upon whether the physical activity was perceived as pleasurable or stressful. Often the relationship of physical activity to immunity, or more specifically to disease susceptibility, is described as a J-shaped curve. In other words, susceptibility to disease decreases as you move from sedentary to moderately active, then increases again as you move to more extreme levels of physical activity or exercise. Athletes engaging in marathon-type events or very intense physical training programs have been shown to be at a greater risk for upper respiratory tract infections (colds and flu). In a study of 2300 marathon runners, those who ran more than 100 kilometres per week suffered twice as many upper respiratory tract infections as those who ran fewer than 35 kilometres per week.

Just how physical activity alters immunity is not well understood. We do know that moderate-intensity physical activity temporarily increases our white blood cells (WBCs), the blood cells responsible for fighting infection. How long does one have increased immunity? It is suggested that after 30 minutes or more of physical activity, WBCs may be elevated for 24 hours or more before returning to normal levels.

Improved Mental Health and Stress Management

Although most people who engage in regular physical activity are not aware of the beneficial physiological changes of their activity apart from those that are most noticeable, such as weight loss or weight maintenance, most do notice the psychological benefits. While these psychological benefits are difficult to quantify, they are frequently mentioned as reasons for continuing to be physically active.

Regular vigorous physical activity has been shown to "burn off" the chemical byproducts released by our nervous system during its normal response to stress. Elimination of these biochemicals reduces our stress response by accelerating the neurological system's return to a balanced state. For this reason, regular physical activity of moderate to vigorous intensity should be an integral component of your stress management plan.

Regular physical activity can improve physical appearance by toning and developing muscles and, combined with a healthy dietary intake, reducing (or maintaining) body fat. Feeling good about personal appearance is an integral component of self-esteem. Other improvements to physical self-esteem result from learning new skills, developing increased ability and capacity in recreational activities, and "sticking with" a physical activity plan.

what do you THINK?

What makes you feel good about being physically active? How does it make you feel, physically and mentally, during and after the activity?

IMPROVING CARDIORESPIRATORY ENDURANCE

Cardiorespiratory endurance, or cardiovascular fitness, refers to the ability of the heart, lungs, and blood vessels to function efficiently. Our lives depend on our cardiorespiratory system's ability to deliver oxygenated blood and nutrients to our body tissues and to remove carbon dioxide and other metabolic waste products. The primary category of physical activity known to improve cardiorespiratory fitness is aerobic exercise. The term *aerobic* means "with oxygen" and describes any type of exercise, typically performed at moderate to vigorous intensity for extended periods of time. Aerobic activities such as brisk walking, jogging, bicycling, skating, and swimming are among the best exercises for improving or maintaining cardiorespiratory fitness.

Aerobic power is the term used to describe the current functional status of the cardiovascular system (that is, the heart, lungs, blood vessels) and refers specifically to the volume of oxygen consumed by the muscles during exercise, maximal aerobic power (often referred to as VO_2max). Maximal aerobic power refers to the maximal capacity of the cardiorespiratory system. The most common measure of maximal aerobic capacity is determined from a walk or run on a treadmill. In this test, you will walk or run at an easy pace, and then, at set time intervals gradually increase the workload (that is, a **graded exercise test** in which a combination of running speed and the angle of incline is used) to arrive at your point of maximal exertion. The higher your cardiorespiratory endurance, the more oxygen you can transport to exercising muscles and the longer you can maintain a high intensity of exercise before exhaustion. Other less valid, but reliable and safer, methods of measuring aerobic capacity are frequently employed and then used to estimate VO_2max. These submaximal tests may use stationary bicycles, walk/run tests, shuttle runs, or walk tests to quantify the aerobic fitness levels in people of all ages and of all abilities. You may have performed one of these aerobic capacity tests in a physical education class.

It is important for you to complete the Physical Activity Readiness Questionnaire (PAR-Q; available at www.csep.ca) prior to engaging in physical activity or any tests to measure your physical fitness. If you answer yes to any of the questions on the PAR-Q or if you have certain medical conditions, such as asthma, diabetes, heart disease, or obesity, you should consult a physician to ensure that physical activity is safe for you. Further, you should engage in a walking/jogging program at low intensity before you attempt to measure your maximal aerobic capacity.

CARDIORESPIRATORY FITNESS PROGRAMS

When creating a cardiorespiratory fitness program, there are many variables to consider. Generally, what is needed is an aerobic physical activity you enjoy that works your heart at a moderate intensity (approximately 70 to 90 percent of your maximum heart rate, which corresponds to a workload of between 55 and 85 percent of your VO_2max) for a continuous length of time (20 to 30 minutes) at least three days per week.

The most effective aerobic exercises for building cardiorespiratory endurance are total body activities involving large muscle groups of your body. If you have

Cardiorespiratory endurance: The ability of the heart, lungs, and blood vessels to function efficiently.

Aerobic power: The current functional status of a person's cardiorespiratory system; measured as VO_2max and referring specifically to the volume of oxygen consumed by the muscles during exercise.

Graded exercise test: A test of aerobic capacity administered by a physician, exercise physiologist, or other trained person.

Palpation of the radial (wrist) or carotid (neck) artery is a simple means of determining heart rate.

been sedentary for quite a while, initiating a physical activity program may be a challenge. The key is to begin slowly at a low intensity in a physical activity that you like and is easily accessible for you to do. To start slowly, for example, if jogging is the physical activity you choose, you should alternate jogging and walking (1 minute of jogging, 1 minute of walking; progress to 2 minutes of jogging, 1 minute of walking, and so on) until you develop a cardiorespiratory fitness level that enables you to jog continuously for 20 to 30 minutes.

Determining Exercise Frequency

If you have been physically inactive for the past few months or longer, the frequency of your aerobic exercise should begin at 3 times per week. If you exercise less frequently (that is, once or twice per week), you will achieve fewer health benefits. Exercising 3 to 5 times per week is the general recommendation for improving cardiorespiratory endurance. Your ultimate goal should be to exercise 5 times a week. To avoid overuse injuries and monotony, vary your physical activities and take a day off when needed.

Determining Exercise Intensity

An aerobic exercise program must employ sustained, moderate- to vigorous-intensity physical activity to improve cardiorespiratory endurance. A common measure of exercise intensity is your heart rate. The exercise intensity required to improve cardiorespiratory endurance is a heart rate between 70 and 90 percent of your maximum heart rate. To calculate your **target heart rate**, subtract your age from 220 (for males) or 226 (for females). The result is your maximum heart rate (HRmax). You then determine your target heart rate by calculating the desired percentage of maximum heart rate—that is, 70 to 90 percent. If you are a 20-year-old male, your estimated maximum heart rate is 200 ($220 - 20 = 200$). Your target heart rate would be somewhere between 140 ($200 \times 0.70 = 140$) and 180 ($200 \times 0.90 = 180$) beats per minute. Those who have been sedentary for a long time should set a lower target heart rate, somewhere between 50 and 60 percent of their maximum. As their cardiorespiratory fitness improves, these previously sedentary individuals can gradually increase their target heart rate using small increments—for example, from 50 to 55 percent, then from 55 to 60 percent. It is not recommended for people engaging in aerobic exercise for health benefits to exceed 90 percent of maximum heart rate.

Once you know your target heart rate, you can determine how close you are to this value during your workout. You'll need to stop exercising briefly to measure your heart rate. To take your pulse, lightly place your index and middle fingers (not your thumb) over one of the major (carotid) arteries in your neck, along either side of your Adam's apple, or on the artery on the inside of your wrist. Be sure to start counting your pulse immediately—the first count is "0"—after you stop exercising, as your heart rate decreases quickly. Using a watch or clock, take your pulse for 6 seconds and multiply this number by 10 (just add a zero to your count) to get the number of beats per minute. If necessary, increase or decrease the pace or intensity of your workout to achieve your target heart rate.

A target heart rate of 70 percent of maximum is sometimes called the "conversational level of exercise" because you are able to talk with a partner while exercising. If you are breathing so hard that talking is

TABLE 5a.1
Health- and Performance-Related Components of Physical Fitness

Health	
Cardiorespiratory endurance	Ability to sustain moderate-intensity whole-body activity for extended time periods
Muscular strength	Ability to apply maximum force with a single muscle contraction
Muscular endurance	Ability to perform muscle contractions repeatedly
Flexibility	Range of motion in a joint or series of joints
Body composition	Ratio of fat to total body weight
Performance	
Agility	Speed in changing direction or in changing body positions
Power	Combination of strength and speed
Balance	Maintenance of a stable body position
Coordination	Ability to have things work together
Reaction time	Ability to adjust or "react" to stimuli
Speed	Ability to move quickly

Source: Adapted from T. Baranowski, et al., "Assessment, Prevalence, and Cardiovascular Benefits of Physical Activity and Fitness in Youth," *Medicine and Science in Sports and Exercise* 24 (June 1992): supplement, S238.

difficult, the intensity of your exercise is too high. Conversely, if you are able to sing or laugh heartily while exercising, the intensity of your exercise is insufficient for improving or maintaining cardiorespiratory endurance.

Determining Exercise Time

Time refers to the number of minutes of exercise performed at the specified intensity during any one session. As previously mentioned, the length of your exercise session depends on the intensity. If the intensity is 70 to 90 percent HRmax, then only 20 to 30 minutes are needed. Although many individuals engage in exercise sessions lasting longer than 30 minutes, greater improvements to cardiorespiratory fitness are not realized.

Frequency, Intensity, or Time?

You will need to adjust the frequency, intensity, and time of your aerobic exercise program to accommodate your improving cardiorespiratory endurance. As you progress and are able to exercise for 20 minutes at 70 percent of your HRmax for three days per week, increase the frequency, time, or intensity of your exercise—but not all three at the same time. Generally, it is recommended to first increase the frequency of your workouts from 3 to 4 days per week, then from 4 to 5 days per week. Once you have adjusted to that change, it is recommended to increase the length of your exercise period in gradual amounts (usually a 10 percent increase in the volume or total amount of exercise). Once you have adjusted to those changes, it is recommended to increase the intensity of your workout gradually from 70 to 90 percent of HRmax.

what do you THINK?

Consider a type (or several types) of physical activity that you like doing and create a workout plan for a month, to improve your cardiorespiratory fitness using the principles discussed in this chapter. What will it take to get you to follow this plan? What will make it challenging? Easier?

Your goal should be to expend 300 to 500 calories per day through leisure-time physical activity, with an eventual weekly goal of 1500 to 2100 calories. The lower the intensity of the activity, the longer the time you will need to obtain the same caloric expenditure. If your preference is for lower-intensity physical activity, the recommendation changes to 60 minutes every day of the week. It should be pointed out that whether the recommendation is for 30 minutes of moderate-intensity physical activity most days of the week or 60 minutes of light-intensity physical activity every day of the week, it is possible to accumulate these activities in 10-minute spurts. See the Focus on Canada box.

A physical activity program over several months or years—exercise training—improves the way your cardiorespiratory system meets your body's oxygen requirements at rest and during exercise and helps you to feel good about yourself. Keep in mind that the physiological health benefits associated with cardiorespiratory endurance activities (reduced blood pressure, decreased resting heart rate, improved blood flow, etc.) take about one year of regular exercise to achieve. However, any physical activity, even if it does not meet all the exercise characteristics mentioned in this chapter, will benefit your overall health and help you to feel better about yourself almost immediately.

Target heart rate: The desired intensity of aerobic exercise for improving or maintaining cardiorespiratory fitness; calculated as a percentage of maximum heart rate (220 [for males] 226 [for females] minus age).

FOCUS ON CANADA

Physical Activity for Healthy Living: How Much Is Enough?

Similar to Eating Well with Canada's Food Guide, Canada's Physical Activity Guide to Healthy Active Living uses a rainbow approach to describe the amount and type of physical activities Canadians need for optimal health benefits (see Figure 5a.1).

The outside of the rainbow includes physical activities we need the most of—endurance activities. These activities should be engaged in 4 to 7 days per week, depending upon the intensity of the activity, and are continuous in nature, thus providing benefits to the heart, lungs, and circulatory system. Examples include cross-country skiing, taking the stairs instead of the elevator, cycling, walking, and mowing the lawn.

The intensity of the physical activities engaged in for cardiorespiratory endurance significantly influences the frequency and time needed for health benefits. If your preferred physical activities involve light effort such as slow-paced walking, stretching, or easy gardening, you need 60 minutes 7 days a week. If the physical activities you engage in are of a moderate effort, such as brisk walking, biking, raking leaves, swimming, or dancing, you need 30 to 60 minutes at least 4 days per week. If your preference is for "workout" kinds of physical activities, then you need 20 to 30 minutes 3 days per week. Examples of workout activities include fitness classes, jogging, fast swimming, or fast dancing. Combinations of physical activities of various intensities can also lead to optimal health benefits.

The next arc of the rainbow describes the type of physical activity that we need the next most of—flexibility activities. It is also recommended that we obtain these types of activities 4 to 7 times per week. These types of physical activities are described as "gentle reaching, bending, and stretching activities to keep your muscles relaxed and joints mobile." Examples include various stretches that are often done after other types of physical activities.

The third arc of the rainbow is for strength activities, which should be done 2 to 4 days per week. These activities will strengthen muscles and bones as well as improve posture. Examples include weight training with hand-held weights, body-weight resistance exercise (curl-ups and push-ups), as well as walking with backpacks.

The last arc of the rainbow describes activities we should try to reduce. Examples included in this arc of the rainbow are sedentary activities such as watching television or movies, and working or playing on a computer.

FIGURE 5a.1

Canada's Physical Activity Guide to Healthy Active Living

Source: Canada's Physical Activity Guide to Healthy Active Living, Cat. No. H39-429/1998-1E ISBN 0-662-86627-7, Health Canada, 2003; available online at: www.phac-aspc.gc.ca/pau-uap/fitness/pdf/guideEng.pdf.

STUDY QUESTIONS

1. Identify the practical, economic, and environmental roadblocks that make it difficult to attain and maintain a physically active lifestyle in Canada. Suggest potential solutions.
2. Describe ways that Canadians of all ages—children, adolescents, adults, and older adults—could begin to incorporate more physical activity into their lives. When answering this question, consider each demographic group in a rural, urban, and suburban environment.
3. What could the various levels of government (federal, provincial/territorial, municipal) do to enhance the physical activity level of Canadians? Should the private sector also get involved? How?
4. What is the role of education in promoting physical activity? How can this role be better played?

Source: Adapted from Public Health Agency of Canada, Canada's Physical Activity Guide to Healthy Living, Cat. No. H39-429/1998-2E. Canada's Physical Activity Guide to Healthy Living can be downloaded from www.phac-aspc.gc.ca/pau-uap/paguide/index.html.

IMPROVING MUSCULAR STRENGTH AND ENDURANCE

Musculoskeletal health (that is, strength, endurance, and flexibility) also significantly impacts health and overall wellness. Specifically, musculoskeletal health is associated with a reduced risk for coronary heart disease and osteoporosis as well as improved glucose tolerance and ease of completing tasks of daily living. **Muscular strength** refers to the maximal amount of force a muscle or group of muscles is capable of exerting in one contraction. The most common way to measure strength is to determine the maximum amount of weight you can lift once. This value is called **one repetition maximum (1RM)**. Your 1RM can also be predicted from a 10RM test. **Muscular endurance** is defined as a muscle's or group of muscles' ability to exert force repeatedly without fatiguing or the ability to sustain a muscular contraction. The more repetitions you can perform successfully (for example, push-ups) or the longer you can hold a certain position (for example, flexed arm hang), the greater your muscular endurance. Muscular endurance is often measured from the number of curl-ups or push-ups an individual can do.

Principles of Strength Development

There are three key principles—tension, overload, and specificity—to follow to increase your muscular strength and endurance.

The Tension Principle

The key to developing strength is to create sufficient tension within a muscle. The most common way to create tension in a muscle is the use of external resistance such as that found in weight lifting. While weight lifting is one method of producing tension in a muscle, many other types of physical activity have the same effect—for example, lifting your own body weight (push-ups or pull-ups) or riding a bicycle up a steep hill. It really does not matter what type of resistance you choose to develop tension in your muscles; what matters is that you use sufficient resistance to improve muscular strength and/or endurance.

The Overload Principle

The overload principle is the most important of the three key principles for improving muscular strength.

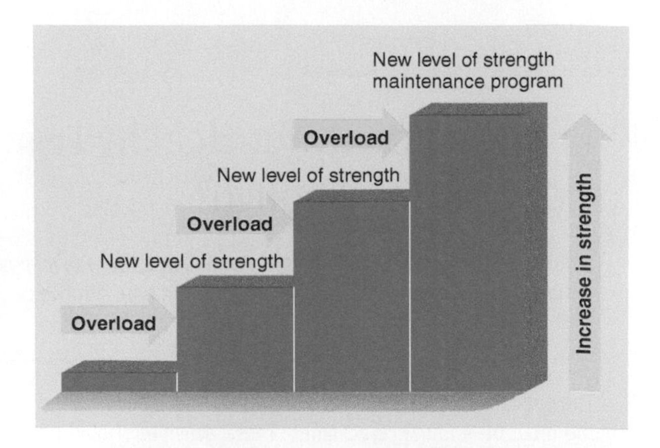

FIGURE 5a.2

The overload principle must be followed to increase strength or endurance. Notice that once the muscle has adapted to the original overload, a new overload must be placed on the muscle for subsequent gains in strength or endurance to occur.

Source: From Philip A. Sienna, *One Rep Max: A Guide to Beginning Weight Training,* Fig. 2.1, 8. © 1989. Wm. C. Brown Communications, Inc., Dubuque, Iowa. Reprinted by permission of Times Mirror Higher Education Group, Inc., Dubuque, Iowa. All rights reserved.

Everyone begins a resistance training program with an initial level of strength. To increase strength, you must then regularly create tension in your muscles greater than what you are accustomed to. This overload forces your muscles to adapt by getting larger (**hypertrophy**), stronger, and thus capable of generating more tension. Figure 5a.2 illustrates a continual process of overload and adaptation resulting in improved strength. If you do not create an overload—if you "underload" your muscles—you will not increase strength. Conversely, if you create too great an overload, you may experience muscle injury, muscle fatigue, and even a loss of strength. Once you reach your strength goal, no further overloading is necessary. Your next challenge is to maintain that level of strength by continuing to engage in a regular (once or twice per week) total-body resistance exercise program.

Musculoskeletal health: The combination of strength, endurance, and flexibility and their influence on various components of health.

Muscular strength: The maximal amount of force that a muscle or groups of muscles is capable of exerting.

One repetition maximum (1RM): The maximum amount of weight/resistance that can be lifted/moved only once.

Muscular endurance: A muscle's or group of muscles' ability to exert force repeatedly or to sustain a contraction without fatiguing.

Hypertrophy: Increased size (girth) of a muscle.

These photographs illustrate concentric and eccentric muscle actions. In A, the abdominal muscles shorten, a concentric muscle action, while producing tension in the lifting phase of a curl-up. In B, the abdominal muscles lengthen, an eccentric muscle action, while producing tension as the body returns to its starting position.

The Specificity of Training Principle

This principle refers to the manner in which a specific body system responds to the physiological demands placed upon it. According to the specificity principle, you get a very specific response to the exercises you do. If the specific overload you impose is designed to improve strength in the muscles of your chest and back, the response to that demand (overload) will be improved strength in the chest and back, not in the overall body. Therefore, to improve overall or total body strength, you must include exercises for all the major muscle groups. You must also ensure that your overload is sufficient to increase strength and not only endurance.

The Recovery Principle

Allow 48 hours for the body to "recover" from and adapt to the resistance training undertaken (that is, to become stronger). This does not mean that you cannot resistance train daily, but rather that you need to design your work out so that you alternate which muscles you concentrate on when resistance training. Keep in mind that your core body is always involved in your training and you may need to take a day off to ensure that it too has sufficient time to heal and adapt to the overloads undertaken.

Types of Muscle Contractions

When your skeletal muscles receive a stimulus from your nervous system to contract, they respond by developing tension and producing a measurable force. Your skeletal muscles contract in three different modes—isometric, concentric, and eccentric—to produce this force. In an **isometric muscle contraction**, force is produced by the muscle without movement. Isometric muscle actions do not create joint motion. Muscles act isometrically to stabilize a particular body part while another body part is moving, or when a maximal resistance is met and the force produced cannot overcome the resistance. One example is the unsuccessful attempt to push a car out of a snow bank. Although you push with all your might, the car does not move (and neither do your joints). The muscles involved are producing force in an isometric way. Another example related to resistance training is trying to lift a barbell that is too heavy for you. The more you try, the more tired your muscles become, but the barbell never leaves the floor. Isometric muscle contractions are important because they are involved in maintaining body stability. Maintaining your balance and body alignment while holding a push-up is another example of isometric muscle contractions.

A **concentric muscle contraction** is one in which force is produced while the muscle shortens. Joint movement is always produced during concentric muscle actions. Raising the body in a curl-up is an example of a concentric action of the abdominal muscles. Usually, but not always, concentric muscle contractions produce movement in a direction opposite to the downward pull of gravity.

Eccentric muscle contraction describes a muscle's ability to produce force while lengthening. Typically, eccentric muscle actions occur when movement is in the same direction as the pull of gravity. If you want to be sure that a given resistance exercise has an eccentric phase, you must use the type of resistance that requires you to achieve the starting position before your next repetition. For example, in a curl-up, you lower your upper body slowly to the starting point of the exercise in an eccentric contraction of the abdominal muscles.

All factors being equal, the greatest amount of force is produced during eccentric muscle contractions, followed by isometric and then concentric muscle contractions. Changes in muscle size and strength are affected by the type of resistance exercise and by the type of muscle contraction(s) you use during your workout. When using free weights (barbells, dumbbells), the typical sequential pattern of concentric–eccentric muscle contractions during resistance training contributes to improved muscle strength and muscle fibre size. If your resistance exercise program uses only concentric muscle actions, you'll need to perform at least twice as many repetitions to achieve the same results as you would attain by using concentric–eccentric combinations.

Methods of Providing Resistance

There are four commonly used methods of applying resistance for muscular strength and endurance training: body weight resistance, and fixed, variable, and accommodating resistance devices.

Body Weight Resistance

Muscular strength and endurance can be improved without exercise equipment, using your body weight as the resistance. For many individuals, using their body weight as resistance in a variety of exercises can be as effective as external resistance in developing and maintaining muscular strength and endurance. Exercises such as curl-ups, push-ups, and pull-ups require your muscles to lift and return your body weight off the floor, involving concentric and eccentric muscle contractions.

Fixed Resistance

Fixed resistance exercises provide a constant resistance throughout a full range of movement. Barbells and dumbbells provide fixed resistance because their weight or the amount of resistance applied does not change as you exercise. However, due to the biomechanics of human motion, the muscle forces that must be exerted to move the weight are lower at some joint angles and higher at others. Any given muscle generates the least amount of force at the beginning and ending positions of a resistance exercise, and the most force when the joint involved in the exercise approximates a right angle (90 degrees). As a result, the disadvantage of fixed resistance exercises is that the extent to which a muscle is overloaded varies throughout the exercise, and the exercise may not fully develop the muscle.

Variable Resistance

Whether found at a health club or in your home workout area, variable resistance equipment alters the resistance encountered by a muscle at all joint angles so that the effort by the muscle is consistent throughout the full range of motion. Variable resistance machines are typically single-station devices (for example, Nautilus), but some have multiple stations at which muscles of the upper and lower extremities can be exercised (for example, Soloflex).

Accommodating Resistance

Accommodating resistance devices (isokinetic machines), maintain a constant speed through the range of motion. The exerciser performs at a maximal level of effort, while the exercise machine controls the speed of the exercise and does not allow any faster motion. The body segment being exercised must move at a rate faster than or equal to the set speed to encounter resistance.

Getting Started

You will find some general principles useful whatever your strength training goals. If sufficient tension is generated within a muscle, it will respond by becoming stronger regardless of the type of muscle action or resistance used. To design your program, first determine your 1RM for each muscle or muscle group you plan to exercise. Then, develop specific training goals as well as the strategies to achieve those goals.

Strength Training

There are almost as many ways to develop muscular strength as there are participants in strength training programs. Given the specificity principle, it is important to select at least one resistance exercise for each major muscle group in the body to develop total body strength. Generally, strength training exercises are done in a set, or series, of multiple repetitions using the same resistance. For increases in muscular strength, the amount of resistance should be at least 60 percent or greater of your 1RM for a given exercise, with 8 to 12 repetitions of the exercise performed per set. Generally, a resistance that you can move or lift only 8 to 10 times is a good place to start. It is further recommended that 1 to 3 sets be performed.

Since resistance training exercises cause microscopic damage (tears) to muscle fibres and the rebuilding process takes about 24 to 48 hours, resistance training programs should incorporate at least one day of rest (and recovery) between workouts to allow the muscle or muscle groups to adapt. Thus, the recommended frequency of programs to build muscular strength is 2 to 4 days per week.

Isometric muscle contraction: Force produced without muscle movement.

Concentric muscle contraction: Force produced while shortening the muscle.

Eccentric muscle contraction: Force produced while lengthening the muscle.

Using your body weight can be an effective way to build or maintain muscular strength and endurance.

To summarize, you should perform each strength building exercise at an intensity greater than 60 percent of your 1RM for 1 to 3 sets of 2 to 6 repetitions, 2 to 4 days per week. See also Table 5a.2.

Muscular Endurance Training

In contrast to improvements in strength, increases in muscular endurance are achieved by performing a relatively high number of repetitions with a relatively low resistance. For endurance, instead of traditional resistance exercise equipment, consider adding variety to your training program with devices equipped with an ergometer, such as a stationary bicycle, rowing machine, or stair-climbing machine. With these and other devices, you can control the cadence of the activity and/or adjust the amount of resistance you encounter. Performing thousands of repetitions during a 20-minute (or longer) workout using a relatively low resistance will quickly develop muscular endurance in the muscles exercised. Other activities that build muscular endurance include hiking, wall climbing, jogging, and cycling. These latter types of exercises also provide cardiorespiratory benefits if you select an intensity that allows you to reach your target heart rate.

TABLE 5a.2

Guide to Manipulating Training Variables to Achieve Different Strength Training Goals

	Endurance	Strength
Sets	2–6	1–3
Repetitions	10–15	2–6
Resistance (% of maximum)	< 60	> 60
Rest between sets (seconds)	30–60	120
Frequency per week (days)	2–4	2–4
Rest between workouts (days)	1–2	1–2

what do you THINK?

In regard to daily living, why is it important to develop your muscular strength and endurance? What type of resistance training program would work best for you? Do you require access to equipment and facilities to engage in this type of program? If so, do you know where to go and how to use this equipment?

You can also build muscular endurance through resistance training by performing 2 to 6 sets of 10 to 15 repetitions of a resistance less than 60 percent of your 1RM 2 to 4 days per week. See also Table 5a.2.

Lifting free weights to build muscular strength and endurance has many advantages.

IMPROVING YOUR FLEXIBILITY

Flexibility refers to the range of motion, or the amount of movement possible, at a particular joint or series of joints. Although this component of physical fitness is often overshadowed by muscular strength and cardiorespiratory endurance, it should not be overlooked because inflexible muscles are susceptible to injury. Improving your range of motion through stretching exercises will enhance the efficiency of your movements as well as your posture. A regular stretching program may also enhance psychological well-being.

Types of Stretching Exercises

Flexibility is most often enhanced by controlled stretching of muscles. The primary strategy is to decrease the resistance to stretch (tension) within a tight muscle targeted for increased range of motion. To do this, you repeatedly stretch the muscle and its two tendons of attachment to elongate them.

The safest exercises for improving flexibility involve **static stretching**. Static stretching techniques slowly and gradually lengthen a muscle or group of muscles. In this regard, various positions and postures are used with the "stretch" held to a point where tension (mild discomfort) is felt within the muscle. This end position is then held for 10 to 30 seconds, and is repeated 2 or 3 times in close succession. With each repetition of a static stretch, your range of motion improves temporarily and when done regularly, range of motion increases for longer periods of time. Stretching regularly (at least four, and preferably seven, days a week) will effectively result in a more permanent elongation of the targeted muscle or muscle group and thus permit a greater range of motion at a given joint.

In regard to athletic performance, static stretching immediately prior to performance reduces the athlete's efforts. Thus it is recommended that if static stretching is part of the warm-up, that it be followed immediately by more dynamic movements.

> **try it NOW!**
> Give yourself a break and stretch! Stretching and improved flexibility are just as important in the classroom and library as they are in the gym. Sitting hunched over a pile of books or leaning in toward your computer for extended periods of time can be a pain in the neck and/or back! When studying, be sure to stretch every 20 minutes or so by doing shoulder rolls, shrugs, and neck stretches (tilt ear to shoulder on both sides, chin to chest) to help work out the kinks. It is also a good idea to stand up and move the whole body a little. These mini-stretch breaks will ease your muscles and your mind.

YOGA, TAI CHI, AND PILATES

Three popular styles of exercise that include stretching are yoga, tai chi, and Pilates. In addition to improving flexibility, these types of exercise may increase muscular strength and endurance as well as focus on the mind body connection through concentration on breathing and body position. Some people see these three activities strongly connected to the development of their spiritual health, particularly when time is spent relaxing, breathing deeply, and trying to clear the mind.

Yoga

Although yoga originated in India about 5000 years ago, it is currently one of the most popular physical activities that involves static stretching. Yoga blends the mental and physical aspects of exercise, a union of mind and body that provides a relaxing and satisfying experience that many find enhances their spiritual

Flexibility: The range of motion, or the amount of movement possible, at a particular joint or series of joints.

Static stretching: Assuming a "stretching" position—at the point of tension—for 10 to 30 seconds in which there is a gradual lengthening of a muscle.

health. If done regularly, the combination of mental focus and physical effort improves flexibility, vitality, posture, agility, and coordination.

The practice of yoga focuses attention on controlled breathing as well as purely physical exercise. In addition to its mental dimensions, yoga incorporates a complex array of static stretching exercises expressed as postures—or asanas. Over 200 postures/asanas exist with about 50 most commonly practiced. During a session, participants move to different asanas and hold them for 30 seconds or more. Asanas, singly or in combination, can be changed and adapted for young and old or to accommodate physical limitations or disabilities. Asanas can also be combined to provide well-conditioned athletes with a challenging workout!

A typical yoga session will move the spine and joints through their full range of motion. Yoga postures lengthen, strengthen, and balance musculature, leading to increased flexibility, stamina, and strength—and many people report a psychological sense of general well-being too. Table 5a.3 details three popular types of yoga.

Tai Chi

Tai chi is an ancient form of exercise that combines stretching, balance, coordination, and meditation. It is designed to increase range of motion and flexibility while reducing muscular tension. Based on Chi Kung, a Taoist philosophy dedicated to spiritual growth and good health, tai chi was developed about 1000 CE by monks to defend themselves against bandits and warlords. It involves a series of positions called "forms," based on Chinese martial arts, performed continuously. Further, tai chi is often described as "meditation in motion" because it promotes serenity through gentle movements—connecting the mind and body.

TABLE 5a.3

Popular Yoga Styles

- **Iyengar yoga** focuses on precision and alignment in the poses. Standing poses are basic to this style and are often held longer than in other styles.
- **Ashtanga yoga** in its pure form is based on a specific flow of poses with an emphasis on strength and agility that creates internal heat. *Power yoga,* a style growing in popularity, is a derivative of ashtanga yoga.
- **Bikram yoga**, or hot yoga, is similar to power yoga but does not incorporate a specific flow of poses. Literally the hottest yoga going, it is performed in temperatures of 38°C, or even a bit higher. Proponents say that the heat increases the body's ability to move and stretch without injury.

what do you THINK?

Why is flexibility often overlooked in workout plans? How does stretching provide physical and mental health benefits?

Pilates

Pilates was developed by Joseph Pilates in 1926. It teaches body awareness, good posture, and easy, graceful body movements. Further, Pilates improves flexibility, agility, coordination, strength, tone, and economy of motion. It may even alleviate back pain. Pilates combines stretching with movement against resistance aided by devices such as tension springs or heavy rubber bands. Pilates differs from yoga and tai chi in that it includes a component specifically designed to increase strength. The method consists of a sequence of carefully performed movements. Some are carried out on specially designed equipment, while others are performed on mats. Each exercise strengthens the muscles involved and has a specific breathing pattern associated with it.

BODY COMPOSITION

Body composition is the final component of a comprehensive health-related physical fitness program. Body composition describes the relative portions of fat and lean tissues in the body. Body composition parameters are influenced by regular physical activity and exercise in terms of total body mass, fat mass, fat-free mass, and regional fat distribution. Generally, aerobic physical activities improve body composition because they expend calories and contribute to weight maintenance and/or loss.

PLANNING YOUR PHYSICAL FITNESS TRAINING PROGRAM

Identifying Your Physical Fitness Goals

Before you start a physical fitness training program, determine your personal health and physical fitness needs, limitations, exercise likes and dislikes, daily schedule, and goals. Whatever your primary reason for starting a training program, your most important goal should be to commit to regular physical activity, exercise, and physical fitness.

Once committed, you must decide what program is best suited to your needs. The amounts and types of exercises required to yield beneficial results vary with the age and physical condition of the exerciser. Regardless of age, first complete the Physical Activity Readiness Questionnaire (available at www.csep.ca) and consult your physician if you respond yes to any of the questions.

It is useful to map your journey by identifying your current physical fitness level and your end goal. Your program should reflect your initial positioning while addressing your individual strengths and weaknesses so that you can move along the chart stage by stage as you pursue your short- and long-term goals.

Designing Your Physical Fitness Program

To optimize your physical fitness training, develop a workout schedule that is both challenging and realistic. An important step in adopting a new behaviour is developing a new routine. Care must be taken to ensure that you do not set yourself up for failure before you begin by choosing an overly ambitious schedule. If you decide to walk 6 times per week, but are able to complete only four sessions, you might feel you failed to achieve your goal. It is very important to set yourself up for success by making your goals realistic and achievable—success in meeting and exceeding your short-term goals will give you the positive energy and confidence to move forward with your program and reach your long-term goals.

For many people, it is also important to keep a record of their workouts. Something as simple as checkmarks on the calendar for the days you exercised may help to keep you motivated from the visual signs of success. More detailed records provide positive feedback and motivation by allowing you to look back to see where you started and how much you have progressed over time. It is also important to regularly evaluate your progress—about every six to eight weeks—and adjust your program accordingly. As previously mentioned, the body adapts quickly to an overload and unless you keep overloading your body your progress will quickly plateau. You must consciously increase the intensity, volume (quantity), or frequency of your workouts over time to continue to make gains.

Your training program can be as simple as outlining which days you will exercise each week, and for how long—leaving the decision as to what type of activity you will do, or where, for that day. Alternately, you can develop a long-term program where each set of variables is carefully calculated and managed. Whatever your approach, all good fitness programs should address the major components of physical fitness—cardiorespiratory endurance, muscular strength and endurance, and flexibility.

Warm-up and Cool-Down

Every exercise session should begin with a warm-up and finish with a cool-down. Your warm-up should include 5 to 15 minutes of large body movements that increase your body temperature, followed by light stretching for the muscle groups you are about to use. The length of your warm-up is dependent upon how psychologically prepared you are to move; if you are geared up and ready to go, the warm-up may not take as long (approximately 5 minutes), whereas if you are not quite in the mood to exercise the warm-up may take longer (approximately 15 minutes). A warm-up should gradually increase heart rate and core body temperature, improve joint lubrication, increase muscles' and tendons' elasticity and flexibility, and enhance your performance during the workout that follows.

The cool-down should be similar to the warm-up, with 5 to 10 minutes of moderate- to low-intensity cardiorespiratory activity, followed by 5 to 10 minutes of stretching exercises. The purpose of the cool-down is to gradually reduce your heart rate, blood pressure, and body temperature to pre-exercising levels. In addition, a cool-down reduces the risk of blood pooling in the extremities, and facilitates quicker recovery between exercise sessions. Because of the body's increased temperature, the cool-down is an excellent time to stretch and increase flexibility.

Cardiorespiratory Endurance

It is important to spend a good portion of your exercise time developing your aerobic fitness. Choose physical activities that you like. Many people find cross training—alternating participation in two or more activities (such as jogging and swimming)—more enjoyable than long-term participation in only one activity. Cross training is also beneficial in that it strengthens a variety of muscles and reduces your risk of overuse injuries. Jogging, brisk walking, swimming, cycling, rowing, step aerobics, and cross country skiing are excellent activities for developing cardiovascular fitness.

Resistance Training

It is important to include strengthening exercises in your training plans as well. Although regular aerobic exercise will contribute to building and maintaining muscular endurance, it will not build or maintain muscular strength. Different exercises using free weights, your own body weight, or machines can be combined in many ways to create an effective resistance-training workout. As previously mentioned, physical activities such as yoga, tai chi, and Pilates are also effective at building strength.

Flexibility

For optimal flexibility, static stretching exercises should be performed every day following a general warm-up to raise the core body temperature and increase the elasticity of muscles and tendons. Many people find that stretching between sets during their resistance training sessions is quite effective. The target muscles are already warm, and since the stretches are performed during the rest time between sets, no additional time for stretching is required at the beginning or end of the workout.

FITNESS-RELATED INJURIES

There are two basic types of injuries stemming from participation in fitness training–related activities: overuse and traumatic.

Causes of Fitness-Related Injuries

Overtraining is the most frequent cause of injuries associated with physical fitness training. **Overuse injuries** occur because of cumulative, day-after-day stresses placed on body parts (tendons, bones, and ligaments). The forces that occur normally during physical activity are not enough to result in an injury, but when applied on a daily basis for weeks or months, they can result in an injury. That is why people who sustain this type of injury typically cannot pinpoint a particular time or day when they were injured. Common sites of overuse injuries are the leg, knee, shoulder, and elbow joints. While participating in your personal fitness program, listen to your body's warning signs. Muscle stiffness and soreness, bone and joint pains, and whole-body fatigue are common warning signs of an overuse injury. To minimize your risk of an overuse injury, vary your physical activities throughout the week. Further, set appropriate and realistic short- and long-term training goals.

Traumatic injuries, which occur suddenly and violently, typically by accident, are the second major type of fitness training–related injuries. Typical traumatic injuries are broken bones, torn ligaments and muscles, contusions, and lacerations. Most traumatic injuries are unavoidable—for example, spraining your ankle by landing on another person's foot after jumping up for a rebound in basketball. If your traumatic injury causes a noticeable loss of function and immediate pain or pain that does not go away after 30 minutes, you should have a physician examine it.

Prevention

To minimize your risk of injuries, it is important to examine the equipment you use—the actual exercise equipment you use and the shoes you wear.

Appropriate Footwear

When you purchase running shoes or sneakers, look for several key components. Proper footwear can decrease the likelihood of foot, knee, or back injuries. Biomechanics research suggests that running is a "collision" sport—that is, the runner's foot collides with the ground with a force three to five times the runner's body weight with each stride. The force not absorbed by the running shoe is transmitted upward into the foot, leg, thigh, and back. Our bodies are able to absorb forces such as these, but may be injured by the cumulative effects of repetitive impacts (for example, running 65 kilometres per week). Therefore, the ability of running shoes to absorb shock is a critical factor to consider when you purchase footwear for your physical activities. Proper fit is also important. In addition, it is crucial to replace footwear regularly (after running approximately 1000 kilometres) to ensure that the shock absorbency is still effective. Other physical activities or sports (basketball, soccer, cycling, mountain climbing) require different footwear performance, and the requirements of the physical activity or sport should be considered when you prepare yourself to engage in those activities or sports.

Appropriate Protective Equipment

It is essential to use well-fitted, appropriate equipment for your physical activities. For some activities, there is specialized protective equipment to reduce your chances of injury. In tennis, for example, the use of the "right" racquet with the "right" tension helps prevent the general inflammatory condition known as "tennis elbow."

Eye injuries can occur in virtually all physical activities, though the risk of injury is much greater in some activities than others. As many as 90 percent of eye injuries resulting from racquetball and squash are preventable with appropriate eye protection—for example, goggles with polycarbonate lenses.

While appropriate clothing and equipment help prevent injuries in any physical activity, a workout partner is also an important safeguard.

According to the Canadian Cycling Association, cycling is one of the most popular recreational activities in Canada and continues to grow every year. The selection of the right-sized bicycle frame and correct seat height, coupled with the use of a bicycle helmet, padded grips/handlebars, and padded cycling gloves, can significantly reduce injuries. In the past, head injuries accounted for 85 percent of all deaths attributable to bicycle accidents; however, the wearing of bicycle helmets has significantly reduced the number of skull fractures and facial injuries among recreational cyclists. Cyclists should wear bicycle helmets that meet the criteria established by the Canadian Standards Association.

> **what do you THINK?**
> In what way do your physical activities put you at risk of injury? What changes can you make in terms of your training program, equipment, or footwear to reduce these risks?

Common Overuse Injuries

The three most common overuse injuries are plantar fasciitis, "shin splints," and "runner's knee."

Plantar Fasciitis

Plantar fasciitis is an inflammation of the plantar fascia, a broad band of dense, inelastic tissue (fascia) that runs from the heel to the toe on the bottom of your foot. The main function of the plantar fascia is to protect the nerves, blood vessels, and muscles of the foot from injury. In repetitive, weight-bearing activities such as walking and running, the plantar fascia may become inflamed. Common symptoms include pain and tenderness under the ball of the foot, at the heel, or at both locations. The pain of plantar fasciitis is particularly noticeable during your first steps out of bed in the morning. If not treated properly, this injury may progress in severity to the point that weight-bearing exercise is too painful to endure. Uphill running is not advised since each uphill stride severely stretches (and thus irritates) the already inflamed plantar fascia. Plantar fasciitis can be prevented by regular stretching of the plantar fascia prior to exercise and by wearing footwear with good arch support and shock absorbency. Stretching the plantar fascia involves slowly pulling all five toes upward toward your head, holding for 10 to 15 seconds, and repeating this 3 to 5 times on each foot before exercising.

Shin Splints

Shin splints is a general term for any pain that occurs on the front part of the lower legs. More than 20 different medical conditions have been identified within the broad description of shin splints. Problems range from stress fractures of the tibia (shinbone) to severe inflammation in the muscular compartments of the lower leg, which can interrupt the flow of blood and nerve conduction to the foot. The most common type of shin splints occurs along the inner side of the tibia and is usually a combination of muscle irritation and irritation of the tissues that attach the muscles to the bone. Typically, there is pain and swelling along the middle one-third of the postero-medial tibia in the soft tissues.

Sedentary people who start a new weight-bearing physical activity program are at the greatest risk for shin splints, though well-conditioned aerobic exercisers who rapidly increase their distance or pace may also be at risk. Running and exercise classes are the most frequent cause of shin splints, but those who do a great deal of walking (for example, postal carriers or restaurant staff) may also develop shin splints.

To minimize your risk, wear shoes with good arch support and shock absorbency. If the severity of your shin splints increases to the point that you cannot comfortably complete your desired physical activity,

Overuse injuries: Injuries that result from the cumulative effects of day-after-day stresses placed on tendons, muscles, and joints.

Traumatic injuries: Injuries that are usually accidental in nature and occur suddenly and violently (for example, fractured bones, ruptured tendons, and sprained ligaments).

HEALTH IN THE MEDIA

Evaluating Sources of Health Information

A quick glance at national newspaper headlines, magazine cover stories, nightly television news programs, and the internet shows how popular it has become to engage in exercise not only to improve health but also to shape one's body. Led by the desire of our aging population to remain physically fit and healthy, there is seemingly no end to the information available. However, the quality of information runs the gamut from physical activity trends, exercise fads, and weight-loss gadgets to scientifically sound research regarding the triangular relationship among physical activity, physical fitness, and health. Take time to carefully consider the original source of the information and the context in which it is presented.

Popular health and fitness magazines can be good sources of information about exercise techniques, program design variables, and training regimens for individuals at all skill levels. However, you must closely examine a magazine's masthead to identify whether or not the editors, staff, and writers have relevant qualifications. A high-quality, reputable health and fitness magazine will complement its staff of professional journalists with a variety of experts in the field—exercise editors, science editors, medical editors, and/or health editors—who hold advanced degrees in their fields and maintain their credentials through membership in respected professional associations. The same goes for television, newspapers, and the internet. The quality of the experts associated with each story or media outlet will be a fairly accurate indicator of the quality of the information. Are the "experts" celebrities and/or consumers who have experienced tremendous results from a particular product? Or are they researchers and scientists with recognized credentials from universities, colleges, and professional associations?

Look for these credentials when assessing the expertise of a source on physical activity and exercise:

BSc or BA—Bachelor of Science or Bachelor of Arts degree in human kinetics, kinesiology, human movement, or related exercise science fields

MSc (MS if US source)—Master of Science in an exercise science–related field

PhD—Doctor of Philosophy in an exercise science–related field

MD—Medical doctor

CSCS—Certified Strength and Conditioning Specialist (National Strength and Conditioning Association www.nsca-cc.org)

ACSM (American College of Sports Medicine)—Exercise Specialist (www.acsm.org)

CSEP (Canadian Society of Exercise Physiology)—Exercise Specialist (www.csep.ca)

see your physician. Specific pain on the tibia or on the fibula (the adjacent, smaller bone) should be examined for possible stress fracture. Reducing the frequency, intensity, and time of weight-bearing exercises may be required. You may also be advised to substitute a non–weight bearing exercise such as swimming, cycling, or rowing during your recovery period.

Runner's Knee

Runner's knee describes a series of problems involving the muscles, tendons, and ligaments of the knee. The most common problem is abnormal movement of the patella or kneecap. Women are more commonly affected than men because of their anatomical structure. Specifically, their wider pelvis results in a lateral pull on the patella by the muscles that act on the knee. In women (and some men), this causes irritation to the cartilage on the back of the patella as well as to the nearby tendons and ligaments. The main symptom is the pain experienced when downward pressure is applied to the patella after the knee is straightened fully. Additional symptoms include swelling, redness, and tenderness around the patella, and a dull, aching pain in the centre of the knee. With these symptoms, your physician will probably recommend that you stop running for a few weeks and reduce daily physical activities that put compressive forces on the patella (for example, exercise on a stair-climbing machine or doing squats with heavy resistance) until you no longer feel any pain around your kneecap.

Treatment

Treatment for virtually all fitness training-related injuries involves **RICE:** rest, ice, compression, and elevation. Rest is required to eliminate the risk of further irritating the injured body part. Ice is applied to relieve pain and to constrict the blood vessels to reduce internal or external bleeding associated with the injury. To prevent frostbite or other irritation to the skin, do not apply directly to your skin; instead, place a layer of wet towelling between the ice and your skin. Ice should be applied to a new injury for approximately 20 minutes every hour for the first 24 to 72 hours. Compression of the injured body part can be accomplished with a 10- or 15-centimetre-wide elastic bandage; this applies indirect pressure to damaged blood vessels to help stop bleeding. Be careful that the compression wrap is not on so tight that it interferes with normal blood

learned, you want to suggest that she add aerobic exercise and flexibility training to her workout. However, because you do little more than walk 30 minutes a day, you are afraid she won't take your suggestion seriously.

Decide how you could approach Silke to urge her to take a more balanced and perhaps more realistic approach to her workout regime.

SKILLS FOR BEHAVIOUR CHANGE

Better, Not Best

A popular, relatively new video game system (introduced in the fall of 2006) that promotes physical activity is the Nintendo Wii. Various games/activities are available (golf, bowling, baseball, tennis, and boxing, for instance), which are played in an interactive setting. The "player" holds a remote in one or both hands to perform the required actions of the game (that is, swing golf club, bowl, swing bat, etc.). The game can be played in the comfort of your own home and at a time that fits your personal schedule. Further simplifying the process and reducing common barriers to physical activity is the fact that you do not need someone to play with (though a number of players/gamers can be included at one time). Sound like a perfect way to build and/or maintain your physical fitness? Not quite. Research by Porcari, Schmidt, and Foster showed that the physical activities engaged in did burn significantly more calories than does the body at rest; however, not as many as the "real" physical activity in the "real" environment would. Specifically it was found that Wii golfing used approximately 3.1 calories per minute compared to 3.9 calories per minute for real golfing. Wii boxing was the most vigorous activity, using 7.2 calories per minute compared to 10.2 calories per minute of the real thing. The bottom line is that Wii provides another option for being physically active, *but* it may not provide the intensity of activity needed to build or maintain your physical fitness.

Source: Adapted from J. Porcari, K. Schmidt, and C. Foster. "As Good as the Real Thing?" *ACE Fitness Matters*, July/August (2008) 7–9.

condition resulting from abnormally low body core temperature—may result. Hypothermia can occur as a result of prolonged, vigorous exercise (for example, snowboarding or rugby) in 4°C to 10°C temperatures, particularly if there is rain, snow, or a strong wind.

As your body core temperature drops from the normal 37°C to 34°C, you will begin to shiver. Shivering—the involuntary contraction of nearly every muscle in your body—is designed to increase your body temperature by generating heat through muscle activity. During this first stage of hypothermia, you may also experience cold hands and feet, poor judgment, apathy, and amnesia. Shivering ceases in most hypothermia victims as their core body temperature drops to between 32°C and 30°C, a sign that the body has lost its ability to generate heat. Death from hypothermia usually occurs at core body temperatures between 26.5°C and 24°C.

To prevent hypothermia, follow these guidelines: analyze weather conditions and your risk of hypothermia before engaging in your planned outdoor physical activity, remembering that wind and humidity are as significant as temperature; use the "buddy system"—that is, have a friend join you for your cold-weather outdoor activities; wear layers of appropriate clothing to prevent excessive heat loss (for example, polypropylene or woolen undergarments, a Gore-Tex windbreaker, and wool hat and gloves); and, finally, don't allow yourself to become dehydrated.

CHAPTER 5b

DIET, NATURAL HEALTH PRODUCTS AND NUTRITION

Taken from *Health: The Basics*, Fifth Canadian Edition, by Rebecca J. Donatelle and Angela M. Thompson

Today, we face dietary choices and nutritional challenges that our grandparents never dreamed of—exotic foreign foods; dietary supplements; artificial sweeteners; no-fat, low-fat, and artificial-fat alternatives; cholesterol-free, trans fat–free, sugar free, low sodium, high-protein, high-carbohydrate, and low-calorie products. Thousands of alternatives bombard us daily. Caught in the crossfire of advertised claims by the food industry and advice provided by health and nutrition experts, most of us find it challenging to make wise dietary choices. The ability to sift through the untruths, half-truths, and scientific realities and select a dietary plan that satisfies individual preferences and needs is an essential health-promoting skill—particularly when you are living away from home for the first time. Past patterns of eating influence current dietary attitudes and behaviours. Understanding the reasons behind your dietary attitudes and behaviours may help you make more positive dietary choices.

HEALTHY EATING

We often take our ability to eat what we want, when we want, where we want for granted. We assume we will have sufficient food to get us through the day, and rarely are forced to eat foods we do not like for survival. Although we have undoubtedly experienced **hunger**, few of us have suffered the type of hunger that continues for days and threatens survival. We often eat because of **appetite**, a learned psychological desire to eat whether or not we are hungry. Our appetite can be triggered by smell, taste, time of day, special occasions, or proximity to favourite foods such as freshly baked bread, pizza, or chocolate chip cookies. Other factors also stimulate our desire to eat, including cultural and social meanings attached to food, convenience and advertising, habit or custom, emotional comfort, nutritional value, social interaction, and regional/seasonal trends. Finding the right balance between eating to maintain body functions (eating to live) and eating to satisfy our appetite and/or cultural needs (living to eat) is a problem for many, as evidenced by the increased prevalence of overweight and obesity in our population.

Many factors influence what we eat, when we eat, why we eat, where we eat, and how much we eat. Social pressures, including family traditions, social events that involve food, and busy work schedules also influence the quality and quantity of our dietary intake. The Your Spiritual and Emotional Health box also discusses some of the cultural influences on our eating attitudes and behaviours.

Although our grandparents typically sat down to eat least three big meals per day, they also laboured heavily in the fields or at other physical work, effectively using the calories consumed. Today, eating three large meals combined with a physically inactive lifestyle—at work and at play—is the perfect recipe for weight and fat gain.

Nutrition is the science that investigates the relationship between physiological function and the elements of the foods we eat. With the abundance of food available in our society, the options available, and easy access to almost every **nutrient** (water, proteins, carbohydrates, fats, vitamins, and minerals) 24 hours a day, Canadians should have few nutritional problems. However, nutritionists believe that our "diet of affluence" is responsible for many diseases and disabilities. This country's history as a land of agricultural abundance accounts for the traditional Canadian diet: high in fats and calories with typically large servings of red meats, potatoes, and rich desserts. More recent trends indicate that Canadians are changing to a white-meat diet (that is, poultry and fish) with less fats and more vegetables and fruits.

Why do so many of us have nutritional problems? Much of our preoccupation with food and our tendency to eat too much of certain foods stems from our early eating habits.

Monitoring Calories

Canadians consume more calories per person per day than many other people in the world. A **calorie** is a unit of measure that indicates the amount of energy obtained from a particular food. Calories are eaten in the form of proteins, fats, and carbohydrates, three of the basic nutrients necessary for life. Three other nutrients also necessary for life—water, vitamins, and minerals—do not contribute calories to our dietary intake even though they provide vital functions.

Excess calorie consumption is a major factor in gaining weight. However, it is not just the quantity of food we eat that results in weight gain and associated diseases: it is also the relative proportion of nutrients consumed and, perhaps more importantly, low levels of physical activity. Canadian adults obtain their dietary energy from proteins (16–18 percent), carbohydrates (50–56 percent), and fats (29–31 percent), close to the recommended levels for their specific age/sex groups. It is the high concentration of fats in the Canadian diet—particularly saturated (largely animal fats) and trans fats (produced when polyunsaturated oils are hydrogenated)—that likely most increase risk

YOUR SPIRITUAL AND EMOTIONAL HEALTH

Cultural Practices and Healthy Eating

Many factors influence healthy eating, including culture. Culture permeates all aspects of life, including food preparation, food selection, and attitudes and behaviours toward eating. Some of the attitudes and behaviours relate to portion sizes, how, where, and when food is consumed as well as who with (or without). Food may also be consumed to sooth the spirit. This textbox focuses primarily on cultural eating of three ethnicities. Traditional dietary intakes such as Mediterranean, Asian, and Western are influenced by ethic and religious beliefs in addition to culture, climate, terrain, material resources, and technology. In regard to our nutrition and overall health, we can learn from other cultural eating practices.

MEDITERRANEAN

The traditional Mediterranean diet found in Spain, southern France and Italy, former Yugoslavia, Greece, Turkey, Cyprus, Crete, Lebanon, Israel, Palestine, Egypt, Libya, Algeria, Tunisia, and Morocco, typically includes a lot of bread and other cereal products (usually made of wheat), vegetables and fruits, fish, cheese, olive oil, tree nuts such as walnuts and almonds, and wine (in non-Islamic countries). Food is flavoured extensively with herbs and spices. Little meat is consumed, and when it is, it is most often included in everyday dishes. The traditional hot drink is coffee, which in modern times is sweetened with sugar. Desserts are also sweet, but consumption is relatively low such that overall sugar intake is low. This traditional Mediterranean diet has been associated with lower incidences of coronary heart disease. It is also thought that this dietary pattern may be protective against cancer.

ASIAN

Although Asian cuisines (including those of India, Sri Lanka, Thailand, Cambodia, Vietnam, China, and Korea) can be very diverse, the traditional Asian diet typically includes rice as its staple cereal and main source of energy. The consumption of vegetables, fruits, and fish varies based upon prosperity. Similar to the Mediterranean diet, herbs and spices are used extensively to flavour food. Tea is the traditional hot drink. Overall, the traditional Asian diet tends to be low in fat and sugar consumption. In addition to lower risks of coronary heart disease, individuals who consume a traditional Asian diet tend to have lower rates of obesity, type 2 diabetes, and some types of cancers.

WESTERN

"Traditional" dietary patterns considered Western are a result of an industrialized food system. The traditional Western diet is energy dense and includes increasingly more and more processed foods. Specifically, the traditional Western diet includes large amounts of meat, milk and milk products, fatty and/or sugary foods (that is, processed meats, pastries, baked goods, confectionery, etc.), and alcoholic drinks. Further, relatively low intakes of vegetables and fruits are common in traditional Western cuisine. As a result, this diet tends to be high in calories, fat, and sugar and low in fibre. Thus, the typical Western diet is associated with overweight and obesity, as well as greater risk for type 2 diabetes, cardiovascular disease, stroke, some cancers, and other chronic diseases.

Source: Adapted from World Cancer Research Fund/American Institute for Cancer Research, 2007, *Food, Nutrition, Physical Activity, and the Prevention of Cancer: A Global Perspective*. Washington DC: AICR.

for various chronic diseases, including heart disease. Elevated concentrations of highly processed sugars also increase risk for other diseases such as tooth decay.

what do you THINK?

Think about your eating habits. Why do you eat the way you do? What/who influences your food choices? How can you change your attitudes and behaviours to eat better?

Hunger: The feeling associated with the physiological need to eat.

Appetite: The desire to eat; often more psychologic than physiological.

Nutrition: The science that investigates the relationship between physiological function and the essential elements of foods we eat.

Nutrients: The constituents of food that sustain us physiologically: water, proteins, carbohydrates, fats, vitamins, and minerals.

Calorie: A unit of measure that indicates the amount of energy obtained from a particular food.

RATE YOURSELF

What's Your EQ (Eating Quotient)?

Keeping up with the latest on what to eat—or not eat—isn't easy. If you think a few facts might have slipped past you, this quiz should help. There's only one correct answer for each question.

1. Fresh fruits and vegetables contain more nutrients than canned or frozen varieties.

   True or False

2. While you are shopping, it makes a difference what area of the store you start in, in terms of keeping your foods safe.

   True or False

3. Fruit drinks count as a serving from the fruit group in the Food Guide.

   True or False

4. Baked potatoes have a higher glycemic index (carbohydrates' ability to raise blood sugar levels quickly) than sweet potatoes or apples.

   True or False

5. A late dinner is more likely to cause weight gain than eating the same meal earlier in the day.

   True or False

6. Nuts are okay to eat if you are trying to stick to a low-fat diet.

   True or False

7. Certain foods, such as grapefruit, celery, or cabbage soup, can burn fat and make you lose weight.

   True or False

8. Which of the following has the most fibre?
   a. chuck roast
   b. dark-meat chicken with skin
   c. skinless chicken wing
   d. they are all about the same

9. Which of the following is the strongest predictor of obesity in Canada today?
   a. region of the country you live in
   b. ethnicity/culture
   c. lack of physical activity
   d. socioeconomic status

10. When you eat a meal, how long does it take for your brain to get the message that you are full?
    a. 10 minutes
    b. 20 minutes
    c. at least an hour
    d. 2 hours or more

11. Which of the following are at the top of the list in bacterial levels among domestically grown vegetables?
    a. green onions, cantaloupe, and cilantro
    b. beets, potatoes, and summer squash
    c. celery, leaf lettuce, and parsley
    d. strawberries, apples, and tomatoes

12. Which of the following foods contains the most grams of fibre per serving?
    a. 1/2 cup of strawberries
    b. 1/2 cup of kidney beans
    c. 1 cup popcorn
    d. 1 medium banana

13. To ensure that you are getting your antioxidants each day, which tip below would be most helpful?
    a. Eat several dark green vegetables and orange, red, and yellow fruits and vegetables.
    b. Eat at least 2 servings of lean red meat per day.
    c. Eat whole-grain foods with at least 2 grams of fibre per serving.
    d. Eat several servings of tuna and salmon per week.

14. Olive oil, one of the heart-healthy monounsaturated fats, is a great source for antioxidants. To reap the most benefits from olive oil, which recommendation should you follow?
    a. Buy it only in amounts that you will use relatively quickly. Nutrients are lost quickly after 12 months sitting on the shelf.
    b. If you buy larger bottles, separate it into smaller bottles and keep the lid on tightly to reduce oxidation from air contact. Refrigerate if possible. Refrigeration causes cloudiness but doesn't affect quality.
    c. Store it in opaque airtight glass bottles or metal tins away from heat and light.
    d. All of the above.

15. Which strategy will help you identify high-fibre breads to maximize your quality carbohydrate intake?
    a. Choose a whole-grain bread that lists a whole grain as the first ingredient.
    b. Try to purchase breads with 1 to 2 grams of fibre per slice.
    c. Look for bread that is dark coloured. The darker it is, the greater the chance that it has lots of good-quality fibre in its recipe.
    d. All of the above.

Answers

1. *False:* There is usually little difference, depending on how produce is handled and how quickly it reaches your supermarket. Canned and frozen produce is typically picked at its peak and may contain more nutrients than fresh produce that was picked overripe or too early, sat in a warehouse, spent days in transit, or sat at improper temperatures for prolonged periods. However, canned or frozen fruits and vegetables may have added salt or sugar, so check labels carefully. Whenever possible, buy local produce fresh from the fields or neighbouring areas.
2. *True:* As a general rule, milk, meat, and other perishables that have been left at room temperature for more than 2 hours have a significant risk of conveying a food-borne illness. Be sure to factor in the time that you spend driving home from the store or running other errands. Start your shopping in the canned and non-refrigerated sections of the store, and save your meat and dairy products and frozen foods until last. Run your other errands before you shop for food, and if you know it will take time to get home, bring a cooler with ice.
3. *False:* Even if fruit juice is an actual ingredient (often it is not), most fruit drinks consist primarily of water and high fructose corn syrup or other sweeteners, colourings, and fruit flavouring. It is always better to eat the whole fruit, because you will get added fibre, more nutrients, and other benefits. Next best are 100 percent fruit juices, preferably with added vitamin C. Lowest on the nutrient quality list are the sweetened, flavoured fruit drinks.
4. *True:* Unfortunately, we'd probably be better off with a sweet potato or apple instead of substituting baked potatoes for fries if we are trying to keep our blood sugar levels down or control diabetes. For more information, check the glycemic index reference books available at most bookstores, or use the handy guide found at www.diabetesnet.com/diabetes_food_diet/glycemic_index.php.
5. *False:* It's not when you eat but what you eat that makes a difference in weight gain. If you ate a 500-calorie salad at 10 PM and it was your only meal, you wouldn't gain weight. However, a 5000 calorie pizza for breakfast, followed by a big lunch and dinner would provide enough total calories to put more than muscle on the hips, buttocks, and waist.
6. *True:* Although they are high in fat, nuts contain mostly unsaturated (good) fat and are good sources of protein, magnesium, and the antioxidants vitamin E and selenium. Moderation is the key.
7. *False:* No foods can burn fat. Some foods with caffeine may speed up your metabolism for a short time, but they do not cause weight loss. One of the best ways to boost your metabolism is to increase your muscle mass through weight training and exercise—not by eating specific foods.
8. *d:* There is no fibre in animal foods. Fibre is found only in plants and plant-based foods such as fruits, beans, whole grains, and vegetables.
9. *d:* Although the other responses are all contributors to obesity, the greatest single predictor of obesity is low socioeconomic status. Although related factors such as education play a role, the poor nutritional quality of foods commonly eaten when people are forced to stretch their food budget—high-fat meats, hot dogs, inexpensive white breads and pastries, and other high-calorie, low-fibre foods—often increases the risk of obesity.
10. *b:* It takes about 20 minutes for your brain to get the message that you are full. To make sure you don't gorge yourself, eat slowly, talk with others, put your fork down after taking a bite, take a drink of water, or do other things to delay your meal. Let your brain catch up to your fork, and slow it down!
11. *a:* The bad news is that in a recent government study of bacterial levels found in domestic produce, green onions, cantaloupe, and cilantro scored the highest in positive tests for two common bacteria: *Salmonella* and *Shigella.* The good news is that out of nearly 1100 samples, only 2 to 3 percent were contaminated, but washing your produce (even the bagged and washed variety) is still a must; run a heavy stream of water over the produce while rubbing the outside under the water.
12. *b:* One-half cup of kidney beans provides 4.5 grams of fibre; the medium banana has 2 grams of fibre; strawberries and popcorn each have 1 gram of fibre per serving.
13. *a:* Antioxidants, particularly vitamins C and E, the mineral selenium, and plant pigments known as carotenoids (which include beta-carotene) are found in green leafy vegetables and orange, yellow, and red vegetables and fruit. Eating several servings of these per day may help avoid risks from selected health problems.
14. *d:* Olive oil does lose nutrients over time, with one year being the general guesstimate of "use by" time. Keeping it in the refrigerator helps prolong shelf life. If the oil smells rancid or if you note mould or other discolouration, discard the bottle.
15. *a:* A true whole-grain bread clearly says so on the label (for example, "100 percent whole wheat" or "100 percent stone-ground whole wheat"). If all the ingredients aren't whole grain, then it's not a true whole-grain bread. The more fibre in each slice, the better; look for a minimum of 3 grams per slice. Colour is not a good indicator of nutrient value. Dyes and colouring may make even the whitest white bread brown.

SCORING

If you answered all of the above correctly, congratulations! You clearly have a good sense of some of the current issues and facts surrounding dietary choices. If you missed one or more questions, read the corresponding section of this chapter to find out more. Don't despair. Nutrition information changes rapidly, and there is a wealth of information available. Check with your instructor for courses you can take to increase your nutritional knowledge. Review the resources that are recommended, and work hard to stay current.

EATING WELL WITH CANADA'S FOOD GUIDE

In July 1942, the Official Food Rules, Canada's first food guide, was introduced. The main objectives of the Official Food Rules were to promote healthy eating, prevent nutritional deficiencies, and improve the health of Canadians while recognizing the impact of wartime food rationing. Although the food guide has been transformed many times, it has never wavered from its original purpose of guiding food selection and promoting the health of Canadians. In addition to new looks and formats, the title of Canada's food guide has changed over time: from Canada's Official Food Rules (1942), to Canada's Food Rules (1944, 1949), to Canada's Food Guide (1961, 1977, 1982), to Canada's Food Guide to Healthy Eating (1992), and now to Eating Well with Canada's Food Guide (2007).

Canada's most recent Food Guide was created because it was important to ensure that it (1) promoted a pattern of eating to meet nutrient needs, (2) promoted health, and (3) minimized the risk of nutrition-related chronic disease. In revising this Food Guide, Health Canada worked closely with three advisory groups; (1) an external group called the Food Guide Advisory Committee, which included 12 individuals representing public health, health policy, nutrition education, disease prevention, industry, and communication; (2) an Interdepartmental Working Group of 13 representatives from several federal departments for which changes to the Food Guide would have an impact; and (3) an Expert Advisory Committee on Dietary Reference Intakes consisting of 11 appointed members. Also part of the process was a stakeholders meeting held in January 2004, followed by a number of meetings throughout the country to update key stakeholders on proposed directions and to seek feedback on the planned approach, tools, and resources available. Finally, a national consultation was launched in Ottawa in November 2005, at which the proposed content and draft design of the new Food Guide were shared, with input sought using an online questionnaire (February to March 2006) and regional meetings in St. John's, Halifax, Montreal, Toronto, Winnipeg, Regina, Calgary, and Vancouver in April 2006.

It takes knowledge, resources, and planning to make healthy food choices, whether eating out, in the dining hall, or cooking meals at home.

The newest version of the Food Guide is intended to help a broader age range of Canadians, since it can be applied to anyone 2 years of age and older. Specifically, the objectives of the new Food Guide are to

- describe a pattern of eating sufficient to meet nutrient needs;
- describe a pattern of eating that reduces risk of nutrition-related health problems;
- describe a pattern of eating that supports the achievement and maintenance of a healthy body weight;
- describe a pattern of eating that reflects the diversity of foods available to Canadians;
- support Canadians' awareness and understanding of what constitutes a pattern of healthy eating; and
- emphasize that healthy eating and regular physical activity are important for health.

Figure 5b.1 shows Eating Well with Canada's Food Guide (2007), including recommended sex-specific servings for children, teens, and adults. Examples of one serving from each of the major food groups are also depicted.

The newest version of the Food Guide continues to incorporate a rainbow approach in its presentation. This use of the "rainbow" is consistent with Canada's Physical Activity Guide and visually depicts that we need some foods in amounts greater than others. New to the latest Food Guide are age- and sex-specific recommendations for children, teens, and adults for each of the four food groups (vegetables and fruit, grain products, milk and alternatives, meat and alternatives). Also new to the Food Guide is a specific recommendation to include a small amount of unsaturated fat each day (that is, 30–45 millilitres or 2–3 tablespoons.). The Food Guide continues to advocate for variety, balance, and moderation in your food intake. It is recommended that you eat as many different foods from each food group as possible to obtain variety. Generally, focusing on having lots of "colour" on your plate helps to achieve variety. In terms of balance, it is recommended that you obtain the minimum number of servings from each food group *before* eating "extras" or "others" (that is, foods that do not fit into a food group, such as chips, soft drinks, chocolate bars, etc.). Finally, moderation refers to total calorie consumption as well as consumption of individual foods. In other words, moderate consumption meets your caloric needs and does not involve excessive consumption, nor does it involve an excessive consumption of one particular food (that is, a whole box of crackers or pint of ice cream). Something else to be remembered is that all foods can be part of healthy eating; some, like "extras" or "others" we simply need to eat less of.

what do you THINK?

Do you use the Food Guide? Why or why not? Examine the current version of the Food Guide (Figure 5b.1). Of which food groups are you most likely to eat the recommended amounts? Which ones are you most likely to skimp on? Why? Do you meet the principles of variety, balance, and moderation? What are some simple changes that you could make right now to help you eat better?

THE DIGESTIVE PROCESS

Food provides the chemicals we need for physical activity and body maintenance. Because our bodies cannot synthesize or produce certain essential nutrients, we must get them from the foods we eat. Nutrients are the elements of food that physiologically sustain us, and, as mentioned, these include water, protein, carbohydrates, fats, vitamins, and minerals. Before foods can be utilized, the digestive system must break them down into smaller, more usable forms. The process by which foods are broken down and absorbed or excreted by the body is known as the **digestive process**.

Even before you take your first bite, your body has already begun a series of complex digestive responses. Your mouth prepares for the food by increasing saliva production. **Saliva** contains mostly water, which aids in chewing and swallowing, but it also contains important enzymes that begin the process of food breakdown. One such enzyme, amylase, initiates the digestive process for carbohydrates. From your mouth, food passes down your **esophagus**, a 23- to 25-centimetre tube that connects the mouth to the stomach. A series of contractions and relaxations by the muscles lining your esophagus gently moves food to the next digestive organ, the **stomach**. Here, food mixes with enzymes and stomach acids. Hydrochloric acid works in combination with pepsin, another enzyme, to break down proteins. In most people, the stomach secretes enough mucus to protect the stomach lining from these harsh digestive juices. In others, there are problems with the lining that result in ulcers or other gastric problems.

Further digestive activity takes place in your **small intestine**, an 8-metre-long coiled tube containing three sections: the duodenum, the jejunum, and the ileum. Each section secretes digestive enzymes that, when combined with enzymes from the liver and the pancreas, contributes to the breakdown of proteins, fats, and carbohydrates. Once broken down, these nutrients are absorbed into the bloodstream and supply body cells with energy. The liver is the major organ that determines whether nutrients are stored, sent to cells or organs, or excreted. Solid wastes consisting of fibre, water, and salts are dumped into the large intestine, where most of the water and salts are reabsorbed into the system and the fibre is passed out through the anus. The entire digestive process takes approximately 24 hours (see Figure 5b.2).

Dietary Reference Intake vs. Recommended Nutrient Intake

Scientists in Canada and the United States collaborated to develop new, common recommendations for nutrient intake. Canada previously used Recommended Nutrient Intake (RNI) while the United States utilized the Recommended Dietary Allowance (RDA), with slight variations between the two. The new recommendations, called Dietary Reference Intakes (DRIs), are based on the amount of water, proteins, carbohydrates, fats, vitamins, and minerals we need to avoid deficiencies and reduce risk for chronic diseases while attempting to avoid overconsumption. The RDA is now a reference standard within the DRIs and represents the average nutrient

Digestive process: The process by which foods are broken down and absorbed or excreted by the body.

Saliva: Fluid secreted by the salivary glands that contains enzymes that assist in the digestion of some foods.

Esophagus: Tube that transports food from the mouth to the stomach.

Stomach: Large muscular organ that temporarily stores, mixes, and digests foods.

Small intestine: Muscular, coiled digestive organ; consists of the duodenum, jejunum, and ileum.

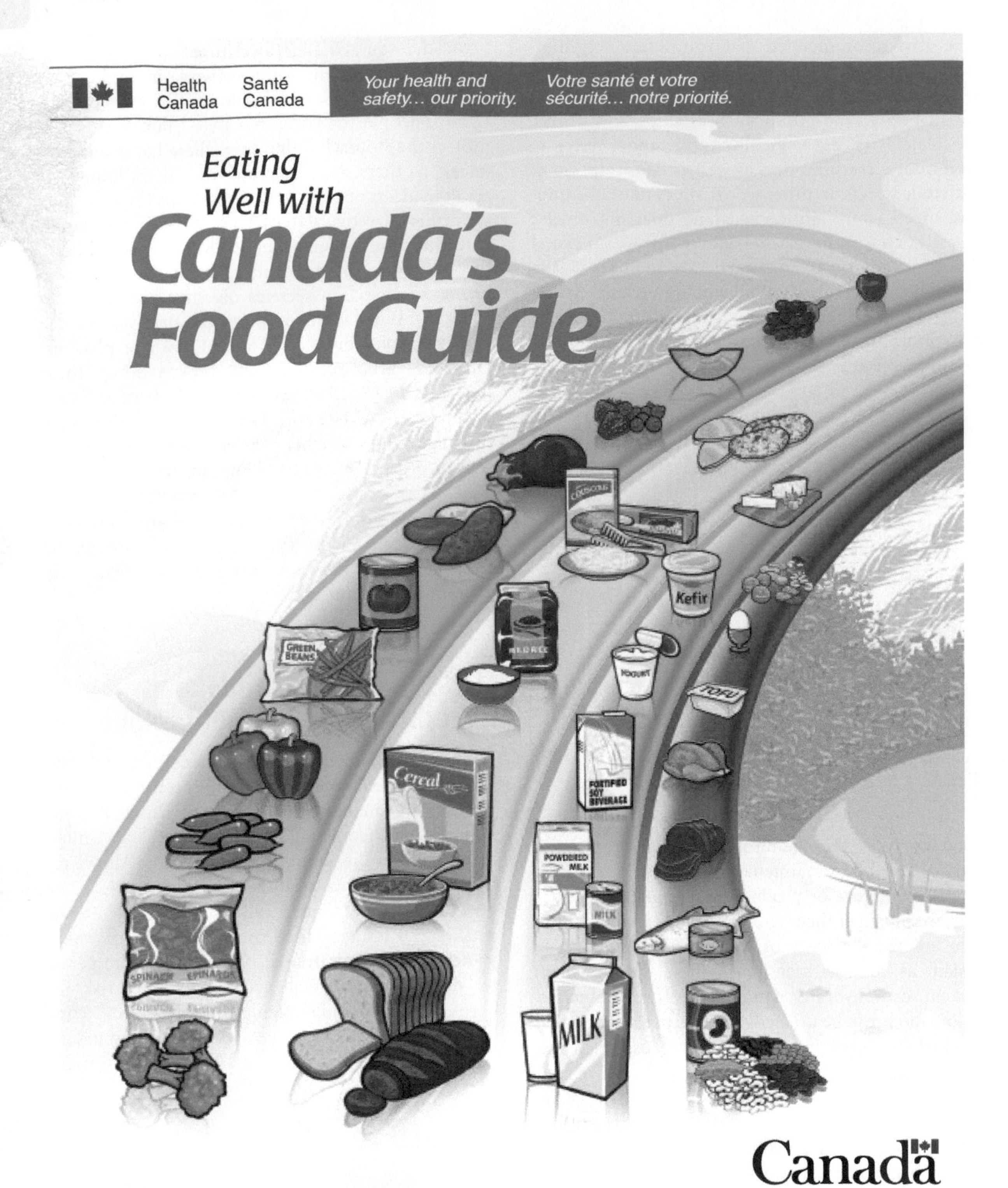

FIGURE 5b.1

Eating Well with Canada's Food Guide

Source: Health Canada, 2009©. Adapted and Reproduced with the permission of the Minister of Public Works and Government Services Canada, 2009.

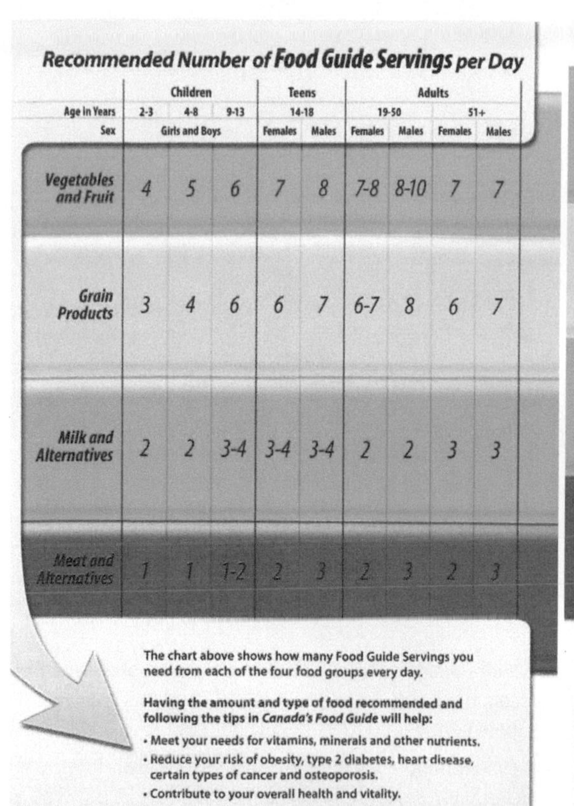

Recommended Number of Food Guide Servings per Day

Age in Years	Children 2-3	Children 4-8	Children 9-13	Teens 14-18		Adults 19-50		Adults 51+	
Sex	Girls and Boys	Girls and Boys	Girls and Boys	Females	Males	Females	Males	Females	Males
Vegetables and Fruit	4	5	6	7	8	7-8	8-10	7	7
Grain Products	3	4	6	6	7	6-7	8	6	7
Milk and Alternatives	2	2	3-4	3-4	3-4	2	2	3	3
Meat and Alternatives	1	1	1-2	2	3	2	3	2	3

The chart above shows how many Food Guide Servings you need from each of the four food groups every day.

Having the amount and type of food recommended and following the tips in *Canada's Food Guide* will help:

- Meet your needs for vitamins, minerals and other nutrients.
- Reduce your risk of obesity, type 2 diabetes, heart disease, certain types of cancer and osteoporosis.
- Contribute to your overall health and vitality.

Make each Food Guide Serving count...
wherever you are – at home, at school, at work or when eating out!

- **Eat at least one dark green and one orange vegetable each day.**
  - Go for dark green vegetables such as broccoli, romaine lettuce and spinach.
  - Go for orange vegetables such as carrots, sweet potatoes and winter squash.
- **Choose vegetables and fruit prepared with little or no added fat, sugar or salt.**
  - Enjoy vegetables steamed, baked or stir-fried instead of deep-fried.
- **Have vegetables and fruit more often than juice.**

- **Make at least half of your grain products whole grain each day.**
  - Eat a variety of whole grains such as barley, brown rice, oats, quinoa and wild rice.
  - Enjoy whole grain breads, oatmeal or whole wheat pasta.
- **Choose grain products that are lower in fat, sugar or salt.**
  - Compare the Nutrition Facts table on labels to make wise choices.
  - Enjoy the true taste of grain products. When adding sauces or spreads, use small amounts.

- **Drink skim, 1%, or 2% milk each day.**
  - Have 500 mL (2 cups) of milk every day for adequate vitamin D.
  - Drink fortified soy beverages if you do not drink milk.
- **Select lower fat milk alternatives.**
  - Compare the Nutrition Facts table on yogurts or cheeses to make wise choices.

- **Have meat alternatives such as beans, lentils and tofu often.**
- **Eat at least two Food Guide Servings of fish each week.***
  - [illegible]
- **Select lean meat and alternatives prepared with little or no added fat or salt.**
  - [illegible]
  - [illegible]
  - [illegible]

Enjoy a variety of foods from the four food groups.

Satisfy your thirst with water!
Drink water regularly. It's a calorie-free way to quench your thirst. Drink more water in hot weather or when you are very active.

* Health Canada provides advice for limiting exposure to mercury from certain types of fish. Refer to www.healthcanada.gc.ca for the latest information.

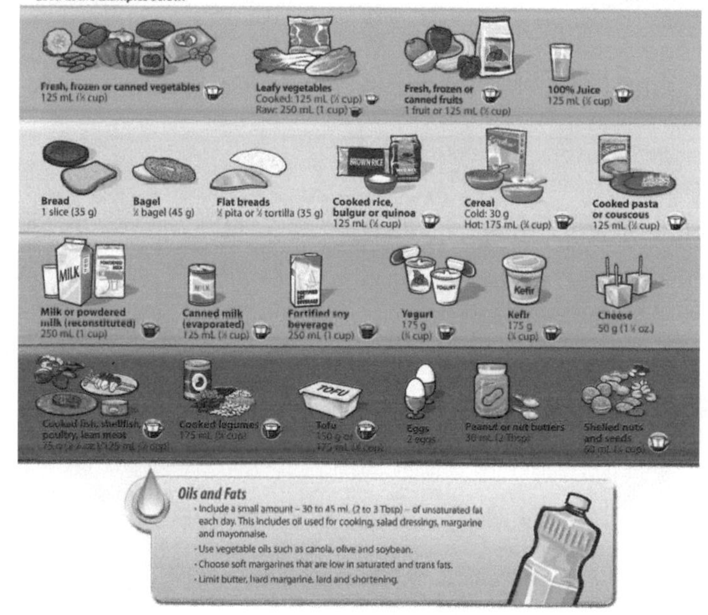

FIGURE 5b.1 (continued)
Eating Well with Canada's Food Guide

FOCUS ON CANADA

Vitamin D: Many Canadians May Not Be Getting Enough

A May 25, 2006 news release from the Dietitians of Canada, the national professional association of dietitians, suggested many Canadians may not be getting enough vitamin D.

Why is there concern about vitamin D?

In addition to playing a vital role in bone health for people of all ages, vitamin D may have a positive effect on some types of cancers, in particular colorectal cancer, and other immune-related diseases.

We normally obtain vitamin D in one of two ways: (1) from the sun via UVB radiation absorbed through our skin, and (2) through our dietary intake, most often from fortified cows' milk.

Who is at greatest risk for inadequate vitamin D?

All Canadians–and anyone else who lives above 370° latitude–may be at risk in the winter months when there is insufficient UVB radiation from the sun, partly because of the reduced daylight hours and partly because of the level of the solstice. Other groups particularly at risk include:

- The elderly–because they produce less vitamin D in their bodies as a result of aging. Other contributing factors include an inadequate dietary intake, and limited exposure to the sunlight because the elderly are more likely to be housebound.
- Individuals with dark skin–because the darker one's skin, the lower the production of vitamin D.
- Exclusively breast-fed infants–because the vitamin D content of breast milk is not sufficient.
- Individuals who wear clothing covering the majority of their body when outside–because there is no exposed skin to absorb vitamin D from the sun and its UVB radiation.
- Individuals with low dietary intakes of vitamin D.

Can diet alone provide enough vitamin D?

As mentioned previously, most of the vitamin D obtained via dietary intake comes from fortified cows' milk. Other dietary sources include fatty fish, such as salmon and sardines, infant formulas, meal replacements, and nutritional supplements.

The dietary reference intakes (DRIs), the new dietary standard for Canada and the United States, recommend that adults up to the age of 50 obtain 200 IU each day, those between the ages of 51 and 70 require 400 IU per day, and individuals over the age of 71 need 600 IU per day. Further, the Osteoporosis Society of Canada recommends that adults over the age of 50 and at risk for osteoporosis obtain 800 IU of vitamin D or the equivalent of 750 mL of milk (around three glasses) per day.

Are vitamin D supplements recommended, and if so how much should one take?

Health Canada and the Canadian Paediatric Society currently recommend that exclusively breast-fed infants receive a daily supplement of 400 IU vitamin D per day.

If children and adults are able to have regular, brief, unprotected daily exposure to the sun and follow Eating Well with Canada's Food Guide, they should obtain sufficient vitamin D. However, adults over the age of 50 at risk of osteoporosis may need to supplement. These individuals should consult their physician and have their dietary intake evaluated by a registered dietitian. A blanket recommendation should not be made for everyone.

STUDY QUESTIONS

1. How much vitamin D do you need?
2. Where do you get your vitamin D from?
3. What can you do to ensure an adequate vitamin D intake?
4. Are vitamin D supplements an essential part of healthy living? Why or why not?

Source: Adapted from Dietitians of Canada News Releases, May 25, 2006, "Vitamin D–Many Canadians May Not Be Getting Enough." Retrieved on May 25, 2006, from www.dietitians.ca/news/media.

intake that meets the requirements of 97 to 98 percent of healthy males and females at a particular age. Another term to become familiar with in regard to nutrient consumption is *adequate intake* (AI). AI refers to the recommended average daily nutrient intake based on observed or experimentally determined estimates of nutrient intake for a group of healthy people.

These estimates are used when an RDA cannot be established and are assumed to be adequate.

OBTAINING ESSENTIAL NUTRIENTS

Water

Most of us are aware that we could survive much longer without food than without water. Even in severe conditions, the average person can go for weeks without certain vitamins and minerals before experiencing

While you may not be conscious of your body's need for water, it is actually the most necessary nutrient.

serious deficiency symptoms. However, **dehydration** (abnormal depletion of body fluids) can cause serious health-related issues within hours, and death after a few days.

Just what function does water serve in the body? Between 50 and 60 percent of our total body weight is water. The water in our system bathes cells, aids in fluid and electrolyte balance, maintains pH balance, and transports molecules and cells throughout the body. Water is the major component of blood, which carries oxygen and nutrients to the tissues and is responsible for maintaining cells in working order.

FIGURE 5b.2
The Digestive System

How much water do you need? Most experts believe that six to eight glasses of water per day are necessary. Because of high concentrations of water in most foods we consume, the actual number of glasses needed each day is somewhat less than this for the average person. The DRIs are somewhat greater than this recommendation, at approximately 13 cups of beverages for men and nine for women. More specifically, the DRI for men between the ages of 19 and 50 years is 3.7 litres of total water per day (includes 3.0 litres of beverages) while the recommendation for women (ages 19 to 50 years) is 2.7 litres (includes 2.2 litres of beverages). Individual needs vary according to dietary factors, age, size, environmental temperature and humidity levels, physical activity, and the effectiveness of the individual's system. It is not unusual for athletes to lose 1 to 2 litres of fluid per hour in hot, humid weather when exercising. To maintain hydration levels, athletes should weigh themselves before and after their workouts and drink one litre of fluid for every kilogram of weight lost. Thirst is not a good indicator of your need for fluids. In fact, if you wait until you are thirsty to replenish your fluids, you have waited too long. The best method of ensuring that your body is adequately hydrated is to monitor the colour of your urine. If it is a pale yellow, your body is sufficiently hydrated; if it is a darker yellow, your body needs fluids.

Are sports drinks necessary? Not likely as often as they are consumed. Most sport drinks are absorbed as effectively as water, and some are absorbed better than juice. In terms of hydration, it is important to note that people are likely to drink more fluid when it is flavoured. The intent of sport drinks is to replenish electrolytes lost through perspiration. They are also

Dehydration: Abnormal depletion of body fluids.

used to replenish glycogen or energy stores. Thus, when your perspiration is profuse for 60 minutes or longer, a sports drink may be necessary. However, for physical activity of shorter duration or that is not accompanied by heavy sweating, a sports drink is not needed; water can adequately meet your needs.

Recently, interest has been given to milk and its potential to hydrate the body and replenish nutrients. Milk is a liquid that not only hydrates but also is a rich source of carbohydrates for energy as well as a rich source of protein, which is vital for muscle repair. Milk also contains the electrolytes sodium and potassium, which are involved in the body's hydration process—and with which sports drinks are often fortified.

Proteins

Next to water, proteins are the most abundant substances in the human body. **Proteins** are major components of nearly every cell and are often referred to as "building blocks" because of their role in the development and repair of bone, muscle, skin, and blood cells. Proteins are also the key elements of the antibodies that protect us from disease, of enzymes that control chemical activities in the body, and of hormones that regulate bodily functions. Moreover, proteins aid in the transport of iron, oxygen, and nutrients to the body's cells. Finally, proteins are also involved in fluid, electrolyte, and acid–base balance (pH). Normally proteins are not a source of energy, but can be broken down to supply energy if carbohydrates and fat are not available. Proteins provide 4 calories of energy per gram of intake.

Most Canadians consume more protein than needed. In particular, they consume too much protein in the form of meat and high-fat dairy products, which are associated with higher blood cholesterol levels. The recommended protein intake for the average person is 0.8 gram per kilogram of body weight per day, equivalent to about 12 to 20 percent of total energy intake. The excess is stored, like other extra calories, as fat.

Proteins are made up of smaller molecules known as **amino acids.** Amino acids are composed of chains that link together like beads on a necklace in differing combinations. More than 22 different amino acids are found in animal tissue, and humans cannot synthesize all of them. The eight amino acids that the adult body cannot make adequately are referred to as **essential amino acids.** They must be obtained from the foods we eat.

Complete (high-quality) proteins are found in foods that naturally contain the eight essential amino acids together. If we consume a food deficient in an essential amino acid, the total amount of protein that can be synthesized by the other amino acids is limited by the missing amino acid(s). It is important to remember that the fact that essential amino acids are present in a food does not guarantee that they will be synthesized. The quality of protein depends on the presence of amino acids in digestible form and in amounts proportional to body requirements.

The most common sources of dietary protein in Canada are meats, poultry, seafood, dairy products, eggs, soy products, legumes, whole grains, and nuts. In addition to providing high-quality proteins, some of these foods (that is, meats, poultry, high-fat dairy products, and eggs) also contain high levels of saturated fat. Selecting leaner cuts of meat, removing the fat and skin from poultry, and choosing low-fat dairy products enables you to get high-quality proteins with less fat.

What about plant sources of protein? Proteins from plant sources are **incomplete proteins** in that they are missing one or two essential amino acids. It is relatively easy for the non–meat eater to combine plant foods effectively and eat complementary sources of plant protein. An excellent example is eating peanut butter on whole-grain bread. Although separately peanut butter and whole wheat bread are deficient in essential amino acids, eating them together provides high-quality protein because all amino acids are eaten at the same time.

As illustrated in Figure 5b.3, plant sources of protein fall into four general categories: legumes (beans, peas, peanuts, and soy products), grains (whole grains, corn, and pasta products), nuts and seeds, and other vegetables, such as leafy greens and broccoli. Mixing two or

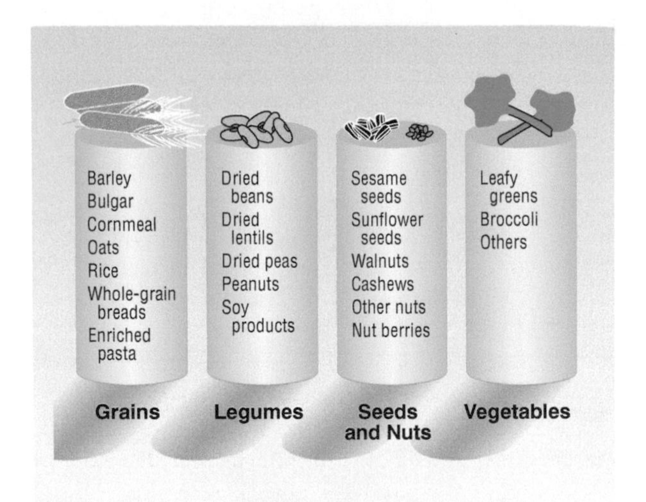

FIGURE 5b.3

Complementary Proteins

Source: Adapted by permission from page 205 of *Nutrition Concepts and Controversies*, 6th ed., by Eva Hamilton, Eleanor Whitney, and Frances Sizer.

more foods from each of these categories at the same meal provides all the essential amino acids necessary to ensure adequate protein absorption. People not interested in obtaining all their protein from plants can combine incomplete plant proteins with complete low-fat animal proteins such as poultry, seafood, and lean cuts of pork or beef. Further, low-fat cottage cheese, skim milk, egg whites, and nonfat dry milk provide high-quality proteins, few calories, and little dietary fat.

Carbohydrates

Carbohydrates supply us with the energy (4 calories per gram) needed to sustain normal daily activity. Long maligned by weight-conscious people, carbohydrates are often metabolized more quickly and efficiently than proteins. Carbohydrates are a quick source of energy for the body, easily converted to glucose, a fuel for the body's cells. Carbohydrates are actually the preferred fuel for red blood and nerve cells—including those in the brain. Carbohydrates also play an important role in the functioning of the internal organs, the nervous system, and the muscles. They are the best source of energy for endurance athletes because they provide an immediate and a time-released energy source as they are digested easily and continuously metabolized in the bloodstream.

There are two major types of carbohydrates: **simple carbohydrates**, found primarily in fruits, and **complex carbohydrates**, found mostly in grains, cereals, dark green leafy vegetables, yellow fruits and vegetables (carrots, yams), cruciferous vegetables (such as broccoli, cabbage, and cauliflower), and root vegetables, such as potatoes. Most Canadians do not eat enough complex carbohydrates and, in particular, not enough fibre (this will be discussed in greater detail later).

Canadians typically consume a lot of simple sugars. A high intake of simple sugars is linked to consumption of soft drinks (also high in children and youth). The most common form is glucose. The human body converts all simple sugars to glucose to provide energy to cells. In its natural form, glucose is sweet and obtained from foods such as corn syrup, honey, molasses, vegetables, and fruits. Fructose is another simple sugar found in fruits and berries. Glucose and fructose are classified as **monosaccharides** because they contain only one molecule of sugar.

Disaccharides are combinations of two monosaccharides or two molecules of simple sugar. Perhaps the best-known disaccharide is table sugar (known as sucrose), which is made of fructose and glucose. Lactose, found in milk and milk products, is also a disaccharide, formed by the combination of glucose and galactose. Disaccharides must be broken down into simple sugars before they can be used by the body.

Polysaccharides are complex carbohydrates formed from the combination of long chains of saccharides. Like disaccharides, they must be broken down into simple sugars before they can be utilized by the body.

The World Health Organization (WHO) recommends an intake of free sugars of less than 10 percent of total caloric intake. Free sugars refer to the monosaccharides and disaccharides added to foods by the manufacturer, food preparer, or consumer as well as sugar naturally occurring in honey, syrups, and fruit juices. A limit of free sugars is recommended because they (1) contribute to the overall density of dietary intake, (2) promote a positive energy balance, and (3) reduce appetite control. Of particular interest regarding the last point is the reduced compensatory decrease in food intake that follows the consumption of high-sugar drinks, like soft drinks, compared to when the equivalent number of calories are consumed in food.

There are two major forms of complex carbohydrates: starches and **fibre**. Starches make up the majority of the complex carbohydrates. We obtain dietary starches from flours, breads, pasta, potatoes, and related foods. Starches are stored in the muscles and liver in a polysaccharide form called **glycogen**. When the body requires a sudden burst of energy, it breaks down glycogen into glucose.

Proteins: An essential constituent of nearly all body cells, necessary for the development and repair of bone, muscle, skin, and blood, and key elements of antibodies, enzymes, and hormones.

Amino acids: The building blocks of protein.

Essential amino acids: Eight of the basic nitrogen-containing building blocks of protein.

Complete (high-quality) proteins: Proteins that contain all eight essential amino acids.

Incomplete proteins: Proteins lacking in one or more essential amino acids.

Carbohydrates: Basic nutrients that supply the body with energy (4 kcal/gram).

Simple carbohydrates: Found primarily in fruits; are quickly digested.

Complex carbohydrates: Found in grains, cereals, and vegetables; require more time to be digested.

Monosaccharide: A simple carbohydrate that contains only one molecule of sugar.

Disaccharide: A combination of two monosaccharides.

Polysaccharide: A complex carbohydrate formed by the combination of long chains of saccharides.

Fibre: Refers to the non-digestible part of plants.

Glycogen: The polysaccharide form in which glucose is stored in the liver.

Carbohydrates and Athletic Performance

Many athletes and/or fitness enthusiasts view carbohydrates as their "health foods." Some of these individuals consume concentrated sugary foods or drinks before or during athletic activity, thinking that the sugars will provide extra energy. However, this practice may actually be counterproductive. One possible problem involves the gastrointestinal tract. If your intestines react to physical activity (or the nervousness before competition) by moving material through the small intestine more rapidly than usual, undigested disaccharides or unabsorbed monosaccharides will reach the colon, which can result in an inopportune bout of diarrhea.

In an attempt to improve performance, endurance athletes often attempt to increase stores of glycogen in their body through a process known as carbohydrate loading, glycogen loading, or glycogen supercompensation. Although a variety of strategies—which vary in duration, dietary manipulation, and the amount and intensity of training—can be used to effectively increase muscle glycogen stores, a common process involves modifying these variables, usually a week or so before competition. Athletes train very hard several days before the competition while eating only a small amount of carbohydrates. Then, the day before competition, they dramatically increase their intake of carbohydrates. This depletion and repletion of carbohydrates forces the body to store increased levels of glycogen, which are presumably then used in the later stages of endurance activities (such as the last kilometre or so of a marathon). There are a variety of techniques to carbohydrate load, with most research on its effectiveness done on men. Canadian researcher, Mark Tarnopolsky and associates reported no significant increase in glycogen stores or performance in women, however. This team of researchers suggested that women's lower total energy requirements (compared to men) may limit their ability to carbohydrate load effectively. Further speculation indicates that the menstrual cycle may also play a role. More research is needed on this topic with women.

Carbo-loading before an endurance event is a strategy used by many athletes to build energy reserves for the last few kilometres.

Carbohydrates and Weight Loss

As previously mentioned, carbohydrates have often been given a bad "rap" when it comes to weight control. As a result, many individuals interested in weight loss often reduce the amount of carbohydrates they consume. Examples of low-carbohydrate diets include (but are not limited to) the Atkins Diet, Protein Power, The Zone, and the South Beach Diet. Although it may seem that a low-carbohydrate dietary intake reduces body weight (at least in the short term), the long-term negative health effects have serious implications.

what do you THINK?

Do you eat enough carbohydrates? Do you eat sufficient complex carbohydrates? What easy changes could you make now to eat better?

Fibre

Fibre is often referred to as "bulk" or "roughage." It is the indigestible portion of plant foods that helps move foods through the digestive system and softens stools by absorbing water. Fibre has a number of definitions: dietary, functional, and total. Dietary fibre refers to the nondigestible parts of plants, such as leaves, stems, and seeds. Functional fibre refers to the nondigestible forms of carbohydrates with health benefits that are extracted from plants or manufactured.

Total fibre refers to the combination of dietary and functional fibre. Although the terms *dietary fibre*, *functional fibre*, and *total fibre* provide the most recent scientific definitions and distinctions for fibre, most people prefer to describe it according to its physical properties—that is, solubility. Insoluble fibres are associated with gastrointestinal benefits and reduce the risk of several forms of cancer. Specifically, insoluble fibres attract water by clinging to it, thus facilitating passage of the contents of the large intestine for excretion. The main insoluble fibres are lignin (found in vegetables), cellulose (found in wheat), and hemicellulose (found in cereals and vegetables). Soluble fibres absorb water and swell to form gels that trap nutrients such as glucose and slow their absorption in the blood. Food then stays longer in the small intestine, providing a feeling of "fullness," which may assist in the regulation of blood sugars and weight control. Sources of soluble fibre include oat bran, oatmeal, barley, and legumes, as well as naturally occurring pectins in some fruits (apples, bananas, grapefruits, oranges, and strawberries).

The best way to increase your intake of dietary fibre is to eat more complex carbohydrates, such as whole grains, fruits, vegetables, dried peas and beans, nuts, and seeds. A few years ago, fibre was thought to be the remedy for just about everything. Current research supports its function in the following:

- protection against colorectal cancer
- protection against breast cancer
- protection against constipation
- protection against diverticulosis
- protection against heart disease
- protection against diabetes
- enhanced weight control

The AI for fibre is 25 grams per day for women and 38 grams per day for men—or an amount equivalent to 14 grams of fibre for every 1000 calories consumed. Most Canadians do not eat sufficient fibre; thus, to increase your dietary intake of fibre, the following steps are recommended:

- Select breads and cereals made with whole grains such as wheat, oats, barley, and rye.
- Choose foods with at least 2 to 3 grams of fibre per serving.
- Choose fresh fruits and vegetables whenever possible. When appropriate, eat the peel or skin of fresh fruits and vegetables (potatoes, pears, apples, mangoes, and kiwi fruit).
- Eat legumes frequently—every day, if possible.
- Drink plenty of fluids.

Fats

Fats (or lipids), another basic nutrient, are perhaps the most misunderstood of the body's required energy sources. Most of us do not realize that fat is a source of essential fatty acids (omega-3 and omega-6) and plays a vital role in the maintenance of healthy skin and hair, insulation of the body organs against shock, maintenance of body temperature, and the proper functioning of the cells themselves. Fats help our food taste better, provide texture to food, and carry the fat-soluble vitamins A, D, E, and K to the cells. They also provide a concentrated form of energy at 9 calories per gram. If fats perform all these functions, why are we frequently reminded to reduce our intake?

Although a moderate consumption of fats is essential to health, overconsumption can be dangerous. The most common form of fat circulating in the blood is the **triglyceride**, which makes up about 95 percent of total body fat. When we consume too many calories, the excess is converted into triglycerides in the liver, which are stored in obvious places on our bodies. The remaining five percent of body fat is composed of substances such as **cholesterol**, which can accumulate on the inner walls of arteries, causing a narrowing of the channel through which blood flows. This buildup, "plaque," is a major cause of arteriosclerosis.

Fat cells consist of chains of carbon and hydrogen atoms. Those not able to hold any more hydrogen in their chemical structure are labelled **saturated fats**. These generally come from animal sources, such as meats and dairy products, and are solid at room temperature. **Unsaturated fats**, which come from plants and most vegetable oils, are generally liquid at room temperature and have room for additional hydrogen atoms in their chemical structure. The terms *monounsaturated fat* and *polyunsaturated fat* refer to the relative number of hydrogen atoms missing. Peanut and olive oils are high in monounsaturated fats, whereas corn, sunflower, and safflower oils are high in polyunsaturated fats.

Fats: Basic nutrients that provide taste and texture to food, absorb vitamins A, D, E, and K, and are needed for the proper functioning of cells, insulation of body organs against shock, maintenance of body temperature, and healthy skin and hair.

Triglyceride: The most common form of fat in the body.

Cholesterol: A form of fat circulating in the blood that can accumulate on the inner walls of arteries.

Saturated fats: Fats that are unable to hold any more hydrogen in their chemical structure; derived mostly from animal sources; solid at room temperature.

Unsaturated fats: Fats that have room for more hydrogen in their chemical structure; derived mostly from plants; liquid at room temperature.

SKILLS FOR BEHAVIOUR CHANGE

Reducing Fat in Your Daily Dietary Intake

The small choices you make daily add up to make a tremendous difference in the amount of fat you eat over time. Trimming just 5 mL (1 tsp.) of fat each day can cut more than 2 kg from your dietary intake in one year—without removing great-tasting foods or causing noticeable changes. Consider the following:

1. "Butter" your toast, muffins, or bagels with "fruit-only" jams instead of butter, margarine, cream cheese, or other high-fat spreads.
   - 15 mL butter or margarine 108 calories 12 g fat
   - 15 mL sugarless jam 8 calories 0 g fat
   - Savings 90 calories 12 g fat
2. Sauté or stir fry meat and vegetables in chicken broth or wine (most of which burns off during cooking) rather than oil.
   - 15 mL oil 240 calories 27 g fat
   - wine or broth 0 calories 0 g fat
   - Savings 240 calories 27 g fat
3. Remove the skin from chicken before cooking.
   - 100 g breast 193 calories 8 g fat
   - 100 g skinless breast 142 calories 3 g fat
   - Savings 51 calories 5 g fat
4. Use low-fat or no-fat salad dressings on your sandwiches and salads.
   - 15 mL mayonnaise 100 calories 11 g fat
   - 15 mL low-fat dressing 7 calories 0 g fat
   - Savings 93 calories 11 g fat
5. Choose nonfat frozen yogurt instead of ice cream.
   - 125 mL ice cream 400 calories 25 g fat
   - 125 mL nonfat yogurt 120 calories 0 g fat
   - Savings 280 calories 25 g fat
6. Mix in a blender three parts low-fat cottage cheese with one part nonfat yogurt and use as a delicious dip, spread, or topping.
   - 30 mL cream cheese 99 calories 10 g fat
   - 30 mL mock cream cheese 20 calories 0 g fat
   - Savings 79 calories 10 g fat
7. Eat broth-based rather than cream-based soups.
   - 250 mL cream of chicken soup 191 calories 15 g fat
   - 250 mL chicken noodle soup 75 calories 2 g fat
   - Savings 116 calories 13 g fat
8. Eat seafood at least twice per week.
   - 85 g top round beef 162 calories 5 g fat
   - 100 g skinless chicken breast 142 calories 3 g fat
   - 85 g cod 70 calories 0.5 g fat
   - Savings 164 calories 7.0 g fat
9. Substitute two egg whites for one whole egg in recipes or omelettes.
   - 1 whole egg 79 calories 6 g fat
   - 2 egg whites 32 calories 0 g fat
   - Savings 47 calories 6 g fat
10. Choose meatless entrées such as lentil soup or vegetarian chili.
   - 270 g beef chili 256 calories 6 g fat
   - 270 g lentil soup 164 calories 1 g fat
   - Savings 92 calories 5 g fat

GENERAL ADVICE

Read food labels carefully and select products that contain no more than 3 grams of fat for every 100 calories,

List the small changes that you can make this week to reduce fat from your dietary intake:

1.
2.
3.
4.
5.

What other things can you do to help reduce your overall fat consumption?

Source: www.EvelynTribole.com

Healthier fats contain polyunsaturated and monounsaturated fatty acids (found in vegetable oils—canola, soybean, olive—soft non-hydrogenated margarines, nuts, seeds, avocados, olives, and fatty fish; it is recommended that we include approximately 45 millilitres (2–3 tablespoons) in our daily dietary intake of these fats). Part of our fat intake should include omega-3 and omega-6, which are polyunsaturated fatty acids. Canadians typically ingest sufficient omega-6 fats in the form of polyunsaturated margarines and sunflower, corn, and sesame oil. However, our intake of omega-3 fatty acids tends to be low. As such, we need to increase our intake of fish, flaxseed, walnuts, canola, and soybean oil.

Another group of fats we need to be aware of are **trans fatty acids** or trans fat. Trans fats are fatty acids produced by adding hydrogen molecules to liquid oil to make the oil solid. Unlike regular fats and oils, these "partially hydrogenated" fats stay solid or semisolid at room temperature. They change into irregular shapes at the molecular level, priming them to clog arteries. Trans fats are used in margarines, commercially baked goods, and many restaurant deep fryers. Trans fats are more harmful than saturated fats because they increase LDL levels and decrease HDL levels in the bloodstream. In other words, they increase our "bad" cholesterol and decrease our "good" cholesterol. Canada was the first country in the world to include trans fat on food labels: starting in December 2005 all prepackaged food sold in Canada had to include the trans fat content. In regard to food labelling, "trans fat free" or "0 trans fat" can be used only if the stated serving amount contains less than 0.2 grams of trans fat or if the total amount of saturated and trans fat in a stated serving is 2 grams or less.

Reducing Fat in Your Diet

Finding the best ways to reduce fat in your dietary intake is largely dependent on your determining what does and does not work for you and your lifestyle. The following basic guidelines are a place to start:

- Know what you are putting in your mouth. Read food labels. No more than 10 percent of your total calories should come from saturated and/or trans fat, and no more than 30 percent should come from all forms of fat combined.
- Choose fat-free or low-fat versions of foods whenever possible.
- Use olive oil for baking, stir frying, and sautéing.
- Whenever possible, use liquid, diet, or whipped margarine: these forms have far less trans fat than solid fat.
- Choose lean meats, seafood, or poultry. Remove skin and visible fat. Broil or bake whenever possible. In general, the more well-done the meat, the fewer the calories from fat. Drain fat after cooking.
- Limit intake of cold cuts, bacon, sausage, hot dogs, and organ meats.
- Select nonfat or low-fat dairy products whenever possible.
- When cooking, substitute chicken broth, wine, vinegar, low-fat/no-fat dressings and low-fat/no-fat sour cream for butter, margarine, oils, regular fat sour cream, mayonnaise, and salad dressings.
- Remember to think of your food intake as an average over a day or several days. If you have a high-fat breakfast or lunch, have a low-fat dinner to balance it out.

For more specific ways to reduce fat in your dietary intake, see the Skills for Behaviour Change box.

Vitamins

Although they do not provide energy (that is, calories), **vitamins** are potent, essential, organic compounds that promote growth and help maintain life and health. Every minute of every day, vitamins help maintain your nerves and skin, produce blood cells, build bones and teeth, heal wounds, and convert food energy to body energy.

Age, heat, and other environmental conditions can destroy vitamins in food. Vitamins are classified as either fat-soluble, meaning that they are absorbed through the intestinal tract with the help of fats, or water-soluble, meaning that they are easily dissolved in water. Vitamins A, D, E, and K are fat soluble; B-complex vitamins and vitamin C are water-soluble. Fat-soluble vitamins tend to be stored in the body, and toxicity can occur if too much is consumed. Water-soluble vitamins are generally excreted and cause few toxicity problems. Table 5b.1 provides a list of vitamins, the recommended dietary intake, best sources, and major functions in the body, as well as the symptoms of deficiency and toxicity.

Despite all media suggestions to the contrary, few Canadians suffer from vitamin deficiencies if they consume the recommended number of servings from each of the food groups most days of the week.

Nevertheless, Canadians continue to purchase and consume large quantities of vitamin supplements. For the most part, vitamin supplements are unnecessary and in certain instances may even be harmful. See also the Health in the Media box.

what do you THINK?

Of all of the nutrients discussed in this chapter, which one do you worry most about not getting enough of? Why? Are there any nutrients you consume too much of? What actions do you plan to make sure your daily dietary intake is adequate?

Trans-fatty acids: Fatty acids produced when polyunsaturated oils are hydrogenated to make them more solid.

Vitamins: Essential organic compounds that promote growth and reproduction and maintain life and health.

TABLE 5b.1

A Guide to Vitamins

Vitamin	Best Sources	Chief Functions in the Body	Deficiency Symptoms	Toxicity Symptoms
Water-Soluble Vitamins				
Vitamin B1 (thiamine) 1.5 mg (RDA & RDI)	Meat, pork, liver, fish, poultry, whole-grain and enriched breads, cereals, pasta, nuts, legumes, wheat germ, oats	Helps carbohydrate convert to energy; supports normal appetite and nervous system function	Beriberi, edema, heart irregularity, mental confusion, muscle weakness, low morale, impaired growth	Rapid pulse, weakness, headaches, insomnia, irritability
Vitamin B2 (riboflavin) 1.7 mg (RDA & RDI)	Milk, dark green vegetables, yogurt, cottage cheese, liver, meat, whole-grain or enriched breads and cereals	Helps carbohydrates, fat, and protein convert to energy; promotes healthy skin and normal vision	Eye problems, skin disorders around nose and mouth	None reported, but an excess of any of the B vitamins can cause a deficiency of the others
Niacin 20 mg NE (RDA & RDI)	Meat, eggs, poultry, fish, milk, whole-grain and enriched breads and cereals, nuts, legumes, peanuts, nutritional yeast, all protein foods	Helps convert nutrients to energy; promotes health of skin, nerves, and digestive system	Pellagra: skin rash on parts exposed to sun, loss of appetite, dizziness, weakness, irritability, fatigue, mental confusion, indigestion	Flushing, nausea, headaches, cramps, ulcer irritation, heartburn, abnormal liver function, low blood pressure
Vitamin B6 (pyridoxine) 2.0 mg (RDA & RDI)	Meat, poultry, fish, shellfish, legumes, whole-grain products, green leafy vegetables, bananas	Protein and fat metabolism; formation of antibodies and red blood cells; helps convert tryptophan to niacin	Nervous disorders, skin rash, muscle weakness, anemia, convulsions, kidney stones	Depression, fatigue, irritability, headaches, numbness, damage to nerves, difficulty walking
Folate 400 μg (DFE & RDA)	Green leafy vegetables, liver, legumes, seeds	Red blood cell formation; protein metabolism; new cell division; prevents neural tube birth defects	Anemia, heartburn, diarrhea, smooth tongue, depression, poor growth	Diarrhea, insomnia, irritability, may mask a vitamin B12 deficiency
Vitamin B12 (cobalamin) 2.4 mg (RDA)	Meat, fish, poultry, shellfish, milk, cheese, eggs, nutritional yeast	Maintenance of nerve cells; red blood cell formation; synthesis of genetic material	Anemia, smooth tongue, fatigue, nerve degeneration progressing to paralysis	None reported
Pantothenic acid 5–7 mg (AI)	Widespread in foods	Coenzyme in energy metabolism	Rare; sleep disturbances, nausea, fatigue	Occasional diarrhea
Biotin 30 μg (AI)	Widespread in foods	Coenzyme in energy metabolism; fat synthesis; glycogen formation	Loss of appetite, nausea, depression, muscle pain, weakness, fatigue, rash	None reported
Vitamin C (ascorbic acid) 60 mg (RDI & RDA)	Citrus fruits, cabbage-type vegetables, tomatoes, potatoes, dark green vegetables, peppers, lettuce, cantaloupe, strawberries	Heals wounds, maintains bones and teeth, strengthens blood vessels; antioxidant; strengthens resistance to infection; aids iron absorption	Scurvy, anemia, depression, frequent infections, bleeding gums, loosened teeth, muscle degeneration, rough skin, bone fragility, poor wound healing	Nausea, abdominal cramps, diarrhea, breakdown of red blood cells in persons with certain genetic disorders; deficiency symptoms may appear at first on withdrawal of high doses

TABLE 5b.1 (Continued)

A Guide to Vitamins

Vitamin	Best Sources	Chief Functions in the Body	Deficiency Symptoms	Toxicity Symptoms
Fat-Soluble Vitamins				
Vitamin A 5000 IU	Fortified milk and margarine, cream, cheese, butter, eggs, liver, spinach, and other dark leafy greens, broccoli, deep orange fruits and vegetables (carrots, sweet potatoes, peaches)	Vision; growth and repair of body tissues; reproduction; bone and tooth formation; immunity; cancer protection; hormone synthesis	Night blindness, rough skin, susceptibility to infection, impaired bone growth, vision problems	Nosebleeds, abdominal cramps, nausea, diarrhea, weight loss, blurred vision, irritability, bone pain, rashes, cessation of menstruation, growth retardation
Vitamin D 400–600 IU (RDA & RDI)	Self-synthesis with sunlight; fortified milk, fortified margarine, eggs, liver, fish	Calcium and phosphorus metabolism (bone and tooth formation); aids body's absorption of calcium	Rickets in children; osteomalacia in adults; abnormal growth, joint pain, soft bones	Raised blood calcium, constipation, weight loss, irritability, weakness, nausea, kidney stones, mental and physical retardation
Vitamin E 30 IU (RDA & RDI)	Vegetable oils, green leafy vegetables, wheat germ, whole-grain products, butter, liver, egg yolk, milk fat, nuts, seeds	Protects red blood cells; antioxidant; stabilization of cell membranes	Muscle wasting, weakness, red blood cell breakage, anemia, hemorrhaging, fibrocystic breast disease	Interference with anticlotting medication, general discomfort
Vitamin K 70–140 μg	Liver, green leafy and cabbage-type vegetables; milk	Bacterial synthesis in digestive tract; synthesis of blood-clotting proteins and a blood protein that regulates blood calcium	Hemorrhaging	Interference with anticlotting medication; may cause jaundice

Source: From J. Thompson and M. Manore, *Nutrition: An Applied Approach*. Copyright © 2005b. Reprinted by permission of Pearson Education, Inc.

Minerals

Minerals are the inorganic, indestructible elements that aid physiological processes in the body. Without minerals, vitamins could not be absorbed. Minerals are readily excreted and usually not toxic. Macrominerals are minerals that the body needs in fairly large amounts: sodium, calcium, phosphorus, magnesium, potassium, sulphur, and chloride. Trace minerals include iron, zinc, manganese, copper, iodine, and cobalt, so-called because only trace amounts of these minerals are needed. Serious problems may result if excesses or deficiencies occur. Specific types of minerals, the recommended dietary intake, best sources, and their major functions in the body, as well as symptoms of deficiency and toxicity are listed in Table 5b.2. Although minerals are necessary for body function, there are limits on how much of them we should consume.

Sodium

Sodium is necessary for the regulation of blood and body fluids, for the transmission of nerve impulses, for heart activity, for muscle contraction, and for other metabolic functions. Sodium also enhances flavour, balances the bitterness of some foods, acts as a preservative, and tenderizes meat. Although vital to our survival—and to the good taste of food—we tend to consume much more sodium than we need. The AI for sodium is 1500 mg per day for the average adult, yet the average Canadian consumes at least 12 times this amount. The most common source of sodium for Canadians is table salt (that is, sodium chloride, which is about 40 percent sodium and 60 percent chloride by weight). The remainder of dietary sodium comes from the water we drink and highly processed foods such as pickles, salty snack foods, processed cheeses, many breads and bakery products, smoked meats and sausages, many fast-food entrées, and soft drinks.

Many experts believe there is a link between excessive sodium intake and hypertension (high blood pressure). As a result, many organizations recommend

Minerals: Inorganic, indestructible elements that aid physiological processes.

TABLE 5b.2

A Guide to Minerals

Mineral	Significant Sources	Chief Functions in the Body	Deficiency Symptoms	Toxicity Symptoms
Calcium AI: 1000 mg/day (men and women aged 19 to 50); 1200 mg/day (men and women over 50)	Milk and milk products, small fish (with bones), tofu, greens, legumes	Principal mineral of bones and teeth; involved in muscle contraction and relaxation, nerve function, blood clotting, blood pressure	Stunted growth in children; bone loss (osteoporosis) in adults	Excess calcium is excreted except in hormonal imbalance states
Phosphorus RDA = 700 mg/day	All animal tissues	Part of every cell; involved in acid-base balance	Unknown	Can create relative deficiency of calcium
Magnesium RDA = 400 mg/day (men); 310 mg/day (women)	Nuts, legumes, whole grains, dark green vegetables, seafood, chocolate, cocoa	Involved in bone mineralization, protein synthesis, enzyme action, normal muscular contraction, nerve transmission	Weakness, confusion, depressed pancreatic hormone secretion, growth failure, behavioural disturbances, muscle spasms	Pharmacological overuse can cause nausea, cramps, dehydration
Sodium AI: 1.5 g/day	Salt, soy sauce; processed foods; cured, canned, and pickled foods	Helps maintain normal fluid and acid-base balance	Muscle cramps, mental apathy, loss of appetite	Hypertension (in salt-sensitive persons)
Chloride AI: 2.3 g/day	Salt, soy sauce; processed foods	Part of stomach acid, necessary for proper digestion, fluid balance	Growth failure in children, muscle cramps, mental apathy, loss of appetite	Normally harmless (different from poisonous chlorine gas); disturbed acid-base balance; vomiting
Potassium AI: 4.7 g/day	All whole foods: meats, milk, fruits, vegetables, grains, legumes	Facilitates many reactions including protein synthesis, fluid balance, nerve transmission, and contraction of muscles	Muscle weakness, paralysis, confusion; can cause death, accompanies dehydration	Causes muscular weakness; triggers vomiting; if given into a vein, can stop the heart
Iodine RDA = 150 μg	Iodized salt, seafood	Part of thyroxine, which regulates metabolism	Goitre, cretinism	Very high intakes depress thyroid activity
Iron RDA = 8 mg/day (men; women over 51); 18 mg/day (women aged 19 to 50)	Beef, fish, poultry, shellfish, eggs, legumes, dried fruits	Hemoglobin formation; part of myoglobin; energy use	Anemia: weakness, pallor, headaches, reduced resistance to infection, inability to concentrate	Nausea, vomiting, dizziness, damage to organs, death
Zinc RDA = 11 mg/day (men); 8 mg/day (women)	Protein-containing foods: meats, fish, poultry, grains, vegetables	Part of many enzymes; present in insulin; involved in making genetic material and proteins, immunity, vitamin A transport, taste, wound healing, sperm creation, normal fetal development	Growth failure in children, delayed development of sexual organs, loss of taste, poor wound healing	Fever, nausea, vomiting, diarrhea
Fluoride AI: 3 to 4 mg/day	Drinking water (if naturally fluoride-containing or fluoridated), tea, seafood	Formation of bones and teeth; helps make teeth resistant to decay and bones resistant to mineral loss	Susceptibility to tooth decay and bone loss	Fluorosis (discolouration of teeth)
Selenium RDA = 55 μg	Seafood, meats, grains	Helps protect body compounds from oxidation	Impaired immune function, depression, muscle pain	Vomiting, nausea, rash, brittle hair and nails

Source: From J. Thompson and M. Manore, *Nutrition: An Applied Approach*. Copyright © 2005b. Reprinted by permission of Pearson Education, Inc.

HEALTH IN THE MEDIA

The Continuing Debate on the Benefits and Risks of Supplemental Vitamins and Minerals

In August 2008, Dietitians of Canada released a report on the benefits and risks of vitamin and mineral supplements.

Given the controversial media attention given to nutritional intake, it is often difficult for consumers to decide what is good or not good for them. Specific to vitamin and mineral supplementation, the difficulty in understanding their importance and relationship to health increased with a flurry of media attention paid to the issue in April 2008. Three articles surfaced around the same time:

1. A Cochrane review (a database that compiles and reviews large numbers of existing research studies) of the use of antioxidants,
2. the Maclean's cover story titled "Vitamins Are Hazardous to Your Health", and
3. a news item that appeared on internet health sites regarding a Harvard newsletter story titled "No One Needs to Take a Multivitamin".

What is a safe dose of vitamins and minerals and is supplementation–general and specific–recommended? Canadian researchers Whiting and Adolphe considered these questions in their recent report published by Dietitians of Canada.

When the DRIs were set, the benefits of vitamins and minerals beyond preventing deficiency diseases were not clearly established. Thus, Whiting and Adolphe conducted a review of recent research to clarify the risks and benefits of high supplemental doses of vitamins and minerals. These authors concluded that both too little and too much of a single nutrient can potentially cause harm. Further, it is important to take into account an individual's dietary habits and lifestyle when making decisions about the appropriateness of recommending vitamin and/or mineral supplements. It was also suggested as a Dietitian Practice Point that "until further research confirms a benefit of high intakes, it is best to keep intake from supplements within the boundaries set by the RDA/AI and the UL. However, risks and benefits of vitamin and mineral intakes with respect to chronic disease risk reduction should be communicated to clients."

Readers may be interested to learn more about Canada's Natural Health Products and their Regulations at: www.hc-sc.gc.ca/dhp-mps/prodnatur/about-apropos/index-eng.php.

Source: Adapted from S.J. Whiting and J. Adolphe. "The Continuing Debate on the Benefits and Risks of Supplemental Vitamins and Minerals." *Current Issues: The Inside Story* August (2008). Retrieved on September 11, 2008 from www.dietitians.ca/news/media/asp.

that Canadians cut back on sodium consumption to reduce their risk for cardiovascular diseases, debilitating bone fractures, and other health problems.

what do you THINK?

Do you use salt frequently? Pay attention to how often you use a salt shaker over the next few days. Do you "salt" your food prior to tasting? Why? Can you get by without salting your food? Have you tried salt-free herbs and spices? Why or why not?

Calcium

The issue of calcium consumption has gained national attention with the rising incidence of osteoporosis among the elderly, particularly among older women. Although calcium plays a vital role in building strong bones and teeth, contracting muscles, clotting blood, transmitting nerve impulses, regulating heartbeat, and balancing fluid within cells, most adult Canadians between ages 19 and 50 do not consume the recommended 1000 milligrams of calcium per day, with particularly inadequate intakes in older Canadians

try it NOW!

Shake your salt habit! Did you know that the average Canadian consumes 1150 mg per 1000 calories eaten (or 2900 mg for 2500 calories)? Extra salt can be found in almost everything from cereal to snack foods. Take simple steps today to reduce your overall sodium intake: read food labels and choose products labelled as low sodium (containing fewer than 500 mg per serving) or sodium/salt free. Order your popcorn without salt, and, when dining out, ask the chef to cook with low-sodium products. Switch to kosher salt, it contains 25 percent less sodium than regular table salt. Instead of adding salt to food you prepare, use fresh or dried herbs for seasonings. Train yourself to taste the natural flavours of food. Once you reduce your sodium intake, you will taste the difference the next time you eat a sodium-laden product. Check out the following website for more information: www.sodium101.ca.

(>50 years), who are advised to consume 1200 milligrams of calcium per day. Another reason to ensure adequate calcium intake relates to obesity prevention. Recent research suggests a positive relationship between calcium intake and healthy weight maintenance (or in other words, people who do not consume sufficient calcium are more likely to be overweight or obese). Of equal importance is to evaluate the trend toward choosing soft drinks instead of milk. Soft drinks not only contain a high percentage of free sugars but also do not provide the necessary nutrients found in milk.

Increasing Your Dietary Calcium Intake

Because calcium intake is so important throughout your life, it is critical that you consume the minimum required each day. More than half our calcium intake usually comes from milk, one of the best sources of dietary calcium. Although many green, leafy vegetables are sources of calcium, some contain oxalic acid, which makes their calcium harder to absorb. Spinach, chard, and beet greens are not particularly valuable sources of calcium, whereas broccoli, cauliflower, and many peas and beans (pinto beans and soybeans) are a source of calcium. Many nuts, particularly almonds, Brazil nuts, and hazelnuts, and seeds such as sunflower and sesame contain calcium as well. Molasses is a source of calcium, as are canned salmon (if you eat the bones) and sardines. Some fruits—such as citrus, figs, raisins, and dried apricots—have moderate amounts.

Of interest to those who drink carbonated soft drinks is that the added phosphoric acid (phosphate) in these drinks can cause you to excrete calcium. Calcium and phosphorus imbalances may lead to kidney stones and other calcification problems, as well as to increased arteriosclerotic plaque.

Vitamin D improves absorption of calcium; thus, exposure to sunlight is like having an extra calcium source. (See also the Focus on Canada box earlier in this chapter.) Stress, on the other hand, contributes to calcium depletion. Although calcium supplements are available, the best way to meet your needs is to consume calcium as part of a balanced, varied dietary intake throughout the day in foods containing protein, vitamin D, and vitamin C for optimum absorption.

Iron

Iron deficiency is the most common nutrient deficiency worldwide, affecting more than 2 billion people or about one third of the population. Although less prevalent an issue in Canada, it is still the most common nutrient deficiency. Females aged 19 to 50 require 18 milligrams of iron per day, and males aged 19 to 50 about 8 milligrams per day. After the age of 50 (postmenopausal for women), men and women each require about 8 milligrams of iron per day. Pregnant women require 27 milligrams of iron per day. Iron deficiencies can lead to **anemia**, a problem resulting from the body's inability to produce hemoglobin, the bright red, oxygen-carrying component of the blood. When this occurs, body cells receive less oxygen, and carbon dioxide wastes are removed less efficiently, resulting in a person feeling tired and run down. Another problem with iron deficiency is that the immune system becomes less effective, which can lead to increased risk of illness. A less common problem, iron toxicity, is caused by too much iron in the blood. Women are more likely than men to suffer from iron deficiency problems, partly because they typically eat less than men and because of blood loss from menstrual flows.

Sex Differences in Nutritional Needs

Men and women differ in body size, body composition, and overall metabolic rates. These differences result in distinctive requirements for most nutrients throughout the life cycle and mean that men and women face unique challenges in meeting their dietary goals. Some of these differences have already been discussed. However, there are some dietary factors that need further consideration. One factor is that women have a lower ratio of lean body mass to adipose (fatty) tissue at all ages, particularly after puberty. Also, after puberty, metabolism is higher in men, meaning that they require more calories than women to do the same things.

Different Cycles, Different Needs

Women also have many more "landmark" times in their lives when their nutritional needs vary significantly. From menarche to menopause, women undergo cyclical physiological changes that can have dramatic effects on metabolism, nutrition needs, and efforts to maintain a nutrition plan. For example, during pregnancy and lactation, nutrition requirements increase substantially for women. Those unable to follow the dietary recommendations may gain more weight during pregnancy and retain it afterward. During the menstrual cycle, many women report significant food cravings that result in overeating. At menopause, nutrition needs change again rather dramatically. With the hormone estrogen reduced, the body needs more calcium to combat losses in bone mineral density.

Eating Too Much Meat!

Although men do not have the same cyclical patterns and dietary needs as women, they often have dietary excesses or habits resistant to change. Consider the following:

- Men who eat red meat as a main dish five or more times a week are four times more at risk of colorectal cancer than men who eat red meat less than once a month.
- Heavy-red-meat-eaters are more than twice as likely to get prostate cancer.
- For every three servings of vegetables or fruits consumed per day, men can expect a 22 percent lower risk of stroke.
- High vegetable and fruit dietary intakes may lower the risk of lung cancer in smokers, from 20 times the risk of nonsmokers to "only" 10 times the risk. They may also protect against oral, throat, pancreas, and bladder cancers, all of which are more common in smokers.
- While obesity seems to be a factor in cancer of the esophagus, an increasingly common malignancy among men, consumption of vegetables and fruits can help protect against it.

Meals like this vegetable and tofu stir-fry provide a vegan with essential vitamins, minerals, and protein. Adding a whole grain, such as brown rice or whole wheat bread/rolls would further enhance this meal by making use of complementary plant proteins.

what do you THINK?

Think about women you know who have difficulty maintaining their weight. What are their ages? What factors may influence them to have more (or less) difficulty than you have? What advantages, if any, do men have in managing their eating behaviours and their weight? How can you help these men and women in their efforts to maintain their weight?

VEGETARIANISM

For a variety of reasons, some people choose not to eat meat; approximately 4 percent of Canadians are identified as **vegetarian**. Vegetarianism can provide a positive alternative to the typical high-fat, high-calorie, meat-based cuisine of most Canadians. However, without knowledge and careful food selection, vegetarians can have several dietary problems.

The term *vegetarian* means different things to different people. Strict vegetarians, or vegans, avoid all foods of animal origin, including dairy products and eggs. The people who fall into this category must carefully plan their dietary intake to ensure they obtain the necessary nutrients. Far more common are people who are lacto-vegetarians. These people eat dairy products but avoid flesh foods; as a result, their diet is often low in fat and cholesterol, but only if they consume skim milk and other low-fat or nonfat dairy products. Ovo-vegetarians add eggs to their diet, while lacto-ovo-vegetarians eat dairy products and eggs. Pesco-vegetarians eat seafood, dairy products, and eggs, while semi-vegetarians eat poultry, seafood, dairy products, and eggs. Some people in the semi-vegetarian category prefer to call themselves non–red meat eaters.

Anemia: Iron-deficiency disease that results from the body's inability to produce hemoglobin.

Vegetarian: A term with a variety of meanings: vegans avoid all foods of animal origin; lacto-vegetarians avoid flesh foods and eat dairy products; ovo-vegetarians avoid flesh foods and eat eggs; lacto-ovo-vegetarians avoid flesh foods and eat dairy products and eggs; pesco-vegetarians avoid meat but eat seafood, dairy products, and eggs; semi-vegetarians eat chicken, seafood, dairy products, and eggs.

Maintaining a healthy dietary intake can be a challenge for post-secondary students, particularly with fast-food chains on most campuses.

Generally, people who follow a vegetarian diet weigh less, have better cholesterol levels, fewer problems with irregular bowel movements (constipation and diarrhea), and a lower risk of heart disease than nonvegetarians. Preliminary evidence suggests that vegetarians may also have a reduced risk for colorectal and breast cancer. Whether these lower risks are due to the vegetarian diet per se or to a combination of lifestyle variables remains unclear.

The modern vegetarian is usually adept at combining the right types of foods to ensure proper nutrient intake. People who eat dairy products and small amounts of poultry or seafood are seldom nutrient-deficient; in fact, while vegans typically get 50 to 60 grams of protein per day, lacto-ovo-vegetarians normally consume between 70 and 90 grams per day, well beyond the DRIs. Vegan diets may be deficient in vitamins B2 (riboflavin), B12, and D. See Table 5b.1 for "best sources" of these vitamins. Vegans are also at risk for calcium, iron, zinc, and other mineral deficiencies, but these nutrients can be obtained from supplements. Strict vegans have to pay much more attention to what they eat than the average person, but by eating complementary combinations of plant products (as shown previously in Figure 5b.3) they can obtain an adequate amount of essential amino acids.

what do you THINK?

Have you ever considered becoming or are you currently a vegetarian? What would be (or is) your reason for making this choice? Do you find it difficult to select vegetarian foods in restaurants or other eating places on your campus? What actions can you take to obtain more vegetarian choices?

BUILDING COMMUNICATION SKILLS

Understanding Nutrition and Health Claims

Nutritional labelling regulations became mandatory for packaged foods distributed from larger businesses on December 12, 2005 and for smaller businesses on December 12, 2007. These regulations require pre-packaged food labels to carry a Nutrition Facts table that lists calories and 13 key nutrients in a specified amount of food (that is, a usual serving). The regulations were introduced in 2003, with many food distributors adapting their food labels to meet the regulations prior to the mandatory dates.

In addition to the labelling regulations, Health Canada updated the requirements of more than 40 nutrient content claims and decided to allow only certain health claims (re: the diet–health relationships) on food labels or in advertisements. It is up to the manufacturer whether to include a nutrition content or diet–health claim on the label or in the advertisement of the food. Often the claims are made–and done so attractively–because they positively influence consumers purchasing habits.

EXAMPLES OF NUTRIENT CONTENT CLAIMS:

Source of fibre–the food must contain at least 2 grams of dietary fibre in the amount of food specified as a serving in the Nutrition Facts table.

Low fat–the food contains no more than 3 grams of fat in the amount of food specified as a serving in the Nutrition Facts table.

Trans fat free – the food contains less than 0.2 grams of trans fat in the amount of food specified or the total amount of saturated and trans fat add up to 2 grams or less per specified serving in the Nutrition Facts table.

Cholesterol-free–the food has a negligible amount of cholesterol (less than 2 mg) in the amount of food specified as a serving in the Nutrition Facts table. The food must also be low in saturated and trans fat.

Sodium-free–the food contains less than 5 mg of sodium in the amount of food specified as a serving in the Nutrition Facts table.

Reduced in calories–the food has at least 25 percent fewer calories than the food it is compared to.

Light–in regard to the nutritional characteristics of a product, "light" is allowed on foods reduced in fat or reduced in calories. "Light" may also be used to describe sensory characteristics associated with a particular food–so long as that characteristic is clearly identified with the claim (for example, light tasting, light coloured).

WHAT DO THE WORDS IN NUTRIENT CONTENT CLAIMS MEAN?

Free–none or hardly any

Low–a small amount

Reduced–at least 25 percent less than in a similar product

Light–allowed only on labels reduced in fat or reduced in calories. If used in reference to the characteristic of the food, the characteristic must accompany the claim.

Source–contains a useful amount

High or good source–contains a high amount

Very high or excellent source–contains a very high amount

WHAT ARE HEALTH CLAIMS?

Only the following diet–health claims can be made:

1. A healthy diet low in saturated and trans fat may reduce the risk of heart disease.
2. A healthy diet with adequate calcium and vitamin D, and regular physical activity, helps to achieve strong bones and may reduce the risk of osteoporosis.
3. A healthy diet rich in a variety of vegetables and fruit may help reduce the risk of some types of cancer.
4. A healthy diet containing foods high in potassium and low in sodium may reduce the risk of high blood pressure, a risk factor for stroke and heart disease.

Source: Adapted from Health Canada: Food and Nutrition, "Interactive Nutrition Label: Get the Facts," retrieved on May 25, 2006, from www.hc-sc.gc.ca and S. Conrad"s. "Current Perspectives on Understanding Fat," retrieved on September 11, 2008 from www.cfcn.ca/in_action/fact_sheets.asp.

Canadians are concerned about their body weight and shape—and should be, since more than half are classified as overweight or obese according to body mass index (BMI) calculations derived from measured height and weight in the most recent Canadian Community Health Survey. Equally alarming is the high percentage of Canadian children and youth considered at risk of overweight or overweight. In addition to a greater number of Canadian adults, children, and youth classified as overweight or obese, their average BMI and fat levels have increased too. Specifically, the average BMI of adults increased from 25.1 in 1978–79 to 27.0 in 2004 and the average level of fat as measured by skinfolds was greater in children and adolescents measured in the 1990s than in those measured in the 1960s. Given the attention to overweight and obesity in the media, you are likely aware of the health risks associated with these conditions. Briefly, these include increased risk of heart disease, stroke, high blood pressure, some types of cancer, type 2 diabetes, gall bladder disease, and osteoarthritis. Of equal concern are the emotional, spiritual, and social health risks associated with obesity partly due to the stigma surrounding it. You are also likely aware of the "simple" solution to obesity often depicted in the media: eat less, do more. However, it is not that simple—if it was, our population would not be experiencing the current levels of overweight and obesity.

This chapter is designed to help you better understand what overweight and obesity really mean, what factors lead to their development, and why weight maintenance is essential to overall health. This chapter also includes practical and realistic strategies for maintaining your weight and learning to appreciate your body size and shape as it is.

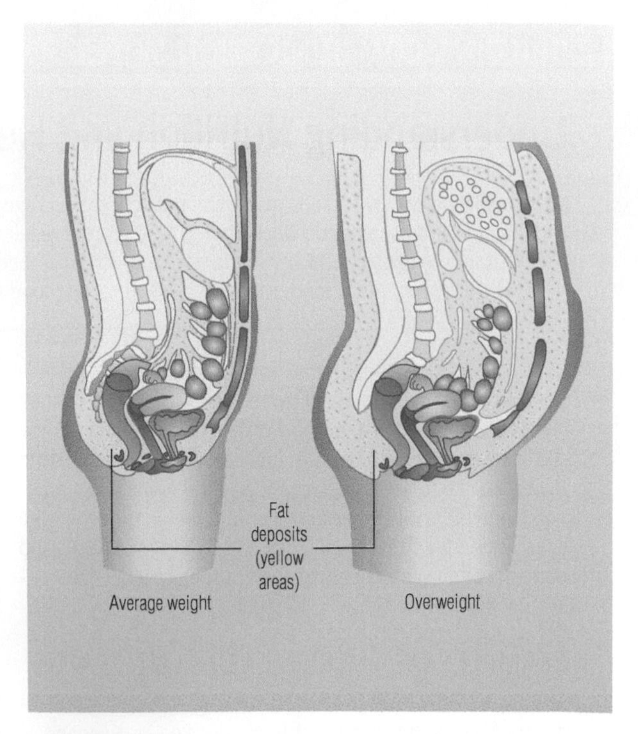

FIGURE 5b.4

The figure compares a person with an average level of body fat to a person with excess body fat. Note the fat deposits directly under the skin (subcutaneous fat) and around the internal organs (visceral fat).

OVERWEIGHT AND OBESITY

Confusion exists in the understanding of the terms *overweight* and *obesity*. Part of the confusion relates to measurement and another part is the inconsistent and inappropriate use of each term. **Overweight** refers to a weight greater than expected for a specific height (and is usually determined from height–weight charts or calculating BMI). **Obesity** refers to an excessive accumulation of body fat such that the individual is at increased risk for developing health problems (see Figure 5b.4). Interestingly, a person can be overweight and not obese. For example, a male weightlifter or football athlete may be overweight according to a height–weight chart and BMI classification because of his high level of lean body or muscle mass but clearly not be obese. Similarly, a person can be obese without being overweight. A female student, 20 years of age, who weighs 54 kilograms and is 160 centimetres tall can have more than 30 percent of her weight coming from fat if she does not exercise, engages in little physical activity, spends lots of time on the computer and studying, and eats a high-fat diet. Thus, weight by itself or in combination with height is not a valid indicator of obesity or fatness.

As previously mentioned, physical health risks associated with obesity or an excessive accumulation of fat include, but should not be limited to, an increased chance of developing atherosclerosis, coronary artery disease, hypertension, colon cancer, postmenopausal breast cancer, type 2 diabetes, gallbladder disease, and osteoarthritis. Excessive fatness may also contribute to a poor body image and reduced self-esteem. Most health professionals agree that a level of total body fat that exceeds 20 percent in men and 30 percent in women puts them at risk for health problems. Table 5b.3 provides general ratings for adults aged 18 to 30 in terms of overall percentages of body fat.

Determining the Right Weight for You

The answer to whether you are at a healthy weight depends on your body structure and how your weight is distributed. Traditionally, people compared their weight to the range given on height-and-weight charts. These charts usually give the "ideal" weight for males and females of a given height and frame size. If you were above your ideal weight, you would then be classified as overweight.

More common today is to determine your weight status based on calculating your **BMI**. BMI is obtained by dividing your weight (in kilograms) by your height (in metres) squared. Weight should be taken without shoes or clothing, and height should be measured without shoes. Table 5b.4 and Figure 5b.5 depict classifications for health risk according to BMI for men and women. In general, a BMI range of 18.5 to 24.9 is considered a healthy weight. BMI values above 25.0 are referred to as overweight and are associated with increased health risk. Although not a measure of fatness per se, a BMI greater than 30 results in an "obese" classification because of the associated health risks found in the population at this level of BMI and greater. As noted in Table 5b.4, obesity is further broken into classes with associated health risks. Specifically, a BMI between 30.0 and 34.9 refers to Obese Class I with high health risk, a BMI between 35.0 and 39.9 refers to Obese Class II and very high health risk, and a BMI greater than 40.0 is classified as Obese Class III with extremely high health risk.

TABLE 5b.3

General Ratings of Body Fat Percentages by Age and Sex

Rating	Males (ages 18–30) (%)	Females (ages 18–30) (%)
Athletic*	6–10	10–15
Good	11–14	16–19
Acceptable	15–17	20–24
Overfat	18–19	25–29
Obese	20 or over	30 or over

* The ratings in the Athletic category are general guidelines for athletes involved in aesthetic or lean-weight sports such as gymnastics, diving, distance running, etc. where a low level of body fat and/or weight often confers a competitive advantage.

TABLE 5b.4

Health Risk Classification for Adults* According to BMI

BMI	Weight Classification	Risk of Developing a Health Problem
30.0	Obese	High
30.1–34.9	Obese Class I	High
35.0–39.9	Obese Class II	Very high
> 40.0	Obese Class III	Extremely high

* These cut-off values and weight and health classifications are not applicable to growing children and adolescents.

Why the difference in acceptable fat levels between men and women? Much of it can be attributed to genetics and, more specifically, related to the structure of the female body and to sex hormones. Body composition is most often broken down into two main components: fat-free mass and fat mass. Fat-free mass is made up of all the body's components other than fat—that is, the structural and functional elements in cells, body water, muscle, bones, and other body organs such as the heart, liver, and kidneys. Compared with men, women have a lower ratio of fat-free mass to fat mass, in part due to the genetic differences in bone size and mass, muscle size, and other variables. Women also experience greater weight and fat fluctuation due to hormonal changes, pregnancy, and menopause.

Body fat is composed of two types: essential fat and storage fat. Essential fat is necessary for normal physiological functioning, such as nerve conduction. Essential fat makes up approximately three to seven percent of total body weight in men and approximately 10 to 15 percent in women. Storage fat, which serves to insulate, pad, and protect the body from cold and trauma, makes up the remainder of our fat. It accounts for only a small percentage of total body weight for very lean people and between 5 and 25 percent of body weight for most healthy Canadian adults. Female bodybuilders, who are among the leanest of female athletes, may have a healthy body fat percentage in the range of 8 to 13 percent, nearly all of which is essential fat.

Similar to too much fat putting one's health at risk, too little fat also can relate to poor health. A minimal amount of fat is necessary for insulating the body, for cushioning between parts of the body and vital organs, and for maintaining several body functions. Although tremendous variation exists, it is generally suggested that in men this lower limit is approximately 3 to 4 percent and for women, 8 percent. Excessively low

Overweight: A weight greater than expected for a specific height.

Obesity: An excessive accumulation of body fat at which level the risk for health problems is increased.

Body mass index (BMI): A technique of weight assessment based on the relationship of weight to height.

Body Mass Index

Legend
Underweight
Weight appropriate
Overweight
Obese

Height (feet / inches)

Weight (pounds)	5'0"	5'1"	5'2"	5'3"	5'4"	5'5"	5'6"	5'7"	5'8"	5'9"	5'10"	5'11"	6'0"	6'1"	6'2"	6'3"	6'4"	Weight (kilograms)
100	20	19	18	18	17	17	16	16	15	15	14	14	14	13	13	12	12	45
105	21	20	19	19	18	17	17	16	16	16	15	15	14	14	13	13	13	47
110	21	21	20	19	19	18	18	17	17	16	16	15	15	15	14	14	13	50
115	22	22	21	20	20	19	19	18	17	17	17	16	16	15	15	14	14	52
120	23	23	22	21	21	20	19	19	18	18	17	17	16	16	15	15	15	54
125	24	24	23	22	21	21	20	20	19	18	18	17	17	16	16	16	15	57
130	25	25	24	23	22	22	21	20	20	19	19	18	18	17	17	16	16	59
135	26	26	25	24	23	22	22	21	21	20	20	19	18	18	17	17	16	61
140	27	26	26	25	24	23	23	22	21	21	20	20	19	18	18	17	17	63
145	28	27	27	26	25	24	23	23	22	21	21	20	20	19	19	18	18	66
150	29	28	27	27	26	25	24	23	23	22	22	21	20	20	19	19	18	68
155	30	29	28	27	27	26	25	24	24	23	22	22	21	20	20	19	19	70
160	31	30	29	28	27	27	26	25	24	24	23	22	22	21	21	20	19	72
165	32	31	30	29	28	27	27	26	25	24	24	23	22	22	21	21	20	75
170	33	32	31	30	29	28	27	27	26	25	24	24	23	22	22	21	21	77
175	34	33	32	31	30	29	28	27	27	26	25	24	24	23	22	22	21	79
180	35	34	33	32	31	30	29	28	27	27	26	25	24	24	23	22	22	82
185	36	35	34	33	32	31	30	29	28	27	27	26	25	24	24	23	23	84
190	37	36	35	34	33	32	31	30	29	28	27	26	26	25	24	24	23	86
195	38	37	36	35	33	32	31	31	30	29	28	27	26	26	25	24	24	88
200	39	38	37	35	34	33	32	31	30	30	29	28	27	26	26	25	24	91
205	40	39	37	36	35	34	33	32	31	30	29	29	28	27	26	26	25	93
210	41	40	38	37	36	35	34	33	32	31	30	29	28	28	27	26	26	95
215	42	41	39	38	37	36	35	34	33	32	31	30	29	28	28	27	26	98
220	43	42	40	39	38	37	36	34	33	32	32	31	30	29	28	27	27	100
225	44	43	41	40	39	37	36	35	34	33	32	31	31	30	29	28	27	102
230	45	43	42	41	39	38	37	36	35	34	33	32	31	30	30	29	28	104
235	46	44	43	42	40	39	38	37	36	35	34	33	32	31	30	29	29	107
240	47	45	44	43	41	40	39	38	36	35	34	33	33	32	31	30	29	109
245	48	46	45	43	42	41	40	38	37	36	35	34	33	32	31	31	30	111
250	49	47	46	44	43	42	40	39	38	37	36	35	34	33	32	31	30	114
	150.0	152.5	155.0	157.5	160.0	162.5	165.0	167.5	170.0	172.5	175.0	177.5	180.0	182.5	185.0	187.5	190.0	

Height (centimetres)

FIGURE 5b.5

What is your weight status? To find out, find your height (either at the top [in feet and inches] or bottom [in centimetres]) and your weight (at the right [in kilograms] or left [in pounds]) and find where these two intersect.

FOCUS ON CANADA

Nutrition: Findings from the Canadian Community Health Survey–Measured Obesity

Information on the prevalence of obesity (based on BMI) in adults gathered from the 2004 Canadian Community Health Survey (CCHS) was released in July 2005. Unique to this survey was that body mass index (BMI) was calculated from measured rather than self-reported height and weight. This is significant because, typically, people overestimate their height and underestimate their weight in measures of self-report, resulting in an underestimation of BMI. Thus, it is important to keep in mind that it is likely that the data reported in previous surveys underestimated the prevalence of overweight and obesity in the Canadian population.

Results from the CCHS indicate that 23.1 percent of adult Canadians (aged 18 or older) were classified as obese (BMI ≥ 30). Further, 36.1 percent of Canadian adults were considered overweight (BMI > 25 < 30). All together, more than half (59.1 percent) of the Canadian population is overweight or obese. Of significant concern is the percentage of the population that meet the criteria for Class II (BMI 35–39.99) and Class III (BMI ≥ 40) obesity; that is, 5.1 percent and 2.7 percent, respectively.

The percentage of males classified as overweight (42.0 percent) was significantly greater than that of females (30.2 percent). Although, there were no significant differences in the estimates of males (22.9 percent) and females for obesity (23.2 percent), when the three classes of obesity (that is, a BMI 30–34.9, BMI 35.–39.9, and BMI ≥ 40.) were combined, there were a greater percentage of females (3.8 versus 1.6 percent) in the Class III category (that is, BMI ≥ 40.0).

Obesity rates were greatest among the 45- to 54-year-olds and lowest in the 18- to 24-year-olds (29.9 vs. 10.7 percent). Overweight was greatest in the 65- to 74-year-olds and lowest in the 18- to 24-year-olds (52.7 vs. 27.0 percent).

In regard to provincial data, the highest rates of obesity were found in Newfoundland and Labrador (33.3 percent), New Brunswick (30.8 percent), and Saskatchewan (30.4 percent), with the lowest prevalence in British Columbia (18.2 percent).

STUDY QUESTIONS:

1. Why do think the rate of overweight and obesity increased in the Canadian population? Is this a real change or simply an issue of more accurate measurement?
2. What effect will this rise in overweight and obesity have on Canada's Health System? On individual health and wellness?

Source: Statistics Canada, 2005, "Nutrition: Findings from the Canadian Community Health Survey, Measured Obesity, Adult Obesity in Canada: Measured Height and Weight," Catalogue No. 82-620-MWE2005001. Retrieved on December 9, 2005, from www.statcan.ca/english/research/82-620-MIE/2005001/articles/adults/aobesity.htm. Adapted and reproduced with permission of the Minister of Public Works and Government Services of Canada, 2007.

body fat in females may lead to amenorrhea or oligomenorrhea, a cessation or disruption of the menstrual cycle respectively. The critical level of body fat necessary to maintain normal menstrual flow is believed to be between 8 and 13 percent, with exceptions to this rule and many additional factors that affect the menstrual cycle. Under extreme circumstances, such as starvation diets and certain diseases, the body exhausts available fat reserves and begins breaking down muscle tissue in a last-ditch effort to obtain sufficient nourishment.

Assessing Your Body Fat Content

Since both too little and too much body fat may pose a health risk, it can be important to know your actual level of body fat. But how is fat measured? Many options are available and an accurate assessment of body fat requires a different type of measurement than what can be obtained using traditional height–weight charts or calculations of BMI. How do you decide which of the techniques available are the best for you? Several factors should be considered before you make this decision. Cost and access may be two of those factors, since some techniques are relatively expensive and inaccessible. Another factor to consider is your reason for wanting to know your body fat content and whether or not it is essential for you to have a precise measure. At the most basic level, if your previously well-fitting jeans are now too tight, you know you have gained weight/fat and ought to take action to prevent further weight gain. Similarly, if your well-fitting jeans continue to fit well, you have maintained your weight.

Although assessments of body composition generally quantify body weight into its basic components—that is, fat-free mass and fat mass—estimates of body fat are considered most important for the health-related components of physical fitness. Further, although the various methods used to measure body fat can be useful, there are limits to the accuracy of measurement, even when the testers are skilful and well trained. Before agreeing to any procedure, be aware of the expense, risks, measurement error, and training of the tester. Further, consider what you will do with the value, once known.

Dual-Energy X-Ray Absorptiometry

Dual-energy X-ray absorptiometry (DXA) measures bone mineral content and lean and fat tissue. This technique requires a low radiation exposure from a low-energy and high-energy photon beam. Based on appropriate computer algorithms and the amount of absorption of the photon beams by the atoms in bone mineral and soft tissues, an estimate of bone mineral, fat-free soft tissue, and fat tissue is made. A strength of the DXA method is that total body fat can be determined as well as regional body fat distribution. Further, some consider DXA to be the most accurate or "gold standard" assessment of body composition.

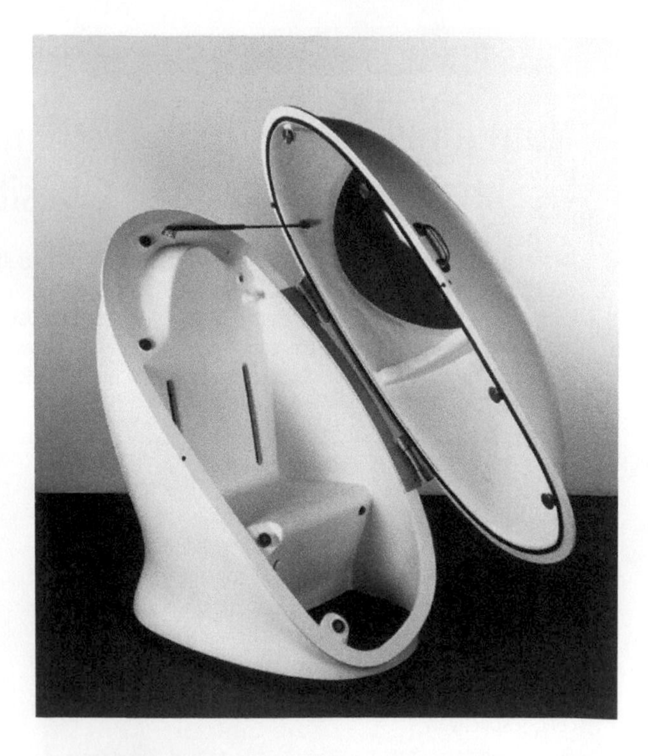

The Bod Pod is an example of air displacement plethysmography.

Hydrostatic Weighing

Hydrostatic weighing was previously considered the gold standard for measuring body composition. This method measures the amount of water a person displaces when completely submerged. Because fat tissue has a lower density than muscle or bone tissue, body fat can be computed using a person's underwater and out-of-water weights.

Air Displacement Plethysmography

Air displacement plethysmography (ADP) has become popular in recent years to measure body composition. Based on the same premises as hydrostatic weighing, total body volume is measured—this time from air displacement—from which an estimate of body fat can be made. Estimates of total body volume (either in water or air) use the formula density = mass ÷ volume. The major assumption and limitation of these two methods is that the density of fat and fat-free mass (fat-free mass being all components of the body except fat) is considered constant. The limitation, then, relates to bone mineral content and density, which is known to vary throughout the life cycle.

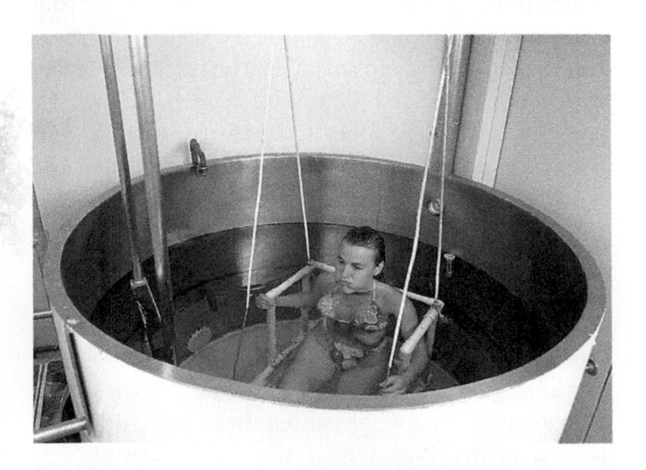

Hydrostatic weighing is one technique used to estimate body fat.

Skinfold Measurements

Perhaps the most commonly used method to estimate body fat is **skinfold measurements**. In this procedure, a person grasps folds of skin and the underlying tissue with the thumb and index finger and then a specially calibrated instrument called a "skinfold" caliper is applied to take the measurement. The eight sites most commonly measured on the right side of the body include the triceps (back of the arm), biceps (front of the arm), subscapular (on the back), iliac crest (on the side of the body—near the "love handles"), supraspinale (along the front of the body over the hip), abdominal (next to the umbilicus—belly button), front thigh (middle of the upper leg), and medial calf (middle, inside of the lower leg). Once these sites

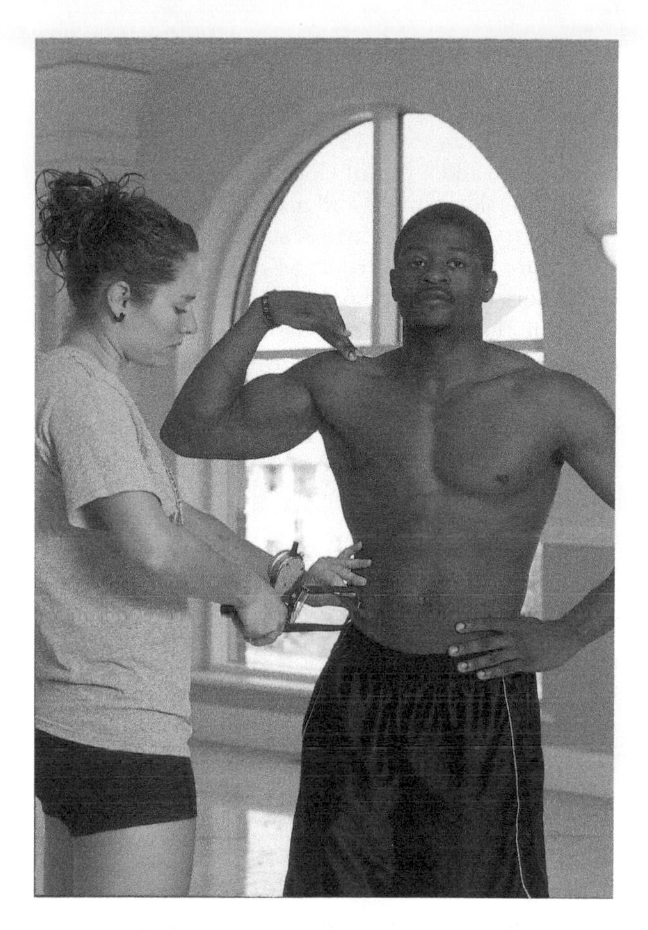

In the hands of a trained professional, skinfold calipers can be used to provide an accurate measure of body fat for people who are not overly fat.

are measured, formulas can be used to predict total body fat. In the hands of trained technicians, this procedure can be fairly accurate. However, the fatter a person is, the more prone this technique is to error. For people who are obese, difficulties in assessment are magnified because of problems distinguishing between flaccid muscles and fat. Also, most skinfold calipers do not expand far enough to obtain measurements from the moderately obese (20 to 40 percent fat) or morbidly obese (more than 40 percent fat). Additional errors in estimating percentage of body fat from skinfold assessments may occur as a result of failure to account for certain age, sex, and ethnic differences in the calculations.

An alternative to predicting percentage of body fat from skinfold measurements is to simply total them. A "sum of skinfolds" also allows for comparison of "before" and "after" measurements. Since approximately 50 percent of body fat lies below the skin (that is, as subcutaneous fat), a loss in total sum of skinfolds indicates a loss of total body fat. Similarly, a gain in sum of skinfolds indicates a gain in total body fat.

what do you THINK?

Is it important to you to know your current level of body fat? Why or why not? Which of the tests would you feel comfortable taking? Would any make you feel uncomfortable? Why or why not?

Waist Circumference

A common method of assessing abdominal body fat is **waist circumference.** A simple measuring tape is used to take the girth, or circumference, measurement at the superior border or top of the iliac crest or hip bones. Regardless of where measured (for example, at the smallest point of the torso, at the level of the umbilicus [that is, belly button], or the top of the hip bones), a larger waist circumference is associated with greater health risk. Specifically, a waist circumference greater than 102 centimetres in men and 88 centimetres in women indicates increased risk of heart disease, type 2 diabetes, metabolic syndrome, hypertension, and hyperlipidemia.

Bioelectrical Impedance Analysis

Another method of determining body fat levels, **bioelectrical impedance analysis (BIA)**, involves sending a weak electric current through the body. The rationale for this technique is based on the greater electrolyte and water content of fat free versus fat tissue. The amount of resistance to the current, along with the person's age, sex, and other physical characteristics, is then fed into a computer that uses a special formula to determine the total amount of fat-free and

Dual-energy X-ray absorptiometry (DXA): A method of body composition assessment in which estimates are made of bone mineral content and lean and fat mass.

Hydrostatic weighing: A method of determining body fat by measuring the amount of water displaced when a person is completely submerged.

Air displacement plethysmography (ADP): A method used to determine body fat from estimates of total body volume.

Skinfold measurements: A method of assessing body fat where double folds of skin and the underlying tissue are measured with skinfold calipers.

Waist circumference: A method of assessing abdominal fat where a measuring tape is used to assess the girth at the top of the iliac crest.

Bioelectrical impedance analysis (BIA): A technique of body fat assessment in which the resistance to a weak electrical current is measured.

fat tissue. This technique has increased in use in recent years, likely because of its convenience, low cost, non-invasiveness, and quick estimate of body fat. Keep in mind however that it is important for the body to be normally hydrated when using BIA because even small fluctuations in body water content alter the assessment. Even with adequate hydration and nutritional status, significant error can result in body composition estimates from BIA.

MANAGING YOUR WEIGHT

At some point in our lives, almost all of us will decide we need to do something about our weight. Many will choose to go on a diet, with initially successful results, but few of us will achieve long-term weight loss. The problem is that we think about losing weight via dieting, or lowering our calorie intake for the short term. Even if combined with increased exercise or physical activity, the change is viewed as temporary. What is needed instead is a lifetime approach to eating well, being physically active, and managing our behaviours around food, physical activity, and sedentary activities.

Keeping Weight Loss in Perspective

Long-term weight loss is difficult for many people and requires support from friends, family, and the community. As mentioned previously, it is often believed that losing weight is simple: we just need to burn more calories than we consume. Putting this principle into practice, however, is far from simple given our cultural attitudes and behaviours toward food and habitual levels of physical activity and sedentary activities. Other factors are involved, too—factors such as stress, food availability and accessibility, and depression. To reach and maintain the weight that is right for you—the weight at which you will be most healthy—you need to develop a lifelong approach to healthy eating, physical activity, and sedentary behaviours. Your eating habits cannot simply be a "diet" that you go on, because then it will be a diet that you can go off of as well. Similarly, your approach to being physically active must also be for your lifetime—while recognizing that there will be times when you will be more or less physically active.

What Is a Calorie?

A calorie is a unit of measurement that indicates the amount of energy obtained from a particular food. A kilogram of body fat contains approximately 7500 calories. So each time you consume 7500 calories more than your body needs, you gain a kilogram (or, roughly, two pounds). Conversely, each time your body expends an extra 7500 calories, you lose a kilogram. If you add a can of Coca-Cola (140 calories) to your daily caloric intake and make no other changes in your dietary intake or physical activity, you would gain a kilogram in approximately 54 days (7500 calories ÷ 140 calories/day = 53.6 days). Conversely, if you walked for half an hour each day at a pace of 9 minutes per kilometre (172 calories burned), you would lose a kilogram in 44 days (7500 calories ÷ 172 calories/day = 43.6 days), assuming you make no other changes to dietary intake or physical activity habits.

Physical Activity

Approximately 90 percent of the daily calorie expenditures of most people occurs as a result of their **resting metabolic rate (RMR)**. RMR is greater than BMR (or **basal metabolic rate**, which is the amount of energy our bodies burn at complete rest; this will be discussed at greater length later in the chapter); RMR includes BMR plus any additional energy expended through daily sedentary activities, such as food digestion, sitting, studying, or standing.

Exercise metabolic rate (EMR) accounts for the remaining 10 percent and specifically refers to the energy expenditure as a result of physical activity. For most of us, this caloric expenditure comes in the form of light daily activities, such as walking, climbing stairs, doing the dishes, running the vacuum, and mowing the lawn. If we increase the level and intensity of our physical activity to moderate or heavy, our EMR may be 10 to 20 times greater and contribute more substantially to our energy needs.

Increasing BMR (which is the energy expenditure of the body under resting conditions at normal room temperature), RMR, or EMR levels will require more

try it NOW!
Set SuPeRSMART goals for weight maintenance or even weight loss. Give your goals a reality check: are they Self-controllable, Public, Rewarded, Specific, Measurable, Achievable, Relevant, and Time Specific? For example, rather than aiming to lose 10 kilograms this month (which is *not* healthy–nor realistic or achievable), set a comfortable goal of not *gaining* any weight and/or losing 1 to 2 kilograms. Realistic goals encourage success by boosting confidence in your ability to make lifelong healthy changes.

A physically active lifestyle is the key to balancing caloric intake with caloric output for weight maintenance.

calories for weight maintenance. An increase in the intensity, frequency, and time or duration of your daily physical activities will have a significant impact on your total calorie expenditure and ability to manage your weight. Current recommendations are that at least 60 minutes of moderate-intensity physical activity each day are required for weight management. Further, emphasis should be placed on cardiorespiratory and strength-related physical activities.

Physical activity makes a greater contribution to EMR when large muscle groups are used. The energy spent on physical activity includes the energy used to move the body's muscles—the muscles of the arms, back, abdomen, legs, and so on—and the extra energy required to increase heartbeat, respiration rate, blood pressure, body cooling, etc. The number of calories expended depends on three factors:

1. the amount of muscle mass being moved
2. the amount of weight being moved
3. the amount of time the activity takes

For example, an activity involving the arms and the legs burns more calories than one involving only the legs, an activity performed by a heavy person burns more calories than one performed by a lighter person, and an activity performed for 40 minutes requires twice as much energy as the same activity performed for 20 minutes. Thus, persons who are obese who walk 1 kilometre burn more calories than people who are slim and walk the same distance. It may also take a person who is obese longer to walk a specified distance, which means they burn energy for a longer time and therefore expend more overall calories than walkers who are thin and complete the walk in a shorter time.

Determining the Caloric Output of Your Physical Activity

The number of calories required to do a physical activity depends on a number of factors, one of which is how much you weigh. The more you weigh, the greater the caloric cost of the physical activity. In other words, you use more calories when you weigh more. Another factor is how intensely—or how hard—you participate in that physical activity. More intense physical activities require more energy to perform. The third factor that influences the number of calories required to do a particular physical activity is time. Obviously, the longer you do the physical activity, the more energy it requires. The latter two factors, intensity of activity and length of time, interact. Most often, more intense physical activities (for instance, running) can only be done for shorter periods of time, and less intense physical activities (for instance, walking) can be done for longer periods of time.

The following physical activities each require about 150 calories of energy to perform (with an average body weight of around 68 kilograms):

- gardening for 30 to 45 minutes
- raking leaves for 30 minutes
- shovelling snow for 15 minutes
- walking 3 kilometres in approximately 30 minutes
- pushing a stroller when walking for 30 minutes
- running 2.25 kilometres in 15 minutes
- climbing the stairs for 15 minutes
- playing touch football for 30 to 45 minutes
- playing basketball (that is, shooting baskets) for 30 minutes
- playing basketball (that is, a game) for 15 to 20 minutes
- playing wheelchair basketball for 20 minutes

Resting metabolic rate (RMR): The energy expenditure of the body while at rest, which includes basal metabolic rate (the metabolic rate of the body at complete rest) plus the energy required by sedentary activities, such as food digestion, sitting, studying, or standing.

Basal metabolic rate (BMR): The energy expenditure of the body under resting conditions at normal room temperature.

Exercise metabolic rate (EMR): The energy expenditure of physical activity.

- bicycling 7.5 kilometres in 30 minutes
- dancing (social) for 30 minutes
- swimming laps for 20 minutes
- water fitness classes for 30 minutes
- jumping rope for 30 minutes

Another way to determine the number of calories required by a particular physical activity is to use established energy costs for that physical activity, along with your body weight (in kilograms) and the time you engaged in that physical activity, to calculate your energy costs. This method takes into account the three factors that are involved in determining the energy costs of physical activity: body weight, intensity, and time.

Table 5b.5 provides a sample of the energy costs of selected physical activities per minute per kilogram. Thus, if you weigh 65 kilograms and go for a 30-minute run at a pace of 5 minutes per kilometre, you will use 362 calories (65 kg × 0.1856 cal/min/kg × 30 minutes = 362 calories). You would need to run for only 24 minutes at a pace of 3.7 minutes per kilometre to use the same approximate number of calories (that is, 65 kg × 0.2350 cal/min/kg × 24 minutes = 367 calories).

Is Dieting Healthy?

Most experts agree that the ultimate goal of a weight-loss program should be improved quality of life and lifetime weight maintenance. Weight goals should be set to reduce health risks and address medical problems and to help people improve their ability to perform daily tasks without undue stress and strain—rather than to achieve an "ideal" weight or shape. In addition, experts agree that weight-loss programs that promote qualitative rather than quantitative changes in food intake improve health and long-term weight maintenance and are more easily sustained than those that force people to severely restrict intake of calories or specific foods. But while the experts seem to agree on these points, many weight-loss programs fail to follow these basic premises. What happens to people who get caught up in "lose weight fast and furiously" campaigns? Researchers are increasingly concerned that:

- dieting to lose weight may be more harmful than helpful in promoting physiological health and psychological well-being
- because dieting only rarely produces successful long-term weight loss, the physiological and psychological stress, damage to self-esteem, and other emotional disturbances are without purpose
- dieting causes repeated cycles of weight loss and regain, changes in metabolic rates, increased risk for cardiovascular problems, and other conditions adverse to health
- dieting contributes to the development of eating disorders such as anorexia and bulimia nervosa, and compulsive eating or binge eating disorder

Most health authorities recommend that, rather than going on a diet, a person should adopt a lifetime approach to healthy eating, physical activity, and sedentary activities aimed at enhancing metabolic rates and maintaining muscle mass.

TABLE 5b.5
Energy Costs of Selected Physical Activities (min/kg)

Physical Activity	Time	Cal/min/kg
Walking (on a grassy surface)	10.5 min/km	0.0794
Cycling	4 min/km	0.0985
Cycling	3.1 min/km	0.1559
Swimming	55 min/km	0.1333
Running	3.7 min/km	0.2350
Running	5 min/km	0.1856

Source: Adapted from B. Getchell, *Physical Fitness: A Way of Life* (Benjamin Cummings, 1992).

what do you THINK?

Consider your approach to eating; Do you think about your food choices (including quantity) as part of your overall approach to being healthy in the long-term? Or do you make decisions related to short-term gain (that is, dieting)? How can you develop a lifetime approach to healthy eating?

Improving Your Eating Habits

Before you can change a given behaviour, you must first determine what causes and relates to that behaviour. Why do you suddenly find yourself at the refrigerator door eating? Why do you take a second and third helping of potatoes or dessert when you know that you have had enough to eat and your body does not need more? Our eating is influenced by a number of things including individual and environmental determinants. Individual determinants include our physiological state (that is, whether or not we are hungry), food preferences, nutritional knowledge, perceptions of healthy eating, and psychological factors. Environmental factors include the interpersonal environment created by our family and peers, the physical environment, which determines food accessibility and availability, the economic and social environment, and the cultural milieu surrounding food choices. Further, food policy has an overarching influence on the individual and environmental factors influencing our eating behaviours.

Many people discovered that one of the best ways of assessing their eating behaviours is to chart exactly when they feel like eating, where they are when they eat, the amount of time they spend eating, other activities they engage in while eating (watching television, reading, or something else), whether they eat alone or with others, what and how much they eat, and how they feel before they take their first bite. If you keep a detailed log each day for a week, you will discover useful clues about what in your environment or in your emotional makeup relates to your eating habits. Typically, these "triggers" centre on issues related to everyday living rather than on real hunger/need to eat. As you record this information, your reasons for eating will often become apparent. Many people discover that they eat compulsively when stressed or when they have problems in their relationships. For others, it is the smell of a particular food (for example, popcorn) or a routine (for example, eating while studying) that causes them to eat, rather than hunger itself.

Once you recognize the factors that relate to your eating, remove the triggers or substitute other activities so that you develop more sensible eating behaviours. Here are some examples (see also Skills for Behaviour Change):

1. When eating dinner, turn off all distractions, including the television, radio, and your computer.
2. Include physical activity in your coffee breaks.
3. Instead of gulping your food, chew slowly, putting your fork down between each bite.
4. Instead of eating by the clock, eat when you are hungry.
5. Eat frequently throughout the day—three smaller meals per day plus snacks—rather than loading up at one meal and skipping others.
6. If you find that you generally eat all that is on a plate, use smaller plates, or serve smaller portions. Serve your plate at the counter/stove rather than having pots/bowls on the table where you are eating.
7. If you find that you are continually seeking your favourite foods, buy them in smaller quantities, serve them in smaller portions, and store them in an inconvenient spot.
8. Eat breakfast every day.
9. Replace soft drinks with water.

what do you THINK?

Based on what you have read so far, what triggers your eating? Is it certain people? Places? Situations? What can you do to manage these triggers?

Selecting a Nutritional Plan

Once you discover what factors influence your eating, you will be on your way to successful weight maintenance. To be successful, however, you must plan for success.

Seek help from reputable sources in choosing a dietary plan that is easy to follow and includes adequate nutrients. Registered dietitians, holistic physicians (only holistic physicians have strong backgrounds in nutrition, which includes some MDs), health educators, exercise physiologists with nutritional backgrounds, and other health professionals can provide reliable information. Avoid quick weight-loss programs that promise miracle results. The majority of these programs are expensive, and most people regain the weight soon after completing them. Ask questions about the credentials of the adviser in any weight-loss program/centre, assess the nutrient value of the prescribed diet, verify that dietary guidelines are consistent with information from reliable dietary research, and analyze how suitable the dietary plan is for your tastes, budget, and lifestyle to avoid putting yourself in a risky, expensive, or unhealthy dietary situation. Any diet that requires radical behaviour changes or cannot be followed for a lifetime is doomed to fail. Dietary plans that do not ask you to sacrifice what you enjoy and that allow you to make choices are usually the most successful.

"Miracle" Diets

Fasting, starvation diets, and other forms of **very low-calorie diets (VLCDs)** are related to significant health risks. Typically, when you deprive your body of food for prolonged periods, it makes adjustments to save you from inevitable organ shutdown. First, it depletes its energy reserves to maintain its supply of glucose. One of the first reserves to which the body turns is lean protein tissue. When this occurs you lose weight rapidly because significant water is lost as well. Over time, the body begins to run out of liver tissue, heart muscle, blood, and so on, as these readily available substances are used to supply energy. Only after

Very-low-calorie diets (VLCDs): Diets with caloric value of 400 to 700 calories per day.

SKILLS FOR BEHAVIOUR CHANGE</HD>

General Tips for Managing Your Weight

PEARSON myhealthlab

WHEN EATING AT HOME

- Eat only in the kitchen or dining room. Keep food out of the living room, bedroom, and study spaces.
- Spread your caloric intake throughout the day by eating smaller meals four to five times a day (this enhances RMR).
- Use a smaller plate and fill it with low-calorie, nutrient-dense foods such as salad without dressing or with a small amount of dressing on the side, and pasta with a low-fat sauce.
- Take more time to eat; at least 20 minutes per meal is recommended. Chew your food carefully, setting your fork down between bites and enjoying the taste.
- Drink a glass of water before your meal.
- Drink a glass of water when you think you are hungry; you may actually be thirsty; hunger is often mistaken for thirst.
- Brush your teeth after eating to signify the end of your meal.
- Limit your purchases of high-calorie, high-fat, low-nutrient foods, even for guests or even on holidays.
- When having desserts, limit yourself to a small taste, or choose lower-calorie, lower-fat options.
- Get in tune with your true feelings of hunger. Eat when you are really hungry, not by the clock.
- Develop stress-management skills that do not involve eating.
- Get enough sleep; individuals with a "sleep debt" are at greater risk for obesity.
- Try not to allow yourself to get too hungry before eating.
- Limit the amount you eat immediately before going to bed.
- Put serving dishes on the counter or stove while you are eating. Leaving them on the table encourages second helpings even when you are no longer hungry.

WHEN EATING OUT

- Ask for it "your way." Request that the cheese be left off, the sauce cut in half, salad dressing on the side, and so on.
- Ask that entrées be broiled, steamed, baked, grilled, poached, or roasted, with only a small amount of fat used for the cooking process.
- When ordering omelettes, ask for a one- or two-egg-yolk version containing only the whites of the other eggs. Limit meat and cheese fillings. Choose vegetable fillings whenever possible.
- Reduce portion size. Order à la carte if possible, with a salad or fresh vegetable on the side.
- Limit how frequently you eat at an all-you-can-eat restaurant.
- Drink at least one glass of water before starting your meal. Try to relax while eating and make your mealtime last. Talk more, put your fork down more frequently, chew more, and generally slow down.
- Order fresh fruits and low- or no-fat yoghurts in place of heavy desserts.
- Frequent restaurants that offer low-fat, high-complex-carbohydrate meals.
- Choose water or low-fat milk as your beverage.

the readily available proteins from these sources are depleted will your body begin to use fat reserves. In this process, known as **ketosis**, the body adapts to prolonged fasting or carbohydrate deprivation by converting body fat to ketones, which can be used as fuel for some brain cells. About 10 days after the typical adult begins a complete fast, the body has used many of its energy stores and death may occur.

try it NOW!

Make healthy substitutions at meal time—a successful key to weight maintenance! The next time you make dinner, take a look at the portions on your plate. Vegetables and whole grains should take up most of the space; if not, substitute a portion of meat, pasta, or cheese for an equal portion of legumes, salad greens, or a favourite vegetable. This will reduce the calorie content of your meal without sacrificing quantity.

In very-low-calorie diets, powdered formulas are usually given to patients under medical supervision. These formulas range from 400 to 700 calories plus vitamin and mineral supplements. Although these diets may be beneficial for people who have failed at all conventional weight-loss methods and who face severe threats to their health complicated by their obesity, they should never be undertaken without close medical supervision. Problems associated with fasting, VLCDs, and other forms of severe calorie deprivation include blood sugar imbalances, cold intolerance, constipation, decreased BMR, dehydration, diarrhea, emotional problems, fatigue, headaches, heart irregularity, ketosis, kidney infections and failure, loss of lean body tissue, weakness, and weight gain due to the yo-yo effect and other problems.

Trying to Gain Weight

Although trying to lose weight poses a major challenge for many, there is a another group of people who, for a variety of metabolic, hereditary, psychological, and other reasons, cannot seem to gain weight no matter how hard they try. If you are one of these individuals, you must determine why you have difficulty in gaining weight—just like someone who has difficulty keeping his or her weight down. Once you have answered this question, there are several things you can do to help yourself:

- Monitor your physical activity. Keep a careful record of calories burned; perhaps you are not eating enough to compensate. In addition to your exercise, monitor your incidental movements (that is, active transportation, fidgeting behaviours, etc.). These contribute to caloric needs as well.
- Eat more. Eat more often. It is possible that you are not eating enough calories to support your body's needs. Eat more frequently, spend more time eating, and eat high-calorie, nutrient-dense foods first if you tend to fill up fast. Take time to shop and to cook, and eat slowly. Make your sandwiches with extra-thick slices of bread and add more filling such as peanut butter, cream cheese, or cheese. Eat second helpings whenever possible and eat high-calorie, nutrient-dense snacks during the day.
- Drink more of your calories; instead of water, choose milk or juice.
- Try to relax. Many people who are underweight also suffer from anxiety and the "hurry syndrome." Slow down and try to manage your reactions to stress.

RISK FACTORS FOR OBESITY

It would seem that the cause of obesity is quite simple: when you take in more calories than you burn, you gain weight—most often in the form of fat. If you do this frequently enough, you will become obese. If we know what the cause is, we should be able to offer a simple solution for prevention, right?

Wrong. Although the calorie balance equation (that is, if calories in equals calories out there is no weight gain) explanation of weight management is valid, it offers only two simple reasons for a person's weight gain: we eat too much and do too little. It does not include the many other sociocultural factors surrounding dietary intake and our physical activity behaviours that contribute to excessive food consumption or low levels of physical activity. It also fails to answer many other critical questions. If we know that eating too much will cause us to gain weight, why do we continue to eat so much? If we know we should be more physically active, why don't we simply get out there and "do it"? Is there a metabolic explanation for obesity? Why is there limited success for permanent weight loss from dieting?

✓• Heredity and Genetic Factors

Are some people born to be fat? Many factors influence why one person becomes obese and another remains thin; genes seem to interact with many of these factors. More than 250 gene markers have been identified as related to obesity in more than 400 studies.

Body Type and Genes

In some animal species, the shape and size of the individual's body is largely determined by the shape and size of its parents' bodies. Many scientists have explored the role of heredity in determining human body shapes or physiques. As early as 1940, Harvard psychologist William Sheldon analyzed weight problems in terms of somatotypes. A somatotype provides a classification of an individual's physique or body as a whole and is comprised of three components: endomorphy, mesomorphy, and ectomorphy. Endomorphy describes the relative fatness of the body, specifically referring to roundness and soft appearance. In Sheldon's work, individuals with a high endomorphic rating often had a large abdomen and typically reported a history of weight problems beginning in childhood. Mesomorphy refers to the relative muscularity of the body; individuals with a high mesomorphic rating have a tendency to gain weight later in life. Ectomorphy describes the relative linearity of the body, with individuals rating high in this component characterized as tall with slender frames and generally experiencing few difficulties with weight control.

Although somatotype may play a role in the development of obesity, most researchers contend that heredity plays a more subtle role. These researchers argue that obesity has a strong genetic determinant (it tends to run in families) and cite statistics suggesting that 40 percent of children with one obese parent and 80 percent of children with two obese parents are also likely to be obese. Studies of identical twins separated at birth and raised in different environments have provided some of the most compelling evidence to date that obesity may be genetically determined.

Ketosis: A condition in which the body adapts to prolonged fasting or carbohydrate deprivation by converting body fat to ketones, which can be used as fuel for some brain activity.

Whether raised in environments with fat or thin family members, twins with obese birth parents tended to be obese in later life. According to another study, identical twins separated and raised in different families who ate widely different diets still grew up to weigh about the same.

Obesity Genes?

Recent research points to the existence of a "fat gene." Rather than inheriting a particular body type that predisposes us to become overweight or obese, it may be that our genes predispose us toward certain satiety and feeding behaviours. This "I need to eat" gene may account for up to one-third of our risk for obesity. The most promising candidate is the GAD2 gene. For some individuals, a variation in this gene increases the production of a chemical that boosts appetite and signals a person to eat.

Another gene getting a lot of attention is an Ob gene (for obesity) which is believed to disrupt the body's "I've had enough to eat" signalling system and may prompt individuals to keep eating past the point of being comfortably full. Research on Pima Indians, a group with an estimated 75 percent obesity rate and 90 percent rate of overweight, points to an Ob gene that is a "thrifty gene." It is theorized that because their ancestors struggled through centuries of famine, during which the Ob gene prompted them to eat as much as possible when food was available and to conserve when not, their basal metabolic rates slowed, which allowed them to store precious fat. Survivors may have passed their genes on to their descendants, which may explain their lower metabolic rates and tendency toward obesity today.

Endocrine Influences: The Hungry Hormones

Over the years, many people attributed obesity to problems with their thyroid gland and resultant hormonal imbalances. They believed that an underactive thyroid impeded their ability to burn calories. Research indicates that less than 2 percent of the population that is obese can trace their weight and/or fat problems to their thyroid, or metabolic or hormonal imbalances. Researchers continue to investigate the influence of various hormones on a person's ability to attain and maintain weight loss, and control appetite and satiety or sense of fullness.

One such hormone that researchers suspect may play a role in our ability to maintain weight loss, based on its role in appetite stimulation, is ghrelin. Specifically, it was noted in a small group of people who were obese and lost weight over six months that their ghrelin levels—which are produced in the stomach—rose before every meal and fell drastically shortly after. Another hormone believed to be involved in the satiety signal from the brain, which tells us to stop eating because we are full, is leptin. Leptin and ghrelin are both believed to be influenced by lack of sleep. More specifically, fewer hours of sleep in standardized experimental sleeping conditions resulted in an increase in hunger accompanied by a decrease in leptin and an increase in ghrelin. Yet another hormone involved in slowing the passage of food through the intestines is called GLP-1. It is believed that GLP-1 may stimulate insulin production and be a key factor in preventing and controlling type 2 diabetes and obesity. It is further speculated that leptin and GLP-1 play complementary roles in weight control, where leptin regulates body weight and fat levels over the long term, calling on the fast-acting appetite suppressants GLP-1 when needed.

* Hunger, Appetite, and Satiety

Scientists distinguish between **hunger**, an inborn physiological response to nutritional needs, and **appetite**, a learned response to food tied to an emotional or psychological craving for food often unrelated to nutritional need. Obese people may be more likely than people at a healthy weight to satisfy their appetite and eat for reasons other than nutrition.

In some instances, the problem with overconsumption may be more related to **satiety** than to appetite or hunger. People generally feel satiated, or full, when they have satisfied their nutritional needs and their stomach signals "no more." For undetermined reasons, people who are obese may not feel full until much later than people who are at a healthy weight.

Theories abound concerning the mechanisms that regulate food intake. Some sources indicate that the hypothalamus (the part of the brain that regulates appetite) closely monitors levels of certain nutrients in the blood. When these levels begin to fall, the brain signals us to eat. In persons who are obese, it is possible that the monitoring system does not work properly and that the cues to eat are more frequent and intense than in people of a healthy weight.

Other sources indicate that people who are at a healthy weight may send more effective messages to the hypothalamus. This concept, known as **adaptive thermogenesis**, states that some people can consume lots of food without gaining weight because the appetite centre of their brains speeds up metabolic activity to compensate for the increased consumption. Still other studies indicate the possibility that specialized types of fat cells, called **brown fat cells**, may send signals to the brain, which controls the thermogenesis response.

Developmental Factors

Some people who are obese may have an excessive number of fat cells. **Hyperplasia**, which refers to an increase in the number of cells, normally occurs during specific periods of the growth process. The only periods during which fat cells normally increase in number is during infancy and the rapid growth period of puberty. However, fat cells can also increase in number when an individual is under chronic positive energy balance (that is, they continuously consume more calories than they burn) and their current fat cells are "full." Fat cells also have the ability to increase in size. This process is called **hypertrophy**, and can occur at any time in childhood, adolescence, and adulthood—if calorie intake exceeds calorie output. Thus, fat gain is tied to the number of fat cells in the body (during infancy and puberty) and the capacity of the fat cells to increase in size (childhood, adolescence, and adulthood).

An adult of average weight and fat levels has approximately 30 to 50 billion fat cells, an adult who is moderately obese has about 60 billion to 100 billion, and an adult who is extremely obese may have as many as 200 billion. The size of fat cells in a young adult of a healthy weight is about 80 to 100 micrometres (μm). (See Figure 5b.5.)

People who are obese and have a large number of fat cells may have difficulty attaining long-term fat loss because there may be a trigger released once they have substantially decreased the size of each fat cell, resulting in an increase in appetite.

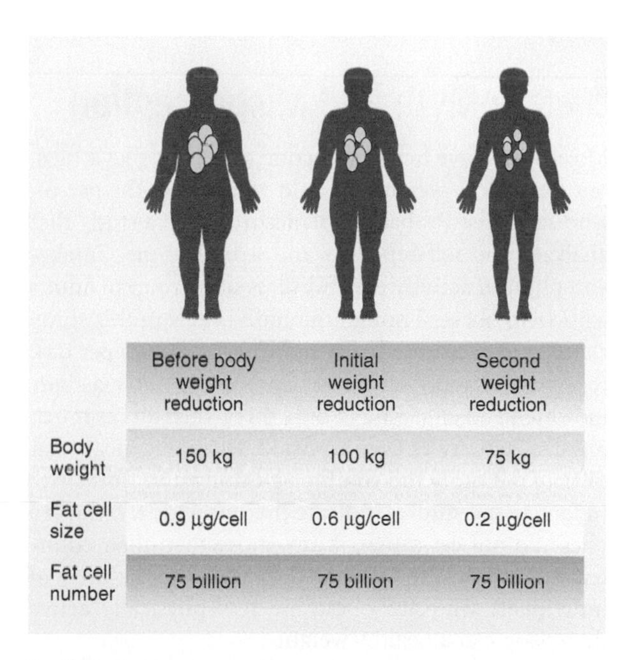

	Before body weight reduction	Initial weight reduction	Second weight reduction
Body weight	150 kg	100 kg	75 kg
Fat cell size	0.9 μg/cell	0.6 μg/cell	0.2 μg/cell
Fat cell number	75 billion	75 billion	75 billion

FIGURE 5b.5

The figure depicts one person at various stages of fat loss. Note that the number of fat cells remains constant but the cells' size decreases.

Metabolic Rates and Weight

Even at rest, our bodies need a certain amount of energy. As previously noted, the amount of energy the body requires at complete rest is called basal metabolic rate (BMR). In physically active individuals, about 60 to 70 percent of all the calories consumed support basal metabolism, which provides the energy (that is, calories) needed for bodily functions such as heartbeat, breathing, maintaining body temperature, and so on. So if you consume 2000 calories per day, between 1200 and 1400 of those calories are required for regular body maintenance. The remaining 600 to 800 calories supply the energy required for your physical activities. The key factor here is the amount of physical activity you do.

BMR fluctuates considerably. In general, the younger you are, the higher your BMR. BMR is greatest when we are younger partly because cells undergo rapid subdivision in young people, which requires a good deal of energy. Thus, BMR is highest during infancy, puberty, and pregnancy, when bodily changes are most rapid.

BMR is also influenced by body composition. Muscle tissue is highly active—even at rest—compared to fat tissue. In essence, the more muscle tissue you have, the greater your BMR. Thus, men usually have a higher BMR than women, because they have a greater muscle mass.

Age is another factor that affects BMR. After the age of 30, BMR slows down by about 1 to 2 percent per year. Therefore, people over 30 commonly find that they either have to eat less or do more physical activity to maintain their body weight. "Middle-aged spread," a reference to the tendency to gain weight or fat after the age of 30, is partly related to this change. A slower BMR, coupled with an inclination to be less physically

Hunger: An inborn physiological response to nutritional needs.

Appetite: A learned response tied to an emotional or psychological craving for food often unrelated to nutritional need.

Satiety: The feeling of fullness or satisfaction after eating.

Adaptive thermogenesis: Theoretical mechanism by which the brain regulates metabolic activity according to caloric intake.

Brown fat cells: Specialized type of fat cell that affects the ability to regulate fat metabolism.

Hyperplasia: An increase in the number of cells.

Hypertrophy: An increase in the size of cells

active, puts many middle-aged people's weight over healthy limits.

In addition, the body has a number of self-protective mechanisms that signal BMR to speed up or slow down. For example, when you have a fever, the energy needs of your cells increase, and this increased activity generates heat and increases your BMR. In starvation situations, the body protects itself by slowing the BMR to conserve energy. Thus, when people repeatedly resort to low-calorie diets, their bodies "reset" their BMRs to lower rates. **Yo-yo diets**, which involve people repeatedly gaining and losing weight, lower BMR in the process, and as a result are doomed to failure. When the dieters begin to eat again after the weight loss, their BMR is set lower, making it almost certain that they will regain the weight lost—and more. After repeated cycles of such dieting/regaining, these people find it increasingly hard to lose weight and increasingly easy to regain it, and so they become fatter. Besides an increase in fat, weight-cycling may also have a negative effect on an individual's risk for heart disease. Specifically, other health risks research indicated that middle-aged men who maintained a steady weight (even if overweight) had a lower risk of heart attack than men whose weight cycled in a yo-yo pattern. Furthermore, it was noted that smaller, maintained weight losses were more beneficial for reducing cardiovascular risk than larger, poorly maintained weight losses.

Related to metabolic rate is a highly controversial theory called the **setpoint theory**. It states that a person's body has a setpoint of weight at which it is programmed to be comfortable. If your setpoint is 70 kilograms, you will gain and lose weight fairly easily within a given range around that setpoint. Can a person change this predetermined setpoint? Proponents of this theory argue that it is possible to raise one's setpoint over time by continually gaining weight and failing to engage in regular physical activity. Conversely, reducing caloric intake and being physically active over a long period of time may slowly decrease one's setpoint.

Psychosocial Factors

The relationship of weight problems to deeply rooted emotional insecurities, needs, and wants remains uncertain. Food is often used inappropriately as a reward for good behaviour in childhood. As adults face various stresses in their lives, food is often also used as a comforting mechanism. Again, the research underlying this theory is controversial. What is certain is that in mainstream Canada, eating tends to be a focal point of people's lives—a major part of our socialization; a social ritual associated with companionship, celebration, and enjoyment.

Eating Cues

At least one major factor in our preoccupation with food is the pressure placed on us by the highly sophisticated, heavily advertised "eating" campaigns launched by the food industry. Although salads and other lower-fat, lower-calorie options are available at most, if not all, fast-food restaurants, we still have the gauntlet of starchy, meaty delights and tasty high-fat fries to choose from. Food-related messages permeate the media, particularly for children and youth. Compared to the foods recommended in Eating Well with Canada's Food Guide, most advertised foods are lower in nutrient density, fibre, and complex carbohydrates and higher in fat, sodium, simple carbohydrates, caffeine, and alcohol.

Increasingly, a large percentage of the foods we eat come from fast-food restaurants. We eat at fast-food restaurants for a number of reasons, including the relatively low cost and the perceived time saved. It should be kept in mind however that: (1) fast food is typically high in calories, fat, sodium, and simple carbohydrates; (2) it tends to all be eaten, even though portions are often much bigger than needed; and (3) it tends to be eaten quickly, so there is not enough time for the "I am full" signal to get to your mouth before the last bite of food is consumed. This is a particular problem for post-secondary students, who encounter fast-food restaurants on campus, in addition to the all-you-can-eat buffets at food hall, combined with a perceived time shortage to focus on a sit-down, healthy, family meal.

Dietary Myth and Misperception

Most of us have heard someone say "I eat like a bird, but I can't lose weight." Should you believe the person who says this? Probably not, according to a study that analyzed the self-reported and actual caloric intakes and physical activity expenditures of a group of adults who were obese. Though the individuals in this study claimed to consume fewer than 1200 calories per day, they were actually eating nearly twice as much as they indicated and engaging in only three-quarters as much physical activity as they reported. Does this mean that obesity is simply the result of gluttony and sloth? No. In fact, many studies indicate that individuals who are obese do not eat much, if any, more than their counterparts at a healthy weight. However, the majority of individuals who are obese are less physically active than people at a healthy weight.

Lifestyle

Of all the factors affecting obesity, perhaps the most critical one relates to lifestyle. About 50 percent of the

Canadian population aged 12 and over were classified as sedentary or inactive in their leisure time. One of the reasons for low levels of physical activity participation may relate to poor or inadequate experiences in physical education classes. Currently, physical education is optional in most high schools (although recently the provinces of Alberta and Nova Scotia have added a physical education requirement to graduate from high school) and is seldom offered daily in elementary and junior schools. Furthermore, many children and youth are transported to and from school on a daily basis. This may limit the desire for active transportation later in life as well as leading to the attitude that one must be transported to one's activities.

You probably know someone who seems to be able to eat a lot and does not appear to do any more physical activity than you, yet never seems to gain weight. It is hard to understand how this person maintains his or her weight. With few exceptions, if you were to follow this person around for a typical day and monitor their level and intensity of physical activity, you would discover the answer to your question. Although the person's day may not include scheduled exercise, it probably includes a high level of physical activity. Walking up a flight of stairs rather than taking the elevator, speeding up the pace while mowing the lawn, getting up to change the TV channel rather than using the remote, and doing housework vigorously all burn extra calories. A major cause of low physical activity levels is the abundance of labour-saving devices in the modern household. Using a blender instead of chopping vegetables or pushing remote-control buttons on the television and stereo equipment as well as on garage doors results in a reduced caloric expenditure compared to previous generations. The automobile is also a great convenience, but using it has significantly reduced our daily physical activity.

what do you THINK?

Based on the risk factors for obesity discussed thus far, which ones do you think pose the greatest risk for you? Why? What can you do about it? What will motivate you to do something about it now?

SOCIAL BIAS AGAINST THE OVERWEIGHT

Although much has been written about the potentially devastating physical consequences of being overweight and obese, the social consequences of excessive weight and/or fat are rarely discussed. Difficulty in finding a suitable job, workplace discrimination, and problems in most every aspect of their social life have been noted for people who are obese.

Research increasingly points to a nation of weight bias. **Weight bias** refers to negative attitudes that have a detrimental effect on interpersonal interactions and activities with individuals who are obese. The stigma against fat people may come in several forms, including verbal types of bias (such as ridicule, teasing, insults, stereotypes, derogatory names, or pejorative language), physical stigma (such as touching, grabbing, or other aggressive behaviours), or other barriers and obstacles for people who are obese, such as the inadequate size of the seats in movie theatres, stadiums, and airplanes. In an extreme form, this stigma results in subtle and overt forms of discrimination, such as the denial of a promotion or a raise.

Bias and stigmatization can lead to social isolation and a host of other problems for individuals who are obese. People who experience bias and stigma have higher rates of depression, poorer psychological adjustment, and higher rates of suicide. They may feel that they are "unlovable" and have difficulties in relationships. They also may have higher rates of disordered eating, issues with self-esteem, more difficulties in obtaining health care, and host of other problems.

what do you THINK?

Are you biased against people who are overweight or obese? When you see a person who is fat, do you make judgments about him or her? His or her level of physical activity? Dietary intake? Personal lifestyle? Would you date someone who was obese? Why or why not? Should certain jobs have weight or fat restrictions? Why or why not?

Yo-yo diet: Cycles in which people repeatedly gain and lose weight. This lowers their BMR, which favours the weight gain process.

Setpoint theory: A theory that suggests fat storage is determined by a thermostatic mechanism in the body that acts to maintain a specific amount of body fat.

Weight bias: Negative attitudes that have a harmful effect on a person's interpersonal interactions and activities with persons who are obese.

CHAPTER 5c

THERAPEUTIC, PERFORMANCE ENHANCEMENT AND RECREATIONAL DRUGS

Taken from *Health: The Basics,* Fifth Canadian Edition, by Rebecca J. Donatelle and Angela M. Thompson

DRUG DYNAMICS

Have you ever walked into a drugstore looking for some cough syrup or a pain reliever and become overwhelmed by the options available? Although there are literally tens of thousands of drugs at our disposal, choices among them should not be made lightly. All drugs are chemical substances that have the potential to alter the structure and function of our bodies. Quite simply, all drug use involves risks. You can minimize these risks by asking appropriate questions of health providers and by being a critical consumer of all drugs.

Drugs work because they physically resemble the chemicals produced naturally within the body (see Figure 5c.1). For example, many painkillers resemble the endorphins (literally "morphine within") manufactured in the body. Most bodily processes result from chemical reactions or changes in electrical charge. Because drugs possess an electrical charge and a chemical structure similar to chemicals that occur naturally in the body, they can affect physiological and psychological functions in many different ways.

A current explanation of drug actions is the receptor site theory, which states that drugs attach themselves to specific **receptor sites** in the body. These sites are specialized cells to which a drug is able to attach because of its size, shape, electrical charge, and chemical properties. Most drugs can attach at multiple receptor sites located throughout the body in such places as the heart and blood system, the lungs, liver, kidneys, brain, and gonads (testicles or ovaries). The physiology of drug activity and its effect on human behaviours is very complex.

try it NOW!

Achieve a drug-free and "natural high." Many people become addicted to drugs because of the positive, short-term effects they exert on mood. Right now, you can take a walk in a beautiful and sense-stimulating location, lose yourself in a favourite song, or visit an amusement park and ride the rollercoaster to satisfy a craving for an endorphin rush or simply to lift your spirits.

Compulsion: Obsessive preoccupation with a behaviour or substance and an overwhelming need to engage in it.

Loss of control: Inability to predict reliably whether any isolated involvement with the addictive substance or behaviour will be healthy or damaging.

Negative consequences: Difficulties such as physical damage, legal trouble, financial ruin, academic failure, relationship difficulties, family dissolution, and others as a result of continued engagement in a substance or behaviour.

Denial: Inability to perceive or accurately interpret the effects of drug use or engaging in a behaviour.

Relapse: The tendency to return to the addictive behaviours or drug after a period of abstinence.

Receptor sites: Specialized cells to which drugs can attach themselves.

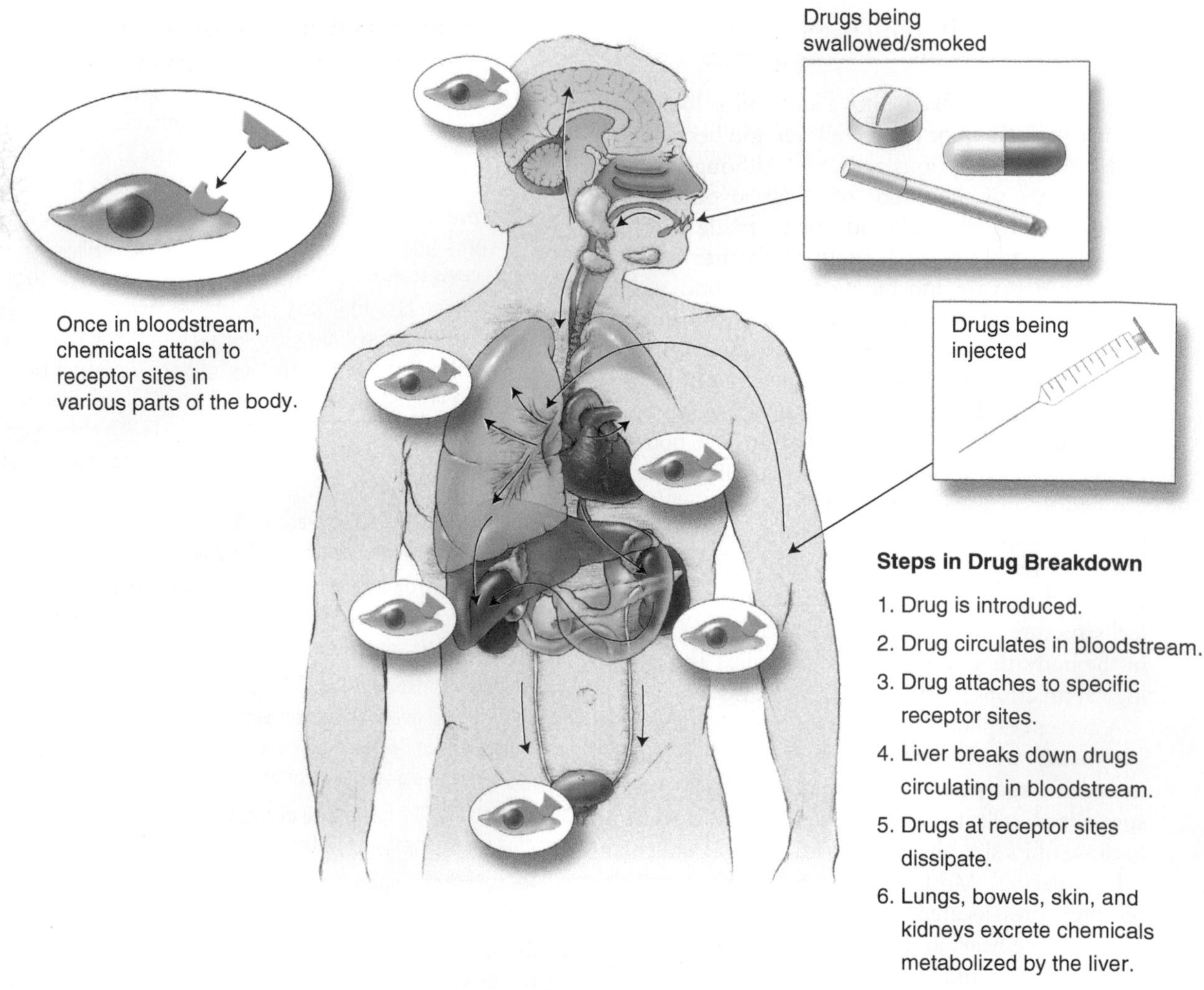

Drugs being swallowed/smoked
Drugs being injected
Once in bloodstream, chemicals attach to receptor sites in various parts of the body.
Steps in Drug Breakdown
1. Drug is introduced.
2. Drug circulates in bloodstream.
3. Drug attaches to specific receptor sites.
4. Liver breaks down drugs circulating in bloodstream.
5. Drugs at receptor sites dissipate.
6. Lungs, bowels, skin, and kidneys excrete chemicals metabolized by the liver.

FIGURE 5c.1
How the Body Metabolizes Drugs

TYPES OF DRUGS

Drugs are divided into six categories: prescription drugs, recreational drugs, over-the-counter (OTC) drugs, herbal preparations, illicit drugs, and commercial drugs. Each category includes drugs that stimulate the body, depress body functions, produce hallucinations, or have the potential to alter a person's mood or behaviours (that is, **psychoactive drugs**).

- **Prescription drugs** can be obtained only with a written prescription from a licensed physician. In 2005 the total expenditure in Canada on drugs (including prescription and non-prescription drugs) was $23.3 billion and is forecasted to reach 26.9 billion in 2007. Prescribed drug expenditure is forecasted to increase to $20.9 billion in 2006 and to $22.5 billion in 2007, accounting for 83.3 and 83.6 percent, respectively, of total drug expenditure in Canada.
- **Recreational drugs** belong to a vague category, with boundaries dependent upon how recreation is defined. Generally, these drugs contain chemicals that people use to help them relax or socialize. These drugs are legal even though they are psychoactive. Alcohol, tobacco, and caffeine are included in this category.
- **Over-the-counter (OTC) drugs** can be purchased without a physician's prescription. Expenditures specifically on OTC products (which are not usually covered by health care) were forecasted to reach $4.4 billion in 2006 and $4.6 billion in 2007.
- **Herbal preparations** form another vague category that includes approximately 750 substances such as herbal teas and other products of botanical origin believed to have medicinal properties.
- **Illicit (illegal) drugs** are the most notorious substances. Although laws governing their use, possession, cultivation, manufacture, and sale differ from

country to country, illicit drugs are generally recognized as harmful. These drugs are psychoactive.

- **Commercial preparations** are the most universally used yet least commonly recognized as products with a drug action. More than 1000 of these substances exist, including seemingly benign items such as perfumes, cosmetics, household cleansers, paints, glues, inks, dyes, gardening chemicals, pesticides, and industrial by-products.

Routes of Administration of Drugs

Route of administration refers to the way in which a drug is taken into the body. Common routes include oral ingestion, injection, inhalation, inunction, and suppository.

Oral ingestion is the most common method for taking drugs and includes tablets, capsules, and liquids that we swallow. Oral ingestion generally results in relatively slow absorption because the drug must pass through the stomach, where it is acted on by digestive juices, and then move on to the small intestine before it enters the bloodstream. Alcohol is the one exception to this rule since the majority of it is absorbed into the bloodstream without digestion.

Many oral preparations are coated to keep them from being dissolved by corrosive stomach acids before they reach the intestine and to protect the stomach lining from irritation. If your stomach contains food, absorption is slower than if your stomach is empty. Some drugs should not be taken with certain foods because they inhibit the drug's action. Others must be taken with food to prevent stomach irritation.

Injection, another common method of taking a drug, involves the use of a hypodermic syringe. This method usually results in rapid absorption, depending on the type of injection. **Intravenous injection**, or injection directly into a vein, puts the drug in its most concentrated form directly into the bloodstream. Effects will be felt within three minutes, making this route extremely effective, particularly in medical emergencies. However, there is risk of serious or even fatal reactions as a result of this effective and efficient administration of a drug. When illicit drugs are injected, the risk of overdose is particularly high. In addition, some serious diseases, such as hepatitis and HIV infection, can be transmitted in this way. For this reason, intravenous injection is also one of the most dangerous routes of administration. **Intramuscular injection** results in much slower absorption of the drug than intravenous injection. This type of injection places the hypodermic needle into muscular tissue, usually in the buttocks or in the triceps on the back of the upper arm. Normally used to administer antibiotics and vaccinations, this route of administration ensures a slow and consistent dispersion of the drug into the body tissues. **Subcutaneous injection** puts the drug into the layer of fat directly beneath the skin. Its common medical uses are for administration of local anesthetics and for insulin replacement therapy. A drug injected subcutaneously will circulate even more slowly than an intramuscularly injected drug because it takes longer to be absorbed into the bloodstream.

Inhalation refers to the ingestion of drugs through the nostrils. This method transfers the drug rapidly into the bloodstream through the alveoli (air sacs) in the lungs. Some examples of inhalation include nasal sprays, cocaine snorting, and the inhalation of aerosol sprays, gases, or fumes from solvents. The drug effects are usually felt immediately after inhalation and do not last long because only small amounts can be absorbed and metabolized in the lungs.

Inunction introduces drugs into the body through the skin. Common examples include the small adhesive patches used to alleviate motion sickness or nicotine patches used to assist individuals when they stop smoking. These patches slowly release their chemicals for a consistent dispersal.

Psychoactive drugs: Drugs that have the potential to alter mood or behaviours.

Prescription drugs: Drugs that can be obtained only with a written prescription from a licensed physician.

Recreational drugs: Legal drugs that people use to relax or socialize.

Over-the-counter (OTC) drugs: Drugs that can be purchased without a physician's prescription.

Herbal preparations: Substances of plant origin believed to have medicinal properties.

Illicit drugs: Drugs whose use, possession, cultivation, manufacture, and/or sale are illegal.

Commercial preparations: Commonly used chemical substances with a drug action, such as cosmetics, household cleaning products, and industrial by-products.

Route of administration: The manner in which a drug is taken into the body.

Oral ingestion: Intake of drugs through the mouth.

Injection: The introduction of drugs into the body via a hypodermic needle.

Intravenous injection: The introduction of drugs directly into a vein.

Intramuscular injection: The introduction of drugs into muscles.

Subcutaneous injection: The introduction of drugs into the layer of fat directly beneath the skin.

Inhalation: The introduction of drugs through the nostrils.

Inunction: The introduction of drugs through the skin.

Whenever you take more than one drug at a time, you should consider how they will interact. For example, women who take oral contraceptives should strictly follow the dosage instructions and be aware that medicines such as penicillin may alter the contraceptive's effectiveness. Asking a pharmacist is a good way to learn about drug interactions.

Suppositories are drugs mixed with a waxy medium that are designed to melt at body temperature. Most suppositories are inserted into the anus past the rectal sphincter muscles. As the wax melts, the drug is released and absorbed through the rectal walls into the bloodstream. Since there are many blood vessels here, the effects of the drug are usually felt within 15 minutes. Other suppositories are inserted in the vagina. These suppositories often involve antifungal agents that treat problems in the vagina itself as opposed to drugs meant to travel in the bloodstream.

DRUG INTERACTIONS

Most people are aware that sharing medications, using outdated prescriptions, taking higher doses than recommended, or using drugs as a substitute for dealing with personal problems may result in serious health consequences. However, many are not aware of the risks of taking several drugs simultaneously. The most dangerous interactions are synergism, antagonism, inhibition, and intolerance. Other negative interactions may occur between drugs and nutrients when consumed together.

Synergism, also known as potentiation, is an interaction of two or more drugs in which the effects of the individual drugs are multiplied beyond what is normally expected. Synergism can be expressed mathematically as $2 + 2 = 10$. A synergistic interaction is most likely to occur when central nervous system depressants such as alcohol, opiates (morphine, heroin), antihistamines (cold remedies), sedative hypnotics (Quaaludes), minor tranquillizers (Valium, Librium, and Xanax), and barbiturates are combined. The worst possible combination is alcohol and barbiturates (sleeping preparations such as Seconal and phenobarbital) because the combination leads to a slowdown of the brain centres that normally control vital functions. Respiration, heart rate, and blood pressure can drop to the point of inducing coma or death.

Prescription drugs carry special labels warning the user of potential drug interactions. Many OTC preparations carry similar warning labels. Because the dangers associated with synergism are so great, you should always check for possible drug interactions before using a prescribed or OTC drug. You should also consider synergistic actions when consuming recreational drugs with or without prescription and/or OTC drugs. Pharmacists, physicians, drug information centres, or community drug education centres can answer your questions. Even if one of the drugs in question is an illegal substance, you should still try to determine the dangers involved in combining it with other drugs. Health-care professionals are legally bound to maintain confidentiality even when they know that a client is using illegal substances. The Building Communication Skills box suggests questions you should ask before taking any prescription or OTC drug. These can be adapted to include recreational and illegal drugs.

what do you THINK?

What types of drugs do you typically use? How do you usually take them? Are you aware of the risks and benefits of their administration?

BUILDING COMMUNICATION SKILLS

Asking the Right Questions

At one time or another you will use prescription or OTC drugs to restore or maintain your health. How can you be certain that you need a medication in the first place, that you are taking the right medication for you, and that your medication is not robbing you of vital nutrients or being rendered ineffective by other drugs you are taking or foods you are ingesting? Only by asking the right questions of the right people can you be sure. Listed below are questions to pose to your physician, your pharmacist, or yourself before you take any drug.

1. What is your diagnosis?
2. Is your physician or pharmacist aware of all the other drugs you take, including prescription drugs (don't forget, birth control pills are drugs), OTCs, recreational drugs, and others?
3. Do you know the name of the medication you are taking? Is it the chemical name, a generic name, or a brand name?
4. Are you certain of how often you should take the medication, for how long you should take it, and in what dosage?
5. Do you know when your medication should be taken in relation to food intake?
6. Do you know if you can drink alcohol while on your medication?
7. What are the known side effects of the medication? What should you do if you experience any of the side effects?
8. Can you stop taking your medication when you start feeling better, or do you continue to take the drug until the prescription is finished?
9. Do you know what you should do if you forget to take your medication at the scheduled time?
10. Do you know what signs and symptoms signal that you are allergic to the medication?
11. Do you know how and where to store your medication?
12. Are there any drug–nutrient interactions that you should be aware of?
13. Are there any potential drug interactions that you should be aware of?
14. Are there any adverse consequences of long-term use of the medication?

Antagonism, although not usually as serious as synergism, can produce unwanted and unpleasant effects. In an antagonistic reaction, one drug blocks the action of the other at the receptor site. The "blocking" drug occupies the receptor site, preventing the second drug from attaching, and this alters its absorption and action.

Inhibition is a type of interaction in which the effects of one drug are eliminated or reduced by the presence of another drug, again with the interaction occurring at the receptor site. A common inhibitory reaction occurs between antacid tablets and Aspirin. Antacids inhibit the absorption of Aspirin, resulting in a less effective pain reliever. Other inhibitory reactions occur between alcohol and contraceptive pills and between antibiotics and contraceptive pills. Specifically, alcohol and antibiotics diminish the effectiveness of birth control pills in some women.

Intolerance occurs when drugs combine in the body, resulting in extremely uncomfortable reactions. The drug Antabuse, used to help individuals addicted to alcohol to give it up, works using this type of interaction. It binds liver enzymes (the chemicals the liver produces to break down alcohol), making it impossible for the body to metabolize alcohol. As a result, the user of Antabuse who drinks alcohol experiences nausea, vomiting, and, occasionally, fever.

Cross-tolerance occurs when a person develops a physiological tolerance to one drug and, as a result, a similar tolerance to other drugs with similar effects. For example, cross-tolerance can develop between alcohol and barbiturates, two depressant drugs.

PRESCRIPTION DRUGS

Even though prescription drugs are administered under medical supervision, the critical consumer should still take precautions. Complications and

Suppositories: Mixtures of drugs and a waxy medium designed to melt at body temperature; usually inserted into the anus or vagina.

Synergism: An interaction of two or more drugs in which the effects of the individual drugs are magnified beyond what is expected of their individual contribution.

Antagonism: A type of interaction in which one drug blocks the action of another at the receptor site.

Inhibition: A type of interaction in which the effects of one drug are eliminated or reduced by the presence of another drug at the receptor site.

Intolerance: A type of interaction in which two or more drugs taken together produce extremely uncomfortable reactions.

Cross-tolerance: The development of a tolerance to one drug that carries over to another similar drug.

serious negative health consequences arising from the use of prescription drugs are common. Responsible decision making about prescription drug use requires the consumer to acquire basic drug knowledge.

Types of Prescription Drugs

Antibiotics are drugs used to fight bacterial infection. Bacterial infections continue to be among the most common serious diseases in the world, with the vast majority cured by antibiotics. There are almost 100 different antibiotics available and dispensed by intramuscular injection or in tablet or capsule form. Some, called broad-spectrum antibiotics, are designed to control diseases caused by a number of bacterial species. These medications may also kill off helpful bacteria in the body, thus triggering secondary infections. For example, some vaginal infections are related to long-term use of antibiotics. Further, it is believed that the misuse of antibiotics has led to an increase in drug-resistant bacteria.

Sedatives are central nervous system depressants that induce sleep and relieve anxiety. Used heavily in the 1950s and 1960s in the form of phenobarbital or Seconal, they gradually fell out of favour because of the risks involved, including a high potential for addiction. Detoxification can be life-threatening and must be medically supervised.

> **what do you THINK?**
> What is the difference between drug use, misuse, and abuse? Give examples of each. Are drug abuse and addiction the same thing? Why or why not? Is it possible to use illicit drugs without becoming addicted to them?

Tranquillizers are another form of central nervous system depressant. They are classified either as major or minor tranquillizers. The most powerful tranquillizers are used in the treatment of major psychiatric illnesses. When used appropriately, these strong sedatives are capable of reducing violent aggressiveness and self-destructive impulses. About 5 percent of Canadians aged 15 and older report using sleeping pills, and 5 percent report using tranquillizers. Women and older Canadians are more likely to report using these medications.

Antidepressants are powerful substances used to treat clinically diagnosed cases of depression. These drugs inhibit the release of certain neurotransmitters in the brain, thereby moderating the user's mood.

Amphetamines are stimulants prescribed less commonly now than in the past. Like other psychoactive drugs, they can be purchased legally and illegally. Amphetamines suppress appetite and elevate respiration, blood pressure, and pulse rate. Tolerance to these powerful stimulants develops rapidly, and the user trying to cut down or quit may experience unpleasant **rebound effects**. These severe withdrawal symptoms, peculiar to stimulants, include depression, irritability, violent behaviours, headaches, nausea, and deep fatigue.

Use of Generic Drugs

Generic drugs are sold under a chemical name rather than a brand name. These alternatives to more expensive brand-name drugs contain the same active ingredients. There is, however, some controversy about the effectiveness of some generic drugs. Differences in minor ingredients can affect the way the drug is absorbed, which may cause discomfort or an allergic reaction in some users. If you experience any allergic reactions to a prescribed generic drug, tell your pharmacist or doctor, who can recommend an alternative drug. A list of medicines that can be interchanged has been approved in Canada. If your doctor or pharmacist fails to offer you the option of using a generic drug, you should ask if such a substitute exists and if it would be safe for you to use it.

OVER-THE-COUNTER (OTC) DRUGS

Over-the-counter (OTC) drugs are non-prescription drugs used in self-diagnosis and self-medication. Canadians spend many millions yearly on OTC preparations for relief of everything from runny noses to ingrown toenails. Most OTC drugs are manufactured from a basic group of 1000 chemicals. Combinations of as few as 2 and as many as 10 of these chemicals result in the many different OTC drugs available today. Perhaps because of the common belief that OTC products are safe and effective, indiscriminate use, misuse, and abuse often occurs. OTC drugs, like any other drugs, have the potential to produce dependency, tolerance, and addiction, as well as adverse toxic reactions.

Types of OTC Drugs

Analgesics are pain relievers. The earliest pain relievers were made of derivatives manufactured from the opium poppy. Today, pain relievers ranging from Aspirin to morphine are among the most commonly

HEALTH IN THE MEDIA

OxyContin

OxyContin is the trade name for the long-lasting form of the prescription opioid (pain reliever) oxycodone. Oxycodone is also an ingredient in Percocet and Percodan. OxyContin contains much higher doses, at 10 to 80 mg. OxyContin is specially formulated for slow release and as such is intended to provide relief from moderate to severe pain for up to 12 hours. Individuals prescribed OxyContin swallow one tablet twice daily. Although most users take this medication appropriately, they should be monitored closely because of their high risk of dependency.

How is OxyContin abused? OxyContin is formulated to be swallowed whole to provide the slow release into the blood stream; however, when it is chewed or crushed, the slow release properties are destroyed. Thus, when users chew or crush tablets the oxycodone effects occur very rapidly causing a high or euphoria which is described as similar to the high from heroin.

Oxycodone is a potent opioid. When large amounts of oxycodone are released into the body all at once (whether chewed, snorted, or injected), there is a high risk of overdose and death similar to a heroin overdose. Symptoms of overdose include laboured or slow breathing, extreme somnolence progressing to coma, cardiac arrest, and death.

OxyContin users who inject the drug have the additional risks associated with sharing needles (that is, hepatitis, HIV).

Addiction is also a problem, with the user requiring larger and larger doses to achieve the desired effect because tolerance quickly develops. Eventually the drug is needed to simply prevent feeling sick. Withdrawal symptoms include muscle aches, nausea, diarrhea, loss of appetite, restlessness, insomnia, runny nose, teary eyes, and sweating.

Source: Centre for Addiction and Mental Health, "What Is OxyContin," 2004. Retrieved March 2, 2006, from www.camh.net/About_Addiction_Mental_Health/Drug_and_Addiction_Information/oxycontin.

used drugs. In fact, most Canadians when surveyed said they had taken pain relievers in the past month. Although pain relievers come in several forms, the most common are Aspirin, acetaminophen (Tylenol, Pamprin, Pandol), ibuprofen (Advil, Motrin, Nuprin), and ibuprofen-like drugs such as naproxen sodium (Aleve, Anaprox) and ketoprofen (Orudis).

Most pain relievers work at the receptor sites by interrupting pain signals. Some are categorized as non-steroidal anti-inflammatory drugs (NSAIDS), also called **prostaglandin inhibitors**. Prostaglandins are chemicals that resemble hormones and are released by the body in response to pain. Scientists believe that the additional pain caused by the release of prostaglandins signals the body to begin the healing process. Prostaglandin inhibitors restrain the release of prostaglandins, thereby reducing the pain. Common NSAIDS include ibuprofen, naproxen sodium, and Aspirin.

Acetylsalicylic acid (ASA), commonly known as Aspirin, relieves pain by inhibiting the body's production of prostaglandins. It brings down fever by increasing the flow of blood to the skin's surface, which causes sweating and therefore cooling of the body. ASA is also commonly used to reduce the inflammation and swelling of arthritis. Furthermore, ASA's anticoagulant (interference with blood clotting) effects make it a useful daily medication for reducing the risk of heart attacks.

Acetaminophen is the active ingredient found in Tylenol and related medications. Like ASA, acetaminophen is an effective analgesic and antipyretic (fever-reducing) drug. It does not, however, provide relief from inflamed or swollen joints. The side effects associated with acetaminophen are generally minimal, though overdose can cause liver damage.

Most analgesics have side effects, the most common of which is drowsiness due to the depression of the central nervous system. Label warnings are important to read. Some warnings caution specifically against

Antibiotics: Prescription drugs designed to fight bacterial infection.

Sedatives: Central nervous system depressants that induce sleep and relieve anxiety.

Tranquillizers: Drugs taken to relax the body and relieve anxiety.

Antidepressants: Drugs used to treat clinically diagnosed depression.

Amphetamines: Drugs that suppress appetite and increase breathing rate, blood pressure, and heart rate.

Rebound effects: Severe withdrawal effects, including depression, nausea, and violent behaviours.

Generic drugs: Drugs marketed by their chemical name rather than a brand name.

Analgesics: Pain relievers.

Prostaglandin inhibitors: Drugs that inhibit the production and release of prostaglandins (released by the body in response to pain).

driving or operating heavy machinery when using analgesics, and most state they should not be taken with alcohol. Specific to ASA, possible side effects include allergic reactions, ringing in the ears, stomach bleeding, and ulcers. Since research has linked ASA to the potentially fatal condition Reye's syndrome, children, teenagers, and young adults (up to age 25) who are at risk for developing this syndrome are recommended to use an alternative analgesic.

Cold, Cough, Allergy, and Asthma Relievers

These substances are popular OTC drugs intended to provide relief of the symptoms of coughs, colds, allergy, and asthma that affect millions of sufferers. The operative word in their titles is **reliever**. Most of these drugs are designed to alleviate or reduce some or all of the discomforting symptoms associated with upper-respiratory-tract maladies. Unfortunately, no drug exists to actually cure these conditions. The drugs available provide temporary relief until the sufferer's immune system prevails. Aspirin or acetaminophen are often included in cold preparations. The basic types of OTC cold, cough, and allergy relievers are

- Expectorants. These drugs are formulated to loosen phlegm, allowing the user to cough and clear congested respiratory passages.
- Antitussives. These drugs are designed to calm or curtail the cough reflex. They are most effective when the cough is "dry," and does not produce phlegm (for which an expectorant is required).
- Antihistamines. These drugs are central nervous system depressants that dry runny noses, clear postnasal drip, clear sinus congestion, and reduce tears.
- Decongestants. These drugs are designed to reduce nasal stuffiness due to colds.
- Anticholinergics. These drugs are often added to cold preparations to reduce nasal secretions and tears.

It is important to read the labels of cough, cold, allergy, and asthma relievers for a number of reasons. First, some cold compounds contain alcohol in concentrations that may exceed 40 percent, while others contain a lot of sugar. Equally important to consider are the various drug ingredients included and the potential interactions as a result. In fact, many cough and cold medications contain expectorants and antitussives, which means conflicting actions could be caused in the body (that is, phlegm loosened to be coughed and cleared combined with a curtailed or reduced cough reflex).

Stimulants

Non-prescription stimulants are sometimes used by students in college or university in the last minute panic to complete assignments or in "all-nighter" study sessions. The active ingredient in most OTC stimulants is caffeine. Although caffeine heightens wakefulness, increases alertness, and relieves fatigue, it also can result in increased nervousness, irritability, anxiety, and involuntary muscle twitches.

Sleeping Aids and Relaxants

These drugs are often used to induce the drowsy feelings that precede sleep. The principal ingredient is an antihistamine called pyrilamine maleate. Chronic reliance on sleeping aids may lead to addiction.

Dieting Aids

Some people use **laxatives** or **diuretics** ("water pills") to achieve weight loss. Since laxatives were designed to relieve constipation, their use to reduce body weight is considered drug misuse. There are health risks for both laxatives and diuretics. Frequent use of laxatives disrupts the body's natural elimination process and may result in constipation or even obstipation (inability to have a bowel movement). In addition to being inefficient in producing weight loss, laxatives deplete the body of needed fluids, salts, and minerals. Further, the user gains the lost weight back upon drinking fluids, and may have created dangerous chemical imbalances with the elimination of potassium and sodium, which have important roles in maintaining electrolyte balance. Depletion of these vital minerals may cause weakness, dizziness, fatigue, and sometimes death.

ILLICIT DRUGS

Illicit drug use is a problem in our society, and though we may not be users ourselves, we are bound to be influenced by them in one way or another. It is important to understand how these drugs work and why people use them. In this section, we focus our attention on illicit drugs—drugs that are illegal to possess, produce, or sell.

On June 19, 1996, the Senate passed Bill C-8, the Controlled Drugs and Substances Act. The Act came into force on May 14, 1997. It replaced Canada's main laws on illicit drugs—the Narcotic Control Act and parts of the Food and Drugs Act. The Controlled Drugs and Substances Act significantly expanded the reach of Canada's drug laws and continued Canada's heavy reliance on a failed policy of criminal prohibition.

Illicit drug users come from all walks of life. Most illicit drug use occurs in places other than dilapidated crack houses, and few users fit the stereotype of the crazed junkie. The reasons we have for using drugs vary from one situation to another and from one person to another. Age, sex, genetic background, culture, education, physiology, personality, life experiences, and expectations are factors that play a role in a person's choice to use illicit drugs.

Health Canada and the Canadian Executive Council on Addictions sponsored the Canadian Addiction Survey 2004 (CAS), which included a random sample of almost 14 000 Canadians aged 15 or older interviewed by telephone. In this survey, 39.2 percent of Canadian women reported use of marijuana (cannabis) in their lifetime, with 10.2 percent indicating use in the past year. Lifetime use of marijuana was 50.1 percent for men and past-year use 18.2 percent. Typical age of initiation was 17 years for both men and women. Illicit drug use varies with age, province, marital status, education and income. Women report a 12.2 percent lifetime use of illicit drugs, while men report a 21.1 percent lifetime use. In 2002, between 1455 and 1695 deaths in Canada were attributed to illicit drugs. Acute care hospital days were estimated to be 318 000 to 352 000.

It is estimated that 185 million people worldwide—or 4.3 percent of the population aged 15 and older—used illicit drugs in the late 1990s. Globally, 0.4 percent of deaths and 0.8 percent of "disability adjusted life years" (that is, the time a person lives with a physical or mental disability) were attributed to illicit drug use. Further, the World Health Organization suggested that "illicit drugs account for the highest proportion of disease burden among low mortality, industrialized countries in the Americas, Eastern Mediterranean, and European regions [and that the] economic reliance on the drug trade, and drug dependence leaves many individuals open to exploitation by criminals and criminal organizations; threatening the health of men, women and children, the rule of law, and ultimately, the vitality and strength of all our communities."

Why do Canadians choose to use illicit drugs? There is no clear answer. Economic despair, issues related to the family or community, a general sense of hopelessness, or a need to relieve boredom may be powerful engines leading to use. These factors, combined with increased availability and diversity of drugs, attitudes and beliefs that illicit drug use is common, and potentially liberal parental attitudes may explain the use of illicit drugs for some.

Social policy also affects drug use, although its effects are extremely hard to evaluate. However, illicit drug use declined significantly during the first five years of Canada's Drug Strategy, when the focus was on the general public. It started rising again during Phase II, when the focus shifted to street youth and high-risk groups. The resurgence of drug use we currently witness is led largely by mainstream youth. Ultimately, we must aim our prevention messages at all youth. According to the Canadian Centre on Substance Abuse, all young people—dropouts and A+ students alike—are vulnerable to drug use and should be viewed as an at-risk population.

Anti-drug programs have been developed to deal with the problems of illegal drug use. The major drawback of most of these programs is their failure to take a multi-dimensional approach. The tendency has been to focus on only one aspect of drug use rather than the many interrelated factors that contribute to the problem. For example, many programs consider the drugs themselves the culprits. Others oversimplify the drug use by exhorting potential users to "just say no," ignoring the fact that drugs are an integral part of many people's social or cultural lives. The pressures to take drugs are often tremendous, and the reasons for using them complex.

People who develop drug problems usually think they can control their use when they start. Initially, their drug use is viewed as a fun and controllable pastime. Peer influence is a strong motivator for drug use, especially among adolescents. Typically, teens and young adults believe that drug use in others is much greater than what it really is. Some people use drugs to cope with feelings of worthlessness and despair, others to battle depression and anxiety. Some view drugs as the quick answer to life's difficulties. Since the majority of illegal drugs produce physiological and psychological dependence, the idea that a person can use these substances regularly without becoming addicted is foolish. To find out if you are controlled by drugs or by a drug user, complete the questionnaires in the Rate Yourself box.

what do you THINK?

Do you think you can control your use of drugs? How do you know? Are the current laws in Canada effective at controlling illicit drug use? Why or why not?

Laxatives: Drugs used to soften stool and relieve constipation.

Diuretics: Drugs that increase the excretion of urine from the body.

RATE YOURSELF

Recognizing a Drug Problem

myhealthlab

ARE YOU CONTROLLED BY DRUGS?

How do you know if you are dependent on the drugs you use? Persons dependent on drugs cannot stop using them; their use hurts themselves and those around them.

Take the following assessment. The more times you respond "yes," the more likely you are controlled by the drugs you use.

	Yes	No
1. Do you use drugs to handle stress or escape from life's problems?	❑	❑
2. Have you unsuccessfully tried to cut down or quit using your drug?	❑	❑
3. Have you ever been in trouble with the law or arrested because of your drug use?	❑	❑
4. Do you think a party or social gathering is not fun unless drugs are available?	❑	❑
5. Do you avoid people or places that do not support your drug use?	❑	❑
6. Do you neglect your responsibilities because you would rather use your drug?	❑	❑
7. Have your friends, family, professors, or employer expressed concern about your drug use?	❑	❑
8. Do you do things under the influence of drugs that you would not normally do?	❑	❑
9. Have you seriously thought that you might have a drug problem?	❑	❑

ARE YOU CONTROLLED BY A DRUG USER?

Is your life controlled by a drug user? Your love and care (codependency) may actually enable the drug user to continue his or her use, hurting you, him- or herself, and others. Take this assessment; the more "yes" checks you make, the more likely that you are being controlled by a drug user.

	Yes	No
1. Do you often have to lie or cover up for the drug user?	❑	❑
2. Do you spend time counselling the person about problems related to his or her drug use?	❑	❑
3. Have you taken on additional financial or family responsibilities to cover this person's drug use?	❑	❑
4. Do you feel that you have to control the drug user's behaviour?	❑	❑
5. At the office or in classes, have you done work/completed assignments or attended meetings for the user?	❑	❑
6. Do you often put your own needs and desires after the user's?	❑	❑
7. Do you spend time each day worrying about your situation?	❑	❑
8. Do you analyze your behaviour to find clues to how it might affect the drug user?	❑	❑
5c. Do you feel powerless and at your wits' end about the user's drug use?	❑	❑

Source: Reprinted by permission of Krames Communications, 1100 Grundy Lane, San Bruno, CA 94066–3030.

CONTROLLED SUBSTANCES

Cocaine

Cocaine is a crystalline white alkaloid powder derived from the leaves of the South American coca shrub (not related to cocoa plants). These leaves have been chewed for thousands of years by people in Peru and Bolivia to lessen hunger and fatigue. Pure cocaine was isolated in 1860 by a German pharmacology graduate student. In the 1880s, Freud praised the powerful stimulant effects of cocaine as the treatment for a variety of illnesses, including depression, as well as for alcohol and opioid addiction. Cocaine use then increased and it was widely and legally available in Canada in medicine and soft drinks. With increased use, the risks of cocaine became clear, and in 1911 Canada passed laws restricting its importation, manufacture, sale, and possession.

Cocaine is generally sold on the street as a hydrochloride salt—a fine, white crystalline powder known as "blow," "C," "coke," "crack," "flake," "free-base," "rock," or "snow," among other names. Street dealers often dilute it with inert (non-psychoactive) but similar-looking substances such as cornstarch, talcum powder, and sugar, or with active drugs such as procaine and benzocaine (used as local anesthetics), or other central nervous system stimulants such as amphetamines.

According to the most recent Canadian Addiction Survey, lifetime cocaine use ranged from 9.4 to 11.8 percent for women ages 15 to 44 years. For men, lifetime cocaine use was greatest in men between the ages of 35 and 44 years at 21.4 percent.

Cocaine affects mood, judgment, and motor skill coordination. Cocaine has its most dramatic effects on vision, as it may cause a higher sensitivity to light, the perception of halos around bright objects, and difficulty focusing. Users have also reported blurred vision, glare problems, and hallucinations, particularly "snow lights"—weak flashes or movements of light in the peripheral field of vision, which tend to make drivers swerve toward or away from the lights. Some users have also reported auditory hallucinations (for example, ringing bells) and olfactory hallucinations (for example, the smell of smoke or gasoline).

Cocaine also heightens feelings such as irritability, excitability, and startle response. Users reported that sudden sounds, such as horns or sirens, caused them severe anxiety coupled with rapid steering or braking reactions, even when the source of the sound was not in the immediate vicinity of their vehicles. Suspiciousness, distrust, and paranoia—other reactions to cocaine—have prompted users to flee in their cars or drive evasively. Further, users report attention lapses while driving, reckless driving, and ignoring relevant stimuli such as changes in traffic signals.

Although cocaine use has declined from its peak in the 1980s, it continues to be a commonly used and abused illicit drug today.

Methods of Cocaine Use

Cocaine can be taken in several ways. The powdered form of the drug is "snorted" through the nose. Smoking (freebasing) and intravenous injections are more dangerous means of using cocaine. When cocaine is snorted, it can cause damage to the mucous membranes in the nose and sinusitis. Further, snorting cocaine can damage the user's sense of smell, and occasionally it creates a hole in the septum. Smoking, or "freebasing," cocaine can result in lung and liver damage. Freebasing is more popular than injecting cocaine because of the risk of contracting diseases such as AIDS and hepatitis by sharing needles. A major risk of freebasing relates to the volatile mixes it requires and the risk of explosion; some users have been killed or seriously burned.

Many cocaine users still occasionally "shoot up." Injecting allows the user to introduce large amounts of cocaine rapidly into the body. Within seconds, there is an incredible sense of euphoria. This intense high lasts only 15 to 20 minutes, and then the user heads into a "crash." To prevent the unpleasant effects of the crash, users often shoot up frequently, which can severely damage their veins. Besides AIDS and hepatitis, users who inject themselves are at risk for skin infections, inflammation of the arteries, and infection of the lining of the heart.

Physical Effects of Cocaine

The effects of cocaine are felt rapidly. Snorted cocaine enters the bloodstream through the lungs in less than one minute and reaches the brain in less than three minutes. When cocaine binds at its receptor sites in the central nervous system, it produces intense pleasure. The euphoria quickly abates and the desire to regain the pleasurable feelings makes the user want more.

Cocaine is an anesthetic and a central nervous system stimulant. In tiny doses, it can slow heart rate. In larger doses, the physical effects are dramatic: increased heart rate and blood pressure, loss of appetite that can lead to dramatic weight loss, convulsions, muscle twitching, irregular heartbeat, even death due to overdose. Other effects of cocaine include temporary relief of depression, decreased fatigue, talkativeness, increased alertness, and heightened self-confidence. Again, however, as the dose increases, users become irritable and apprehensive and their behaviours may turn paranoid or violent.

Cocaine: A powerful stimulant drug with strong psychological effects

ALCOHOL, TOBACCO, AND CAFFEINE

Unacknowledged Drugs with Risk for Addictions

CONSIDER THIS . . .

Teresa is a waitress at a local restaurant. In the entryway there is a large warning sign about the dangers of drinking alcohol while pregnant. While taking a drink order from a woman, Teresa notices that the woman is in maternity clothes and in the advanced stages of pregnancy. Teresa takes the order and tells the restaurant manager that she feels uneasy serving alcohol to a pregnant woman. The manager says, "Mind your own business," and tells her to take the woman the drink. Teresa delivers the drink. During the course of the evening, she takes several more drinks to the same woman.

Should Teresa refuse to serve the pregnant woman? Why or why not? What are Teresa's moral or ethical obligations? If the baby is born with alcohol-related problems, should the mother be sued for endangering her child?

Objectives

- Describe the alcohol-use patterns of post-secondary students as well as the physiological and behavioural effects of alcohol consumption.
- Explain the symptoms, causes, and treatments of alcoholism, its cost to society, and its effects on the family.
- Identify the social issues involved in tobacco use, including those surrounding smokeless tobacco.
- Explain the physiological short- and long-term effects of smoking.
- Compare the benefits and risks of caffeine consumption.

When you hear references to the dangers of drugs, what comes to mind? Usually the term *drugs* conjures images of people using cocaine, heroin, marijuana, LSD, PCP, and other illegal substances. Although people use the word *drugs* to refer to one set of dangerous substances, they often refuse to categorize alcohol as a drug, primarily because its consumption is socially accepted and alcohol sales are booming. Similarly, tobacco and caffeine are seldom considered drugs, also likely because of their legality and acceptable use. In the fiscal year ending March 31, 2007, Canada's beer and liquor sales were $18.0 billion, an increase of 4.9 percent from the years before and an amount equivalent to almost 218.7 million litres of alcoholic beverages.

Although beer continues to be the alcoholic drink of choice for most Canadians in terms of volume and dollar value, more consumers are turning to wine, where sales now capture 28 percent of the market (compared to 21 percent 10 years previously).

Most of us think of alcohol the way it is portrayed in ads or in the movies: a way of having fun with company and an important adjunct to a romantic dinner or a cozy evening in front of the fireplace. And moderate use of alcohol can be part of celebrations or special times without health risk. In fact, research shows that low levels of use may actually reduce some health risks. Still, alcohol is a drug that affects your physical and mental behaviours. Further, the tragedies associated with alcohol receive far less attention than cocaine-related deaths, drug busts, and efforts to eradicate marijuana crops. Nevertheless, they are far more common—with potentially devastating effects on people of all ages.

ALCOHOL: AN OVERVIEW

Although 79.3 percent of Canadians reported alcohol consumption in the past year, only 44 percent reported drinking weekly. Males are more likely than females to report drinking in the past year (82.0 versus 76.8 percent), and the highest past-year drinking rates (90.8 percent) are found in the 18- to 19-year-old age group. In the Canadian Addiction Survey, a light infrequent drinker is classified as someone who reported drinking alcohol less than once a week, with fewer than five drinks consumed; in contrast, a light frequent drinker consumes fewer than five drinks per occasion more than once a week. A heavy infrequent drinker is someone who consumes five or more drinks at a time less than once a week, while a heavy frequent drinker consumes five or more drinks more than once per week. Using these definitions, 36.0 and 62.0 percent of Canadian males and females aged 15 or older, respectively were classified as light infrequent drinkers, 40.9 and 29.2 percent were light frequent drinkers, 9.0 and 5.1 percent were heavy infrequent drinkers, and 14.2 and 3.7 percent were heavy frequent drinkers. Clearly, males are more likely to drink than females, more frequently and in greater quantity.

In terms of alcohol sales, beer remains the most popular choice, capturing 47 percent of sales. The market share of spirits is 25 percent and of wine is 28 percent. Reports from 2004 indicated that when total sales were considered, consumers in Quebec and Newfoundland and Labrador purchased the most (115 litres per capita per year), while consumers in Saskatchewan purchased the least (94.4 litres). Per capita purchases of beer were also highest in Quebec and Newfoundland and Labrador and lowest in British Columbia. Consumers

While alcohol has long been seen as a "social lubricant" by post-secondary students, alcohol abuse and associated behaviours continue to be serious problems on many campuses.

in Newfoundland and Labrador also bought the most spirits. The greatest wine purchasers came from Quebec, Alberta, and British Columbia.

Alcohol can benefit and harm an individual. Most scientific evidence about the benefit as well as the harm comes from industrialized countries such as Canada, cultures where alcohol consumption is largely accepted and where dietary intake and inactive lifestyles lend themselves to heart diseases. Moderate alcohol consumption reduces, in certain age groups, the risk of coronary heart disease and ischemic stroke. Low-risk drinking guidelines suggest consuming no more than 14 standard drinks for men or 9 standard drinks for women per week. Despite this individual benefit, the harm associated with the misuse and abuse of alcohol still constitutes a major public health problem in developed and developing countries. In fact, in Canada 22.6 percent (30.2 percent men; 15.1 percent women) of the population reporting exceeding these low-risk guidelines over the past year.

Almost 10 percent of current drinkers report some sort of harm to themselves as a result of their drinking in the past year. Of these, 3 percent report negative effects on friendships and social life and 5.4 percent report negative effects to their physical health. More alarming is that 32.7 percent of the respondents to the Canadian Addiction Survey reported being harmed the past year because of someone else's drinking. Of these, 10 percent indicated family or marriage difficulties, 22.1 percent reported being insulted or humiliated, 15.5 percent indicated serious arguments or quarrels, 15.8 percent reported verbal abuse, 10.8 percent were pushed or shoved, and 3.2 percent were physically assaulted. Alcohol is a significant factor in hospital admissions, road deaths, industrial accidents, accidental drowning, homicide, and suicide. It is estimated that 6507 Canadians lost their lives as a result of alcohol consumption in 1995, with the largest number of deaths stemming from impaired driving accidents, and that 82 014 Canadians were hospitalized due to alcohol misuse. Total costs of alcohol abuse in 2002 (the latest data available) when measured in terms of health care, law enforcement, loss of productivity in the work place and home, and premature death or disability were estimated to be $14.6 billion or 36.6 percent of the total costs for substance abuse (also includes tobacco and illicit drugs).

> **what do you THINK?**
> Are binge drinking and alcohol abuse the same thing? Why or why not? If you drink to get drunk does that indicate a problem? Why or why not?

✓ Alcohol and the Post-Secondary Student

Alcohol is the most widely used, misused, and abused recreational drug in our society. It is also the most popular drug on campuses, where approximately 94.5 percent of students consume alcoholic beverages. The Addiction Research Foundation estimates that one-third of Ontario students consume more than 15 drinks per week: a level that puts them at health risk. A greater number of alcohol users live in residence (41 percent), are between 17 and 22 years of age (65 percent), and have lower grades (49.5 percent D students, 22.6 percent A students).

University or college is a critical time to become conscious of and responsible about your drinking. A number of social factors are involved in campus drinking. There is little doubt that alcohol is a part of campus culture and tradition. It is used to relieve tensions and to celebrate. Its ability to lower inhibitions makes it the "social lubricant" of choice for many students, giving them an easy way to initiate conversations, create friendships, and find a date and/or companion for the evening.

How do students view the drinking patterns of themselves and their peers? Students consistently report that their friends drink much more than they do. Further, actual consumption is higher than self-reports. Such misinformation may promote or be used to excuse excessive drinking practices among post-secondary students.

Binge drinking on campuses continues to be a big problem. **Binge drinking** is defined as the consumption of five drinks in a row by men or four in a row by women on a single occasion. The express purpose of binge drinking is to become intoxicated.

Although everyone is at risk for alcoholism and alcohol-related problems, post-secondary students are particularly vulnerable for the following reasons:

- Alcohol exacerbates their already high risk for suicide, automobile accidents, and falls.
- Many university and college customs, norms, traditions, and mores encourage several dangerous practices and patterns of alcohol use, misuse, and abuse.
- Campuses are heavily targeted by advertising and promotions from the alcohol industry, including the employment of liquor representatives and distributors on most campuses.
- It is more common for post-secondary students than their peers to drink excessively in a variety of drinking games and other dangerous drinking practices.
- Post-secondary students are particularly vulnerable to peer influences and have a strong need to be accepted by their peers.

In an effort to prevent alcohol abuse, many universities and colleges institute strong policies against excessive consumption. Furthermore, help is made available to students with drinking problems. Today, individual and group counselling are offered on most campuses, and more attention is directed toward the prevention of alcohol abuse. Several student organizations also promote responsible drinking and responsible party hosting. Many campuses also provide "safe" rides home.

what do you THINK?

Do you worry about how much you drink? Do you compare the amount you drink to your friends' intake? If you drink less than your friends, does that mean your drinking is not a problem? What is a responsible–and appropriate–level of alcohol consumption for you? For your friends? What do you do to ensure your safety when drinking? What about the safety of your friends?

Rights versus Responsibilities

Most of us recognize the dangers associated with alcohol consumption in general, yet we tend to deny that such things could happen to us. We are aware of the relationship between alcohol and traffic accidents, spouse battering and child abuse, violent crimes, unprotected sexual activity, and family disruption, but we also like to believe that these tragedies happen only to

When drinking alcohol, it is important to choose beverages containing a lower percentage of alcohol such as wine or beer, as well as to eat prior to and while drinking to reduce blood alcohol content.

Binge drinking: Drinking to become intoxicated; five drinks in a single sitting for men and four drinks for women.

Ethyl alcohol (ethanol): A drug produced by fermentation and found in many beverages.

HEALTH IN THE MEDIA

Contributing Factors to Alcohol Abuse and Related Problems on Campus

Many students are not aware of the reality of alcohol use, misuse, and abuse on their campuses. The following statistics provide a brief glimpse into the issues.

- Alcohol kills more people under the legal drinking age than cocaine, marijuana, and heroin combined.
- Half a million students aged 15 to 24 are unintentionally injured each year while intoxicated.
- One night of heavy drinking can impair the ability to think abstractly for up to 30 days, limiting a student's ability to understand a professor's lecture, think through a football play, write a paper, or take an exam.
- College and university administrators estimate that alcohol is a factor in 29 percent of dropouts, 38 percent of academic failure, and 64 percent of violent behaviours.
- Over the past decade, there has been a threefold increase in the number of college and university women who report having been drunk on 10 or more occasions in the previous month.
- Areas of a campus offering cheap beer prices have more crime, including trouble between students and police or other campus authorities, arguments, physical fighting, property damage, false fire alarms, and sexual misconduct.
- Alcohol is involved in more than two-thirds of suicides among post-secondary students, 90 percent of sexual assaults, and 95 percent of violent crime on campus.
- The likelihood that a woman will be raped is far greater on campuses with a high rate of binge drinking.
- Each year, more than 100 000 students aged 18 to 24 reported being too intoxicated to know if they had consented to having sex.
- College and university binge drinking occurs more often among male students, students who reside on campus, varsity athletes, and members of fraternities and sororities. Approximately 40 percent of fraternity and sorority members report being frequent binge drinkers, and college or university athletes are 50 percent more likely to binge drink than non-athletes.
- Rates of binge drinking among high-risk students (younger, white males) are lower on more diverse campuses.
- Post-secondary students under the legal drinking age are more prone to binge drinking and pay less for their alcohol than their older classmates. Though underage students drink less often, they consume more per occasion than older students.
- One risk of binge drinking and excessive alcohol consumption is "passing out." During this time, the drinker who passed out could vomit, choke on his or her own vomit, and die. If someone passes out at a party or later at home, it is important to place him or her in the recovery position (that is, on his or her side, upper arm extended with the lower arm bent such that the hand is under his or her cheek) and stay with them until they have "slept it off."

Sources: Data were compiled from the numerous studies cited throughout this chapter and from M. Mohler-Kuo et al., "College Rapes Linked to Binge-Drinking Rates," *Journal of Studies on Alcohol* 65.1 (2004); H. Wechsler, "Watering Down the Drinks: The Moderating Effect of College Demographics on Alcohol Use in High Risk Groups," *American Journal of Public Health* 93.11 (2003): 1929–1933; T. F. Nelson et al., "Alcohol and Collegiate Sports Fans," *Addictive Behaviors* 28.1 (2003): 1–11; R. W. Hingson et al., "Magnitude of Alcohol-Related Mortality and Morbidity among U.S. College Students Aged 18–24," *Journal of Studies on Alcohol* 63.2 (2002): 136–144.

other people. Many students refuse to acknowledge that alcohol is a drug simply because they do not wish to see themselves as drug users. Our society condones, approves, and often encourages the consumption of alcoholic beverages. It also informs how to drink responsibly, yet the reality is that seldom do a person's words match their actions, particularly in the university or college environment, where excessive consumption of alcohol is often the norm, not the exception.

If you make the choice to drink, you should do so judiciously, with complete information about the risks. The physiological and psychological reactions of the human body to alcohol are strong. For this reason, you should approach the drug carefully be and well informed. To avoid the devastating effects of alcohol abuse, you must adhere to the same principles of prevention that apply to any potentially harmful substance. The Canadian Centre for Substance Abuse and the Centre for Addiction and Mental Health recommend fewer than 14 standard drinks per week for men, fewer than 9 standard drinks per week for women, and not more than 2 standard drinks on any one day.

PHYSIOLOGICAL AND BEHAVIOURAL EFFECTS OF ALCOHOL

The intoxicating substance found in beer, wine, liquor, and liqueurs is **ethyl alcohol**, or **ethanol**. It is produced during a process called **fermentation**, whereby plant sugars are broken down by yeast organisms, yielding ethanol and carbon dioxide. Fermentation continues until the solution of plant sugars (called mash) reaches a concentration of 14 percent alcohol. At this point, the alcohol kills the yeast and halts the chemical reactions that produce it.

Manufacturers then add other ingredients that dilute the alcohol content of the beverage, such as in beer and wine. Other alcoholic beverages are produced through further processing called **distillation**, during which alcohol vapours are released from the mash at high temperatures. The vapours are then condensed and mixed with water to make the final product, such as in fortified wines and spirits.

The **proof** of an alcoholic drink is a measure of the percentage of alcohol in the beverage. The word *proof* comes from "gunpowder proof," a reference to the gunpowder test, whereby potential buyers tested the distiller's product by pouring it on gunpowder and attempting to light it. If the alcohol content was at least 50 percent, the gunpowder would burn; otherwise the water in the product would put out the flame. Thus, alcohol percentage is 50 percent of the given proof. For example, 80-proof whiskey or scotch is 40-percent alcohol by volume. The proof of a beverage provides an indication of its strength. Therefore, consuming the same amount (that is, volume) of lower-proof drinks will produce fewer alcohol effects than higher-proof drinks. Most spirits are 40 percent alcohol, wines are between 12 and 15 percent alcohol, and ales are between 6 and 8 percent. The alcoholic content of most beers is between 2 and 6 percent, varying according to the type of beer.

Behavioural Effects

Behaviour changes caused by alcohol vary with the setting and with the individual. Alcohol may allow shy people to be less inhibited and more willing to talk to others. It may also cause a depressed person to become even more depressed. In people reluctant to share emotions, it may bring out violence and aggression. In many cases, alcohol will do for the drinker what the drinker expects and wants it to do, making it possible for the user to blame his or her inappropriate behaviours on the alcohol. It is because of this expected effect, combined with reduced inhibitions, that a person who normally does not dance well tears a strip off the dance floor. In other words, a person who normally inhibits dancing behaviours may actually dance better after a drink or two, simply because his or her inhibitions have been reduced.

Blood alcohol concentration (BAC) is the ratio of alcohol to total blood volume. It is the factor used to measure the physiological and behaviour effects of alcohol. Despite individual differences, alcohol produces some general behaviour effects based on BAC (see Table 5c.1). At a BAC of 0.02, a person feels slightly relaxed and his or her mood—whatever that may be—is generally enhanced. At a BAC of 0.05, relaxation increases, there is some motor impairment, and a willingness to talk becomes apparent. At a BAC of 0.08, the person feels euphoric and there is further motor impairment. At a BAC of 0.10, the depressant effects of alcohol become apparent, drowsiness sets in, and motor skills are further impaired, followed by a loss of judgment. Thus, a driver may not be able to estimate distances or speed, and some drinkers lose their ability to make value-related decisions and may do things they would not do when sober. As BAC increases, the drinker suffers increased physiological and psychological effects. All these changes are negative; that is, physical and mental functions are impaired not enhanced.

People can acquire physiological and psychological tolerance to the effects of alcohol through regular use. The nervous system adapts over time, so greater quantities of alcohol are required to produce the same physiological and psychological effects. Furthermore, some people learn to modify their behaviours so that they appear to be sober even when their BAC is quite high. This ability is called **learned behavioural tolerance**.

Absorption and Metabolism

Alcohol is rapidly absorbed into the bloodstream from the small intestine, and less rapidly from the stomach and colon. In proportion to its concentration in the bloodstream, alcohol decreases activity in parts of the brain and spinal cord. The drinker's blood alcohol concentration depends on

- the amount consumed in a given time
- the drinker's size, sex, body build, and metabolism
- the type and amount of food in the stomach

Fermentation: The process whereby yeast organisms break down plant sugars to yield ethanol.

Distillation: The process whereby mash is subjected to high temperatures to release alcohol vapours, which are then condensed and mixed with water to make the final product.

Proof: A measure of the percentage of alcohol in a beverage.

Blood alcohol concentration (BAC): The ratio of alcohol to total blood volume; the factor used to measure the physiological and behaviour effects of alcohol

TABLE 5c.1

Psychological and Physiological Effects of Various Blood Alcohol Concentration Levels

Number of Drinks†	Blood Alcohol Concentration*	Psychological and Physiological Effects
1	0.02%–0.03%	No overt effects, slight mood elevation
2	0.05%–0.06%	Feeling of relaxation, warmth; slight decrease in reaction time and in fine-muscle coordination
3	0.08%–0.09%	Balance, speech, vision, and hearing slightly impaired; feelings of euphoria, increased confidence; loss of motor coordination
4	0.11%–0.12%	Coordination and balance becoming difficult; distinct impairment of mental faculties, judgment
5	0.14%–0.15%	Major impairment of mental and physical control; slurred speech, blurred vision, lack of motor skills
7	0.20%	Loss of motor control—needs help moving about; mental confusion
10	0.30%	Severe intoxication; minimum conscious control of mind and body
14	0.40%	Unconsciousness, threshold of coma
17	0.50%	Deep coma
20	0.60%	Death from respiratory failure

†One drink = one beer (4–5% alcohol, 375 mL), one highball (31 mL whiskey), or one glass table wine (157 mL).
*For each hour elapsed since the last drink, subtract 0.015% blood alcohol concentration, or approximately one drink.

Source: Modified from data given in Ohio State Police Driver Information Seminars and the National Clearinghouse for Alcohol and Alcoholism Information, Rockville, MD.

Once alcohol has passed into the bloodstream, you cannot slow its absorption by eating or drinking. Mood also influences the rate of absorption, since emotions affect how long it takes for the contents of the stomach to empty into the intestine. Powerful moods, such as stress and tension, are likely to cause the stomach to "dump" its contents into the small intestine. That is why alcohol is absorbed much more rapidly when people are tense than when they are relaxed.

Consuming fruit sugar may shorten the duration of alcohol's effect by increasing the rate of elimination from the blood (that is, metabolism). In the average adult, the rate of metabolism is about 8.5 grams (that is, about two-thirds of a drink) of alcohol per hour. This rate varies dramatically among individuals, however, depending on the user's drinking history, physique, sex, liver size, and genetic factors.

Alcohol is metabolized in the liver, where it is converted by the enzyme alcohol dehydrogenase to acetaldehyde. It is then rapidly oxidized to acetate, converted to carbon dioxide and water, and eventually excreted from the body. Acetaldehyde is a toxic chemical that can cause immediate symptoms such as nausea and vomiting as well as long-term effects such as liver damage.

Like food, alcohol contains calories. Proteins and carbohydrates (starches and sugars) each contain 4 kilocalories per gram while fat contains 9 kilocalories per gram. Alcohol, although similar in structure to carbohydrates, contains 7 kilocalories per gram. Although a source of energy—and therefore considered a food—alcohol is not considered a nutrient because it is not essential to our body, nor does it perform any necessary function.

A drinker's BAC depends on his or her weight and body fat, the water content in the body tissues, the concentration of alcohol in the beverage consumed, the rate of consumption, and the volume of alcohol consumed. Heavier people have larger body surfaces through which to diffuse alcohol; therefore, they have lower concentrations of alcohol in their blood than thin people after drinking the same amount. Because alcohol does not diffuse as rapidly into body fat as into water, alcohol concentration is higher in a person with more body fat. Because a woman is likely to have more body fat and less water in her body tissues than a man

what do you THINK?

Have you or someone you know ever chosen specifically to alter conditions so as to increase BAC (that is, to get drunk quicker)? Are these wise practices? Why or why not?

TABLE 5c.2

Calculation of Estimated Blood Alcohol (BAC) for Men and Women

	Number of Drinks: Males									
Body Weight (kg)	**1**	**2**	**3**	**4**	**5**	**6**	**7**	**8**	**9**	**10**
45.4	0.043	0.087	0.130	0.174	0.217	0.261	0.304	0.348	0.391	0.435
56.8	0.034	0.069	0.103	0.139	0.173	0.209	0.242	0.278	0.312	0.346
68.2	0.029	0.058	0.087	0.116	0.145	0.174	0.203	0.232	0.261	0.290
79.5	0.025	0.050	0.075	0.100	0.125	0.150	0.175	0.200	0.225	0.250
90.9	0.022	0.043	0.065	0.087	0.108	0.130	0.152	0.174	0.195	0.217
102.3	0.022	0.045	0.068	0.091	0.113	0.136	0.159	0.182	0.204	0.227
113.6	0.020	0.041	0.061	0.082	0.101	0.122	0.142	0.162	0.182	0.202

	Number of Drinks: Females									
Body Weight (kg)	**1**	**2**	**3**	**4**	**5**	**6**	**7**	**8**	**9**	**10**
45.4	0.050	0.101	0.152	0.203	0.253	0.304	0.355	0.406	0.456	0.507
56.8	0.040	0.080	0.120	0.162	0.202	0.244	0.282	0.324	0.364	0.404
68.2	0.034	0.068	0.101	0.135	0.169	0.203	0.237	0.271	0.304	0.338
79.5	0.029	0.058	0.087	0.117	0.146	0.175	0.204	0.233	0.262	0.292
90.9	0.026	0.050	0.076	0.101	0.126	0.152	0.177	0.203	0.227	0.253
102.3	0.022	0.045	0.068	0.091	0.113	0.136	0.159	0.182	0.204	0.227
113.6	0.020	0.041	0.061	0.082	0.101	0.122	0.142	0.162	0.182	0.202

Body weight: Calculations are for people who have a normal body weight for their height, who are free of drugs or other affecting medications, and who are neither unusually thin nor obese.

Drink equivalents:
1 drink = 43 mL (1.5 oz) of rum, rye, scotch, brandy, gin, vodka, etc.
1 drink = 341-mL (12-oz) bottle of normal-strength (5%) beer
1 drink = 85 mL (3 oz) of fortified wine
1 drink = 142 mL (5 oz) of table wine

Using the chart: Find the appropriate figure using the proper chart (male or female), body weight, and number of drinks consumed. Then subtract the time factor (see Time Factor Table, below) from the figure on the chart to obtain the approximate BAC. For example, for a 68-kg man who has had 4 drinks in 2 hours, take the figure 0.116 (from the chart for males) and subtract 0.030 (from the Time Factor Table) to obtain a BAC of 0.086 percent.

Time Factor Table

Hours since first drink	1	2	3	4	5	6
Subtract from BAC	0.015	0.030	0.045	0.60	0.075	0.090

Source:

of the same weight, she will have a higher BAC than a man after drinking the same amount of alcohol. (See Table 5c.2.)

Learned behavioural tolerance: The ability of drinkers to modify their behaviours so that they appear sober even when they have high BAC levels.

Women and Alcohol

Body fat is not the only contributor to the differences in alcohol's effects on men and women. Compared to men, women have half as much alcohol hydrogenase, the enzyme that breaks down alcohol in the stomach before it has a chance to get to the bloodstream and the brain. Therefore, if a man and a woman drink the same amount of alcohol, the woman's BAC will be approximately 30 percent higher than the man's, leaving her more vulnerable to slurred speech, careless driving, and other drinking-related impairments. Table 5c.2 compares blood-alcohol levels by sex, weight, and consumption. Although this table provides an estimate of probable BAC levels, many additional factors may cause considerable variation. For this reason, you should always err on the side of caution when gauging your BAC.

Breathalyzer and Other Tests

The breathalyzer tests used by law enforcement officers are designed to determine BAC based on the amount of alcohol exhaled in the breath. Urinalysis yields a BAC based on the concentration of unmetabolized alcohol in the urine. Breath analysis, urinalysis, and blood tests are used to determine whether a driver is over the legal limit, with blood tests providing the most accurate measures.

Immediate Effects

Alcohol is a central nervous system (CNS) depressant. The primary action of ethanol is to reduce the frequency of nerve transmissions and impulses at synaptic junctions. This reduction of nerve transmissions causes a significant reduction in CNS functions, with resulting decreases in respiratory rate, pulse rate, and blood pressure. As CNS depression deepens, vital functions become noticeably reduced. In extreme cases, coma and death can result (see also Table 5c.1).

Alcohol is a diuretic that increases urinary output. Although this effect might be expected to lead to automatic **dehydration** (loss of water), the body actually retains water, most of it in the muscles or in the cerebral tissues. This is because water is usually pulled out of the **cerebrospinal fluid** (fluid within the brain and spinal cord) instead, leading to what is known as mitochondrial dehydration at the cellular level within the nervous system. Mitochondria are miniature organs within cells responsible for specific functions. They rely heavily on fluid balance. When mitochondrial dehydration occurs from drinking, the mitochondria cannot carry out their normal functions, resulting in symptoms that include the "morning-after" headaches suffered by some drinkers.

Alcohol is also an irritant to the gastrointestinal system and may cause indigestion and heartburn if consumed on an empty stomach. Long-term use of alcohol causes repeated irritation that has been linked to cancers of the esophagus and stomach. In addition, people who engage in brief drinking sprees during which they consume unusually high amounts of alcohol put themselves at risk for irregular heartbeat or even total loss of heart rhythm, which can cause disruption in blood flow and possible damage to the heart muscle.

A **hangover** is sometimes experienced the morning after consuming alcohol. The symptoms of a hangover are familiar to those who drink: headache, upset stomach, anxiety, depression, thirst, and, in severe cases, an almost overwhelming desire to crawl back into bed. People who get hangovers often also stay up too late or engage in other behaviours likely to leave them feeling unwell the next day. The causes of hangovers are not well known, but the effects of congeners are suspected. **Congeners** are toxic forms of alcohol metabolized more slowly than ethanol. Your body metabolizes the congeners after the ethanol is gone from your system, and their toxic by-products are thought to contribute to the hangover. It usually takes 12 hours to recover from a hangover. Bed rest, plenty of fluids, solid food, and a pain reliever may reduce the discomforts of a hangover; however, nothing cures it but time.

> **what do you THINK?**
> Think about the last time you consumed alcohol. How much did you consume? Over how long? Calculate your blood alcohol content using the information presented in Table 5c.2. How long did it take until your BAC was reduced to 0?

Drug Interactions

When you use any drug (and alcohol is a drug), you need to be aware of the possible interactions with prescription drugs, over-the-counter drugs, or other drugs you are taking or considering taking. Table 5c.3 summarizes possible interactions.

Long-Term Effects

Effects on the Nervous System

Since alcohol is a CNS depressant, the nervous system is especially sensitive to it. Even people who drink moderately experience a decrease in brain size and weight accompanied by a slight loss of intellec tual ability. The damage that results from alcohol use

TABLE 5c.3

Drugs and Alcohol: Actions and Interactions

Drug Class/Name(s)	Effects with Alcohol
Anti-alcohol: Antabuse	Severe reactions to even small amounts: headache, nausea, blurred vision, convulsions, coma, possible death.
Antibiotics: Penicillin, Cyantin	Reduces therapeutic effectiveness of antibiotics.
Antidepressants: Elavil, Sinequan, Tofranil, Nardil	Increased central nervous system (CNS) depression, blood pressure changes. Combined use of alcohol and MAO inhibitors, a specific type of antidepressant, can trigger massive increases in blood pressure, even brain hemorrhage and death.
Antihistamines: Allerest, Dristan	Drowsiness and CNS depression. Impairs driving ability.
ASA: Aspirin, Anacin, Excedrin, Bayer	Irritates stomach lining. May cause gastrointestinal pain, bleeding.
Depressants: Valium, Ativan, Placidyl	Dangerous CNS depression, loss of coordination, coma. High risk of overdose and death.
Narcotics: Heroin, Codeine, Darvon	Serious CNS depression. Possible respiratory arrest and death.
Stimulants: Caffeine, Cocaine	Masks depressant action of alcohol. May increase blood pressure, physical tension.
Tylenol, Acetaminophen	Risk of liver damage, particularly with heavy alcohol consumption and maximum recommended doses of acetaminophen.

Source: Adapted by permission from *Drugs and Alcohol: Simple Facts about Alcohol and Drug Combinations* (Phoenix: DIN Publications, 1988), No. 121.

is localized primarily in the left side of the brain, which is responsible for written and spoken language, logic, and mathematical skills. The degree of shrinkage appears to be directly related to the amount of alcohol consumed. In terms of memory loss, the evidence suggests that having one drink every day is less likely to result in damage than saving up for a binge and consuming seven or eight drinks in a night.

Cardiovascular Effects

The cardiovascular system is affected by alcohol in a number of ways. Evidence suggests that the effect of alcohol on the heart is not all bad. Some studies suggest that moderate drinkers suffer fewer heart attacks, have less cholesterol buildup, and are less likely to die of heart disease than either nondrinkers or heavy drinkers. However, drinking is not recommended as a preventive measure against heart disease because the benefits do not outweigh the risks. Alcohol contributes to high blood pressure and a slightly increased heart rate and cardiac output. Those who report drinking three to five drinks a day, regardless of ethnicity or sex, have higher blood pressure than those who drink less, or not at all.

People who engage in brief drinking sprees, during which they consume unusually large amounts of alcohol, also suffer some risks, including irregular heartbeat or total loss of heart rhythm. This condition has been called "holiday heart syndrome" because it typically occurs around holidays such as Thanksgiving, Christmas, and New Year's Eve—occasions when drinkers are likely to overindulge. It can cause disruption in blood flow and possible damage to the heart muscle. Prolonged drinking can also lead to deterioration of the heart muscle, a condition called cardiomyopathy.

Dehydration: Loss of fluids from body tissues.

Cerebrospinal fluid: Fluid within and surrounding the brain and spinal cord tissues.

Hangover: The physiological reaction to excessive drinking, including such symptoms as headache, upset stomach, anxiety, depression, diarrhea, and thirst.

Congeners: Forms of alcohol metabolized more slowly than ethanol that produce toxic by-products.

Cirrhosis: The last stage of liver disease associated with chronic heavy use of alcohol, during which liver cells die and damage is permanent.

Alcoholic hepatitis: Condition resulting from prolonged use of alcohol in which the liver is inflamed. It can result in death.

Liver Disease

One of the most common diseases related to alcohol abuse is **cirrhosis** of the liver. It is among the top 10 causes of death in Canada. One result of heavy drinking is that the liver begins to store fat—a condition known as "fatty liver." If there is insufficient time between drinking episodes, this fat cannot be transported to storage sites and the fat-filled liver cells stop functioning. Continued drinking causes a further stage of liver deterioration called fibrosis, in which the damaged area of the liver develops fibrous scar tissue. Cell function can be partially restored at this stage with proper nutrition and abstinence from alcohol. However, if the person continues to drink, cirrhosis results: liver cells die and the damage is permanent. **Alcoholic hepatitis** is a serious condition resulting from prolonged use of alcohol. A chronic inflammation of the liver develops, which may be fatal in itself or progress to cirrhosis.

Cancer

Heavy drinkers (more than 5 drinks per day, more than 12 times per year) are at higher risk for certain types of cancer, particularly those of the gastrointestinal tract. The repeated irritation caused by long-term use of alcohol has been linked to cancers of the esophagus, stomach, mouth, tongue, and liver. Research also indicates a link between breast cancer and moderate consumption in women. A landmark study found that women between the ages of 34 and 59 who consumed between three and nine drinks a week were 30 percent more likely than nondrinkers to develop breast cancer. It is unclear how alcohol exerts its carcinogenic effects, though it is thought that it inhibits the absorption of carcinogenic substances, permitting them to be taken to sensitive organs.

Other Effects

An irritant to the gastrointestinal system, alcohol may cause indigestion and heartburn if consumed on an empty stomach. It also damages the mucous membranes and leads to inflammation of the esophagus, chronic stomach irritation, problems with intestinal absorption, and chronic diarrhea. Alcohol abuse is a major cause of chronic inflammation of the pancreas, the organ that produces digestive enzymes and insulin. Chronic abuse of alcohol inhibits enzyme production, which further inhibits the absorption of nutrients. Drinking alcohol can block the absorption of calcium, a nutrient that strengthens bones. This should be of particular concern to women, because as women age their risk for osteoporosis (bone thinning and calcium loss) increases. Heavy consumption of alcohol worsens this condition.

Evidence also suggests that alcohol impairs the body's ability to recognize and fight foreign bodies such as bacteria and viruses. Thus, individuals become more susceptible to colds and flues.

Fetal Alcohol Spectrum Disorders

Alcohol consumed by the mother has harmful effects on fetal development. Alcohol consumed during the first trimester of pregnancy poses the greatest threat to organ development, while exposure during the last trimester, when the brain is developing rapidly, is most likely to affect CNS development.

A series of disorders collectively called **fetal alcohol spectrum disorder (FASD)** is caused by prenatal exposure to alcohol and leads to lifelong developmental and cognitive disabilities among Canadian children. FASD occurs when alcohol ingested by the mother passes through the placenta into the fetus's bloodstream. Because the fetus is so small, its BAC will be much higher than that of the mother. Thus, consumption of alcohol during pregnancy affects the fetus far more seriously than the mother.

FASD is the leading cause of developmental delay in Canada and North America, with an incidence estimated at 1 to 6 in 1000 live births. FASD includes the following disorders related to alcohol consumption during pregnancy: **fetal alcohol syndrome (FAS)**, **fetal alcohol effects (FAE)**, partial fetal alcohol effects, alcohol-related neurodevelopmental disorders, and neurobehavioural disorder–alcohol exposed. FAS is characterized by retarded growth prenatally and postnatally, facial anomalies, CNS dysfunction as noted by intellectual impairment, structural abnormalities, developmental delay, and complex behavioural problems. One-fifth of FAS children have difficulty sleeping and are hyperactive. Many have severe learning disabilities and are dyslexic. Congenital heart problems are more common than in normal babies, as are genitor-urinary problems. There is an increased incidence of spina bifida, hip dislocation, and delayed skeletal maturation. FAE is used to describe children with prenatal exposure to alcohol but only some FAS characteristics.

what do you THINK?

Why do we hear so little about FASD given that it is the leading cause of developmental delay in North America? If you or your partner were pregnant, would you drink? Why or why not? How would you handle the societal pressures to consume alcohol?

Deciding when and how much to drink is no simple matter. Irresponsible consumption of alcohol can easily result in disaster.

As there is no definitive information regarding a safe quantity of alcohol during pregnancy, women who are or wish to become pregnant should abstain from alcohol. Health professionals should reassure women who have consumed small amounts of alcohol occasionally during pregnancy that the risk is likely minimal. Pregnant women should also know that not drinking at any time during a pregnancy will benefit themselves and their babies.

In June 1992, the Standing Committee on Health and Welfare, Social Affairs, Seniors, and the Status of Women released its report *Fetal Alcohol Syndrome: A Preventable Tragedy.* Since then, Health Canada has worked with health-care professionals to identify and implement prevention strategies; produced pamphlets and videos on FAS; and, with the Association of Canadian Distillers and the Brewers' Association of Canada, sponsors a national information service resource centre providing links to support groups, prevention projects, and experts on FASD (1-800-559-4514).

Drinking and Driving

The leading cause of death for all age groups from 5 to 34 years old (including university and college students) is traffic accidents. Young people between 15 and 29 years old account for 38 percent of motor vehicle fatalities. The rate is highest for 20- to 24-year-olds, at 14.7 percent. Impaired driving is a major cause of death, killing about 1350 Canadians each year and injuring many more.

ALCOHOLISM

Alcohol use becomes **alcohol abuse** or **alcoholism** when there is excessive consumption or a level of consumption that interferes with work, school, or social and family relationships. Alcoholism is one of many addictions or dependencies on substances or behaviours that have mood-altering consequences.

As noted previously, 8.8 percent of Canadians between the ages of 15 and 65 reported harm to self in the past year as a result of their drinking. Of the past-year drinkers, 6.2 percent indicated heavy drinking (five or more drinks for males and four or more drinks for women on a single occasion) at least once per week, with men between the ages of 18 and 24 years the most likely to report heavy drinking. Further, 22.6 percent of past-year drinkers exceeded the low-risk drinking guidelines (that is, consuming no more than 14 standard drinks for men or 9 standard drinks for women per week). Again, men between the ages of 18 and 24 were most likely to exceed these guidelines.

As previously noted, the most common areas affected by excessive drinking are physical health (5.4 percent), financial position (4.7 percent), and social health (3.0 percent). Almost one-third (32.7 percent) of Canadians say they have had problems from other people's drinking, such as being disturbed by loud parties (23.8 percent), being insulted or humiliated (22.1 percent), having a serious argument (15.5 percent), being physically abused (14.0 percent), and experiencing marital difficulties (10.0 percent). There were 8103 deaths and 1 587 054 acute care hospital days attributed to alcohol in Canada in 2002. Motor vehicle accidents accounted for the largest number of alcohol-related deaths, while accidental falls and alcohol dependence syndrome accounted for the largest number of alcohol-related hospitalizations.

Fetal alcohol spectrum disorder (FASD): A broad category of disorders relating to consumption of alcohol during pregnancy; includes fetal alcohol syndrome, fetal alcohol effects, partial fetal alcohol effects, alcohol-related neurodevelopmental disorders, and neurobehavioural disorder–alcohol exposed.

Fetal alcohol syndrome (FAS): A disorder that may result in the fetus if a mother regularly consumes alcohol during pregnancy. Among its effects are mental retardation, small head, tremors, and abnormalities of the face, limbs, heart, and brain.

Fetal alcohol effects (FAE): A syndrome describing children with a history of prenatal alcohol exposure but without all the physical or behavioural symptoms of FAS. Among its symptoms are low birthweight, irritability, and possible permanent mental impairment.

Alcohol abuse (alcoholism): Use of alcohol that interferes with work, school, or personal relationships or that entails violations of the law.

FOCUS ON CANADA

The Public Rates Drinking and Driving as One of Canada's Most Serious Social Issues

According to the 2002 Road Safety Monitor, an annual national opinion poll conducted by the Traffic Injury Research Foundation (TIRF), most Canadians believe that drinking and driving is a priority social issue, and the most important road safety issue that they face.

Drinking and driving occurrence in Canada:

- 86 percent of Canadians rated drinking and driving as a serious problem.
- 16.1 percent of drivers reported driving within two hours of consuming alcohol in the 30-day period prior to the survey.
- 7.9 percent of drivers admitted to driving when they thought they were over the legal limit at some point in 2002.
- It is estimated that, during 2002, there were more than 8 million trips in which the driver was impaired.

A relatively small group of individuals makes our roads particularly dangerous:

- Fewer than 3 percent of drivers account for more than 80 percent of all impaired driving trips.
- Young drivers (aged 16 to 18) and older drivers (aged 65 and over) are least likely to drive after drinking.
- Canadians aged 18 to 34 are most likely to report driving after drinking.

Canadian drivers support the following initiatives aimed at decreasing the incidence of drinking and driving:

- Requiring drivers suspected of drinking to perform sobriety tests
- Mandatory breath testing of drivers involved in collisions
- Alcohol ignition interlocks
- Immediate impoundment of vehicles driven by impaired drivers
- A zero blood alcohol content restriction for convicted offenders
- Greater use of police spot checks

Source: Adapted from the Traffic Safety Research Foundation, 2002 Road Safety Monitor.

How, Why, Whom?

As with other addictions, tolerance, psychological dependence, and withdrawal symptoms must be present to qualify a person as addicted to alcohol. Addiction usually results from chronic use over a period of time that may vary from person to person. People who have problems with alcohol, including irresponsible users, are not necessarily people who are addicted to it. The stereotype of the person on skid row addicted to alcohol applies to only 5 percent of those who are affected. The remaining 95 percent of individuals addicted to alcohol live in some type of extended family unit. They can be found at all socioeconomic levels and in all professions, ethnic groups, geographic locations, and religions. You have a 1 in 10 chance or risk of becoming addicted to alcohol. Individuals addicted to alcohol tend to have a number of attitudes behaviours in common. People who recognize in themselves any of these attitudes and behaviours discussed in the following paragraphs should seek professional help to determine whether alcohol has become a controlling factor in their lives.

Women are the fastest-growing component of the population becoming addicted to alcohol. They tend to become addicted at a later age and after fewer years of heavy drinking than men. Women at highest risk for alcohol-related problems are those living common law in their 20s or early 30s, or who have a husband or partner who drinks heavily.

The Causes of Alcoholism

We know that alcoholism is a disease with biologic, psychological, and social/environmental components, but we do not know what role—or how much of a role—each of these components plays.

Biologic and Family Factors

Research into the hereditary and environmental causes of alcoholism has found higher rates of alcoholism among family members of individuals addicted to alcohol. In fact, according to researchers, alcoholism is four to five times more common among the children of those who are addicted to alcohol than in the general population.

Individuals categorized with type 1 alcoholism are individuals who had at least one parent who was a problem drinker and grew up in an environment that encouraged heavy drinking. Their drinking is reinforced by family and social events that include heavy drinking. These individuals share certain per-

YOUR SPIRITUAL AND EMOTIONAL HEALTH

The Emotional Trauma of Losing a Loved One to Impaired Driving

The loss of someone you love is always devastating. When the death is sudden and violent, it can be even more traumatic. Hurt, anger, sadness, and frustration are some of the emotions a senseless and violent death causes. The loss of a loved one because of an impaired driving crash brings an abrupt end to that person's life, his or her future dreams and aspirations. There is no chance to say good-bye, no time to say thank you or I am sorry. There are loose ends that will never be tied. In particular, someone who has lost a child or a partner often feels guilty that he or she could not protect them.

The violence of auto accidents often leaves the victims unrecognizable. The hospital or funeral home may not permit viewing of the body, which can lead families into painful fantasies about how their loved one looked; or they may doubt that the person actually died. For many families, seeing the body gives them closure that the person they loved is really gone.

Central to the trauma that families and friends experience after a crash is the senselessness of the death. The fact that the death could have been prevented and is clearly someone's fault is one of the most painful parts of grieving. Knowing that someone chose to be negligent is hard to understand. Many people report feelings of intense anger, even rage, at the offender.

Anger can be central to the grieving process. There is anger not only at the offender but also "the system" and at other family members. Because people experience the sudden loss differently, some may feel anger at the way other family members appear to be moving on or not moving on. Even anger toward the person who has died–due to feelings of abandonment–is not unusual. Anger covers up the underlying sadness that may be more difficult to endure.

Anxiety and fear are also common. Suddenly families realize their vulnerability, a concept that may not have been fully understood before. Often people hold on to the belief that bad things do not happen to good people. When that idea is destroyed, it may be replaced with fear and a sense of powerlessness that is overwhelming.

The emotional aftermath of losing a loved one to impaired driving is filled with feelings and experiences not even touched upon in this short discussion. The road to feeling better is often blocked; many people feel they will not be happy again. While it is true that life will never be the same, families do survive the ordeal. Many manage to gain strength and find happiness again. Ultimately, what people are left with is sorrow. Sorrow encompasses the knowledge that you will always feel sadness over the tragic loss of your loved one; however, it is also a step away from being overwhelmed by grief.

Source: Mothers Against Drunk Driving (MADD) Canada. Retrieved August 26, 2009 from the Transport Canada website: www.tc.gc.ca/roadsafety/safedrivers/impaireddriving/smashed.

sonality characteristics; they avoid novelty and harmful situations and are concerned about the thoughts and feelings of others. Individuals classified with type 2 alcoholism are typically males only. These men are the biological sons of fathers who in addition to being alcoholics have a history of violence and drug use. These men display the opposite characteristics of individuals considered type 1 alcoholics; they do not seek social approval, they lack inhibition, and they are prone to novelty-seeking behaviours.

Scientists are on the trail of an "alcohol gene," but so far they have not found one. In 1990, it appeared that a specific gene linked to alcoholism had been discovered. It turned out, however, that not only was the gene not found consistently in every person addicted to alcohol studied, it also existed in some individuals who were not alcoholics.

Because the effects of heredity and environment are so difficult to separate, some researchers have chosen to examine this issue through twin and adoption studies. So far, these studies have produced inconclusive results. However, a slightly higher rate of similar drinking behaviours has been demonstrated among identical twins. Further, sons living away from their biologic parents who are alcoholics tend to more closely resemble them in drinking behaviours than they do their adoptive or foster parents.

Social and Cultural Factors

There are numerous factors that may mitigate or exacerbate problems with alcohol. Many individuals begin to drink because of peer pressure—because everyone else is doing it. Others may begin drinking as a way to dull the pain of an acute loss or an emotional or social problem. For example, students may drink to escape the stress involved in university or college life, disappointment over unfulfilled expectations, difficulties in forming relationships, or the loss of the security of home, loved ones, and close friends. Unfortunately, the emotional discomfort that causes many people to turn to alcohol also ultimately causes them to become even more uncomfortable as the depressant effect of

try it **NOW!**

Make a conscious effort to alter your drinking habits. Take these measures to be sure you do not become extremely intoxicated the next time you go out; switch to light beers or another beverage with a lower alcohol content; drink slowly; have a glass of water after each drink containing alcohol; eat a meal before going out drinking to slow the rate of absorption.

the drug begins to take its toll. Thus, the person who is already depressed may become even more depressed, antagonizing friends and other social supports until these supports turn away.

Family attitudes toward alcohol also influence whether or not a person will develop a drinking problem. It has been demonstrated that people raised in cultures in which drinking is a part of religious or ceremonial activities or in which alcohol is a traditional part of the family meal are less prone to alcohol dependency. In contrast, in societies in which alcohol purchase is carefully controlled and drinking is regarded as a rite of passage to adulthood, such as that found in Canada, the tendency for abuse appears to be greater.

what do you **THINK?**

What are the attitudes and behaviours in your family toward alcohol? What are the attitudes and behaviours of your friends toward alcohol? What are the attitudes and behaviours regarding alcohol on your campus? Whose attitudes and behaviours towards alcohol are most reflected in your current attitudes and behaviours toward alcohol?

Certain social factors have been linked with alcoholism as well. These include urbanization, the weakening of links to the extended family and a general loosening of kinship ties, increased mobility, and changing religious and philosophic values. Apparently, then, some combination of heredity and environment plays a decisive role in the development of alcoholism.

Effects of Alcoholism on the Family

Recently, it has been recognized that not only the person addicted to alcohol but also his or her entire family suffers. Although most research focuses on family effects during the late stages of alcoholism, the family unit actually begins to react early on as the person starts to show symptoms of addiction to alcohol.

Many families affected by alcoholism have no idea what normal family life is like. Family members unconsciously adapt to the behaviours of the person who is addicted to alcohol by adjusting their own behaviours. To minimize their feelings about the addiction or out of love for him or her, family members take on various abnormal roles. These roles actually help keep the person drinking. Children in such dysfunctional families generally assume at least one of the following roles:

- Family hero: tries to divert attention from the problem by being really good, almost too good to be true
- Scapegoat: draws attention away from the family's primary problem through delinquency or misbehaviour
- Lost child: becomes passive and quietly withdraws from upsetting situations as well as family life
- Mascot: disrupts tense situations by providing comic relief

For children in alcoholic homes, life is a struggle. They have to deal with constant stress, anxiety, and embarrassment. Because the individual who is an alcoholic is often the centre of attention, the children's wants and needs are usually ignored. It is not uncommon for these children to be victims of violence, abuse, neglect, or incest. As previously noted, when such children grow up they have a greater tendency to become alcoholics themselves than do children from nonalcoholic families.

Over time, we have come to recognize the unique problems of adult children of individuals addicted to alcohol whose difficulties in life stem from a lack of parental nurturing during childhood. Among these problems are an inability to develop social attachments, a need to be in control of all emotions and situations, low self-esteem, and depression.

Fortunately, not all individuals who grew up in alcoholic families are doomed to have lifelong problems. Many of these people develop a resiliency in response to their family's problems and enter adulthood armed with positive strengths and valuable career-oriented skills, such as the ability to assume responsibility, strong organizational skills, and realistic expectations of their jobs and those of others.

Costs to Society

As previously noted, the alcohol industry in Canada registered sales of more than $18 billion in the fiscal year ending March 31, 2007, providing employment for more than 14 000 persons and generating significant revenue for provincial and federal governments. The average beverage sales per capita per year for Canadians was $667.

The benefits of alcohol sales to the economy should be considered alongside the consequences of alcohol abuse and addiction. Wider society suffers the consequences of individuals' alcohol abuse. The figure of $18.45 billion, or 2.7 percent of GDP, represents the most optimistic estimate of the cost of addiction to society. The actual number could be significantly higher. Of this amount, alcohol abuse accounts for $7.5 billion.

Women and Alcoholism

In the past, women have consumed less alcohol and had fewer alcohol-related problems than men. Now, a greater percentage of women, especially college- and university-aged women, are choosing to drink and many are drinking more heavily.

Studies indicate that there are now almost as many women as men who become alcoholics. However, there appear to be differences between men and women when it comes to alcohol abuse:

1. Women attribute the onset of problem drinking to a specific life stress or traumatic event more frequently than men.
2. Women's alcoholism starts later and progresses more quickly than men's; this phenomenon is called "telescoping."
3. Women tend to be prescribed mood-altering drugs more often than men; women thus face the risks of drug interaction or cross-tolerance more often.
4. Men not addicted to alcohol tend to divorce their spouses who are addicted nine times more often than they do their spouses without an alcohol addiction; women addicted to alcohol are thus not as likely to have a family support system to aid them in their recovery.
5. Women addicted to alcohol do not tend to receive as much social support as men in their treatment and recovery.
6. Unmarried, divorced, or single-parent women tend to have significant economic problems that may make entry into a treatment program especially difficult.

what do you THINK?

Think about your campus and the cultural norms surrounding alcohol use. Do women drink as frequently as men? Why or why not? Do women on campus drink heavily? Why or why not? Does the campus culture view men's and women's drinking in the same way? What supports are available on campus for individuals with a drinking problem? What supports are available in the local community?

RECOVERY

Most individuals addicted to alcohol and problem drinkers who seek help have experienced a turning point or dramatic occurrence, such as a failed relationship or confrontation at work. Regardless of the reasons for seeking help, it has finally been recognized that alcohol controls the person's life—this is a critical component of recovery. The first step on the road to recovery is to regain that control and to assume responsibility for personal actions.

The Family's Role

Family members of an individual addicted to alcohol sometimes take action before that person does. They may go to an organization or a treatment facility to seek help for themselves and their relative. An effective method of helping an individual addicted to alcohol confront the disease is a process called **intervention**. Essentially, an intervention is a planned confrontation with the person who is an alcoholic that involves several family members plus professional counsellors. The family members express their love and concern, telling the person who has the addiction that they will no longer refrain from acknowledging the problem and affirming their support for appropriate treatment. A family intervention is often the turning point for a growing number of individuals addicted to alcohol.

Treatment Programs

There are hundreds of residential care facilities in Canada for the treatment of alcohol and drug addiction, funded by a mix of municipal, provincial, and federal sources. There are also outpatient, detox, walk-in, and crisis centres. Treatment programs are based on various models and offered in many other languages in addition to French and English. Upon admission to a treatment facility, the individual is given a complete physical exam to determine whether there are underlying medical problems that will interfere with treatment. Individuals addicted to alcohol who quit drinking typically experience withdrawal symptoms, such as

- hyperexcitability
- confusion
- sleep disorders

Intervention: A planned confrontation with a person addicted to alcohol in which family members and/or friends express their concern about the drinking.

- convulsions
- agitation
- tremors of the hands
- brief hallucinations
- depression
- headache
- seizures

In a small percentage of individuals, alcohol withdrawal results in a severe syndrome known as **delirium tremens (DTs)**. Delirium tremens is characterized by confusion, delusions, agitated behaviours, and hallucinations.

Withdrawal from alcohol is very difficult and medically risky—more so than for many other addictive substances or behaviours. Thus, for any long-term addiction to alcohol, medical supervision is usually necessary. Detoxification, the process by which individuals addicted to alcohol end their dependence, is commonly carried out in a medical facility where they can be monitored to prevent fatal withdrawal reactions. Withdrawal usually takes 7 to 21 days. Shortly after detoxification, treatment begins for psychological addiction. Most treatment facilities keep their patients from three to six weeks. Treatment at private treatment centres costs several thousand dollars, but some insurance programs or employers will assume most of this expense.

Family Therapy, Individual Therapy, and Group Therapy

Various individual and group therapies are also available. In family therapy, the person and family members gradually examine the psychological reasons underlying the addiction. In individual and group therapy, individuals addicted to alcohol learn positive coping skills for use in situations that have regularly caused them to drink. On some campuses, the problems associated with alcohol abuse are so great that student health centres are offering their own treatment programs.

Other Types of Treatment

Two other treatments are drug and aversion therapy. For drug therapy, disulfiram (trade name Antabuse) is the drug of choice for treating individuals addicted to alcohol. If alcohol is consumed, the drug causes unpleasant intolerant effects such as headache, nausea, vomiting, drowsiness, and hangover. These symptoms discourage one from drinking. Aversion therapy is based on conditioning therapy. It works on the premise that the sight, smell, and taste of alcohol will acquire aversive properties if repeatedly paired with a noxious stimulus. For a period of 10 days, the individual takes drugs that induce vomiting when combined with alcohol. These treatments work best in conjunction with counselling.

Alcoholics Anonymous (AA) is a private, nonprofit, self-help organization founded in 1935. The organization, which relies on group support to help people stop drinking, currently has more than one million members, with branches all over the world. People attending their first AA meeting will find that last names are never used. Neither is anyone forced to speak. Members are taught to believe that their alcoholism is a lifetime problem. They share their stories with the group and are asked to place their faith, and control of the habit, in the hands of a "higher power." The road to recovery is taken one step at a time. AA offers specialized meetings for individuals who are homosexual, atheist, HIV-positive, and professionals.

Alcoholics Anonymous also has auxiliary groups to help spouses or partners, friends, and children of individuals addicted to alcohol. Al-Anon is the group dedicated to helping adult relatives and friends of the person who is addicted understand the disease and learn how they can be part of the recovery process. The support gained from talking with others with similar problems is one of the greatest benefits derived from participation in Al-Anon. Many members learn how to exert greater control over their own lives. Some are able to rid themselves of the guilt they feel about their participation in their loved one's alcoholism.

Alateen, another AA-related organization, is designed to help adolescents live with a parent or parents who are alcoholics. Teens are taught that they are not at fault for their parents' problems with alcohol. They learn skills to develop their self-esteem so they can function better socially. Alateen also helps the children of people addicted to alcohol to overcome their guilt feelings.

Relapse

Roughly 60 percent of individuals addicted to alcohol relapse (resume drinking) within the first three months of treatment. Why is the relapse rate so high? Treating an addiction requires more than getting the person who is addicted to stop using; it also requires getting the person to break a pattern of behaviours that has dominated his or her life—often for some time.

People seeking to regain a healthy lifestyle must not only confront their addiction, but also guard against the tendency to relapse. Individuals with compulsive personalities need to learn to understand themselves and take control. Others need to view treatment as a long-term process that takes a lot of effort beyond attending a weekly self-help group meeting. In order to work, a recovery program must offer the individual addicted to alcohol ways to increase self-esteem and resume personal growth.

SMOKING

Health consequences of the tobacco epidemic in developed and developing countries are devastating. By 2020, tobacco use is expected to kill more people than any single disease. Since the middle of the twentieth century, tobacco products have killed more than 60 million people in developed countries alone.

Canadians have been smoking less since 1966, when 54 percent of men and 28 percent of women were smokers. The Canadian Tobacco Use Monitoring Survey reported (from data collected between February and June 2008) that slightly more than 4.9 million Canadians were current smokers, representing 18 percent of the population 15 years of age and older. More men than women smoke (20 versus 16 percent). Thirteen percent of Canadians report smoking daily and another 5 percent report occasional smoking. Daily smokers consume, on average, 15 cigarettes per day. In the 15- to 19-year-old group, 15 percent reported smoking; 8 percent reported smoking daily, with an average of 11.3 cigarettes. Seven percent of 15- to 19-year-olds were occasional smokers. In the 20- to 24-year-old group, 19 percent reported daily smoking, with another 9 percent reporting occasionally lighting up. In this age group, males who smoke daily consume more cigarettes per day than females (16.4 versus 9.6).

Despite the reduced rate of smoking in the population, it remains the number one preventable cause of death in Canada. Every year, smoking kills five times more Canadians than car accidents, murder, suicide, and alcohol abuse combined. Deaths attributed to tobacco in 2002 totalled 37 209, or 16.6 percent of all deaths, while acute-care hospital days attributable to tobacco were 2 210 155, or 10.3 percent of all hospital days.

what do you THINK?

What would it be like if Canada were smoke-free? Is your campus smoke-free? If not, what would it take to get it there? Has Canada and each of its provinces gone far enough to protect the rights of nonsmokers? Why or why not? What about smokers and their rights?

Tobacco and Its Effects

Tobacco is available in several forms. Cigarettes, cigars, and pipes are used for burning and inhaling tobacco. **Snuff** is a finely ground form of tobacco that can be inhaled, chewed, or placed against the gums. **Chewing tobacco**, also known as "smokeless tobacco," is placed between the gums and teeth for sucking or chewing.

The chemical stimulant nicotine is the major psychoactive substance in these products. In its natural form, **nicotine** is a colourless liquid that turns brown upon oxidation (exposure to oxygen). When tobacco leaves are burned in a cigarette, pipe, or cigar, nicotine is released and inhaled into the lungs. Sucking or chewing tobacco releases nicotine into the saliva, and is then absorbed through the mucous membranes in the mouth.

Smoking is the most common form of tobacco use. Smoking delivers a strong dose of nicotine to the user, along with an additional 5000 chemicals, 50 of which are known to cause cancer. Among these chemicals are various gases and vapours that carry particulate matter in concentrations that are 500 000 times as great as the most air-polluted cities in the world. Particulate matter condenses in the lungs to form a thick, brownish sludge called tar. **Tar** contains various carcinogenic (cancer-causing) agents such as benzopyrene and chemical irritants such as phenol. Phenol has the potential to combine with other chemicals to contribute to the development of lung cancer.

In healthy lungs, millions of tiny hairlike tissues called cilia sweep away foreign matter. Once the foreign material is swept up and collected by the cilia, it can be expelled from the lungs by coughing. Nicotine impairs the cleansing function of the cilia by paralyzing them for up to one hour following the smoking of a single cigarette. Tars and other solids in tobacco smoke are thus allowed to accumulate and irritate sensitive lung tissue.

Tar and nicotine are not the only harmful chemicals in cigarettes. In fact, tars account for only 8 percent of the components of tobacco smoke. The remaining 92 percent is made up of various gases, the most dangerous

Delirium tremens (DTs): A state of confusion brought on by withdrawal from alcohol. Symptoms include hallucinations, anxiety, and trembling.

Alcoholics Anonymous (AA): An organization whose goal is to help individuals addicted to alcohol stop drinking; includes auxiliary branches such as Al-Anon and Alateen.

Snuff: A powdered form of tobacco sniffed and absorbed through the mucous membranes in the nose or placed inside the cheek and sucked.

Chewing tobacco: A stringy type of tobacco placed in the mouth and then sucked or chewed.

Nicotine: The stimulant chemical in tobacco products.

Tar: A thick, brownish substance condensed from particulate matter in smoked tobacco.

of which is **carbon monoxide**. In tobacco smoke, the concentration of carbon monoxide is 800 times higher than the level considered safe. In the human body, carbon monoxide reduces the oxygen-carrying capacity of the red blood cells by binding with the receptor sites for oxygen. Smoking thus diminishes the capacity of the circulatory system to carry oxygen, causing oxygen deprivation in many body tissues. The heat from tobacco smoke, which can reach 880°C, is also harmful to the smoker. Inhaling hot gases and vapours exposes sensitive mucous membranes to irritating chemicals that weaken the tissues and contribute to the development of cancers of the mouth, larynx, and throat.

Filtered cigarettes designed to reduce levels of gases such as hydrogen cyanide and hydrocarbons may actually deliver more hazardous carbon monoxide to the user than non-filtered brands. Some smokers use low-tar and nicotine products (that is, mild, special, or "lite") thinking these are safer forms of cigarettes. True, they contain 10 percent less carbon monoxide and 8 percent less nicotine, but they contain the same level of the other harmful chemicals. Furthermore, since there is less nicotine, smokers tend to inhale more deeply when smoking this kind of cigarette and actually inhale more of the dangerous chemicals than they would if they smoked regular cigarettes.

what do you THINK?

Why do you think the rates of smoking have decreased in recent years? What "antismoking" methods/policies/laws do you think have been successful? What other methods/policies/laws might you suggest?

Clove cigarettes contain about 40 percent ground cloves (a spice) and about 60 percent tobacco. Many users mistakenly believe that these products are made entirely of ground cloves and that smoking them eliminates the risks associated with tobacco. In fact, clove cigarettes contain higher levels of tar, nicotine, and carbon monoxide than regular cigarettes. In addition, the numbing effect of eugenol, the active ingredient in cloves, allows smokers to inhale the smoke more deeply.

Nicotine is a powerful CNS stimulant that produces an aroused, alert mental state. Nicotine also stimulates the adrenal glands, increasing the production of adrenaline. The physical effects of nicotine stimulation include increased heart and respiratory rate, constriction of blood vessels, and subsequent increased blood pressure because the heart must work harder to pump blood through the narrowed vessels. Because smoking increases the "stickiness" of the blood, there is an increased risk of developing blood clots when you smoke. This risk is further elevated when smoking is combined with use of oral contraceptives.

Nicotine decreases the stomach contractions that signal hunger. It also decreases blood sugar levels. These factors, along with decreased sensation in the taste buds, reduce appetite. For this reason, many smokers eat less and weigh, on average, 3 kilograms less than nonsmokers. Beginning smokers usually feel the effects of nicotine with their first puff. These symptoms, called **nicotine poisoning**, include dizziness, lightheadedness, rapid, erratic pulse, clammy skin, nausea, vomiting, and diarrhea. The effects of nicotine poisoning cease when tolerance to the chemical develops. Medical research indicates that tolerance develops almost immediately in new users, perhaps after the second or third cigarette. In contrast, tolerance to most other drugs, such as alcohol, develops over a period of months or years.

Smoking—A Learned Behaviour

Taking up smoking is a gradual process. It begins with forming a predisposition to smoking—that is, a perception that smoking is a normal behaviour accepted and pervasive in society or one's peer group. Smoking usually starts with an experimental stage when it happens repeatedly but irregularly; then regular use, followed by addiction. The transition from first experimenting with smoking to daily use usually takes an average of two to three years.

About 85 percent of smokers start before age 16. New smokers do not expect to become addicted, believing instead that they will be able to quit whenever they want to, discounting the prospect of addiction and the potential adverse health effects of that future addiction. Only 10 percent of smokers begin after the age of 18. It seems probable that the level of knowledge and experience acquired by age 18 relate to the decision not to start smoking.

Tobacco product promotions are intended to convey a positive brand image and convey as many "impressions" (exposures to the consumer) as possible in order to create and maintain the perception that tobacco use is desirable, socially acceptable, healthy, sexy, and more pervasive in society than it really is. These promotions are primarily directed to young people, particularly young women, partly because the tobacco companies know that most people make the decision as to whether or not to smoke by the age of 16.

This positive image of tobacco use is precisely the perception that people need in order to feel reassured about smoking. Promotion affects tobacco consumption in three interrelated ways:

- by influencing the smoking decision process among starters through helping to shape and reinforce their belief that it's okay to smoke
- by influencing the amount consumed by smokers

- by hindering the quitting decision process among those who are addicted by acting as a reassuring cue to smoke

Smokeless Tobacco

Smokeless tobacco is just as addictive as cigarettes due to its nicotine content. Although there is nicotine in all tobacco products, smokeless tobacco contains more of the substance than cigarettes. An average-sized dip or chew held in your mouth for 30 minutes gives as much nicotine as smoking four cigarettes. Thus, a two-can-a-week snuff dipper gets as much nicotine as a one-and-a-half-pack-a-day smoker.

One of the major risks of chewing tobacco is **leukoplakia**, a condition characterized by leathery white patches inside the mouth produced by contact with irritants in tobacco juice. Smokeless tobacco also impairs the senses of taste and smell, causing the user to add salt and sugar to food, which may contribute to high blood pressure and obesity. Some smokeless tobacco products contain high levels of sodium (salt), which also contributes to high blood pressure. Another risk of using smokeless tobacco is caused by the addition of fibreglass to the tobacco, which helps cut the lining in the mouth to facilitate the uptake of nicotine by the bloodstream. In addition, dental problems are common among users: contact with tobacco juice causes receding gums, tooth decay, bad breath, and discoloured teeth. Damage to the teeth and jawbone can contribute to early loss of teeth. Users of all tobacco products may not be able to use the vitamins and other nutrients in food effectively. In some cases, vitamin supplements may be recommended by a physician.

what do you THINK?

Why do people use smokeless tobacco? Do you think the health risks of smokeless tobacco are well understood? Should smokeless tobacco be forbidden in public places just as cigarettes are banned? Why do you think chewing tobacco has attracted athletes? Do you think the use of smokeless tobacco should be banned in high school, college, and university athletics? Why or why not?

Environmental Tobacco Smoke

As the population of nonsmokers rises, so does the demand for the right to breathe clean air. As a result, smoking is banned in many public places, particularly those that are indoors.

Environmental tobacco smoke (ETS) is divided into two categories: mainstream smoke and secondhand smoke (also called sidestream smoke). **Mainstream smoke** refers to smoke drawn through tobacco while inhaling; **secondhand smoke** refers to smoke from the burning end of a cigarette and the smoke exhaled by a smoker. People who breathe smoke as a result of someone else's smoking are said to be involuntary or passive smokers.

This 25-year-old cancer survivor has undergone surgery to remove neck muscles, lymph nodes, and his tongue. He began using smokeless tobacco at age 13; by age 17, he was diagnosed with squamous cell carcinoma. He now speaks out about the dangers of smokeless tobacco.

Although involuntary smokers breathe less tobacco than active smokers, they still face risks from exposure to tobacco smoke. Secondhand smoke actually contains more carcinogenic substances than the smoke that a smoker inhales directly—about twice as much tar and nicotine, 5 times as much carbon monoxide, and 50 times as much ammonia. There is also evidence that secondhand smoke may pose an even greater risk for death due to heart disease than for

Carbon monoxide: A gas found in cigarette smoke that binds at oxygen receptor sites in the blood.

Nicotine poisoning: Symptoms often experienced by beginning smokers; they include dizziness; diarrhea; lightheadedness; rapid, erratic pulse; clammy skin; nausea; and vomiting.

Leukoplakia: A condition characterized by leathery white patches inside the mouth produced by contact with irritants in tobacco juice.

Environmental tobacco smoke (ETS): Smoke from tobacco products, including sidestream and mainstream smoke.

Mainstream smoke: Smoke drawn from a cigarette, cigar, or pipe while inhaling.

Secondhand smoke: Cigarette, pipe, or cigar smoke released into the air and inhaled by nonsmokers (as well as smokers).

Global anti-smoking efforts

Day by day, smoking is becoming a thing of the past in Canada. The number of smokers declines every year, in tandem with an increase in efforts by government and health activists to tighten up restrictions on the sale and use of tobacco.

Smoking has been banned from most offices for some time, but the bans have now extended to bars, restaurants and other public places. Some cities have banned indoor smoking outright, shutting down separate smoking rooms altogether.

Canada is considered to be at the forefront of anti-smoking legislation, but the rest of the world is beginning to catch up. Here's a sampler of homegrown and global anti-smoking measures:

Efforts in Canada

NEWFOUNDLAND AND LABRADOR

The province's Smoke-free Environment Act was amended on July 1, 2005, to ban smoking in all public places, including bars and bingo halls.

PRINCE EDWARD ISLAND

Without a specially ventilated smoking room, smokers are out of luck in public places and workplaces. Also, food can't be served in these rooms.

NOVA SCOTIA

Halifax regional council unanimously adopted a policy in October 2009 to restrict smoking at about 480 outdoor venues where children are present, such as parks, rinks and sports fields.

Smoking in public spaces was banned provincewide after Dec. 1, 2006, with a minimum fine of $2,000 for those who choose to light up. The only exceptions are designated rooms in nursing homes and long-term-care facilities.

Prominent displays of tobacco products in stores are also prohibited under the act.

Taxi cabs, bowling alleys, schoolyards and other public places were smoke-free as of Jan. 1, 2003. In bars and restaurants, smoking is restricted after 9 p.m. to an enclosed room that's separately ventilated and available only to adults. As well, tobacco can be seized from people under 19.

Nova Scotia has banned smoking in prison. In April 2008, the province also outlawed smoking in vehicles carrying children.

NEW BRUNSWICK

As of October 2004 there has been a provincewide ban on smoking in all public areas. Restaurants and bars can't have smoking sections or glassed-in smoking areas.

QUEBEC

All private designated smoking rooms were eliminated by May 30, 2008.

Restaurants, bars, clubs, bingo halls, casinos and shelters became smoke-free on May 31, 2006. Smoking is also forbidden within nine metres of any doorway leading to a health or social services institution, college, university or child-care facility.

A ban on smoking in all public places started in June 2006.

It's illegal to sell tobacco by mail order, over the internet, on school grounds or in health-care, social services or child-care facilities.

ONTARIO

Retail behind-counter displays of tobacco were banned after 2008. In 2009, Ontario also outlawed smoking in vehicles carrying children.

On June 1, 2006, the Smoke-Free Ontario Act prohibited smoking in all workplaces and enclosed spaces open to the public, except for private homes and hotel rooms.

In Toronto in 2004, all bars, pool halls, bingo halls, casinos, and racetracks became smoke-free, with fines ranging from $205 to $5,000. A plan to outlaw smoking rooms by 2005 was sent back to council for review.

The Northwestern (Ontario) Health Unit banned smoking in all public places and private businesses as of Jan. 1, 2003, with fines ranging from $5,000 to $25,000.

The City of Ottawa banned smoking in all workplaces and public spaces, with no allowance for designated smoking rooms, on Aug. 1, 2001.

It's illegal to sell tobacco at hospitals, psychiatric facilities, nursing homes, long-term-care facilities and charitable institutions.

MANITOBA

The Non-Smokers' Health Protection Act banned smoking in public areas, with the exception of group-living facilities and hotel rooms, as of October 2004. Restaurants and bars can't have smoking sections or glassed-in smoking areas.

As of January 2002, it became illegal to smoke in any indoor location in Winnipeg where minors are present. Some coffee shops and restaurants avoid this problem by banning children.

All public places in Winnipeg became smoke-free as of Sept. 1, 2003.

SASKATCHEWAN

Saskatchewan in 2009 outlawed in all enclosed places of employment, including offices, warehouses, vehicles and some mines.

On Jan. 19, 2005, the Supreme Court of Canada ruled the province could reinstate the "shower curtain law" that requires store owners to keep tobacco products out of sight.

As of January 2005, all public places, including outdoor areas and veterans' clubs, became smoke-free under the Tobacco Control Act, with fines of up to $10,000 for smokers who violate it.

Bingo parlours, bars, casinos, restaurants and bowling alleys after Dec. 31, 2002, were required to designate 40 per cent of their space as non-smoking. By 2004, this percentage increased to 60 per cent.

ALBERTA

The Smoke-free Places Act, effective January 2006, restricts smoking in public places and workplaces where minors are allowed. Casinos, bingo halls, and bars don't fall under these restrictions.

Some Albertan municipalities have enacted tougher bylaws, and Peace River, Stettler, Wainwright, Drumheller, Olds, Airdrie and Jasper are 100 per cent smoke-free in public places. Calgary banned all smoking in public places, including restaurants and bars, as of Jan. 1, 2007.

People under age 18 who are caught smoking or in possession of tobacco products after April 1, 2003, can be fined $100 and have their cigarettes seized.

In Edmonton, there has been no smoking in public places where children are served, except for lounges, since May 22, 2001.

BRITISH COLUMBIA

In 2009, British Columbia outlawed citizens from lighting a cigarette in a vehicle in the presence of a person under the age of 16. A province wide ban on smoking in public places began in 2008.

You can't smoke in public places like restaurants, bars, bingo halls, bowling alleys and casinos. Restaurant and bar owners may construct open smoking rooms where staff may volunteer to serve.

Victoria banned smoking in all workplaces and public spaces, with no allowance for designated smoking rooms, as of Aug. 1, 2001.

YUKON

In May 2008, the Yukon became the last of the provinces and territories to ban smoking in public places.

NORTHWEST TERRITORIES

In March 2006, legislation was passed confirming and enforcing the Workers Compensation ban on smoking in workplaces.

The Workers Compensation Board bans smoking in all enclosed businesses and work sites on May 1, 2004, including bars. Smoking rooms are only allowed in workplaces that are private residences.

NUNAVUT

Smoking was banned in all enclosed businesses and work sites on May 1, 2004, by the Workers Compensation Board. This includes bars. It also bans smoking within 15 metres of schools and three metres of entrances.

Source: CBC.CA

death due to lung cancer. Secondhand smoke is estimated to cause more deaths per year than any other environmental pollutant.

Lung cancer and heart disease are not the only risks involuntary smokers face. Children exposed to secondhand smoke also have a greater chance of developing other respiratory problems, such as cough, wheezing, asthma, and chest colds, along with a decrease in pulmonary performance. The greatest effects of secondhand smoke are seen in children under the age of five.

Cigarette, cigar, and pipe smoke in enclosed areas present other hazards to nonsmokers. The level of carbon monoxide from cigarette smoke contained in enclosed places is 4000 times higher than the standard recommended by the US Environmental Protection Agency for a definition of clean air. An estimated 10 to 15 percent of nonsmokers are extremely sensitive (hypersensitive) to cigarette smoke. These people experience itchy eyes, difficulty breathing, painful headaches, nausea, and dizziness in response to minute amounts of smoke.

Efforts to reduce the hazards associated with passive smoking have been gaining momentum in recent years. As previously mentioned, smoking is now illegal in most public places, including government buildings, restaurants, cafés, coffee shops, shopping malls, schools, and universities. Hotels and motels, if not completely smoke-free, set aside rooms for nonsmokers, and car rental agencies designate certain vehicles for nonsmokers. Smoking has also been banned for some time on all domestic airline flights. Recently, some regions have declared vehicles containing children under the age of 18 years to be smoke-free as well.

QUITTING

From what we know about smoking cessation and the various programs that have developed to support people in their efforts, quitting is often a lengthy process involving several unsuccessful attempts before success is finally achieved. Even successful quitters suffer occasional slips, emphasizing the fact that quitting smoking is a dynamic process that may actually be never-ending.

Breaking the Nicotine Addiction

Nicotine addiction may be one of the toughest addictions to overcome. When smokers quit, **nicotine withdrawal** occurs; the symptoms of withdrawal include irritability, restlessness, nausea, vomiting, and intense cravings for tobacco. The person who quits has several options to manage the symptoms of withdrawal.

Nicotine Replacement Products

Non-tobacco products that put nicotine in the bloodstream have helped some people stop using tobacco. The two most common nicotine-replacement products are nicotine chewing gum and the nicotine patch, both available by prescription. Some individuals use a prescription chewing gum containing nicotine, called Nicorette, to help with the withdrawal symptoms by reducing their nicotine consumption gradually over time. Under the guidance of a physician, the individual chews between 12 and 24 pieces of gum per day for up to six months, with a plan for reducing consumption over time. Nicorette delivers about as much nicotine as a cigarette, but because it is absorbed through the mucous membrane of the mouth, it does not produce the same rush as the nicotine that is inhaled from a cigarette. As a result, the individual who stopped smoking does not experience withdrawal symptoms, and fewer cravings for nicotine are felt as the dosage is reduced until the person is completely weaned. There is some controversy surrounding the use of nicotine replacement gum. Opponents believe that it substitutes one addiction for another. Successful quitters counter that it is a valid way to help break a deadly habit without suffering the unpleasant withdrawal symptoms and cravings that often lead ex-smokers to resume smoking.

The nicotine patch, first marketed in 1991, is a popular method for those attempting to quit smoking. It is generally used in conjunction with a comprehensive smoking-behaviour cessation program. A small, thin patch is placed on the smoker's upper body to deliver a continuous flow of nicotine through the skin for 24-hours, helping to relieve the body's cravings for nicotine. The patch is worn for 8 to 12 weeks under the guidance of a physician. During this time, the dose of nicotine in the patch is gradually reduced until the smoker is fully weaned from nicotine. Occasional side-effects include mild skin irritation, insomnia, dry mouth, and nervousness. The patch is relatively inexpensive compared to the price of a pack of cigarettes, and some insurance plans will pay for it.

Breaking the Habit

For many smokers, the road to quitting includes some type of antismoking therapy. Among the more common therapy techniques are aversion therapy, operant conditioning, and self-control therapy. Prospective quitters must decide which method or combination of methods will work best for them.

Nicotine withdrawal: Symptoms, including nausea, headaches, and irritability, suffered by smokers who cease using tobacco.

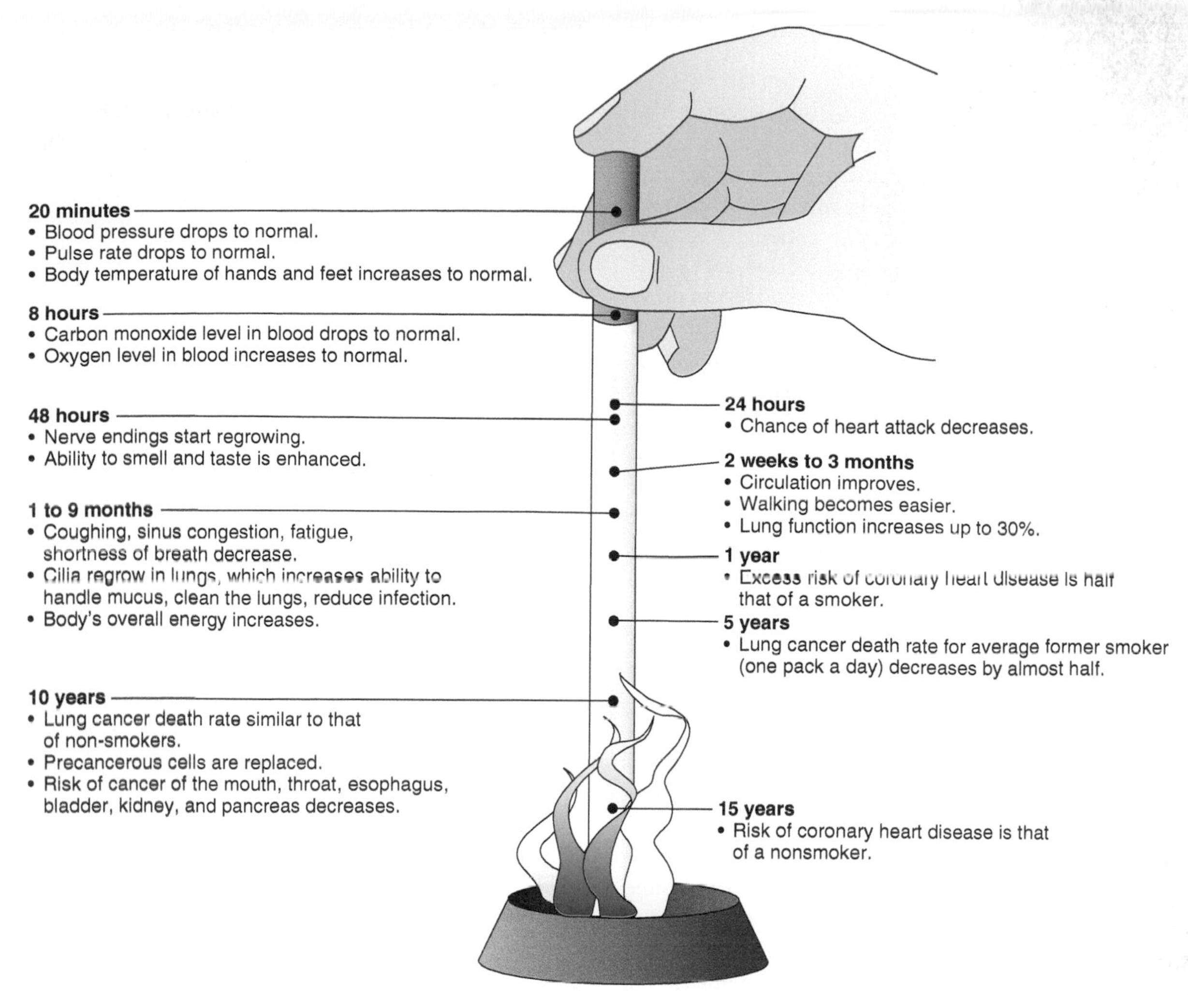

20 minutes
• Blood pressure drops to normal.
• Pulse rate drops to normal.
• Body temperature of hands and feet increases to normal.
8 hours
• Carbon monoxide level in blood drops to normal.
• Oxygen level in blood increases to normal.
48 hours
• Nerve endings start regrowing.
• Ability to smell and taste is enhanced.
1 to 9 months
• Coughing, sinus congestion, fatigue, shortness of breath decrease.
• Cilia regrow in lungs, which increases ability to handle mucus, clean the lungs, reduce infection.
• Body's overall energy increases.
10 years
• Lung cancer death rate similar to that of non-smokers.
• Precancerous cells are replaced.
• Risk of cancer of the mouth, throat, esophagus, bladder, kidney, and pancreas decreases.
24 hours
• Chance of heart attack decreases.
2 weeks to 3 months
• Circulation improves.
• Walking becomes easier.
• Lung function increases up to 30%.
1 year
• Excess risk of coronary heart disease is half that of a smoker.
5 years
• Lung cancer death rate for average former smoker (one pack a day) decreases by almost half.
15 years
• Risk of coronary heart disease is that of a nonsmoker.

FIGURE 5c.2

When Smokers Quit

Within 20 minutes of smoking cessation, the body begins a series of changes that continues for years.

Source: G. Hanson and P. Venturelli, *Drugs and Society,* 5th ed. (Sudbury, MA: Jones and Bartlett, 1998), 320 © Jones and Bartlett, www.jbpub.com. Reprinted with permission.

Programs that combine several approaches have shown the most promise.

Benefits of Quitting

Many tissues damaged by smoking can repair themselves. As soon as smokers stop, their bodies begin the repair process. Within eight hours, carbon monoxide and oxygen levels return to normal, and "smoker's breath" disappears. Within a few days of quitting, the mucus clogging airways is broken up and eliminated. Circulation and the senses of taste and smell improve within weeks. Many ex-smokers who have kicked the cigarette habit say they have more energy, sleep better, and feel more alert. By the end of one year, the risk for lung cancer and stroke decreases. Within two years, the risk for heart attack drops to near-normal. At the end of 10 smoke-free years, the ex-smoker can expect to live out his or her normal life span. Figure 5c.2 shows the health benefits of quitting smoking.

what do you THINK?

What could you do to help someone quit smoking? What are the most common barriers to quitting? When trying to stop smoking, why do people often interpret a relapse as a total failure? Alternatively, how could a relapse be viewed?

CAFFEINE

Caffeine is the most popular and widely consumed drug in Canada. Almost half of Canadians drink coffee every day, and many others consume caffeine in some other form (tea, colas, chocolate), mainly for its well-known "wake-up" effect. Drinking coffee is legal and socially encouraged. Many people believe caffeine is not a drug and is not really addictive. Coffee and other caffeine-containing products seem harmless. If you share these attitudes, think again; research links caffeine to several health problems. **Caffeine** is a drug derived from the chemical family called **xanthines**. Two related chemicals, theophylline and theobromine, are found in tea and chocolate, respectively. Xanthines are mild CNS stimulants that enhance mental alertness and reduce feelings of fatigue. Other stimulant effects include increases in heart muscle contractions, oxygen consumption, metabolism, and urinary output. These effects are felt within 15 to 45 minutes of ingesting a product that contains caffeine.

Side effects of xanthines include wakefulness, insomnia, irregular heartbeat, dizziness, nausea, indigestion, and sometimes mild delirium. Some people also experience heartburn. As with other drugs, the user's psychological outlook and expectations will influence the effects. Different products contain different concentrations of caffeine. A 156-mL (5-ounce) cup of coffee contains 65 to 115 milligrams. Caffeine concentrations vary with the brand and strength of the brew. Small chocolate bars (28 grams) contain up to 15 milligrams of caffeine and theobromine. Table 5c.4 outlines the caffeine content of various products.

TABLE 5c.4
Caffeine Content of Various Products

Product	Caffeine Content (average mg per serving)
Coffee (156-mL cup)	
Regular brewed	65–115
Decaffeinated brewed	3
Decaffeinated instant	2
Tea (175-mL cup)	
Hot steeped	36
Iced	31
Bottled (375 mL)	15
Soft drinks (375-mL serving)	
Jolt Cola	100
Dr. Pepper	61
Mountain Dew	54
Coca-Cola	46
Pepsi	36–38
Chocolate	
28 grams baking chocolate	25
28 grams chocolate candy bar	15
1/2 cup chocolate pudding	4–12
Over-the-counter drugs	
No Doz (2 tablets)	200
Excedrin (2 tablets)	130
Midol (2 tablets)	65
Anacin (2 tablets)	64

Source: Office of Department of Health and Welfare, October 2001.

Caffeine Addiction

As the effects of caffeine wear off, users may feel let down—mentally or physically depressed, tired, and weak. To counteract this, people commonly choose to drink another cup of coffee. Habitually engaging in this practice leads to tolerance and psychological dependency. Until the mid-1970s, caffeine was not medically recognized as addictive. Chronic caffeine use and its attendant behaviours were called "coffee nerves." This syndrome is now recognized as caffeine intoxication, or **caffeinism**. Symptoms of caffeinism include chronic insomnia, jitters, irritability, nervousness, anxiety, and involuntary muscle twitches. Withdrawing the caffeine may compound the effects and produce severe headaches. (Some physicians ask their patients to take a simple test for caffeine addiction: do not consume anything containing caffeine, and if you get a severe headache within four hours, you are addicted and experiencing withdrawal symptoms.) Because caffeine meets the requirements for addiction—tolerance,

Caffeine: A stimulant found in coffee, tea, chocolate, and some soft drinks.

Xanthines: The chemical family of stimulants to which caffeine belongs.

Caffeinism: Caffeine intoxication brought on by excessive caffeine use; symptoms include chronic insomnia, irritability, anxiety, muscle twitches, and headaches.

psychological dependency, and withdrawal symptoms—it can be classified as addictive. Although you would have to drink 67 to 100 cups of coffee in a day to produce a fatal overdose of caffeine, you may experience sensory disturbances after consuming only 10 cups of coffee within a 24-hour period. These symptoms include tinnitus (ringing in the ears), spots before the eyes, numbness in arms and legs, poor circulation, and visual hallucinations. Because 10 cups of coffee is not an extraordinary amount to drink in one day, caffeine use clearly poses health threats.

The Health Consequences of Long-Term Caffeine Use

Long-term caffeine use has been suspected of being linked to a number of serious health problems, ranging from heart disease and cancer to mental dysfunction and birth defects. Further, high consumption (more than six cups of coffee) of unfiltered coffees such as French press and boiled/perked coffee are linked to elevated low-density-lipoprotein concentrations. However, no strong evidence exists to suggest that moderate caffeine use (less than 300 milligrams daily, approximately three cups of coffee) produces harmful effects in healthy, nonpregnant people. In fact, there may be some benefit to frequent moderate consumption of coffee—whether decaffeinated or caffeinated—in terms of reducing risk for type 2 diabetes, though more research is warranted to better understand the mechanisms providing this benefit. Coffee and other products containing caffeine also have potential benefits as ergogenic aids, facilitating athletic performances and potentially positively altering carbohydrate and fat metabolism during exercise.

It appears that caffeine does not cause long-term high blood pressure and is not linked to strokes; nor is there any evidence of a relationship between caffeine and heart disease. However, people who suffer from irregular heartbeat are cautioned against using caffeine because the resultant increase in heart rate might be life-threatening. Both decaffeinated and caffeinated coffee products contain ingredients that can irritate the stomach lining and be harmful to people with stomach ulcers. For years, caffeine consumption was linked with fibrocystic breast disease, a condition characterized by painful, noncancerous lumps in the breasts. Although these conclusions have been challenged, many clinicians advise patients with mammillary cysts to avoid or limit their caffeine use.

Go to MyHealthLab at **www.pearsoned.ca/myhealthlab.** Here you will find self-assessments, case studies, links to health on the net, and much more.

DISCUSSION QUESTIONS

1. When it comes to drinking alcohol, how much is too much? How often is too often? How can you control your consumption of alcohol so that you do not drink too much or too often?
2. What factors may cause someone to progress from being a social drinker to becoming addicted to alcohol? What effect does alcoholism have on the family of the person who becomes addicted?
3. Describe your campus culture regarding alcohol. Create a video/commercial that portrays this culture and the risks associated with it.
4. Discuss the varied forms in which you can ingest tobacco. In each form, how do chemicals enter your system? What are the physiological effects of nicotine?
5. Discuss the risks of smokeless tobacco. Do you think that smokeless tobacco should be banned from all levels of sport? Why or why not?
6. People who smoke often claim they have the right to smoke in public places. From what you have learned about secondhand smoke, how would you argue against an individual's right to smoke in public?
7. Do you drink coffee or other beverages that contain caffeine? Do you limit your consumption of these beverages? Why or why not? Are you addicted to caffeine? How could you find out? What are the risks of caffeine addiction or excessive caffeine consumption?
8. Describe the health risks and potential benefits of coffee and caffeine consumption.

APPLICATION EXERCISE

Reread the "Consider This . . ." scenario at the beginning of the chapter and answer the following questions.

1. What responsibility do the restaurant owner and employees have for protecting the fetus?
2. What responsibility does the mother have for protecting her fetus?
3. If you were the waiter/waitress, what would you do?

MYSEARCHLAB EXERCISE

1. Log on to www.MySearchLab.com.
2. Retrieve article AN 36236940, "Factors That Predict Self-Perceived Problem Drinking among College Students," by E. E. Eshbaugh.
3. Respond to the following questions:
   a. Why do you think most students are not able to identify their own risky behaviours regarding alcohol consumption—that is, drinking more than four (for a female) or five (for a male) drinks on one occasion?
   b. What are the risks of binge drinking? Consider all components of health and wellness.
   c. How might students on your campus be convinced that a moderate consumption of alcohol should be the norm, not the exception?

CHAPTER 5d

STRESS MANAGEMENT

Taken from *Health: The Basics*, Fifth Canadian Edition, by Rebecca J. Donatelle and Angela M. Thompson

STRESS AND THE POST-SECONDARY STUDENT

Stress related to university or college life is more far-reaching than simply the pressure to excel academically. Post-secondary students experience numerous distressors, including changes related to being away from home for the first time, climatic differences between home and school, pressure to make friends in a new and sometimes intimidating setting, the feeling of anonymity imposed by larger classes, test-taking anxiety, and pressures related to time management. Some students are stressed by athletic team requirements, on-campus food selection, roommates' habits, peers' expectations, new questions about personal values and beliefs, relationship problems, fraternity or sorority demands, financial worries, changed sleeping habits (including reduced sleep), and the need to be technologically savvy. For older students, worries about competing with 18-year-olds may also be distressful, in addition to the pressure of determining their future career path and managing responsibilities regarding their family and home. Technological advances have created new pressures for students to be engaged in computer and computer-related tasks for longer time periods, which may cause mental as well as physical duress (that is, anxiety about not finding required information, sifting through the abundance of materials discovered to find credible information, and repetitive strain injuries related to overuse and poor body mechanics). Most colleges and universities offer stress management workshops through their health centres or student counselling departments.

You should not ignore the following symptoms of stress overload. If you experience one or more of these symptoms, act promptly to reduce their impact:

- difficulty keeping up with classes or difficulty concentrating on and finishing tasks
- frequent clashes with close friends, family, or intimate partners about trivial issues such as housekeeping
- frequent mood changes or overreaction to minor problems
- lethargy caused by lack of sleep or excessive frustration
- lack of interest in social activities or tendency to avoid others
- avoidance of stressors through use of drugs or alcohol or through other extreme behaviours
- sleep disturbances, TV or computer/technology-related addiction, free-floating anxiety, or an exaggerated sense of self
- difficulty in maintaining an intimate relationship
- lack of interest in sexual relationships or inability to participate in satisfactory sexual relationships
- tendency to be intolerant of minor differences of opinion
- hunger and cravings or tendency to overeat or to eat while thinking of other things
- lack of awareness of sensory cues
- inability to listen or tendency to jump from subject to subject in conversation
- stuttering or other speech difficulties
- accident-proneness
- difficulty finding the right words to say or misspeaking quite frequently

> **what do you THINK?**
> What are your signs and symptoms of stress? What about your university or college life causes you to react with a stress response? What can you do about these factors?

STRESS MANAGEMENT

Stress can be challenging or defeating depending upon how we learn to view it. The most effective way to avoid defeat is to develop a number of skills known collectively as stress management. Stress management consists primarily of finding balance in our lives. We balance rest, relaxation, physical activity, dietary intake, work, school, family, community responsibilities, finances, and social activities. As we balance our lives, we make the choice to react constructively to our stressors. Robert Eliot, a cardiologist and stress researcher, offers two rules for people trying to cope with life's challenges: "Don't sweat the small stuff," and remember that "it's all small stuff."[22]

Dealing with Stress

The first step of stress management is to examine thoroughly any problem involving stress. Figure 5d.1

Psychological hardiness: A personality characteristic characterized by control, commitment, challenge, choices, and connectedness.

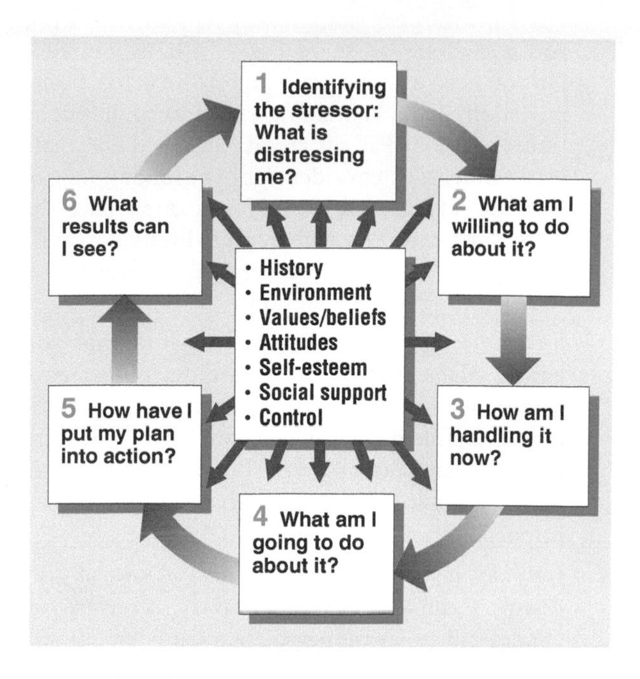

FIGURE 5d.1

A Decision-Making Model for Stress Management

Source: Adapted from Lester A. Lefton, *Psychology,* 5th ed., 485 (Figure 15d.5). © 1994 by Allyn & Bacon. Reprinted by permission.

shows a decision-making model for managing your response to stress. As the model shows, dealing with stress involves assessing all aspects of a stressor, examining how you currently respond to it and how you may be able to change your response, and evaluating various methods of coping with stress. Some stressors we cannot change, such as professors' assignments or unexpected distressors like car accidents or storm damage. Inevitably, we will take classes that bore us and for which we find no application to real life. And, of course, we feel powerless when a loved one has died. These facts themselves cannot be changed; only our reactions or responses to these situations can be altered.

Assessing Your Stressors

After recognizing a stressor, you need to assess it. Can you alter the circumstances in any way to reduce the amount of distress you are experiencing, or must you change your behaviours and reactions? For example, if five term papers for five different courses are due during the semester, you will probably quickly assess that you cannot alter the circumstances: your professors are unlikely to change their requirements. You can, however, alter your behaviours by working on one or two of the papers well before the due dates and spacing the others over time to avoid last-minute stress from trying to write them all in the week before they are due. Another example is your boss being vague about directions for assignments. You cannot change the boss; you can, however, ask the boss to clarify what is expected of you—in writing, if an oral response is insufficient.

Recognizing and Changing Your Responses

Recognizing and changing your responses to stressors requires self-reflection, practice, and emotional control. It is important to recognize your typical physical and mental responses to stress so that you can manage these responses more effectively in future situations. If your roommate is habitually messy and this causes you stress, you can choose from several responses. For example, you can express your anger by yelling, you can pick up the mess and leave a nasty note, or you can defuse the situation with humour. The first response that comes to mind is not always the best response. Stop before you react, to gain the time you need to find an appropriate response. Ask yourself, "What is to be gained from my response?" or "How will my response mediate this type of behaviour in the future?" Many people change their responses to potentially stressful events through cognitive coping strategies. These strategies help them prepare for stressors through gradual exposure to increasingly higher stress levels.

Learning to Cope

Everyone copes with stress and their stress responses in different ways. For some people, drinking and taking drugs helps them to cope. Others choose to get help from counsellors. Still others try to get their minds off stress by engaging in physical activity or relaxation techniques. *Stress inoculation,* a newer technique, helps people prepare for stressful events ahead of time. For example, if you are petrified about speaking in front of your class, practising in front of a friend or a mirror may inoculate you and prevent you from freezing up on the day of your presentation. Some health experts compare stress inoculation to a vaccine. Stress inoculation

- increases the predictability of stressful events
- fosters coping skills
- generates self-talking

- encourages confidence about successful outcomes
- builds a commitment to personal action and responsibility for an adaptive course of action

Regardless of how you cope with a given situation, your conscious effort to deal with it is an important step in stress management.

Downshifting

Today's lifestyles are hectic and pressure-packed, with self-imposed stress often a result of trying to keep up. Many people are wondering if "having it all" is worth it, and as a result are taking a step back and simplifying their lives. This simplification is known as "downshifting." Moving from a big city to a small town or moving from a big house to a smaller home and a host of other changes typify downshifting. Some dedicated downshifters have given up television, phones, and even computers.

Downshifting involves a fundamental alteration in values and honest introspection about what is important in life. When you consider any form of downshift or perhaps even start your career this way, it's important to move slowly and consider the following:

- *Determine your ultimate goal.* What is most important to you, and what will you need to reach that goal? What can you do without? Where do you want to live? Where do you want to work?
- *Make a short- and long-term plan for simplifying your life.* Set up your plan in doable steps, and work slowly toward each step. Determine those people and organizations to whom it is important to give your time and say no to those requests from people and organizations that do not share your same values.
- *Complete a financial inventory.* How much money will you need to do the things you want to do? Will you live alone or share costs with roommates? Do you need a car, or can you rely on active transportation, such as walking or cycling, or public transportation? Pay off credit cards and eliminate existing debt, or consider debt consolidation. Get used to paying with cash. If you don't have the cash, don't buy. Remember, your lifestyle may be different as a student compared to when you were working or living at home.
- *Select the right career.* Look for work that you enjoy; salary should not be the deciding factor. Can you be happy in a lower-paying job that is less stressful and provides you with sufficient challenge and the opportunities for the personal and professional growth that you consider important?
- *Consider options for saving money.* Downshifting doesn't mean you renounce money; it means you choose not to let money dictate your life. It's still important to save. If you are just getting started, you need to prepare for emergencies and future plans.
- *Clear out/clean out.* A cluttered life can be distressing. Take an inventory of material items, and get rid of things you haven't worn or used the last year or so. Donate these items to appropriate charities.

try it NOW!

A penny for your thoughts! Negative self-talk can contribute to feelings of stress. Try this idea to see how often you have negative emotional responses. Place a handful of pennies in your right-hand pocket, and each time you catch yourself having a negative thought about yourself, remove a penny from your right pocket and place it in your left pocket. Once you have an idea of how extensive your negative self-talk is, you can take steps to replace negative thoughts with positive ones.

Managing Emotional Responses

Have you ever gotten all worked up about something you thought was happening only to find that your perceptions were totally wrong or that a communication problem resulted in a misinterpretation of events? This happens to most of us. We often get upset by our faulty perceptions rather than reality. For example, imagine you find out that your friends were invited to a party but you were not. You are likely to become angry as well as disappointed. Self-doubt will likely follow, and you will wonder if anybody likes you. Yet the reality may be that you were invited, but your invitation got lost or misplaced.

Stress management requires that you examine your emotional responses, including your self talk and explanatory style. With any emotional response to a distressor, you are responsible for your emotions and resulting behaviours. Learning to tell the difference between normal emotions and those based on irrational beliefs can help you to express them in a healthy and more appropriate way. Admitting your feelings and allowing them to be expressed either through communication or action is a stress management technique that can help you get through many difficult situations. Talking yourself through the situation—in a positive way—and explaining yourself to others, accepting responsibility when appropriate, and avoiding blaming others for your mistakes or setbacks are also part of managing your emotional responses and behaviours. It is also important in this regard to develop appropriate expectations for yourself and others.

Learning to Laugh and Cry

For some people, learning to express emotions freely is a difficult task. However, it is a task worth learning. Have you ever noticed that you feel better after a good laugh or cry? It was not your imagination. Laughter and crying stimulate the heart and temporarily invigorate many body systems. Heart rate and blood pressure then decrease significantly, allowing the body to relax.

Managing Social Interactions

The importance of social interaction should not be underestimated in your stress management plans. Consider the nature and extent of your friendships. Do you have a friend or several friends with whom you can share intimate thoughts and feelings? Is there someone you can call for help or in the case of an emergency? Do you trust your friends to be supportive? Do you think your friends will be honest and tell you if you are doing something risky or inappropriate? Having someone to listen to you when needed and to give helpful advice is an invaluable stress management tool. It is less important to have a wide circle of acquaintances than it is to have a few really good friends. Different friends often serve different needs, so having more than one friend is beneficial. In university and college, friends often fulfill roles that family members held in the past. As you continue to develop and cultivate friendships, look for individuals who:

- have values similar to your own
- have similar interests that you can enjoy together
- have different interests that force you to grow and explore new ideas
- are good listeners, give and share freely, are tolerant, and do not rush to judgment
- are trustworthy
- consider your needs in addition to theirs
- are not unusually critical, negative, selfish, or pessimistic.
- are responsible and value doing well in school
- know when and how to have fun
- are willing to be physical activity buddies or study partners with a mutual interest in a healthy lifestyle
- know how to laugh, cry, engage in meaningful conversation, and feel comfortable with silence

Just as it is important to find these characteristics in your friends, it is also important for you to bring these qualities to your friendships. Sometimes, focusing on others can help you get your problems into perspective and control.

Making the Most of Support Groups

Support groups can also be an important part of stress management. Friends, family members, and co-workers can provide us with emotional and physical support. Although the ideal support group differs for each of us, you should have one or two close friends in whom you are able to confide and neighbours with whom you can trade favours. You should participate in community activities at least once a week. Part of your support group may also involve a significant other; a healthy, committed relationship can provide vital support.

If you do not have a close support group, you should know where to turn when the pressures of life seem overwhelming. Family members are often a steady base of support on which you can rely. Most colleges and universities have counselling services available at no cost for short-term crises. Members of the clergy, instructors, and residence supervisors may also be supportive resources. You should also be able to find counselling services in the local community. All services are confidential.

Taking Mental Action

Stress management calls for mental action in two areas. First, positive self-esteem, which can help you cope with stressful situations, comes from learned habits. If you have the mental habit of assuming you can handle the challenges that come your way, you will be less likely to feel overwhelmed. Successful stress management involves mentally developing and practising self-esteem skills. For example, when things seem overwhelming, remind yourself of situations you have handled well in the past and challenges you have already overcome; do not assume the situation is beyond your control. Second, because you can not always anticipate what the next distressor will be, you need to develop the mental skills necessary to manage your reaction to stresses when they happen. The ability to think about and react quickly to stress comes with time, practice, experience with a variety of stressful situations and coping methods, and patience. Most of all, you must strive to become more aware of situations that potentially induce stress and act quickly to deal with them. Rather than seeing stressors as adversaries, learn to view them as exercises in life, challenges to be overcome, or obstacles to be cleared.

Changing the Way You Think

Once you realize that some of your thoughts or self-talk may be negative, irrational, or overreactive, making a conscious effort to reframe or change the way you've been thinking and focusing on more positive ways of thinking is a key element of stress management. Here are some specific actions you can take to develop these mental skills.

- *Worry constructively.* Do not waste time and energy worrying about things you can not change or things that may never happen. For example, do not fret over the weather forecast even if rain or a storm is predicted for when you want to travel for the week end. Wait until the week end comes to adjust your plans accordingly.
- *Look at life as being fluid.* Accept change as a natural part of living and growing rather than resisting it. For example, if your roommate decides to move out, see that as an opportunity to live with someone different, to experience a new friendship.
- *Consider alternatives.* Remember that there is seldom only one appropriate action. Anticipating options will help you plan for change and adjust more rapidly. For example, when faced with several assignments or mid-term exams scheduled for the same day, there are a variety of approaches you can take. You might speak to each professor and outline your situation hoping for some rescheduling, or you may simply start each assignment right away and plan your time accordingly.
- *Have moderate expectations.* Aim high, but be realistic about your circumstances and capabilities. Be realistic about your grades—90s are rare in college and university! Aiming to maintain honours status may be more appropriate for you.
- *Weed out trivia.* Do not sweat the small stuff, and remember that most of it is small stuff. So, if someone took the last piece of pizza ahead of you in the food line, do not sweat about it; move on to your next option or wait until more pizza is brought out.
- *Do not rush into action.* Think before you act. You can use the 24–48 hour rule. If something happens that angers or disappoints you; leave it for 24 hours. If you are still disturbed, address the situation. If you leave it for 48 hours, it must not be important enough for you to follow up.
- *Keep things in perspective.* Try not to exaggerate the importance of what has happened. Yes, failing an exam or a paper is not a good thing. Still, consider how much it is actually worth—and in the whole scheme of things, how significant is it?
- *Focus on the positive.* Become selectively aware of the positive aspect of negative or unplanned situations. For example, if you get caught up in traffic, plan your day ahead. Or if your partner ends your relationship, think about the extra time you will have to yourself or for your friends and family.
- *See stumbling blocks as challenges rather than barriers.* Expect challenges and difficulties rather than resisting them. So, when your schedule becomes full with many papers to write, exams to prepare for, and classes to attend, see that as the opportunity to learn how to organize your time well and to follow a planned agenda versus just seeing it as "stressful."
- *When you think "I can't do it," break the task into smaller pieces and work on one small part at a time.* For example, if you have a paper and a laboratory report due on the same day, break each down into logical pieces and work on one piece at a time.
- *Reframe.* Rather than seeing the situation as a stumbling block, see it as a challenge and an opportunity. For example, if your date is no longer available to go out, see the unexpected evening alone as an opportunity to unwind and indulge in a bath rather than getting angry or frustrated.

Taking Physical Action

Learning to use physical activity to prevent, alleviate, and manage stress will complement the emotional strategies you employ in stress management.

Physical Activity

Moderate and vigorous intensity physical activities play a critical role in stress management. When engaged in moderate or vigorous intensity physical activity, the body releases endorphins (mood-enhancing, pain-killing hormones) in the bloodstream. Being physically active also increases energy, reduces hostility, and improves mental alertness. Vigorous physical activity is particularly effective as an immediate response to stress because it can immediately alleviate or reduce the stress symptoms/response. Engaging in physical activity on a regular basis yields even more substantial benefits. Try to get at least 20 to 30 minutes of aerobic exercise 3 or 4 times a week for the added benefits to the hormonal regulation of stress. A quiet walk can also refresh your mind, calm your stress response, and replenish your adaptation energy stores. Plan walking breaks alone or with friends. In fact, walking and talking is often an effective way to manage stress—physically and emotionally. Stretch after prolonged periods of study at your desk. A short period of physical activity may provide the break you really need.

YOUR SPIRITUAL AND EMOTIONAL HEALTH

Relaxation Techniques for Stress Management

You probably experience stressful situations every day—at school, at work, at home, even at play. Stress results from a combination of many factors often beyond our control. While stress cannot be eliminated completely, you can learn how to manage your responses in a positive way. Take steps to manage your response to stressful situations by using the following simple techniques:

1. **Diaphragmatic or deep breathing:** Typically, we breathe only using the upper chest and thoracic region rather than involving the abdominal region. Diaphragmatic breathing refers to deep breathing that maximally expands the chest by including the lower abdomen. This technique is commonly used in yoga exercises. Diaphragmatic breathing process occurs in three stages:
   - *Stage 1:* Assume a comfortable position. Whether sitting or lying down on your back, find the most natural position to be in. Close your eyes, unbutton your shirt or binding clothes, remove your belt, or unbutton your pants. Often it works best to hold your hands over your abdomen and get used to feeling the rise and fall of your stomach.
   - *Stage 2:* Concentrate on the act of breathing. Shut out external noise. Focus on inhaling, exhaling, and the route the air is following. Try saying to yourself, "Feel the warm air coming into your nose, warming your windpipe, and flowing into your lungs, expanding first your chest and then your belly.
   - *Stage 3:* Visualize. The above stages seem to work best when combined with visualization. A common example is to visualize clean, fresh, invigorating air slowly entering the nose and then being exhaled as grey, stale air. Such processes, particularly when they involve the whole body, seem to help individuals become refreshed from their experience.
2. **Progressive muscle relaxation:** Progressive muscle relaxation involves systematically contracting and relaxing each of several muscle groups; breathing deeply and concentrating on the muscles being contracted and relaxed are part of this process. Again, find a comfortable position and begin a deep-breathing cycle. The difference from diaphragmatic breathing is that, as you concentrate on inhaling, you will also contract a particular muscle group (for example, the hand and fingers). Hold that position for a short period and then, as you exhale, slowly release the muscles that you have been contracting. Repeat and add more muscle groups. You might start with the hands, then move to the forearms, the entire arms, the neck, then move to the shoulders, back, buttocks, thighs, lower legs, and finish with the feet. You can add components of other relaxation techniques to this experience by saying, "My hands are getting warmer, my arm is getting warmer," and so on as you work to gain maximum control of blood flow and muscle tension in a region.

Source: Paragraph on qigong from C. Dold, "The New Yoga," *Health* (May 2004): 73–77.

Relaxation

Like physical activity, relaxation can help you to cope with stressful feelings, preserve adaptation energy stores, and dissipate the excess hormones associated with the GAS: (General Adaptation Syndrome). Relaxation may involve a warm bath, or some time sitting quietly and listening to music, or it may involve sitting comfortably repeating a mantra (a word to help you relax). There are various forms of relaxation that can be undertaken. Generally, relaxation helps you to refocus your energies and should be practised daily. When you begin to feel your body respond to stress—eustress or distress—make time to relax to give yourself added strength and to alleviate the negative physical effects of the GAS. As your body relaxes, your heart rate lowers, your blood pressure and metabolic rate decrease, and many other body-calming effects occur, allowing you to channel energy more effectively. See also the Your Spiritual and Emotional Health box.

Eating Well

Is food a destressor? Do Mom's chocolate chip cookies or Grandma's apple pie really make you feel better? Whether foods can calm us and nourish our psyches is a controversial question. Much of what has been published about hyperactivity and its relation to the consumption of sweets has been shown to be scientifically invalid. And high-potency stress-tabs that are supposed to provide you with resistance against stress-related ailments are nothing more than gimmicks. However, what is clear is that having a balanced, healthy dietary intake will provide you with the stamina needed to get through problems and may stress-proof you in ways not fully understood. It is also known that undereating, overeating, emotional eating, and a dietary intake that is insufficient in variety, balance, and moderation can create distress in the body.

Learning Time Management

Time—everybody needs more of it, especially students trying to balance the demands of classes, social life, part-time jobs, family obligations, and time needed for relaxation and physical activity. The following tips regarding time management should become a part of your stress management program:

- *Clean off your desk.* According to Jeffrey Mayer, author of *Winning the Fight between You and Your Desk,* most of us lose time looking for things that are lost on our desks or in our homes. Go through the things on your desk, recycle the unnecessary papers, and organize the remaining papers in "to do" piles.
- *Never handle papers more than once.* When bills and other papers come in, take care of them immediately. Write out a cheque and hold it for mailing. Get rid of the envelopes. Read your mail and file it or toss it. If you haven't looked at something in over a year, recycle it. The same can be said for your email. Read it, handle it, and then delete it. Do not open and read your email unless you are ready to manage each message.
- *Prioritize your tasks.* Make a daily "to do" list and stick to it. Categorize the things you must do today, the things that you have to do but not immediately, and the things that it would be nice to do. Prioritize the Must Do Now and Have to Do Later items and put deadlines next to each. Only consider the Nice to Do items if you finish the others or if the Nice to Do list includes something fun for you.
- *Avoid interruptions.* When you've got a project that requires your total concentration, schedule uninterrupted time. Unplug the phone or let your voice mail get it. Turn off the instant messaging and email software on your computer. Close your door and post a Do Not Disturb sign. Go to a quiet room in the library or student union where no one will find you. Protect your time so you can use it well.
- *Do not be afraid to say no.* Too often, we overcommit ourselves. It is okay to say "No, I am too busy," "No, I am not really interested," or "I would like to help out; however, I am already committed to too many projects at this time."
- *Reward yourself for being efficient.* If you planned to take a certain amount of time to finish a task and you finish early, take some time for yourself. Have a cup of coffee or hot chocolate. Go for a walk. Read for pleasure. Differentiate between rest breaks and work breaks. Work breaks simply mean that you switch tasks for a while. Rest breaks get you away from work and let you spend time for yourself.
- *Use time to your advantage.* If you are a morning person, plan your work to take advantage of that time. If you know that by Friday afternoon you will be tired and worn out, plan to work on tasks that require minimal concentration. Take breaks when needed. Use physical activity as an energizer.
- *Become aware of your own time patterns.* For many of us, minutes and hours drift by without us even noticing them. Chart your daily schedule, hour by hour, for one week. Note the time that was wasted, when it was wasted, and think of the reasons that may have led to that. Note also the time spent in productive work or restorative pleasure. Determine how you could be more productive and make more time for yourself.
- *Remember that time is precious.* Many people learn to value their time only when they face a terminal illness. Value each day. Time spent not enjoying life is a tremendous waste of potential.

Being able to talk comfortably to someone close to you is part of stress management.

Using Alternative Stress Management Techniques

The popularity of stress management has increased the amount of advertising for various "stress fighters" such as hypnosis, massage therapies, and meditation. Some universities and colleges may provide these services through extended health coverage. Most should also be available in your local community.

TAKING CHARGE

Managing Stress Behaviours

Stress is not something that you can run from or wish into non-existence. To control stress, you must meet it head-on and use the resources needed to ensure that your coping skills are fine-tuned and capable of helping you. In planning your personal strategies for coping with stress, consider the following:

MAKING DECISIONS FOR YOU

Following a few simple guidelines may help you not only to enjoy more guilt-free time but also to become more productive during work hours.

- *Plan life, not time*. Determining what you want from life rather than what you can get done may help change the way you use time. Evaluate all your activities, even the most trivial, to determine whether they add to your life. If they don't, get rid of them.
- *Decelerate*. Rushing is part of the Canadian work ethic and mindset that says "Busy is better." It can be addictive. When rushed, ask yourself if you really need to be. What is the worst that could happen if you slow down? Tell yourself at least once a day that failure seldom results from doing a job slowly or too well. Failures happen when rushing causes a lack of attention to detail.
- *Learn to delegate and share*. The need to feel in control is powerful. If you are unusually busy, leave details to someone else. Do not be afraid to ask others to help or to share the workload and responsibilities.
- *Learn to say no*. Give priority to what is most critical to your life, your job, or your current situation. Decide what things you can do, what things you must do, and what things you want to do, and delegate the rest to someone else either permanently or until you complete some of your priority tasks. Before you take on a new responsibility, finish or drop an old one.
- *Schedule time alone*. Find time each day for quiet thinking, reading, physical activity, or other enjoyable activities.

CHECKLIST FOR CHANGE: ASSESSING YOUR LIFE STRESSORS

- Have you assessed the major stressors in your life? Are they people, events, or specific activities?
- Have you thought about what you may be doing to elevate your stress levels? Do you often worry about things that never happen?
- Have you thought about what you could change to reduce your stress response?
- Do you have a network of friends and family members who can help you reduce your stress levels? Do you know how and where to access professional advice if needed?
- Have you thought about what changes you would like to work on first? Have you developed a plan of action? When do you plan to start?

CHECKLIST FOR CHANGE: ASSESSING COMMUNITY STRESSORS

- Have you considered what in your environment may be perceived as stressful for you and those around you?
- Do you have control over these stressors? How could they be changed? How would changing them make a difference?
- What on your campus or in your living situation is perceived as stressful for you or your friends? What could you do to manage these stressors?
- What advice might you give to your school administrators to help them reduce unnecessary stress among students?

CRITICAL THINKING

You just scraped by to pay your tuition bill in January, and then your university announced a large tuition hike for next year. You already work a part-time job, and seem to spend all your "free time" studying. The stress you have now is beginning to get to you, and you realize that you will have to work another 5 to 10 hours per week just to pay your bills next year. And tuition is likely to go up in your final year as well. How can you manage your time and finances so you can complete your degree?

Begin with your current situation: How can you make better use of your time? Could you prioritize your week in such a way that you could find the extra time to work? Finally, even if you make enough money, you need to deal with the increased stress. What will you do to keep the stress under control?

Massage Therapy

If you have ever had someone massage your stiff neck or aching feet, you know that massage is an excellent means of relaxation and thus a potential form of stress management. Massage therapists use techniques that vary from the aggressive methods typical of Swedish massage to more gentle methods such as acupressure and Esalen massage. Before selecting a massage therapist, check his or her credentials carefully. He or she should have training from a reputable program that teaches scientific principles for anatomical manipulation. Each province and territory has different requirements to become a registered massage therapist—check out the Canadian Massage Therapy Alliance website at www.cmta.ca for specific information.

Meditation

Another way to relax and to manage stress is through meditation. **Meditation** generally focuses on visualization and deep breathing, allowing tension to leave the body with each exhalation. There is no "right" way to meditate. Although there are several common forms of meditation, most involve sitting quietly and comfortably for 15 to 20 minutes, focusing on a particular word or symbol, controlling breathing, and getting in touch with your inner self. The deep breathing typically used is described in the Your Spiritual and Emotional Health textbox. Visualization can be added to this deep breathing. Visualization, or the creation of mental scenes, works by engaging your imagination of the physical senses of sight, sound, smell, taste, and feel to replace stressful stimuli with peaceful or pleasurable thoughts. Your choice of mental images is unlimited and should reflect a scene that brings you peace; this might be a beach or mountain lake, a mountain range, or a field of flax or grain blowing in the wind.

Taken from *An Introduction to Health Psychology*, Second Edition, by Val Morrison and Paul Bennett

HELPING PEOPLE TO COPE WITH TRAUMA

Post-traumatic stress disorder

The American Psychiatric Association (American Psychiatric Association 2000) states that for a person to be given a diagnosis of **post-traumatic stress disorder** (PTSD) they must have experienced or witnessed an event that involved actual or threatened death or serious injury, or a threat to the physical integrity of self or others, and that their immediate response involved intense fear, helplessness or horror. In the longer term, the individual must have experienced three clusters of symptoms lasting one month or more:

1. *Intrusive memories*: the trauma is re-experienced through intrusive thoughts, flashbacks or nightmares. Flashbacks often feel as real as the event but may be fragmentary or partial. Emotions and sensations associated with the trauma may be relived with similar intensity to those felt at the time. Images are often described as if being in a film of the incident. Initially, the person may feel that they are actually 'in' the film: as they recover, their perspective may shift to that of outside observer watching a film. That is, they begin, almost literally, to feel more detached from the trauma.
2. *Avoidance*: this may involve mental defence mechanisms such as being unable to recall aspects of the trauma, emotional numbness or detachment from others, as well as physically avoiding reminders of the trauma.
3. *Arousal*: persistent feelings of over-arousal that may be evidenced by irritability, being easily startled or hyper-vigilant, suffering insomnia, or having difficulty concentrating.

Meditation: A relaxation technique that involves deep breathing and potentially visualization

post-traumatic stress disorder a disorder that forms a response to experiencing a traumatic event. The key elements are unwanted repetitive memories of the event, often in the form of flashbacks, attempts at avoidance of such memories, and a generally raised level of arousal.

Many health workers may witness other people at times of either threatened or actual death. Emergency ambulance workers, for example, are frequently involved in incidents involving serious trauma, death and high levels of personal distress. For this reason, the prevalence of PTSD in this group is alarmingly high. Bennett *et al.* (2004), for example, found that 21 per cent of their sample of working emergency ambulance personnel were experiencing some degree of PTSD. Many patients also experience PTSD as a consequence of events that led them to hospital or which occurred in hospital, although the exact prevalence of PTSD among such people is difficult to determine, as some studies use much stricter criteria for a 'diagnosis' of PTSD than others. Among cancer patients, for example, two studies using very rigorous criteria for the diagnosis of PTSD have reported a 3 per cent prevalence among women with breast cancer (Green *et al.* 1998) and 5 per cent of people undergoing bone marrow transplant in the treatment of cancer (Widows *et al.* 2000). Using less rigid criteria, Meeske *et al.* (2001) reported that 20 per cent of their sample of adults who had been treated successfully for cancer an average of eleven years previously still met the full criteria for PTSD. A small percentage of people may have residual symptoms of PTSD twenty years after diagnosis and treatment (Kornblith *et al.* 2003). About 10 per cent of people who have had a myocardial infarction may also experience PTSD (e.g. Bennett *et al.* 2002).

Post-traumatic stress may not just affect those with the condition. High rates of PTSD have also been found among the parents of children diagnosed as having cancer. Landolt *et al.* (2003), for example, found that 16 per cent of the fathers and 24 per cent of the mothers of children diagnosed with either cancer or diabetes met the diagnostic criteria for PTSD five–six weeks after the diagnosis was given.

PREVENTING PTSD: PSYCHOLOGICAL DEBRIEFING

Because of the serious impact that PTSD can have on an individual, much research and clinical work has been conducted to try to prevent PTSD occurring following traumatic incidents. The most frequently used approach is called **psychological debriefing**. Many emergency services such as the ambulance and police services regularly use psychological debriefing to help staff to cope following traumatic incidents (Smith and Roberts 2003). This usually comprises a single-session interview conducted close to the time of a traumatic event during which the individual talks about the event and their emotional reactions to it in a detailed and systematic manner. The therapist leads the person through the event in a very structured manner, asking them to talk about the events that have occurred and their emotional, cognitive and behavioural responses to those events. It is hoped that this procedure helps the individual to come to terms with any emotional trauma they have experienced and prevent the development of PTSD.

The procedure is at least partly justified by theorists such as Brewin and Holmes (2003), who have suggested that the symptoms of PTSD result from traumatic memories remaining isolated from the general memory system, with flashbacks and other unwanted recall of events being the result of cognitive attempts to integrate isolated traumatic memories into general memory. Once such memories are fully integrated into the memory system, they lose their emotional charge and are no more salient than other more general memories. This process of integration is facilitated by thinking and rethinking about the memories until full integration has been achieved. Debriefing may encourage the integration of memories into general memory from the outset and prevent them becoming isolated and emotionally distressing.

How effective psychological debriefing is in achieving its goals is, unfortunately, somewhat questionable. In a meta-analysis of trials using debriefing, Rose *et al.* (2001) concluded that it may not only be ineffective in preventing PTSD, it may actually *increase* risk for the disorder. None of the studies they analysed found that debriefing lowered risk for PTSD in the three–four months following a traumatic incident. More worrying were the results of the two studies that reported longer-term findings. Both found that those who received debriefing were at nearly twice the risk of developing PTSD than those who did not receive the intervention. That is, debriefing seemed to inhibit long-term recovery from psychological trauma. A number of explan-ations have been proposed for these findings:

- 'Secondary traumatisation' may occur as a result of further exposure to a traumatic incident within a short time of the event.
- Debriefing may 'medicalise' normal distress and increase the expectancy of developing psychological symptoms in those who would otherwise not have done so.
- Debriefing may prevent the potentially protective responses of denial and distancing that may occur in the immediate aftermath of a traumatic incident.

These findings seem particularly worrying, given the continued widespread use of debriefing. It may well be that in the immediate aftermath of a trauma, the person may benefit from some degree of avoidance of thinking about the trauma, only allowing themselves to think about it and deal with it over a longer period.

psychological debriefing a procedure in which people who have been through a particular trauma talk through the trauma in a structured way with a counsellor.

TREATING PTSD

Following a traumatic incident, many people experience PTSD-like symptoms for a limited period. Many will also recover from them in the weeks following the incident. However, where these are persistent and distressing (for at least one month), people may be diagnosed as having PTSD. In such cases, the optimum treatment seems to be very similar to debriefing, as it involves repeated exposure to memories of the event. This may take place over a period of several sessions, until integration of isolated memories into general memory is achieved and the symptoms no longer occur. This type of intervention, known as **exposure therapy**, may lead to an initial increase in distress as upsetting images, previously avoided where possible, are deliberately recollected. To minimise this distress, Leskin *et al.* (1998) recommended a graded exposure process in which the individual initially recalls and talks about particular elements of a traumatic event at a level of detail they choose over several occasions until they no longer find them upsetting. Any new and potentially more distressing memories remain the focus of the next stages of the intervention.

exposure therapy a form of therapy involving exposure to traumatic memories, based on the theoretical assumption that continued exposure will result in a gradual reduction in the level of fear associated with such memories.

RESEARCH FOCUS

Donahue, S.A., Jackson, C.T., Shear, K.M. *et al.* (2006). Outcomes of enhanced counseling services provided to adults through Project Liberty. *Psychiatric Services*, 57: 1298–305d.

Disasters, such as the terrorist attacks on the World Trade Centre (WTC), can have significant detrimental consequences for the mental health of those involved. This study evaluated the effectiveness of a programme established in New York following the September 11th attack on the WTC to minimise its effect on the population of New York. It is not a well-controlled randomised controlled trial. Instead, it attempted to provide a realistic assessment of the effectiveness of the interventions provided in the years following the attack, when the researchers and clinicians were grappling with a very real health problem.

Immediately following the attack on the WTC, the Federal Emergency Management Agency (FEMA) implemented Project Liberty to provide crisis counselling and public education services for residents of New York City and surrounding counties. Individual crisis counselling services were provided to 687,848 people, and approximately 550,000 received public education. More than a year after the attacks, reports from Project Liberty providers indicated that additional services were needed for some individuals still struggling with serious disaster-related problems. In response to this, FEMA funded an additional 'enhanced services' programme of counselling for individuals who remained significantly affected by the attacks. To select people into the programme, individuals who needed three or more sessions of counselling were screened for presence of depression, PTSD, or an abnormal grief reaction. Where these conditions were found, individuals were offered the enhanced services. These comprised cognitive-behavioural intervention for depression or PTSD and/or a grief intervention that included strategies for dealing with loss and re-engaging in satisfying life activities and techniques for working with problem emotions (guilt and anger). Both interventions were designed to last between ten and twelve sessions.

PARTICIPANTS AND PROCEDURE

Over the period of the study, 214 individuals who only received crisis counselling agreed to be contacted, and 153 (71 per cent) completed a telephone interview. Of the 119 people who received enhanced services over this time, 102 agreed to be interviewed and 93 (91 per cent) completed the telephone interview. A total of 76 (75 per cent) completed a second telephone interview approximately forty days later.

TELEPHONE INTERVIEW

The telephone interview assessed participants' experiences during the attacks, their reasons for contacting Project Liberty, demographic characteristics, extent of symptoms, functional impairment and interventions received. In addition, they measured:

- *Depression and PTSD symptoms.* Respondents reported whether they had experienced a series of symptoms consistent with depression or PTSD for two weeks or longer during the previous month.
- *Complicated grief.* If respondents indicated that someone they knew died during the attacks, they were asked to respond to five questions measuring complicated grief (e.g. How much does your grief still interfere with your life?). A score of 8 or more indicated probable complicated grief.
- *Daily functioning.* Respondents rated their current functioning in five domains using 4-point Likert scales: job or school, maintaining relationships with family and friends, handling daily household activities, ability to take care of physical health, and staying involved in community activities.

FINDINGS

Comparisons between counselling groups

The crisis counselling and enhanced services samples did not differ in age or gender composition. There was no significant difference in respondents' assessment of being in immediate danger during the attacks, but a significantly greater proportion of enhanced-services recipients reported knowing someone who died as a result of the attacks, having been involved in rescue efforts, or having lost their job because of them. At the time of the first interview, the enhanced-services recipients reported significantly more symptoms of depression and PTSD, more intense grief, and were more likely to be defined as 'cases' of depression or PTSD. Forty-two per cent of the enhanced-services sample met the criteria for a major depressive disorder, and 39 per cent met the criteria for PTSD. Enhanced-services recipients were also significantly more impaired in all domains of their daily functioning.

Changes over time

Enhanced-services recipients reported a significant reduction in the number of depressive symptoms from the first to the second interview (mean score time 1 = 4.2; time 2 = 2.8), significantly reduced intensity of grief (mean 7.4 versus 4.8), and significantly improved daily functioning in three of five life domains (job and school, personal relationships and household activities). The number of PTSD symptoms was also notably reduced (6.1 versus 5.1). These scores were similar to those of the crisis-counselling recipients about one year earlier.

DISCUSSION

This investigation has several limitations, and findings should be considered preliminary. Perhaps the greatest methodological weakness was the lack of randomisation into treated and

RESEARCH FOCUS *(CONT.)*

untreated individuals. The changes in the enhanced service could have occurred naturally over time, and not be a result of the enhanced intervention. Accordingly, while the study suggests that individuals with severe and enduring problems following the September 11th attacks benefited from the interventions, this cannot be stated definitively. The authors can be forgiven this weakness–they placed the wellbeing of those involved over methodological rigour.

Reactivation of memories by this procedure involves describing the experience in detail, focusing on what happened, the thoughts and emotions experienced at the time, and any memories that the incident triggered. This approach can be augmented by a variety of cognitive-behavioural techniques, including relaxation training and cognitive restructuring. Relaxation helps the individual to control their arousal when recalling distressing events, or at other times in the day when they are feeling tense or on edge. Cognitive restructuring can help them to change any distorted cognitions they had in response to the event and make them less threatening ('I'm going to die!' to 'It felt like I was going to die, but actually most people survive a diagnosis of . . .').

A number of studies have found exposure-based therapy to be superior to no treatment and interventions such as supportive counselling and relaxation therapy without exposure. Foa *et al.* (1991), for example, compared the effectiveness of a waiting-list control condition, self-instruction training as developed by Meichenbaum (see above), supportive counselling, and an exposure programme. Participants in each of the active interventions experienced more improvements than those in the waiting-list condition. However, by the three-month follow-up, people in the exposure programme reported the least intrusive memories and arousal.

The most recent treatment for PTSD is known as **eye movement desensitisation and reprocessing** (EMDR). This approach was discovered by chance by Shapiro (1995). In a now famous story of how the approach was initially developed, she noticed that while walking in the woods her disturbing thoughts began to disappear and were less upsetting than before. She linked this change to her eyes spontaneously moving rapidly backwards and forwards in an upward diagonal while walking. Since then, the procedure has been developed into a standardised intervention, and its effectiveness has been evaluated in a number of clinical trials. The intervention involves recall of trauma memories as visual images. The participant is then asked to link these images with a negative cognition associated with the memory but framed in the present tense ('I am terrified'). The individual rates the strength of emotion evoked by this process on a scale of 0–100. They are then asked to track the therapist's finger as it is moved increasingly quickly across their line of vision. After twenty-four such movements, the patient is instructed to 'blank it out' or 'let it go' and asked to rate their level of emotion. This procedure is repeated until the patient experiences minimal distress to the presence of the image and negative cognition. If no changes occur, the direction of eye movements is changed.

EMDR incorporates exposure to elements of the trauma stimulus. It is therefore important to determine whether the addition of the eye movements enhances the effect of exposure. This does not seem to be the case. While EMDR is certainly more effective than no treatment, it may be no more effective than standard exposure methods. Reviewing the evidence, Davidson and Parker (2001) used meta-analysis to compare the effectiveness of EMDR with no treatment, non-specific treatments and the exposure methods described above. While their analyses indicated a benefit for EMDR when compared with no treatment or non-specific treatments, its benefits were similar to or less than those resulting from exposure approaches.

eye movement desensitisation and reprocessing (EMDR) a form of therapy for post-traumatic stress disorder involving exposure to traumatic memories while repeatedly moving the eyes. Its method of working is not clear. However, the most popular theory is that when the eyes move back and forth this creates brain activity similar to that which occurs during REM (rapid eye movement) sleep. This may help the brain to process the 'stuck' material, enabling the person to arrive at an adaptive resolution.

CHAPTER 5e

ACHIEVING THE BALANCE OF PSYCHOSOCIAL HEALTH

Taken from *Health: The Basics,* Fifth Canadian Edition, by Rebecca J. Donatelle and Angela M. Thompson

Most of us feel "down" occasionally; still, we get through the day in a reasonably productive, if not altogether exciting, way. We eventually sort through seemingly overwhelming problems, suppress our anxieties, and use our social support system (families, friends, and significant others) to help us through the low times. For some, though, these down times become persistent, nagging experiences that vary from small "downers" to "black holes" that are increasingly difficult to emerge from. Whether caused by temporary setbacks or major blows, these miserable moods sap our energy, reduce our physical reserves, waste our time, diminish our spirit, and take the joy out of our lives. They may even lead to a serious mental illness. Eventually, they may shorten our life span—reducing quantity as well as quality of life. How we feel and think about ourselves, those around us, and our circumstances can tell us a lot about our psychosocial health. Like our physical health, our psychosocial health can have a profound impact on the quality and quantity of our lives. We can enhance our psychosocial health just as we can our physical health, by becoming aware of relevant attitudes and behaviours and making changes where and when necessary.

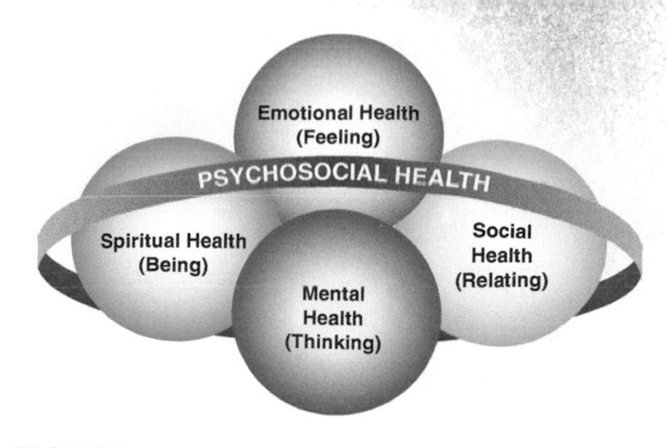

FIGURE 5e.1

Psychosocial Health as a Complex Interaction of Mental, Emotional, Social, and Spiritual Health

DEFINING PSYCHOSOCIAL HEALTH

Psychosocial health encompasses the mental, emotional, social, and spiritual dimensions of health (see Figure 5e.1). People who are psychosocially healthy develop these dimensions to optimal levels. They have an endless reserve for facing the normal ups and downs of life. They respond to challenges, disappointments, joys, frustrations, and pain by summoning up personal resources acquired through years of experience, and when a needed resource is not available, they find ways to develop it. Their resiliency is strong and they are actively involved in the process of living each day to the fullest.

Psychosocial health is the result of a complex interaction of a person's history and his or her conscious and unconscious thoughts about and interpretations of the past. Although definitions of psychosocial health vary, people who are psychosocially healthy share several basic characteristics:

- *They feel good about themselves.* People who are psychosocially healthy are not overwhelmed by fear, love, anger, jealousy, guilt, or worry. They know who they are, have a realistic sense of their capabilities, and respect themselves even though they realize they are not perfect.
- *They feel comfortable with other people.* People who are psychosocially healthy have satisfying and lasting personal relationships and do not take advantage of others; nor do they allow others to take advantage of them. They give and receive love, consider others' interests, respect personal differences, and feel responsible for their fellow human beings.
- *They control tension and anxiety.* People who are psychosocially healthy recognize the underlying causes and symptoms of stress in their lives and consciously avoid illogical or irrational thoughts, unnecessary aggression, hostility, excessive excuse making, and blaming others for their problems. They use resources and learn skills to control reactions to stressful situations, including constructively expressing positive and negative feelings and learning to tolerate their frustrations.
- *They are able to meet the demands of life.* People who are psychosocially healthy try to solve problems as they arise, to accept responsibility for their thoughts and actions, and to plan ahead. They break down problems into manageable bits and work through them one piece or step at a time. They set realistic goals, think for themselves, and make independent decisions. Acknowledging that change is a normal part of life, they welcome new experiences.
- *They curb hate and guilt.* People who are psychosocially healthy acknowledge and combat their tendencies to respond with hate, anger, thoughtlessness, and selfishness. They do not take vengeance, nor do they allow feelings of inadequacy to build. They do not try to knock others aside to get ahead but rather reach out to help others—even those they may not be fond of.

Psychosocial health: The mental, emotional, social, and spiritual dimensions of health.

A study of spirituality among post-secondary students from 46 diverse universities and colleges indicated that spirituality played a role in student health, grades, and other aspects of student life. The researchers of this study found a correlation between spirituality and health achievement, with more spiritually oriented students having better health, higher grades, more involvement in charitable organizations or volunteerism, and more interest in helping others. Other studies also indicated a correlation between spirituality and positive health outcomes. For example, mindfulness therapies have been used effectively to treat depression, to reduce stress in outpatient therapy and in the nursing profession, with anxiety and heart disease treatments, and for other problems.

A Spiritual Resurgence

An increase in spiritual awareness does not necessarily equate with an increase in beliefs in a god or supreme being of some kind. Some people find spiritual fulfillment in music, poetry, literature, art, nature, or intimate relationships. For some, spirituality refers to a quest for self and selflessness—learning about oneself and learning how to willingly give of oneself to others. Understanding and appreciating oneself as a result of self-reflection can also help us to deepen or appreciate our life experiences more fully rather than just live through them. This topic has received much scholarly and popular attention. The fact that self-help books that focus on spirituality consistently top the bestseller lists demonstrates a renewed interest in spirituality within contemporary society.

Putting Spirituality into Practice

How can you enhance the spiritual dimension of your psychosocial health? As noted, some people turn to a formal religion—for instance by attending religious services, engaging in prayer, or taking part in the organized study or discussion of religious texts (such as the Bible or the Koran). Others will find meaningful volunteer experiences or spend more time in personal reflection. Regardless of what you choose to do, keep in mind that enhancing your spiritual health is as time-consuming and requires as much effort as building your physical fitness or changing your dietary intake. The Skills for Behaviour Change textbox

SKILLS FOR BEHAVIOUR CHANGE

Strategies for Finding Your Spiritual Side

Spirituality involves connectedness to others and to the broader community, so it is important that we take time for meaningful interactions with our friends, family, and people within the community with whom we may not interact regularly. What types of actions foster connectedness?

VOLUNTEER

he ability to notice when others are in trouble, and reaching
t to help them through volunteering, is an excellent way to
connected with others and enhance your own health. In
ftermath of Hurricane Katrina, thousands of people vol-
ed their time, money, and effort to help an entire pop-
tthat was suffering. Recognizing that we are all part of
reser system of humanity and that we have roles and
spirlities to help others in times of need is a key part of
clean Volunteering by helping your older neighbours
ing in me, working at an animal shelter, or participat-
responsih or highway cleanup is all a part of being
of things. finding a place to help in the greater scheme
are feeling ering can be a huge boost for you when you
r wondering how you fit in.

TAKE TIME REFLECT

Connecting with
spiritual side. Make elf is another method of finding your
ual out of taking a few moments each day to think about who you are, what you value, why you feel good, or what things are troubling you. Setting aside this special time to reflect will become a sacred time meant just for you and can help you relieve tension, seek out answers to problems you are experiencing, or simply empty your mind and enjoy this time to yourself.

GET INVOLVED IN SERVICE LEARNING

Service learning involves making meaningful and productive relationships with the greater community. Community agencies and programs benefit from an enthusiastic, hardworking group of students. The students in turn have an opportunity to learn new skills and grow; they learn to look at the greater community and world around them, rather than remaining absorbed in college life and thoughts of papers due, the party on Friday night, and basketball practice.

features a few strategies you can implement to develop your spirituality.

FACTORS INFLUENCING PSYCHOSOCIAL HEALTH

Although it is relatively easy to define psychosocial health, it is much more difficult to explain why some people are psychosocially well almost all the time, others some of the time, and still others almost never. What factors influence your mental, emotional, social, and spiritual health? Are these factors changeable? What can you do to improve your psychosocial health? How can you enhance the positive qualities you already possess? See Table 5e.1 for tips regarding mental fitness.

Most of our mental, emotional, social, and spiritual reactions to life are a direct outcome of our experiences, along with social and cultural expectations. Each of us is born with the innate capacity to experience emotions. Some of us apparently have a

what do you THINK?

When you think of mental, emotional, social, and spiritual health, what do you think? What are your strengths and weaknesses in each? How can you enhance your strengths? How can you reduce the influence of your weaknesses?

TABLE 5e.1

Mental Fitness Tips

- **Daydream** – Close your eyes and imagine yourself in a dream location. Breathe slowly and deeply. Whether it's a beach, a mountaintop, a hushed forest or a favourite room from your past, let the comforting environment wrap you in a sensation of peace and tranquility.
- **"Collect" positive emotional moments** – Make it a point to recall times when you have experienced pleasure, comfort, tenderness, confidence, or other positive emotions.
- **Learn ways to cope with negative thoughts** – Negative thoughts can be insistent and loud. Learn to interrupt them. Don't try to block them (that never works), and don't let them take over. Try distracting yourself or comforting yourself if you can't solve the problem right away.
- **Do one thing at a time** – For example, when you are out for a walk or spending time with friends, turn off your cellphone and stop making that mental "to do" list. Take in all the sights, sounds, and smells you encounter.
- **Exercise** – Regular physical activity improves psychological well-being and can reduce depression and anxiety. Joining an exercise group or a gym can also reduce loneliness, since it connects you with a new set of people sharing a common goal.
- **Enjoy hobbies** – Taking up a hobby brings balance to your life by allowing you to do something you enjoy because you want to do it, free of the pressure of everyday tasks. It also keeps your brain active.
- **Set personal goals** – Goals don't have to be ambitious. You might decide to finish that book you started three years ago; to take a walk around the block every day; to learn to knit or play bridge; to call your friends instead of waiting for the phone to ring. Whatever goal you set, reaching it will build confidence and a sense of satisfaction.
- **Keep a journal (or even talk to the wall!)** – Expressing yourself after a stressful day can help you gain perspective, release tension, and even boost your body's resistance to illness.
- **Share humour** – Life often gets too serious, so when you hear or see something that makes you smile or laugh, share it with someone you know. A little humour can go a long way to keeping us mentally fit!
- **Volunteer** – Volunteering is called the "win–win" activity because helping others makes us feel good about ourselves. At the same time, it widens our social network, provides us with new learning experiences and can bring balance to our lives.
- **Treat yourself well** – Cook yourself a good meal. Have a bubble bath. See a movie. Call a friend or relative you haven't talked to in ages. Sit on a park bench and breathe in the fragrance of flowers and grass. Whatever it is, do it just for you.

Source: Canada Mental Health Association.

predisposition toward more emotionality than others. How we express our emotions has a lot to do with our interpretations of what we experience. These interpretations are often learned reactions to environmental and social stimuli.

External Influences

Our psychosocial health is based on how we perceive our experiences. While some experiences are under our control, others are not. External influences refer to those factors that we do not control, such as who raised us and the physical environment in which we live.

Influences of the Family

Our families have a significant influence on our psychosocial development. Children raised in healthy, nurturing, happy families where they learn about being responsible and accountable are more likely to become well-adjusted, productive adults. Children raised in dysfunctional families in which violence, sexual, physical, or emotional abuse, negative behaviours, distrust, anger, dietary deprivation, drug abuse, parental discord, or other negative characteristics are present may have a harder time adapting to life. In dysfunctional families, security, unconditional love, and trust are lacking and the children are often confused and psychologically bruised. Yet not all people raised in dysfunctional families become psychosocially unhealthy. Conversely, not all people from healthy family environments are psychosocially healthy. Obviously more factors are involved in our "process of becoming" than just our family.

Influences of the Wider Environment

While isolated negative events may do little damage to psychosocial health, persistent stressors, uncertainties, and threats may cause significant problems. Children raised in environments where crime is rampant and daily safety is in question, for example, have an increased risk of psychosocial health issues among other things. Drugs, crime, violent acts, school failure, unemployment, and a host of other bad things can happen to good people. That said, it is believed that certain protective factors—such as having one or more positive role models in the midst of chaos, or a high level of self-esteem—may help children from even the worst environments be healthy and well adjusted.

Another important influence on psychosocial health is access to health services and programs designed to support the maintenance or enhancement of psychosocial health. Going to a support group or seeing a trained counsellor or therapist is often a crucial first step in prevention and intervention efforts. Unfortunately, individuals from a poor socioeconomic background (who often need the services most) may have more difficulty accessing such services.

Internal Influences

Although your life experiences influence you in fairly obvious ways, many internal factors also work subtly to shape who you are and who you become. Some of these factors include your traits, hormonal functioning, physical health status (including neurological or nervous system functioning), level of physical fitness, and selected elements of your mental and emotional health. If issues occur with any of these factors, overall psychosocial health can decline.

Self-Efficacy and Self-Esteem

During our formative years, our successes and failures in school, sports, friendships, intimate relationships, jobs, and in every other aspect of life subtly shape our perceptions and beliefs about our personal worth and ability to help ourselves. These perceptions and beliefs in turn become internal influences on our psychosocial health.

Self-efficacy describes our belief about whether or not we can successfully engage in and execute a specific behaviour. If we experience success in academics, sports, or popularity, we typically expect to be successful in these aspects in the future. If we fail an exam, were chosen last to be on a team, or have not been able to make friends easily, we may believe that failure is inevitable in this regard. In general, the more self-efficacious we are and the more our experiences have been positive, the more likely we are to keep trying to execute a specific behaviour successfully. People who have a high level of self-efficacy are also more likely to feel that they have **personal control** over situations or believe their internal resources allow them to control events. On the other hand, a person with low self-efficacy may give up easily or not even try to change his or her behaviours. Learning new skills and having successful experiences improves confidence and leads to the expectation of future success.

Self-esteem refers to our sense of self-respect or self-worth. It can be defined as an evaluation of ourselves and personal worth as individuals. People with high self-esteem tend to feel good about themselves and to express a positive outlook on life. People with low self-esteem tend to not be happy with themselves, to demean themselves, and to doubt their ability to succeed.

Past successes and happy experiences, often recalled through photos, mementos, and recollections, contribute to a person's psychosocial health.

Our self-esteem forms as a result of the relationships we have with our parents and family during our formative years, with our friends as we grow older, with our significant others as we form intimate relationships, and with our teachers, co-workers, and others important to us throughout our lives. If we feel loved and valued in each of these relationships, we believe that we are inherently loveable individuals and have a strong sense of self esteem.

Learned Helplessness versus Learned Optimism

People who continually experience failure may develop a pattern of responding known as **learned helplessness**, in which they give up and fail to take action to help themselves. This attitude and resultant behaviours are due in part to society's tendency toward *victimology*, laying the blame for an individual's problems on other people and on the circumstances rather than placing responsibility on the individual. Although viewing ourselves as victims may help us to feel better temporarily, it does not address the underlying cause or causes of a problem. Ultimately, not taking responsibility for our actions erodes self-efficacy and fosters learned helplessness by developing an attitude that there is nothing we can do to improve the situation or the outcome, so we may as well give up.

Countering learned helplessness is the theory that we can also learn to be optimistic; this phenomenon is called, not surprisingly, **learned optimism**. Scientists studying learned optimism have found that it is possible for an individual to make a conscious choice to take a more positive stance towards the world. By changing our self-talk, examining our reactions and the way we assess what happens to us in life, and blocking negative thoughts, replacing those thoughts with positive thoughts, we can actually "learn" how to be optimistic.

Personality

Our personality is the unique mix of characteristics that distinguishes us from others. Hereditary, environmental, cultural, and experiential factors influence how we develop our personality. For each of us, the amount of influence exerted by any of these factors differs. Our personality determines how we react to the challenges of life. It also determines how we interpret the feelings we experience and how we resolve the conflicts we feel about being denied the things we need or want.

It is believed that we have the power not only to understand our own behaviours but also to actively change them, and that we thus can shape our personalities. Although much has been written about the importance of a healthy personality, there is little consensus about what exactly it is. In general, however, people who possess the following traits appear to be psychologically healthy:

- *Extroversion*: The ability to adapt to a social situation and demonstrate assertiveness as well as power or interpersonal involvement.
- *Agreeableness*: The ability to conform, be likeable, and demonstrate friendly compliance as well as love.
- *Openness to experience*: The willingness to demonstrate curiosity and independence (also referred to as *inquiring intellect*).
- *Emotional stability*: The ability to maintain control of feelings.

Self-efficacy: Belief in your ability to perform a task successfully.

Personal control: Belief that our efforts can and do influence situations and interactions with others.

Self-esteem: Sense of self-respect or self-worth.

Learned helplessness: An attitude of giving up and not trying because of past failures.

Learned optimism: Pattern of responding that focuses on the positive, because you choose to view each situation positively and with a sense of hope.

- *Conscientiousness*: The qualities of being dependable and demonstrating self-control, discipline, and a need to achieve.

> **what do you THINK?**
> Which factors of psychosocial health have the greatest positive impact on your life? What are the negative influences? Which are influencing your life most now? How resilient are you? How can you build resiliency?

Life Span and Maturity

Although the exact determinants of personality are impossible to define, we do know that our personalities are dynamic. Our temperament changes as we age, as illustrated by the extreme emotions experienced in adolescence as we search for our independence and experience an influx of hormones. Most of us learn to control our emotions as we advance toward adulthood.

The college or university years mark another critical transition period for young adults. This transition to independence is easier if students have successfully accomplished earlier developmental tasks such as learning how to solve problems, to make and evaluate decisions, to define and adhere to personal values, and to establish casual and intimate relationships. Management of personal finances, career management strategies, interpersonal communication skills, and parenting skills (for those who choose to become parents) are among the developmental tasks post-secondary students must accomplish. Older students often have to balance the responsibilities of family, career, and school.

If you have not fulfilled earlier tasks, you will continue to grow but may find your life interrupted by recurrent "crises" left over from earlier stages. For example, if you did not learn to trust others in childhood, you may have difficulty establishing intimate relationships in late adolescence or early adulthood.

Resiliency and Developmental Assets

It has become well established that some people are much better prepared to meet the challenges of life than others. The combination of certain personality traits coupled with a supportive environment can equip one to deal effectively with life's many challenges. Individuals with this set of traits and circumstances are able to cope and even thrive in times of great stress or pressure. **Resiliency**, or *protective factors*, is a term used to describe those traits or characteristics that protect an individual or community from threat or harm. In a sense, these traits may serve to inoculate one against potential ill health. People with assets, whether financial, emotional, spiritual, physical, mental, or social, and other positive forces in their lives are likely to be resilient and bounce back when facing life's challenges.

✓ ENHANCING PSYCHOSOCIAL HEALTH

You may believe that your psychosocial health is fairly well developed by the time you reach college or university. However, attaining self-fulfillment is a lifelong, conscious process that involves building self-efficacy and self-esteem, understanding and controlling emotions, maintaining support networks, and learning to solve problems and make decisions.

Developing and Maintaining Self-Esteem and Self-Efficacy

There are several ways to build self-esteem and self-efficacy. These include developing a support group, being a support for others, completing required tasks, forming realistic expectations, making and taking time for yourself, maintaining your physical health, and examining your problems and seeking help.

Developing a Support Group

One of the best ways to gain self-esteem and self-efficacy is through a support group—peers who share your values. A support group can make you feel good about yourself and help you to take an honest look at your actions and choices. Although you might seek support in a wholly new group, remember that old ties are often the strongest. Keeping in contact with old friends and family members can provide a foundation of unconditional love that will help you through the many life transitions ahead.

Being a Support for Others

Feel better about yourself by helping others to feel good about themselves. Write more "thank you" cards, postcards, and "thinking of you" notes. This will build your self-esteem and that of your friends. Become more interesting by being more interested (in people, current events, and so on). Send news clippings to friends. Join a discussion, political action, or recreational group.

Completing Required Tasks

Another way to boost your self-esteem or self-efficacy is to complete required tasks successfully and on time. You are not likely to succeed in your studies if you leave term papers until the last minute, fail to keep up with the reading for your courses, and do not ask for clarification of points confusing you. Some university and college campuses provide study groups for various content areas. Your school's student services department may offer tips for managing time, understanding assignments, dealing with professors, and preparing for test taking. Poor grades, or grades that do not meet a student's expectations, are major contributors to diminished self-esteem and to emotional distress among post-secondary students.

Forming Realistic Expectations

Having realistic expectations of yourself—and others—is another method of boosting self-esteem and self-efficacy. College or university is a time to explore your potential. If you expect perfect grades, a steady stream of Saturday-night dates and a Hollywood-type romantic involvement, a good job, and a beautiful home and car, you may be setting yourself up for failure. Assess your current resources and the direction in which you are heading. Set small, incremental goals that are possible for you to meet. Rather than suggesting, "I'm going to get better grades" without some realistic actions or achievable, definable goals to support your intentions, decide that tomorrow you will spend two hours studying or go to the library to do research on a paper, or decide to talk to your professor to see what he or she recommends to help you to better understand a particular topic.

Making and Taking Time for You

Taking time to enjoy yourself is another way to boost your psychosocial health. Making that time available is critical. For some people, participating in a sport improves self-esteem and self-efficacy via a sense of achievement and/or success. For others, meditating, doing volunteer work, getting a massage, or meeting a new challenge, such as successfully auditioning for a play, can enhance psychosocial health. Viewing each new activity as something to look forward to and an opportunity to grow is an important part of keeping the excitement in your life.

Maintaining Physical Health

Maintaining physical health also contributes to self-esteem and to overall psychosocial health. Regular physical activity fosters a sense of well-being and improves mood. Nourishing meals that provide variety, balance, and moderation help you to feel good about yourself. Combined, regular physical activity and healthy eating lead to weight maintenance rather than the usual weight gain, or "Frosh 15" (the 7 kilograms—or 15 pounds), experienced by many college or university students. Getting adequate sleep and managing your stress are two other behaviours critical to maintaining your physical and psychosocial health.

Examining Problems and Seeking Help

Examining your problems and seeking help when needed will also boost your self-esteem and self-efficacy. Facing and solving problems can be one of life's most satisfying experiences. You do not necessarily have to deal with your problems alone. Help can come in the form of a friend, a group, or a mental health professional.

Getting Adequate Sleep

Getting adequate sleep is a key contributor to physical and psychosocial functioning. Many of us do not get enough sleep and some get too much sleep. Sleep serves at least two biological purposes: (1) conservation of energy, so that we are rested and ready to perform during high-performance daylight hours; and (2) restoration, so that neurotransmitters depleted during waking hours can be replenished. This process clears the brain of daily minutiae to prepare for a new day.

what do you THINK?

Considering the suggestions listed above and in Table 5e.2, which are you actively engaged in to enhance your self-esteem and self-efficacy? How can you more actively work at enhancing your self-esteem and self-efficacy?

Resiliency: Those traits or characteristics that protect an individual or community from threat or harm.

TABLE 5e.2

Tips for Building Self-Esteem

- **Pay attention to your own needs and wants.** Listen to what your body, your mind, and your heart are telling you.
- **Take good care of yourself.** Eat healthy foods, limit junk foods, exercise, and plan fun activities for yourself.
- **Take time to do things you enjoy.** Make a list of things you enjoy doing. Then do something from that list every day.
- **Do something that you have been putting off.** Cleaning out your closet, or paying a bill that you've been putting off will make you feel like you've accomplished something.
- **Give yourself rewards.** Acknowledge that you are a great person by rewarding yourself occasionally.
- **Wear clothes that make you feel good about yourself.** You don't have to spend a lot to find clothes that make you feel good. Check out local thrift stores and consignment shops for great bargains.
- **Spend time with people.** People who make you feel better about yourself are great self-esteem boosters. Avoid people who treat you badly or make you feel bad about yourself.
- **Display items that you like.** You may have items that remind you of your achievements, your friends, or special times. Keep those special items close by.
- **Make your meals a special time.** Get rid of distractions such as the television, and really concentrate on enjoying your meal, whether you are by yourself or with others.
- **Learn something new every day.** Take advantage of any opportunity to learn something new every day–you'll feel better about yourself and be more productive.
- **Do something nice for another person.** There is no greater way to feel better about yourself than to help someone in greater need. Check out local volunteer opportunities, or make a special effort to be nice to those around you, such as your parents or siblings.

Most of us can identify with that tired, listless feeling caused by sleep deprivation during periods of peak stress. Either we do not make enough time to sleep, we have difficulty falling asleep, or we do not stay asleep once we get there. Lack of sleep is especially common among post-secondary students given their relatively high workload and levels of anxiety and stress. Women, in particular, have problems with sleep.

How much sleep do we need? That depends on a number of factors. There is a genetically based need for sleep and it differs for each person, though six to nine hours is generally recommended. Sleep duration is also controlled by *circadian rhythms*, which are linked to the hormone *melatonin*. People alter their sleep patterns by staying up late, drinking coffee, getting lots of exercise, eating a heavy meal, or using an alarm or other wake-up device. *Sleep inertia* is a term used to describe the cognitive impairment, disorientation, and grogginess we experience when we first get up in the morning. This sleep inertia may impair our ability to think clearly and function effectively in tasks that occur shortly after we wake up. To wake up effectively and well rested, you should go to bed and get up regularly at the same time. Exercise and a healthy breakfast (that is, three of the four food groups, low in fat, high in fibre) also help us to feel awake. Further, a coffee or tea upon awakening may speed the wakefulness process and for some people who must wake up quickly and be alert—such as physicians, pilots, truck drivers, and students with an 8:00 a.m. exam—this "jump start" may be necessary in order to perform effectively.

Most of us follow characteristic stages of sleep, ranging from wakefulness to drowsiness to light sleep, and then move to a deeper sleep. The most important period of sleep, a deeper sleep, is called "rapid eye movement" (REM) sleep and is essential to feeling rested and refreshed. In REM sleep, heart rate increases, respiration speeds up, and dreaming tends to occur. If we miss REM—which we do in an alcohol-induced sleep—we are left feeling groggy and sleep deprived.

Though many people turn to over-the-counter sleeping pills, barbiturates, or tranquillizers to get some sleep, the methods presented in Table 5e.3 for conquering sleeplessness are less harmful.

TABLE 5e.3

Getting a Good Night's Sleep

- **Go to bed and rise on a regular schedule.** It is important to go to bed and get up at about the same time every day.
- **Ensure your sleep environment is conducive to sleep.** Remove excessive noises, darken the room, and ensure you have quality bed and bedding.
- **Limit caffeine and alcohol.** Caffeine can linger in your body for up to 12 hours and may relate to insomnia. Although alcohol may initially make you drowsy, it affects REM sleep and the sleep–wake cycle.
- **Avoid eating a heavy meal or drinking large amounts of liquids before bed.**
- **Engage in regular physical activity.** You sleep better when you have been physically active, particularly if the activity has been outdoors. Keep in mind, however, that it is best to not be physically active right before bed; physical activity acts as a stimulant, speeding the body's metabolism and making it harder to fall asleep immediately after.
- **Nap only in the afternoon.** This works in conjunction with your circadian rhythm, and if you do, make it a "cat-nap," no longer than 20 minutes so that you do not interfere with your night sleep.
- **Establish a relaxing nighttime ritual that puts you in the mood to sleep.** Take a warm shower, relax in a comfortable chair, read, listen to music, or do something else that is quiet. Doing this consistently will tell your mind and body it is time to wind down.
- **Do not bring work to bed.**
- **If you are unable to fall asleep after 30 minutes, get up and do something else.** If you wake up in the middle of the night and cannot return to sleep, get up and do something quiet to repeat your night time ritual. Do not make your sleeplessness a cause for additional worry. Insomnia is not a crime. Not everyone needs eight hours of sleep. You can feel well—and be quite healthy—on fewer.

Understanding the Mind–Body Connection

Can negative emotions and stress make us physically sick? Can positive emotions and happiness help us feel well? Do positive emotions boost the immune system? Although considerable research has attempted to answer these questions, much remains unknown. For decades, research focused primarily on negative emotions and disease; however, little is known about the role of positive emotions in preserving health and protecting against disease. Many believe that this end of the emotional continuum may hold the key to future advances in health, and that mind–body health science may expand into new areas and may be accorded a higher level of importance as a result. One emotion that appears to have particularly positive benefits is *happiness.*

Happiness and Physical Health

Happiness refers to a number of positive states in which individuals actively embrace the world around them. As researchers examined characteristics of happy people, they found that this emotion had a profound impact on the body. Specifically, researchers found that happiness, or related mood states such as hopefulness, optimism, and contentment reduced the risk or limited the severity of cardiovascular disease, pulmonary disease, type 2 diabetes, hypertension, colds, and other infections. Laughter increases heart and respiration rates, and reduces stress hormones in the same way as physical activity. For this reason, it has been promoted as a possible risk reducer for those with hypertension and other forms of cardiovascular disease.

If happiness is good for your health, how does one "get happy"? **Subjective well-being (SWB)** refers to that uplifting feeling of inner peace or overall "feel-good state," which includes happiness. SWB is defined by three central components:

1. *Satisfaction with present life.* People high in SWB tend to like their work and are satisfied with their current personal relationships. They are sociable,

Happiness: Feeling of contentment created when expectations and physical, psychological, and spiritual needs are met and life is enjoyed.

Subjective well-being (SWB): An uplifting feeling of inner peace and/or an overall feel-good state.

outgoing, and willing to open up to others. They also like themselves and enjoy good health and self-esteem.

5e. *Relative presence of positive emotions.* People with high SWB more frequently feel pleasant emotions, mainly because they perceive the world around them in a generally positive way. They have an optimistic outlook, and they expect success in what they undertake.

3. *Relative absence of negative emotions.* Individuals with a strong sense of SWB experience fewer and less severe episodes of negative emotions, such as anxiety, depression, and anger.

Researchers also suggest that people may be biologically predisposed to happiness. In fact, happiness may be related to actual differences in brain physiology: *neurotransmitters,* the chemicals that transfer messages between neurons, may function more efficiently in happy people. Others suggest that we can develop happiness by practising positive psychological actions.

You do not have to be happy all the time to achieve overall subjective well-being. It is normal or usual to experience disappointment, unhappiness, and times when life seems unfair. In these situations, people with SWB are typically resilient, able to look on the positive side, able to get themselves back on track fairly quickly, and less likely to fall into despair over setbacks. Happiness does not depend on age, sex, ethnicity, race, or socioeconomic status. Take the quiz on happiness and see how satisfied you are with life (Figure 5e.3).

Humans are remarkably resourceful creatures. We respond to great loss, such as the death of a loved one or a traumatic event, with an initial period of grief, mourning, and sometimes anger. Yet, with time and the support of others, we move forward and find satisfaction and peace once again. Typically, we learn from suffering and emerge stronger and more capable of dealing with the next crisis. Most find some measure of happiness after the initial shock and pain of loss.

Does Laughter Enhance Psychosocial Health?

Remember the last time you laughed so hard that you cried or that your belly ached? Remember how relaxed you felt afterward? Researchers are beginning to understand the role and importance of humour in our lives and health, as noted in the following:

- Stressed people with a strong sense of humour become less depressed and anxious than those whose sense of humour is less well developed.
- Students who use humour as a coping mechanism report that it predisposes them to a positive mood.
- Telling a joke, particularly one that involves a shared experience, increases one's sense of belonging and social cohesion.

try it NOW!

Laugh for health! Laughing not only feels good, it also is good for you. Next time you are in a funk or feeling tired and out of sorts, seek out a laugh or two. Read a funny book, watch a favourite comedy, call a good friend, or play with a pet. You may be surprised how a few chuckles can make you feel better all over.

How happy are you?

Read the following statements, and then rate your level of agreement with each one using the 1–7 scale.

1	2	3	4	5	6	7
Strongly disagree	Disagree	Slightly disagree	Neither agree nor disagree	Slightly agree	Agree	Strongly agree

1. In most ways, my life is close to my ideal. ________
2. The conditions of my life are excellent. ________
3. I am satisfied with my life. ________
4. So far I have gotten the important things I want in life. ________
5. If I could live my life over, I would change almost nothing. ________

Total score: ________

Scoring:
31–35: You are very satisfied with your life 26–30: Satisfied 21–25: Slightly satisfied
20: You are neither satisfied nor dissatisfied 15–19: Slightly dissatisfied 10–14: Dissatisfied 5–9: Very dissatisfied

FIGURE 5e.3
Satisfaction with Life Scale

Source: W. Pavot and E. Diener, "Review of the Satisfaction with Life Scale," *Psychological Assessment* 5 (1993): 164–175e.

Clearly, laughter enhances mental and emotional health. It also promotes social health: people like to be around others who are fun and who laugh easily. Learning to laugh puts more joy into everyday experiences and increases the likelihood that people will keep company with us.

Positive emotions such as joy, interest, and contentment serve valuable life functions. Joy is associated with playfulness and creativity. Interest encourages us to explore our world, which enhances knowledge and cognitive ability. Contentment allows us to savour and integrate experiences, an important step in achieving mindfulness and insight. By building our physical, social, and mental resources, these positive feelings empower us to cope effectively with life's challenges. While the actual emotions may be transient, their effects can be permanent and provide lifelong enrichment.

Psychosocial Health and Well-Being

In the 1970s and '80s, a number of widely publicized studies of the health of widowed and divorced people indicated higher rates of illness and death than those of married people. Moreover, tests revealed below-normal immune-system functioning with follow-up studies indicating unusually high rates of cancer among people who were depressed. Are these studies conclusive evidence of the mind–body connection? Probably not, because they did not take into account other factors relevant to health and disease. For example, some researchers suggest that people who are divorced, widowed, or depressed are more likely to drink and smoke, use drugs, eat and sleep poorly, and fail to engage in regular physical activity—all of which negatively affect the immune system. Another possibly relevant factor is that such people may be less tolerant of illness and more likely to report their problems.

Keep in mind that the immune system changes measured in various studies of the mind–body connection are relatively small. (They are nowhere near as large as what is found in people with AIDS, for example.) The health consequences of such minute changes are difficult to gauge because the body can tolerate a certain amount of reduced immune function without illness developing. The exact amount the body is able to tolerate and under what circumstances are still unresolved questions. Thus, although there is a large body of evidence pointing to an association between emotions and physical health, there is still much to learn about this relationship. In the meantime, maintaining an optimistic mindset continues to be sound advice as it relates to improved quality of life, regardless of whether or not it also improves quantity of life.

A powerful strategy for maintaining psychosocial health is to make time for friends and activities you enjoy and that bring laughter into your life.

WHEN THINGS GO WRONG

In spite of our best efforts to remain psychosocially healthy, circumstances and events in our lives sometimes are more than we can handle. Abusive relationships, stress, anxiety, loneliness, financial upheavals, and other traumatic events can sap our spirits, causing us to turn inward or act in ways that are not healthy. Chemical imbalances, drug interactions, trauma, neurological disruptions, and other physical problems may also contribute to these not-so-healthy behaviours. **Mental illnesses** are disorders that disrupt thinking, feeling, moods, and behaviours, and cause a varying degree of impaired functioning in daily life.

Similar to a physical disease, mental illnesses can range from mild to severe and exact a heavy toll on the quality of life of the individual affected and those who come in contact with him or her. It is estimated that one in five Canadians will directly experience a mental illness at some point in his or her lifetime.

Depression

Depression is the most common emotional disorder in Canada: 6 percent of Canadians aged 18 and over have experienced a major depressive episode. It was

Mental illnesses: Disorders that disrupt thinking, feeling, moods, and behaviours and cause a varying degree of impaired functioning in daily life.

estimated from the 2000/01 Canadian Community Health Survey that 9.9 percent of Canadians over the age of 12 had a possible or probable risk of depression. Females have a greater risk of depression than males (15e.3 versus 7.5 percent). Individuals between 20 and 24 years of age have the greatest possible and probable risk of depression (13.3 percent), while individuals over the age of 75 have the lowest risk (5.1 percent).

There are two acknowledged forms of depression: endogenous and exogenous depression. **Endogenous depression** is of biochemical origin. Neurotransmitters (chemicals that transmit nerve impulses across synapses) in the brain responsible for mood elevation become unbalanced for unknown reasons. A decrease in these neurotransmitters gives rise to outward expressions of depression. If not treated, endogenous depression may become chronic. **Exogenous depression**, on the other hand, is usually caused by an external event such as the loss of something or someone of great value. People who experience exogenous depression can slide into chronic depression if unable to work through the grieving process necessary for overcoming event-related depression.

Similar symptoms appear in the two types of depression: lingering sadness; inability to find joy in pleasure-giving activities; loss of interest in work and reduced concentration; diminished or increased appetite; unexplainable fatigue; sleep disorders, including insomnia or early-morning awakenings; loss of sex drive; withdrawal from friends and family; feelings of hopelessness and worthlessness; and a desire to die. A depressed person may be unable to get out of bed in the morning or may find it impossible to leave the house.

A depressed person usually suffers from low self-esteem. He or she may feel alone—separated from and unable to communicate with others. After a while, depression becomes a vicious circle. The person feels helpless and trapped, having no way out. He or she may feel that depression is a deserved punishment for real or imagined failings. Prolonged depression may cause a person to feel utterly worthless and to view suicide as the only way out.

Facts about Depression

Although depression appears to be one of the fastest-growing psychosocial health problems, the general public is uninformed and misinformed about many aspects of it. The following points may help you to understand it.

- *Depression is not a natural reaction to crisis and loss.* Something has happened to the mood and thinking of people who are depressed such that they experience pervasive pessimism, helplessness, despair, and lethargy, sometimes coupled with agitation. Individuals who are depressed may have difficulty at work and they tend to have chronically negative interpersonal relationships. Symptoms may come and go, get worse, or stay stable; they do not get better without treatment. People who are depressed forget what it is like to feel normal.

Without appropriate treatment, depression and anxiety can become overwhelming problems that affect psychosocial well-being and physical health.

- *People will not "snap out of" depression by using a little willpower.* Telling a depressed person to "snap out of it" is like telling a person with diabetes to produce more insulin. Medical intervention in the form of antidepressant drugs and therapy is often necessary. Depression also tends to recur—more than half of those afflicted once will experience a recurrence. Understanding the seriousness of the disease and supporting people in their attempts to recover is important.
- *Frequent crying is not a hallmark of depression.* Some depressed people do not cry at all. In fact, biochemists theorize that crying may actually ward off depression by releasing chemicals that the body produces as a positive response to distress.
- *Depression is not "all in the mind."* In fact, depressive illnesses originate with an inherited chemical imbalance in the brain. Depression-like symptoms can also be a side-effect of certain physiological conditions (or their treatment), such as thyroid disorders, Lyme disease, diabetes, multiple sclerosis, hepatitis, mononucleosis, rheumatoid arthritis, and pancreatic cancer.
- *No single psychotherapy method works for all cases of depression.* A variety of methods are available. What works best for each person is a treatment that is tailored to him or her and deals with his or her personal circumstances and experiences.

Treating Depression

Depression is one of the most treatable of mental health problems; with various types of treatments available, including lifestyle modification (that is, engaging in regular moderate- to vigorous-intensity physical activity, eating well, managing stress, getting adequate sleep, developing a strong social support system, and so on); talking to a physician, counsellor, psychologist, or psychiatrist; attending a support group; or taking a medication. Selecting the best treatment for a specific person involves determining his or her type and degree of depression and its possible causes. Psychotherapeutic and pharmacologic modes of treatment are recommended for clinical (severe and prolonged) depression. Drugs often relieve the symptoms of depression, such as loss of sleep or appetite, while psychotherapy can improve the social and interpersonal functioning of a person who is depressed. Treatment may be weighted toward one or the other mode depending on the specific situation. In some cases, psychotherapy alone may be the most successful treatment. The two most common psychotherapeutic therapies for depression are cognitive and interpersonal therapy.

Cognitive therapy aims to help an individual look at life rationally and to correct habitually pessimistic thought patterns. It focuses on the here and now rather than analyzing the past. To pull a person out of depression, cognitive therapists usually need 6 to 18 months of weekly sessions comprising reasoning and behavioural exercises. *Interpersonal therapy* is sometimes combined with cognitive therapy. It also addresses the present but differs from cognitive therapy in that its primary goal is to manage chronic human relationship problems. Interpersonal therapists focus on individuals' relationships with their families and other people.

Antidepressant drugs relieve symptoms in nearly 80 percent of people with chronic depression. In recent years, drug therapies have become so common that it is not unusual to know someone taking them. Despite their commonness, caution is warranted regarding the use of antidepressants. Many emergency-room visits occur when people misuse their antidepressants, in particular when they try to quit "cold turkey" or when they have drug interactions. Clinics have been established in large metropolitan areas to offer group support for depressed people. Some clinics treat all types of depressed people; others restrict themselves to specific groups, such as widows, adolescents, or families and friends of people with depression.

Seasonal Affective Disorder

Seasonal affective disorder (SAD), a type of depression, affects approximately 2 to 3 percent of Canadians. As much as 25 percent of the population in Canada experiences a milder form of the disorder known as the "winter blues." SAD strikes during the winter months and is associated with reduced exposure to sunlight. People with SAD suffer from irritability, apathy, carbohydrate craving and weight gain, increases in sleep time, and general sadness. Researchers believe that SAD is caused by a malfunction in the hypothalamus, the gland responsible for regulating responses to external stimuli. Stress may also play a role in SAD.

Certain factors seem to put people at risk for SAD. Women are four times more likely to suffer from SAD than men. Although SAD occurs in people of all ages, those between 20 and 40 years of age appear to be the most vulnerable. Certain families also appear to be at risk. People living in cities with cold, bright winters and with an active winter culture often have lower rates of SAD than expected. Vancouver has relatively high rates of SAD due to frequent overcast skies; Saskatchewan has lower rates due to the frequency of sunshine in the winter. Some people experience a reduction in symptoms if they move south.

There are some simple but effective therapies for SAD. The most beneficial appears to be light therapy, in which an individual is exposed to lamps that mimic sunlight. In fact, following four days of daily light exposure, 80 percent of individuals experienced relief from their symptoms. Other forms of treatment include dietary modifications (eating more foods high in complex carbohydrates), increased physical activity, stress management, sleep restriction (limiting the number of hours slept in a 24-hour period), psychotherapy, and antidepressants.

Anxiety Disorders

Anxiety disorders are the most common of mental health problems, occurring in about 1 in 10 people and more frequently in women than in men. Anxiety disorders refer to a group of disorders that affect behaviour, thoughts, emotions, and physical health. These include obsessive-compulsive disorder, phobias, panic disorders, and post-traumatic stress disorder. People with anxiety disorders have intense, prolonged feelings of fright and distress for no apparent reason.

Endogenous depression: A type of depression with a biochemical basis.

Exogenous depression: A type of depression with an external cause, such as the death of a loved one or marital break up.

Seasonal affective disorder (SAD): A type of depression that occurs in the winter months, when sunlight levels are low.

Anxiety disorders: Disorders characterized by persistent feelings of threat and anxiety in coping with everyday problems.

It is believed that anxiety disorders are caused by a combination of genetics and personal circumstances. Anxiety disorders can be effectively treated with a combination of pharmaceutical intervention and cognitive-behavioural therapy.

Obsessive-Compulsive Disorders

An **obsessive-compulsive disorder (OCD)** is an anxiety disorder that affects the thoughts, behaviours, emotions, and sensations of those who experience it. Obsessions—intrusive and illogical—are persistent ideas, thoughts, impulses, or images. Common OCDs revolve around contamination (therefore the need to wash one's hands many times before eating), doubts (such as not being sure whether the lights were turned off), and disturbing sexual or religious thoughts. More harmful behaviours include pulling out one's hair, eyebrows, or eyelashes, and other forms of self-mutilation.

It is believed that OCDs have a neurological and genetic basis. They occur equally in men and women of all ages, though usually before 40 years of age, and most often begin during adolescence or early childhood.

Phobias

A **phobia** is an anxiety disorder that involves a deep and persistent fear of a specific object, activity, or social situation, and results in a compelling desire to avoid the source of fear. Phobias are thought to be more prevalent in women than in men. Simple phobias, such as fear of spiders, flying, or heights, can be treated successfully with behavioural therapy. Social phobias (fears related to interaction with others), such as fear of public speaking, inadequate sexual performance, and eating in public places, require more extensive therapy.

Panic Disorders

Another type of anxiety disorder is panic disorders which are expressed via a **panic attack**, the sudden onset of disabling terror. These attacks can happen at any time: while sleeping, sitting in traffic, or just before you deliver your class presentation. Suddenly and unexpectedly, your heart starts to race, your face turns red, you can't catch your breath, you feel nauseated, you start to perspire, and you may feel like you are going to pass out or are having a heart attack. Panic attacks may have no obvious link to environmental stimuli, or they may be learned responses to environmental stimuli. Researchers believe that panic attacks are caused by some physiological change or biochemical imbalance in the brain; they are still searching for the mechanisms that trigger such attacks.

Canadians are becoming more familiar with their psychosocial health, the risk factors for poor psychosocial health, and their treatment options, partly because of people like James Bartleman, who shared his story of depression at the National Canadian Mental Health Association Conference.

Post-Traumatic Stress Disorder

Sometimes people experience something so unexpected and so shattering that is has a serious effect on them long after the danger has passed. Examples of these experiences include traumas such as rape, abuse, assault, war, natural disasters (hurricanes, tornadoes, floods, forest fires), or airplane or car crashes. People who suffer serious after-effects of such experiences are afflicted by **post-traumatic stress disorder (PTSD)**. Common symptoms include flashbacks in which the terrifying experience is relived, nightmares, depression, detachment, and feelings of anger and irritability.

Schizophrenia

Perhaps the most frightening of all mental disorders is **schizophrenia**, a disease that affects about 1 percent of the Canadian population. Schizophrenia is characterized by alterations of the senses (including auditory

FOCUS ON CANADA

CMHA Applauds Work of Senate Committee, Wants Recommendations to Move Forward

On May 9, 2006, the Canadian Mental Health Association (CMHA)* applauded the Senate Committee on Social Affairs, Science and Technology on the 118 recommendations it made in a report on mental health, mental illness, and addictions in Canada. This report (titled *Out of the Shadows at Last*) is the result of a three-year study of mental health and addiction. In the report, the Senate Committee recommends that a 5-percent tax be placed on alcoholic beverages to assist with the funding of the $5.4-billion plan to transform Canada's mental health system.

The CMHA looks forward to working with the government, its agencies, and other stakeholders across the country to make the recommendations a reality.

It should be noted that Canada is one of the only G-8 countries currently without a national strategy for mental health and mental illness. The CMHA actively supports the Senate Committee's recommendation for a call for a strategy on mental health and mental illness for the people of Canada. The organization recommends that the federal government work with the provincial and territorial governments and key stakeholders in the mental health community to develop and implement a national strategy

The CMHA also strongly supports the Senate Committee's recommendation for the establishment of a Mental Health Commission that will bring together key stakeholders to improve the quality of life of those affected directly and indirectly by mental illness. Finally, the CMHA endorsed the Senate Committee's recommendation for the creation of a Mental Health Transition Fund, which would be used to assist individuals with mental illness in obtaining affordable housing.

The complete report can be downloaded from www.parl.gc.ca/39/1/parlbus/commbus/senate/com-e/soci-e/rep-e/rep02may06-e.htm.

* The CMHA is a leading national, voluntary organization within the mental-health sector. For more than 90 years, it has existed to promote the mental health of Canadians and to serve mental-health consumers and their families and friends through education, public awareness, research, advocacy, and direct services.

Source: Adapted from Canadian Mental Health Association, "CMHA Applauds Work of Senate Committee, Wants Recommendations to Move Forward." Retrieved on May 26, 2006, from www.cmha.ca/bins/print_page.asp?cid=6-20-21-1229-1355&lang=1.

and visual hallucinations); the inability to sort out incoming stimuli and make appropriate responses; an altered sense of self; and radical changes in emotions, movements, and behaviours. Individuals with this disease often cannot function in society, unless treated pharmacologically.

Schizophrenia is now recognized as a biological brain disease. It has become evident that the brain damage involved occurs very early in life, possibly as early as in the second trimester of fetal development. However, the disease most commonly has its onset in late adolescence.

Schizophrenia is treatable but not curable. Treatments usually include some combination of hospitalization, medication, and supportive psychotherapy. Supportive psychotherapy, as opposed to psychoanalysis, is used to help the individual acquire skills for living in society.

Despite its genetic roots, a stigma remains attached to the disease. Families of individuals with schizophrenia often experience anger and guilt. They often need help in the form of information, family counselling, and advice on how to meet the needs for shelter, medical care, vocational training, and social interaction of the family member with schizophrenia.

SEX ISSUES IN PSYCHOSOCIAL HEALTH

Studies indicate that sex bias often gets in the way of correct diagnosis of psychosocial disorders. In one study, 175 mental health professionals of both sexes were asked to diagnose an individual on the basis of a summarized case history. Some were told that the individual was male, others female. The sex of the patient made a substantial difference in the diagnosis

Obsessive-compulsive disorder (OCD): A disorder characterized by obsessive thoughts or habitual behaviours.

Phobia: A deep and persistent fear of a specific object, activity, or situation that results in a compelling desire to avoid the source of the fear.

Panic attack: The sudden, rapid onset of disabling terror.

Post-traumatic stress disorder: A disorder characterized by terrifying flashbacks, detachment, and anxiety following a severe traumatic event.

Schizophrenia: A mental illness characterized by irrational behaviours, severe alterations of the senses (hallucinations), and, often, an inability to function in society.

(though the sex of the clinician did not). When clinicians thought the case history was from a female, they were more likely to diagnose hysterical personality, a "women's disorder." When they believed the case history was from a male, the more likely diagnosis was antisocial personality, a "male disorder."

Depression and Sex

For reasons not well understood, women are twice as likely to develop depression than men. Researchers have proposed biological, psychological, and social explanations. The biological explanation relates to women's hormone level changes observed during the menstrual cycle, pregnancy, miscarriage, postpartum period, pre-menopause, and menopause. Women also face various stressors related to their multiple roles and responsibilities—work, child-rearing, household work, relationships, and caring for older parents—at rates much greater than men. Although men's hormone levels appear to remain relatively stable throughout life, they too experience depression. For men, depression is often masked by alcohol or drug use or by the socially acceptable habit of working excessively long hours. Typically, men who are depressed present as irritable, angry, and discouraged rather than hopeless and helpless.

Not only do researchers note different rates of depression in men and women, they also observe sex differences in coping strategies, or the response to certain events or stimuli, and thus propose that women's strategies put them at greater risk. Results indicate that men distract themselves from a depressed mood, whereas women tended to focus on it. If focusing on depressed feelings intensifies these feelings, women's response style then may make them more likely than men to become clinically depressed.

PMS: Physical or Mental Disorder?

A major controversy regarding sex bias is the inclusion of a diagnosis for premenstrual syndrome (PMS) and premenstrual dysphoric disorder (PMDD) in the American Psychiatric Association's *Diagnostic and Statistical Manual of Mental Disorders*, fourth edition (known as *DSM-IV*). PMS is characterized by depression, irritability, and other symptoms of increased stress typically occurring just prior to menstruation and lasting for a day or two. Whereas PMS is somewhat disruptive and uncomfortable, it does not interfere with daily function; PMDD does. To be diagnosed with PMDD, a woman must have at least five symptoms of PMS for a week to ten days, at least one of which is serious enough to interfere with her ability to function at work or at home. In these more severe cases, antidepressants may be prescribed.

SUICIDE: GIVING UP ON LIFE

Statistics Canada reported 3613 suicides in Canada for 2004 (2734 men and 879 women)—equivalent to a rate of 11.3 per 100 000 people, lower than the worldwide rate of 14.5 per 100 000 people reported by the World Health Organization. The pressures, joys, disappointments, challenges, and changes within the college or university environment are believed to be in part responsible for these rates. However, young adults who choose not to go to post-secondary school and who search for the directions to their career and relationship goals and other life aspirations are also at risk for suicide. Experts estimate that there may actually be more cases than are reported due to the difficulty in determining the causes of suspicious deaths. Suicide is often a consequence of poor coping skills, lack of social support, lack of self-esteem, and the inability to see one's way out of a bad or negative situation. Suicide can also be viewed as an extreme form of violence—anger, rage, and hopelessness turned inward rather than outward.

University or college students are more likely than the general population to attempt suicide; suicide is the second leading cause of death in people between the ages of 15 and 24. Although women attempt suicide at four times the rate of men, more than three times as many men as women actually succeed in ending their lives. Men may be more "successful" than women because they often choose more violent measures to kill themselves (that is, firearms versus an overdose of painkillers). The suicide rate among First Nations peoples is reported to be three to eight times that of non-Aboriginal Canadians.

People likely to commit suicide include those who (1) are experiencing a serious physical or mental illness, (2) are abusing alcohol or drugs, (3) are experiencing a major loss—such as the death of a loved one, unemployment, or divorce, (4) are experiencing major changes in life—for example, teenagers and seniors, and (5) have made previous suicide attempts.

Many of us will be touched by a suicide at some time. In most cases, the suicide does not occur unpredictably. In fact, it is estimated that 8 out of 10 people who attempt suicide or die by suicide hint or talk openly about it beforehand. Further, suicide is considered a process, not an event, with most contemplating their fate over a relatively long period of time.

Warning Signals of Suicide

Common warning signals of suicide include

- talk of suicide—for example, "no one cares if I live or die"

HEALTH IN THE MEDIA

Prescribing Antidepressants for Depression in 2005: Recent Concerns and Recommendations

In 2005, a review was conducted after the safety of prescribed antidepressants (selective serotonin reuptake inhibitors [SSRIs], selective serotonin and noradrenalin reuptake inhibitors [SNRIs], and other novel antidepressants) was questioned as a first-line treatment for major depressive disorders (MDD) in adults and in children and adolescents because of the drugs' potential to cause or enhance aggression and suicide. Results from this review led to the following clinical recommendations for prescribing antidepressants:

- In adults, including the elderly, SSRIs, SNRIs, and other novel agents remain the best first-line treatments for MDD.
- In children and adolescents, only fluoxetine should be used as a first-line treatment for MDD.
- In children and adolescents, SSRIs other than fluoxetine can be used as a second-line treatment when depression is severe, chronic, and associated with other comorbid conditions or if psychosocial treatments have not worked. SNRIs and other novel agents should be used only as a third-line treatment because of their greater risk of adverse events.
- It is essential to closely monitor patients for suicidality (emerging or worsening suicidal thoughts, behaviours, and attempts), particularly in the early phases of treatment—weekly contact in the first month of antidepressant treatment is recommended. It is also critical to inform the patients and families (when appropriate) of the potential side-effects that may increase suicidality (anxiety, agitation, hypomania, and activation syndrome).

Further research is recommended; specifically to determine risks and benefits to antidepressant use in children, adolcscents, and the elderly.

Source: Adapted from R. W. Lam and S. H. Kennedy, "CPA Position Statement: Prescribing Antidepressants for Depression in 2005: Recent Concerns and Recommendations," *The Canadian Journal of Psychiatry*, 49.12, 1–6. Retrieved May 30, 2006 from www.canmat.org/suicidality_antidepressant/suicidality-antidepressant.html.

- making a plan or increased risk taking
- writing or drawing about suicide (in a diary, for example)
- a preoccupation with death; giving away valued possessions
- a withdrawal from friends and family and from activities once found pleasurable
- hero worship of people who have died by suicide
- increased use of alcohol or drugs
- recent loss of a friend, family member, or parent, especially if they died by suicide
- conflicting feelings or sense of shame about being gay or straight
- mood swings, emotional outbursts, high level of irritability or aggression
- feelings of hopelessness

Taking Action to Prevent Suicide

Suicide is often seen as the only way out of an intolerable situation. People who commit suicide are in such pain they cannot see any other way out. Crisis counsellors and help lines may help temporarily, but the only way to prevent suicide is to get rid of conditions, situations, and substances that may precipitate attempts, including alcohol, drugs, loneliness, isolation, and access to guns. If someone you know threatens or displays warnings signs of suicide, take the following actions:

- *Monitor the warning signals.* Ensure that there is someone around the person as much as possible.
- *Find a safe place to talk with the person.* Allow as much time as necessary. Talking about suicide can only decrease the likelihood that someone will act on suicidal feelings.
- *Take any threat seriously.* Don't brush them off.
- *Do not belittle the person's feelings or say that he or she doesn't really mean it or couldn't succeed at suicide.* To some people, these comments offer the challenge of proving you wrong.
- *Let the person know how much you care about him or her.* State that you are there if he or she needs help.
- *Listen.* Try not to discredit or be shocked by what the person says to you. Empathize, and keep the person talking. Talk about stressors and listen to responses.
- *Ask the person directly, "Are you thinking of hurting or killing yourself?"*
- *Help the person think about alternatives.* Go with the person for help.
- *Make a plan with the person for the next few hours or days.* Help this person make contact with an

appropriate health-care professional or make the contact yourself. Take this person to an appropriate health-care facility to meet with a counsellor.

- *If the person has a plan, remove any pills or guns; call 911 for help immediately.*
- *Tell your friend's spouse, partner, parents, brothers and sisters, or counsellor.* Do not keep your suspicions to yourself. Don't let a suicidal friend talk you into keeping your discussions confidential. Let your friend know you must share this information with a professional. If your friend is successful in a suicide attempt, you will have to live with the consequences of your inaction. Counselling services available on campus can help you talk with your friend and suggest options for you.

what do you THINK?

If your roommate showed warning signs of suicide, what would you do? Whom would you contact first? Where on campus might your friend get help? In your community?

SEEKING PROFESSIONAL HELP

Many Canadians feel that seeking professional help for psychosocial problems is an admission of personal failure. Typically, any physical health problem, such as an abscessed tooth or prolonged severe pain, sends us to the nearest dentist or physician. On the other hand, we tend to ignore psychosocial problems until they pose a serious threat to our well-being—and even then, we may refuse to ask for the help needed. Despite this custom, however, an increasing number of Canadians are turning to mental health professionals for help. Researchers believe that more people want help today because "normal" living has become more difficult. Breakdown in support systems, high expectations of the individual by society, and dysfunctional families are cited as the three major reasons more people ask for help.

CHAPTER 5f

PREVENTING AND FIGHTING DISEASE

Taken from *Health: The Basics,* Fifth Canadian Edition, by Rebecca J. Donatelle and Angela M. Thompson

Heart disease and cancer continue to be the two leading causes of death in Canada. Increasing dramatically in prevalence is type 2 diabetes, with significant personal and societal consequences. Not surprisingly, the actions you take today have a significant impact on reducing your risk for these diseases now and in the future.

CARDIOVASCULAR DISEASES

Cardiovascular disease (CVD) is a class of diseases of the heart and blood vessels, which are the leading cause of death worldwide. In Canada, CVD account for more than 32 percent of all deaths. This mortality (that is, death) rate for CVD has decreased from 47 percent in 1979.

How do health experts account for this decline? There are no simple answers. Advances in medical techniques, earlier and better diagnostic procedures and treatments, better emergency medical assistance programs, and training of people in cardiopulmonary resuscitation (CPR) have greatly aided individuals with CVD. Refinements in surgical techniques and improvements in heart transplants and artificial heart devices have enabled many to live longer lives. Despite these medical advances in treatment of CVD, the onus remains on the individual for prevention, since 80 percent of premature deaths from CVD could be prevented through a healthy dietary intake, regular physical activity, and avoiding tobacco. More specifically, you can reduce your risk for CVD by controlling high blood pressure and reducing your dietary intake of saturated fats and cholesterol. By maintaining your weight, decreasing your sodium intake, engaging in regular physical activity, and changing your lifestyle to reduce your stress response, you can lower your blood pressure. You can also monitor the levels of fat and cholesterol in your blood and adjust your dietary intake to prevent your arteries from becoming clogged. Understanding how your cardiovascular system works will help you to understand your risks for CVDs and what can be done to reduce these risks.

try it NOW!

Learn about your risk of developing CVD!

Right now, you can find out about your likelihood of developing CVD and take steps to modify your risk. The Heart and Stroke Foundation has a website with various online tools that identify individual risk. Visit: www.heartandstroke.com and click on "risk assessment."

UNDERSTANDING YOUR CARDIOVASCULAR SYSTEM

The **cardiovascular system** refers specifically to the network of elastic tubes through which blood flows as it carries oxygen and nutrients to all parts of the body. It includes the heart, lungs, arteries, arterioles (small arteries), and capillaries (minute blood vessels). It also includes venules (small veins) and veins, the blood vessels though which blood flows as it returns to the heart and lungs.

Under normal circumstances, the human body contains approximately six litres of blood. This blood transports nutrients, oxygen, waste products, hormones, and enzymes throughout the body. It also regulates body temperature, cellular water levels, and acidity levels of body components, and aids in bodily defence against toxins and harmful microorganisms. An adequate blood supply is essential to health and well-being.

How does the heart ensure that blood is constantly recirculated to body parts? The four chambers of the heart work together to deliver oxygenated blood where it is needed and to remove carbon dioxide (see Figure 5f.1). The

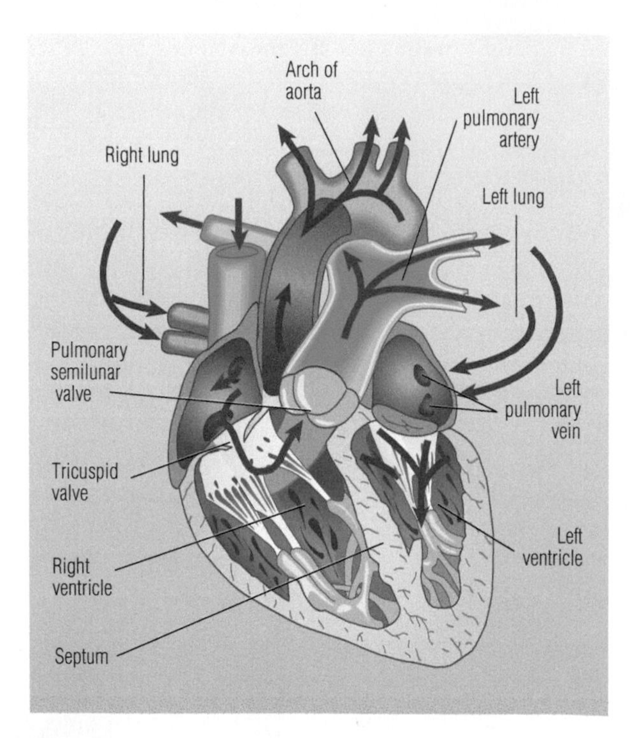

FIGURE 5f.1
Anatomy of the Heart

Cardiovascular diseases (CVD): Diseases of the heart and blood vessels.

Cardiovascular system: A complex system comprising the heart and blood vessels that transports nutrients, oxygen, hormones, and enzymes throughout the body and regulates temperature, the water levels of cells, and the acidity levels of body components.

two upper chambers of the heart, called **atria**, or auricles, are large collecting chambers that receive blood from the rest of the body. The two lower chambers, known as **ventricles**, pump the blood out again. Small valves regulate the steady, rhythmic flow of blood between chambers and prevent inappropriate backwash. The tricuspid valve, located between the right atrium and the right ventricle, the pulmonary (pulmonic) valve, between the right ventricle and the pulmonary artery, the mitral valve, between the left atrium and left ventricle, and the aortic valve, between the left ventricle and the aorta, allow blood to flow in only one direction.

Heart activity depends on a complex interaction of biochemical, physiological, and neurological signals. The following is a simplified version of the steps involved:

1. Deoxygenated blood enters the right atrium after circulating through the body.
2. From the right atrium, blood moves to the right ventricle and is pumped through the pulmonary artery to the lungs, where it receives oxygen.
3. Oxygenated blood from the lungs then returns to the left atrium of the heart.
4. Blood from the left atrium is forced into the left ventricle.
5. The left ventricle pumps blood through the aorta to the body.

Different types of blood vessels are required for different parts of this process. **Arteries** carry blood away from the heart—except for pulmonary arteries, which carry deoxygenated blood to the lungs, where they pick up oxygen and drop off carbon dioxide. As they branch off from the heart, the arteries divide into smaller blood vessels called **arterioles**, and then into even smaller blood vessels called capillaries.

Capillaries have thin walls that permit the exchange of oxygen, carbon dioxide, nutrients, and waste products with body cells. Carbon dioxide and waste products are transported to the lungs and kidneys through **veins** and venules (small veins).

For the heart to function properly, the four chambers must beat in an organized manner. This is governed by an electrical impulse that directs the heart muscle to move when the impulse moves across it, resulting in a sequential contraction of the four chambers. This signal starts in a small bundle of highly specialized cells, the **sinoatrial node (SA node)**, located in the right atrium. The SA node serves as a form of natural pacemaker for the heart. People with damaged or nonfunctional natural pacemaker activity have a mechanical pacemaker inserted to ensure the smooth passage of blood through the sequential phases of the heartbeat.

At rest, the average adult heart beats 70 to 80 times per minute. A woman's resting heart rate tends to be slightly higher than a man's. A person's heart with a high level of physical fitness beats about 50 to 60 times per minute. To supply the working muscles with the nutrients they need, the heart beats harder when engaged in physical activity. When the mind and body experience severe stress, the heart may beat over 200 times per minute, particularly in an individual who is overweight and/or with a low level of physical fitness. A healthy heart functions more efficiently and is better able to accommodate to overwork than an unhealthy one.

what do you THINK?

Do you know your resting heart rate? Do you know how to find it? What influences your heart rate? Measure your heart rate at various times throughout the day and become familiar with the settings and circumstances that influence it.

TYPES OF CARDIOVASCULAR DISEASES

Although most of us associate CVD with heart attacks, there are a number of different types. The four most common forms include:

- atherosclerosis (characterized by deposits of plaque in the inner lining of the arteries)
- coronary heart disease (a result of atherosclerotic plaque building up in the arteries such that coronary artery blood flow is reduced; when the blood flow is severely restricted or blocked a heart attack [myocardial infarction] results; when the blood flow is reduced [approximately 75 percent], but not blocked, chest pain [angina pectoris] often occurs)
- stroke (cerebrovascular accident that occurs as a result of reduced blood supply to the brain)
- hypertension (chronic high blood pressure)

Other less common forms of CVD include irregular heartbeat (arrhythmia), congestive heart failure, and congenital and rheumatic heart disease.

Irrespective of lifestyle behaviours, some individuals are at a greater risk than others for CVD. Generally, risk increases with age; men are at a greater risk than women, and individuals of African, South Asian, and First Nations descent are at greater risk than other ethnicities. Others are at risk because of their lifestyle choices. These will be discussed later in this chapter.

Atherosclerosis

Atherosclerosis is a type of arteriosclerosis. **Arteriosclerosis** is a general term for the narrowing or "hardening" of the arteries. The end result of arteriosclerosis is reduced blood flow to vital organs. Atherosclerosis is characterized by deposits of fatty substances, cholesterol, cellular waste products, calcium, and fibrin (a clotting material in the blood) in the inner lining of an artery. The resulting build-up is referred to as atherosclerotic **plaque**. Plaque may partially or totally block the blood's flow through an artery. When plaque develops, two things can happen: (1) bleeding (hemorrhage) into the plaque or (2) formation of a blood clot (thrombus) on the plaque's surface. If either of these occurs and an artery is blocked, the chances of a heart attack or stroke increase.

Atherosclerosis does not suddenly occur. In fact, evidence suggests that atherosclerotic plaque begins to form in the womb, and worsens as the years pass. As such, atherosclerosis is not an all-or-nothing disease but occurs in varying degrees. Further, there are lifestyle choices individuals make in regard to physical activity and dietary intake that significantly influence the amount of plaque that develops. If the arteries are occluded (blocked with plaque) to about 75 percent in the heart, angina pectoris (chest pain) results. When the arteries are 90 to 95 percent occluded and a blood clot attempts to travel through them, a myocardial infarction (heart attack) or ischemic stroke (if the blood clot is in occluded arteries in the brain) occurs.

The process of plaque buildup begins when the protective inner lining of the artery (endothelium) becomes damaged, allowing fat, cholesterol, and other substances in the blood to affix to the arterial walls, eventually obstructing blood flow. The three major causes of such damage are (1) dramatic fluctuations in blood pressure, (2) elevated levels of cholesterol, triglycerides, and glucose in the blood, and (3) cigarette smoking. Viral infections may also be contributing factors. Cigarette smoke aggravates and speeds up the development of atherosclerosis, particularly in the coronary arteries, the aorta, and the arteries of the legs because of the damage caused to the inner arterial walls.

what do you THINK?

Did you know that deposits of atherosclerotic plaque are likely forming in your arteries right now? Do you know your cholesterol and triglyceride levels? Do you know your blood pressure? Have your parents or grandparents been diagnosed with high cholesterol or high blood pressure? What actions should you take to reduce your risk for atherosclerosis?

Coronary Heart Disease

Coronary heart disease (CHD), also called coronary artery disease, is the major disease of the cardiovascular system. It is the result of atherosclerotic plaque accumulation such that a blockage occurs in one or more of the coronary arteries and blood flow is impeded. As previously mentioned, chest pain or angina pectoris results when the blockage is equivalent to 75 percent or more while complete blockage results in a heart attack.

A **heart attack**, or **myocardial infarction**, involves a blockage of the normal blood supply to an area of the heart. This condition is often brought on by a **coronary thrombosis**, or blood clot in the coronary artery. When blood does not flow readily, there is a corresponding decrease in oxygen flow. The most common symptoms of a heart attack include

- uncomfortable pressure or pain in chest lasting more than a few seconds
- mild to intense pain spreading to the shoulders, neck, or arms
- lightheadedness, fainting, sweating, nausea, or shortness of breath
- anxiety, nervousness, and/or cold, sweaty skin
- paleness or pallor
- increased or irregular heart rate
- feeling of impending doom

Atria: The two upper chambers of the heart, which receive blood.

Ventricles: The two lower chambers of the heart, which pump blood through the blood vessels.

Arteries: Vessels that carry blood away from the heart.

Arterioles: Small arteries.

Capillaries: Minute blood vessels that branch out from the arterioles; through which the exchange of oxygen, carbon dioxide, nutrients, and waste products happens.

Veins: Vessels that carry blood back to the heart.

Sinoatrial node (SA node): Node serving as a form of natural pacemaker for the heart.

Arteriosclerosis: Refers to narrowing and hardening of the arteries.

Atherosclerosis: A type of arteriosclerosis characterized by plaque deposits in the inner lining of arteries.

Plaque: Combination of fatty substances, cholesterol, cellular waste products, calcium, and fibrin.

Heart attack or **Myocardial infarction:** A blood clot that prevents blood from flowing through the heart.

Coronary thrombosis: A blood clot in a coronary artery.

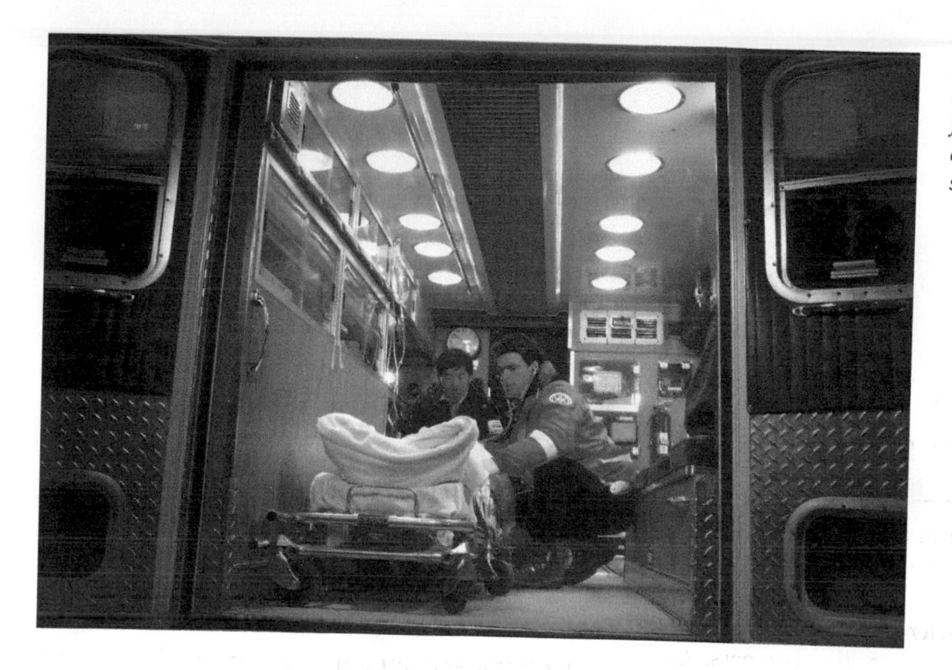

Because 40 percent of heart attack victims die within the first two hours, immediate attention is vital to the patient's survival.

Since many women do not experience the symptoms above, in women the following may be indicative of a heart attack: unusual fatigue, shortness of breath, and sleep disturbances.

If the heart blockage is extremely minor, the otherwise healthy heart will adapt over time by using small unused or underused blood vessels to reroute the needed blood. This system, known as **collateral circulation**, is a form of self-preservation that allows a damaged heart muscle to heal itself. When heart blockage is more severe, the body is unable to adapt on its own and outside lifesaving support is critical. The two hours following a heart attack are believed to be the most critical period for treatment; more than 40 percent of heart attack victims die within this time. Following this time period, 12 percent of Canadians who experience a heart attack die within 30 days. Long-term survival after 30 days reaches 91 to 93 percent.

It is believed that normal nonatherosclerotic arteries can also go into spasm and cause circulatory impairment. Excessive calcium and potassium are among the suspected causes of these spasms.

As a result of atherosclerosis and other circulatory impairments, the heart's oxygen supply is often reduced, a condition known as ischemia. Individuals with **ischemia** often suffer from varying degrees of **angina pectoris** or chest pains. Many of these individuals experience short episodes of angina when they exert themselves physically. Symptoms of angina range from a slight feeling of indigestion to a feeling that the heart is being crushed. Generally, the more serious the oxygen deprivation, the more severe the pain.

Currently, several methods of treating angina are available. In mild cases, rest is critical. The most common treatments for more severe cases involve using drugs that affect (1) the supply of blood to the heart muscle or (2) the heart's demand for oxygen. Pain and discomfort are often relieved with nitroglycerin, a drug used to relax (dilate) veins, thereby reducing the amount of blood returning to the heart and thus lessening its workload. Patients whose angina is caused by spasms of the coronary arteries are often given drugs called calcium channel blockers. These drugs prevent calcium atoms from passing through coronary arteries and causing heart contractions. They also appear to reduce blood pressure and to slow heart rates. **Beta blockers** are another major type of drug used to treat angina. The chemical action of beta blockers serves to control potential overactivity of the heart muscle.

When a stroke occurs, the result is the death of brain cells. Consequences of a stroke include speech impairment, memory loss, and loss of motor control. Although some strokes affect parts of the brain that regulate heart and lung function and result in death within minutes, others are mild and result in temporary dizziness or slight weakness or numbness. Mild strokes are called **transient ischemic attacks** and often indicate an impending major stroke. The key to surviving a stroke is to obtain medical treatment within three hours of the first symptom. Althoughalmost three-quarters of Canadians recognize at least one warning sign of stroke, only half would call 9-1-1 if they or someone they knew was experiencing the warning sign. The most common symptoms include

- sudden weakness or numbness of the face, arm, or leg on one side of the body
- sudden dimness or loss of vision, particularly in only one eye

- loss of speech, or trouble talking or understanding speech
- sudden, severe headache with no known cause
- unexplained dizziness, unsteadiness, or sudden fall, especially with any of the previous symptoms

Stroke

Like the heart muscle, brain cells must have a continuous and adequate supply of oxygen in order to survive. A **stroke** (also called a cerebrovascular accident) occurs when the blood supply to the brain is cut off. Strokes (see Figure 5f.2) may be caused by a **thrombus** (blood clot), an **embolus** (a wandering clot), or an **aneurysm** (a weakening in a blood vessel that causes it to bulge and, in severe cases, burst).

Hypertension

Hypertension or chronic high blood pressure is unique because it is a CVD itself, and a risk factor for CHD and stroke. When blood pressure is chronically elevated, the workload on the heart is greater, which may damage the heart's ability to pump blood effectively throughout the body and result in heart muscle damage. High blood pressure may also damage the interior walls of the arteries, which facilitates atherosclerotic plaque accumulation.

Sustained high blood pressure, or **hypertension**, that cannot be attributed to any specific cause is known as **essential hypertension**. Approximately 90 percent of all cases of high blood pressure fit this category. **Secondary hypertension** refers to high blood pressure caused by specific factors, such as kidney disease, obesity, or tumours of the adrenal glands.

Blood pressure is measured in two parts and is expressed as two numbers separated by a slash—for example, 120/80, or 120 over 80. Both values are measured in millimetres of mercury (mmHg). The first number refers to **systolic pressure**, or the pressure on the walls of the arteries when the heart contracts, pumping blood to the rest of the body. The second value refers to **diastolic pressure**, or the pressure on the arterial walls during the heart's relaxation phase. During this phase, blood re-enters the chambers of the heart, preparing for the next heartbeat. As shown in Table 5f.1, a blood pressure reading of 120 over 80 mmHg is generally considered normal. Systolic values between 120 and 139 mmHg or diastolic values of 80 to 89 mmHg are usually considered prehypertensive, and a blood pressure reading greater than 140 over 90 mmHg is classified as hypertensive. Research indicates that risk for CVD doubles for each increase of 20/10 mmHg above 115/75.

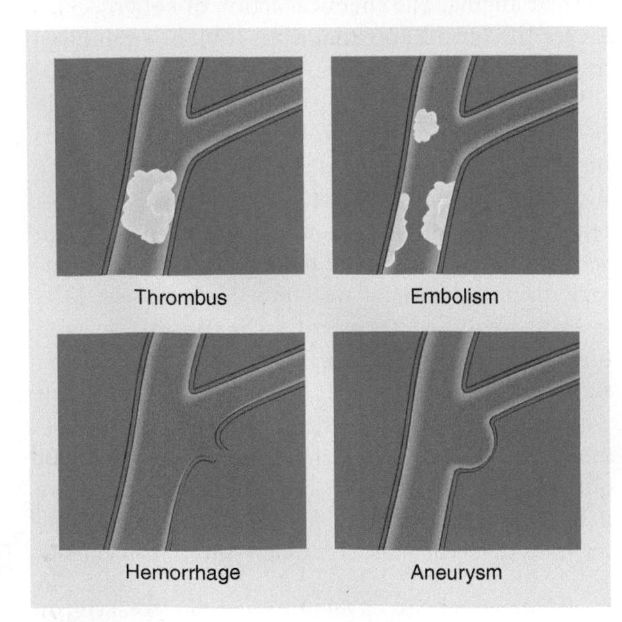

FIGURE 5f.2
Common Blood Vessel Disorders

Collateral circulation: Following the complete occlusion of a coronary artery, rerouting of needed blood through unused or underused blood vessels.

Ischemia: Insufficient blood flow relative to the demand of the tissue which results in a decrease in oxygen

Angina pectoris: Severe chest pain occurring as a result of reduced oxygen flow to the heart.

Beta blockers: A type of drug used to treat angina; controls potential overactivity of the heart muscle.

Transient ischemic attacks: Mild form of stroke; often an indicator of impending major stroke.

Stroke: Results when the blood supply to the brain is severely reduced or cut off.

Thrombus: Blood clot.

Embolus: Blood clot forced through the circulatory system.

Aneurysm: A weakened blood vessel that may bulge under pressure and, in severe cases, burst.

Hypertension: Chronic high blood pressure; 140/80 mmHg or greater.

Essential hypertension: Hypertension as a result of unknown causes.

Secondary hypertension: Hypertension as a result of another condition such as kidney disease, obesity, or tumours of the adrenal glands.

Systolic pressure: The upper number in the blood pressure fraction, refers to the pressure on the walls of the arteries when the heart contracts.

Diastolic pressure: The lower number in the blood pressure fraction, refers to pressure on the walls of the arteries during the relaxation phase of heart activity.

TABLE 5f.1

Blood Pressure Classifications

Classification	Systolic Reading (mmHg)	Diastolic Reading (mmHg)
Normal	<120	<80
Prehypertension	120–139	80–89
Hypertension		
Stage 1	140–159	90–99
Stage 2	≥160	≥100

Note: If systolic and diastolic readings fall into different categories, treatment is determined by the highest category. Readings are based on the average of two or more properly measured, seated readings on each of two or more health care provider visits.

Source: National Heart, Lung, and Blood Institute, *The Seventh Report of the Joint National Committee on Prevention, Detection, Evaluation, and Treatment of High Blood Pressure* (NIH Publication No. 03-5233) (Bethesda, MD: National Institutes of Health, May 2003).

Arrhythmia, Congestive Heart Failure, and Congenital and Rheumatic Heart Disease

Arrhythmia refers to an irregular heartbeat. It may be suspected, for instance, when a person complains of a racing heart in the absence of physical activity or anxiety; *tachycardia* is the medical term for an abnormally fast heartbeat. On the other end of the continuum is *bradycardia*, or abnormally slow heartbeat. When a heart goes into **fibrillation**, it exhibits a sporadic, quivering pattern of beating resulting in extreme inefficiency in moving blood through the cardiovascular system. If untreated, this condition may be fatal. Not all arrhythmias are life-threatening. Excessive caffeine or nicotine consumption can trigger arrhythmia. For the most part, in the absence of other symptoms, arrhythmias are not serious. However, severe cases may require drug therapy or an external electrical stimulus to prevent further, more serious complications.

Congestive heart failure occurs when the heart muscle is damaged or overworked and lacks the strength to continue the blood circulating process. Individuals afflicted with rheumatic fever, pneumonia, or other cardiovascular problems in the past often have weakened heart muscles. In addition, the walls of the heart and the blood vessels may be damaged from previous radiation or chemotherapy treatments for cancer. These weakened muscles respond poorly when stressed; blood flow out of the heart is diminished, and the return flow of blood through the veins begins to back up, causing congestion in the tissues. This pooling of blood causes enlargement of the heart and decreases the amount of blood that can be circulated. Blood begins to accumulate in other body areas, such as in the vessels in the legs and ankles or the lungs, causing swelling or difficulty in breathing. If untreated, congestive heart failure results in death. Most cases respond well to diuretics (water pills) for relief of fluid accumulation, digitalis, a drug that increases the pumping action of the heart, and a vasodilator that expands blood vessels and decreases resistance, allowing blood to flow more easily, thus reducing the workload on the heart.

Approximately 1 out of every 125 children is born with some form of **congenital heart disease** (heart disease present at birth). These diseases range from slight murmurs caused by valve irregularities which some children outgrow, to serious complications in heart function that can only be corrected with surgery. The underlying causes of congenital heart diseases are unknown but believed to be related to hereditary factors; maternal diseases, such as German measles (rubella), occurring during fetal development; or chemical intake (particularly alcohol) by the mother during pregnancy. Due to advances in pediatric cardiology, the prognosis for children with congenital heart defects is better now than ever before.

Rheumatic heart disease is attributed to rheumatic fever, an inflammatory disease caused by an unresolved streptococcal infection of the throat ("strep throat") that may affect many connective tissues of the body, especially those of the heart, the joints, the brain, or the skin. In a small number of cases, the streptococcal infection can lead to an immune response in which antibodies attack the heart as well as the bacteria.

CONTROLLING YOUR RISKS FOR CARDIOVASCULAR DISEASES

The four primary risk factors for CVD are high blood pressure (hypertension), high blood fats (hyperlipidemia), smoking, and physical inactivity. Secondary risk factors include, stress, obesity, and diabetes. These primary and secondary risk factors are primarily under your control. There are other risk factors, such as age, sex, ethnicity, and hereditary factors that you cannot control.

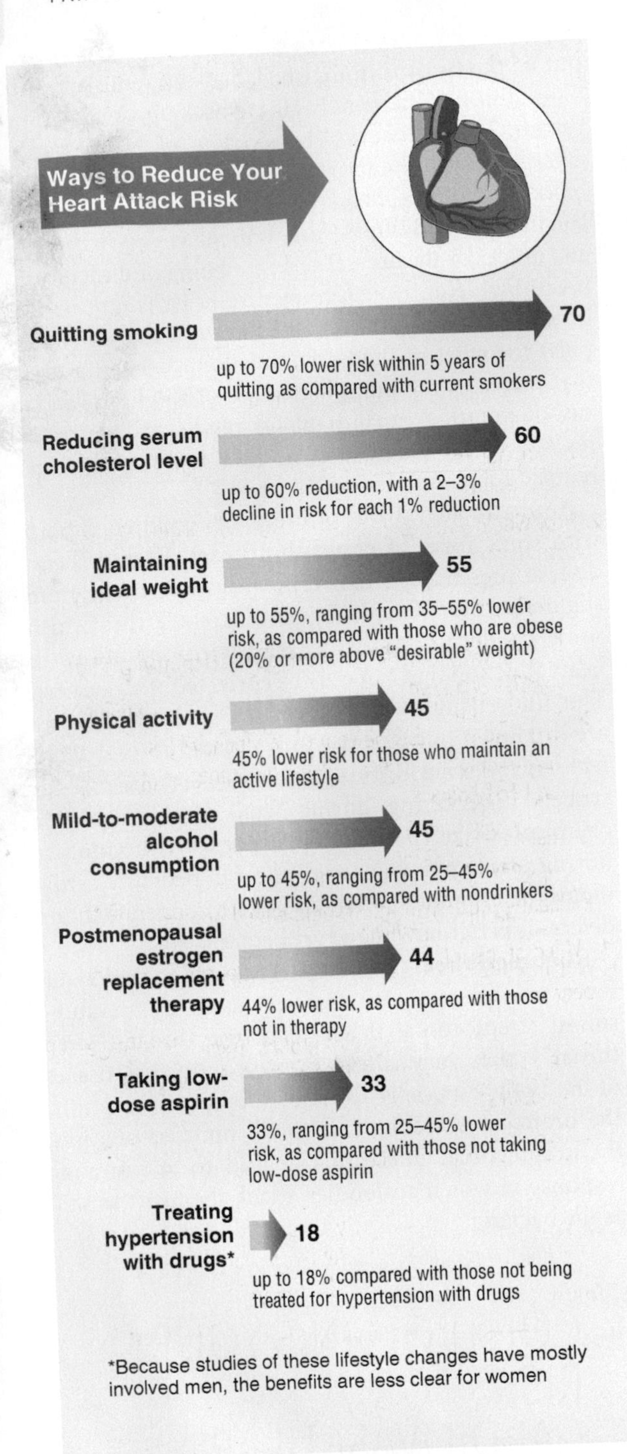

FIGURE 5f.3

Estimated Average Reduction in Risk for Heart Attack*

*Estimated risk reductions refer to the independent contribution of each risk factor to heart attack and do not address the wide range of known or hypothesized reactions among them.

Source: Adapted from information appearing in J. E. Mason, "Medical Progress: The Primary Prevention of Myocardial Infarction," *New England Journal of Medicine* 326 (May 21, 1992): 1406–1416.

Knowledge of the factors that contribute to CVD and how to make lifestyle changes that reduce your risk may motivate you to make the necessary health-promoting lifestyle changes. Figure 5f.3 summarizes known ways to reduce your risk for heart attack. These risks have an elevated impact when combined. For example, if you have high blood pressure, high cholesterol, a family history of heart disease, and smoke cigarettes, you run a much greater risk of having a heart attack or other CVD than someone with only one risk. To assess your risks for heart disease, see the Rate Yourself box.

Risks You Can Control

High Blood Pressure

As mentioned previously, high blood pressure (hypertension) is a unique risk factor for CHD because it is also a CVD itself. It is considered the leading risk for stroke and a major factor for heart disease. In general, the higher your blood pressure, the greater your risk for CHD. High blood pressure is known as the "silent killer," because it usually has no symptoms. The latest data available from Statistics Canada (2005) indicate that 14.9 percent of the population 12 years of age or older have been diagnosed by a health professional with high blood pressure. Overall, more women (15.7%) than men (14.1%) have been diagnosed, though this may relate to women living longer than men. Very few 12- to 19-year-olds (0.5 percent) or 20- to 34-year-olds (2.5 percent) have high blood pressure. In the 35- to 44-year-old age group, 6.6 percent have high blood pressure. Rates more than double in the 45- to 54-year-old age group, with 15.6 percent having high blood pressure. In the older age groups, rates of high blood pressure increase dramatically, with 29.8 percent of 55- to 64-year-olds, 42.3 percent of 65- to 74-year-olds and 46.6 percent of all individuals over the age of 75 having high blood pressure. After the age of 65, more females than males have high blood pressure, with the greatest difference noted in the over-75 group (50.8 versus 40.3 percent). Individuals of African and South Asian descent are not only three

Arrhythmia: An irregularity in heartbeat.

Fibrillation: A sporadic, quivering pattern of heartbeat resulting in inefficient moving of the blood.

Congestive heart failure: Occurs when the heart muscle is damaged or overworked and lacks the strength to maintain blood circulation.

Congenital heart disease: Heart disease present at birth.

Rheumatic heart disease: A heart disease caused by unresolved streptococcal infection of the throat.

RATE YOURSELF

Understanding Your Risk for CVD

Each of us has a unique level of risk for various diseases. Some of these risks you can take action to change; others are risks that you need to consider as you plan a lifelong strategy for overall risk reduction. Respond to each of the following, then total your points in each section. The higher your score, the greater your risk. If you answer "don't know" for any question, talk to your parents or other family members as soon as possible to find out if you have any unknown risks.

PART I: ASSESS YOUR FAMILY RISK FOR CVD

1. Do any of your primary relatives (mother, father, grandparents, siblings) have a history of heart disease or stroke?

   Yes ____ (1 point) No____ (0 points) Don't Know ____
2. Do any of your primary relatives (mother, father, grandparents, siblings) have diabetes?

   Yes ____ (1 point) No____ (0 points) Don't Know ____
3. Do any of your primary relatives (mother, father, grandparents, siblings) have high blood pressure?

   Yes ____ (1 point) No____ (0 points) Don't Know ____
4. Do any of your primary relatives (mother, father, grandparents, siblings) have a history of high cholesterol?

   Yes ____ (1 point) No____ (0 points) Don't Know ____
5. Would you say that your family consumed a high-fat diet (lots of red meat, dairy, butter/margarine) during your time spent at home?

   Yes ____ (1 point) No____ (0 points) Don't Know ____

   Total ____

PART II: ASSESS YOUR LIFESTYLE RISK FOR CVD

1. Is your total cholesterol level higher than it should be?

   Yes ____ (1 point) No____ (0 points) Don't Know ____
2. Do you have high blood pressure?

   Yes ____ (1 point) No____ (0 points) Don't Know ____
3. Have you been diagnosed as prediabetic or diabetic?

   Yes ____ (1 point) No____ (0 points) Don't Know ____
4. Do you smoke?

   Yes ____ (1 point) No____ (0 points) Don't Know ____
5. Would you describe your life as being highly stressful?

   Yes ____ (1 point) No____ (0 points) Don't Know ____

   Total ____

PART III: ASSESS YOUR ADDITIONAL RISKS FOR CVD

1. How would you best describe your current weight?
   a. Lower than what it should be for my height and weight (0 points)
   b. About what it should be for my height and weight (1 point)
   c. Higher than it should be for my height and weight (1 point)
2. How would you describe the level of exercise that you get each day?
   a. Less than what I should be exercising each day (1 point)
   b. About what I should be exercising each day (0 points)
   c. More than what I should be doing each day (0 points)
3. How would you describe your dietary behaviours?
   a. Eating only the recommended number of calories per day (0 points)
   b. Eating less than the recommended number of calories per day (0 points)
   c. Eating more than the recommended number of calories per day (1 point)
4. Which of the following best describes your typical dietary behaviours?
   a. I eat from the major food groups, trying hard to get the recommended amount of fruits and vegetables. (0 points)
   b. I eat too much red meat and consume too much saturated fat from meats and dairy products each day. (1 point)
   c. Whenever possible, I try to substitute olive oil or canola oil for other forms of dietary fat. (0 points)
5. Which of the following best describes you?
   a. I watch my sodium intake and try to reduce stress in my life. (0 points)
   b. I have a history of Chlamydia infection. (1 point)
   c. I try to eat 5 to 10 milligrams of soluble fibre each day and to substitute a soy product for an animal product in my diet at least once each week. (0 points)

Total ____

Source: TOTAL FITNESS AND WELLNESS, 4th ed., by Scott K. Powers, Stephen L. Dodd and Virginia J. Noland. © 2006, pp. 277–278. Reprinted by permission of Pearson Education, Inc. Upper Saddle River, New Jersey.

Controlling the amount and type of fat you eat is one thing you can do to lower your risk for heart disease

times more likely to become hypertensive than the general population, but they are also more likely to develop the problem at younger ages.

Normal blood pressure varies for different individuals, depending on weight, physical fitness, sex, and ethnicity. As previously mentioned, 120 over 80 mmHg is a normal blood pressure level and a blood pressure of 140/90 mmHg or greater is considered hypertensive. Recently, Canadian blood pressure guidelines suggested that a blood pressure of more than 135/85 measured at home may also indicate high blood pressure. Further, these guidelines indicated that a blood pressure reading between 130/85 and 139/89 mmHg should be considered high-normal blood pressure. Currently it is estimated that more than 2.5 million Canadians have high-normal blood pressure and approximately 1 million of them will develop full-blown high blood pressure over the next four years.

If your blood pressure exceeds 140 over 90, you should make lifestyle changes to lower it (engage in regular physical activity, eat healthily, manage your stress, and attain a healthy body weight). Regular aerobic exercise normally lowers blood pressure by 5 to 15 mmHg. Controlling your sodium intake can also reduce your risk since it contributes to approximately 17 000 cases of stroke and heart disease in Canada each year. Even though the average Canadian consumes more than 3100 mg of sodium per day, the adequate daily intake has been set at between 1200 and 1500 mg each day. Since the majority of the sodium we consume comes from processed foods, reducing consumption of these would assist in lowering your intake. If these lifestyle changes do not reduce your blood pressure to more normal values, you may need to take medication. Similarly, if your blood pressure is pre-hypertensive (that is, between 120/80 and 140/90), you should adjust your lifestyle in an attempt to lower your blood pressure to what is considered normal.

Blood Fat and Cholesterol Levels

You do not actually consume LDLs or HDLs directly in your diet, rather a dietary intake high in saturated fats raises your LDL cholesterol levels. This sends the body's blood-clotting system into high gear, increasing the viscosity of the blood in just a few hours, which in turn increases risk for heart attack or stroke. A fatty diet also elevates the amount of cholesterol in the blood, contributing to atherosclerosis. Foods particularly high in saturated fat include coconut oil, palm kernel oil, butter, cream, whole milk, and beef. Regular physical activity, reducing saturated and trans fat intake, and increasing monounsaturated fat and omega-3 fat intakes can benefit your blood lipid profile and reduce risk for heart disease (see Chapter 5 for more details). A total cholesterol concentration of less than 5.2 millimoles per litre (mmol/L) or 200 milligrams per decilitre (mg/dL) indicates a low risk for heart disease, while values greater than 5.2 mmol/L (or 240 mg/dL) indicate high risk. Values between 200 and 240 mg/dL are considered moderate risk.

Although risk values are established for total cholesterol, it is really the individual components that you need to be concerned about. **Low-density lipoproteins (LDLs)** are often referred to be "bad" cholesterol because they tend to build up or accumulate on artery walls. In contrast, **high-density lipoproteins (HDLs)** or "good" cholesterol remove cholesterol from artery walls, thus serving as a protector. In theory, if LDL levels get too high (greater than or equal to 3.4 mmol/L) or HDL levels too low (less than 0.9 mmol/L)—largely because of too much saturated fat in the diet, lack of physical activity, high stress, or genetic predisposition—cholesterol will accumulate on the arterial walls and lead to CVD. The goal then is to manage the ratio of HDL to total cholesterol by lowering LDLs or raising HDLs or both. Regular physical activity and a healthy dietary intake low in saturated and trans fat (see also Chapter 5 for more details) continue to be the best method for maintaining healthy ratios.

Triglycerides, the type of fat we normally consume, are also manufactured by our bodies. As people get older or fatter or both, their triglyceride and cholesterol levels tend to rise. According to the Heart and Stroke Foundation of Canada, a triglyceride level greater than or equal to 2.3 mmol/L increases risk for CVD.

Low-density lipoproteins (LDLs): A combination of protein, triglycerides, and cholesterol in the blood that accumulate on arterial walls.

High-density lipoproteins (HDLs): A combination of protein, triglycerides, and cholesterol in the blood that facilitate the transport of LDLs to the liver for metabolism and elimination from the body.

Triglycerides: The most common form of fat in the body, consumed and manufactured in the body.

FOCUS ON CANADA

Obesity Link to Heart Disease Confirmed

Dr. Jean-Pierre Després, Director of Research Cardiology at Laval's University Hospital in Quebec, is a member of the International Day for Evaluation of Abdominal Obesity (IDEA) study, which examined the relationship of abdominal obesity to cardiovascular disease in 170 000 individuals in 63 countries. The results of this study confirmed that abdominal obesity, as measured by waist circumference in men and women, was associated with the presence of cardiovascular disease. More specifically, it was found that a 14- or 14.9-centimetre increase in waist circumference, in men and women respectively, increased the risk of cardiovascular disease from 21 to 40 percent. Furthermore, this study showed that a 16-year increase in age tripled the likelihood of an adult developing cardiovascular disease.

Dr. Després commented, "this is the first time a study of this magnitude has been conducted worldwide in a primary care population," and "these figures show that patients do not feel that having their waist measured is intrusive. The importance and the clinical significance of these results will stimulate initiation of additional studies that will aid us in identifying patients most at risk and help us to evaluate the impact that new treatments will have on the overall cardiometabolic risk of these patients."

Source: "Obesity Link to Heart Disease Confirmed," report by Jennifer Tryon, *Global National*, March 14, 2006: www.canada.com/nationalpost/news/story.html?id=5ee25c66-9c9b-4fe7-a05a-be185d60cddc$k=95067.

Cigarette Smoking

The link between cigarette smoking and heart disease has been firmly established. The risk for CVD is 70 percent greater for smokers than for nonsmokers. Further, the more a person smokes, the greater his or her risk of developing heart disease. Smokers who have a heart attack are more likely to die suddenly (within one hour) than non-smokers. Evidence also indicates that chronic exposure to environmental tobacco smoke (passive smoking or secondhand smoke) also increases risk of heart disease. If the effects of smoking are combined with other risk factors, the danger is greater than the sum of the added effects.

Cigarette smoking increases the risk of heart disease in several ways. First, the drug nicotine, a central nervous system stimulant, increases heart rate, heart output, blood pressure, and oxygen use by heart muscles. In other words, nicotine causes the heart to work harder. Second, the carbon monoxide in cigarette smoke displaces oxygen in heart tissue, resulting in the heart being forced to work harder to get enough oxygen to the working tissues. Third, nicotine can lead to irregular heart rates (that is, arrhythmias) that may result in sudden death. Finally, cigarette smoke damages the lining of the arteries, allowing plaque to accumulate more easily. This additional accumulation constricts the vessels, increasing blood pressure and forcing the heart to work harder.

Physical Inactivity

Inactivity is another primary risk factor for CVD. The good news is that you don't have to be an exercise fanatic to reduce your risk for CVD. Even moderate levels of low-intensity physical activity are beneficial if done regularly and on a long-term basis. Such activities include walking for pleasure, gardening, housework, and dancing.

Engaging in physical activity on a regular basis reduces risk for heart disease in a number of ways. First, physical activity of a sufficient intensity strengthens the heart, improves circulation, and improves your blood profile by increasing HDLs. Because of the increases in HDL, there is a reduced level of atherosclerotic plaque development. Third, physical activity plays an important role in reducing hypertension, maintaining body weight, and managing and preventing the stress response.

Obesity

Obesity also may increase risk for CVD. A body with excessive fat causes strain to the heart in its efforts to push blood through the many kilometres of capillaries that supply each kilogram of fat with needed nutrients. As such, people who are overweight or obese and sedentary are more likely to develop heart disease and stroke even if they have no other risk factors. Moreover, evidence indicates that where fat accumulates or is distributed on the body may affect a person's risk for CHD. Specifically, if excess fat accumulates around your upper body and waist (apple-shaped), you are at a greater risk than if your excess fat accumulates around your hips and thighs (pear-shaped). A waist girth greater than 102 centimetres for men and 88 centimetres for women significantly relates to elevated triglyceride levels, low HDL concentrations, and hypertension.

Diabetes

Individuals with diabetes, particularly those who have taken insulin for a number of years (that is, individuals with type 1 diabetes), have an increased risk for CVD. In fact, heart disease is the leading cause of death among individuals with diabetes. Because people who are obese have a higher risk for diabetes, distinguishing between the effects of the two conditions is difficult. Individuals with diabetes also tend to have elevated blood fat levels, increased atherosclerosis, and a tendency toward deterioration of small blood vessels, particularly in the eyes and extremities. Through a prescribed regimen of diet, physical activity, and medication, individuals with diabetes can control much of their increased risk for heart disease.

Individual Response to Stress

Some people react to stress on a daily basis. These stress reactions occur because of or in reaction to normal, usual daily activities. Consequently, these people typically have inconsistent, yet high, blood pressure when it is taken in an "unrested" state. However, when these people are asked to lie down and stay in a "rested" state for 10 minutes or more, their blood pressure often normalizes. In one study, one out of five people had an extreme cardiovascular reaction to stressful stimulation. These people experience alarm and resistance so strongly that, when under stress, their bodies produce large amounts of stress chemicals, which in turn lead to tremendous strain for the cardiovascular system. These people are called "hot reactors." Although their blood pressure may be normal when they are not under stress—for example, in a doctor's office—it increases dramatically in response to even small amounts of everyday tension. "Cold reactors" are those who are able to experience stress without harmful cardiovascular responses. Cold reactors may internalize stress, but their self-talk and perceptions about the stressful events lead them to a non-response state in which their cardiovascular system remains virtually unaffected. Other research investigating the relationship of personality to heart disease suggests that personality plays a role in effective coping of the stress response.

Risks You Cannot Control

There are some risk factors for CVD that you cannot prevent or control. These include

- Heredity: Having a family history of heart disease increases risk significantly.
- Age: Eighty percent of all fatal heart attacks occur in people over the age of 65. The risk for CVD increases with age for both sexes.
- Sex: Men are at a greater risk for CVD until older age. Women under 35 years of age generally have a fairly low risk for CVD. (For a more detailed discussion, see the next section.)
- Ethnicity: First Nations and Inuit people have three times the rate of heart problems of Canadians in general. Also at greater risk for heart disease are individuals of African and South Asian descent.

what do you THINK?

Complete the "Understanding Your Risk" box. What is your greatest risk factor for heart disease right now? What is your second biggest risk factor? What action will you take immediately to reduce your risk? Will it be difficult to take this action? Why or why not?

WOMEN AND CARDIOVASCULAR DISEASE

Many more women die from heart disease and stroke than from breast cancer. Currently, two in three women have one or more of the major risk factors for heart disease. While men have more heart attacks and have them earlier in life, women have a much lower chance of survival. Although we understand the mechanisms that cause heart disease in men and women, their experiences in the health-care system, their reactions to life-threatening diseases, and a host of other technological and environmental factors may play a role in their survival rates.

Risk Factors for Heart Disease in Women

Premenopausal women are unlikely to have a heart attack unless they also have diabetes, high blood pressure, kidney disease, or a genetic predisposition to high cholesterol levels. Family history, oral contraceptive use, and smoking also increase the risk for heart disease in premenopausal women.

Once her estrogen production drops with menopause, a woman's chance of developing heart disease rises rapidly. In fact, a 60-year-old woman has the same heart attack risk as a 50-year-old man, and by her late 70s, a woman has the same heart attack risk as a man her age.

Cholesterol is another factor to consider in women's increased risk for heart disease as they age. Although women aged 25 and over tend to have lower cholesterol levels than men of the same age, when they reach 45 years things change. Most men's cholesterol levels become more stable, while LDL and total cholesterol levels in women rise, with the gap widening after the age of 55. Studies of men indicate that for every 1-percent drop in cholesterol, there is a 2-percent decrease in CVD risk. If this holds true for women, prevention efforts focusing on dietary interventions and physical activity may significantly help postmenopausal women reduce their risk for CVD.

When data from seven cycles of the National Population Health Survey from 1994/1995 to 2006/2007 were examined in a longitudinal format, results indicated that women's risk of heart disease was significantly elevated if she also had depression—even after adjusting for other risk factors (for example, marital status, income, high blood pressure, diabetes, BMI, smoking, leisure-time physical activity, alcohol consumption, and use of hormone replacement therapy). This same relationship was not found in men.

Recognizing Heart Disease in Postmenopausal Women

Postmenopausal women often do not display the same recognizable symptoms of heart disease as men. The first sign of heart disease in men is generally a myocardial infarction. In women, the first sign is usually uncomplicated angina pectoris. Because chest discomfort rather than pain is the common manifestation of angina in women, and because angina has a much more favourable prognosis in women than in men, many physicians ignore the condition in their female patients or treat it too casually.

A heart attack also causes different symptoms in women than in men. In men, a heart attack usually manifests itself as crushing chest pain radiating to the shoulders, arms, neck, jaw, or back as well as dizziness, paleness, difficulty breathing, sweating, nausea, vomiting, or anxiety. In women, a heart attack results in much more vague symptoms such as pain in the neck, jaw, or arms; heaviness in the shoulders, back, or the pit of the stomach; and feeling out of breath, tired, sweating, nausea, or vomiting. If these symptoms are experienced for two minutes or longer, it is critical to seek help immediately (call 9-1-1) or get to the nearest hospital that offers emergency cardiac care.

In the past decade, three main reasons why signs of heart disease in women may be overlooked have been postulated: (1) physicians may often be sex-biased in their delivery of health care, tending to concentrate on women's reproductive organs rather than on the whole body; (2) physicians tend to view heart disease in men as a more severe problem because they traditionally have a higher incidence of the disease; and (3) women decline major procedures more often than men. Other explanations for diagnostic and therapeutic difficulties encountered by women with heart disease include

- Delay in diagnosing a possible heart attack, due to the complexity of interpreting chest pain in women because symptoms of heart attack are vague and much different than in men.
- Typically less aggressive treatment of women who have had a heart attack.
- Their older age, on average, and frequency of other health problems.
- Women's coronary arteries are often smaller than men's, making surgical or diagnostic procedures more difficult technically.
- Their increased incidence of post-infarction angina or heart failure.

what do you THINK?

How do men and women differ in their experiences with heart disease? How might women play a role in the underdiagnosis of their heart disease? What actions do you think individuals can take to help improve this situation for women? What actions can communities and medical practitioners take?

NEW WEAPONS AGAINST HEART DISEASE

The victim of a heart attack today has a variety of options not available a generation ago. Medications can strengthen heartbeat, control arrhythmias, remove fluids in cases of congestive heart failure, and relieve pain. Further, bypass surgery and angioplasty have become relatively commonplace procedures in hospitals throughout the nation.

Techniques of Diagnosing Heart Disease

Several techniques can be used to diagnose heart disease, including electrocardiogram, angiography, and positron emission tomography scans. An **electrocardiogram** is a record of the electrical activity of the heart measured during a stress test. Patients walk or run on treadmills while their hearts' functions are monitored. Another method of testing for heart disease is **angiography** (often referred to as "cardiac catheterization"), in which a needle-thin tube called a catheter is threaded through blocked heart arteries, a dye is injected, and an X-ray is taken to discover which areas are blocked. A more recent and even more effective method of measuring heart activity is **positron emission tomography**, also called a **PET scan**, which produces three-dimensional images of the heart as blood flows through it. During a PET scan, a patient receives an intravenous injection of a radioactive tracer. As the tracer decays, it emits positrons that are picked up by the scanner and transformed by a computer into colour images of the heart.

Other tests include the following:

- Radionuclide imaging (includes such tests as thallium test, multinucleated gated angiography scan, and acute infarct scintigraphy). In these procedures, substances called radionuclides are injected into the bloodstream. Computer-generated pictures can then show them in the heart. These tests can show how well the heart muscle is supplied with blood, how well the heart's chambers are functioning, and which part of the heart has been damaged.
- Magnetic resonance imaging (MRI). This test uses powerful magnets to look inside the body. Computer-generated pictures can show the heart muscle, identify damage from a heart attack, diagnose certain congenital heart defects, and evaluate disease of larger blood vessels such as the aorta.
- Ultrafast computed tomography (CT). This is an especially fast form of X-ray of the heart designed to evaluate bypass grafts, diagnose ventricular function, and measure calcium deposits.
- Digital cardiac angiography. This modified form of computer-aided imaging records pictures of the heart and its blood vessels.

Angioplasty versus Bypass Surgery

During the 1980s, **coronary bypass surgery** seemed to be the ultimate technique for treating patients who had coronary blockages or suffered heart attacks. In coronary bypass surgery, a blood vessel taken from another site in the patient's body (usually the saphenous vein in the leg or the internal mammary artery) is implanted to transport blood by bypassing blocked arteries. The effectiveness of bypass operations, particularly for elderly people, has been questioned, particularly with less invasive treatment options now available.

A procedure called **angioplasty** (also called balloon angioplasty) has fewer risks and is believed by many to be more effective than bypass surgery in selected cardiovascular cases. This procedure is similar to angiography. A needle-thin catheter is threaded through blocked heart arteries. The catheter has a balloon at the tip, which is inflated to flatten fatty deposits against the artery walls, allowing blood to flow more freely. Angioplasty patients are generally awake but sedated during the procedure and spend only one or two days in the hospital after treatment. Most people can return to work within five days. Only about 1 percent of all angioplasty patients die during or soon after the procedure. Risks of this procedure include spontaneous collapse of the vessel worked on in 3 to 7 percent of cases, and in about 30 percent of all angioplasty operations, the treated arteries become clogged again within six months. Some patients may undergo the procedure as many as three times within a five-year period. Some surgeons argue that given angioplasty's high rate of recurrence, bypass may still be a more effective method of treatment.

Other research suggests that in many instances, drug treatments may be as effective in prolonging life as invasive surgical techniques, but it is critical that doctors follow an aggressive drug treatment program and more important that patients comply. Among the most effective treatments are beta blockers and calcium channel blockers, used to reduce high blood pressure and treat other symptoms. Cholesterol-lowering medications are also effective.

Research indicates that low doses of Aspirin (80 milligrams daily or every other day) are beneficial to heart patients because of their blood-thinning properties. It should be pointed out that higher doses do not provide additional protection. Aspirin is even recommended as a preventive strategy for individuals without current heart disease symptoms. However, given the additional risks from emergency surgery or accidental bleeding, Aspirin should be taken as a preventive measure only if your physician recommends it.

Thrombolysis

Whenever a heart attack occurs, prompt action is the key factor in the patient's eventual prognosis. When a

Electrocardiogram: A record of the electrical activity of the heart measured during a stress test.

Angiography: A technique for examining blockages in heart arteries. A catheter is inserted into the arteries, a dye injected, and an X-ray taken to find the blocked areas.

Positron emission tomography (PET scan): Method for measuring heart activity by injecting a patient with a radioactive tracer scanned electronically to produce a three-dimensional image of the heart and arteries.

Coronary bypass surgery: A surgical technique in which one or more blood vessels are implanted to bypass one or more clogged coronary arteries.

Angioplasty: A technique in which a catheter with a balloon at the tip is inserted into a clogged artery; the balloon is inflated to flatten fatty deposits against artery walls, allowing blood to flow more freely.

coronary artery gets blocked, the heart muscle doesn't die immediately, but time determines how much damage occurs. If a victim gets to an emergency room and is diagnosed fast enough (within two hours), a form of reperfusion therapy called **thrombolysis** can sometimes be performed. Thrombolysis involves injecting an agent such as TPA (tissue plasminogen activator) to dissolve the clot and restore some blood flow, thereby reducing the amount of tissue that dies from ischemia. These drugs must be used within one to three hours of a heart attack for best results, and once again, the importance of dialling 9-1-1 when the symptoms of a heart attack are first noticed cannot be over-emphasized.

what do you THINK?

With all the new diagnostic procedures and treatments for prevention and intervention of CVD, how can a health consumer ensure that he or she will get the best treatment when needed? Where can one go for information? Why might women, members of certain minority groups, and the elderly need a "health advocate" who can help them get through the system?

DIABETES: INCIDENCE AND MORTALITY

Diabetes is a serious, widespread, and costly chronic disease. It is characterized by high blood sugar (glucose) levels. Untreated diabetes results in numerous health problems, including blindness, amputation, and kidney dysfunction. From 1996/1997 to 2005 (the most recent data available), the number of Canadians 12 years and older diagnosed with diabetes almost doubled. These estimates indicate that 4.9 percent of the Canadian population has diabetes. At all ages except for 15 to 19 years and 20 to 35 years, males are more likely to have diabetes than females. Further, diagnoses increase with age, particularly after the age of 54 years, with 10.1 percent of people between the ages of 55 to 64 years and 14.6 of all individuals over the age of 65 years having a positive diagnosis.

What causes diabetes? In healthy people, the pancreas, a powerful enzyme-producing organ, produces the hormone insulin in sufficient quantities to allow the body to use or store glucose. When the pancreas fails to produce enough insulin to regulate sugar metabolism or when the body fails to use insulin effectively, diabetes develops. Individuals with diabetes exhibit hyperglycemia, or elevated blood sugar levels, and high glucose levels in their urine. Other symptoms include excessive thirst, frequent urination, hunger, a tendency to tire easily, wounds that heal slowly, numbness or tingling in the extremities, changes in vision, skin eruptions, and in women, a tendency toward vaginal yeast infections.

Type 1 diabetes, also called insulin-dependent diabetes and formerly referred to as juvenile-onset diabetes, is an autoimmune disease in which the immune system destroys the insulin-making beta cells. It most often appears in childhood or adolescence, with rare cases diagnosed in early to mid-adult years. People with type 1 diabetes typically depend on insulin injections or oral medications because their body does not produce the insulin it needs.

In type 2 diabetes, also called non-insulin dependent diabetes and formerly called adult-onset diabetes, insulin production is deficient or the body is unable to utilize all available insulin. Type 2 diabetes accounts for 90 to 95 percent of all diabetes cases and in the past did not appear until after the age of 40 years—hence the term "adult-onset." Currently, type 2 diabetes is diagnosed across the age spectrum, including children and adolescents, and because of the frequency of diagnoses in younger individuals (reflective of current Canadian lifestyle), it can no longer be considered an adult-onset disease. Specifically, type 2 diabetes is linked to obesity and physical inactivity, both of which can be modified to control and prevent diabetes and improve health. Further, if people with type 2 diabetes change their lifestyle (that is, become more physically active, eat well, lose weight), they may be able to avoid the need for oral medications or insulin indefinitely.

A third type of diabetes, gestational diabetes, can develop in women during pregnancy. Although once believed to be only a transient event that disappeared after pregnancy, today experts realize that women with gestational diabetes have an increased risk of developing type 2 diabetes within 5 to 10 years of giving birth. This is particularly true for women who do not lose the weight they gained during pregnancy and for those with subsequent pregnancies and weight gain with each one.

Understanding Risk Factors

Diabetes tends to run in families. As previously mentioned, being obese, coupled with low levels of physical activity, dramatically increases risk of type 2 diabetes. This, too, often runs in families—not because of a genetic link, but rather an environmental or lifestyle link. Older persons and mothers of babies weighing more than 4 kilograms at birth are also at increased risk. About 80 percent of all individuals with type 2 diabetes are obese at the time of diagnosis. Weight loss, better nutrition, control of blood glucose levels, and regular physical activity are important factors in lowering blood sugar and improving the efficiency of cellular use of insulin. These lifestyle improvements can also help to prevent overwork of the pancreas and the development of diabetes. In fact, recent findings indicate that regular, moderate intensity physical activity and a healthy diet can reduce one's risk of type 2 diabetes significantly. Individuals of African Canadian descent and First Nations and Inuit Canadians have much higher rates of type 2 diabetes than others, which is most likely related to lifestyle factors such as low levels of physical activity and poor dietary intakes.

Controlling Diabetes

Most physicians attempt to control type 1 and latter stages of type 2 diabetes with a variety of insulin drugs. Most drugs are taken orally, although self-administered hypodermic injections are prescribed when other treatments are inadequate. Recent breakthroughs in individual monitoring, implantable insulin monitors and pumps, and insulin inhalers have given many people with diabetes the opportunity to lead more normal lives. Some people with type 2 diabetes can manage their diagnoses effectively by losing weight, engaging in regular physical activity, and eating foods rich in complex carbohydrates, low in sodium, and high in fibre.

Physical activity, particularly walking, is often prescribed to assist with the management of type 2 diabetes. These recommendations should be individualized and should specifically identify the quantity and quality of walking required. More than 10 000 steps may be needed, as well as a walking speed that elicits improvements in cardiorespiratory fitness.

Complications Associated with Diabetes

Depending on the type and severity of the disease, diabetes results in many complications and increases the severity of existing conditions, including

- CVD. Heart disease and stroke cause about 65 percent of deaths among people with diabetes. More than 70 percent of people with diabetes have hypertension.
- Eye disease and blindness. Diabetes is the leading cause of blindness.
- Kidney disease. The kidneys in many people with diabetes often fail. Dialysis is a common treatment for these individuals.
- Amputations. More than 60 percent of nontraumatic amputations of lower limbs are a result of diabetes. Foot care programs that include regular exams and patient education could prevent as many as 85 percent of these amputations.
- Pregnancy complications. Poorly controlled diabetes can cause major birth defects in 5 to 10 percent of all pregnancies and accounts for 15 to 20 percent of spontaneous abortions.
- Flu- and pneumonia-related deaths. People with diabetes have a threefold increase of dying as a result of complications from the flu or pneumonia compared to people without diabetes.

CANCER INCIDENCE AND MORTALITY

An estimated 171 000 new cases of cancer and 75 300 deaths from cancer will occur in Canada in 2009. It is projected that 40 percent of women and 45 percent of men will develop cancer in their lifetime and that one of every four Canadians will die of cancer (24 percent of women; 29 percent of men). The greater number of new cases of cancer is primarily due to an aging population. Mortality from cancer is declining for males of all ages, for women under the age of 70, and most rapidly in children and adolescents.

Lung cancer continues to be the leading cause of premature death due to cancer, accounting for 28.3 percent of all cancer deaths in men and 26.3 percent in women. It is expected that 23 400 new cases (12 800 for males and 10 700 for females) of lung cancer will be diagnosed in 2009. It should be pointed out that although lung cancer is the number one cancer killer of men and women, it is only the second highest for new cases. In men there are more new cases of prostate cancer (25 500) expected in 2009, while in women more new cases of breast cancer (22 700) are expected. The third-highest expected cancer incidence for 2009 for men and women is colorectal cancer, with 12 100 and 9900 new cases, respectively.

Not everyone is equally at risk for all types of cancers. Cancer incidence and mortality vary greatly by age, sex, ethnicity, and socioeconomic status. Because cancer risk is strongly associated with lifestyle and behaviours, differences in ethnic and cultural groups can provide clues to factors involved in its development. Culturally influenced values and belief systems can also affect whether or not a person seeks care, participates in screenings, or follows recommended treatment options. In Canada, cancer incidence and mortality are higher in the Atlantic provinces and Quebec and lowest in British Columbia.

Thrombolysis: Injection of an agent to dissolve clots and restore some blood flow, thereby reducing the amount of tissue that dies from ischemia.

What Is Cancer?

Cancer is the name given to a large group of diseases characterized by the uncontrolled growth and spread of abnormal cells. It may be hard to understand how normal, healthy cells become cancerous, but if you think of a cell as a small computer, programmed to operate in a particular fashion, the process may become clearer. Under normal conditions, healthy cells are protected by the immune system as they perform their daily functions of growing, replicating, and repairing body organs. When something interrupts normal cell programming, uncontrolled growth and abnormal cellular development result in a new growth of tissue. This new tissue serves no physiological function and is called a **neoplasm**. When this neoplasmic mass forms a clump of cells it is known as a **tumour**.

Not all tumours are **malignant** (cancerous); in fact, most are **benign** (non-cancerous). Benign tumours are generally harmless unless they grow to obstruct or crowd out normal tissues or organs. A benign tumour of the brain, for instance, is life-threatening when it grows and causes blood restriction resulting in a stroke. The only way to determine whether a given tumour or mass is benign or malignant is through **biopsy**, or microscopic examination of cell development.

Benign and malignant tumours differ in several key ways. Benign tumours are generally composed of ordinary-looking cells enclosed in a fibrous shell or capsule that prevents their spreading to other body areas. Malignant tumours are usually not enclosed in a protective capsule and can therefore spread to other organs. This process, known as **metastasis**, makes some forms of cancer particularly aggressive in their ability to overcome bodily defences. By the time they are diagnosed, malignant tumours have frequently metastasized throughout the body, making treatment extremely difficult. Unlike benign tumours, which merely expand to take over a given space, malignant cells invade surrounding tissue, emitting clawlike protrusions that disrupt chemical processes within healthy cells. More specifically, malignant cells disturb the ribonucleic acid (RNA) and deoxyribonucleic acid (DNA) within the normal cells. Tampering with these substances that control cellular metabolism and reproduction produces mutant cells that differ in form, quality, and function from normal cells.

What Causes Cancer?

After decades of research, most cancer epidemiologists believe that the majority of cancers are preventable and can be avoided by healthier choices in lifestyle and environment. In fact, the recently released "Policy and Action for Cancer Prevention Food Nutrition, and Physical Activity: A Global Perspective," by the World Cancer Research Fund in conjunction with the American Institute for Cancer Research, clearly stated that two-thirds of all cancers could be prevented based on lifestyle changes. One-third could be prevented by not using tobacco and another one-third could be prevented by being physically active and eating well. Many specific causes of cancer are well documented, the most important of which are smoking, obesity, and a few organic viruses. Most research supports the idea that cancer is caused by external (chemicals, radiation, viruses, and lifestyle) and internal (hormones, immune conditions, and inherited mutations) factors. These causal factors may act together or in sequence to promote cancer development. We do not know why some people have malignant cells in their body and never develop cancer while others may take 10 years or more to develop the disease. Many factors are believed to cause cancer, and a combination of these factors can dramatically increase one's risk of the disease.

One theory proposes that cancer results from spontaneous errors during cell reproduction. Perhaps cells that are overworked or aged are more likely to break down, causing genetic errors that result in mutant cells. Another theory suggests that cancer is caused by some external agent or agents that enter a normal cell and initiate the cancerous process. Numerous environmental factors, such as radiation, chemicals, hormonal drugs, immunosuppressant drugs (drugs that suppress the normal activity of the immune system), and other toxins are considered possible **carcinogens** (cancer-causing agents) (see Figure 5f.4); perhaps the most common carcinogen is the tar found in cigarettes. The greater the dose or exposure to environmental hazards, the greater the degree of risk. Thus, people forced to work, live, and pass through areas that have high levels of environmental toxins may be at greater risk of cancer.

A third theory came out of research on certain viruses believed to cause tumours in animals. This research led to the discovery of **oncogenes**, suspected cancer-causing genes present on chromosomes. Although oncogenes are typically dormant, scientists theorize that certain conditions, such as age, stress, and exposure to carcinogens, viruses, and radiation may activate these oncogenes. Once activated, they begin to grow and reproduce in an out-of-control manner. Scientists are uncertain whether only people who develop cancer have oncogenes or whether we all have **proto-oncogenes**, genes that can become oncogenes under certain conditions. Many **oncologists** (physicians who specialize in the treatment of malignancies) believe that the oncogene theory may lead to a greater understanding of how individual cells function and may bring us closer to developing an effective treatment for cancer.

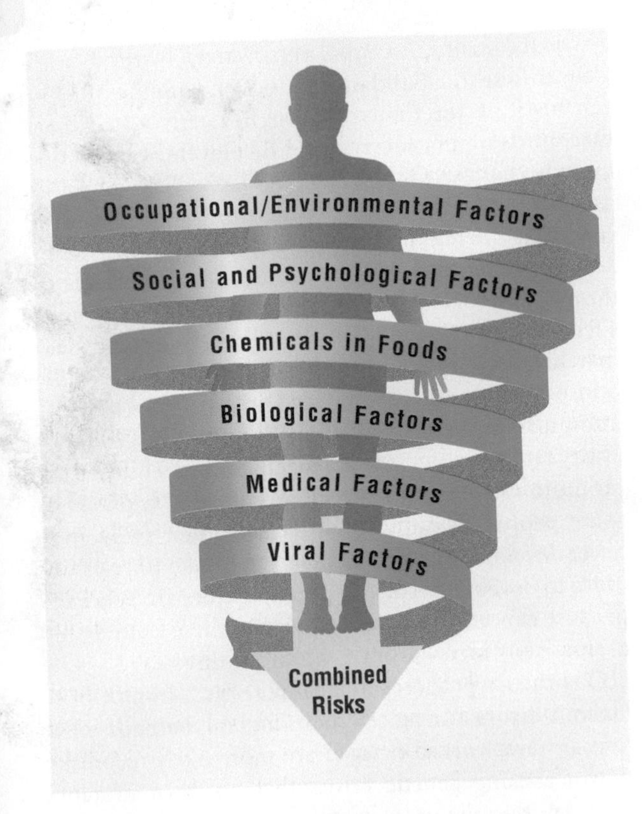

FIGURE 5f.4
Suspected Causes of Cancer

Risks for Cancer

Lifestyle

Anyone can develop cancer; however, most cases affect adults beginning in middle age. In fact, nearly 80 percent of cancers are diagnosed at ages 55 and over. Cancer researchers refer to one's cancer risk when they assess risk factors. *Lifetime risk* refers to the probability that an individual, over the course of a lifetime, will develop cancer or die from it. In 2009, as noted previously, 45 percent of men and 40 percent of women have a lifetime risk of developing cancer.

Relative risk is a measure of the strength of the relationship between risk factors and a particular cancer. Basically, relative risk compares your risk if you engage in certain known risk behaviours with that of someone who does not engage in such behaviours. For example, if you smoke, you have a 20-fold relative risk of developing lung cancer compared to a nonsmoker. In other words, the chances of getting lung cancer are about 20 times greater in a smoker than in a nonsmoker.

Over the years, researchers have found that certain behaviours result in a higher incidence of cancer. In particular, dietary intake, sedentary lifestyle (and resultant obesity), consumption of alcohol or cigarettes, stress, and other lifestyle factors seem to play a role. Further confirming this theory is that colon and rectal cancer occur more frequently among persons with a high-fat, low-fibre dietary intake, in those who don't eat enough fruits and vegetables, and in those who are physically inactive.

Keep in mind that a high relative risk does not guarantee cause and effect. It merely indicates the likelihood of a particular risk factor being related to a particular outcome. In other words you can modify your lifestyle behaviours to reduce your risk.

Smoking

Of all the potential risk factors for cancer, smoking is among the greatest; it is the leading cause of preventable death in the world today. In developing countries, smoking is responsible for 80 percent of all deaths from lung cancer. In Canada, tobacco is responsible for nearly one in five deaths annually. Recent declines in smoking have likely had a direct effect on the overall decrease in lung cancer rates; however, as previously noted, lung cancer remains the leading cause of cancer death in men and women.

Researchers once believed that cigarettes caused only cancers of the lung, pancreas, bladder, and kidney, and (synergistically with alcohol) the larynx, mouth, pharynx, and esophagus. However, recent evidence indicates that several other types of cancer are also related to tobacco use. Most notably, cancers of the stomach, liver, and cervix are directly related to long-term smoking.

Cancer: A large group of diseases characterized by the uncontrolled growth and spread of abnormal cells.

Neoplasm: A new growth of tissue that serves no physiologic function, resulting from uncontrolled, abnormal cellular development.

Tumour: A neoplasmic mass that grows more rapidly than surrounding tissues.

Malignant: Very dangerous or harmful; refers to a cancerous tumour.

Benign: Harmless; refers to a non-cancerous tumour.

Biopsy: Microscopic examination of tissue to determine if a cancer is present.

Metastasis: Process by which cancer spreads from one area to different areas of the body.

Carcinogens: Cancer-causing agents.

Oncogenes: Suspected cancer-causing genes present on chromosomes.

Proto-oncogenes: Genes that can become oncogenes under certain conditions.

Oncologists: Physicians who specialize in the treatment of malignancies.

Obesity

It is difficult to sort through the volumes of evidence about the role of nutrients, obesity, sedentary lifestyle, and related variables in the development of cancer. That said, cancer is more common among people who are obese, and risk increases as level of obesity increases. A study of more than 900 000 adults indicates a significant relationship between a high body mass index (BMI) and death rates for cancers such as that of the esophagus, colon, rectum, liver, kidney, and pancreas. Women with a high BMI have a higher mortality rate from breast, uterine, cervical, and ovarian cancers; men with a high BMI have higher death rates from prostate and stomach cancers. In this study, 34 percent of all cancer deaths were attributable to overweight and obesity. Other findings relevant to the obesity–cancer link are as follows:

- The relative risk of breast cancer in postmenopausal women is 50 percent higher for women who are obese.
- The relative risk of colon cancer in men is 40 percent higher for men who are obese.
- The relative risks of gallbladder and endometrial cancer are five times higher in individuals who are obese compared to those at a healthy weight.

Biologic Factors

Some early cancer theorists believed that we inherit a genetic predisposition toward certain forms of cancer. Cancers of the breast, stomach, colon, prostate, uterus, ovaries, and lungs do appear to have a heredity link. Specifically, a woman has a much higher risk of developing breast cancer if her mother, sisters, or daughters (i.e., primary relatives) had the disease, particularly if they had it at a young age. Hodgkin's disease and certain leukemias also show familial patterns. Whether these familial patterns are attributable to genetic susceptibility or to the fact that people in the same families experience similar environmental risks remains uncertain.

Sex also affects the likelihood of developing certain forms of cancer. For example, breast cancer occurs primarily among females, although men occasionally get breast cancer. Of the 22 900 new cases expected in 2009, 180 will be in males. Obviously, factors other than heredity and familial relationships affect which sex develops a particular cancer. In the 1950s and 1960s, for example, women rarely contracted lung cancer. But with increases in the number of women who smoked and the length of time they smoked, lung cancer became a leading cause of cancer deaths for Canadian women in the 1980s. Although sex plays a role in certain cases, other variables, such as lifestyle, are probably more significant in other cases.

Occupation and Environment Factors

Various occupational hazards are known to cause cancer when exposure levels are high or exposure is prolonged. Overall, however, workplace hazards account for only a small percentage of all cancers. One of the most common occupational carcinogens is asbestos, a fibrous substance once widely used in the construction, insulation, and automobile industries. Nickel, chromate, and chemicals such as benzene, arsenic, and vinyl chloride have been shown to be carcinogens for humans. Also, people who routinely work with certain dyes and radioactive substances may have increased risks for cancer. Working with coal tars, as in the mining profession, or working near inhalants, as in the auto-painting business, is also hazardous. Those who work with herbicides and pesticides also appear to be at higher risk, although the evidence is inconclusive to date for low-dose exposures.

Because people are sometimes forced to work near hazardous substances, it is imperative that worksites enact policies and procedures designed to minimize or eliminate toxic exposure.

Ionizing radiation—radiation from X-rays, radon, cosmic rays, and ultraviolet radiation (primarily UV-B radiation)—is the only form of radiation linked to cancer. (See the section on skin cancer.)

While reports about cancer-case clusters in communities around nuclear power facilities have raised public concerns, studies show that clusters do not occur more often near nuclear power plants than they do by chance in wider geographical areas.

Social and Psychological Factors

Although orthodox medical personnel are skeptical of overly simplistic prevention centres that focus on humour and laughter as the way to prevent cancer, we cannot rule out the possibility that negative emotional states contribute to disease development. People who are lonely, depressed, and lack social support are more susceptible to cancer than their mentally and emotionally healthy counterparts. Similarly, people under chronic stress and those with poor nutrition or sleep habits develop cancer at a slightly higher rate than the general population. Experts believe that severe depression or prolonged stress may reduce the activity of the body's immune system, thereby wearing down bodily resistance to cancer.

Chemicals in Foods

Among the food additives suspected of causing cancer is sodium nitrate, a chemical used to preserve and give colour to red meat. Research indicates that the actual carcinogen is not sodium nitrate but nitrosamines,

HBV, HCV, and Liver Cancer

Viruses such as hepatitis B (HBV) and C (HCV) are believed to stimulate cancer cells in the liver because they are chronic diseases that cause inflammation of liver tissue. This may prime the liver for cancer or make it more hospitable for cancer development. Global increases in HBV and HCV rates and concurrent increases in liver cancer rates provide evidence of such an association.

HPV and Cervical Cancer

Nearly 100 percent of women with cervical cancer have evidence of human papilloma virus (HPV) infection, believed to be a major cause of cervical cancer. HPV is a group of more than 100 different types of viruses, of which 40 are transmitted through sexual activity. In fact, it is estimated that at least 75 percent of sexually active men and women in Canada will have at least one HPV infection in their lifetime. HPV types 16 and 18 are responsible for 70 percent of all cervical cancers while HPV types 6 and 11 are responsible for 90 percent of genital warts. A vaccine that protects against these HPV types is available for young women in Canada and should be viewed as a complement to cervical cancer screening (that is, the Pap test), not a replacement.

what do you THINK?

Given what you've read and heard about the immunization available to reduce your risk of developing cervical cancer, would you take it? Why or why not? If you have the immunization, what lifestyle behaviours will you still have to incorporate to (1) further reduce your risk for and/or ensure early detection of cervical cancer, and (2) to prevent the transmission of other sexually transmitted infections?

Medical Factors

Some medical treatments increase a person's risk for cancer. One famous example is the widespread use of the prescription drug diethylstilbestrol (DES), widely used from 1940 to 1960 to control problems with bleeding during pregnancy and to reduce the risk of miscarriage. It was not until the 1970s that the dangers of this drug became apparent in daughters of mothers who took it during their pregnancy, as they were found to have an increased risk for cancers of the reproductive organs. Another example is the use of estrogen replacement therapy for postmenopausal women because of the potential risk of increased uterine cancer. Ironically, chemotherapy, which is used to treat cancer, may also increase risk for other forms of cancer.

TYPES OF CANCER

As noted previously, the term *cancer* refers to hundreds of different diseases. Four broad classifications are made according to the type of tissue from which the cancer arises.

- Carcinomas—Epithelial tissues (tissues covering body surfaces and lining most body cavities) are the most common sites for cancers. Carcinoma of the breast, lung, intestines, skin, and mouth are examples. These cancers affect the outer layer of the skin and mouth as well as the mucous membranes. They metastasize through the circulatory or lymphatic system initially and form solid tumours.
- Sarcomas—Sarcomas occur in the mesodermal, or middle, layers of tissue—for example, in bones, muscles, and general connective tissue. They metastasize primarily via the blood in the early stages. These cancers are less common but generally more virulent than carcinomas. They also form solid tumours.
- Lymphomas—Lymphomas develop in the lymphatic system—the infection-fighting regions of the body—and metastasize through the lymph system. Hodgkin's disease is one type of lymphoma. Lymphomas also form solid tumours.
- Leukemia—Cancer of the blood-forming parts of the body, particularly the bone marrow and spleen, is called leukemia. A non-solid tumour, leukemia is characterized by an abnormal increase in the number of white blood cells.

The seriousness and general prognosis of a particular cancer are determined through careful diagnosis by trained oncologists. Once laboratory results and clinical observations have been made, cancers are rated by level and stage of development. Those diagnosed as "carcinoma in situ" are localized and are often curable. Cancers given higher level or stage ratings have spread farther and are less likely to be cured.

PART VI: AGING, DEATH AND DYING

CHAPTER 6a

THEORIES ON AGING

Taken from *Health: The Basics*, Fifth Canadian Edition, by Rebecca J. Donatelle and Angela M. Thompson

Growing old does not have to entail declining physical and mental health. Health promotion, disease prevention and wellness-oriented activities prolong vigour and productivity, even among those who may not have always led a model lifestyle or made healthy choices a priority. Getting older can mean getting better in many ways—particularly socially, psychologically, spiritually, and intellectually.

The manner in which you view aging (either as a natural part of living or as an inevitable move toward disease and death) is an important factor in how successfully you will adapt to life's transitions. If you view these transitions as opportunities for growth—as changes that lead to improved mental, emotional, spiritual, and physical phases in your development as a human being—your journey will be smooth. Explore your own knowledge of aging in the Rate Yourself box.

Aging has traditionally been described as the patterns of life changes that occur in members of all species as they grow older. Some believe that it begins at the moment of conception. Others contend that it starts at birth. Still others believe that true aging does not begin until we reach our 40s. Typically, chronologic age (that is, age based on birthdate) is used to assign a person to a particular life-cycle stage. However, people of different chronologic ages view age very differently. To the 4-year-old, a university or college student seems quite old. To the 20-year-old, parents in their 40s are over the hill. Have you ever heard your 65-year-old grandparents talking about "those old people down the street"? Views of aging are also coloured by occupation. For example, a professional linebacker may find himself too old to play football in his mid-30s. Airline pilots and police officers often retire in their 50s, while professors, senators, and prime ministers may work well into their 70s.

REDEFINING AGING

Discrimination against people based on age is known as **ageism**. When directed against the elderly, this type of discrimination carries with it social ostracism and negative portrayals of older people. A developmental task approach to life-span changes tends to reduce the potential for ageist or negatively biased perceptions about what occurs as a person ages chronologically. The study of individual and collective aging processes, called **Gerontology**, explores the reasons for aging and the ways in which people cope with and adapt to this process. Gerontologists have identified several types of age-related characteristics that should be used to determine where a person is in terms of biologic, psychological, social, legal, and functional life-stage development:

- *Biologic age* refers to the relative age or condition of the person's organs and body systems. Arthritis and other chronic conditions often accelerate biologic age.
- *Psychological age* refers to a person's adaptive capacities, such as coping abilities and intelligence, and to the person's awareness of his or her individual capabilities, self-efficacy, and general ability to adapt to a given situation.
- *Social age* refers to a person's habits and roles relative to society's expectations. People in a particular life stage often share similar tastes in music, television shows, and decor.
- *Legal or chronologic age* is probably the most common definition of age in Canada. Legal age is based on chronological years and is used to determine such things as voting rights, driving privileges, drinking age, eligibility for Old Age Security and Canada Pension Plan benefits, and a host of other rights and obligations.
- *Functional age* refers to the ways in which people compare to others of a similar age. It is difficult to separate functional aging from other types of aging, particularly chronologic and biologic aging.

WHAT IS NORMAL AGING?

Contemporary gerontologists analyze the vast majority of people who continue to live full and productive lives throughout their later years. In the past, our youth-oriented society viewed the onset of the physiological changes of aging as something to be dreaded. The aging process was seen primarily from a pathological (disease) perspective, and therefore as a time of decline; the focus was not on the gains and positive aspects of normal adult development throughout the life span. Many of these positive developments occur in the areas of emotional and social life as older adults learn to cope with and adapt to the many changes and crises that life has in store for them.

Aging: The patterns of life changes that occur in a species as they grow older.

Ageism: Discrimination based on age.

Gerontology: The study of individual and collective aging processes.

RATE YOURSELF

Aging Quiz

Test your knowledge of healthy aging by taking the following test. Answer true or false to each statement. The answers are listed below.

1. Men usually outlive women.
2. If your parents had Alzheimer's disease, you will also get it.
3. Dietary intake and physical activity can reduce the risk of developing osteoporosis.
4. Heart disease affects women as much as men.
5. The older you get, the less sleep you need.
6. People should reduce their caloric intake as they age.
7. People take more medications as they age.
8. As your body changes with age, so does your personality.
9. Intelligence declines with age.
10. Most older people live alone.
11. Most people become "senile" if they live long enough.
12. Physical strength tends to decline with age.
13. Most older adults limit their travel to be closer to home.
14. Older adults have the lowest income of all adult groups.
15. Most older adults have no interest in, or capacity for, sexual activity.
16. People tend to become more religious with age.
17. People tend to change their driving habits as they age.
18. Older people are more likely to commit suicide than younger people.
19. Many older people are preoccupied with death.
20. Most older people new to Canada speak neither English nor French.

ANSWERS

1. False. Women have an average life expectancy greater than men. In 2003, a boy born is expected to live to 77.4 years, while a girl born in the same year is expected to live to 82.4 years or 5 years longer.
2. False. Between 90 and 95 percent of people with Alzheimer's disease have a form of the disease not necessarily linked to family history. Only 5 percent of Alzheimer's cases are a result of a genetic link.
3. True. Bone loss can be reduced by eating foods rich in calcium (for example, milk and other dairy products; dark green, leafy vegetables; canned salmon; sardines; and tofu) and engaging in regular, weight-bearing physical activity, such as walking and resistance training.
4. True. Heart disease is one of the leading causes of death for men and women.
5. False. Although quality of sleep declines when we age, required sleep time does not. Further, sleep tends to get more fragmented as we get older.
6. True. Older people need fewer calories because of decreases in metabolic function and physical activity. If an involuntary weight gain or loss of 5 kilograms or more occurs in six months, a physician should be consulted.
7. True. Most Canadian older adults take some form of prescription or over-the-counter medication. Further, older adults (85+) are more likely than younger older adults (65–74) to take more than one medication (65 versus 52 percent).
8. False. Other than personality changes associated with Alzheimer's disease and other forms of dementia, personality does not change appreciably as you age.
9. False. Although studies show that the elderly have a slower reaction time and take longer to learn something new, their intellect is maintained and can be improved as they get older.
10. False. The majority of Canadian older adults (69 percent) live with their family or extended family.
11. False. Dementia ("senility" is not the correct term) is not a normal part of aging. One in 50 older adults between the ages of 65 and 74, one in nine older adults between the ages of 75 and 84, and one in three older adults over the age of 85 will develop dementia.
12. True. Physical strength does decrease with age—as does the quality of the muscles. Decreases in strength can be reduced by regular participation in physical activity, including resistance training.
13. False. In fact, some older adults are more likely to travel abroad than younger adults.
14. True. In 1997, 19 percent of all older adults (65+) had an income below the low-income cut-off. Women (24 percent) are more likely than men (11.7 percent) to have a low income.
15. False. Aging does not equate to a loss of interest in or capacity for sex.
16. False. Despite a perception that people tend to become more religious with age, this is not true. This perception may reflect a difference between generations rather than a characteristic of aging.
17. True. To accommodate the changes associated with aging many older adults modify their driving behaviour by planning their trips, driving less, limiting highway travel, and avoiding driving in poor weather or at night.
18. False. Overall, older adults in Canada are less likely to commit suicide than are younger adults.
19. False. Older adults' attitudes toward death are variable, though some trends can be noted. Specifically, older adults are less anxious and more matter-of-fact about death. Most young adults avoid thinking about or discussing death.
20. True. The majority (61 percent) of older immigrants to Ontario from 1996 to 1999 spoke neither English nor French.

Source: Adapted from the Ontario Gerontology Association, "Aging Quiz." Retrieved on May 16, 2006, from http://ontgerontology.on.ca.

Gerontologists have devised several categories for specific age-related characteristics. For example, people who reach the age of 65 are considered to fit the general category of "old age." They receive special consideration in the form of government assistance programs such as the old age pension. People aged 65 to 74 are viewed as the **young-old** those aged 75 to 84 are the **middle-old** group; those 85 and over are classified as the **old-old**.

You should note that chronological age is not the only component considered when objectively defining aging. The question is not how many years a person has lived, but how much life a person has packed into those years. This quality-of-life index, combined with the inevitable chronological process, appears to be the best indicator of the "aging gracefully" phenomenon. The eternal question then becomes, "How can I age gracefully?" Most experts agree that the best way to experience a productive, full, and satisfying old age is to take appropriate action to lead a productive, full, and satisfying life *prior* to old age. Essentially, older people are the product of their lifelong experiences, moulded over years of happiness, heartbreak, and day-to-day existence.

WHO ARE THE ELDERLY?

Contrary to popular belief, the elderly are not and never will be the "forgotten minority." The 65-and-over age group will unquestionably continue to be a major force in the social, political, and economic plans of the nation because of their sheer numbers (see Table 6a.1) and buying power. Canadian seniors are living longer lives in better health than in the past. By the year 2010, a whole generation of 1960s "flower children," who once proclaimed that no one over 30 could be trusted, will become 65 years old. Whereas people aged 65 and older made up less than 10 percent of the population in 1981, they are projected to make up more than 20 percent by 2031. In 2006, it was estimated that 13.7 percent of the Canadian population were 65 years of age or older (see Table 6a.2).

TABLE 6a.1
Canada's Elderly

Age	Total	Men	Women
65–69	1 193 500	574 400	619 100
70–74	1 042 600	488 600	554 000
75–79	864 300	377 700	486 500
80–84	625 300	241 700	383 600
85–89	322 500	107 100	215 400
90 and over	169 500	44 600	125 000

Source: Statistics Canada, "Population by Sex and Age Group." Retrieved on May 16, 2006, from www40.statcan.ca/101/cst01/demo10a.htm.

what do you THINK?

How do you define aging? What do you think of becoming old? How much interaction do you have with people over the age of 65?

try it NOW!

Estimate your life expectancy. How long you live involves more than good genes. Health behaviours that you can control have a direct impact on whether or not you will live to see 100. Visit this life expectancy calculator to see how long you are likely to live, given your history and current habits: www.livingto100.com

For a more detailed profile of today's elderly, download "Canada's Aging Population," a report prepared by Health Canada in collaboration with the Interdepartmental Committee on Aging and Seniors Issues, at www.globalaging.org/elderrights/world/canada.pdf.

THEORIES ON AGING

Biologic Theories

Explanations about the biologic causes of aging include:

- The wear-and-tear theory, which states that, like everything else in the universe, the human body wears out. Inherent in this theory is the idea that

TABLE 6a.2

Age Structure of Population, Medium-Growth Scenario (in millions)

Number

Age	2000	2006	2016	2026	2036	2051
0 to 14	5869	5527	5241	5382	5203	5053
15 to 64	21 018	22 400	23 477	23 056	22 765	22 440
65 and over	3863	4302	5702	7753	9067	9366
Total	30 750	32 229	34 420	36 191	37 035	36 860

Percentage

Age	2000	2006	2016	2026	2036	2051
0 to 14	19.1	17.1	15.2	14.9	14.0	13.7
15 to 64	68.3	69.5	68.2	63.7	61.5	60.9
65 and over	12.6	13.3	16.6	21.4	24.5	25.4

Source: Statistics Canada, "2006 Census: Portrait of the Canadian Population in 2006, by Age and Sex: Highlights." Retrieved on March 30, 2009, from www12.statcan.ca/census-recensement/2006/as-sa/97-551/p1-eng.cfm.

the more you abuse your body and/or the more you do not treat it as well as you can, the faster it will wear out.

- The cellular theory, which states that at birth we have only a certain number of usable cells, and these cells are genetically programmed to divide or reproduce only a limited number of times. Once these cells reach the end of their reproductive cycle, they begin to die and the organs they make up begin to show signs of deterioration. The rate of deterioration varies from person to person, and the impact of the deterioration depends on the system involved.
- The autoimmune theory, which attributes aging to the decline of the body's immunological system. Studies indicate that as we age, our immune systems become less effective in fighting disease. Lifestyle can contribute negatively to this process in bodies subjected to too much stress, lack of sleep, a poor dietary intake, inactivity, and so on. Although autoimmune diseases occur in all age groups, some gerontologists believe that they increase in frequency and severity with age.
- The genetic mutation theory, which proposes that the number of cells exhibiting unusual or different characteristics increases with age. In this theory, it is believed that aging relates to the amount of mutational damage within the genes. The greater the mutation, the greater the chance that cells will not function properly, leading to eventual dysfunction of body organs and systems.

For many, the secret to aging well is to remain physically active, eat well, and enjoy the company of good friends.

Young-old: People aged 65 to 74 years.
Middle-old: People aged 75 to 84 years.
Old-old: People 85 years and over.

CHAPTER 6b

CHANGES IN THE BODY AND MIND WITH AGING

Taken from *Health: The Basics*, Fifth Canadian Edition, by Rebecca J. Donatelle and Angela M. Thompson

Psychosocial Theories

Numerous psychological and sociological factors also have a strong influence on the manner in which people age. Psychologists have formulated theories of personality development that encompass the human life span. These theories emphasize adaptation and adjustment. In the developmental model, it is noted that people must progress through eight critical stages during their lifetime. If a person does not receive adequate stimulation or develop effective methods of coping with life's stresses from infancy onward, problems are likely to develop later in life. According to this theory, attitudes, behaviours, and beliefs related to maladjustments in old age are often a result of problems encountered in earlier stages of a person's life. Specifically, the developmental theory focuses on the crucial issues of middle and old age because it is believed that during these periods people face a series of increasingly stressful tasks. Those who are poorly adjusted psychologically or who have not developed appropriate coping skills are likely to undergo a painful aging process.

A key element in these theories is the incorporation of age-related factors into lifelong behaviour patterns. Both models (biological and psychosocial) emphasize that successful aging involves maintaining emotional as well as physical well-being. Most probably, a combination of psychosocial and biologic factors as well as environmental "trigger mechanisms" cause each of us to age in a unique manner.

CHANGES IN THE BODY AND MIND

Answers to the question of what is "typical" or "normal" when applied to aging are highly speculative. In order to assess the typical aging process, we should ask ourselves what we can reasonably expect to happen to our bodies as we grow older. Keep in mind that despite physical changes that occur, 76 percent of seniors 65 to 74 years old and 68 percent of seniors over 75 years of age reported their health to be "good," "very good," or "excellent."

Physical Changes

Although the physiological consequences of aging differ in their severity and timing from person to person, there are standard changes that occur.

The Skin

As we age, the skin becomes thinner and loses elasticity, particularly in the outer surfaces. Fat deposits, which add to the soft lines and shape of the skin, begin to diminish. Starting at about age 30, lines develop on the forehead as a result of smiling, squinting, and other facial expressions. These lines become more pronounced, with added "crow's-feet" around the eyes, during the 40s. During a person's 50s and 60s, the skin begins to sag and lose colour, leading to pallor in the 70s. Body fat in underlying layers of skin continues to be redistributed away from the limbs and extremities into the trunk region of the body. Age spots become more numerous because of excessive pigment accumulation under the skin. The sun tends to increase pigment production, leading to more age spots.

Bones and Joints

Bones are the most metabolically active tissue in our bodies, in a continual state of modelling or remodelling. Bone mineral accrual exceeds bone mineral loss during our growing years. Then, once we are fully grown, our bone mineral accrual and loss are at about the same rate, with our bones maintaining their integrity and strength. Then, in mid-to-late adult life, generally during menopause in women, and a little later in men, bone mineral loss exceeds bone mineral accumulation, resulting in a deterioration of bone tissue in which bones become fragile and brittle and at an increased risk of fracture. This loss of bone mineral content occurs in men and women, although it tends to occur at a faster rate in women, especially after menopause. Loss of bone mineral content contributes to **osteoporosis**, a condition characterized by weakened, porous, and fractured bones.

Although many people consider osteoporosis a disease of the elderly, it is actually a progressive disorder with roots firmly established in childhood and adolescence. In fact, osteoporosis prevention begins in childhood by developing the strongest bones possible with the greatest reservoir of bone mineral content. When you hear of osteoporosis, you likely envision a slumped-over individual with a characteristic "dowager's hump" in the upper back, but this is the rare extreme. Bone loss occurs over many years and without symptoms until fractures occur. The spine, hips, and wrists are the most common sites of fractures, though other bones of the body may be involved.

Osteoporotic fractures of the hip, vertebrae, proximal humerus, pelvis, and wrist increase in incidence with age and are more common among women. It is estimated that one in four women aged 60 years and over will have an osteoporotic fracture. Further, about one-third of all women aged 65 and over have vertebral osteoporosis. About 70 percent of all fractures among individuals over the age of 45 result from osteoporosis. Several risk factors for developing osteoporosis have been identified:

- Sex: Women's risk is four times greater than men's. Their peak bone mass is lower than men's, and they experience an accelerated rate of bone loss after menopause.
- Age: After the third and fourth decade of life, most individuals begin to lose bone mass and are more susceptible—particularly if sedentary.
- Low bone mass: Low bone mass is one of the strongest predictors of osteoporosis. Measurement of bone density is an important aspect of risk assessment. Low bone mass is often a result of inadequate bone-growth stimulation (inactivity), poor dietary intake (lack of total calories and insufficient calcium intake), estrogen suppression (delayed onset of menarche, amenorrhea), and smoking.
- Early menopause: The early occurrence of menopause, whether natural or caused by surgery, means that the positive effects of estrogen occur for a shorter period of time. (Decreases in sex hormones—estrogen in females and testosterone in males—increase risk for osteoporosis.) Menstrual disturbances, such as those caused by anorexia nervosa or bulimia nervosa or excessive exercise without an adequate dietary intake, may similarly result in an early loss of bone minerals.
- Thin, small-framed body: Petite, thin women usually have a relatively low bone mass and are therefore at greater risk for osteoporosis.
- Ethnicity: Caucasians and Asians are at higher risk of developing osteoporosis than individuals of African descent. Individuals of African descent have greater bone density, on average, than individuals of Caucasian or Asian descent. And women of African descent have about half the incidence of hip fractures of women of Caucasian descent.
- Lack of calcium and vitamin D: A lifetime of low calcium and vitamin D intake may result in a lower than expected peak bone mineral content and above-average loss of bone mineral content throughout adulthood.
- Lack of physical activity: Immobilized, bedridden, and inactive people have less muscle and bone mass.
- Cigarette smoking: Since cigarette smoking suppresses estrogen, bone mineral accrual is negatively affected.
- Heredity: Hereditary factors may play a role in the development of osteoporosis; these factors relate to body size as well as the body's efficiency at using calcium and other minerals to build bone.

The goal of treatment and prevention of osteoporosis is to decrease the likelihood and severity of bone fractures. Currently accepted treatments of established osteoporosis include enhancing calcium and vitamin D intake, engaging in daily weight-bearing physical activity, fall-prevention measures, and potentially hormonal supplementation (in individuals not at high risk for certain forms of cancer). One study indicated that increasing calcium intake to 1380 mg per day—an amount that exceeds the current DRI for calcium—reduces bone loss and increases bone mineralization in women aged 58 to 77. Other therapies for osteoporosis, such as sodium fluoride, various metabolites of vitamin D, and bisphosphonates, are under investigation.

The most effective method of preventing osteoporosis is to develop strong, dense bones during growth. Critical to developing strong bones is sufficient calcium intake during childhood and young adulthood as well as weight-bearing or weight resistance (that is, bone-growth-stimulating) physical activity. For adolescent males and females (ages 15 to 18 years), an adequate intake of calcium is 1300 mg per day. Children and adolescents should also do 30 minutes of vigorous-intensity and 60 minutes of moderate-intensity physical activities almost every day of the week. Once strong bones are developed, the next critical step is to maintain them and delay the onset of bone mineral loss. This can most effectively be done by maintaining a healthy dietary intake and remaining physically active. Regular physical activity of weight-bearing joints, maintenance of muscular strength and flexibility, and an adequate intake of calcium are probably your best routes of osteoporosis prevention during early, middle, and late adulthood.

Another bone condition that affects a large number of people is osteoarthritis, a progressive breakdown of joint cartilage. Osteoarthritis becomes more common with age and is a leading cause of disability.

The Head

With age, features of the head enlarge and become more noticeable. Increased cartilage and fatty tissue cause the nose to grow 1.25 cm wider and another 1.25 cm longer. Earlobes get thicker and grow longer, while overall head circumference increases 0.6 cm per decade, even though the brain itself shrinks.

The Urinary Tract

One problem often associated with aging is **urinary incontinence**, which ranges from passing a few drops

Osteoporosis: A degenerative bone disease characterized by loss of bone mineral density resulting in an increased fracture risk.

Urinary incontinence: The inability to control urination.

of urine while laughing or sneezing to having little or no control when and where urination takes place. This condition affects 22 percent of older men and 35 percent of older women. Incontinence poses major social, physical, and emotional problems for the elderly. Embarrassment and fear of wetting oneself may cause an older person to become isolated and avoid social functions. Caregivers may become frustrated. Prolonged wetness and the inability to properly care for oneself can lead to irritation, infections, and other problems. However, incontinence is not an inevitable part of the aging process. Most cases are caused by highly treatable underlying neurological problems that affect the central nervous system, medications, infections of the pelvic muscles, weakness in the pelvic walls, or other problems. When the problem is treated, incontinence usually vanishes.

The Heart and Lungs

Assuming physical fitness levels do not fluctuate dramatically, resting heart rate remains about the same during an adult's life. Stroke volume (the amount of blood the muscle pumps per beat), however, diminishes as heart muscles deteriorate. Vital capacity, or the amount of air that moves when you inhale and exhale at maximum effort, also declines with age. Aerobic physical activity is effective at reducing and slowing the age-related deterioration expected in heart and lung function.

✱ Eyesight

By the age of 30, the lens of the eye begins to harden, causing specific problems by the early 40s. The lens begins to yellow and loses transparency, while the pupil of the eye begins to shrink, allowing less light to penetrate. Activities such as reading become more difficult, particularly in dim light. By age 60, depth perception declines and farsightedness often develops. A need for glasses usually develops in the 40s that evolves into a need for bifocals in the 50s and trifocals in the 60s. **Cataracts** (clouding of the lens) and **glaucoma** (elevation of pressure within the eyeball) become more likely. There may eventually be a tendency toward colour-blindness, especially for shades of blue and green. **Macular degeneration** is the breakdown of the light-sensitive part of the retina responsible for the sharp, direct vision needed to read or drive. Its effects can be devastating to independent older adults.

✱ Hearing

Our ability to hear high-frequency consonants (for example, *s*, *t*, and *z*) diminishes with age. Much of the actual hearing loss experienced as we age relates to our inability to distinguish extreme ranges of sound from normal conversational tones—which can make it harder for older individuals to hear what someone is saying if the surrounding environment is noisy, compared to younger people in the same situation.

Taste

Our sense of taste declines as we age. At age 30, each tiny elevation on the tongue (called papilla) has 245 taste buds. By the age of 70, we have only 88 left. The mouth gets drier as salivary glands secrete less fluid. The ability to distinguish sweet, sour, bitter, and salty diminishes. Thus, many older people compensate for their diminished sense of taste by adding salt, sugar, and other flavour enhancers to their food.

Smell and Touch

Our sense of smell also diminishes with age. As a result of this loss, coupled with the loss in taste, food is often less appealing when we get older. This lack of appeal may be one factor that contributes to the tendency for our older population to be malnourished. Pain receptors also become less effective and our tactile senses decline.

Mobility

Nearly half of older Canadians report some disability, usually related to mobility and agility; one-third require help with housework and shopping. The incidence and severity of disability increase with age.

Sexual Changes

As people age, they experience noticeable changes in sexual function. The degree and rate of change varies from person to person. As men age, the following changes generally occur:

- The ability to get and maintain an erection diminishes.
- The length of the refractory period between orgasms increases.
- The orgasm itself becomes shorter.

Women experience the following changes with age:

- Menopause usually occurs between the ages of 45 and 55. At this time, women may experience hot flashes, mood swings, weight gain, development of facial hair, and other hormone-related problems.
- The walls of the vagina become less elastic, and the epithelium thins, making sexual activity less comfortable.

- Vaginal secretions diminish, particularly during sexual activity (though this problem can be reduced with the use of a lubricant).
- The breasts decrease in firmness. Loss of fat in various areas leads to fewer curves, with a decrease in the soft lines of the body.

While these physiologic changes may sound discouraging, the fact is that many older people enjoy satisfying sexual activity throughout their lives. Indeed, one study refuted long-held beliefs that sexual desire decreases as we age. The results showed that nearly half the population over 60 years of age engaged in sexual activity at least once a month, and 40 percent would like to have sex more frequently.

Body Comfort

Because of the loss of body fat, thinning of the epithelium, and diminished glandular activity, elderly people generally have greater difficulty regulating body temperature. This change means that their ability to withstand extreme cold or heat may be limited, thus increasing their risks of hypothermia, heat stroke, and heat exhaustion.

Many of these changes related to body comfort are exacerbated by poor nutrition. For a variety of reasons, getting adequate nutrition is a problem for many seniors. Using assessments based on risk factors associated with malnutrition, researchers have determined that 40 to 50 percent of community-dwelling seniors have a moderate to high risk of becoming malnourished, especially among those who live alone. The limited data on frailer seniors suggest that the picture is much worse. Poor nutrition worsens the impact of chronic disease, reduces resistance to infections, slows healing, and increases use of the health-care system. Identifying seniors at risk for malnutrition is important to enable them to maintain an optimal quality of life and age successfully.

what do you THINK?

Of the health conditions listed in this section, which ones are preventable? Which ones can be delayed?

Mental Changes

Intelligence

Stereotypes concerning inevitable intellectual decline among the elderly have been largely refuted. Research demonstrated that much of our previous knowledge about elderly intelligence was based on inappropriate testing procedures. Given an appropriate length of time, elderly people may learn and develop skills in a similar manner to younger people. Researchers have also determined that what many elderly people lack in speed of learning they make up for in practical knowledge—that is, the "wisdom of experience."

Memory

Have you ever wondered why your grandfather seems unable to remember what he did last weekend even though he can graphically depict the details of a social event that occurred 40 years ago? This phenomenon is not unusual among the elderly. Research indicates that although short-term memory may fluctuate on a daily basis, the ability to remember events from past decades remains largely unchanged.

Adaptability

Although it is widely believed that people become more like one another as they age, nothing could be further from the truth. Having lived through a multitude of experiences and faced diverse joys, sorrows, and obstacles, the typical older person has developed unique methods of coping. These unique adaptive variations make for interesting differences in how the elderly confront the many changes brought on by the aging process. Thus as a group, older Canadian are heterogeneous.

Depression

Most adults continue to lead healthy, fulfilling lives as they grow older. Some research indicates, however, that depression may be the most common psychological problem as we age. Still, those aged 25 to 44 years have greater depression rates (approximately 10 percent) than those older than 65 (5 percent).

Dementia

Over the years, older people have often been the victims of ageist attitudes. People chronologically old were often labelled "senile" whenever they displayed memory failure, errors in judgment, disorientation, or erratic behaviours. (The term *senile* is seldom used

Cataracts: Clouding of the lens that interrupts the focusing of light on the retina, resulting in blurred vision or eventual blindness.

Glaucoma: Elevation of pressure within the eyeball, leading to hardening of the eyeball, impaired vision, and possible blindness.

Macular degeneration: Disease that breaks down the macula, the light-sensitive part of the retina responsible for sharp, direct vision.

Georgia O'Keeffe retained her intellectual and artistic abilities into old age.

today except to describe a very small group of organic disorders.) Today, scientists recognize that these same symptoms can occur at any age and for various reasons, including disease or the use of OTC or prescription drugs. When the underlying problems are corrected, memory loss and disorientation also improve.

Alzheimer's Disease

Dementias are progressive brain impairments that interfere with memory and normal intellectual functioning. Although there are many types of **dimentia**, one of the most common forms is **Alzheimer's disease**. Alzheimer's affects an estimated one in 20 people between the ages of 65 and 75 and one in five people over the age of 80. The total number of people with Alzheimer's disease is expected to increase. Estimates are that the incidence of dementia could triple by 2031. This possibility presents a real economic burden for the future. While the disease is associated in most people's minds strictly with the elderly, it has been diagnosed in people as young as their late 40s. In fact, about 5 percent of all cases occur before age 65.

Alzheimer's refers to a degenerative disease of the brain in which nerve cells stop communicating with one another. Ordinarily, brain cells communicate by releasing chemicals that allow the cells to receive and transmit messages for various behaviours. In Alzheimer's patients, the brain does not produce enough of these chemicals, cells cannot communicate, and eventually the cells die. This degeneration happens in the sections of the brain that affect memory, speech, and personality, leaving the parts that control other bodily functions, such as heartbeat and breathing, working fine. Thus, the mind's ability to function decreases while the body continues to work more or less fine. Alzheimer's happens slowly and progressively, and it may be as long as 20 years before symptoms are noticed. It is generally detected first by family members, who note memory lapses and personality changes. Medical tests rule out other underlying causes and neurological tests confirm the diagnosis.

What are the symptoms of Alzheimer's? Alzheimer's disease is characteristically diagnosed in three stages. During the first stage, symptoms include forgetfulness, memory loss, impaired judgment, increasing inability to handle routine tasks, disorientation, lack of interest in one's surroundings, and depression. These symptoms accelerate in the second stage, which also includes agitation and restlessness (especially at night), loss of sensory perceptions, muscle twitching, and repetitive actions. Many patients become depressed at this stage and there is a tendency to be combative and aggressive. In the final stage, disorientation is often complete. The person becomes completely dependent on others for eating, dressing, and other activities. Identity loss and speech problems are common symptoms. Eventually, control of bodily functions may be lost.

Once Alzheimer's disease strikes, the patient's remaining life expectancy is cut in half. Treatment includes several prescription drugs. Some physicians prescribe vitamin E because it may help protect brain cells from free radical damage. Researchers are also examining anti-inflammatory drugs, theorizing that Alzheimer's may develop in response to an inflammatory ailment. Others are focusing on stimulating the brains of those prone to Alzheimer's, believing that as people learn, more connections between brain cells are formed that may offset those that are lost.

✓ HEALTH CHALLENGES OF OLDER CANADIANS

The elderly are disproportionately victimized by a number of societally induced problems. Other problems result when older people do not develop the

FOCUS ON CANADA

Canada's Aging Population Runs Greater Dementia Risk

by Steven Wharry, Canadian Medical Association Journal

The Alzheimer Society of Canada is warning that the number of Canadians battling dementia is set to explode as the population ages.

Steve Rudin, executive director of the Alzheimer Society told *CMAJ* that a study published in *Neurology* predicts that about 109 000 Canadians will develop dementia in the next year alone, while the total number of those suffering from the syndrome will reach 364 000.

"These numbers are very alarming and with this huge number of new cases the implications for our health care system are profound," said Rudin. "The financial and social costs risk being overwhelming."

The estimates are based on data from the Canadian Study of Health and Aging (CSHA) report, which dementia experts warn contain some dire predictions: in 2011, new cases of dementia are expected to reach 145 300 a year; the total number of cases will be 475 000; by 2031 there will be an estimated 778 000 Canadians with Alzheimer's disease and related dementias.

Rudin states that long-term care facilities and services to help these individuals and initiatives such as a national home care program need to be examined to help families cope with caring for stricken family members.

"The population in the 85-plus age group is the fastest growing segment of the population," states Joan Lindsay, co-investigator of the CSHA study and chief of the Aging Related Diseases Division of Health Canada. "The increase in the numbers of people with dementia is a direct result of the growth in the 'oldest of the old' segment of our population."

Dementia is a syndrome that includes loss of memory, judgment, reasoning, and ability to function. Alzheimer's disease is a degenerative brain disorder that destroys vital brain cells. The cause is unknown and the Alzheimer Society and other organizations continue to fund research aimed at finding a cure.

"Given the vast numbers of people predicted to get this disease, it's even more urgent for us to find a cause and a cure," said Rudin. "We must also develop better methods for diagnosis, caregiving and providing needed services."

Source: "Canada's Aging Population Runs Greater Dementia Risk," by Steve Wharry. Reprinted from eCMAJ News Desk 15-Dec-00; by permission of the publisher.

ability to cope with life's various hurdles. Still other problems come from a perceived loss of control in older people over the circumstances of their lives—when they watch loved ones die, are forced to retire, face problems with personal health, and confront an uncertain economy on a fixed income. Developing adequate coping and decision-making skills in your earlier years, as well as strong social supports, may significantly reduce your risk for problems in old age.

Alcohol Use and Abuse

A person prone to alcoholism during their younger and middle years is more likely to continue drinking during his or her later years. The older individual addicted to alcohol is no more common than the younger person, despite the stereotype of the old, lost soul hiding his or her sorrows in a bottle. Alcohol abuse is five times more likely in older men than in older women. Almost half of all older men and even more older women do not drink at all. Those who do drink consume less than younger persons, at only five to six drinks per week.

Prescription Drug Use: Unique Problems for Older Canadians

It is extremely rare for older people to use illicit drugs, but some do overuse, misuse, and grow dependent upon prescription and OTC drugs. Beset with numerous aches, pains, and inexplicable as well as diagnosable maladies, some older Canadians take between four and six prescription drugs a day in addition to vitamin and/or mineral supplements and regular use of OTCs such as Aspirin. Anyone who combines drugs runs the risk of dangerous and/or uncomfortable drug interactions. The risks of adverse effects are greater for people with circulation impairments and declining kidney and liver functions. Older people displaying symptoms of these drug-induced effects, including bizarre behaviour patterns or an appearance of being out of touch, are often misdiagnosed as experiencing dementia.

Dementia: Refers to mental deterioration, loss of memory, and judgment and orientation problems.

Alzheimer's disease: A chronic condition involving changes in nerve fibres of the brain; results in mental deterioration.

HEALTH IN THE MEDIA

Baby Boomers Sport Waistline Woes

In Andrew Wister's new book (*Baby Boomer Health Dynamics: How Are We Aging?* UTP, 2005), he calls obesity "the new tobacco." Despite today's baby boomers' making many healthier lifestyle choices such as not smoking, reducing alcohol consumption, and engaging in physical activity or exercise, they are not aging any better than their forefathers 25 years ago. One thing boomers experience at a much higher rate than their forefathers and -mothers is obesity. In fact, the number of people classified as obese has doubled in the past 15 years. Clearly the lifestyle improvements have not been sufficient to counteract the quantity and quality of our food consumption.

To examine the exercise–obesity paradox, Wister, Chair of the Department of Gerontology at Simon Fraser University, analyzed data from six Canadian health surveys. From these analyses, it was noted that 25 percent of the energy we take in (that is, calories) comes from the "other" food group of Canada's Food Guide to Healthy Eating (updated and now called Eating Well with Canada's Food Guide). Twenty percent of all meals were eaten outside the home, many at fast food restaurants which continue to serve exceedingly large portions. Further, it was noted that as many as 27 percent of people eat at least one meal per week in their car.

These changes have a direct impact on individual and national levels of obesity. Given the sheer number of boomers, combined with an increase in the number classified as obese, our health-care system is likely to become overburdened in the coming years as the boomers age.

Source: Adapted from Centre on Aging, "Research through the Life Course," *The Bulletin* 14.1 (January 2006): 12. Retrieved on May 16, 2006, from www.coag.uvic.ca.

Over-the-Counter Remedies

Although older Canadians today appear to be more receptive to medical treatment than previous generations, a substantial segment of the over-60 population avoid orthodox medical treatment, viewing it as only a last resort. As might be expected, ASA and laxatives head the list of commonly used OTC medications for relief of arthritic pain and the irregular bowel activity sometimes experienced by older Canadians.

Physical Activity

An inevitable physical change the body undergoes as it ages is **sarcopenia**, age-related declines in muscle mass. The less muscle you have, the less energy you require, even when physically active. The lower your metabolic rate, the more likely you will gain weight—particularly when your caloric intake remains the same. Regular moderate-intensity physical activity that gets your heart beating faster will help to reduce the expected age-related declines in quality and quantity of muscle. Further, regular resistance training will increase (or maintain) muscle mass, boost metabolism, strengthen your bones, prevent osteoporosis, and in general help older Canadians to feel better and function more effectively and efficiently.

Canada's Physical Activity Guide to Healthy Active Living for Older Adults (available at www.phac-aspc.gc.ca/pau-uap/paguide/older/index.html) recommends that older adults choose a variety of endurance, flexibility, and strength and balance activities such that they accumulate 30 to 60 minutes of moderate-intensity physical activity most days of the week. It is further noted that these activities can be accumulated in 10-minute blocks of time.

Dietary Concerns

As with many bodily processes, the digestion of food slows with age. Nevertheless, the body still requires nutrients consumed in moderate quantities and in the right combination. Certain nutrients are especially important to healthy aging:

- Calcium: Many elderly people do not consume adequate calcium, or they may take it as an individual supplement without vitamin D, which is necessary for calcium absorption in the body. Adequate calcium intake should be part of a lifelong regimen of preventive health care to reduce loss of bone mineral content. For individuals over the age of 50, a calcium intake of 1200 mg per day is recommended.
- Vitamin D: As noted above, vitamin D is essential to enable adequate calcium absorption. As people age, particularly in and beyond their 50s and 60s, they do not absorb vitamin D as readily from foods. More recently, vitamin D has been

Learning to cope with challenges and make effective decisions early in life develops attitudes and skills that contribute to a full and satisfying old age.

identified as protective from a number of chronic diseases. Further, it is clear, particularly during the winter months in Canada, that most Canadians cannot obtain sufficient vitamin D from the sun. Supplementation may therefore be warranted.

- Protein: As older adults become concerned about cholesterol and fatty foods, and as their budgets shrink, one nutrient often cut back on is protein. Meat costs more, takes longer to cook, and has a "fat" stigma associated with it. Many older people cut back on protein to a point below the DRIs. Because protein is necessary to maintain muscle mass, deficiencies can spell trouble.

Gender Issues: Caring for Older Canadians

According to the most recent census data, older women fill a disproportionate place in Canadian society. In 2005, for example, 56.5 percent of Canadians over the age of 65 years were women. This difference in the number of older women increases with age. In the same year, women made up 58.4 percent of people aged 75 to 84, and 69.2 percent of Canadians aged 85 or older. This is also a relatively new phenomenon—as recently as 1950, there were more older men than women. Because women live longer then men on average, older women are more likely than older men to be living alone, and thus to lack the support in the home that helps keep them independent. Women over the age of 75 were the largest consumers of home-care services, with 20 percent reporting using these services.

The rate of institutionalization is twice as high among older people without a spouse as for married older people; one reason is that a married person has a built-in potential caretaker. Further, women are more likely than men to experience poverty and multiple chronic health problems, a situation referred to as **comorbidity**. Consequently, more older women than men are likely to need assistance from children, other relatives, friends, and neighbours.

what do you THINK?

Why are women often the primary caregivers for aging spouses or other family members? What issues might there be with such caregiving? How can caregivers cope with the stresses of their situation?

Sarcopenia: Age-related declines in the quality and quantity of muscle tissue.

Comorbidity: The presence of a number of diseases at the same time.

CHAPTER 6c

UNDERSTANDING DEATH AND DYING

Taken from *Health: The Basics*, Fifth Canadian Edition, by Rebecca J. Donatelle and Angela M. Thompson

Death eventually comes to everyone. Although this can be a depressing thought, we must accept the inevitable. The acceptance of death helps shape our attitudes about the importance of life. Throughout history, humans have attempted to determine the nature and meaning of death. This questioning continues today. Although we will touch on moral, spiritual, and philosophical questions about death, we will not explore such issues in depth in this chapter. Rather, our primary focus is to present dying and death as a normal part of life and to discuss how we can cope with it.

Confrontations with death elicit different feelings depending on many factors, including age, religious beliefs, family orientation, health, personal experience, and the circumstances of the death itself. To cope effectively with dying and death, we must address the individual needs of those involved. Why is it that we wish to deny, or even postpone, death?

Defining Death

Dying is the process of decline in body functions resulting in the death of an organism. **Death** can be defined as the "final cessation of the vital functions" and refers to a state in which these functions are "incapable of being restored." This definition has become more significant as medical and scientific advances have made it increasingly possible to postpone death. Although irreversible cessation of circulatory and respiratory functions acceptably defines death, irreversible cessation of brain function is also equivalent to death even though the heart continues to beat while the individual is on a respirator.

In 1968, following the publication of the Harvard criteria for the diagnosis of brain death, the Canadian Medical Association (CMA) provided guidelines, revised in 1974 and 1975. In 1976, guidelines were established in the United Kingdom, and in 1981, revised guidelines were published in the *Journal of the American Medical Association*. Brain death must be determined clinically by an experienced physician in accordance with accepted medical standards. The following definitions facilitate classification of various phases of biologic death:

- Cell death: The gradual death of a cell after all metabolic activity has ceased. The rate of cellular death varies according to the tissue involved. For example, higher-functioning brain cells die five to eight minutes after respiration ceases; striated muscle cells die two to four hours later; kidney cells die after about seven hours; and epithelial cells (hair and nails) die several days later. Rigor mortis, the temporary stiffening of muscles, is associated with cell death.
- Local death: The death of a body part or portion of an organ without the death of the entire organism. For example, a kidney may fail, part of the heart muscle may die, or a limb or section of intestine may die as a result of loss of circulation.
- Somatic death: The death of the entire organism, as opposed to death of a part of an organ or an extremity.
- Apparent death: The cessation of vital physiologic functions, particularly spontaneous cardiac and respiratory activities, which produces a state simulating actual death but from which recovery is possible through resuscitative efforts.
- Functional death: Extensive and irreversible damage to the central nervous system, with respiration and circulatory function maintained by artificial means.
- Brain death: The cessation of brain function, as evidenced by loss of all reflexes and electrical activity of the brain or by irreversible coma. Brain death is confirmed by an electroencephalogram reading of electrical activity of brain cells.

The Canadian Medical Association established the following criteria for the clinical diagnosis of brain death:

1. An etiology has been established capable of causing brain death, and potentially reversible conditions have been excluded (drug intoxication, treatable metabolic disorders, core temperature less than 32.2°C, shock, and peripheral nerve or muscle dysfunction due to disease or neuromuscular-blocking drugs).
2. The patient is in deep coma and shows no response within the cranial nerve distribution to stimulation of any part of the body. In particular, there should be no motor response within the cranial nerve distribution to stimuli applied to any body regions. There should be no spontaneous or elicited movements arising from the brain. However, various spinal reflexes may persist in brain death.
3. Brain-stem reflexes are absent. Pupillary light and corneal, vestibulo-ocular, and pharyngeal reflexes must be absent. The pupils should be midsize or larger and must be unresponsive to light. Care

Dying: The process of decline in body functions resulting in the death of an organism.

Death: The "final cessation of the vital functions" and the state in which these functions are "incapable of being restored."

should be taken that atropine or related drugs that could block the pupillary response to light have not been given to the patient.

4. The patient does not breathe when taken off the respirator for an appropriate time.
5. The conditions listed above persist when the patient is reassessed after a suitable interval to ensure that the non-functioning state of the brain is persistent and to reduce the possibility of observer error.

The CMA also suggests that a physician consult with another experienced physician before determining death.

what do you THINK?

How long do you think you will live? Do you have concerns about the quality of your life up until you die? How can you obtain not only a long life, but also a healthy quality of life?

In some cultures, death is not feared but viewed as a passage to a better state of being that is to be celebrated.

Denying Death

We can look at our attitudes toward death as falling on a continuum. At one end of the continuum, death is viewed as the enemy of humankind. Medical science promotes this idea of death. At the other end of the continuum, death is accepted and welcomed. For people whose attitudes fall at this end, often those with a deep religious faith or spiritual belief, death is a passage to a better state of being. Most of us perceive ourselves somewhere in the middle of this continuum. From this perspective, death is a bewildering mystery that elicits fear and apprehension, as well as profoundly influencing our attitudes, beliefs, and actions throughout our lives.

In Canada, a high level of discomfort is associated with dying and death. As a result, we often avoid speaking about the subject. You may be denying death if you:

- avoid people who are grieving after the death of a loved one so you do not have to talk about it
- fail to validate a dying person's situation by talking to the person as if nothing were wrong
- substitute euphemisms for the word *death* (a few examples are "passed away," "kicked the bucket," "no longer with us," "gone to heaven," or "gone to a better place")
- give false reassurances to dying people by saying things like "everything is going to be okay"
- shut off conversation about death by silencing people trying to talk about it
- avoid touching a dying person

Although some experts indicate that the denial of death has always been a predominant characteristic of our society, we must keep in mind that societal norms contribute to this denial. The miraculous feats of science and medicine during the first half of the century created an attitude closer to death-defying than to death-denying. However, the pendulum appears to be swinging back. Today, a growing number of people are rejecting "high-tech" death—death postponed through the use of life-support technology—in favour of more personal, and perhaps more humane, alternatives. The concept of death as an enemy may be giving way to acceptance of dying as a natural part of life.

THE PROCESS OF DYING

Dying is a complex process that includes physical, intellectual, social, spiritual, and emotional dimensions. Accordingly, we must consider the process of dying from several perspectives. The preceding section primarily examined the physical indicators of death. It is also essential to consider the emotional aspects of dying and "social death" in establishing an appreciation for the multifaceted nature of life and death.

Coping Emotionally with Death

Science and medicine enable us to understand changes associated with growth, development, aging, and social roles throughout the life span, but they have not revealed the nature of death. This may partially explain why the transition from life to death evokes mystery and emotion. Although emotional reactions to dying vary, there seem to be many similarities in this process.

Much of our knowledge about reactions to dying stems from the work of Elisabeth Kübler-Ross, a major figure in modern **thanatology**, the study of death and dying. In 1969, Kübler-Ross published *On Death and Dying*, a sensitive analysis of the reactions of terminally ill patients. This pioneering work encouraged the development of death education as a discipline and prompted efforts to improve the care of patients who were dying. In her book, Kübler-Ross identified five psychological stages that terminally ill patients often experience as they approach death: denial, anger, bargaining, depression, and acceptance. Health professions immediately embraced this "stage theory" and hastily applied it in clinical settings. However, research evidence supporting the concept of stages of grief is neither extensive nor convincing. Although it is normal to grieve when a severe loss has been sustained, some people never go through this process and instead remain emotionally calm. Others pass back and forth between the stages.

A summation of Kübler-Ross's five stages follows:

- Denial: ("Not me, there must be a mistake.") This is usually the first stage, experienced as a sensation of shock and disbelief. A person intellectually accepts his or her impending death but rejects it emotionally. The individual is too confused and stunned to comprehend "not being" and thus rejects the idea. When this anxiety level diminishes, the individual is able to sort through the powerful web of emotions surrounding his or her impending death.
- Anger: ("Why me?") Anger is another common reaction to the realization of imminent death. The person becomes angry at the prospect of dying when others, including loved ones, are healthy and not threatened. The person dying perceives the situation as "unfair" or "senseless" and may be hostile to friends, family, physicians, and/or the world in general.
- Bargaining: ("If I am allowed to live, I promise . . . ") This stage generally occurs at about the middle of the progression toward acceptance of death. During this stage, the dying person may resolve to be a better person in return for an extension of life or may secretly pray for a short reprieve from death in order to experience a special event, such as a family wedding or birth.
- Depression: ("It is really going to happen to me and I cannot do anything about it.") Depression eventually sets in as vitality diminishes and the person begins to experience distressing symptoms with increasing frequency. The individual's deteriorating condition becomes impossible for him or her to deny, and feelings of doom and tremendous loss may become unbearably pervasive. Feelings of worthlessness and guilt are also common in this depressed state because the person dying may feel responsible for the emotional suffering of loved ones and the arduous but seemingly futile efforts of caregivers.
- Acceptance: ("I am ready.") This is often the final stage. The individual stops battling with emotions and becomes tired and weak. The need to sleep increases, and wakeful periods become shorter and less frequent. With acceptance, the person does not "give up" and become sullen or resentfully resigned to death, but rather becomes passive. According to one dying person, the acceptance stage is "almost void of feelings . . . as if the pain had gone, the struggle is over, and there comes a time for the final rest before the long journey." As he or she lets go, the dying person may no longer welcome visitors and may not wish to engage in conversation. Death usually occurs quietly and painlessly while the individual is unconscious.

Subsequent research indicated that each individual has a distinct mix and process of grieving. A person may move from denial to depression, to anger, to denial again, and so on. Even if it is not accurate in all its particulars, Kübler-Ross's theory offers valuable insights for those seeking to understand or cope with the process of dying.

Thanatology: The study of death and dying.

Social Death

The need for recognition and appreciation within a social group is nearly universal. Although the size and nature of the social group may vary widely, the need to belong exists in all of us. Loss of value or of appreciation by others can lead to **social death**, an often irreversible situation in which a person is not treated like an active member of society. Dramatic examples of social death include the exile of nonconformists from their native countries or the excommunication of dissident members of religious orders. More often, however, social death is inflicted by avoidance of social interaction. Numerous studies indicate that people are treated differently when they are dying. The isolation that accompanies social death in terminally ill patients may be promoted by the following:

- The dying person is referred to as if he or she were already dead.
- The dying person may be inadvertently excluded from conversations.
- Dying patients are often moved to terminal wards and given minimal care.
- Bereaved family members are avoided, often for extended periods, because friends and neighbours are afraid of feeling uncomfortable in the presence of grief.
- Medical personnel may make degrading comments about patients in their presence.

A decrease in meaningful social interaction often strips dying and bereaved people of recognition as valued members of society at a time when belonging is critical. Some dying people choose not to speak of their inevitable fate in an attempt to make others feel more comfortable and thus preserve vital relationships.

Near-Death Experiences

We cannot speak of the process of dying without mentioning near-death experiences. Thousands of similar reports have been given by people who almost died or were actually pronounced dead and subsequently recovered. The descriptions of feelings, perceptions, and visions associated with being near death have many common features. Three phases have been identified: resistance, life review, and transcendence. During the initial phase, resistance, the dying person is aware of extreme danger and struggles desperately to escape from the unseen threat. Many people report a sensation of expanding fear. The second phase, life review, has been described as a feeling of being outside one's body and beyond danger. During this period, the dying person feels a sensation of security while observing his or her physical body from an emotionally detached perspective. The dying person's life experiences may also seem to pass by in rapid review. The last phase, transcendence, is characterized by a reported feeling of euphoria, contentment, and even ecstasy. Some people recall a sensation of being unified with nature and of having an awareness of infinity. In February 2000, Pam Barrett, long-time leader of the Alberta New Democratic Party, abruptly resigned from politics after a near-death experience due to an allergic reaction. She termed the experience "a spiritual awakening," and said that it had forced her to re-evaluate all aspects of her life.

* Coping with Loss

The death of a loved one may be extremely difficult to cope with. The dying person, as well as close family and friends, frequently suffers emotionally and physically from the impending loss of critical relationships and roles. Words used to describe feelings and behaviours related to losses resulting from death include bereavement, grief, grief work, and mourning. These terms are related but not identical. A discussion of them may help you to understand the emotional processes associated with loss and the cultural constraints that often inhibit normal coping behaviours (see Figure 6c.1).

Bereavement is generally defined as the loss or deprivation experienced by a survivor when a loved one dies. Because relationships vary in type and intensity, reactions vary. The death of a parent, spouse, sibling, child, friend, or pet will result in different kinds

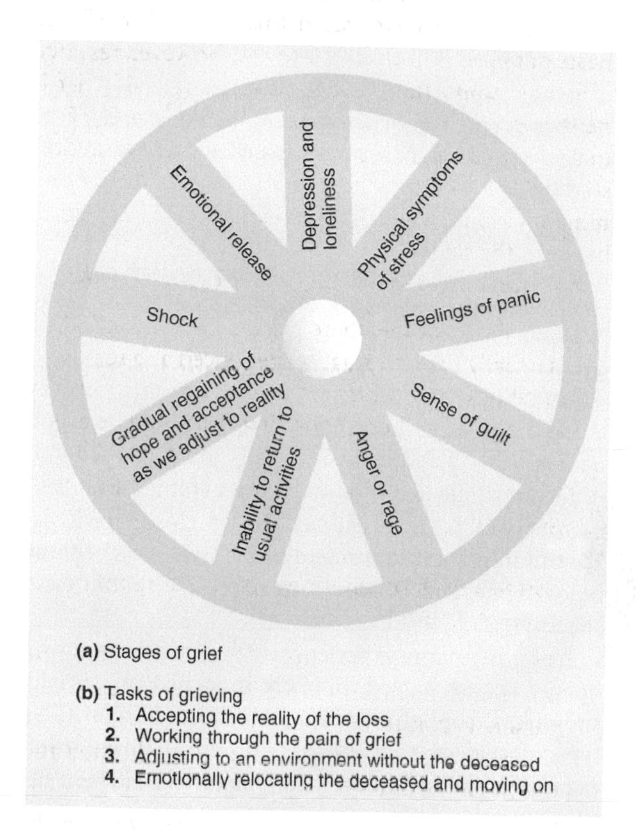

FIGURE 6c.1

The Stages and Tasks of Grief

(a) People react differently to loss, and most eventually adjust. Generally, the stronger the social support system, the smoother the progression through the stages of grief.
(b) Worden's developmental tasks associated with grief are another way to understand the grieving process.

YOUR SPIRITUAL AND EMOTIONAL HEALTH

Bereavement and Grief

Each of us uses various methods to relieve sorrow and bereavement. Similar to other types of stress (see Chapter 3), the stress caused by grief affects people mentally and physically. If an individual is having an especially difficult time dealing with grief, he or she may become depressed or physically ill. There are a number of feelings that people experience while coming to terms with a loss, including:

- shock, numbness, bewilderment, a sense of disbelief, and possibly denial
- feelings of emptiness and intense suffering
- dreams or hallucinations that their loved one is still alive
- feelings of despair as one comes to terms with the loss
- feelings of sadness and the inability to feel pleasure
- tense, restless anxiety alternated with lethargy and fatigue
- avoiding reminders of the deceased alternated with reclaiming memories
- sadness mixed with anger
- self-blame for treating the deceased badly

Physical symptoms of grief include weakness, sleep disturbances, loss of appetite, headaches, back pain, indigestion, shortness of breath, heart palpitations, and occasional dizziness and nausea.

WHY WE GRIEVE

All cultures have various rituals to mourn the death of a loved one. Mourning customs help to confirm social bonds, reorder personal relationships, and establish a new identity for the bereaved. Within our society, people often die in hospitals or away from their families. These changes to the social fabric have made it difficult for some to see death as a natural part of life, and to come to terms with the death of a loved one. Friends and social groups are especially important for helping the bereaved adjust to their loss and move on with his or her life.

WHAT YOU CAN DO TO HELP THE BEREAVED

People who have experienced a death need sympathetic company, reassurance, and willingness among or by others to listen. What the bereaved say they want most are offers of specific practical support, expressions of concern, and the presence of people close to them. Statements such as "time heals" and vague offers of help that do not materialize are more annoying than helpful. People should not discourage expressions of grief or shut off discussions about the person who died, since that is part of the healing process. Understanding that this is a highly emotional time for the bereaved and assuring them that their anger, guilt, and other feelings are normal and part of the grieving process is the most supportive thing you can do.

of feelings. The death of loved ones will leave "holes" in the lives of the bereaved or of close survivors. We can think of bereavement as the awareness of these holes. Time and courage are necessary to fill these spaces.

When a person experiences a loss that cannot be openly acknowledged, publicly mourned, or socially supported, coping may be much more difficult. This type of grief is referred to as **disenfranchised grief.** Some examples of a death that may lead to disenfranchised grief include

- Death of a divorced spouse: Unresolved anger and hurt along with fond memories are conflicting feelings that may prevent the resolution of feelings surrounding the ex-spouse's death.
- Death of a secret lover: When a lover dies and no one but the partner knew of the relationship, grief is often hidden. Examples would include a partner in an extramarital relationship or a lover of a gay person who is not openly gay.

Social death: An irreversible situation in which a person is not treated as an active member of society.

Bereavement: The loss or deprivation experienced when a loved one dies.

Disenfranchised grief: Grief concerning a loss that cannot be openly acknowledged, publicly mourned, or socially supported.

what do you THINK?

Have you, or someone close to you, experienced the stages of grief? What would you add to or take away from the description given?

- Death of a gay lover: Gays and lesbians—even those who are "out"—may find it difficult to mourn the deaths of their lovers when they themselves are not accepted by their own families or the families of their lovers. The situation can be even more difficult if the lover died of AIDS, because of the unjust stigma and discrimination associated with this disease.

A special case of bereavement occurs in old age. Death is an intrinsic part of growing old. The longer we live, the more deaths we are likely to experience. These deaths include physical, social, spiritual, and emotional losses as our bodies deteriorate and more and more of our loved ones die. The theory of bereavement overload has been proposed to explain the effects of multiple deaths and the accumulation of sorrow in the lives of some elderly people. This theory suggests that the gloomy outlook, disturbing behaviour patterns, and apparent apathy that characterize these people may be related more to bereavement overload than to intrinsic physiological degeneration in old age.

Grief is a mental state of distress that occurs in reaction to significant loss, including one's own impending death, the death of a loved one, or a quasi-death experience. Grief reactions include any adjustments needed for one to "make it through the day" and may include changes in patterns of eating, physical activity, sleeping, working, and even thinking.

The term **mourning** is often incorrectly equated with the term *grief*. As we have noted, grief refers to a wide variety of feelings and actions that occur in response to bereavement. *Mourning*, in contrast, refers to culturally prescribed and accepted time periods and behaviour patterns for the expression of grief. In Judaism, for example, "sitting shivah" is a designated mourning period of seven days that involves prescribed rituals and prayers. Depending on a person's relationship with the deceased, various other rituals may continue for up to a year.

By accepting dying as a part of the continuum of life, many people are able to make necessary readjustments after the death of a loved one. This holistic concept, which accepts dying as a part of the total life experience, is shared by believers and non-believers.

What Is "Normal" Grief?

Grief responses vary widely from person to person. Despite these differences, a classic acute grief syndrome often occurs when a person acknowledges a death. This common grief reaction can include the following:

- periodic waves of physical distress lasting from 20 minutes to an hour
- a feeling of tightness in the throat
- choking and shortness of breath
- a frequent need to sigh
- a feeling of emptiness
- a feeling of muscular weakness
- an intense feeling of anxiety described as actually painful

Other common symptoms of grief include insomnia, memory lapse, loss of appetite, difficulty in concentrating, a tendency to engage in repetitive or purposeless behaviours, an "observer" sensation or feeling of unreality, difficulty in making decisions, lack of organization, excessive speech, social withdrawal or hostility, guilt feelings, and preoccupation with the image of the deceased. Susceptibility to disease increases with grief and may even be life-threatening in severe and enduring cases.

Coping with Grief

A bereaved person may suffer emotional pain and exhibit a variety of grief responses for many months after the death of a loved one. The rate of healing depends on the amount and quality of "grief work" that a person does. **Grief work** is the process of integrating the reality of the death with everyday life and learning to feel better. Often, the bereaved person must deliberately and systematically work at reducing denial and coping with the pain that results from memories of the deceased. This process takes time and requires emotional effort.

INDEX

Note: "f" indicates a figure and "t" indicates a table.

B

I